3 tools designed to help you learn with

What Is Life? A Guide to Biology with Physiology

1	2	3
Book Companion Website	Student Success Guide	Prep-U

Free Book Companion Website

www.whfreeman.com/phelanphys1e

All students have FREE, unrestricted access to the Companion Website which offers a variety of study tools that reflect the textbook's coverage and goals. Free website Tools include:

- **Q** Animations
- Podcasts
- Lecture Companion Art
- Chapter Quizzes
- Key Terms Flashcards

Printed Student Success Guide

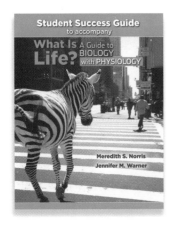

The Student Success Guide contains over 200 pages of study tools to help you better understand key concepts and improve your exam scores. Including:

- Multiple-choice and short-answer practice questions
- Learning objectives
- Outlines of key chapter concepts fully illustrated with text figures
- Visual glossary of key terms

To order a copy of the Student Success Guide online, go to **www.whfreeman.com/phelanphys1e**

 ✓PrepU
Smarter than the average quiz

MORE! Learn about Prep-U, the online student quizzing tool that comes free with this textbook...

PrepU
Smarter than the average quiz

Prep-U is the online quizzing system that comes **free*** with this textbook created by Jay Phelan, author of **What Is Life? A Guide to Biology with Physiology.**

Take custom quizzes and find out what you don't know *before* the exam!

Take Practice Quizzes

Get ready for exams by quickly building quizzes over the chapter/s you choose. Prep-U contains over 5,000 high-quality questions prepared specifically for this textbook.

Get Personalized Results

Instant quiz results help you learn from your mistakes. Your results also determine the questions you will see on your next quizzes. Quiz questions are generated to fit your specific needs.

See How You Are Doing

Your "How Am I Doing?" page shows your overall Prep-U performance compared to your classmates, reveals your strengths and weaknesses, and tells you which chapters you need to study more.

Your Prep-U **activation code** is on the card facing this page.
Log-in at www.prep-u.com now!

What Is Life?

A Guide to BIOLOGY with PHYSIOLOGY

What Is Life?

A Guide to BIOLOGY with PHYSIOLOGY

Jay Phelan

University of California, Los Angeles

Custom Edition for Drexel University

Volume One

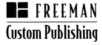

FREEMAN
Custom Publishing

Publisher: Peter Marshall

Senior Development Editor: Elizabeth Howe

Consulting Development Editor: Jane Tufts

Art Development Editor: Tommy Moorman

Illustrations: Tommy Moorman, Erin Daniel

Senior Media Editor: Patrick Shriner

Associate Director of Marketing: Debbie Clare

Managing Editor for First Editions: Elaine Palucki, PhD

Associate Editor for First Edition Supplements: Beth McHenry

Assistant Editor: Marni Rolfes

Managing Editor: Philip McCaffrey

Project Editor: Dusty Friedman

Art Director: Diana Blume

Text Design: Lissi Sigillo

Photo Editor: Christine Buese

Photo Researchers: Deborah Anderson, Elyse Rieder

Production Manager: Julia DeRosa

Composition and Layout: Sheridan Sellers

Printing and Binding: Worldcolor Dubuque

ISBN-13: 978-1-4292-5812-8

ISBN-10: 1-4292-5812-8

Printed in the United States of America

W. H. Freeman Custom Publishing
W. H. Freeman and Company
41 Madison Avenue
New York, NY 10010

www.whfreeman.com/custompub

BRIEF CONTENTS

CONTENTS

PART 1 The Facts of Life

1 • Scientific Thinking

YOUR BEST PATHWAY TO UNDERSTANDING THE WORLD

2 • Chemistry

RAW MATERIALS AND FUEL FOR OUR BODIES

3 • Cells

THE SMALLEST PART OF YOU 76

4 • Energy

FROM THE SUN TO YOU IN JUST TWO STEPS

5 • DNA, Gene Expression, and Biotechnology

WHAT IS THE CODE AND HOW IS IT HARNESSED?

6 • Chromosomes and Cell Division

CONTINUITY AND VARIETY

7 • Mendelian Inheritance

FAMILY RESEMBLANCE: HOW TRAITS ARE INHERITED 248

20 • Introduction to Animal Physiology

21 • Circulation and Respiration

22 • Nutrition and Digestion

AT REST AND AT PLAY: OPTIMIZING HUMAN PHYSIOLOGICAL FUNCTIONING 790

23 • Nervous and Motor Systems

ACTIONS, REACTIONS, SENSATIONS, AND ADDICTIONS: MEET YOUR NERVOUS SYSTEM 836

24 • Hormones

MOOD, EMOTIONS, GROWTH, AND MORE: HORMONES AS MASTER REGULATORS 888

25 • Reproduction and Development

FROM TWO PARENTS TO ONE EMBRYO TO ONE BABY

26 • Immunity and Health

HOW THE BODY DEFENDS AND MAINTAINS ITSELF

To Julia

About the Author

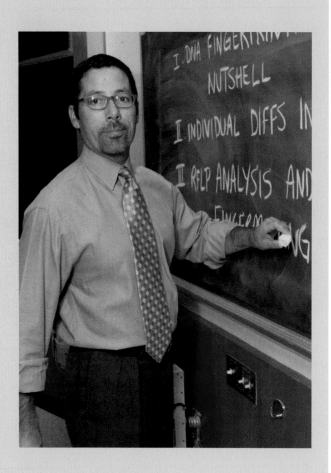

Jay Phelan teaches biology at UCLA, where he has taught introductory biology to more than 8,000 majors and non-majors students over the past twelve years. He received his Ph.D. in evolutionary biology from Harvard in 1995, and his master's and bachelor's degrees from Yale and UCLA. His primary area of research is evolutionary genetics, and his original research has been published in *Evolution*, *Experimental Gerontology*, and the *Journal of Integrative and Comparative Biology*, among other journals. His research has been featured on *Nightline*, CNN, the BBC, and National Public Radio; in *Science Times* and *Elle*; and in more than a hundred newspapers. He is the recipient of more than a dozen teaching awards.

With economist Terry Burnham, Jay is the co-author of the international best-seller *Mean Genes: From Sex to Money to Food—Taming Our Primal Instincts*. Written for the general reader, *Mean Genes* explains in simple terms how knowledge of the genetic basis of human nature can empower individuals to lead more satisfying lives.

Dear Readers,

Biology is about you and it touches on your life every day, in dozens of ways. It's creative. It's fun. And understanding it is increasingly essential to your life. I wrote this book because I want to help you become biologically literate: to talk confidently and knowledgeably about science with your friends, and to understand and appreciate both the beauty and the utility of this subject.

There are two versions of *What Is Life? A Guide to Biology.* One of them, *What Is Life? A Guide to Biology with Physiology,* includes all of the chapters of the other version, with an additional ten chapters on plant and animal physiology. It's not always possible to include these chapters in a one-term course, but they include a rich introduction to the importance of biology to understanding the processes central to how many organisms work, with particular significance for human health.

You will find here an overview of the key themes in biology as well as the specifics about topics meaningful to your life. You'll find answers to the questions that you're curious about, whether you are a future lawyer, teacher, entrepreneur, parent, consumer, citizen, or all of the above:

- Why are humans one of the only species to have friendships?
- Is DNA fingerprinting foolproof?
- Why do dieters lose so much "water weight" during the beginning of a diet?
- Why isn't it always wise to take aspirin or other medicine when you have a fever?
- How does caffeine combat fatigue?

In this book, as in life, there are **interesting questions everywhere.** As you read, red Qs pose questions with real relevance to you, and point toward specific passages where you can uncover the answers. If you look at those bits of the text and don't think the answer is there, look again and think some more. You may be surprised at what you know. The **StreetBio Knowledge You Can Use** section at the end of each chapter unpacks biology-related questions with a practical twist, such as *How clean is that food you just dropped?* (See Chapter 13.)

There's much more to this book than just words. Flip through its pages and look at the **photographs.** For twenty years, I have searched for the best photos to illustrate biological concepts. I hand-picked every photo here with a special purpose in mind—it should provoke, engage, and inspire you, while helping you to make connections between complex ideas.

Because the subject is so varied, I don't want you to lose sight of "the big picture." And so, in organizing each chapter I have broken down the topics into **discrete sections.** At the end of each, I highlight the **Take-Home Message** in clear and concise terms. While there may be a lot of material, in these manageable chunks you can master it. The impact of science on your life is increasing every day. I hope that you embrace this exciting world of knowledge and that you gain as much satisfaction and enjoyment reading this book as I have received in putting it together for you.

Sincerely,

Jay Phelan

Acknowledgments

As a new graduate student at Harvard, I heard from experienced teaching fellows that if you were interested in learning how to be an effective teacher, it was essential to seek out extraordinary mentors. Based on word of mouth, I became involved with E. O. Wilson's course in Evolutionary Biology and Irven DeVore's course in Human Behavioral Biology. Both were known to be unusually provocative, challenging, and entertaining classes for non-science majors.

I aggressively pursued teaching positions in both classes—which I held onto tightly for 12 semesters. Working under these legendary instructors, I was set on a course that inspired and prepared me to write this book. The two courses were quite different from each other, but at their core both were built on two beliefs that are central to this book and to my thinking about education: (1) Biology is creative, interesting, and fun. (2) Biology is relevant to the daily life of every person. There was a palpable sense that, in teaching non-science majors especially, we had a responsibility to provide our students with the tools to thrive in a society increasingly permeated by scientific ideas and issues, and that one of our most effective strategies would be to convey the excitement we felt for biology and the enormous practical value it has to help us understand the world.

I thank Professors Wilson and DeVore for all that they have shared with me.

My development as a scientist and, particularly, my appreciation for rigorous and methodical thinking have been shaped by the kind support and wise guidance of Richard Lewontin. I have also been fortunate to have as a long-time mentor and collaborator Michael Rose, who has instilled in me a healthy skepticism about any observation in life that is not fivefold replicated. And for almost daily insightful input on matters relating to scientific content, teaching, writing, and more, I thank Terry Burnham.

There are many other friends and colleagues I wish to thank for helping me with *What Is Life? A Guide to Biology with Physiology.* In researching and writing the book and in developing the numerous courses I teach, I have benefited from more than a decade of perceptive and valuable contributions too numerous to list from Glenn Adelson, Alon Ziv, Michael Cooperson, and Alicia Moretti. I am tremendously appreciative of all they have done for me.

For a project covering so many topics and years, it is essential to have a close group of trusted, tolerant, and knowledgeable colleagues, I am grateful to Harold Owens, Greg Graffin, Jeff Egger, Andy Tobias, Elisabeth Tobias, Joshua Malina, Melissa Merwin-Malina, Bill U'ren, Chris Bruno, Michelle Richmond, and Meredith Dutton, who have offered advice, guidance, and support, far beyond the call of duty. Numerous colleagues at UCLA provided assistance and support, including Steve Strand, Cliff Brunk, Fred Eiserling, Emil Reisler, Deb Pires, Lianna Johnson, Gaston Pfluegl, Bob Simons, Frank Laski, Jeff Thomas, and Tracy Newman.

I owe a tremendous debt to Sara Tenney, without whose vision and knowledge this project could never have been begun. Thank you, Sara. W. H. Freeman is an extremely author-centric publisher. Throughout the process of creating this book, from the first inception of the idea through the production of all the supplementary materials, Liz Widdicombe, Brian Napack, and John Sargent have been tremendously supportive. I am grateful for their welcoming me into their publishing family. Publisher Peter Marshall has been a tenacious, versatile, and skillful manager of the entire team. I am very fortunate to have such a wise leader overseeing all aspects of this project.

The team of editors that worked with me on this book—and two people in particular—improved it immeasurably. I cannot adequately convey my gratitude to development editor Jane Tufts, whose meticulous attention to detail, commitment to accuracy, and almost obsessive drive to create a thorough and readable book are apparent on every page. And development editor Beth Howe, who oversaw every aspect of the writing and production of the book, attending to issues of content and design while making insightful contributions throughout, expertly managed the thousand details necessary to put everything together.

It is impossible to teach biology without illustrations. My deepest gratitude goes to Tommy Moorman for creating such innovative and effective figures for the book. Tommy's vision for an elegant and beautiful art program completely integrated with the text is apparent on every page. Working with him to develop each illustration in this book has been one of my most enjoyable and satisfying professional collaborations. Thanks also go to Erin Daniel and Alison Kendall for assisting with the creation of the illustrations. For excellent assistance with photo research, thanks to Deborah Anderson, Christine Buese, and Elyse Rieder.

I wish to thank Harvey Pough for providing excellent drafts of Chapters 11–13 and contributing to Chapter 16. Thanks are due to Kelly Hogan for writing a fine draft of chapter 26.

For creating the innovative media and print materials that accompany the book, I am thankful for the vision of my excellent media editor, Patrick Shriner, and for the work of supplements editor Beth McHenry. I thank all of the authors who have created instructor and student resources for this book. I also appreciate the contributions of Renee Altier, Kimberly White, and Larry Jankovic to Prep-U. Sheri Snavely provided significant guidance in developing pedagogical strategies throughout the book; I also appreciate her thoughtful and smart advice at nearly every step in the publishing process. Copyeditor Linda Strange helped to ensure consistency and readability throughout the text. I thank Chris Hunt for compiling the thorough index, and Elaine Palucki for coordinating reviews. The rest of the life sciences editorial team at W. H. Freeman, too, have been knowledgeable and supportive, particularly Kate Parker, Marc Mazzoni, Jerry Correa, Susan Winslow, Susan Moran, Lisa Samols, and Marni Rolfes.

For their efficiency and commitment to producing a beautiful book, I am most grateful to the W. H. Freeman production team: Mary Louise Byrd, Diana Blume, Julia DeRosa, Philip McCaffrey, and Ellen Cash. Sheridan Sellers did an artistic job of page composition. Thank you! Thanks are also due to Dusty Friedman for keeping the book on track.

The people on the marketing team at W. H. Freeman have contributed enormously in helping with the challenging task of introducing a new book to students and instructors across the country. Debbie Clare, Steve Rigolosi, Brenda Bravener, and John Britch have been enthusiastic and dedicated in creating materials and strategies to assist instructors in evaluating the ways that *What Is Life? A Guide to Biology with Physiology* can aid them as they develop their own courses and strategies for success.

Finally, I thank my family—Kevin Phelan, Patrick Phelan, Erin Enderlin, and my parents—for their unwavering support and interest as I wrote this book. Reading draft after draft and following each revision, they made valuable contributions at every stage. I thank Jack, Charlie, and Sam, too. Most of all, for her generous and passionate support of this project from day one, her substantive contributions to both the content and presentation of ideas, and so much more, I thank Julia.

Contact the author with your feedback.

The content of this book has been greatly improved through the counsel of reviewers and students. Your comments, suggestions, and criticism are also welcome; they are essential in guiding its ongoing evolution. Please contact the author at **jay@jayphelan.com**. (He's serious about this.)

We thank the many reviewers who aided in the development of this text.

Text Development

Stephanie J. Aamodt, University of Louisiana–Shreveport
M. Stephen Ailstock, Anne Arundel Community College
Sylvester Allred, Northern Arizona University
Jessica K. Baack, Montgomery Community College–Rockville
Marilyn Banta, Texas State University–San Marcos
Sarah Barlow, Middle Tennessee State University
Rebecca A. Bartow, Western Kentucky University
Brian J. Baumgartner, Trinity Valley Community College
José Bava, El Camino Community College
Cynthia Bida, Henry Ford Community College
William Blanton, St. Phillip's College
Lisa L. Boggs, Southwestern Oklahoma State University
Charlotte Borgeson, University of Nevada–Reno
Susan L. Bower, Pasadena City College
Peggy Brickman, University of Georgia
Jason Brown, Young Harris College
Carole L. Browne, Wake Forest University
Neil J. Buckley, State University of New York–Plattsburgh
Anne E. Bunnell, East Carolina University
Joseph Burdo, Bridgewater State University
David Byres, Florida Community College–Jacksonville
William Caire, University of Central Oklahoma
Michael S. Carr, Oakton Community College
Kelly Carrillo Burke, College of the Canyons
Jeannie Chapman, University of South Carolina–Spartansburg
Thomas Chen, Santa Monica College
Roger Choate, Oklahoma City Community College
Thomas F. Chubb, Villanova University
Nira Clark, Southwestern College
Erica Cline, University of Washington
George Clokey, University of Wisconsin–Whitewater
Sandi Connelley, Rochester Institute of Technology
Erica Corbett, Southeastern Oklahoma State University
Anthony D. Cornett, Valencia Community College–Osceola
Becky Croteau, Lincoln Land Community College
Karen Curto, University of Pittsburgh
Don C. Dailey, Austin Peay State University
Michael S. Dann, Pennsylvania State University
Douglas W. Darnowski, Indiana University–Southeast
Garry Davies, University of Alaska
Renee Dawson, University of Utah

Lewis E. Deaton, University of Louisiana–Lafayette
Tom Deaton, Auburn University
Elizabeth Anne Desy, Southwestern Minnesota State University
Sandra G. Devenny, Delaware County Community College
Doreen R. Dewell, Whatcom Community College
Mary E. Dominiecki, Slippery Rock University
Danielle DuCharme, Waubonsee Community College
Charles Dunn, Austin Community College
Frank DuRoy, Essex County College
Kari Eamma, Tarrant County Community College–Northeast
Heidi Engelhardt, Brandon University
Marirose T. Ethington, Genesee Community College
Rebecca A. Fetherson, University of Dayton
Anita Flick, North Carolina State University
Robert C. Frankis, University of New Mexico
Monica C. Frazier, Columbus State University
Anne Galbraith, University of Wisconsin–La Crosse
Elizabeth Gerbec, University of Wisconsin–River Falls
Sandra Gibbons, Moraine Valley College
Phil Gibson, University of Oklahoma
Philip G. Gibson, Gwinnett Technical College
Andrew Goliszek, North Carolina A & T State University
Stephen M. Gómez, Central New Mexico Community College
Becky C. Graham, University of West Alabama
Cara Gubbins, Butte College
Charles (Billy) Gunnels IV, Florida Gulf Coast University
Janelle M. Hare, Morehead State University
Carla Hass, Pennsylvania State University
Colleen Hatfield, California State University–Chico
J. L. Henriksen, Bellevue Community College
Deena Hergert, Rock Valley College
John A. Hnida, Peru State College
Berta Hopkins, Spartanburg Community College
Thomas Horvath, State University of New York–Oneonta
Laurie Host, Harford Community College
Adam W. Hrincevich, Louisiana State University
Catherine Hurlbut, Florida Community College at Jacksonville
Dianne Jennings, Virginia Commonwealth University
Mitrick A. Johns, Northern Illinois University
Robert D. Johnson Jr., Pierce College
Victoria Johnson, San Jose State University

Martin A. Kapper, Central Connecticut State University
Arnold J. Karpoff, University of Louisville
Todd Kelson, Brigham Young University–Idaho
Stephen T. Kenny, Yakima Valley Community College
Jennifer M. Kilbourne, Community College of Baltimore County
Joanne Kilpatrick, Auburn University–Montgomery
Brenda Knotts, Eastern Illinois University
Michael Koban, Morgan State University
Catherine Koo, Caldwell College
Olga R. Kopp, Utah Valley University
Anna Koshy, Houston Community College
Jerome A. Krueger, South Dakota State University
Jim Krupa, University of Kentucky
Josephine Kurdziel, University of Michigan
Archana Lal, Independence Community College
Ellen Shepard Lamb, University of North Carolina–Greensboro
Thomas Landefeld, California State University–Dominquez Hills
Leah LaPerle Larkin, University of New Mexico
Lynn Larsen, Portland Community College
Kathleen H. Lavoie, State University of New York–Plattsburgh
David E. Lemke, Texas State University
Gregory P. Lewis, Furman University
Harvey Liftin, Broward Community College
Sammy J. Liles, Lexington Community College
Cynthia W. Littlejohn, University of Southern Mississippi
Jonathan Lochamy, Georgia Perimeter College
Melanie Loo, California State University–Sacramento
Juan M. López-Bautista, University of Alabama
Blasé Maffia, University of Miami
Jose Maldonado, El Paso Community College–Valle Verde
Jeffrey M. Marcus, Western Kentucky University
Lloyd Douglas Martin, St. Edward's University
Betsy Maxim, Austin Community College
M. Victoria McDonald, University of Central Arkansas
Karen McFarland, Austin Peay State University
Mark A. McGinley, Texas Technical University
Malinda McMurry, Morehead State University
Cassandra Meeks, Oklahoma City College
Karen Meisch, Austin Peay State University
John Mersfelder, Sinclair Community College
Shahroukh Mistry, Westminster College
Jeanne Mitchell, Truman State University
Beth A. Montelone, Kansas State University
Cynthia L. Morin, Lincoln University of Missouri
Royden Nakamura, California Polytechnic–San Luis Obispo
Rocky Nation, Southern Wesleyan University
Allan D. Nelson, Tarleton State University
Kim Nelson, Pennsylvania State University
Tania Nezrick, Kishwaukee College
David Niebuhr, College of William and Mary
Meredith Sommerville Norris, University of North Carolina–Charlotte
Alexander E. Olvido, Virginia State University
Betsy Ott, Tyler Junior College
Joanna M. Padolina, Virginia Commonwealth University
Randi Papke, Southwestern Illinois College

Mary Paulson, Central Washington University
Krista Peppers, Central Arkansas University
John M. Pleasants, Iowa State University
Michael Plotkin, Mt. San Jacinto College
Gregory J. Podgorski, Utah State University
Ronald Porter, Pennsylvania State University
Melissa Presch, California State University–Fullerton
Eric Rabitoy, Citrus College
Karen Raines, Colorado State University
Erin Rempala, San Diego Mesa College
Dawn Ranish, Nova Southeastern University
Angela M. Reevely, Lonestar College
Melody Ricci, Victor Valley College
Kathleen Richardson, Portland Community College
Dave Rintoul, Kansas State University
Steven Rissing, The Ohio State University
Robert R. Robbins, Utah Valley State College
Bill Rogers, Ball State University
Troy T. Rohn, Boise State University
Thomas Rooney, Wright State University
Heather Rushforth, University of North Carolina–Greensboro
Susan T. Rouse, Southern Wesleyan University
Lynette Rushton, South Puget Sound Community College
Michael L. Rutledge, Middle Tennessee State University
Shamili Ajgaonkar Sandiford, College of DuPage
Amanda Schaetzel, Front Range Community College
John Schampel, Phoenix College (AZ)
Fayla Schwartz, Everett Community College
Jennifer Scoby, Illinois Central College
Erik P. Scully, Towson University
Juanita C. Sharpe, Chicago State University
Marilyn Shopper, Johnson County Community College
Michele Shuster, New Mexico State University
Neil E. Simister, Brandeis University
Colleen Sinclair, Towson University
Anu Singh-Cundy, Western Washington University
Jennifer Skillen, College of Southern Nevada
Kerri M. Skinner, University of Nebraska–Kearny
Pamela Skoubis, DePaul University
Marc Allen Smith, Sinclair Community College
Nancy G. Solomon, Miami University of Ohio
Roberta Lynn Soltz, Central Washington University
Bryan G. Spohn, Florida Community College at Jacksonville–Kent Campus
Amanda Starnes, Emory University
Leo Sternberg, University of Miami
Joan C. Stover, South Seattle Community College
Christine Stracey, University of Florida
Sukanya V. Subramanian, Collin County Community College
Franklyn Tan Te, Miami Dade Community College
William J. Thieman, Ventura College
Pamela Thinesen, Century College
Elizabeth M. Thomas, West Virginia University
Gene Thomas, Solano Community College
Michael W. Thompson, Middle Tennessee State University

Jeffry Thornsberry, Northwest Missouri State University
William Unsell, The University of Central Oklahoma
Paul Ustach, San Joaquin Delta College
Martin A. Vaughan, Indiana University/Purdue University at Indianapolis
Kim Vietti, Illinois Central College
Hung Vu, Tarrant County College
Jack Waber, West Chester University of Pennsylvania
Jennifer M. Warner, University of North Carolina–Charlotte
John E. Whitlock, Hillsborough Community College
Elizabeth Willott, University of Arizona
Clifford Wilson, Chicago State University
Mark Woelfle, Vanderbilt University
Carol Wymer, Morehead State University
Calvin Young, Fullerton College
Kerry Yurewicz, Plymouth State University
Michelle Zimmerman, Indiana University Southeast
Brenda Zink, Northeastern Junior College

Art Development

Ann Aguanno, Marymount Manhattan College
Neil Baker, Ohio State University
Marilyn Banta, Texas State University–San Marcos
Christine Barrow, Prince George's Community College
Mark Belk, Brigham Young University
Kristen Byrd, Tarrant Community College (Northeast)
Kelly Carrillo Burke, College of the Canyons
William Caire, University of Central Oklahoma
Claudia Cash, Tarrant Community College (Northeast)
Debra Chapman, Wilkes University
Genevieve C. Chung, Broward Community College
Jeffrey Scott Coker, Elon University
Sandi Connelley, Rochester Institute of Technology
Michael S. Dann, Pennsylvania State University
Renee Dawson, University of Utah
Francisco Delgado, Pima Community College
Sandra G. Devenny, Delaware County Community College
Doreen R. Dewell, Whatcom Community College
Hartmut G. Doebel, George Washington University
Diane Lynn Doidge, Grand View College
James Doyle, College of the Holy Cross
Kari Eamma, Tarrant Community College (Northeast)
Dave Eakin, Eastern Kentucky University
Gerald Farr, Texas State University–San Marcos
Paul Farnsworth, University of New Mexico
Brandon L. Foster, Wake Technical and Community College
Patrick Galliart, North Iowa Community College
David Gordon, Pittsburg State University
Charles (Billy) Gunnels IV, Florida Gulf Coast University
Joe Harsh, Butler University
Bernard Hauser, University of Florida
Jane J. Henry, Baton Rouge Community College
Mark A. Holland, Salisbury University

Laurie Host, Harford Community College
Virginia E. Irintcheva, Black Hawk College–Quad City Campus
Philip Jardim, City College of San Francisco
Denim M. Jochimsen, University of Idaho
Judy Kaufman, Monroe Community College
Ariel R. Krakowski, Laney College
Carissa Krane, University of Dayton
Dan E. Krane, Wright State University
Maria Kretzman, Glendale College
Kathleen H. Lavoie, State University of New York–Plattsburgh
Mary LeFever, Columbus State Community College
Jeff Kiggans, Monroe Community College
Jose Maldonado, El Paso Community College–Valle Verde
Stephen Matheson, Calvin College
James McCaughern-Carucci, Quinnipiac University
Karen McFarland Meisch, Austin Peay State University
Dorian R. McMillan, College of Charleston
Caroline McNutt, Schoolcraft College
Lori A. Pitkofsky, Rampano College
Joel Piperburg, Millersville University
Michael P. Robinson, Miami University
Wendy F. Rothwell, University of California–Santa Cruz
Matt Schmidt, SUNY–Stonybrook
Jason F. Schreer, State University of New York–Potsdam
Jennifer J. Scoby, Illinois Central College
Dawn Sherry, Macon State University
Cara Shillington, Eastern Michigan University
Patricia L. Smith, Valencia Community College
Jill M. Tall, Youngstown State University
Jeffrey Thomas, California State University–Northridge
Bruce Tomlinson, State University of New York–Fredonia
Joy B. Trauth, Arkansas State University
Alan R. Wasmoen, Metropolitan Community College
Brad Wetherbee, University of Rhode Island
Michael Windelspecht, Appalachian State University
David E. Wolfe, American River College
Kerry Yurewicz, Plymouth State University

Accuracy Reviewers

Adrienne Alaie-Petrillo, Hunter College
Sylvester Allred, Northern Arizona University
Brian Bagatto, University of Akron
Christine Bezotte, Elmira College
Kelly Carrillo Burke, College of the Canyons
Michael Carr, Oakton Community College
Michelle Cawthorn, Georgia Southern University
Erica Champion, Yale University
William Crampton, University of Central Florida
Michael S. Dann, Pennsylvania State University
Renee Dawson, University of Utah
Jean DeSaix, University North Carolina at Chapel Hill
D. Michael Denbow, Virginia Polytechnic Institute and State University
Sherri Graves, Sacramento City College

Janelle M. Hare, Morehead State University

Bernard Hauser, University of Florida

Albert Herrera, University of Southern California

John A. Hnida, Peru State College

Kelly Hogan, University of North Carolina–Chapel Hill

Jane Horlings, Saddleback College

Anne Houtman, California State University–Fullerton

Victoria Johnson, San Jose State University

Nancy Kinkaid, Troy University

Ariel R. Krakowski, Laney College

Paul Marshall, Northern Essex Community College

Jennifer Metzler, Ball State University

Michael Silva, El Paso Community College

Ignatius Tan, New York University

Pamela Thinesen, Century College

Jeffrey Thomas, California State University–Northridge

Christopher Thompson, Loyola University Maryland

Martin A. Vaughan, Indiana University/Purdue University at Indianapolis

William A. Velhagen, New York University

Michael Wenzel, California State University–Sacramento

John E. Whitlock, Hillsborough Community College

David Wolfe, American River College

Focus Group Attendees

Text and Content Development

(2004, Los Angeles)

Garen Baghdasarian, Santa Monica College

Thomas Chen, Santa Monica College

Elizabeth Ciletti, Pasadena City College

Mary Colavito, Santa Monica College

Ana Ester Escandon, Los Angeles Harbor College

Phyllis Hirsh, East Los Angeles College

Melody Ricci, Victor Valley College

(2004, Memphis)

T. Wayne Barger, Tennessee Technical University

Don Baud, University of Memphis

Jay Blundon, Rhodes College

Martha P. Brown, University of Memphis

Dave Eakin, Eastern Kentucky University

Stan Eisen, Christian Brothers University

Jack Grubaugh, University of Memphis

Min-Ken Lao, Furman University

(2004, Chicago)

Sandra Bobick, Community College of Alleghany

Christopher Dobson, Grand Valley State University

Sondra Dubowsky, Allen County Community College

Eileen Gregory, Rollins College

Tracy Harris, Florida Keys Community College

Robert Krasner, Providence College

Bernard A. Marcus, Genesee Community College

Laurel B. Roberts, University of Pittsburgh

Lyndell P. Robinson, Lincoln Land Community College

Brian Schmaefsky, Kingwood College

Janet Vigna, Grand Valley State University

Daniel W. Ward, Waubonsee Community College

(2006, Florida)

Peggy Brickman, University of Georgia

Anne E. Bunnell, East Carolina University

Cara Gubbins, Butte College

Janelle M. Hare, Morehead State University

John A. Hnida, Peru State College

Mitrick A. Johns, Northern Illinois University

Kathleen H. Lavoie, State University of New York–Plattsburgh

Blasé Maffia, University of Miami

Gregory J. Podgorski, Utah State University

Susan T. Rouse, Southern Wesleyan University

Jennifer M. Warner, University of North Carolina–Charlotte

Physiology

(2009, San Francisco)

Dan Alex, Chabot College

Dennis Anderson, Oklahoma City Community College

Sean Brumbaugh, Santa Rose Junior College

Tom Chen, Santa Monica College

Genevieve Chung, Broward Community College (Central)

Melinda Downing, Merritt College

Danielle DuCharme, Waubonsee Community College

Gerald Farr, Texas State University–San Marcos

Ari Krakowski, Laney College

Jennifer Lange, Chabot College

Pramila Sen, Houston Community College

Michael Windelspecht, Appalachian State University

Art Development

(2007, Atlanta)

Renee Dawson, University of Utah

Charles (Billy) Gunnels IV, Florida Gulf Coast University

Bernard Hauser, University of Florida

Arnold J. Karpoff, University of Louisville

Stephen R. Kelso, University of Illinois–Chicago

Meredith Sommerville Norris, University of North Carolina–Charlotte

Therese M. Poole, Georgia State University

Mary Celeste Reese, Mississippi State University

Bill Rogers, Ball State University

Kim Cleary Sadler, Middle Tennessee State University

Amy S. Wernette, Hazard Community College

Media and Supplements

(2007, Santa Monica)

Michael Bucher, College of San Mateo

Kelly Carrillo Burke, College of the Canyons

John A. Hnida, Peru State College

Anne Houtman, California State University–Fullerton
Hinrich Kaiser, Victor Valley College
Melanie Loo, California State University–Sacramento
Gregory J. Podgorski, Utah State University
Melissa Presch, California State University–Fullerton
Calvin Young, Fullerton College

(2008, Miami)

Barbara Blonder, Flagler College
Charlotte Borgeson, University of Nevada–Reno
Kris Curran, University of Wisconsin–Whitewater
Kari Eamma, Tarrant Community College
Evelyn Frazier, Florida Atlantic University
John Janovy, University of Nebraska–Lincoln
Jennifer Schramm, Chemeketa Community College
Greg Sievert, Emporia University
Heather Vance Chalcraft, East Carolina University
Martin A. Vaughan, Indiana University/Purdue University at Indianapolis

Comparative Reviewers

Zulfiqar Ahmad, East Tennessee State University
Julie H. Aires, Florida Community College at Jacksonville
William Anyonge, Xavier University
Tami Asplin, North Dakota State University
Randy Brewton, University of Tennessee–Knoxville
Dustin Brisson, University of Pennsylvania
Jeannie Chapman, University of South Carolina–Upstate
Thomas Chen, Santa Monica College
Craig Clifford, Northeastern State University
William Gareth Richard Crampton, University of Central Florida
Chris Davison, Long Beach City College
Tiffany Doan, Central Connecticut State University
Ernest F. DuBrul, University of Toledo
Eugene Fenster, Metropolitan Community College–Longview
Rebecca Fetherson, University of Dayton
Teresa G. Fischer, Indian River State College
Anita Pardue Flick, North Carolina State University
Paul Florence, Jefferson Community and Technical College
Evelyn Frazier, Florida Atlantic University
Diane Wilkening Fritz, Northern Kentucky University
Dennis W. Fulbright, Michigan State University
Douglas C. Gayou, University of Missouri–Columbia
Betsy Gerbec, University of Wisconsin–River Falls
Oliver Ghobrial, Santa Fe College
Julie Gibbs, College of DuPage
Florence K. Gleason, University of Minnesota
Bruce Griffis, Kentucky State University
Tim Grogan, Valencia Community College
Charles J. Grossman, Xavier University
Luis S. Guerra, South Texas College
Pieter de Haan, Berkeley City College

Mary F. Haskins, Rockhurst University
Keith R. Hench, Kirkwood Community College
Sherry Hickman, Hillsborough Community College
Mark Hollier, Georgia Perimeter College
Robert A. Holmes, Hutchinson Community College
Laurie Host, Harford Community College
Robert Iwan, Inver Hills Community College
Philip Jardim, City College of San Francisco
Dianne Jennings, Virginia Commonwealth University
David Knowles, East Carolina University
Kim Lackey, University of Alabama
Ellen Lamb, University of North Carolina at Greensboro
David Loring, Johnson County Community College
Bill Mackay, Edinboro University of Pennsylvania
Barbara Mania-Farnell, Purdue University–Calumet
Tom J. McConnell, Ball State University
Wallace M. Meyer, College of the Redwoods
Thelma Miller-Anderson, Hillsborough Community College
Michael R. Millward, University of Cincinnati
Brenda Moore, Truman State University
Michael Muller, University of Illinois–Chicago
Zia Nisani, Antelope Valley College
Tanya Noel, York University
James Nolan, Georgia Gwinnett College
Laura Palmer, Pennsylvania State University–Altoona
Louis Pech, University of Wisconsin Centers–Marathon County
Joel B. Piperberg, Millersville University
Karen Plucinski, Missouri Southern State University
Aggie Posthumus, Olivet Nazarene University
Bonnie Ripley, Grossmont College
Troy Rohn, Boise State University
Matthew Rowe, Sam Houston State University
Yelena Rudayeva, Palm Beach Community College
Arthur Sandquist, Washburn University
Donald Slish, Plattsburgh State University
Christine Stracey, University of Florida
Anthony J. Stancampiano, Oklahoma City Community College
Tim Strakosh, State University of New York–Fredonia
Richard P. Stringer, Harrisburg Area Community College
Mark Sturtevant, Oakland University
Sukanya Subramanian, Collin County Community College
Rob Swatski, Harrisburg Area Community College
Kimberly Taugher, Diablo Valley College
Jeffrey Thornsberry, Northwest Missouri State
Nina Thumser, Indiana University of Pennsylvania
Jonathan Titus, State University of New York–Fredonia
Mike Tveten, Pima Community College Northwest
Katherine M. Van de Wal, Community College of Baltimore County–Essex Campus
Leslie VanderMolen, Humboldt State University
Fred Vogt, Elgin Community College
William A. Wehbi, University of Pennsylvania

John E. Whitlock, Hillsborough Community College
Jennifer Wiatrowski, Pasco-Hernando Community College
Christina Willis, Rockhurst University

Donald S. Wood, Odessa College
Aimee Wurst, Lincoln University of Missouri
Lan Xu, South Dakota State University

We thank the hundreds of students and faculty at the schools listed below for class-testing elements of the text.

Q Questions

Borough of Manhattan Community College
Broward Community College
Central New Mexico Community College
Colorado Mountain College
Florida Community College–Jacksonville
Heartland Community College
Johnson County Community College
Kutztown University of Pennsylvania
Lincoln Land Community College
Metropolitan Community College
Mt. San Jacinto College
Portland State University
Rowan University
Seattle Central Community College
Suffolk County Community College–Ammerman
Tarrant County Community College (Northeast)
University of Northern Colorado
Wake Technical Community College

Chapters

(2007)
College of San Mateo
Georgia Perimeter College
Georgia State University
Hazard Community College
Southwestern College
University of Arizona
University of Louisville
University of North Carolina–Charlotte
University of Utah
Utah State University
Virginia Commonwealth University

(2008)
Bluegrass Community College
California State University–Northridge
Chaffey College

Clark Atlanta University
Columbus State University
Daytona Community College
Edinboro University
Genesee Community College
George Washington University
Glendale College
Lake Land College
Long Beach Community College
Los Angeles Harbor College
Macon State University
Marshall University
McPherson College
Millersville University of Pennsylvania
Milwaukee Area Technical College
Owensboro Community College
Oxnard College
Philadelphia University
Prince George's Community College
Quinnipiac University
Rock Valley College
Sacramento City College
Salem State College
San Jose State University
Sinclair Community College
Southwestern College
St. Clair Community College
University of New Mexico
University of Rhode Island
Valencia Community College

(2009)
Central Carolina Community College
Florida Community College at Jacksonville
Maple Woods Community College
Morton College
Virginia Commonwealth University
Virginia Polytechnic Institute and State University

The media and supplements package was created with the input of many dedicated and experienced non-majors biology instructors.

Reviewers

Ann Aguanno, Marymount Manhattan College
Charlotte E. Borgeson, University of Nevada–Reno
Kelly Carillo Burke, College of the Canyons
Michelle Cawthorn, Georgia Southern University
G. Chung, Broward Community College
Michael S. Dann, Pennsylvania State University
Gerald Farr, Texas State University–San Marcos
Debra B. Folsom, Pasadena City College
Julie V. Gibbs, College of DuPage
Stephen M. Gómez, Central New Mexico Community College
Jane J. Henry, Baton Rouge Community College
Jane Horlings, Saddleback College
Carina Endres Howell, Lock Haven University
John Janovy Jr., University of Nebraska–Lincoln
Hinrich Kaiser, Victor Valley College
Judy Kaufman, Monroe Community College
Charlease Kelly-Jackson, Claflin University

Patrick J. Lewis, Sam Houston State University
Cindy S. Malone, California State University–Northridge
Jon Milhon, Azusa Pacific University
Meredith Sommerville Norris, University of North Carolina–Charlotte
Greg Podgorski, Utah State University
Lawrence F. Roberge, Florida Community College–Jacksonville
William D. Rogers, Ball State University
Georgianna Saunders, Missouri State University
Jason Schreer, SUNY–Potsdam
Marilyn Shopper, Johnson County Community College
Carol St. Angelo, Hofstra University
Eric Stavney, North Seattle Community College
Alicia Steinhardt, Hartnell College
Jamey Thompson, Hudson Valley Community College
Helen Walter, Diablo Valley College
Jennifer M. Warner, University of North Carolina–Charlotte
Michael Windelspecht, Appalachian State University

The **What Is Life?** media and supplements package was created with the input of hundreds of non-majors biology instructors and through the hard work of our experienced and committed media and supplements contributor team.

Instructor's Manual—Classroom Catalysts
Verona A. Barr, Heartland Community College
Stephen M. Gómez, Central New Mexico Community College
Paul H. Marshall, Northern Essex Community College
Lawrence Roberge, Laboure College
David E. Wolfe, American River College

Connecting Biology to Life: Application Books
Mike Tveten, Pima Community College, Tucson

eBook and Non-Majors Biology Study Tools
Robert Iwan, Inver Hills Community College
Eric Stavney, North Seattle Community College

Figure Conversion Engine Tool
Ann Aguanno, Marymount Manhattan College

Image Bank Advisor
Jane J. Henry, Baton Rouge Community College

Keynote Lecture Presentation
Michael C. Bucher, College of San Mateo

PowerPoint Lecture Outlines
Kristen L. Curran, University of Wisconsin–Whitewater
Danielle DuCharme, Waubonsee Community College
Jennifer Lange, Chabot College
Mark S. Manteuffel, St. Louis Community College

Prep-U Instructor's Test Bank and Prep-U for Students
Glenn Adelson, Lake Forrest College
Jay Phelan, University of California, Los Angeles
Alon Ziv, Prep-U

Q Animations
Anne Bunnell, East Carolina University
G. Chung, Broward College
Johnny El-Rady, University of South Florida
Eric Stavney, North Seattle Community College
Julie V. Gibbs, College of DuPage

Student Success Guide for Phelan's What Is Life?
Meredith S. Norris, University of North Carolina–Charlotte
Jennifer M. Warner, University of North Carolina–Charlotte

Questions About Life Reader
Heather Vance-Chalcraft, East Carolina University

Student Worksheets
Michael C. Bucher, College of San Mateo

Hands-On Biology:Laboratories for Distance Learning
Mimi Bres, Arnold Weisshaar, and Cassandra Moore-Crawford, Prince George's Community College (all)

Exploring Biology: Case Studies
Michelle Cawthorn, Georgia Southern University
Jennifer L. Holzman, Emory University

What Is Life?

A Guide to BIOLOGY with PHYSIOLOGY

1

Scientific Thinking

Your best pathway
to understanding
the world

Already a scientist? It starts with curiosity.

① Science is a collection of facts and a process for understanding the world.

1·1

What is science? What is biology?

You are already a scientist. You may not have realized this yet, but it's true. Because humans are curious, you have no doubt asked yourself or others questions about how the world works and wondered how you might find the answers.

- Does the radiation released by cell phones cause brain tumors?
- Are antibacterial hand soaps better than regular soap?
- Do large doses of vitamin C reduce the likelihood of getting a cold?

These are all important and serious questions. But you've probably also pondered some less weighty issues, too.

- Why is morning breath so stinky? And can you do anything to prevent it?
- Why is it always windy on streets with tall buildings?
- Does taking aspirin before drinking alcohol lead to faster intoxication?

And if you really put your mind to the task, you will start to find questions all around you whose answers you might like to know (and, like those above, whose answers you will learn as you read this book).

- Why is it that seaside towns are not as hot in the summer or as cold in the winter as inland communities?

- Why do so few women get into barroom brawls?
- What is "blood doping" and does it really improve athletic performance?
- Why is it so much easier for an infant to learn a complex language than it is for a college student to learn biology?

Still not convinced you're a scientist? Then here's some good news: science doesn't require advanced degrees or secret knowledge dispensed over years of technical training. It does, however, require an important feature of our species—a big brain—as well as curiosity and a desire to learn about the world around us and inside us. But curiosity, casual observations, and desire can only take you so far. In today's world there are important and pressing issues that require some understanding of science, what it can and can't do, and what it can and can't explain. Nutritional claims on foods and dietary supplements, human behavior, health and disease, how drugs can cure or poison you, the interactions of plants, animals, and their environments, global warming, the continuity and diversity of life in all its forms—by learning more about science, you can think about, learn about, and understand issues like these and things about yourself, your life, and the world around you.

To satisfy your curiosity and to explain seemingly unexplainable, mysterious, or magical things, curiosity and the desire to learn are not enough. Explaining how something works or why something happens requires methodical, objective, and rational observation and analysis that are not clouded with emotions or preconceptions about what is being studied and observed.

Science is not simply a body of knowledge or a list of facts to be remembered. It is an intellectual activity, encompassing observation, description, experimentation, and explanation of natural phenomena. Put another way, science is a pathway by which we can come to discover and better understand the world around us. Later in this chapter, we explore specific ways in which we can most effectively use scientific thinking in our lives. But first let's look at how our understanding of the world can be enhanced by asking the single question that underlies scientific thinking:

Q Can we trust the packaging claims that companies make?

How do you know that is true?

Once you begin asking this question—of others and of yourself—you are on the road to a better understanding of the world.

The following story about a popular and successful over-the-counter medicine shows the importance of questioning the truth of many "scientific" claims you see on merchandise packages or read in newspaper or on the internet. For more than 10 years, a product called "Airborne" was marketed and sold to millions of customers. On the packaging and in advertisements, the makers asserted that Airborne tablets could ward off colds and boost your immune system (**FIGURE 1-1**). Not surprisingly, Airborne was a great success and generated

FIGURE 1-1 Some products claim to improve our health, but how do we know if they work?

more than $100 million in revenue, and became one of the fastest selling health products ever. Then some consumers posed a reasonable question to the makers of Airborne: how do you know that it wards off colds?

To prove their claims, the makers of Airborne pointed to the results of a "double-blind, placebo-controlled study" conducted by a company specializing in clinical drug trials. We'll discuss exactly what those terms mean later in the chapter; for now we just need to note that as a result of a class-action lawsuit, it became clear that no such study had been conducted and that there was *no* evidence to back up Airborne's claims. The Airborne company removed the claims from the packaging and agreed to refund the purchase price to anyone who had bought Airborne. It also removed any reference to its "clinical trials," with the company's CEO saying that people "are really not scientifically minded enough to be able to understand a clinical study."

Are you insulted by the CEO's assumption about your intelligence? You should be. Did you or your parents (along with millions of other people) fall for Airborne's false claims? Possibly. But here's some more good news: you don't have to be at the mercy of slick packaging, false advertising, cranks, or charlatans that claim a product can ward off colds, make you lose 10 pounds in 7 days, make you healthier by cleansing your intestines, or increase or decrease the size of various body parts. You can learn to be skeptical and suspicious (in a good way) of such claims. You can learn exactly what it means to have scientific proof or evidence that something is absolutely true. And you can learn this by learning what it means to think scientifically.

Scientific thinking is an important and productive element in the study of a wide variety of topics: it can help you understand economics, psychology, history, and many other subjects. Our focus in this book is **biology,** the study of living things. Taking a scientific approach, we will investigate the facts and ideas in biology that are already known and will study the process by which we come to learn new things. As we move through the four parts of the book, we explore the most important questions in biology.

- What is the chemical and physical basis for life and its maintenance?

- How do organisms use genetic information to build themselves and to reproduce?

- What are the diverse forms that life on earth takes and how has that diversity arisen?

- How do organisms interact with each other and with their environment?

3

In this chapter, we explore how to think scientifically and how to use the knowledge we gain to make wise decisions. Although we generally restrict our focus to biology, scientific thinking can be applied to nearly every endeavor, and so in this chapter we use a wide range of examples—including some examples from beyond biology—as we learn how to think scientifically. Although the examples will vary greatly, they all convey a message that is key to scientific thinking: it's okay to be skeptical and you don't need to take things on faith.

Fortunately, learning to think scientifically is not difficult—and it can be fun, particularly because it is so empowering. **Scientific literacy,** a general, fact-based understanding of the basics of biology and other sciences, is increasingly important in our lives, and literacy in matters of biology is especially essential. As we see in the next section, issues hinging on biological ideas and processes are turning up in nearly every facet of our lives, from medicine to nutrition to personal relationships to politics, and even to crime and justice.

TAKE-HOME MESSAGE 1·1

Through its emphasis on objective observation, description, and experimentation, science is a pathway by which we can discover and better understand the world around us.

1·2

Biological literacy is essential in the modern world.

In the past, it was possible to get through life with little or no knowledge of science, but now scientific literacy has become a necessity. A brief glance at any newspaper will reveal just how many important health, social, medical, political, economic, and legal issues pivot on complex scientific data and theories.

- Why are unsaturated fats healthier for you than saturated fats?
- What are allergies? Why do they strike children from clean homes more than children from dirty homes?

- Why is friendship so common among humans yet extremely rare elsewhere in the animal kingdom?
- Why do new agricultural pests appear faster than new pesticides?
- What does scientific testing reveal about the accuracy of eyewitness testimony in courtrooms?

Biological literacy is the ability to (1) use the process of scientific inquiry to think creatively about real-world issues that have a biological component, (2) communicate these thoughts to others, and (3) integrate these ideas into your

FIGURE 1-2 In the news. Every day, news sources report on social, political, medical, and legal issues related to science.

What Is Science?   Scientific Method   Experimental Design   Decision Making

decision making. Biological literacy doesn't involve just the big issues facing society or just abstract ideas (**FIGURE 1-2**). It also matters to you personally. Should you take aspirin when you have a fever? Are you using the wrong approach if you try to lose weight and, after some initial success, you find your rate of weight loss diminishing? Is it a good idea to consume moderate amounts of alcohol?

> " Scientific issues permeate the law. I believe [that] in this age of science we must build legal foundations that are sound in science as well as in law. The result, in my view, will further not only the interests of truth but also those of justice.
>
> — U.S. Supreme Court Justice Stephen Breyer, at the annual meeting of the American Association for the Advancement of Science, February 1998 "

Biological issues—including global warming, fossil fuel use, stem cell research, and the proliferation of genetically modified foods—have also become important in political campaigns. And all around you, you will encounter products bearing too-good-to-be-true claims and technical-sounding language designed to lure you into purchasing them. Lack of biological literacy will put you at the mercy of "experts" who may try to confuse you or convince you of things in the interest of (their) personal gain. Scientific thinking will help you make wise decisions for yourself and for society.

TAKE-HOME MESSAGE 1·2

Biological issues permeate all aspects of our lives. To make wise decisions, it is essential for individuals and societies to attain biological literacy.

1·3

The scientific method is a powerful approach to understanding the world.

> " If science proves some belief of Buddhism wrong, then Buddhism will have to change.
>
> — The 14th Dalai Lama, *New York Times*, December 2005 "

It's a brand new age, and science, particularly biology, is everywhere. We are called upon more and more frequently to make decisions that hinge on our abilities to grasp biological information and to think scientifically. To illustrate the value of scientific thinking in understanding the world, let's look at what happens in its absence, by considering some unusual behaviors in the common laboratory rat.

Rats can be trained without much difficulty to push a lever to receive a food pellet from a feeding mechanism (**FIGURE 1-3**). When the mechanism is altered so that there is a 10-second delay between the lever being pushed and the food pellet being dispensed, however, strange things start to happen. In one cage, the rat will push the lever and then, very methodically, run and push its nose into one corner of the cage. Then it moves to another corner and again pushes its nose against the cage. It repeats this behavior at the third and fourth corners of the cage, after which the rat stands in front

of the feeder and the pellet is dispensed. Each time the rat pushes the lever it repeats the nose-in-the-corner sequence before moving to the food tray.

In another cage, with the same 10-second delay before the food pellet is dispensed, a rat pushes the lever and then

FIGURE 1-3 "In the absence of the scientific method . . ." Rats develop strange superstition-like behaviors if there is a 10-second delay between when they push a lever and when food is delivered.

proceeds to do three quick back-flips in succession. It then moves to the food tray for the food pellet when the 10 seconds have elapsed. Like the nose-in-the-corner rat, the back-flip rat will repeat this exact behavior each time it pushes the lever.

In cage after cage of rats with these 10-second-delay food levers, each rat eventually develops its own peculiar series of behaviors before moving to the food dish to receive the pellet. Why do they do this? Because it seems to work! They have discovered a method by which they can get a food pellet. To some extent, the rats' behaviors are reasonable. They associate two events—pushing the lever and

Q Why and when do people develop superstitions? Can animals be superstitious?

engaging in some sequence of behaviors—with another: receiving food. In a sense, they have taken a step toward understanding their world, even though the events are not actually related to each other.

Humans can also mistakenly associate actions with outcomes in an attempt to understand and control their world. The irrational belief that actions that are not logically related to a course of events can influence its outcome is called **superstition.** In the absence of scientific thinking, individuals can develop incorrect ideas, such as superstitions about how the world works (**FIGURE 1-4**). For example, Nomar Garciaparra, a

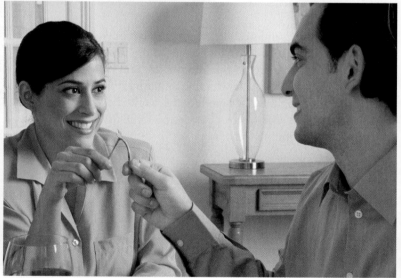

FIGURE 1-4 Superstitions abound. As comforting as myths and superstitions may be, they are no substitute for really understanding how the world works.

What Is Science?   Scientific Method   Experimental Design   Decision Making

baseball player for the Oakland Athletics, engages in a precise series of toe taps and adjustments to his batting gloves before he bats.

Beyond superstitions, humans have developed a variety of ways of understanding their world. Ancient Greeks, for example, understood that the evils of the world flew out of Pandora's box when, despite Zeus's strict orders not to open the box, her curiosity got the best of her and she lifted the lid. In the Kalahari desert, the African Bushmen tell the tale that their creator, Kaang, ordered them not to build fires. Because their ancestors forgot these orders and built a fire, Kaang punished them by destroying their friendship with animals. Although Bushmen and animals could communicate with each other in ancient times, now the animals simply fear the Bushmen.

Thousands of different narratives from all over the world exist to help people understand the world around them. These stories explain everything from birth and death to disease and healing. On the creation of the earth and universe alone, more than 4,000 narratives have been catalogued.

As helpful and comforting as stories and superstitions may be (or as helpful as people *think* they are!), they are no substitute for really understanding how the world works: for really understanding, for example, that you are sick not because the gods are displeased with you but because the water you are drinking is contaminated, and that, if the water can be purified, then you won't get sick. This kind of understanding does not come all at once by some magical power; instead, it begins when someone wonders about why something is the way it is and then decides to try to find out the answer. This process of examination and discovery is called the **scientific method.**

The scientific method usually begins with someone observing a phenomenon and proposing an explanation for it. Next, the proposed explanation is tested through a series of experiments. If the experiments reveal that the explanation is accurate, and if the experiments can be done by others with the same result,

then the explanation is considered to be valid. If the experiments do not support the proposed explanation, then the explanation must be revised or alternative explanations that more closely reflect experimental results must be proposed and tested. This process continues as better, more accurate explanations are found.

While the scientific method reveals much about the world around us, it doesn't explain everything. There are many other methods through which we can gain an understanding of the world. For example, much of our knowledge about plants and animals does not come from the use of the scientific method, but rather comes from systematic, orderly observation, without the testing of any explicit hypotheses. Other disciplines also involve understandings of the world based on non-scientific processes. Knowledge about history, for example, comes from the systematic examination of past events as they relate to humans, while the "truths" in other fields, such as religion, ethics, and even politics, often are based on personal faith, traditions, and mythology.

Scientific thinking can be distinguished from these alternative ways of acquiring knowledge about the world in that it is **empirical.** Empirical knowledge is based on experience and observations that are rational, testable, and repeatable. The empirical nature of the scientific approach makes it self-correcting: in the process of analyzing a topic, event, or phenomenon with the scientific method, incorrect ideas are discarded in favor of more accurate explanations. In the next sections, we look at how to put the scientific method into practice.

TAKE-HOME MESSAGE 1·3

There are numerous ways of gaining an understanding of the world. Because it is empirical, rational, testable, repeatable, and self-correcting, the scientific method is a particularly effective approach.

❷ A beginner's guide: what are the steps of the scientific method?

Scientific thinking relies on rational, testable, and repeatable observations.

1·4

Thinking like a scientist: how do you use the scientific method?

"Scientific method"—this term sounds like a rigid process to follow, much like following a recipe. In practice, however, the scientific method is not a single pathway that is always rigidly followed from start to finish. Rather, it is an adaptable process that includes many different methods. This flexibility makes the scientific method a more powerful process that can be used to explore a wide variety of thoughts, events, or phenomena, not only in science, but in other areas as well.

The basic steps in the scientific method are:

Step 1. Make observations.

Step 2. Formulate a hypothesis.

Step 3. Devise a testable prediction.

Step 4. Conduct a critical experiment.

Step 5. Draw conclusions and make revisions.

Once begun, though, the process doesn't necessarily continue linearly through the five steps until it is concluded (**FIGURE 1-5**). Sometimes, observations made in the first step can lead to more than one hypothesis and several testable predictions and

experiments. And the conclusions drawn from experiments often suggest new observations, refinements to hypotheses, and, ultimately, increasingly precise conclusions.

THE SCIENTIFIC METHOD

STEP 1	STEP 2	STEP 3	STEP 4	STEP 5
Make observations.	Formulate a hypothesis.	Devise a testable prediction.	Conduct a critical experiment.	Draw conclusions and make revisions.

💡 *The scientific method rarely proceeds in a straight line. Conclusions, for example, often lead to new observations and refined hypotheses.*

FIGURE 1-5 The scientific method: five basic steps and one flexible process.

What Is Science?   Scientific Method   Experimental Design   Decision Making

Q What should you do when something you believe in turns out to be wrong?

An especially important feature of the scientific method is that its steps are self-correcting. As we continue to make new observations, a hypothesis about how the world works might change. If our observations do not support our current hypothesis, that hypothesis must be given up in favor of one that is not contradicted by any observations. This may be the most important feature of the scientific method: *it tells us when we should change our minds.*

Because the scientific method is a general strategy for learning, it needn't be used solely to learn about nature or scientific things. In fact, we will investigate how it works by looking at a specific question that has recently begun to benefit from analysis using the scientific method:

• How reliable is eyewitness testimony in criminal courts?

For more than 200 years, courts in the United States have viewed eyewitness testimony as unassailable. Few things are seen as more convincing to a jury than an individual testifying that she can identify the person she saw commit a crime (**FIGURE 1-6**). Common sense has told us that events we see with our own two eyes are as they appear. But is eyewitness identification always right? Can the scientific method tell us whether this

Hold the fries. We apply an understanding of science when we choose foods from the menu that have fewer calories and less saturated fat.

FIGURE 1-6 "With your own two eyes . . ." How reliable is eyewitness testimony in criminal courts?

belief—or some other belief—is true? As we describe how to use the scientific method to answer questions about the world, it will become clear that the answer is a resounding *yes*. To show how the scientific method can be used to examine a wide variety of issues, we will also look at how the scientific method can be used to answer three additional questions:

• Does echinacea reduce the intensity or duration of the common cold?
• Does chemical runoff give rise to hermaphrodite fish?
• Does shaving hair from your face, legs, or anywhere else cause it to grow back coarser or darker?

TAKE-HOME MESSAGE 1·4

The scientific method (observation, hypothesis, prediction, test, and conclusion) is a flexible, adaptable, and efficient pathway to understanding the world, because it tells us when we must change our beliefs.

Step 1: Make observations.

Scientific study always begins with observations. At the first stage in the scientific method, we simply look for interesting patterns or cause-and-effect relationships. This is where a great deal of the creativity of science comes from. In the case of eyewitness testimony, we know now that new technologies have made it possible to assess whether tissue such as hair or blood from a crime scene came from a particular suspect. Armed with these tools, the Justice Department recently reviewed 28 criminal convictions that had been overturned by DNA evidence. They found that in most of the cases, the strongest evidence against the defendant during the trial had been eyewitness identification. The observation here is that many defendants who are later found to be innocent were initially convicted based on eyewitness testimony.

Opportunities for other interesting observations are unlimited. Using the scientific method, we can (and will) answer our three other questions.

Many people have claimed that consuming extracts of the herb echinacea can reduce the intensity or duration of symptoms of the common cold. For this reason, echinacea is a widely used herbal treatment (**FIGURE 1-7**). Returning to our fundamental question underlying the scientific method, we can ask: how do you know that is true?

• Does taking echinacea reduce the intensity or duration of the common cold?

Some people have noted that chemicals in sewage runoff—particularly those related to the hormone estrogen—seem to cause male fish to turn into hermaphrodites, organisms that have the reproductive organs of both sexes. Is this true?

• Does chemical runoff give rise to hermaphrodite fish?

And finally, some people have suggested that shaving hair from your face, legs, or anywhere else causes the hair to grow back coarser and darker. Is this true?

| STEP 1 | STEP 2 | STEP 3 | STEP 4 | STEP 5 |

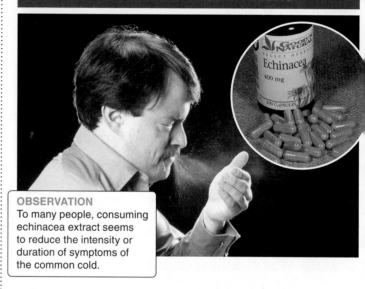

STEP 1: MAKE OBSERVATIONS

OBSERVATION
To many people, consuming echinacea extract seems to reduce the intensity or duration of symptoms of the common cold.

FIGURE 1-7 The first step of science: making observations about the world.

• Does hair that is shaved grow back coarser or darker?

Using the scientific method, we can answer all of these questions.

TAKE-HOME MESSAGE 1·5

The scientific method begins by making observations about the world, noting apparent patterns or cause-and-effect relationships.

What Is Science? | Scientific Method | Experimental Design | Decision Making

1·6

Step 2: Formulate a hypothesis.

Based on observations, we can develop a **hypothesis** (*pl.* **hypotheses**), a proposed explanation for observed phenomena. What hypotheses could we make about the eyewitness testimony observations described in the previous section? We could start with the hypothesis: "Eyewitness testimony is always accurate." We may need to modify our hypothesis later, but this is a good start. At this point, we can't draw any conclusions. All we have done is summarize some preliminary observations into a possible explanation for what we have observed.

To be most useful, a hypothesis must accomplish two things.

1. It must clearly establish mutually exclusive alternative explanations for a phenomenon. That is, it must be clear that if the proposed explanation is not supported by evidence or further observations, a different hypothesis is a more likely explanation.

2. It must generate testable predictions (**FIGURE 1-8**). This characteristic is important because we can only evaluate the validity of a hypothesis by putting it to the test. A hypothesis that can never be shown, by some form of observation, to be untrue is not a useful hypothesis. Consider, for example, the hypothesis that your dog loves you. If, for any observation someone makes, you can explain how that observation is consistent with your hypothesis, then the hypothesis is not useful (even if your dog really does love you).

For example we could disprove the "Eyewitness testimony is always accurate" hypothesis by demonstrating that, in certain circumstances, individuals who have witnessed a crime might misidentify the criminal when asked to select the suspect from a lineup.

Often researchers will pose a hypothesis as a negative statement proposing that there is no relationship between two factors, such as "Echinacea has no effect on the duration and severity of cold symptoms." Or "There is no difference in the coarseness or darkness of hair that has been shaved." A hypothesis that states a *lack* of relationship between two factors is called a **null hypothesis.** These hypotheses are equally valid but are easier to disprove. This is because a single piece of evidence or a single new observation that contradicts a null hypothesis is sufficient to reject it and conclude that an alternative hypothesis is true, or that it is highly probable that an alternative is true. So, once you have one piece of solid evidence that your null hypothesis is not true, you gain little by collecting further data. Conversely, it is impossible to prove a hypothesis is absolutely and permanently true: all evidence or further observations that support a hypothesis are valuable, but they do not rule out the possibility

STEP 1   STEP 2   STEP 3   STEP 4   STEP 5

STEP 2: FORMULATE A HYPOTHESIS

HYPOTHESIS
Echinacea reduces the duration and severity of the common cold.

FIGURE 1-8 Hypothesis: the proposed explanation for a phenomenon.

that some future evidence or observation might show that the hypothesis is not true.

For our other observations, we could state our hypotheses in two different ways:

Hypothesis: Echinacea reduces the duration and severity of the symptoms of the common cold.

Null hypothesis: Echinacea has no effect on the duration or severity of the symptoms of the common cold.

Hypothesis: Estrogens in sewage runoff turn fish into hermaphrodites.

Null hypothesis: Estrogens in sewage runoff have no effect in turning fish into hermaphrodites.

Hypothesis: Hair that is shaved grows back coarser and darker.

Null hypothesis: There is no difference in the coarseness or color of hair that is shaved relative to hair that is not shaved.

TAKE-HOME MESSAGE 1·6

A hypothesis is a proposed explanation for an observed phenomenon.

Step 3: Devise a testable prediction.

This step of the scientific method really is part of the previous step. Formulating a hypothesis is important, but not all hypotheses are created equal. Some, in fact (such as the hypothesis about your dog loving you), are of no use at all when it comes to helping us better understand the world. For a hypothesis to be useful, it must generate a prediction. That is, it must suggest that under certain conditions we will be able to observe certain outcomes. Put another way, a good hypothesis helps us make predictions about novel situations. This is a powerful feature of a good hypothesis: it guides us to knowledge about new situations.

All of this is rather abstract. Let's get more concrete with the four hypotheses we are considering. Keep in mind that when you do not understand some aspect of the world, any one of several possible explanations could be true. In devising a testable prediction from a hypothesis, the goal is to propose a situation that will give a particular outcome if your hypothesis is true, but will give a different outcome if your hypothesis is not true.

Hypothesis: Eyewitness testimony is always accurate.

Prediction: Individuals who have witnessed a crime will correctly identify the criminal regardless of whether multiple suspects are presented one at a time or all at the same time in a lineup.

This is a good, testable prediction because if our hypothesis is true, then our prediction will always be true. On the other hand, if one method of presenting suspects consistently causes incorrect identification of the criminal, our hypothesis cannot be true and must be revised or discarded.

Hypothesis: Echinacea reduces the duration and severity of the symptoms of the common cold (**FIGURE 1-9**).

Prediction: If echinacea reduces the duration and severity of the symptoms of the common cold, then individuals taking echinacea should get sick less frequently than those not taking it, and when they do get sick, their illness should not last as long.

Hypothesis: Estrogens in sewage runoff turn fish into hermaphrodites.

Prediction: If estrogens in sewage runoff turn fish into hermaphrodites, then exposing fish to estrogens should cause more fish to turn into hermaphrodites than when fish are not exposed to estrogens.

STEP 1   STEP 2   STEP 3   STEP 4   STEP 5

STEP 3: DEVISE A TESTABLE PREDICTION

Individuals treated with echinacea

Individuals not treated with echinacea

PREDICTION
If echinacea reduces the duration and the severity of symptoms of the common cold, then:
• Individuals taking echinacea should get sick less frequently than those not taking it.
• Individuals who get sick should recover more quickly.

FIGURE 1-9 Devising a testable prediction. For a hypothesis to be useful, it must generate a testable prediction.

Hypothesis: Hair that is shaved grows back coarser and darker.

Prediction: If shaving leads to coarser, darker hair growing back, then if individuals shaved one leg only, the hair that re-grows on that leg should become darker and coarser than the hair growing on the other leg.

As you begin to think scientifically, you will find yourself making a lot of "if . . . then" types of statements: "*If* that is true," referring to some hypothesis or assertion someone makes, or perhaps to a claim made by the manufacturer of a new health product, "*then* I would expect that . . ." proposing your own prediction about a related situation. Once you've made a testable prediction, the next step is to go ahead and test it.

TAKE-HOME MESSAGE 1•7

For a hypothesis to be useful, it must generate a testable prediction.

Step 4: Conduct a critical experiment.

Once we have formulated a hypothesis that generates a testable prediction, we conduct a **critical experiment,** an experiment that makes it possible to decisively determine whether a particular hypothesis is correct. There are many crucial elements in designing a critical experiment, and Section 1-11 covers the details of this process. For now, it is important just to understand that, with a critical experiment, if the hypothesis being tested is not true, we will make observations that compel us to reject that hypothesis.

In this step of the scientific method, a bit of cleverness can come in handy. Suppose we were to devise a critical experiment to test our hypothesis "Eyewitness testimony is always accurate." First, we stage a mock crime such as a purse snatching in front of a group of observers who do not know the crime is staged. Next, we ask observers to identify the criminal. To one group of observers we might present six "suspects" all at once in a lineup. To another group of observers, we might present the six suspects one at a time. The beauty of this experiment is that we actually know who the "criminal" is. With this knowledge, we can evaluate with certainty whether an eyewitness's identification is correct or not.

This exact experiment was done with an additional, devious little twist: the researcher did not include the actual "criminal" in any of the lineups of six "suspects." If eyewitness testimony is always accurate, however, this slight variation should not matter. We would predict that the observers in both groups (the lineup group and the one-at-a-time group) would indicate that the criminal was not present. In the next section, we will see what happened. Right now, let's devise critical experiments for our other hypotheses.

Hypothesis: Echinacea reduces the duration and severity of the symptoms of the common cold. The critical experiment for the echinacea hypothesis has been performed, and it is about as close to a perfect experiment as possible. Researchers began with 437 people who volunteered to be exposed to viruses that cause the common cold. Exposure to the cold-causing viruses was a bit unpleasant: all of the volunteers had cold viruses (in a watery solution) dripped into their noses. Research subjects were then secluded in hotel rooms for five days, and doctors examined them for the presence of the cold virus in their nasal cavity and for any cold symptoms (**FIGURE 1-10**).

The subjects were randomly divided into four groups. In two of the groups, each individual began taking a pill each day for

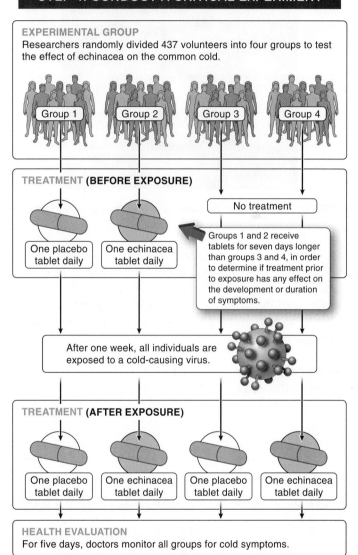

FIGURE 1-10 "When you need to know . . ." A critical experiment makes it possible to conclusively determine whether a hypothesis is correct.

a week prior to exposure to the cold virus. Those in one group received echinacea tablets while those in the other took a **placebo,** a pill that looked identical to the echinacea pill but contained no echinacea or other active ingredient. Neither

FIGURE 1-11 Does shaving hair cause it to grow back coarser or darker?

hypothesis, researchers placed cages containing male trout downstream from sewage treatment plants on several rivers in England. They then examined the fish for the presence of egg in their testes and tested their blood for the presence of an egg-production hormone that is not normally found in males.

Hypothesis: Hair that is shaved grows back coarser and darker. A critical experiment does not have to be complex or high-tech. All that matters is that it can decisively determine whether or not a hypothesis is correct. This point is illustrated by an experiment published in the scholarly journal *Archives of Facial Plastic Surgery.* Researchers decided to test the hypothesis that shaving hair causes it to grow back coarser or darker. A group of volunteers had one of their eyebrows selected at random and completely shaved off. The subjects were then evaluated for eyebrow re-growth over the course of the next six months, with observers also analyzing photographs of the individuals (**FIGURE 1-11**).

Q Does shaving or cutting hair make it grow back more thickly?

In the next section we'll see how our hypotheses survive being confronted with the results of the critical experiments described above and how we can move toward drawing conclusions.

TAKE-HOME MESSAGE 1·8

A critical experiment is one that makes it possible to decisively determine whether a particular hypothesis is correct.

the subject nor the doctor administering the pills (and later checking for cold symptoms) knew what the pills contained. In the other two groups, the individuals did not begin taking the pills until the day on which they were exposed to the cold virus. Again, one group got the echinacea pill and the other group got the placebo.

Hypothesis: Estrogens in sewage runoff turn fish into hermaphrodites. To try to determine the validity of this

1·9

Step 5: Draw conclusions, make revisions.

Once the results of the critical experiment are in, they are pulled apart, examined, and analyzed. Researchers look for patterns and relationships in the evidence they've gathered from their experiments; they draw conclusions and see whether their findings and conclusions support their hypotheses. If an experimental result is not what you expected, that does not make it a "wrong answer." Science includes a great deal of trial and error, and if the conclusions do not support the hypothesis, then you must

Q Is eyewitness testimony in courts always right?

revise your hypothesis, which often spurs you to conduct more experiments. This step is a cornerstone of the scientific method because it demands that you must be open-minded and ready to change what you think.

The results of the purse-snatching experiment were surprising. When the suspects (which, as you'll recall, did not include the actual "criminal") were viewed together in a lineup, the observers/witnesses erroneously identified someone

STEP 5: DRAW CONCLUSIONS AND MAKE REVISIONS

FIGURE 1-12　Drawing conclusions and making revisions.

as the purse snatcher about a third of the time. When the suspects were viewed one at a time, the observers made a mistaken identification less than 10% of the time.

In this or any other experiment, it does not matter whether we can imagine a reason for the discrepancy between our hypothesis and our results. What is important is that we have demonstrated that our initial hypothesis—"Eyewitness testimony is always accurate"—is not supported by the data. Our observations suggest that, at the very least, the accuracy of an eyewitness's testimony depends on the method used to present the suspects. Based on this result, we might then adjust our hypothesis to: "Eyewitness testimony is more accurate when suspects are presented to witnesses one at a time."

We can then devise new and more specific testable predictions to try to further refine a hypothesis. In the case of eyewitness testimony, further investigation suggests that when suspects or pictures of suspects are placed side by side, witnesses compare them and tend to choose the suspect that *most resembles* the person they remember committing the crime. When viewed one at a time, suspects can't be compared in this way and witnesses are less likely to make misidentifications.

Q Does echinacea help prevent the common cold?

Hypothesis: Echinacea reduces the duration and severity of the symptoms of the common cold (**FIGURE 1-12**). In the echinacea study, the results were definitive. Those who took the echinacea were just as likely to catch a cold, and, once they caught the cold, the symptoms lasted for the same amount of time. In short, echinacea had no effect at all. Several similar studies have been conducted, all of which have shown that echinacea does not have any beneficial effect. As one of the researchers commented afterward, "We've got to stop attributing any efficacy to echinacea."

Although it seems clear that our initial hypothesis that echinacea prevents people from catching colds and reduces the severity and duration of cold symptoms is not correct, further experimentation might involve altering the amount of echinacea given to the research subjects or the length of time they take echinacea before exposure to the cold-causing viruses.

Hypothesis: Estrogens in sewage runoff turn fish into hermaphrodites. The results of the sewage experiment showed that, in every single river tested, male fish downstream from the runoff developed eggs in their testes and had significant levels of the egg-production hormone in their blood. Further research stimulated by these results has investigated a variety of common industrial chemicals to see whether they can stimulate production of the egg-development hormone in male fish under laboratory conditions, in an attempt to identify which particular chemical component in the sewage causes the male fish to change.

Hypothesis: Hair that is shaved grows back coarser and darker. In the hair-shaving experiment, the observers discovered that it was impossible to distinguish which eyebrow had been shaved. This was not a surprise to dermatologists evaluating the study because all of the living parts involved in hair growth are below the surface of the skin. (Plucking hairs can damage the root of the hair, potentially affecting future hair growth, but that is another story, awaiting further study.)

The outcomes in all of these studies show that after the results of a critical experiment have been gathered and interpreted, it is important not just to evaluate the initial hypothesis but also to consider any necessary revisions or refinements to it. This revision is an important step; by revising a hypothesis, based on the results of experimental tests, we can explain the observable world with greater and greater accuracy.

TAKE-HOME MESSAGE 1·9

Based on the results of experimental tests, we can revise a hypothesis and explain the observable world with increasing accuracy. A great strength of scientific thinking, therefore, is that it helps us understand when we should change our minds.

1·10

When do hypotheses become theories, and what are theories?

It's an unfortunate source of confusion that, among the general public, the word "theory" is often used to refer to a hunch or a guess or speculation—that is, something we are not certain about—while to scientists, the word means nearly the opposite: a hypothesis of which they are most certain. To reduce misunderstandings, we examine two distinct levels of understanding that scientists use in describing our knowledge about natural phenomena.

Hypothesis As we have seen, hypotheses are at the very heart of scientific thinking. A hypothesis is a proposed explanation for a phenomenon. A good hypothesis leads to testable predictions. Commonly, when non-scientists use the word "theory"—as in, "I've got a theory about why there's less traffic on Friday mornings than on Thursday mornings"—they actually mean that they have a hypothesis.

Theory A **theory** is an explanatory hypothesis for natural phenomena that is exceptionally well supported by the empirical data. A theory can be thought of as a hypothesis that has withstood the test of time and is unlikely to be altered by any new evidence. Like a hypothesis, a theory is testable; but because it has already been repeatedly tested and no

observations or experimental results have contradicted it, a theory is viewed by the scientific community with nearly the same confidence as a fact. For this reason, it is inappropriate to describe something as "just a theory" as a way of asserting that it is not likely to be true.

Theories in science also tend to be broader in scope than hypotheses. In biology, two of the most important theories (which we explore in more detail in Chapters 3 and 8) are *cell theory,* that all organisms are composed of cells and all cells come from pre-existing cells, and the *theory of evolution by natural selection,* that species can change over time and all species are related to each other through common ancestry.

TAKE-HOME MESSAGE 1·10

Scientific theories do not represent speculation or guesses about the natural world. Rather, they are hypotheses— proposed explanations for natural phenomena—that have been so strongly and persuasively supported by empirical observation that the scientific community views them as very unlikely to be altered by new evidence.

What Is Science?   Scientific Method   Experimental Design   Decision Making

❸ Well-designed experiments are essential to testing hypotheses.

Controlled experiments increase the power of our observations. Here, flasks containing Panax (Asian ginseng) are prepared.

1•11

Controlling variables makes experiments more powerful.

From our earlier discussion of critical experiments, you have a sense of how important it is to have a well-planned, well-designed experiment. Some experiments are just better than others when it comes to figuring out how the world works. At their most basic level, experiments help us figure out the cause-and-effect relationship between two things. In the previous sections, for example, we hypothesized about the relationship between witnessing a crime and being able to identify the person who committed it, between taking echinacea and catching a cold and having it for a period of time, between water pollution and hermaphrodite fish, and between shaving and the subsequent coarseness and color of hair. In performing experiments, our goal is to figure out whether one thing influences another thing; if an experiment enables us to draw a correct conclusion about that cause-and-effect relationship, it is a good experiment.

In our initial discussion of experiments, we just described what the experiment was without examining why the researchers chose to perform the experiment the way they did. In this section, we explore some of the ways to maximize

an experiment's power, and we'll find that, with careful planning, it is possible to increase an experiment's ability to discern causes and effects.

First, let's consider some elements common to most experiments. These include:

1. Treatment. This is any experimental condition applied to the research subjects. It might be the shaving of one of an individual's legs, or the pattern used to show "suspects" (all at once or one at a time) to the witness of a staged crime, or a dosage of echinacea given to an individual.

2. Experimental group. This is a group of subjects who are exposed to a particular treatment—for example, the individuals given echinacea rather than placebo in the experiment described above. It is sometimes referred to as the "treatment group."

3. Control group. This is a group of subjects who are treated identically to the experimental group, with one exception: they are not exposed to the treatment. An example would be the individuals given placebo rather than echinacea.

4. Variables. These are the characteristics of an experimental system that are subject to change. They might be, for example, the amount of echinacea a person is given, or a measure of the coarseness of an individual's hair. When we speak of "controlling" variables—the most important feature of a good experiment—we are describing the attempt to minimize any differences (which are also called "variables") between a control group and an experimental group other than the treatment itself. That way, any differences in the outcomes we observe between the groups are most likely due to the treatment.

Let's look at an example that illustrates the importance of considering all these elements when designing an experiment.

Stomach ulcers are erosions of the stomach lining that, due to the highly acidic condition of that part of the digestive tract, can be very painful. In the late 1950s, a doctor reported in the *Journal of the American Medical Association* that stomach ulcers

could be effectively treated by having a patient swallow a balloon connected to some tubes that circulated a refrigerated fluid. He argued that by super-cooling the stomach, acid production was reduced and the ulcer symptoms relieved. He had convincing data to back up his claim: in all 24 of his patients who received this "gastric freezing" treatment, their condition improved. As a result, the treatment became widespread for many years (**FIGURE 1-13**).

Although there was a clear hypothesis ("Gastric cooling reduces the severity of ulcers") and some compelling observations (all 24 patients experienced relief), this experiment falls short of qualifying as a good example of the scientific method. Why? Because it was not designed well. In particular, there was no clear group with whom to compare the patients who received the treatment. In other words, who is to say that just going to the doctor or having a balloon put into your stomach doesn't improve ulcers? The results of this doctor's experiment do not rule out these interpretations.

GASTRIC FREEZING EXPERIMENTS

EXPERIMENT 1

EXPERIMENTAL GROUP
24 individuals with gastric ulcers

TREATMENT
Balloon with refrigerated fluid is placed in the stomach.

RESULTS
100% of patients are healed after procedure.

EXPERIMENT 2

CONTROL GROUP
78 individuals with gastric ulcers

TREATMENT
Balloon with room-temperature fluid is placed in the stomach.

RESULTS
38% of patients are healed after procedure.

EXPERIMENTAL GROUP
82 individuals with gastric ulcers

Balloon with refrigerated fluid is placed in the stomach.

34% of patients are healed after procedure.

CONCLUSIONS

• The results of experiment 2 show that experiment 1 was not well designed. Experiment 1 does not control variables with a control group and has far fewer subjects.

• Gastric freezing does not confer any benefit to patients with gastric ulcers.

Without a control group, it is impossible to draw any conclusions about the effectiveness of an experimental treatment.

FIGURE 1-13 No controls. A poorly designed experiment: gastric freezing and stomach ulcers.

What Is Science?   Scientific Method   Experimental Design   Decision Making

A few years later, another researcher decided to do a more carefully controlled study. He recruited 160 ulcer patients and gave 82 of them the gastric freezing treatment. The other 78 received a similar treatment in which they swallowed the balloon but had room-temperature water pumped in. The latter was an appropriate control group because the subjects were treated exactly like the experimental group, with the exception of only a single difference between the groups—whether they experienced gastric freezing or not. The new experiment could test for an effect of the gastric freezing, while controlling for the effects of other, lurking variables that might affect the outcome.

Surprisingly, although the researcher found that 34% of those in the gastric freezing group improved, he also found that 38% of those in the control group improved. These results indicated that gastric freezing didn't actually confer any benefit when compared with a treatment that did not involve gastric freezing. Not surprisingly, the practice was abandoned. (We will discuss below why the control group might have had such a high rate of improvement.)

Q Is arthroscopic surgery for arthritis beneficial for the 300,000 people in the United States who have it each year? How do we know?

More recently, a well-controlled experiment demonstrated that arthroscopic knee surgery, a treatment for osteoarthritis performed on more than 300,000 people in the United States each year, produced moderate benefits to the patient. But the study demonstrated even greater benefits to patients in a control group who were subjected not to the arthroscopic procedure but rather to "sham" surgery, in which the surgeon made three superficial incisions in the knee, manipulated the knee a bit, and clanged the instruments around in the operating room. As a consequence of this study, many doctors have begun abandoning the use of arthroscopic surgery for the treatment of osteoarthritis—which once accounted for more than a billion dollars in surgical procedures each year. (This type of surgery is still useful for the treatment of some other knee problems, including the repair of ligament and cartilage damage.)

A surprising result from both the gastric freezing studies and the arthroscopic surgery study was that they demonstrated the **placebo effect,** the frequently observed, poorly understood, phenomenon in which people respond favorably to *any* treatment, regardless of whether it is as simple as swallowing a sugar pill or as unpleasant as having to swallow a balloon and have it inflated in their stomach. The placebo effect highlights the need for comparison of treatment effects with an appropriate control group. We want to know whether the treatment is actually responsible for any effect seen; if the control group receiving the placebo or sham treatment has an outcome like that of the experimental group, we can conclude that the treatment itself does not have an effect.

Another pitfall to be aware of in designing an experiment is to ensure that the person(s) conducting the experiment don't influence the experiment's outcome. An experimenter can often unwittingly influence the results of an experiment. For example, eyewitnesses to crimes more frequently identify someone that the police suspect rather than other individuals in the lineup when the police officer conducting the lineup knows which individual is the suspect.

This phenomenon is seen in the story of a horse named Clever Hans. Hans was considered clever because his owner claimed that Hans could perform remarkable intellectual feats, including multiplication and division. When given a numerical problem, the horse would tap out the answer number with his foot. Controlled experiments, however, demonstrated that Hans was only able to solve problems when he could see the person asking the question and when that person knew the answer (**FIGURE 1-14**). It turned out that the questioners revealed, unintentionally and through very subtle body language, the answers.

FIGURE 1-14 Math whiz or ordinary horse? The horse Clever Hans was said to be capable of mathematical calculations, until a controlled experiment demonstrated otherwise.

Themes in Biology

The Clever Hans phenomenon highlights the benefits of instituting even greater controls when designing an experiment. In particular, it highlights the value of **blind experimental design,** in which the experimental subjects do not know which treatment (if any) they are receiving, and **double-blind experimental design,** in which neither the experimental subjects nor the experimenter knows which treatment a subject is receiving.

Another hallmark of an extremely well designed experiment is that it combines the blind/double-blind strategies we've just described in a **randomized,** controlled, double-blind study. In this context, "randomized" refers to the fact that, as in the echinacea study described above, the subjects are randomly assigned into experimental and control groups. In this way, researchers and subjects have no influence on the composition of the control and treatment groups.

The use of randomized, controlled, double-blind experimental design can be thought of as an attempt to imagine all the possible ways that someone might criticize an experiment and to design the experiment so that the results cannot be explained by anything but the effect of the treatment. In this way, the experimenter's results either support the hypothesis or invalidate it—in which case, the hypothesis must be rejected. If multiple explanations can be offered for the observations and evidence from an experiment, then it has not succeeded as a critical experiment.

Suppose you want to know whether a new drug is effective in fighting the human immunodeficiency virus (HIV), the virus that leads to AIDS. Which experiment would be better, one in which the drug is added to HIV-infected cells in a test tube under carefully controlled laboratory conditions, or one in which the drug is given to a large number of HIV-infected individuals? There is no definitive answer. In laboratory studies, it is possible to control nearly every environmental variable. In their simplicity, however, lab studies may introduce difficulties. Complex and naturally varying factors in human subjects, such as nutrition and stress, may have important interactions with the experimental drug that influence its effectiveness. These interactions will not be present and taken into account in the controlled lab study. Good experimental design is more complex than simply following a single recipe. The only way to determine the quality of an experiment is to assess how well the variables that were not of interest were controlled, and how well the experimental treatment tested the relationship of interest.

TAKE-HOME MESSAGE 1·11

To draw clear conclusions from experiments, it is essential to hold constant all those variables we are not interested in. Control and experimental groups should vary only with respect to the treatment of interest. Differences in outcomes between the groups can then be attributed to the treatment.

1·12

Repeatable experiments increase our confidence.

Q *Can science be misleading? How can we know?*

In 2005, a study showed that some patients being treated for HIV infection who were also taking an epilepsy drug called valproic acid had significantly reduced numbers of HIV particles in their blood. Newspaper headlines announced this finding—"AIDS Cure Possible, Study Suggests"—and raised many people's hopes. Two years later, however, a study of people who were already taking valproic acid and anti-HIV drugs concluded that those on valproic acid had not benefited at all from the drug (**FIGURE 1-15**). It's not certain why the later study didn't produce the same results as the first study, but the second study did address two serious shortcomings of the first study—namely, that the first study

was much smaller, involving only four patients, and that no control group was used. This pair of studies reveals the importance of repeatability in science.

A powerful way to demonstrate that observed differences between a treatment group and a control group truly reflect the effect of the treatment is for the

Q *Do megadoses of vitamin C reduce cancer risk?*

researchers to conduct the experiment over and over again. Even better is to have other researcher groups repeat the experiment and get the same results. Researchers describe this desired characteristic of experiments by saying that an experiment must be "reproducible" and "repeatable."

What Is Science?   Scientific Method   Experimental Design   Decision Making

📧 Email   🖨 Print   A A A Text Size

8/7/08

Texas Tech Researchers May Have Found AIDS Cure

Posted: Aug 7, 2008 09:59 PM

Texas Tech University in partnership with Harvard University is on the research forefront of a possible vaccine for HIV, the virus that causes AIDS.

To give you some idea of how big this story is, on Thursday it was the number one story on Newsweek's website and it will be the lead in their next magazine.

NewsChannel 11 met with the president of the Texas Tech Health Sciences Center, Doctor John Baldwin and Texas Tech Chancellor Kent Hance. Both men are optimistic about this research and its possible impact on the world and Texas Tech.

💡 *Repeatability is essential! Scientific conclusions are more reliable when experiments have been repeated (and modified, if necessary).*

Valproic Acid Does Not Reduce Latent HIV Reservoir in Resting CD4 Cells

By Liz Highleyman

Some prior studies have suggested that valproic acid (Depakote), a drug used to treat epilepsy and bipolar disorder, might help eradicate HIV from the body. Two studies published in the June 19, 2008 issue of *AIDS*, however, indicate that it has little long-term effect.

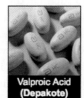

Valproic Acid (Depakote)

Study 1

David Margolis and colleagues from the University of North Carolina previously reported that valproic acid plus intensified antiretroviral therapy could "flush" HIV out of long-lived latently infected CD4 T-cells and potentially reduce the resting CD4 cell reservoir. They later conducted a study to test the ability of valproic acid to deplete resting CD4 cell infection in patients receiving standard HAART.

Infection of resting CD4 cells was measured in 11 patients with stable undetectable HIV viral load using a standard HIV RNA assay twice rior to, and twice after, adding 1000 mg valproic acid to their standard antiretroviral regimen. Resting CD4 T-cell infection frequency was measured by outgrowth assay, and low-level viremia was quantified in 9 patients using a highly sensitive single-copy plasma HIV RNA assay.

FIGURE 1-15 Once is not enough. Experiments and their outcomes must be repeatable for their conclusions to be valid and widely accepted.

An experiment that can be done over and over again by a variety of researchers with the same results is an effective defense against biases (which we discuss in the next section) and reflects a well-designed experiment. Experiments whose results cannot be confirmed by repeated experiments or by experiments performed by other researchers are the downfall of many dramatic claims. Even though chemist Linus Pauling had not one, but two Nobel prizes, he was never able to convince the scientific community that megadoses of vitamin C are an effective treatment for cancer. Every time other individuals tried to repeat Pauling's studies, properly matching the control and treatment groups, they found no difference. Vitamin C just isn't effective against cancer—a conclusion that the vast majority of the medical community now believes. The scientific method is profoundly egalitarian: more important than a scientist's credentials are sound and reproducible results.

When a study is repeated (also referred to as "replicating" a study), sometimes a tiny variation in the experimental design can lead to a different outcome; this can help us isolate the variable that is primarily responsible for the outcome of the experiment. Alternatively, when experiments are repeated and the same results are obtained, our confidence in them is increased.

TAKE-HOME MESSAGE 1·12

Experiments and their outcomes must be repeatable for their conclusions to be considered valid and widely accepted.

We've got to watch out for our biases.

Q Can scientists be sexist? How would we know?

In 2001, the journal *Behavioral Ecology* changed its policy for reviewing manuscripts that were submitted for publication. Its new policy instituted a double-blind process, whereby neither the reviewers' nor the authors' identities were revealed. Previously, the policy had been a single-blind process in which reviewers' identities were kept secret but the authors' identities were known to the reviewers. In an analysis of papers published between 1997 and 2005, it turned out that after 2001, when the double-blind policy took effect, there was a significant increase in the number of published papers in which the first author was female (**FIGURE 1-16**). Analysis of papers published in a similar journal that maintained the single-blind process over that period revealed no such increase.

This study reveals that people, including scientists, may have biases—sometimes subconscious—that influence their behavior. It also serves as a reminder of the importance of proper controls in experiments. If knowing the sex of the author influences a reviewer's decision on whether a paper should be published, it is possible that researchers' biases can creep in and influence their collection of data and analysis of results. (Even the decision of what—and what not—to study can be influenced by our biases.)

It can be hard to avoid biases. Consider a study that required precise measuring of the fingers of the left and right hands—comparing the extent to which people in different groups were physically symmetrical. The researcher noted that when she measured individuals from the group she predicted would be more symmetrical, she felt a need to re-measure if the reading on her digital ruler indicated a big asymmetry. Because she was thinking that the person's fingers *should* be

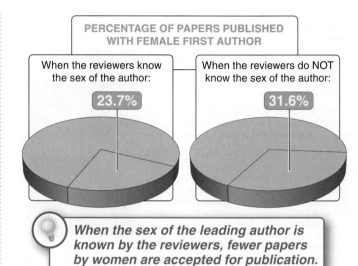

PERCENTAGE OF PAPERS PUBLISHED WITH FEMALE FIRST AUTHOR

When the reviewers know the sex of the author: 23.7%

When the reviewers do NOT know the sex of the author: 31.6%

When the sex of the leading author is known by the reviewers, fewer papers by women are accepted for publication.

FIGURE 1-16 Bias against female scientists? The journal *Behavioral Ecology* accepted more papers from female authors when the reviewers were not aware of the author's sex.

symmetrical, she assumed that she had made an error. She felt no such need to re-measure for subjects in the other group, when asymmetries confirmed her hypothesis. To control for this bias, the researcher connected her digital ruler to a computer and, without ever having the number displayed, transmitted the measurement directly to the computer when she pushed a button. In this way, she was able to make each measurement without introducing any regular bias.

TAKE-HOME MESSAGE 1·13

Biases can influence our behavior, including our collection and interpretation of data. With careful controls, it is possible to minimize such biases.

22 CHAPTER 1 • SCIENTIFIC THINKING

What Is Science?　　Scientific Method　　Experimental Design　　Decision Making

❹ The scientific method can help us make wise decisions.

What can you believe? Reading labels is essential to evaluating products and the claims about them.

1·14

Statistics can help us in making decisions.

In Section 1-12 we saw that researchers repeatedly found, through experimentation, that megadoses of vitamin C do not reduce cancer risk. If you put yourself in the researchers' shoes, you might wonder how you'd figure out that the vitamin C did not reduce cancer risk. Perhaps there were 100 individuals in the group receiving megadoses of vitamin C: some of them developed cancer and some of them did not. And among the 100 subjects in the group not receiving the megadoses, some of the individuals developed cancer and some did not. How do you decide whether the vitamin C actually had an effect? This knowledge comes from a branch of mathematics called **statistics,** a set of analytical and mathematical tools designed to help researchers gain understanding from the data they gather. To understand statistics, let's start with a simple situation.

Suppose you measure the height of two people. One is a woman who is 5 feet 10 inches tall. The other is a man who is 5 feet 6 inches tall. If these were your only two observations

of human height, you might conclude that female humans are taller than males. But suppose you measure the height of 100 women and 100 men chosen randomly from a population. Then you can say, "of the 100 men, the average man is 5 feet 9.5 inches, and of the 100 women, the average woman is 5 feet 4 inches." Better still, the data can illuminate for you not only the average, but also some measure of how much variation there is from one individual to another. Statistical analysis can tell you not only that the average man in this study is 5 feet 9.5 inches tall, but that two-thirds of the men are between 5 feet 6.5 inches tall (3 inches less than the average) and 6 feet 0.5 inches tall (3 inches more than the average). You will often see this type of range stated as "5 feet 9.5 inches ± 3 inches" ("plus or minus 3 inches"). Similarly, the data might show that the female subjects in the study are 5 feet 6 inches ± 3 inches," indicating that two-thirds of the women are between 5 feet 3 inches and 5 feet 9 inches tall. As we discussed in Section 1-11, on experimental design, and as this example shows, larger numbers of participants are

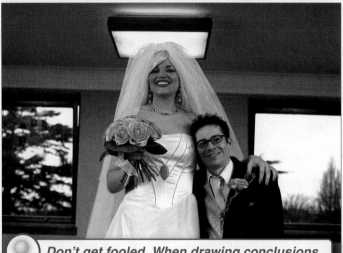

HUMAN HEIGHT AND STATISTICS

Don't get fooled. When drawing conclusions about a natural phenomenon, such as height, it is best to choose subjects at random and to include as many as possible.

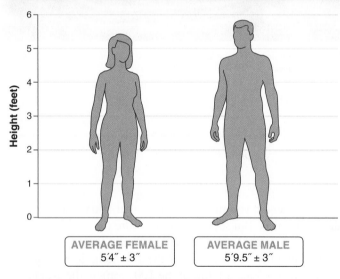

AVERAGE FEMALE
5′4″ ± 3″

AVERAGE MALE
5′9.5″ ± 3″

FIGURE 1-17 Drawing conclusions based on limited observations is risky. Measuring a greater number of people will generally help us draw more accurate conclusions about human height.

better than smaller numbers if you want to draw general conclusions about natural phenomena such as the height of men and women (**FIGURE 1-17**).

Using data to describe the characteristics of individuals participating in a study is useful, but often we want to know whether data support (or do not support) a hypothesis. If the scientific method is to be effective in helping us understand the world, it must help us make wise decisions about concrete things. For example, suppose we want to know whether having access to a textbook helps a student perform

better in a biology class. Statistics can help us answer this question. After conducting a study, let's say we find that students who had access to a textbook scored an average of 81% ± 8% on their exams, while those who did not scored an average of 76% ± 7%.

In this example, it is difficult to distinguish between the two possible conclusions.

Possibility 1: Students having access to a textbook DO perform better in biology classes. In other words, our sampling of this class revealed a true relationship between the two variables, textbook access and class performance.

Possibility 2: Students having access to a textbook DO NOT perform better in biology classes. The variation in the scores in the two groups may be too large to allow us to notice any effect of having access to a textbook. Instead, the difference in average scores for the two groups may mean that more of the high-performing students just happened, through random chance, to be in the group given access to a textbook.

But what if the students with access to a textbook scored, on average, 95% ± 5%, while those without access scored only 60% ± 5%. In this case, we would be much more confident that there is a significant effect of having access to a textbook (**FIGURE 1-18**), because even with the large variation in the scores seen in each group, the averages are still very different from each other.

Statistical methods help us to decide between these two possibilities and, importantly, to state how confident we are that one or the other is true. The greater the difference between two groups (95% versus 60% is a greater difference than 81% versus 76%), and the smaller the variation in each group (± 5% in the 95% and 60% groups, versus ± 8% and ± 7% in the 81% and 76% groups), the more confident we are of the conclusion that there is a significant effect of the treatment (having access to a textbook, in this case). In other words, in the case where the groups of students scored 95% or 60%, depending on whether or not they had access to a textbook, it is possible that having a textbook did not actually improve performance and that this observed difference was just the result of chance. But this conclusion is very, very unlikely.

Statistics can also help us identify relationships (or the lack of relationships) between variables. For example, we might note that when there are more firefighters at a fire, the fire is larger and causes more damage. This is a **positive correlation,** meaning that when one variable (the number of firefighters) increases, so does the other (the severity of the fire). Should we conclude that firefighters make fires worse? No. While correlations can reveal relationships between variables, they

What Is Science?   Scientific Method   Experimental Design   Decision Making

FIGURE 1-18 Drawing conclusions based on statistics. Statistical analyses can help us organize and summarize the observations that we make and the evidence we gather in an experiment.

Students without textbooks score an average of 60% ± 5%

Students with textbooks score an average of 95% ± 5%

Statistics can quantify and summarize large amounts of data, making it possible to draw more accurate conclusions.

don't tell us *how* the variables are related or whether change in one variable causes change in another. (You may have heard or read the phrase "correlation is not causation," which refers to this sort of situation.) Before drawing any conclusions about more firefighters causing larger fires, we need to know about the type of fire and its size when the firefighters arrived, because those factors will significantly influence the ultimate amount of damage. To estimate the effect of the number of firefighters on the amount of damage, we would need to compare the amount of damage from fires of similar size that are fought by different numbers of firefighters.

Ultimately, statistical analyses can help us organize and summarize the observations that we make and the evidence we gather in an experiment. These analyses can then help us decide whether any differences we measure between experimental and control groups are likely to be the result of the treatment, and how confident we can be in that conclusion.

TAKE-HOME MESSAGE 1·14

Because much variation exists in the world, statistics can help us evaluate whether any differences between a treatment group and control group can be attributed to the treatment rather than random chance.

1·15

Pseudoscience and misleading anecdotal evidence can obscure the truth.

One of the major benefits of being familiar with the scientific way of thinking is that it can prevent you from being taken in or fooled by false claims. There are two types of "scientific evidence" that frequently are cited in the popular media and are responsible for people erroneously believing that links between two things exist, when in fact they do not. These are:

1. **Pseudoscience,** in which individuals make scientific-sounding claims that are not supported by trustworthy, methodical scientific studies.

2. **Anecdotal observations,** in which, based on only one or a few observations, people conclude that there is or is not a link between two things.

Pseudoscience is all around us, particularly in the claims made on the packaging of consumer products and food (**FIGURE 1-19**). Beginning in the 1960s, for example, consumers encountered the assertion by the makers of a sugarless gum that "4 out of 5 dentists surveyed recommend sugarless gum for their patients who chew gum." If you ask yourself the question

FIGURE 1-19 Pseudoscientific claims are often found on food products.

"How do they know what they know?" and can't answer it, you may be looking at pseudoscience. Maybe the statement is factually true, but the general relationship it implies may not be. How many dentists were surveyed? If the gum makers surveyed only five dentists, then the statement may not represent the proportion of *all* dentists who would make such a recommendation. And how were the dentists sampled? Were they at a shareholders meeting for the sugarless gum company? What alternatives were given—perhaps gargling with a tooth-destroying acid? You just don't know. That's what makes it pseudoscience.

Pseudoscience capitalizes on a belief shared by most people: that scientific thinking is a powerful method for learning about the world. The problem with pseudoscience is that the scientific bases for a scientific-sounding claim are not clear. The claims generally sound reasonable, and they are persuasive in convincing people to purchase one product over another. But one of the beauties of real science is that you never have to just take someone's word about something. Rather, you are free to evaluate people's research methods and results and decide for yourself whether their conclusions and claims are appropriate.

We are all familiar with anecdotal evidence. Striking stories that we read or hear, or our own experiences, can shape our views of cause and effect. We may find compelling parallels between suggestions made in horoscopes and events in our

lives, or we may think that we have a lucky shirt, or we may be moved by a child whose cancer went into remission following treatment involving eating apricot seeds. Yet, despite lacking a human face, data are more reliable than anecdotes, primarily because they can illustrate a broader range of observations, capturing the big picture.

Anecdotal observations can seem harmless and can be emotionally powerful. But because they do not include a sufficiently large and representative set of observations of the world, they can lead people to draw erroneous conclusions, often with disastrous consequences. One important case of anecdotal evidence being used to draw general conclusions about a cause-and-effect relationship between two things involves autism, a developmental disorder that impairs social interaction and communication, and the vaccination for measles, mumps, and rubella (commonly called the MMR vaccine) that is given to most children.

In 1998, the prestigious medical journal *The Lancet* published a report by a group of researchers that described a set of symptoms (diarrhea, abdominal pain, bloating) related to bowel inflammation in 12 children who exhibited the symptoms of autism. The parents or physicians of 8 of the children in the study said that the behavioral symptoms of autism appeared shortly after the children received MMR vaccination. For this reason, the authors of the report recommended further study of a possible link between the MMR vaccine, the bowel problems, and autism.

Q Does the measles, mumps, and rubella vaccine cause autism?

In a press conference, one of the paper's authors suggested a link between autism and the MMR vaccine, recommending single vaccines rather than the MMR triple vaccine until it could be proved that the MMR vaccine did not trigger autism. This statement caused a major health scare that only recently has begun to subside. Noting that there had been a significant increase in the incidence of autism in the 1990s and early 2000s, the press and many people took the claims made by the researcher at the press conference as evidence that the MMR vaccine causes autism. Over the course of the next few years, the number of children getting the MMR vaccine dropped significantly, as parents sought to reduce the risk of autism in their children (**FIGURE 1-20**).

Unfortunately, this is a notable case of poor implementation of the scientific method, with numerous flaws leading to an incorrect conclusion. Most important among these is that

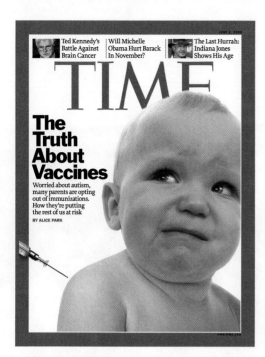

FIGURE 1-20 Headline news. A misguided fear of "catching" autism has caused some parents to decline immunizations for their children.

experiments on this subject, and all have been definitive in their conclusion that there is no link between the MMR vaccine and autism. Here are a few of these studies:

1. A study of all children born in Denmark between 1991 and 1998 found no difference in the incidence of autism among the 440,655 children who were vaccinated with the MMR vaccine and the 96,648 children who were not vaccinated.

2. A 2005 study in Japan showed that after use of the MMR vaccine was stopped in 1993, the incidence of autism continued to increase.

3. A study of 1.8 million children in Finland who were followed up for 14 years after getting the MMR vaccine found no link at all between the occurrence of autism and the vaccine.

At this point, the consensus of the international scientific community is that there is no scientific evidence for a link between the MMR vaccine and autism.

> " Science is a way to call the bluff of those who only pretend to knowledge. It is a bulwark against mysticism, against superstition, against religion misapplied to where it has no business being. If we're true to its values, it can tell us when we're being lied to. "
>
> — Carl Sagan, in *The Demon-Haunted World: Science as a Candle in the Dark,* 1997

The study was small (only 12 children), the sample was carefully selected rather than randomized (that is, the researchers selected the study participants based on the symptoms they showed), and no control group was included for comparison (for example, children who had been vaccinated but did not exhibit autism symptoms). On top of this, the study, even flawed as it was, did not actually find or even report a link between autism and the MMR vaccine. That purported link only came from the unsupported, suggestive statements made by one of the study's authors at the press conference.

On their own, the design flaws in the study would be sufficient to invalidate the one author's claims about the link between autism and the MMR vaccine, but there are more weaknesses in the research. It later was discovered that before the paper's publication, the study's lead author (the one who spoke at the press conference) had received large sums of money from lawyers seeking evidence to use in lawsuits against the MMR vaccine manufacturers. It also came to light that he had applied for a patent for a vaccine that was a rival to the most commonly used MMR vaccine. In the light of these undisclosed biases, 10 of the paper's 12 authors published a retraction of their original interpretation of their results.

In the years since this paper was published, many well-controlled large-scale studies have conducted critical

So what explains the observation that there are more autism cases now than in the past? It seems that the increased number of autism cases is a function of better identification of the condition by doctors and of changes in the process by which autism is diagnosed. Another reason for the perceived link between autism and the MMR vaccine was simply the coincidence that most children receive the vaccine at around 18–19 months of age, which happens to be the age at which the first symptoms of autism are usually noticed. In the end, what we learn from this is that we must be wary that we do not generalize from anecdotal observations or let poorly designed studies obscure the truth.

TAHE-HOME MESSAGE 1·15

Pseudoscience and anecdotal observations often lead people to believe that links between two phenomena exist, when in fact there are no such links.

There are limits to what science can do.

The scientific method is a framework that helps us make sense of what we see, hear, and read in our lives. Science and scientific thinking guide us in recognizing facts and help us in the interpretations of data, analyses of hypotheses, and drawing of conclusions. In doing so, scientific thinking reveals and illuminates explanations about how to think about various events and phenomena, and it can help us make decisions in diverse areas of our lives, not just "scientific" areas. There are, however, limits to what science can do.

The scientific method will never prove or disprove the existence of God. Nor is it likely to help us understand the mathematical elegance of Fermat's last theorem or the beauty of Shakespeare's sonnets. As one of several approaches to the acquisition of knowledge, the scientific method is, above all, empirical. It differs from non-scientific approaches such as mathematics and logic, history, music, and the study of artistic expression in that it relies on *measuring* phenomena in some way. The generation of value judgments and other types of non-quantifiable, subjective information—such as religious assertions of faith—falls outside the realm of science. Despite all of the intellectual analyses the scientific method gives rise to and the objective conclusions it makes possible, it does not, for example, generate moral statements and it cannot give us insight into ethical problems. What "is" (i.e., what we observe in the natural world) is not necessarily what "ought" to be (i.e., what is morally right). It may or may not be.

Further, much of what is commonly considered to be science, such as the construction of new engineering marvels or the heroic surgical separation of conjoined twins, is not scientific at all. Rather, these are technical innovations and developments. While they frequently rely on sophisticated scientific research, they represent the application of research

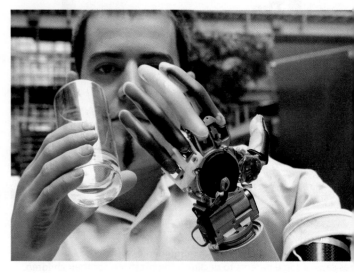

The application of science to solve a problem can result in sophisticated technical innovations, like this thought-controlled prosthetic arm.

findings to varied fields such as manufacturing and medicine to solve problems.

As we begin approaching the world from a more scientific perspective, we can gain important insights into the facts of life, yet must remain mindful of the limits to science.

TAKE-HOME MESSAGE 1·16

Although the scientific method may be the most effective path toward understanding the observable world, it cannot give us insights into the generation of value judgments and other types of non-quantifiable, subjective information.

What Is Science?   Scientific Method   Experimental Design   Decision Making

❺ On the road to biological literacy: what are the major themes in biology?

Finding unity in all the diversity: the Hall of Biodiversity, American Museum of Natural History, New York.

1·17 --

A few important themes tie together the diverse topics in biology.

Driven forward by the power of the scientific method, modern biology is in the midst of an explosion of new and exciting developments. Now more than ever, biology is influencing and even transforming our lives. Its increasing relevance outside the world of scientists is felt in a multitude of areas, including breakthroughs in agriculture, innovative developments in criminology, and increased understanding and awareness of environmental issues and the need for widespread changes in behavior.

In this guide to biology, as we explore the many facets of biology and its relevance to life in the modern world, you will see two unifying themes recurring throughout.

Hierarchical organization. Life is organized on many levels within individual organisms including atoms, cells, tissues, and organs. And in the larger world, organisms themselves are organized into many levels: populations, communities, and ecosystems within the biosphere.

The power of evolution. Evolution, the change in genetic characteristics of individuals within populations over time, accounts for the diversity of organisms, but also explains the unity among them.

These two major themes connect the diverse topics, as we make our way through four chief areas of focus:

1. The chemical, cellular, and energetic foundations of life

2. The genetics, evolution, and behavior of individuals

3. The staggering diversity of life and the unity underlying it

4. Ecology, the environment, and the subtle and important links between organisms and the world they inhabit

Armed with an appreciation for the scientific method and the broader themes you'll encounter in your study of biology, let's continue our exploration of life!

TAKE-HOME MESSAGE 1·17

Although the diversity of life on earth is tremendous, the study of life is unified by the themes of hierarchical organization and the power of evolution.

Knowledge You Can Use

When should you change what you think? Risky behaviors while driving.

Q: Should drunk driving be illegal? Why? Almost everyone believes that people should not drive when they've been drinking. Even after just one or two drinks, a driver is more than twice as likely to cause a fatal traffic accident as a sober driver. With three to five drinks, the risk is almost 10 times greater than when sober. People see the data and understand; the conclusion is not difficult: you put yourself and others at risk when driving drunk.

Q: What about people who claim that they can drive safely even when they are drunk? People believe that their own risks are much lower than they really are. Based on an analysis of U.S. National Highway Traffic Safety data, traffic risks among 16- to 21-year-olds after consuming alcohol are 2–10 times greater than their perceptions of the risks. For instance, people often feel that their reaction times are just as quick whether they are sober or drunk.

Q: If observations and analyses revealed an equally risky and preventable behavior on the road, would it be advisable to prohibit that behavior, too? They have! Such observations and analyses have been made and have resulted in many states banning the use of handheld cell phones and text-messaging while driving. Let's consider two studies.

In a study using a driving simulator, individuals were evaluated when talking on a cell phone or after they had consumed alcohol to the point of intoxication (they used vodka and orange juice in this University of Utah study). The results? The driving of individuals using cell phones was as much impaired as the driving of those who were drunk. One very interesting and perhaps surprising result: handheld and hands-free phones impaired driving equally; it seems that it is inattention, rather than reduced dexterity, that is responsible for the impairment.

Another study, analyzing the cell phone records of individuals who were in real traffic collisions, came to the same conclusion, finding that cell phone users were 4–5 times more likely to get into an accident than non-distracted drivers. When you use a cell phone while driving, you put yourself and others at the same level of risk as if you were driving drunk.

Q: What observations could be made that would cause *you* not to use your cell phone while driving?

What can you conclude? Scientific observations can reveal unexpected truths about the world and, in doing so, can cause us to change what we think and how we behave. If we consider one risk (such as driving drunk) unacceptable, should we consider an equal risk (such as driving while using a cell phone) also unacceptable? Science can't answer that, but it can help you to understand the world better and to think more consciously about decisions you may be making without even realizing it.

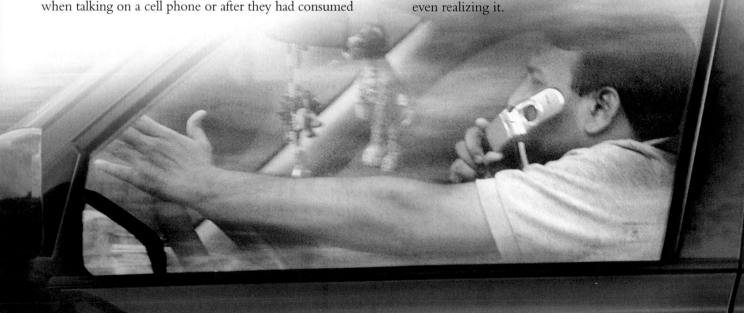

1 Science is a collection of facts and a process for understanding the world.

Through its emphasis on objective observation, description, and experimentation, science is a pathway by which we can discover and better understand the world around us. Biological issues permeate all aspects of our lives. To make wise decisions, it is essential for individuals and societies to attain biological literacy. There are numerous ways of gaining an understanding of the world. Because it is empirical, rational, testable, repeatable, and self-correcting, the scientific method is a particularly effective approach.

2 A beginner's guide: what are the steps of the scientific method?

The scientific method (observation, hypothesis, prediction, test, and conclusion) is a flexible, adaptable, and efficient pathway to understanding the world because it tells us when we must change our beliefs. The scientific method begins by making observations about the world, noting apparent patterns or cause-and-effect relationships. A hypothesis is a proposed explanation for a phenomenon. For a hypothesis to be useful, it must generate a testable prediction. A critical experiment is one that makes it possible to decisively determine whether a particular hypothesis is correct. Based on the results of experimental tests, we can revise our hypothesis and explain the observable world with increasing accuracy. A great strength of scientific thinking, therefore, is that it helps us understand when we should change our minds. Scientific theories do not represent speculation or guesses about the natural world. Rather, they are hypotheses—proposed explanations for natural phenomena—that have been so strongly and persuasively supported by empirical observation that the scientific community views them as very unlikely to be altered by new evidence.

3 Well-designed experiments are essential to testing hypotheses.

To draw clear conclusions from experiments, it is essential to hold constant all those variables we are not interested in. Control and experimental groups should vary only with respect to the treatment of interest. Differences in outcomes between the groups can then be attributed to the treatment. Experiments and their outcomes must be repeatable for their conclusions to be valid and widely accepted. Biases can influence our behavior, including our collection and interpretation of data. With careful controls, we can minimize such biases.

4 The scientific method can help us make wise decisions.

Because much variation exists in the world, statistics can help us evaluate whether differences between a treatment group and control group can be attributed to the treatment rather than random chance. Pseudoscience and anecdotal observations often lead people to believe that links between two phenomena exist, when in fact there are no such links. Although the scientific method may be the most effective path toward understanding the observable world, it cannot give us insights into the generation of value judgments and other types of non-quantifiable, subjective information.

5 On the road to biological literacy: what are the major themes in biology?

Although the diversity of life on earth is tremendous, the study of life is unified by the themes of hierarchical organization and the power of evolution.

KEY TERMS

anecdotal observation, p. 25
biological literacy, p. 4
biology, p. 3
blind experimental design, p. 20
control group, p. 17
critical experiment, p. 13

double-blind experimental design, p. 20
empirical, p. 7
experimental group, p. 17
hypothesis (*pl.* hypotheses), p. 11
null hypothesis, p. 11

placebo, p. 13
placebo effect, p. 19
positive correlation, p. 24
pseudoscience, p. 25
randomized, p. 20
science, p. 3
scientific literacy, p. 4

scientific method, p. 7
statistics, p. 23
superstition, p. 6
theory, p. 16
treatment, p. 17
variable, p. 18

1. Science is:
   a) a field of study that requires certain "laws of nature" to be taken on faith.
   b) both a body of knowledge and an intellectual activity encompassing observation, description, experimentation, and explanation of natural phenomena.
   c) a process that can be applied only within the scientific disciplines, such as biology, chemistry, and physics.
   d) the only way to understand the natural world.
   e) None of the above.

2. All of the following are elements of biological literacy except:
   a) the ability to use the process of scientific inquiry to think creatively about real-world issues having a biological component.
   b) reading the most important books in biology.
   c) the ability to integrate into your decision making a consideration of issues having a biological component.
   d) the ability to communicate with others about issues having a biological component.
   e) All of the above are elements of biological literacy.

3. Superstitions are:
   a) held by many humans, but not by any non-human species.
   b) just one of many possible forms of scientific thinking.
   c) true beliefs that have yet to be fully understood.
   d) irrational beliefs that actions not logically related to a course of events influence its outcome.
   e) proof that the scientific method is not perfect.

4. In a recent study, patients treated with a genetically engineered heart drug were able to walk on a treadmill 26 seconds longer than those not receiving the drug, and they showed no side effects from taking the drug. Can we conclude that this drug is an effective treatment for heart disease?
   a) No. Genetically engineered drugs cannot be tested by the scientific method; they require comparative observations.
   b) No. It is not clear how many subjects were in the study.
   c) No. It is not clear that the drug is not a placebo.
   d) Yes.
   e) No. It is not clear that the proper controls were included.

5. Empirical results:
   a) rely on intuition.
   b) are generated by theories.
   c) are based on observation.
   d) cannot be replicated.
   e) must support a tested hypothesis.

6. In a well-designed experiment:
   a) the prediction will be highly probable if the experiment shows the explanation is correct.
   b) the prediction will be highly improbable if the experiment shows the explanation is incorrect.
   c) the null hypothesis will not be tested.
   d) the prediction will most likely be correct.
   e) Both a) and b) are correct.

7. Which of the following statements is correct?
   a) A hypothesis that does not generate a testable prediction is not useful.
   b) Common sense is usually a good substitute for the scientific method when trying to understand the world.
   c) The scientific method can be used only to understand scientific phenomena.
   d) It is not necessary to make observations as part of the scientific method.
   e) All of the above are correct.

8. The placebo effect:
   a) is the frequently observed, poorly understood phenomenon that people tend to respond favorably to any treatment.
   b) reveals that sugar pills are generally as effective as actual medications in fighting illness.
   c) reveals that experimental treatments cannot be proven effective.
   d) demonstrates that most scientific studies cannot be replicated.
   e) is an urban legend.

9. Before experimental drugs can be brought to market, they must undergo many rigorous trials to ensure they deliver their medical benefits effectively and safely. One method commonly used in this process is to compare the effect of a drug with that of a placebo in double-blind tests. Which of the following correctly describes a double-blind test?
   a) The researchers apply two-layered blindfolds to the study participants so they cannot see whether they are receiving the drug or a placebo.
   b) Neither the researchers nor the study participants know who is receiving the drug and who is receiving the placebo.
   c) The researchers know who is receiving the drug and who is receiving the placebo, but do not know what the supposed effects of the drug should be.
   d) The researchers do not know who receives the drug or the placebo, but the participants know and tell them later.
   e) None of the above.

10. In controlled experiments:
   a) one variable is manipulated while others are held constant.
   b) all variables are dependent on each other.
   c) all variables are held constant.
   d) all variables are independent of each other.
   e) all critical variables are manipulated.

11. If a researcher collects data by using the same experimental setup as in another study, but using different research subjects, the process is considered:
   a) an uncontrolled experiment.
   b) intuitive reasoning.
   c) extrapolation.
   d) replication.
   e) exploration.

12. You hear the males of a particular bird species calling in their natural environment and question why they call. You design an experiment to try to answer your question. You cage one male bird and record his calling rate in response to four treatments, varying the number of conspecific (of the same species) males and the number of conspecific females that the male subject can see. The treatments are: no conspecific birds; 10 conspecific males; 10 conspecific females; 5 conspecific males and 5 conspecific females. Your results are: the rate at which the male subject calls is the same across all four treatments. Which of the following is a null hypothesis that your experimental design could reject?
a) Males of the species do not call.
b) Males of the species call more often than do females.
c) Males of the species call at a rate that is independent of the sex composition of the audience.
d) Males of the species call less often than do females.
e) Males of the species call when called to.

13. Statistical methods make it possible to:
a) prove any hypothesis is true.
b) determine how likely it is that certain results have occurred by chance.
c) unambiguously learn the truth.
d) reject any hypothesis.
e) test non-falsifiable hypotheses.

14. Anecdotal evidence:
a) is a more efficient method for understanding the world than the scientific method.
b) tends to be more reliable than data based on observations of large numbers of diverse individuals.
c) is a necessary part of the scientific method.
d) is often the only way to prove important causal links between two phenomena.
e) can seem to reveal links between two phenomena, but the links do not actually exist.

15. A relationship between phenomena that has been established based on large amounts of observational and experimental data is referred to as:
a) a theory.
b) a fact.
c) an assumption.
d) a conjecture.
e) a hypothesis.

16. Which of the following issues would be least helped by application of the scientific method?
a) developing more effective high school curricula
b) evaluating the relationship between violence in videogames and criminal behavior in teens
c) determining the most effective safety products for automobiles
d) formulating public policy on euthanasia
e) comparing the effectiveness of two potential antibiotics

17. What is the meaning of the statement "correlation does not imply causation"?
a) Just because two variables vary in a similar pattern does not mean that changing one variable causes a change in the other.
b) It is not possible to demonstrate a correlation between two variables.
c) When a change in one variable causes a change in another variable, the two variables are not necessarily related to each other in any way.
d) It is not possible to prove the cause of any naturally occurring phenomenon.
e) Just because two variables vary in a similar pattern does not mean that they have any relationship to each other.

SHORT-ANSWER QUESTIONS

1. A pharmaceutical company plans to test a potential anti-cancer drug on human subjects. The drug will be administered in pill form. How should this study be designed so that appropriate controls are in place?

2. Lately there have been many claims concerning the health benefits of green tea. Suppose you read a claim that alleges drinking green tea causes weight loss. You are provided with the following information about the studies that led to this claim.

People were weighed at the beginning of the study.

People were asked to drink two cups of green tea every day for 6 weeks.

People were weighed at the end of the study.

People who drank green tea for 6 weeks lost some weight by the end of the study.

It was concluded that green tea is helpful for weight loss.

This study obviously had some holes in its design. Assuming no information other than that provided above, indicate at least four things that could be done to improve the experimental design.

3. Use of the word "theory" can imply different things to different people. Statements referring to evolution as "just a theory" imply that a scientific theory is much like a hunch, something that can easily be disproved. How is a scientific theory different from any other type of "theory"? What requirements must be met before a hypothesis is considered to be a scientific theory?

See Appendix for answers. For additional study questions, go to www.prep-u.com.

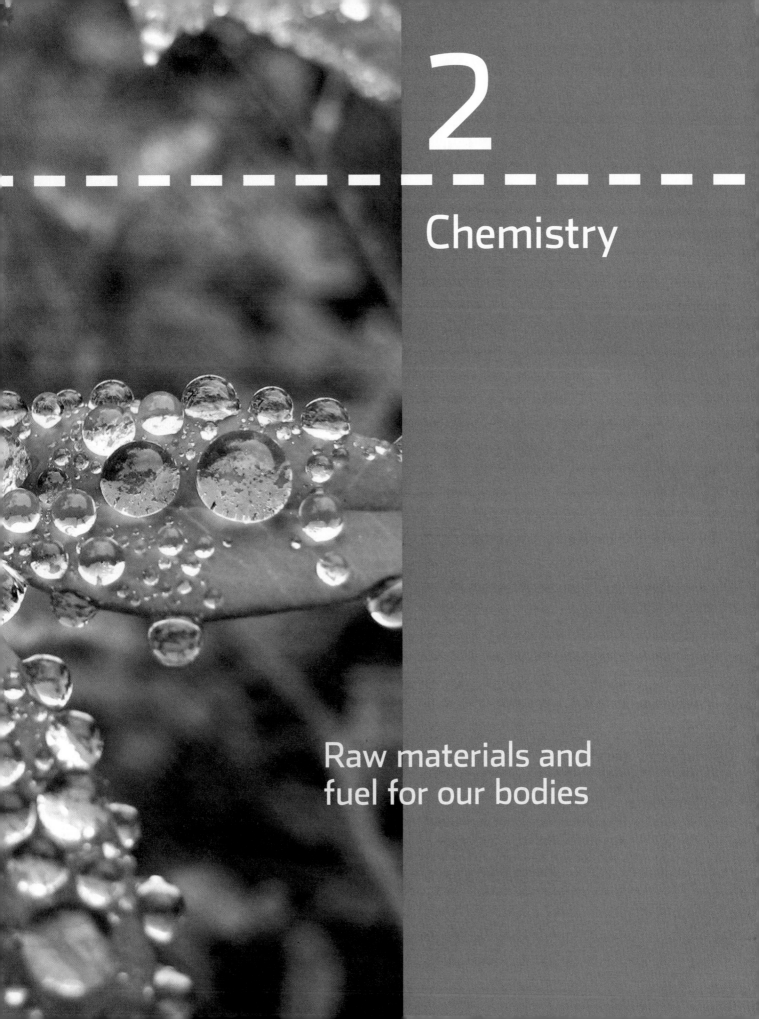

2
Chemistry

Raw materials and
fuel for our bodies

❶ Atoms form molecules through bonding.

A collection of salt crystals, made from cesium chloride.

2·1

Everything is made of atoms.

A little bit of chemistry goes a long way in the study of biology and in understanding a great deal about your everyday life. Will eating those beans in your soup keep you up all night in gastrointestinal distress? Just knowing whether the beans are lentils or lima beans—each contains slightly different types of sugar molecules—will give you an answer. Will the butter you spread on your toast sabotage your efforts to lose weight? Understanding a little about the carbon–hydrogen connections in the fat molecules can help you decide.

The chemistry that is most important in biology revolves around a few important elements. An **element** is a substance that cannot be broken down chemically into any other substances. Gold and carbon and aluminum are elements you might be familiar with. Whatever the element, if you keep cutting it into ever smaller pieces, each of the pieces behaves exactly the same as any other piece. The smallest piece of pure gold will still have the softness, reflectivity, and malleability characteristic of that element (**FIGURE 2-1**).

If you could continue cutting, you would eventually separate the gold into tiny pieces that could no longer be divided

Gold   Carbon

Copper

Although we associate pennies with the element copper, all pennies minted after 1982 are made with a zinc core and are plated with copper.

FIGURE 2-1 Familiar elements. Elements are substances that cannot be broken down chemically into any other substances.

Atoms   Water   Carbohydrates   Lipids

without losing their gold-like properties. These are the individual component pieces of an element, called **atoms.** An atom is a bit of matter that cannot be subdivided any further without losing its essential properties. The word "atom" is from the Greek for "indivisible."

Everything around us, living or not, can be reduced to atoms. All atoms—whether of the element gold or some other element such as oxygen or aluminum or calcium—have the same basic structure. At the center of an atom is a **nucleus,** which is usually made up of two types of particles, called protons and neutrons. **Protons** are particles that have a positive electrical charge and **neutrons** are particles that have no electrical charge. The amount of matter in a proton or neutron, its **mass,** is about the same (**FIGURE 2-2**).

Whirling in a cloud around the nucleus of every atom are negatively charged particles called **electrons.** An electron weighs almost nothing—less than one-twentieth of one percent of the weight of a proton. (The mass of an atom—its **atomic mass**—is made up of the combined mass of all of its protons and neutrons; for our purposes here, electrons are so light that their mass can be ignored.) Particles that have the same charge repel each other; those with opposite charges are attracted to each other. Because all electrons have the same charge, the electrons in an atom repel each other. But because they are negatively charged, they are attracted to the positively charged protons in the nucleus. This attraction holds electrons close enough to the nucleus to keep them from flying away,

A KEY TO THE ELEMENTS

ATOMIC NUMBER
The number of protons found in the atom's nucleus

ELEMENT SYMBOL
Abbreviation of the element's name

ELEMENT NAME

ATOMIC MASS
Combined mass of the atom's protons and neutrons

Periodic table of elements

ELEMENT COLOR CODE
The following colors are used throughout this book for elements commonly found in living organisms.

Hydrogen Carbon Nitrogen Oxygen Sodium
Phosphorus Sulfur Chlorine Potassium Calcium

FIGURE 2-3 The vital statistics of atoms. A guide to reading the periodic table.

while the energy of their fast movement keeps them from collapsing into the nucleus.

Atoms are tiny. Enlarge an atom by a billion times and it would only be the size of a grapefruit. Paradoxically, most of the space taken up by an atom is empty. That is, because the nucleus is very small and compact, the electrons zip about relatively far from the nucleus. If the nucleus were the size of a golf ball, the electrons would be anywhere from half a mile to six miles away.

What distinguishes one element, such as chlorine, from another, such as neon or oxygen? Atoms of different elements have a different number of protons in the nucleus. A chlorine atom has 17 protons, a neon atom has 10 protons, and an oxygen atom has 8 protons. Each element is given a name (and an abbreviation, such as O for oxygen and C for carbon) and an **atomic number** that corresponds to how many protons it has (**FIGURE 2-3**). All the known elements can be arranged in a scheme, in the order of their atomic number, called the "periodic table." So far, about 90 elements have been discovered that are present in nature and about 25 others can be made in the laboratory. Everything you see around you is made up of some combination of those naturally occurring elements.

THE ATOM: BASIC STRUCTURE

Nucleus

Hydrogen atom
1 Proton
0 Neutrons
1 Electron

Carbon atom
6 Protons
6 Neutrons
6 Electrons

Forces of attraction between positive and negative charges hold the fast-moving electrons (negative) close to the nucleus (positive).

Nucleus:
Proton Neutron Electron

FIGURE 2-2 The atom. At the center of an atom is a nucleus containing protons and (in all elements except hydrogen) neutrons. The nucleus is surrounded by electrons whirling about in a cloud.

Proteins

Nucleic Acids

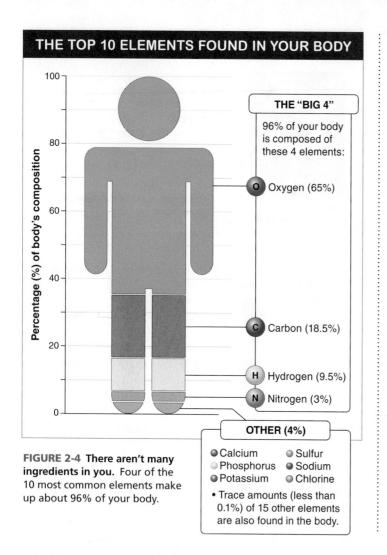

THE TOP 10 ELEMENTS FOUND IN YOUR BODY

THE "BIG 4"

96% of your body is composed of these 4 elements:

O Oxygen (65%)

C Carbon (18.5%)

H Hydrogen (9.5%)

N Nitrogen (3%)

OTHER (4%)

- Calcium
- Phosphorus
- Potassium
- Sulfur
- Sodium
- Chlorine

- Trace amounts (less than 0.1%) of 15 other elements are also found in the body.

FIGURE 2-4 There aren't many ingredients in you. Four of the 10 most common elements make up about 96% of your body.

Of all the elements found on earth, only 25 are found in your body. The "Top 10" most common of these make up 99.9% of your body (**FIGURE 2-4**). And just four elements make up more than 96% of your body. These "Big 4" are oxygen, carbon, hydrogen, and nitrogen. With knowledge about the Big 4, you can understand a huge amount about nutrition and physiology (how your body works), so we'll focus on the properties of these four elements later in this chapter.

The number of protons in an atom's nucleus determines what element it is. The number of neutrons in the nucleus is usually equal to the number of protons. Since protons and neutrons have approximately the same mass, the mass of the atom is about double its atomic number. The element oxygen, for example, has the atomic number 8 because it has 8 protons, so we expect it to have an atomic mass of 16, simply the mass of the 8 protons and 8 neutrons added together—which it generally does. (As noted above, we can ignore the mass of the electrons.)

TAKE-HOME MESSAGE 2·1

Everything around us, living or not, is made up of atoms, the smallest unit into which material can be divided without losing its essential properties. All atoms have the same general structure. They are made up of protons and neutrons in the nucleus, and electrons, which circle far around the nucleus.

2·2 --

An atom's electrons determine how (and whether) the atom will bond with other atoms.

While the number of protons identifies an element, it is an atom's electrons that determine how (and whether) it bonds with other atoms. Electrons move so quickly that it is impossible to determine, at any given moment, exactly where an electron is. Electrons are not just moving about haphazardly, though. Speeding around the nucleus, they tend to stay within a prescribed area. This area is called an "electron shell," and an atom may have several shells, each shell occupied by its own set of electrons. Within a shell, the electrons stay far apart because their negative charges repel one another.

The first electron shell is closest to the nucleus and can hold two electrons (**FIGURE 2-5**). If an atom has more than two

electrons, as most atoms do, the other electrons are arranged in other shells. The second shell is a bit farther away from the nucleus and can hold as many as eight electrons. There can be as many as seven shells in total, holding varying numbers of electrons.

Atoms become stable when their outermost shell is filled to capacity. Those with this configuration behave like loners, neither reacting nor combining with other atoms. On the other hand, when atoms have outer shells with vacancies, they are likely to interact with other atoms, giving, taking, or sharing electrons to achieve that desirable state: a full outer shell of electrons. In fact, based on the number of electron

Atoms   Water   Carbohydrates   Lipids

ELECTRON SHELLS

Electrons move around the nucleus in designated areas called electron shells. An atom can have as many as seven electron shells in total.

First electron shell
(capacity: 2 electrons)

Second electron shell
(capacity: 8 electrons)

Vacancy

Oxygen atom

> The chemical characteristics of an atom depend upon the number of electrons in its outermost shell.

ATOM STABILITY

Atoms become stable when their outermost shell is filled to capacity. Stable atoms tend not to react or combine with other atoms.

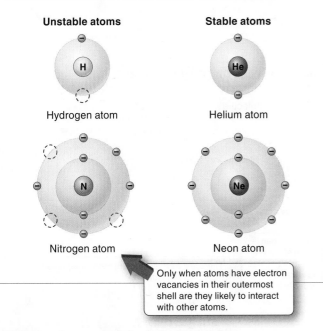

Unstable atoms	Stable atoms
H	He
Hydrogen atom	Helium atom
N	Ne
Nitrogen atom	Neon atom

> Only when atoms have electron vacancies in their outermost shell are they likely to interact with other atoms.

FIGURE 2-5 Electrons and the shells they inhabit.

vacancies in the outermost shell of an atom, it's possible to predict how amenable to bonding that atom will be, and even which other atoms its likely bonding partners will be.

An atom that loses one or more electrons becomes positively charged, while an atom that acquires electrons becomes negatively charged. This transfer of electrons is driven by the fact that atoms with full outer electron shells are more stable.

Donated electron

Sodium ion	Chloride ion
⊕ 11 Protons	⊕ 17 Protons
11 Neutrons	17 Neutrons
⊖ 10 Electrons	⊖ 18 Electrons

NET CHARGE   ➕ Positive   ➖ Negative

FIGURE 2-6 Ions are electrically charged atoms.

Normally, an atom has the same number of electrons as protons. Sometimes an atom may have one or more extra electrons or may lack one or more electrons relative to the number of protons. An atom with extra electrons becomes negatively charged, and an atom lacking one or more electrons is positively charged. Such a charged atom is called an **ion** (**FIGURE 2-6**). Due to their electrical charge, ions behave very differently from the atoms that give rise to them. As we'll see later in the chapter, ions are more likely to interact with other, oppositely charged ions.

TAKE-HOME MESSAGE 2·2

> The chemical characteristics of an atom depend on the number of electrons in its outermost shell. Atoms are most stable and least likely to bond with other atoms when their outermost electron shell is filled to capacity.

Proteins   Nucleic Acids

2·3

Atoms can bond together to form molecules or compounds.

When you eat a meal, it is like filling your car's tank with gasoline; you have a source of energy that can be used to fuel activities like running, thinking, building muscle, and maintaining the machinery of life. That energy initially comes from the sun and is captured and stored by plants. When we eat plants or eat other animals that eat plants, we ingest the energy stored in the plant material. But how exactly is energy stored in plants? It is stored in bonds that join atoms together. Eventually the bonds are broken, the energy is released, and it can be used to fuel the body's activities.

Groups of atoms held together by bonds are called **molecules.** It usually requires energy to build bonds and "glue" atoms together. Conversely, when molecules are broken down—such as when animals (including humans) consume molecules in their diet—bonds are broken, releasing the energy that was used to create them. In a sense, molecules are created as a short-term storage of energy that can be harnessed later.

There are three principal types of bonds that hold multiple atoms together. The type of bonding that any atom is likely to take part in depends almost entirely on the number of electrons in its outermost shell.

Covalent Bonds **Covalent bonds** are strong bonds formed when two atoms share electrons. The simplest example of a covalent bond is the bonding of two hydrogen atoms to form H_2 (**FIGURE 2-7**), the simplest of all molecules. A hydrogen atom has an atomic number of 1: it has a single proton in its nucleus and a single electron circling around the nucleus in the first shell. Because the atom is most stable when the first shell has two electrons, two hydrogen atoms can each achieve a complete outermost shell by sharing electrons. The nuclei come close together (but not too close, since they are positively charged) and the two electrons circle around both of the nuclei, almost in a figure 8. The new H_2 molecule is very stable because, now that both atoms have two electrons in their outermost shell, they are no longer likely to bond with other atoms.

Oxygen, with an atomic number of 8, has two electrons in its innermost shell and six in its outermost shell. Consequently it needs to form two covalent bonds to fill its outermost shell. Sometimes two oxygen atoms join together to form O_2. Each oxygen atom shares two electrons with the other, filling the outermost shell of both. The sharing of two electrons between two atoms is called a **double bond** (see Figure 2-7). O_2 is the most common form in which we find oxygen in the world.

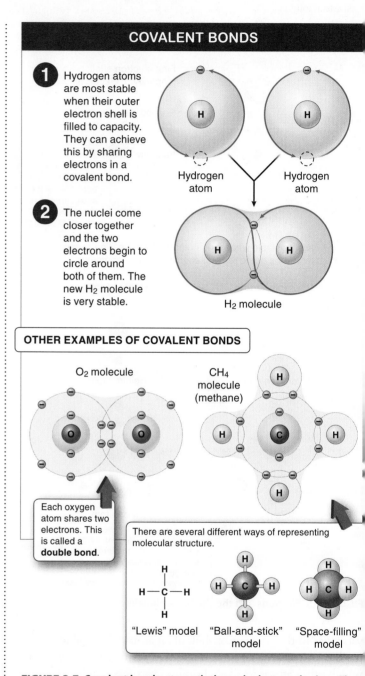

COVALENT BONDS

1 Hydrogen atoms are most stable when their outer electron shell is filled to capacity. They can achieve this by sharing electrons in a covalent bond.

Hydrogen atom   Hydrogen atom

2 The nuclei come closer together and the two electrons begin to circle around both of them. The new H_2 molecule is very stable.

H_2 molecule

OTHER EXAMPLES OF COVALENT BONDS

O_2 molecule

CH_4 molecule (methane)

Each oxygen atom shares two electrons. This is called a **double bond**.

There are several different ways of representing molecular structure.

"Lewis" model   "Ball-and-stick" model   "Space-filling" model

FIGURE 2-7 Covalent bonds: strength through electron sharing. The molecular structures formed by covalent bonding can be represented on paper in several different ways.

Carbon is a particularly extroverted molecule. It has an atomic number of 6, meaning that two electrons fill its first shell and four remain to occupy the second shell. Because four electron vacancies are left, carbon can, and frequently does, form four covalent bonds, joining up with other atoms in a wide variety

Atoms   Water   Carbohydrates   Lipids

of molecules. Methane, the chief component of natural gas, is formed when one atom of carbon covalently bonds with four atoms of hydrogen (see Figure 2-7). It has the chemical formula CH_4.

Ionic Bonds Atoms can also bond together without sharing electrons. In **ionic bonds,** one atom transfers one or more of its electrons completely to another. As a result of this transfer, each atom becomes an ion, since each has an unequal number of protons and electrons. The atom gaining electrons becomes negatively charged, while the atom losing electrons becomes positively charged. Rather than forming molecules, ionic bonds form **compounds,** in which the two oppositely charged ions attract each other. Unlike the much stronger covalent bonds, in ionic bonds each electron circles around a single nucleus. Ions

of equal and opposite charges are attracted to each other and the compound is neutral—that is, it has no charge (**FIGURE 2-8**).

Hydrogen Bonds Ionic and covalent bonds link two or more atoms together. **Hydrogen bonds,** on the other hand, are important in bonding multi-atom molecules together. A hydrogen bond is formed between a hydrogen atom in one molecule and another atom, often an oxygen or nitrogen atom, in another molecule (or, in a very large molecule, in another part of the same molecule). This bond is based on the attraction between positive and negative charges (**FIGURE 2-9**).

The atoms taking part in hydrogen bonds are not ions, so where do the electrical charges come from? The hydrogen atom is already covalently bonded to another atom in the

IONIC BONDS

1 One atom transfers one or more electrons completely to another. The result is two oppositely charged ions.

Donated electron

Sodium ion ⊕   ⊖ Chloride ion

OPPOSITE CHARGES ATTRACT

2 The two oppositely charged ions attract each other, forming a compound.

NaCl compound

NaCl crystals (table salt)

NaCl crystal structure

When multiple Na^+ ions and Cl^- ions are attracted to each other, a NaCl crystal structure forms.

FIGURE 2-8 Ionic bonds: transfer of electrons from one atom to another. The resulting charged atoms (ions) attract each other.

HYDROGEN BONDS

In water, the hydrogen nucleus, with only a single positively charged proton, doesn't attract the negatively charged electrons as much as does the larger nucleus of the oxygen atom (which has eight positively charged protons). As a consequence, all of the electrons spend more time near the oxygen. This makes that side of the molecule slightly negative and the hydrogen side slightly positive.

Polarity

Covalent bonds

Water molecule

Hydrogen bonds are formed between the slightly positively charged hydrogen atoms of one water molecule and the slightly negatively charged atoms of another.

Hydrogen bond

FIGURE 2-9 Hydrogen bonds: attraction between a polar atom or molecule and a hydrogen atom. As we'll see later in the chapter, the hydrogen bonding between H_2O molecules gives water some of its characteristic properties.

Proteins   Nucleic Acids

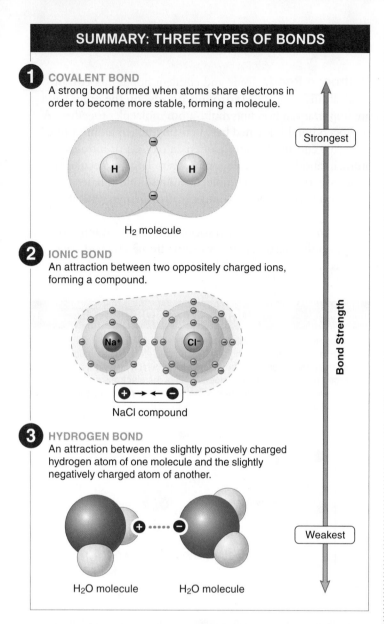

SUMMARY: THREE TYPES OF BONDS

1 COVALENT BOND
A strong bond formed when atoms share electrons in order to become more stable, forming a molecule.

H₂ molecule

2 IONIC BOND
An attraction between two oppositely charged ions, forming a compound.

NaCl compound

3 HYDROGEN BOND
An attraction between the slightly positively charged hydrogen atom of one molecule and the slightly negatively charged atom of another.

H₂O molecule   H₂O molecule

Strongest

Bond Strength

Weakest

FIGURE 2-10 Three ways in which atoms and molecules are bound.

same molecule and shares its electron. That electron circles both the hydrogen nucleus and the nucleus of the other atom, but the electron is not shared equally. Given that the other atom always has more than the one proton found in the hydrogen nucleus, the electron contributed by hydrogen spends more of its time near the other, more positively charged nucleus than near the hydrogen nucleus. Having an extra electron nearby causes the larger atom to be slightly negatively charged, while the hydrogen atom becomes slightly positively charged.

In a sense, the covalently bonded molecules become like a magnet, with distinct positive and negative sides (see Figure 2–9). Magnet–like molecules with distinct positive and negative regions like this are said to be "polar." They are attracted to other polar molecules, lining up in particular orientations such that the positive regions of one molecule are near the negative regions of another. These attractions between polar molecules are called hydrogen bonds. Although they are only about one-thirtieth as strong as covalent bonds, hydrogen bonds are responsible for many of the unique characteristics of water that make it one of the most important molecules for life on earth. See **FIGURE 2-10** for a review of the three types of bonds discussed in this section.

TAKE-HOME MESSAGE 2·3

Atoms can be bound together in three different ways. Covalent bonds, in which atoms share electrons, are the strongest. In ionic bonds, the next strongest, one atom transfers its electrons to another and the two oppositely charged ions are attracted to each other, forming a compound. Hydrogen bonds, the weakest of the three types, involve the attraction between a hydrogen atom and another polar atom or molecule.

2·4

A molecule's shape gives it unique characteristics.

When many atoms bond together, the resulting molecule or compound acquires a "personality" that results from the accumulated properties of the atoms and their interactions with each other. The arrangement of atoms within a molecule also determines the molecule's shape: the atoms may be lined up in a row or may stack in a pyramid or may pack in a more globular formation, like a piece of popcorn. Whatever form

the atoms take, a molecule's shape will determine many of its physical properties. Let's consider two important consequences of shape: how a molecule tastes and how it smells.

When you put a piece of chocolate into your mouth, your brain quickly registers a sweet taste. What exactly does that mean? Why does chocolate taste sweet, while a piece of fish

Atoms   Water   Carbohydrates   Lipids

may taste salty? The human tongue has various types of taste receptors; some detect bitter tastes, some sweet, some sour, some salty, and others savory. A molecule of the sugar glucose in that piece of chocolate triggers a sensation of sweetness when it binds to one of our sweet-taste receptors.

How sweet something tastes depends on the shape of its molecules—how well the molecules fit into the sweet-sensing receptors. Glucose molecules fit very well—slightly more snugly than the sucrose molecules in table sugar (**FIGURE 2-11**). Molecules of fructose, a sugar found in fruits and some vegetables, fit even better.

Food chemists have been able to create artificial sweeteners that have a better and better fit with receptors. Aspartame and saccharin, for example, are 150 times and 450 times sweeter than table sugar. Splenda is 600 times sweeter. This means that with very tiny amounts of artificial sweetener, we can sense a sweetness equivalent to a much greater amount of table sugar.

Insect mating behavior is also heavily influenced by molecular interactions that depend on molecular shape. Male gypsy moths, for example, will fly as far as two miles just because a molecule they encounter fits into one of their receptors and tells them that a sexually receptive female is nearby (**FIGURE 2-12**). At the heart of this behavior is something chemically similar to how taste receptors sense

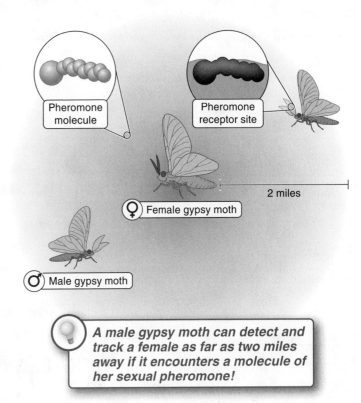

A male gypsy moth can detect and track a female as far as two miles away if it encounters a molecule of her sexual pheromone!

FIGURE 2-12 Molecular shape and function. A molecule's shape can give it a particular smell—and even be essential to its function as a sexual attractant.

the sweetness of a piece of chocolate. Rather than being in a piece of food, though, the molecules the insects "taste" are airborne.

Taste is just one special case illustrating the chemical importance of a molecule's shape. More generally, every interaction between molecules is influenced by the fit between the molecules. Next we will look at the shape and bonding characteristics of one of the most important biological molecules, water, and how they give that molecule superhero-like properties.

? Why does your brain register chocolate as tasting sweet and potato chips as salty?

FIGURE 2-11 The shape of a molecule matches the shape of its taste receptors.

TAKE-HOME MESSAGE 2·4

The chemical and physical properties of a molecule—such as how the molecule tastes or smells, or its likelihood of bonding with other molecules—depend on the shape in which the atoms are linked together and on the electrons exposed in their outermost shells.

❷ Water has features that enable it to support all life.

Water flowing down a Japanese waterfall.

2·5

Hydrogen bonds make water cohesive.

Predators chasing after green basilisk lizards in Central America sometimes get the shock of a lifetime (and lose their lunch in the process). When chased, the lizards run quickly across rocks and dirt—nothing unusual for a lizard. Then, when they come to the edge of a stream or river, these fleeing lizards show their uniqueness and earn their nickname, the "Jesus lizard." Without stopping, a Jesus lizard runs right across the surface of the water, leaving stunned predators behind at the water's edge. How do these animals do it?

The Jesus lizard, like numerous insects such as the water strider, makes use of the fact that water molecules have tremendous cohesion. That is, they stick together with unusual strength. This molecular cohesiveness is due to hydrogen bonds between the water molecules.

Each water molecule is V-shaped (**FIGURE 2-13**; see also Figure 2-9). The hydrogen atoms are at the ends of the two arms and the oxygen is at the bottom end of the V, between the two

hydrogen atoms. Oxygen's strongly positively charged nucleus pulls the circling electrons toward itself and holds on to them for more than its fair share of the time. Consequently, the oxygen at the bottom of the V has a slight negative charge and the end of the water molecule containing the hydrogen atoms has a slight positive charge.

Because of their unequally shared electrons, water molecules are polar; like a magnet, they have a positively charged and a negatively charged side (see Figure 2-9). Consequently, large numbers of water molecules orient themselves in an orderly arrangement that positions the negative side of one molecule near the positive side of another. Hydrogen bonds form between the relatively positively charged hydrogen atoms and the relatively negatively charged oxygen atoms of *adjacent* water molecules.

Hydrogen bonds are much weaker than covalent bonds and they don't last very long. Nonetheless, to the Jesus lizard, the

Atoms   Water   Carbohydrates   Lipids

Pressure applied to
water surface

Hydrogen
bond

V-shaped water molecules are
held together by hydrogen bonds.
The bonds are just strong enough
to give water a surface tension
with net-like properties.

? *How are these animals
able to walk on water?*

FIGURE 2-13 Walking on water! Hydrogen bonds make this possible for some animals.

cumulative effect of all the hydrogen bonds in water is to link together all the water molecules in the stream just enough to give the water a surface tension with some net-like properties. If the lizard were too fat or too slow, its weight would overwhelm the hydrogen bonds and the lizard would push the molecules apart and sink like a rock.

TAKE-HOME MESSAGE 2·5

Water molecules easily form hydrogen bonds, giving water great cohesiveness.

2·6

Water has unusual properties that make it critical to life.

All life on earth depends on water; organisms are made up mostly of water and require it more than any other molecule. Hydrogen bonding among water molecules gives water several important properties that contribute to its crucial role in the biology of all organisms.

1. Cohesion. We saw in the previous section how the connection of water molecules through hydrogen bonds makes water cohesive, resulting in, for example, high surface tension. The cohesiveness of water molecules also makes it possible for tall trees to exist (**FIGURE 2-14**). Leaves need water. Molecules of water in the leaves are continually lost to the atmosphere through evaporation or are used up in the process of photosynthesis. In order to get more water, plants must pull it up from the soil. The problem for many plants,

such as the giant sequoia trees, is that the soil may be 300 feet below the leaf. Hydrogen bonds, however, allow water molecules to pull up adjacent water molecules to which they have hydrogen-bonded. The chain of linked molecules extends all the way down to the soil, where another water molecule is pulled in via the roots each time a water molecule evaporates from a leaf far above.

2. Large heat capacity. Walking across a sandy beach on a hot day, you can feel how easily sand heats up. By comparison, stepping from the beach into the cooler ocean reveals that water resists warming. It takes a lot of energy to change the temperature of water even a small amount. Why? Again, we must look to hydrogen bonding for our answer.

Proteins   Nucleic Acids

WATER: STRONG COHESIVENESS

Because of the cohesive properties of water, trees such as the giant sequoia are able to transport water molecules from the soil to their leaves 300 ft. above.

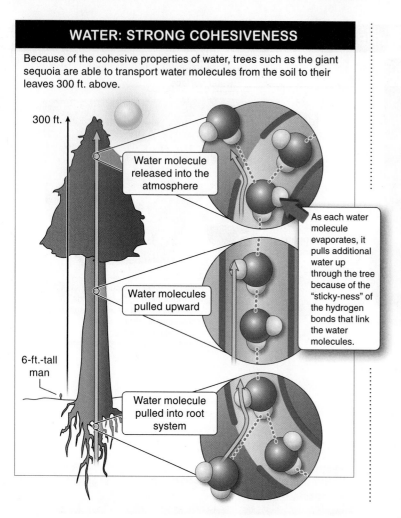

300 ft.

Water molecule released into the atmosphere

Water molecules pulled upward

6-ft.-tall man

Water molecule pulled into root system

As each water molecule evaporates, it pulls additional water up through the tree because of the "sticky-ness" of the hydrogen bonds that link the water molecules.

FIGURE 2-14 Like a giant straw. Hydrogen bonds cause water molecules to "stick" together, so that they can be pulled up through the giant sequoia.

The temperature of a substance is a measure of how quickly all of the molecules are moving. The molecules move more quickly when energy is added in the form of heat. When we heat water, the added energy doesn't immediately increase the movement of the individual water molecules. Rather, it disrupts some of the hydrogen bonds between the molecules (**FIGURE 2-15**). As quickly as they can be disrupted, though, hydrogen bonds form again somewhere else. And since the water molecules themselves don't increase their movement, the temperature doesn't increase. The net effect is that even if you release a lot of energy into water, the temperature doesn't change much. For this reason, because so much of your body is water, you are able to maintain a relatively constant body temperature.

Large bodies of water, especially oceans, can absorb huge amounts of heat from the sun during warm times of the year, reducing temperature increases on the land. Similarly, during cold times of the year the ocean slowly cools, giving off heat that reduces the temperature drop on shore.

Q Why *do coastal areas have milder, less variable climates than inland areas?*

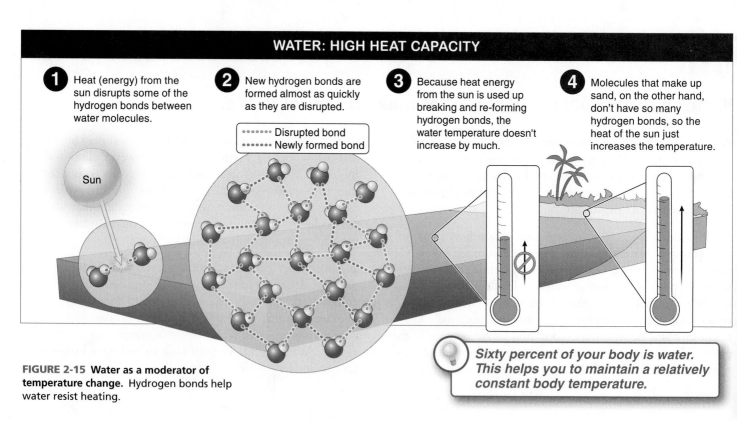

WATER: HIGH HEAT CAPACITY

1 Heat (energy) from the sun disrupts some of the hydrogen bonds between water molecules.

2 New hydrogen bonds are formed almost as quickly as they are disrupted.

········· Disrupted bond
······· Newly formed bond

3 Because heat energy from the sun is used up breaking and re-forming hydrogen bonds, the water temperature doesn't increase by much.

4 Molecules that make up sand, on the other hand, don't have so many hydrogen bonds, so the heat of the sun just increases the temperature.

Sun

Sixty percent of your body is water. This helps you to maintain a relatively constant body temperature.

FIGURE 2-15 Water as a moderator of temperature change. Hydrogen bonds help water resist heating.

Atoms   Water   Carbohydrates   Lipids

3. Low density as a solid. Ice floats. This is unusual, since most substances *increase* in density when frozen; as the molecules slow down, they pack together more and more efficiently—and densely. Consequently, the solid sinks. Water, however, becomes less dense and, as you might expect by now, this is due to hydrogen bonding. As the temperature drops and water molecules slow down, rather than becoming more and more tightly packed, they become less so. Each V-shaped water molecule bonds with four partners, via hydrogen bonds, forming a crystalline lattice in which the molecules are held slightly farther apart than in the liquid, causing ice to be less dense than water (**FIGURE 2-16**).

4. Good solvent. If you put a pinch of table salt into a glass of water, it will quickly dissolve. This means that all the charged sodium (Na⁺) and chloride (Cl⁻) ions that were ionically bonded together become separated from one another. The sodium and chloride ions were initially attracted to each other because they are polar molecules (ions), each carrying a slight charge. Water is able to pry them apart because, as a polar molecule, it, too, carries charges. The positively charged sodium ions are attracted to the negatively charged side of the water molecule, and the negatively charged chloride ions are

WATER: A GOOD SOLVENT

When placed in water, ionic compounds such as NaCl are broken down into separate Na⁺ and Cl⁻ ions. Positively charged Na⁺ ions are attracted to the negatively charged side of the H₂O molecule, while negatively charged Cl⁻ ions are attracted to the positively charged side.

NaCl crystal (table salt)

Dissolved Na⁺ and Cl⁻ ions

Na⁺

Cl⁻

FIGURE 2-17 Solutions. Water pries apart ionic bonds, dissolving ionic compounds.

attracted to the positively charged side (**FIGURE 2-17**). Many substances are, like water, polar. That is why, like salt, they easily dissolve in water.

Non-polar molecules (such as oil) have neither positively charged regions nor negatively charged regions. Consequently, the polar water molecules are not attracted to them. Instead, when oil is poured into a container of water, the water molecules distance themselves from the oil, leaving the oil molecules in isolated aggregations that never dissolve.

Because so much salt is dissolved in the oceans, many of the water molecules have their positively charged sides facing Cl⁻ ions. Simultaneously, many molecules of water are turned the other way, with their negatively charged sides facing Na⁺ ions. Consequently, the orderly lattices of hydrogen bonds found in ice cannot form in salt water, and it does not freeze well.

Q Why don't oceans freeze as easily as freshwater lakes?

WATER: LOWER DENSITY WHEN FROZEN

FROZEN WATER
Hydrogen bonding arranges water molecules into a crystalline lattice, keeping them slighty farther apart and, therefore, less dense.

LIQUID WATER
Water molecules move about freely, allowing them to be closer to one another.

RELATIVE AREA OCCUPIED BY THE SAME NUMBER OF H₂O MOLECULES: Frozen water Liquid water

FIGURE 2-16 Ice floats. When frozen, water becomes less dense.

TAKE-HOME MESSAGE 2·6

The hydrogen bonds between water molecules give water several of its most important characteristics, including cohesiveness, a reduced density as a solid, the ability to resist temperature changes, and broad effectiveness as a solvent.

Proteins   Nucleic Acids

Living systems are highly sensitive to acidic and basic conditions.

There's a lot more going on in water than meets the eye. Most of the molecules are present as H$_2$O, but at any instant some of them break into two parts: H$^+$ and OH$^-$. In pure water, the amount of H$^+$ and OH$^-$ must be exactly the same, since every time a molecule splits, one of each type of ion is produced. But in some fluids containing other dissolved materials, this balance is lost: the fluid can have more H$^+$ or more OH$^-$.

The amount of H$^+$ or OH$^-$ in a fluid gives it some important properties. In particular, the amount of H$^+$ in a solution is a measure of its acidity and is called **pH.** The greater the number of free hydrogen ions floating around, the more acidic the solution is.

Pure water is in the middle of the pH scale, with a pH of 7.0. Any fluid with a pH below 7.0 has more H$^+$ ions (and fewer OH$^-$ ions) and is considered an **acid.** Any fluid with a pH above 7.0 has fewer H$^+$ ions (and more OH$^-$ ions) and is considered a **base.** The pH scale, like the Richter scale for earthquakes, is logarithmic, although in the case of pH, the *lower* the number the *greater* the acidity: a decrease of 1 on the scale represents a 10-fold increase in the hydrogen ion concentration (**FIGURE 2-18**). A decrease of 2 represents a 100-fold increase. This means that a cola, with a pH of about 3.0, is 10,000 times (!) more acidic than a glass of water, with a pH of 7.0.

H$^+$ ions are essentially free-floating protons. Acids can donate their H$^+$ ions to other chemicals. In fact, H$^+$ is a very reactive little ion. Its presence gives acids some unique properties. For instance, the hydrogen ions in acids can bind with atoms in metals, causing them to corrode. That's why you can dissolve nails by dumping them in a bucket of acid (or cola).

Your stomach produces large amounts of hydrochloric acid (HCl) and has a pH between 1 and 3. (HCl is acidic because most of the hydrogen ions split off from the chlorine, raising the H$^+$ concentration of the fluid.) The acid in your stomach helps to kill most bacteria that you ingest. It also greatly enhances the breakdown of the chemicals in the food you eat and the efficiency of digestion and absorption. You may have

THE pH SCALE

H$^+$ ion   Water   OH$^-$ ion

ACIDS

Acids are fluids that have a greater proportion of H$^+$ ions to OH$^-$ ions.

- H$^+$ ions are very reactive.
- Strong acids are corrosive to metals.
- Acids break down food in your digestive tract.
- Acids are generally sour in taste.

BASES

Bases are fluids that have a greater proportion of OH$^-$ ions to H$^+$ ions.

- OH$^-$ ions bind with H$^+$ ions, neutralizing acids.
- Strong bases are caustic to your skin.
- Bases can be found in many household cleaners.
- Bases are generally bitter in taste and soapy.

0 1 2 3 4 5 6 7 8 9 10 11 12 13 14

Battery acid · Soda · Beer · Coffee · Water · Blood · Baking soda · Ammonia · Bleach

Soda, with a pH of about 3.0, is 10,000 times more acidic than a glass of water, with a pH of 7.0!

FIGURE 2-18 pH is a measure of acidity.

Atoms   Water   Carbohydrates   Lipids

BUFFERS IN BLOOD STABILIZE pH

When blood pH level becomes too acidic...

7
0 14

a buffer chemical absorbs excess H⁺ ions.

H⁺

When blood pH level becomes too basic...

7
0 14

a buffer chemical releases H⁺ ions.

H⁺

Blood pH level returns to normal.

7
0 14

FIGURE 2-19 Maintaining a constant internal environment. Buffers in blood prevent potentially damaging pH swings.

Buffers keep the pH of blood close to 7.4.

learned firsthand of the high acidity of your stomach fluids if you have experienced heartburn or the sour taste of vomit.

Bases have very low concentrations of H⁺ and relatively high concentrations of OH⁻. Baking soda is a common basic substance. Some bases are called "antacids" because the OH⁻ ions in bases can bind with excess H⁺ ions in acidic solutions, neutralizing the acid. Base-containing products such as Alka-Seltzer and Milk of Magnesia reduce the unpleasant feeling of

heartburn and acid indigestion that sometimes arise from the overproduction of acids by the stomach. Bases are commonly used in household cleaning products and generally have a bitter taste and a soapy, slippery feel.

The pH of blood is usually 7.4. Given that most cellular reactions produce or consume H⁺ ions, there ought to be great swings in the pH of our blood. Unfortunately, our bodies can't tolerate such swings. Most of the chemicals that aid in the chemical reactions in our blood or cells stop functioning properly if the pH swings up or down by less than half a point. Fortunately, our bodies contain some chemicals that act like bank accounts for H⁺ ions (**FIGURE 2-19**). Called **buffers,** these chemicals can quickly absorb excess H⁺ ions to keep a solution from becoming too acidic, and they can quickly release H⁺ ions to counteract any increases in OH⁻ concentration. Therefore, buffers are chemicals that act to resist changes in pH.

TAKE-HOME MESSAGE 2·7

The pH of a fluid is a measure of how acidic or basic the solution is and depends on the concentration of dissolved H⁺ ions present. Acids, such as vinegar, can donate protons to other chemicals; bases, including baking soda, bind with free protons.

Proteins   Nucleic Acids

❸ Carbohydrates are fuel for living machines.

Worldwide, more corn is produced (by weight) than any other grain.

2·8

Carbohydrates include macromolecules that function as fuel.

Hardly a day goes by without an item in a magazine or newspaper or on TV talking about whether carbohydrates are good or bad for us. Sports drinks such as Gatorade are filled with carbs, and in the days before a big game or race, athletes often "carbo-load" by eating bowls of pasta. Yet other dietary supplements and "power" bars tout that they are low-carb and effective in weight loss by causing the body to resort to using fat for energy. Meanwhile, nutritionists, doctors, and many diet programs exhort people to increase the amount of fiber— another type of carbohydrate—in their diet. What exactly are they all talking about?

There are four types of **macromolecules**—large molecules made up from smaller building blocks or subunits—in living organisms: carbohydrates, lipids, proteins, and nucleic acids. **Carbohydrates** are molecules that contain mostly carbon, hydrogen, and oxygen: they are the primary fuel for running all of the cellular machinery and also form much of

FIGURE 2-20 All carbohydrates have a similar structure and function.

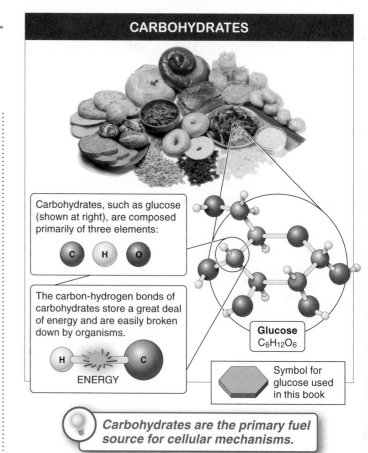

CARBOHYDRATES

Carbohydrates, such as glucose (shown at right), are composed primarily of three elements:

C   H   O

The carbon-hydrogen bonds of carbohydrates store a great deal of energy and are easily broken down by organisms.

H   C
ENERGY

Glucose
$C_6H_{12}O_6$

Symbol for glucose used in this book

Carbohydrates are the primary fuel source for cellular mechanisms.

Atoms   Water   Carbohydrates   Lipids

the structure of cells in all life forms. Sometimes they contain atoms of other elements, but they must have carbon, hydrogen, and oxygen to be considered a carbohydrate (**FIGURE 2-20**). Further, a carbohydrate generally has approximately the same number of carbon atoms as it does H_2O units. For instance, the best-known carbohydrate, glucose, has the composition $C_6H_{12}O_6$ (6 carbons and, as a little math will show us, 6 H_2O units; notice that $6 \times H_2 = H_{12}$ and $6 \times O = O_6$). A carbohydrate called maltose has the composition $C_{12}H_{22}O_{11}$.

Carbohydrates function well as fuels because their many carbon-hydrogen bonds store a great deal of energy. These

C–H bonds are easily broken, and organisms can capture the energy released and put it to use.

TAKE-HOME MESSAGE 2·8

Carbohydrates are the primary fuel for running all cellular machinery and also form much of the structure of cells in all life forms. Carbohydrates contain carbon, hydrogen, and oxygen, and generally have the same number of carbon atoms as they do H_2O units. The C–H bonds of carbohydrates store a great deal of energy and are easily broken by organisms.

2·9

Simple sugars are an effective, accessible source of energy.

Carbohydrates are classified into several categories, based on their size and their composition. The simplest carbohydrates are the **monosaccharides** or **simple sugars.** These simple sugars contain anywhere from three to seven carbon atoms and, when they are broken down, the products usually are not carbohydrates. Two common monosaccharides are glucose, found in the sap and fruit of many plants, and fructose, found primarily in fruits and vegetables, as well as in honey. Fructose is the sweetest of all naturally occurring sugars. The suffix *-ose* tells us that a substance is a carbohydrate.

SOME COMMON MONOSACCHARIDES

| Glucose | Fructose | Galactose |
| $C_6H_{12}O_6$ | $C_6H_{12}O_6$ | $C_6H_{12}O_6$ |

The carbohydrate of most importance to living organisms is glucose. This simple sugar is found naturally in most fruits, but most of the carbohydrates that you eat, including table sugar (called sucrose) and the starchy carbohydrates found in bread and potatoes, are converted into glucose in your digestive system. The glucose then circulates in your blood at a concentration of about 0.1%. Circulating glucose, also called "blood sugar," has one of three fates (**FIGURE 2-21**):

1. **Fuel for cellular activity.** Once it arrives at and enters a cell, glucose can be used as an energy source. Through

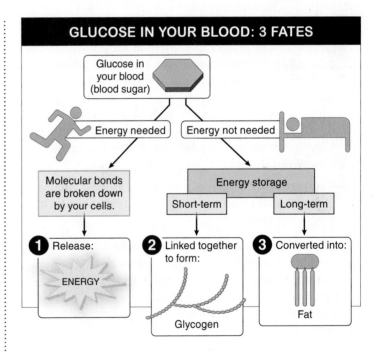

FIGURE 2-21 What happens to sugar in your blood?

a series of chemical reactions, the cell breaks the bonds between the atoms of the glucose molecule (a process explained in detail in Chapter 4) and then uses the released energy to fuel cellular activity, including the muscle contractions that enable you to move and the nerve activities that enable you to think.

2. **Stored temporarily as glycogen.** If there is more glucose circulating in your bloodstream than is necessary

Proteins   Nucleic Acids

FIGURE 2-22 **Some competitive athletes carbo-load to maintain high energy levels.**

Why do dieters lose large amounts of "water weight" during the first few days of a diet?

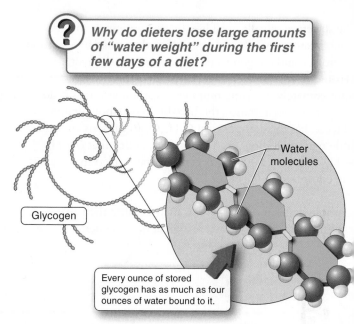

Water molecules

Glycogen

Every ounce of stored glycogen has as much as four ounces of water bound to it.

FIGURE 2-23 **Water weight.** Water molecules bound to glycogen account for much of the weight lost early in a diet.

to meet your body's current energy needs, the excess glucose can be temporarily stored in various tissues, primarily your muscles and liver. The stored glucose molecules are linked together to form a large web of molecules called **glycogen.** When you need energy later, the glycogen can easily be broken down to release glucose molecules back into your bloodstream. Glycogen is the primary form of short-term energy storage in animals.

3. **Converted to fat.** Finally, additional glucose circulating in your bloodstream can be converted into fat, a form of long-term energy storage.

"Carbo-loading" is a method by which athletes can, for a short time, double or triple the usual amount of glycogen stored in their muscles and liver, increasing the store of fuel available for extended exertion and delaying the onset of fatigue during an endurance event (**FIGURE 2-22**).

What is "carbo-loading"?

Carbo-loading is usually done in two phases, a depletion phase and a loading phase. The depletion phase begins six or seven days before a competition. In this phase, the combination of a super-low carbohydrate intake and exhaustive exercise depletes glycogen in the muscles. The loading phase takes place during the two days before the competition. During this phase, a super-high carbohydrate diet is combined with reduced exercise to achieve a higher

blood glucose than is necessary, so that much of the excess glucose is stored as glycogen.

Glycogen also plays a role in the initial rapid weight loss people experience when dieting. If you reduce your caloric intake—perhaps as part of a low-carbohydrate diet—such that your body is burning more calories than you are consuming, your body must use stored forms of energy. The first, most accessible molecules that can be broken down for energy in the absence of sufficient sugar in your bloodstream are glycogen molecules in your muscles and liver. Large amounts of water are bound to glycogen. In fact, every ounce of stored glycogen has as much as 4 ounces of water bound to it. As that glycogen is removed from your tissue, so, too, is the water. This accounts for the initial dramatic weight loss that occurs before your body resorts to using stored fat, at which point the rate of weight loss slows considerably (**FIGURE 2-23**).

TAKE-HOME MESSAGE 2·9

The simplest carbohydrates, including glucose—the most important carbohydrate to living organisms—are monosaccharides or simple sugars. They contain from three to seven carbon atoms.

Atoms   Water   Carbohydrates   Lipids

2·10

Complex carbohydrates are time-released packets of energy.

In contrast to the simple sugars, **polysaccharides** contain more than one sugar unit or building block. For example, two simple sugars can be joined together into a **disaccharide,** such as sucrose (table sugar) and lactose (the sugar found in milk). When more than two simple sugars are joined together—sometimes as many as 10,000—the resulting polysaccharide is called a **complex carbohydrate** (**FIGURE 2-24**). Depending on how the simple sugars are bonded together, polysaccharides may function as "time-release" stores of energy or as structural materials that may be completely indigestible by most animals. An example of such a structural material is the polysaccharide cellulose—the primary component of plant cell walls.

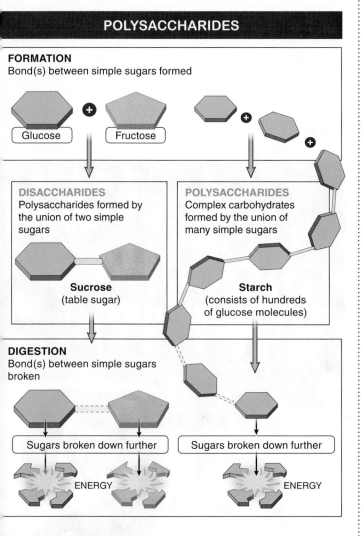

POLYSACCHARIDES

FORMATION
Bond(s) between simple sugars formed

Glucose + Fructose

DISACCHARIDES
Polysaccharides formed by the union of two simple sugars

Sucrose
(table sugar)

POLYSACCHARIDES
Complex carbohydrates formed by the union of many simple sugars

Starch
(consists of hundreds of glucose molecules)

DIGESTION
Bond(s) between simple sugars broken

Sugars broken down further

ENERGY

Sugars broken down further

ENERGY

FIGURE 2-24 Chains of sugars. Polysaccharides are made from simple sugars bound together.

Like simple sugars, many disaccharides and polysaccharides are important sources of fuel. Unlike simple sugars, however, disaccharides and polysaccharides must undergo some preliminary processing before the energy can be released from their bonds. Let's look at what happens when we eat some sucrose, common table sugar. Sucrose is the primary carbohydrate in plant sap. It is a disaccharide composed of two simple sugars, glucose and fructose, linked together. Because humans can't directly use sucrose, the body must first break the bond linking the glucose and fructose. Only then can the individual monosaccharides be broken down into their component atoms and the energy from the broken bonds be harvested and used. Similarly, lactose is a disaccharide made up of a molecule of glucose and a molecule of galactose bound together. As with sucrose, we must break the bond before we can extract any usable energy from a molecule of lactose.

Energy can also be stored in a complex carbohydrate called **starch,** which consists of a hundred or more glucose molecules joined together in a line. In plants, starch is the primary form of energy storage, found in roots and other tissues (see Figure 2-24). Commonly cultivated grains such as barley, wheat, and rye are high in starch content, and corn and rice are more than 70% starch. Although it is composed exclusively of glucose molecules linked together, starch does not taste sweet. Because of its molecular shape it does not stimulate the sweetness receptors on the tongue. The glycogen that stores energy in your muscles and liver is also a complex carbohydrate, so it is sometimes referred to as "animal starch" (although it has a more branched structure than starch and carries more glucose units linked together).

Complex carbohydrates are like "time-release" fuel pellets. The glucose molecules become available slowly, one by one, as the bonds between glucose units are broken. As an interesting demonstration of the gradual release of glucose from complex carbohydrates, put a piece of potato or bread into your mouth and let it rest on your tongue. Initially, it does not have a sweet taste. After a few minutes, though, you will begin to taste some sweetness as the chemicals in your saliva break the starch down into glucose.

The relative amounts of complex carbohydrates and simple sugars in foods cause them to have very different effects when you eat them. Oatmeal (along with rice and pasta), for example, is rich in complex carbohydrates. Fresh fruits, on the other hand, are rich in simple sugars, such as fructose.

Proteins   Nucleic Acids

Before heading to the library for a long study session, students would be wise to consume oatmeal rather than fresh fruits. Why?

Consequently, although the fruit will give a quick burst of energy as the sugars are almost immediately available, the fuel will soon be gone from the bloodstream. The simple sugars in the oatmeal will become available only gradually, as the complex carbohydrates of the oats are slowly broken down into their simple sugar components (**FIGURE 2-25**).

TAKE-HOME MESSAGE 2·10

Multiple simple carbohydrates are sometimes linked together into more complex carbohydrates. Types of complex carbohydrates include starch, which is the primary form of energy storage in plants, and glycogen, which is a primary form of energy storage in animals.

Depending on their structure, dietary carbohydrates can lead to quick-but-brief or slow-but-persistent increases in blood sugar.

FIGURE 2-25 Short-term versus long-term energy? Complex carbohydrates and simple sugars differ in the way they make energy available to you.

2·11

Not all carbohydrates are digestible.

Despite their general importance as a fuel source for humans, not all carbohydrates can be broken down by our digestive system. Two different complex carbohydrates—both indigestible by humans—serve as structural materials for invertebrate animals and plants: **chitin** (pronounced KITE-in) and **cellulose** (**FIGURE 2-26**). Chitin forms the rigid outer skeleton of most insects and crustaceans (such as lobsters and crabs). Cellulose forms a huge variety of plant structures that are visible all around us. We find cellulose in trees and the wooden structures we build from them, in cotton and the clothes we make from it, in leaves and in grasses. In fact, it is the single most prevalent compound on earth.

Surprisingly, cellulose is almost identical in composition to starch. Nonetheless, because of one small difference in the chemical bond between the simple-sugar units, cellulose has a slightly different three-dimensional structure. And, as we noted earlier, even tiny differences in the shape of a molecule can have a huge effect on its behavior. In this case, the

FIGURE 2-26 Carbohydrates can serve as structural materials.

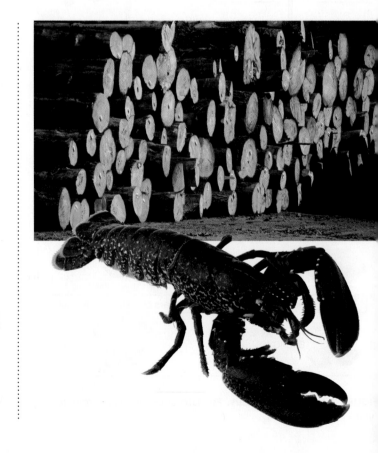

Atoms · Water · Carbohydrates · Lipids

Though indigestible in humans, fiber still aids in digestion and has numerous health benefits.

FIGURE 2-27 Fiber. It's not digestible but it's still important for our diet.

difference in shape makes it impossible for humans to digest cellulose as they can starch. Consequently, the cellulose we eat passes right through our digestive system unused.

Although it is not digestible, cellulose is still important to human diets. The cellulose in our diet is known as "fiber" (**FIGURE 2-27**). It is also appropriately called "roughage" because, as the cellulose of celery stalks and lettuce leaves passes through our digestive system, it scrapes the wall of the digestive tract. Its bulk and the scraping stimulate the more rapid passage of food and the unwanted, possibly harmful products of digestion through our intestines. That is why fiber reduces the risk of colon cancer and other diseases (but it is also why too much fiber can lead to diarrhea.)

Unlike humans, termites have some microorganisms living in their gut that are able to break down cellulose. That's why they can chew on wood and, with the help of the cellulose-digesting boarders in their gut, can break down the cellulose and extract usable energy from the freed glucose molecules.

TAKE-HOME MESSAGE 2·11

Some complex carbohydrates, including chitin and cellulose, cannot be digested by most animals. Such indigestible carbohydrates in the diet, called fiber, aid in digestion and have many health benefits.

Proteins   Nucleic Acids

❹ Lipids store energy for a rainy day.

A well-insulated harbor seal, in Alaska.

2·12

Lipids are macromolecules with several functions, including energy storage.

Lipids are a second group of macromolecules important to all living organisms. Lipids, just like carbohydrates, are made primarily from atoms of carbon, hydrogen, and oxygen, but the atoms are in different proportions. In particular, while carbohydrates usually have two hydrogen atoms for every oxygen, lipids have more hydrogen atoms for each carbon. As a result, lipids have significantly more C–H bonds and contain significantly more stored energy.

What exactly is a lipid? That's not as easy to answer as you might expect. Lipids come in a wide variety of structures. They don't have any unique subunits (such as the simple sugars that make up disaccharides and polysaccharides) or particular ratios of atoms that serve as defining features. Consequently, lipids are defined based on their physical characteristics. Most notably, lipids do not dissolve in water

Q Why does a salad dressing made with vinegar and oil separate into two layers shortly after you shake it?

and are greasy to the touch—think of salad dressings.

Lipids are insoluble in water because, in sharp contrast to water, they consist mostly of hydrocarbons, which are non-polar. Non-polar molecules (or parts of molecules) tend to minimize their contact with water and are considered **hydrophobic** ("water-fearing"). Lipids cluster together when mixed with water, never fully dissolving. Molecules that readily form hydrogen bonds with water, on the other hand, are considered **hydrophilic** ("water-loving").

One familiar type of lipid is *fat,* the type most important in long-term energy storage and insulation (**FIGURE 2-28**). (Penguins and walruses can maintain relatively high body temperatures, despite living in very cold habitats, due to

Atoms   Water   Carbohydrates   Lipids

TYPICAL FEATURES OF LIPIDS
• Non-polar molecules that do not dissolve in water
• Greasy to the touch
• Significant source of energy storage

THREE TYPES OF LIPIDS

FATS	STEROLS	PHOSPHOLIPIDS
FUNCTION Long-term energy storage and insulation	**FUNCTION** Regulate growth and development	**FUNCTION** Form the membranes that enclose cells

FIGURE 2-28 The many purposes of lipids.

TAKE-HOME MESSAGE 2·12

Lipids are insoluble in water and greasy to the touch. They are valuable to organisms for long-term energy storage and insulation, in membrane formation, and as hormones.

their thick layer of insulating fat.) Lipids also include *sterols,* which include *cholesterol* and many of the sex hormones that play regulatory roles in animals, and *phospholipids,* which form the membranes that enclose cells. We examine each type of lipid below.

2·13

Fats are tasty molecules too plentiful in our diets.

All fats have two distinct components: they have a "head" region and two or three long "tails" (**FIGURE 2-29**). The head region is a small molecule called **glycerol.** It is linked to "tail" molecules known as **fatty acids.** A fatty acid is simply a long hydrocarbon—that is, a chain of carbon molecules, often a dozen or more, linked together with one or two hydrogen atoms attached to each carbon.

The fats in most foods we eat are **triglycerides,** which are fats having three fatty acids linked to the glycerol molecule. For this reason, the terms "fats" and "triglycerides" are often used interchangeably. Triglycerides that are solid at room temperature are generally called "fats," while those that are liquid at room temperature are called "oils."

Fat molecules contain much more stored energy than carbohydrate molecules. That is, the chemical breakdown of fat

FIGURE 2-29 Triglycerides have glycerol heads and fatty acid tails.

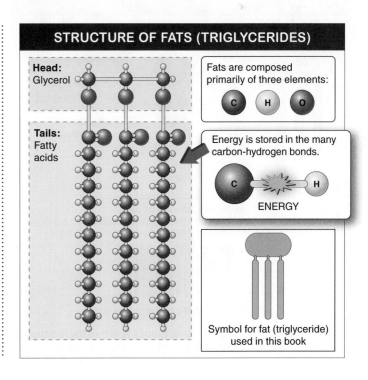

STRUCTURE OF FATS (TRIGLYCERIDES)

Head: Glycerol

Tails: Fatty acids

Fats are composed primarily of three elements:

C   H   O

Energy is stored in the many carbon-hydrogen bonds.

C — H

ENERGY

Symbol for fat (triglyceride) used in this book

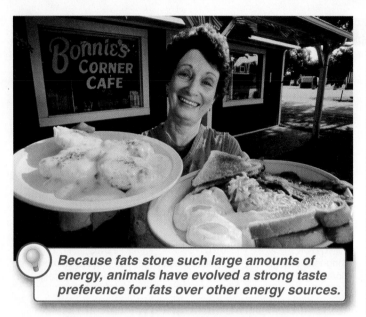

Because fats store such large amounts of energy, animals have evolved a strong taste preference for fats over other energy sources.

FIGURE 2-30 Animals (including humans!) prefer the taste of fats.

molecules releases significantly more energy. A single gram of carbohydrate stores about 4 calories of energy, while the same amount of fat stores about 9 calories—not unlike the difference between a $5 bill and a $10 bill. Because fats store such a large amount of energy, animals have evolved a strong taste preference for fats over other energy sources (**FIGURE 2-30**). Organisms evolving in an environment of uncertain food supply will build the largest surplus by consuming molecules that hold the most amount of energy in the smallest mass. This feature helped the earliest humans to survive, millions of years ago, but today puts us in danger from the health risks of obesity now that fats are all too readily available.

An important distinction is made between "saturated" and "unsaturated" fats (**FIGURE 2-31**). These terms refer to the hydrocarbon chain in the fatty acids. If each carbon atom in the hydrocarbon chain of a fatty acid is bonded to two hydrogen atoms, the fat molecule carries the maximum

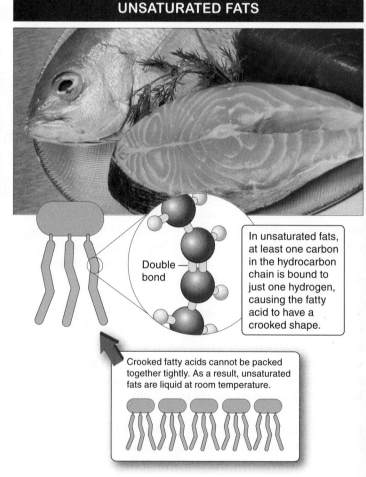

SATURATED FATS

In saturated fats, each carbon in the hydrocarbon chain is bound to two hydrogen atoms.

Straight fatty acids can be packed together tightly. As a result, saturated fats are solid at room temperature.

UNSATURATED FATS

Double bond

In unsaturated fats, at least one carbon in the hydrocarbon chain is bound to just one hydrogen, causing the fatty acid to have a crooked shape.

Crooked fatty acids cannot be packed together tightly. As a result, unsaturated fats are liquid at room temperature.

FIGURE 2-31 Degrees of saturation. Fatty acids (and thus the fats that contain them) can be unsaturated or saturated; unsaturated fats can be saturated artificially, making them tastier but less healthful.

Atoms   Water   Carbohydrates   Lipids

Q Chocolate chip cookie recipes call for some lipids. How will the "chewy-ness" of the cookies differ depending on whether you use butter or vegetable oil as the lipid? Which cookies will be better for your health?

number of hydrogen atoms and is said to be a **saturated fat.** Most animal fats, including those found in meat and eggs, are saturated. They are not essential to your health and, because they accumulate in your bloodstream and can narrow the vessel walls, they can cause heart disease and strokes.

Hydrogenation is the artificial addition of hydrogen atoms to an unsaturated fat. This can improve a food's taste, texture, and shelf-life.

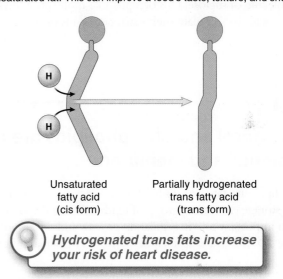

Unsaturated fatty acid (cis form)

Partially hydrogenated trans fatty acid (trans form)

Hydrogenated trans fats increase your risk of heart disease.

FIGURE 2-32 Hydrogenation improves a food's taste, texture, and shelf-life (but at a cost).

An **unsaturated fat** is one in which some of the carbon atoms are bound to only a single hydrogen. Most plant fats are unsaturated. Unsaturated fats may be *mono-unsaturated* (if a fatty acid hydrocarbon chain has only one pair of neighboring carbon atoms in an unsaturated state—that is, has only one double bond) or *polyunsaturated* (if more than one pair of carbons is unsaturated—there's more than one double bond). Unsaturated fats are still high in calories, but because they can lower cholesterol, they are generally preferable to saturated fats. Foods high in unsaturated fats include avocados, peanuts, and olive oil. Relative to other animals, fish tend to have less saturated fat.

The shapes of unsaturated fat molecules and saturated fat molecules are different. When saturated, the hydrocarbon tails of the fatty acids all line up very straight and the fat molecules can be packed together tightly. The tight packing causes the fats, such as butter, to be solid at room temperature. When unsaturated, the fatty acids have kinks in the hydrocarbon tails and the fat molecules cannot be packed together as tightly (see Figure 2-31). Consequently, unsaturated fats, such as canola oil and vegetable oil, do not solidify as easily and are liquid at room temperature.

The ingredient list for many snack foods includes "partially hydrogenated" vegetable oils. The hydrogenation of an oil means that a liquid, unsaturated fat has had hydrogen atoms added to it so that it becomes more saturated. This can be useful in creating a food with a more desirable texture, since increasing a fat's degree of saturation changes its consistency and makes it more solid at room temperatures. By attaining just the right degree of saturation, it is possible to create foods, such as chocolate, that are near the border of solid and liquid and "melt in your mouth" (**FIGURE 2-32**). Unfortunately, hydrogenation also makes the food less

Q Many snack foods contain "partially hydrogenated" vegetable oils. Why might it be desirable to add hydrogen atoms to a vegetable oil?

healthful because saturated fats are less reactive—your body is less likely to break them down—and so are more likely to accumulate in your blood vessels, increasing the risk of heart disease.

Hydrogenation of unsaturated fats is problematic from a health perspective because it creates **trans fats,** the "trans" referring to the unusual orientation of the added hydrogen atoms, which differs from that in other dietary fats—which have their hydrogens in an orientation called "cis." Trans fats cause your body to produce more cholesterol, further raising the risk of heart disease, and they also reduce your body's production of a type of cholesterol that protects against heart disease.

Proteins   Nucleic Acids

Q Olestra is a recently developed "fake fat" chemical that gives foods the taste of fat, without adding the calories of fats. What chemical structure might make this possible?

Because of the well-documented links between dietary fats and heart disease, many people are trying to reduce their fat intake. "Fake fats" make this possible. They are designed to be similar to fats in taste and texture, but have one big difference: they cannot be digested by humans. One such "fake fat" is olestra. Olestra, instead of being a triglyceride fat with three fatty acid tails linked to a glycerol molecule, has eight separate hydrocarbon fatty acids attached to a molecule of sucrose. This octopus-like molecule allows the fatty acids to stimulate their usual taste buds on your tongue, telling your brain that you are eating a fat. The complex shape of the molecule, however, prevents your body's digestive chemicals from grabbing onto it and breaking it down. As a consequence, it passes through your digestive system without being digested. It's not a perfect solution, however. Olestra reduces absorption of some vitamins, and in some people causes abdominal cramping.

TAKE-HOME MESSAGE 2·13

Fats, including the triglycerides common in the food we eat, are one type of lipid. Characterized by long hydrocarbon tails, fats effectively store energy in the many carbon-hydrogen and carbon-carbon bonds. Their caloric density is responsible for humans' preferring fats to other macromolecules in the diet, and is responsible for their association with obesity and illness in the modern world.

2·14

Cholesterol and phospholipids are used to build sex hormones and membranes.

Not all lipids are fats, nor do lipids necessarily function in energy storage. A second group of lipids, called the **sterols,** plays an important role in regulating growth and development (**FIGURE 2-33**). This group includes some very familiar lipids: cholesterol and the steroid hormones such as testosterone and estrogen. These molecules are all modifications on one basic structure formed from four interlinked rings of carbon atoms.

Cholesterol is an important component of most cell membranes. For this reason, it is an essential molecule for living organisms. It has a bad reputation in most Western cultures, though, that is mostly well deserved. When we ingest too much cholesterol (present in animal-based foods such as egg yolks, red meat, and cream) and high levels of cholesterol circulate in our bloodstream, the cholesterol can attach to blood vessel walls and cause them to thicken. In turn, this thickening can lead to high blood pressure, a major contributor to strokes and heart attacks. For these reasons, nutritionists advise limiting the consumption of foods high in cholesterol.

Surprisingly, however, most of the cholesterol in our blood doesn't come directly from the food we consume. Instead, cells in our liver produce almost 90% of the circulating cholesterol. How do they do it? By transforming the saturated fats in our diet. The best way to reduce cholesterol levels, then, may be to consume fewer saturated fats.

The steroid hormones estrogen and testosterone are built through slight chemical modifications to cholesterol. These

STEROLS

CHOLESTEROL
- Important component of cell membranes in animals
- Can attach to vessel walls and cause them to thicken, which may lead to high blood pressure, stroke, and heart attack

Sterols are all based on a structure featuring four carbon rings.

STEROID HORMONES
- Regulate sexual development, maturation, and sex cell production
- Estrogen influences memory and mood
- Testosterone stimulates muscle growth

Estrogen

Testosterone

FIGURE 2-33 Not all lipids are for energy storage. Cholesterol, estrogen, and testosterone are all lipids.

Atoms   Water   Carbohydrates   Lipids

hormones are among the primary molecules that direct and regulate sexual development, maturation, and sperm and egg production. In both males and females, estrogen influences memory and mood, among other traits. Testosterone has numerous effects, one of which is to stimulate muscle growth. As a consequence, athletes often take synthetic variants of testosterone to increase their muscularity. But the use of these supplements is often accompanied by dangerous side effects, including extreme aggressiveness (" 'roid rage"), high cholesterol, and, following long-term use, cancer. As a consequence, nearly all athletic organizations have banned their use (**FIGURE 2-34**).

Phospholipids and waxes are also lipids. **Phospholipids** (**FIGURE 2-35**) are the major component of the membrane that surrounds the contents of a cell and controls the flow of chemicals into and out of the cell. They have a structure similar to fats, but with two differences: they contain a phosphorus atom (hence *phospho*lipids) and they have two fatty acid chains rather than three. We will explore the

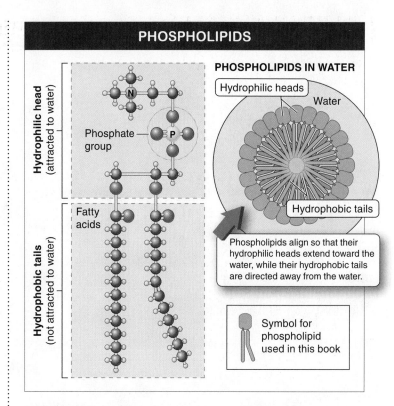

FIGURE 2-35 Lipid versatility. Phospholipids have important roles in many organisms.

significant role of phospholipids in cell membranes in the next chapter.

Waxes resemble fats but have only one long-chain fatty acid linked to the glycerol head of the molecule. Because the fatty acid chain is highly non-polar, waxes are strongly hydrophobic; that is, these molecules do not mix with water but repel it. Their water resistance accounts for their presence as a natural coating on the surface of many plants and in the outer coverings of many insects. In both cases, the waxes prevent the plants and animals from losing the water essential to their life processes. Many birds, too, have a waxy coating on their wings, keeping them from becoming water-logged when they get wet.

TAKE-HOME MESSAGE 2·14

Cholesterol and phospholipids are lipids that are not fats. Both are important components in cell membranes. Cholesterol also serves as a precursor to steroid hormones, important regulators of growth and development.

FIGURE 2-34 Dangerous bulk. Steroids can increase muscularity, but with serious health consequences.

Proteins   Nucleic Acids

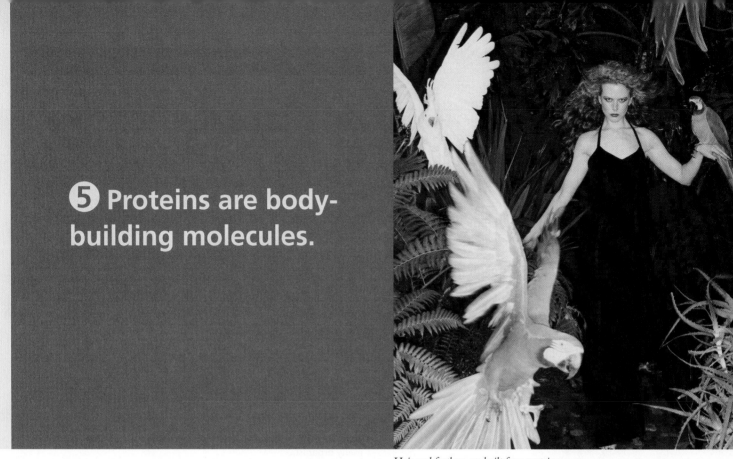

❺ Proteins are body-building molecules.

Hair and feathers are built from proteins.

2•15

Proteins are versatile macromolecules that serve as building blocks.

You can't look at a living organism and not see proteins (**FIGURE 2-36**). Inside and out, **proteins** are the chief building blocks of all life. They make up skin and feathers and horns. They make up bones and muscles. In your bloodstream, proteins fight invading microorganisms and stop you from bleeding to death from a shaving cut. Proteins control the levels of sugar and other chemicals in your bloodstream and carry oxygen from one place in your body to another. And in just about every cell in every living organism, proteins called **enzymes** initiate and assist every chemical reaction that occurs.

Although proteins perform several very different types of functions, all are built in the same way and from the same raw materials in all organisms. In the English language, every sentence is made up of words and every word is formed from one or more of the 26 letters of the alphabet. With 26 letters we can write anything, from sonnets to cookbooks to biology textbooks. Proteins, too, are constructed from a

sort of alphabet. Instead of 26 letters there are 20 molecules, known as **amino acids.** Unique combinations of these 20 amino acids are strung together, like beads on a string, and the resulting protein has a unique structure and chemical behavior.

Let's look more closely at the structure of the amino acids in the protein alphabet. They all have the same basic two-part structure: one part is the same in all 20 amino acids, and the other part is unique, differing in each of the 20 amino acids.

Proteins contain the same familiar atoms as carbohydrates and lipids—carbon, hydrogen, and oxygen—but differ in an important way: they also contain nitrogen. At the center of every amino acid is a carbon atom, with its four covalent bonds (**FIGURE 2-37**). One bond attaches the carbon to something called a **carboxyl group,** which is a carbon bonded to two oxygen atoms. The second bond attaches the central carbon to

| Atoms | Water | Carbohydrates | Lipids |

PROTEIN DIVERSITY

Proteins perform a variety of different functions. They all, however, are built the same way and from the same raw materials in organisms.

STRUCTURAL
Hair, fingernails, **feathers**, horns, cartilage, tendons

PROTECTIVE
Help fight invading microorganisms, coagulate **blood**

REGULATORY
Control cell activity, constitute some **hormones**

CONTRACTILE
Allow **muscles** to contract, heart to pump, sperm to swim

TRANSPORT
Carry molecules such as **oxygen** around your body

FIGURE 2-36 Proteins everywhere! Proteins are the chief building blocks of all organisms.

a single hydrogen atom. The third bond attaches the central carbon to an **amino group,** which is a nitrogen atom bonded to three hydrogen atoms. These components—the central carbon with its attached hydrogen atom, carboxyl group, and

AMINO ACIDS

The side chain is the unique part of each of the 20 amino acids, varying in size, shape, and charge.

FIGURE 2-37 Amino acid structure. Amino acids are made up of an amino group, carboxyl group, and a side chain.

amino group—are the foundation that identifies a molecule as an amino acid and, as multiple amino acids are joined together, forms the "backbone" of the protein.

The fourth bond of the central carbon attaches to a functional group or side chain. This side chain is the unique part of each of the 20 amino acids. In the simplest amino acid, glycine, for example, the side chain is simply a hydrogen atom. In other amino acids, the side chain is a single CH_3 group or three or four such groups. Most of the side chains include both hydrogen and carbon, and a few include nitrogen or sulfur atoms. The side chain determines an amino acid's chemical properties, such as whether the amino acid molecule is polar or non-polar.

TAKE-HOME MESSAGE 2·15

Unique combinations of 20 amino acids give rise to proteins, the chief building blocks of the physical structures that make up all organisms. Proteins perform myriad functions, from assisting chemical reactions to causing blood clotting to building bones to fighting microorganisms.

2·16

Proteins are an essential dietary component.

The atoms present in the plant and animal proteins we eat—especially the nitrogen atoms—are essential to the constant growth, repair, and replacement that take place in our bodies. As we eat protein and break it down into its amino acids through digestion, our bodies are collecting the amino acids needed for various building projects. Proteins also store energy in their bonds and, like carbohydrates and lipids, they can be used to fuel living processes.

The amount of protein we need depends on the extent of the building projects underway at any given time. Most individuals need 40–80 grams of protein per day. Bodybuilders, however, may need 150 grams a day or more to achieve the extensive muscle growth stimulated by their training; similarly, the protein needs of pregnant or nursing women are very high.

Q Food labels indicate an item's protein content. Why is this insufficient for determining whether you are protein deficient, even if your protein intake exceeds your recommended daily amount?

Contrary to the impression you might get from the labels you see on food packaging, all proteins are not created equal (**FIGURE 2-38**). Every different protein has a different composition of amino acids. And while our bodies can manufacture certain amino acids as they are needed, many other amino acids must come from our diet. Those that we must get from our diet—about half of the 20 amino acids—are called "essential amino acids." For this reason, we shouldn't just speak of needing "x grams of protein per day." We need to consume all of the essential amino acids every day.

Many foods, containing "complete proteins," have all of the essential amino acids. Animal products such as milk, eggs, fish, chicken, and beef tend to provide complete proteins. Most vegetables, fruits, and grains, on the other hand, more often contain "incomplete proteins," which do not have all

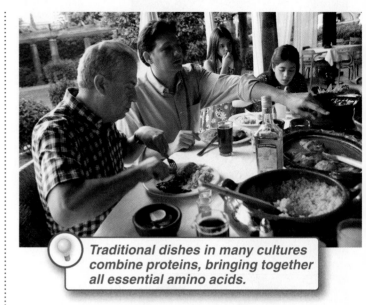

Traditional dishes in many cultures combine proteins, bringing together all essential amino acids.

FIGURE 2-38 All proteins are not created equal. Some foods have "complete proteins" with all the essential amino acids. Other foods have "incomplete proteins" and we must consume proteins from multiple sources to get all the essential amino acids.

the essential amino acids. If you consume only one type of incomplete protein in your diet, you may be deficient in one or more of the essential amino acids. But two incomplete proteins that are "complementary proteins," when eaten together, can provide all the essential amino acids. Traditional dishes in many cultures often include such pairings (see Figure 2-38). Examples are corn and beans in Mexico, rice and lentils in India, and rice and black-eyed peas in the southern United States.

TAKE-HOME MESSAGE 2·16

Twenty amino acids make up all the proteins necessary for growth, repair, and replacement of tissue in living organisms. Of these amino acids, eight are essential for humans: they cannot be synthesized by the body so must be consumed in the diet. Complete proteins contain all eight essential amino acids, while incomplete proteins do not.

Atoms   Water   Carbohydrates   Lipids

Proteins' functions are influenced by their three-dimensional shape.

Proteins are formed by linking individual amino acids together with a **peptide bond,** in which the amino group of one amino acid is bonded to the carboxyl group of another. Two amino acids joined together form a *dipeptide* and several amino acids joined together form a *polypeptide*. The sequence of amino acids in the polypeptide chain is called the **primary structure** of the protein and can be compared to the sequence of letters that spells a specific word (**FIGURE 2-39**).

Amino acids in a polypeptide chain don't remain in a simple straight line like beads on a string. The chain begins to fold as side chains come together and hydrogen bonds form between various atoms in the chain. The two most common patterns of hydrogen bonding between amino acids cause the chain to either twist in a corkscrew-like shape or form a zigzag folding pattern. This hydrogen bonding between amino acids gives a protein its **secondary structure.**

The protein eventually folds and bends upon itself, and additional bonds continue to form between atoms in the side chains of amino acids that are near each other. Eventually, the protein folds into a unique and complex three-dimensional shape called its **tertiary structure.** The exact form comes about as the secondary structure folds and bends, bringing together amino acids that then form bonds such as hydrogen bonds or covalent sulfur–sulfur bonds (see Figure 2-39).

Some protein molecules have a **quaternary structure** in which two or more polypeptide chains are held together by bonds between amino acids in the different chains. Hemoglobin, the protein molecule that carries oxygen from the lungs to the cells where it is needed, is made from four polypeptide chains, two "alpha" chains and two "beta" chains.

Some proteins are attached to other types of macromolecules. *Lipoproteins,* for example, circulate in the bloodstream carrying fats. They are formed when cholesterol and a triglyceride (both lipids) combine with a protein. *Glycoproteins* are combinations of carbohydrates and proteins. These are found on the surfaces of nearly all animal cells and play a role in helping the immune system to distinguish between your own cells and foreign cells. (We learn more about glycoproteins in the next chapter, which discusses cells.)

STRUCTURE OF PROTEINS

PRIMARY STRUCTURE
The sequence of amino acids in a polypeptide chain, similar to the sequence of letters that spell out a specific word

SECONDARY STRUCTURE
The corkscrew-like twists or pleated folds formed by hydrogen bonds between amino acids in the polypeptide chain

TERTIARY STRUCTURE
The complex three-dimensional shape formed by multiple twists and bends in the polypeptide chain based on interactions between the side chains

QUATERNARY STRUCTURE
Two or more polypeptide chains bonded together

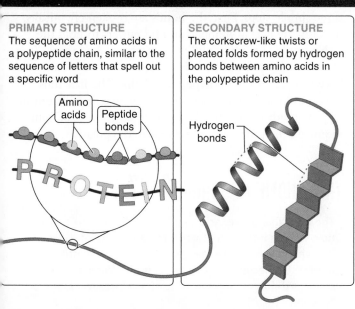

Amino acids — Peptide bonds — PROTEIN

Hydrogen bonds

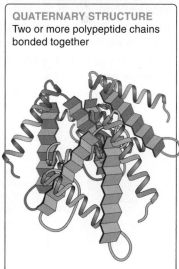

FIGURE 2-39 Protein structure. The functions of proteins are influenced by their three-dimensional shape.

Proteins   Nucleic Acids

Q Egg whites contain a lot of protein. Why does beating them change their texture, making them stiff?

The overall shape of a protein molecule determines its function—how it behaves and the other molecules it interacts with. For proteins to function properly, they must retain their three-dimensional shape. When their shapes are deformed, they usually lose their ability to function. We can see proteins deformed when we fry an egg. The heat breaks the hydrogen bonds that give the proteins their shape. The proteins in the clear egg white unfold, losing their secondary and tertiary structure. This disruption of protein folding is called **denaturation** (**FIGURE 2-40**).

Almost any extreme environment will denature a protein. Take a raw egg, for instance, and crack it into a dish containing baking soda or rubbing alcohol. Both chemicals are sufficiently extreme to turn the clear protein opaque white, as in fried egg whites.

Q Why is wet hair easier to style than dry hair?

Hair is a protein whose shape most of us have modified at one time or another. Styling hair—whether curling or straightening it—involves altering some of the hydrogen bonds between the amino acids that make up the hair protein, changing its tertiary structure. When your hair gets wet, the water is able to disrupt some of the hydrogen bonds, causing some amino acids in the protein to form hydrogen bonds with the water molecules instead. This enables you to change your hair's shape—making it straighter or, if you manipulate it around curlers, making it curlier—if you style it while it's wet. The hair can then hold this shape when it dries as the hydrogen bonds to water are replaced by other hydrogen bonds between amino acids of

FIGURE 2-41 **Curly or straight?** Proteins determine it!

the hair protein as the water evaporates. Once your hair gets wet again, however, unless it is combed, brushed, or wrapped in a different style, it will return to its natural shape.

Whether your hair is straight or curly or somewhere in between also depends on your hair protein's amino acid sequence and the three-dimensional shape it confers (**FIGURE 2-41**). This amino acid sequence is something you're born with (that is, it's genetically determined). The chains are more or less coiled, depending on the extent of covalent and hydrogen bonding between different parts of the coil. Many hair salons make use of the ability to alter covalent bonds to change hair texture semi-permanently. They are able to do this in three simple steps. First, the bonds are broken chemically. Second, the hair is wrapped around curlers to hold the polypeptide chains in a different position. And third, chemicals are put on the hair to create new covalent bonds between parts of the polypeptide chains. The hair thus becomes locked in a new position. (New hair will continue to grow with its genetically determined texture, of course, requiring the procedure to be repeated regularly.)

Q Why do some people have curly hair and others have straight hair?

TAKE-HOME MESSAGE 2·17

The particular amino acid sequence of a protein determines how it folds into a particular three-dimensional shape. This shape determines many of the protein's features, such as which molecules it will interact with. When a protein's shape is deformed, the protein usually loses its ability to function.

FIGURE 2-40 **Denaturation.** When proteins are unfolded, they lose their function.

Atoms　　　　　　　Water　　　　　　　Carbohydrates　　　　　　　Lipids

Enzymes are proteins that initiate and speed up chemical reactions.

Protein shape is particularly critical in **enzymes,** molecules that help initiate and accelerate the chemical reactions in our bodies. Enzymes emerge unchanged—in their original form—when the reaction is complete and thus can be used again and again. Here's how they work.

Think of an enzyme as a big piece of popcorn. Its tertiary or quaternary structure gives it a complex shape with lots of nooks and crannies. Within one of those nooks is a small area called the "active site" (**FIGURE 2-42**). Based on the chemical properties of the atoms lining this pocket, the active site provides a place for the participants in a chemical reaction, the reactants or **substrate** molecules, to nestle briefly.

Enzymes are very choosy: they bind only with their appropriate substrate molecules, much like a lock that can be opened with only one key (see Figure 2-42). The exposed atoms in the active site have electrical charges that attract rather than repel the substrate molecules, and only the substrate molecules can fit into the active-site groove.

Once the substrate is bound to the active site, a reaction can take place—and usually does so very quickly. An enzyme can help to bring about the reaction in a variety of ways. These include:

1. Stressing, bending, or stretching critical chemical bonds, increasing the likelihood of their breaking.

2. Directly participating in the reaction, perhaps temporarily sharing one or more electrons with the substrate molecule, thereby giving it chemical features that increase its ability to make or break other bonds.

3. Creating a "micro-habitat" that favors the reaction. For instance, the active site might be a water-free, non-polar environment, or it might have a slightly higher or lower pH than the surrounding fluid. Both of these slight alterations might increase the likelihood that a particular reaction occurs.

4. Simply orienting or holding substrate molecules in place so that they can be modified.

Sometimes a protein "word" is misspelled—that is, the sequence of amino acids is incorrect. If an enzyme is altered even slightly, the active site may change and the enzyme no longer functions. Slightly modified, non-functioning enzymes

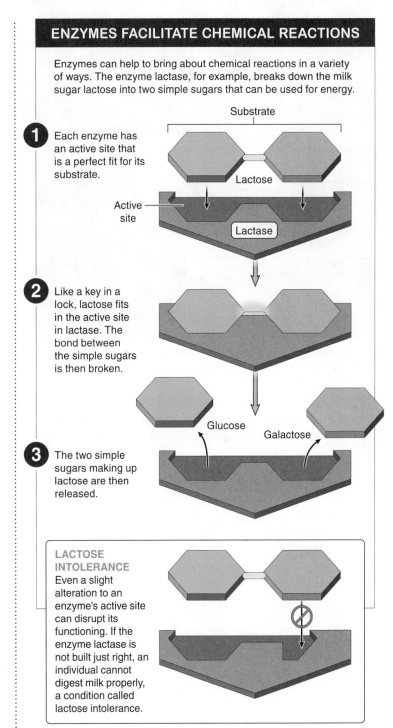

ENZYMES FACILITATE CHEMICAL REACTIONS

Enzymes can help to bring about chemical reactions in a variety of ways. The enzyme lactase, for example, breaks down the milk sugar lactose into two simple sugars that can be used for energy.

1 Each enzyme has an active site that is a perfect fit for its substrate.

Substrate

Lactose

Active site

Lactase

2 Like a key in a lock, lactose fits in the active site in lactase. The bond between the simple sugars is then broken.

Glucose

Galactose

3 The two simple sugars making up lactose are then released.

LACTOSE INTOLERANCE
Even a slight alteration to an enzyme's active site can disrupt its functioning. If the enzyme lactase is not built just right, an individual cannot digest milk properly, a condition called lactose intolerance.

FIGURE 2.42 Lock and key. Enzymes are *very* specific about which molecules and reactions they will catalyze.

Proteins   Nucleic Acids

Without a functioning version of the enzyme lactase, some people are unable to break down the disaccharide lactose in milk.

are responsible for a large number of diseases and physiological problems; an example is the inability to break down the amino acid phenylalanine (in a condition known as phenylketonuria).

Q *Why do some adults get sick when they drink milk?*

One protein "misspelling" is responsible for the condition called lactose intolerance. Normally, during digestion, the lactose in milk is broken down into its component parts, glucose and galactose (see Figure 2-42). These simple sugars are then used for energy. But some people are unable to break the bond linking the two simple sugars because they lack a functioning version of the enzyme lactase that assists in this process. Consequently, the lactose passes through their stomach and small intestine undigested. Then, when it reaches the large intestine, bacteria living there consume the lactose. The problem is that, as they break down the lactose, they produce some carbon dioxide and other gases. These gases are trapped in the intestine and lead to severe discomfort.

These unpleasant symptoms can be avoided by not consuming milk, cheese, yogurt, ice cream, or any other dairy products, but they can also be avoided by taking a pill containing the enzyme lactase. It doesn't matter how the enzyme gets into your digestive system; as long as it's there the lactose in the milk can be broken down.

TAKE-HOME MESSAGE 2·18

Enzymes are proteins that help initiate and speed up chemical reactions. They aren't permanently altered in the process, but rather can be used again and again.

Atoms | Water | Carbohydrates | Lipids

❻ Nucleic acids store the information on how to build and run a body.

Three turns of the DNA double helix (from a scanning tunneling micrograph).

2·19

Nucleic acids are macromolecules that store information.

We have examined three of life's macromolecules: carbohydrates, lipids, and proteins. We turn our attention now to the fourth: **nucleic acids,** macromolecules that store information and are made up of individual units called **nucleotides.** All nucleotides have three components: a molecule of sugar, a phosphate group (containing a phosphorus atom bound to four oxygen atoms), and a nitrogen–containing molecule (**FIGURE 2-43**).

There are two types of nucleic acids: **deoxyribonucleic acid (DNA)** and **ribonucleic acid (RNA).** Both play central roles in directing the production of proteins in living organisms, and by doing so play a central role in determining all of the inherited characteristics of an individual. In both types of nucleic acids, the molecule has the same type of backbone: a sugar molecule attached to a phosphate group attached to another sugar, then another phosphate, and so on. Attached to each sugar is one of the nitrogen–containing molecules called DNA **bases** (so named because of their chemical structure).

FIGURE 2-43 The molecules that carry genetic information. The structure of nucleic acids.

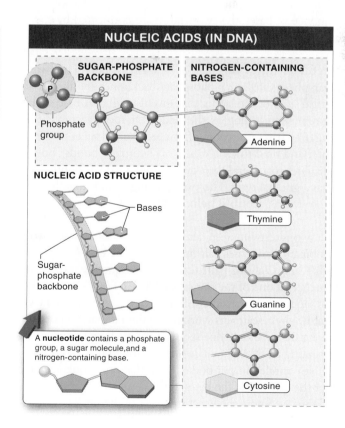

NUCLEIC ACIDS (IN DNA)

SUGAR-PHOSPHATE BACKBONE

NITROGEN-CONTAINING BASES

Phosphate group

Adenine

NUCLEIC ACID STRUCTURE

Bases

Thymine

Sugar-phosphate backbone

Guanine

A **nucleotide** contains a phosphate group, a sugar molecule, and a nitrogen-containing base.

Cytosine

69

A 10-unit nucleic acid therefore would have 10 bases, one attached to each sugar within the sugar-phosphate-sugar-phosphate backbone. But the base attached to each sugar is not always the same. It can be one of several different bases. For this reason, a nucleic acid is often described by the sequence of bases attached to the sugar-phosphate-sugar-phosphate backbone.

Nucleic acids are able to store information by varying which base is attached at each position in the molecule. At each position in a molecule of DNA, for example, the base can be any one of four possible bases: adenine (A), thymine (T), guanine (G), or cytosine (C). Just as the meaning of a sentence is determined by which letters are strung together, the information in a molecule of DNA is determined by its sequence of bases. One molecule may have the sequence adenine, adenine, adenine, guanine, cytosine, thymine, guanine—abbreviated as AAAGCTG. Another molecule may have the sequence CGATTACCCGAT. Because the information differs in each case, so, too, does the protein for which the sequence codes, as we'll see.

TAKE-HOME MESSAGE 2·19

The nucleic acids DNA and RNA are macromolecules that store information in their unique sequences of nucleotides, their building-block molecules. Both nucleic acids play central roles in directing protein production in organisms.

2·20

DNA holds the genetic information to build an organism.

A molecule of DNA has two strands, each a sugar-phosphate-sugar-phosphate backbone with a base sticking out from each sugar molecule. The two strands wrap around each other, each turning in a spiral. Although each strand has its own sugar-phosphate-sugar-phosphate backbone and sequence of bases, the two strands are connected by the bases protruding from them.

You can picture a molecule of DNA as a ladder. The two sugar-phosphate-sugar-phosphate backbones are like the long vertical sides of the ladder that give it height. A base sticking out represents a rung on the ladder. Or, more accurately, half a rung. The bases protruding from each strand meet in the center and bind to each other (via hydrogen bonds), holding the ladder together. DNA differs from a ladder slightly, in that it has a gradual twist. The two spiraling strands together are said to form a **double helix** (FIGURE 2-44).

The two intertwining spirals fit together because only two combinations of bases pair up together. The base A always pairs with T, and C always pairs with G. Consequently, if the base sequence of one of the spirals is CCCCTTAGGAACC, the base sequence of the other must be GGGGAATCCTTGG. That is why researchers working on the Human Genome Project describe only one sequence of nucleotides when presenting a DNA sequence—even though that DNA is double-stranded in our bodies. With that one sequence, we can infer the identity of the bases in the complementary sequence and thus we know the exact structure of the nucleic acid.

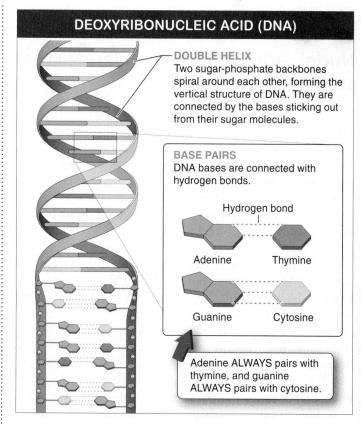

DEOXYRIBONUCLEIC ACID (DNA)

DOUBLE HELIX
Two sugar-phosphate backbones spiral around each other, forming the vertical structure of DNA. They are connected by the bases sticking out from their sugar molecules.

BASE PAIRS
DNA bases are connected with hydrogen bonds.

Hydrogen bond

Adenine   Thymine

Guanine   Cytosine

Adenine ALWAYS pairs with thymine, and guanine ALWAYS pairs with cytosine.

FIGURE 2-44 A gradually twisting ladder. The structure of DNA.

Atoms   Water   Carbohydrates   Lipids

The sequences of bases containing the information about how to produce a particular protein have anywhere from a hundred to several thousand bases. In a human, all of the DNA in a cell, containing all of the instructions for every protein that a human must produce, contains about 3 billion base pairs. This DNA is generally in the nucleus of a cell.

2·21

RNA is a universal translator, reading DNA and directing protein production.

The process of building a protein from a DNA sequence is not a direct one. Rather, it incorporates a middleman, RNA, that is also a nucleic acid (**FIGURE 2-45**). Segments of the DNA are read off, directing the production of short strips of RNA that contain the information, taken from the DNA, about the amino acid sequence in a protein. The RNA moves to another part of the cell and then directs the piecing together of amino acids into a three-dimensional protein. We explore this in greater detail in Chapter 5.

RNA differs from DNA in three important ways. First, the sugar molecule of the sugar-phosphate-sugar-phosphate backbone differs slightly, containing an extra atom of oxygen. Second, RNA is single stranded. The sugar-phosphate-sugar-phosphate backbone is still there, as are the bases that protrude from each sugar. The bases, however, do not bind with anything else—do not form base pairs with another RNA strand. And third, while RNA has the bases A, G, and C, it replaces the thymine with a similar base called uracil (U).

Whether we're looking at the nucleotides that make up RNA and DNA or the lipids used to build sex hormones and cell membranes, we see a recurring theme in the construction of biological macromolecules: from relatively simple sets of building blocks linked together, infinitely complex molecules can be formed. Complex webs of one simple sugar, bonded together as glycogen, for instance, provide fuel for organisms. Similarly, sequences of amino acids of 20 different types, joined together, specify the structure of all of the proteins found in every species on earth.

RIBONUCLEIC ACID (RNA)

RNA STRUCTURE
There are three important structural differences between RNA and DNA.

Uracil

The sugar molecule in the backbone contains an extra oxygen.

2 RNA has only one sugar-phosphate backbone, while DNA has two.

3 Instead of thymine, RNA has a similar base called uracil.

RNA FUNCTION
RNA acts as a middleman molecule. It takes instructions for production of a protein from DNA, moves them to another part of the cell, and directs the building of a protein.

DNA → RNA → Protein

FIGURE 2-45 **The middleman between DNA and protein.** The structure of RNA.

Proteins   Nucleic Acids

Knowledge You Can Use

Did you know? Melt-in-your-mouth chocolate may not be such a sweet idea.

Food chemists have figured out how to make chocolate that melts in your mouth. Is that a good thing?

Q: **Why are some fats "liquidy," like oil, and others solid? The less saturated a fat is, the more "liquidy" it is at room temperature.** Most animal fats are saturated and are solid at room temperature. Best example: butter. Most plant fats are polyunsaturated fats and are liquid at room temperature. Best example: vegetable oils.

Q: **Can oils be made more solid? It's possible to increase the saturation of plant fats.** Just heat them up and pass hydrogen bubbles through the liquid. In creating partially hydrogenated plant oils, this process reduces the number of carbon-carbon double bonds and **makes the oil more solid.** (It's easy, it's cheaper than just using butter, and it increases foods' shelf-life.)

Q: **Does that improve their taste?** By precisely controlling the level of saturation in plant fats, **it is possible to create foods** that are solid but have such a low melting point **that they quickly melt on contact with the warmth of your mouth.** This seems great, but . . .

Q: **Is there a downside? The saturation of vegetable fats creates trans fats,** due to the position taken by the newly added hydrogen atoms in the molecule. Trans fats increase levels of LDL ("bad") cholesterol and decrease HDL ("good") cholesterol, narrowing blood vessel walls and increasing the risk of heart disease and strokes.

Conclusion: Partially hydrogenated vegetable oils can give food a perfect texture and a pleasing feel in your mouth. But the **creaminess comes with a high cost** when it comes to your health.

1 Atoms form molecules through bonding.

An atom is the smallest unit into which material can be divided without losing its essential properties. Atoms are made up of protons and neutrons in the nucleus and electrons that circle far around that nucleus. Molecules are atoms linked together.

2 Water has features that enable it to support all life.

Water molecules easily form hydrogen bonds, giving water great cohesiveness and the ability to resist temperature changes, and making it a versatile solvent. The pH of a fluid is a measure of how acidic or basic a solution is.

3 Carbohydrates are fuel for living machines

Carbohydrates, made up of carbon, oxygen, and hydrogen, are the primary fuel for all cellular machinery and also form much of the structure of cells. The simplest carbohydrates, including glucose, are called monosaccharides or simple sugars. Multiple simple carbohydrates sometimes link together into more complex carbohydrates, including starch, which is the primary form of energy storage in plants, and glycogen, which is a primary form of energy storage in animals. Some carbohydrates are not digestible by humans.

4 Lipids store energy for a rainy day.

Lipids are macromolecules—made up primarily of carbon, hydrogen, and oxygen—that are insoluble in water. Lipids are important for energy storage, hormones, and membrane structure. Their breakdown of dietary fats releases more energy per gram than other macromolecules.

5 Proteins are body-building molecules.

Cells and tissues are primarily built from proteins, sequences of amino acids that fold into complex, three-dimensional shapes. The atoms, especially nitrogen, present in the plant and animal proteins that an organism eats are essential to the organism's growth and repair. The amino acid sequence of a protein determines how it folds into a three-dimensional shape. This shape determines many of the protein's features, such as which molecules it will interact with. Enzymes are proteins that help initiate and speed up chemical reactions. They aren't permanently altered in the process.

6 Nucleic acids store the information on how to build and run a body.

The nucleic acids DNA and RNA are macromolecules that store information by having unique sequences of molecules. Both play central roles in directing protein production in organisms. The sequence of nucleotide bases contains the information about how to produce a particular protein. RNA acts like a universal translator of the genetic code into proteins. It reads DNA sequences and directs the production of a sequence of amino acids.

KEY TERMS

1. The atomic number of carbon is 6. Its nucleus must contain:
   a) 6 neutrons and 6 protons.
   b) 3 protons and 3 neutrons.
   c) 6 neutrons and no electrons.
   d) 6 protons and no electrons.
   e) 6 protons and 6 electrons.

2. The second orbital shell of an atom can hold ___ electrons.
   a) 2   d) 6
   b) 3   e) 8
   c) 4

3. A covalent bond is formed when:
   a) two non-polar molecules associate with each other in a polar environment.
   b) a positively charged particle is attracted to a negatively charged particle.
   c) one atom gives up electrons to another atom.
   d) two atoms share electrons.
   e) two polar molecules associate with each other in a non-polar environment.

4. When you put a piece of chocolate on your tongue, your brain registers a sensation of sweetness. What aspect of molecules is responsible for their having a particular taste?
   a) the total number of protons in the molecule
   b) the number of hydrogen bonds in the molecule
   c) the total number of electron shells in the atoms of the molecule
   d) the ratio of covalent bonds to ionic bonds joining the atoms of the molecule
   e) the molecule's shape

5. Which of the following phenomena is most likely due to the high cohesiveness of water?
   a) Lakes and rivers freeze from the top down, not the bottom up.
   b) The "Jesus lizard" can run across the surface of liquid water for short distances.
   c) Adding salt to snow makes it melt.
   d) The temperature of Santa Monica Bay, off the coast of Los Angeles, fluctuates less than the air temperature throughout the year.
   e) All of the above are due to the cohesiveness of water.

6. Water can absorb and store a large amount of heat while increasing only a few degrees in temperature. Why?
   a) The heat must first be used to break the hydrogen bonds rather than raise the temperature.
   b) The heat must first be used to break the ionic bonds rather than raise the temperature.
   c) The heat must first be used to break the covalent bonds rather than raise the temperature.
   d) An increase in temperature causes an increase in adhesion of the water.
   e) An increase in temperature causes an increase in cohesion of the water.

7. A chemical compound that releases H^+ into a solution is called:
   a) a proton.   d) a hydroxide ion.
   b) a base.   e) a hydrogen ion.
   c) an acid.

8. Which of the following foods is not a significant source of complex carbohydrates?
   a) fresh fruit
   b) rice
   c) pasta
   d) oatmeal
   e) All of the above are significant sources of complex carbohydrates.

9. Sucrose (table sugar) and lactose (the sugar found in milk) are examples of:
   a) naturally occurring enzymes.
   b) simple sugars.
   c) monosaccharides.
   d) disaccharides.
   e) polyunsaccharide sugars.

10. Which of the following statements about starch is incorrect?
    a) Starch is the primary form of energy storage in plants.
    b) Starch consists of a hundred or more glucose molecules joined together in a line.
    c) Starch tastes sweet because it is made from glucose.
    d) Starch is a polysaccharide.
    e) All of the above statements about starch are correct.

11. Which of the following statements about fiber is incorrect?
    a) Dietary fiber reduces the risk of colon cancer.
    b) Fiber in the diet slows the passage of food through the intestines.
    c) Humans are unable to extract any caloric value from fiber.
    d) The cellulose of celery stalks and lettuce leaves is fiber.
    e) Fiber passing through the digestive system scrapes the wall of the digestive tract, stimulating mucus secretion and aiding in the digestion of other molecules.

12. In an unusually detailed dissection of your dinner, you isolate an unknown fatty acid. It is a liquid at room temperature (that is, has a low melting point) and contains carbon-carbon double bonds. What are you most likely to be eating?
    a) a plant   d) a chicken
    b) a cow   e) a lamb
    c) a pig

13. An unsaturated fatty acid is one in which:
    a) carbon-carbon double bonds are present in the hydrocarbon chain.
    b) the hydrocarbon chain has an odd number of carbons.
    c) the hydrocarbon chain has an even number of carbons.
    d) no carbon-carbon double bonds are present in the hydrocarbon chain.
    e) not all of the carbons in the hydrocarbon chain are bonded to hydrogen atoms.

14. Which statement about phospholipids is incorrect?
    a) Because their phosphate groups repel each other, they are used as organisms' chief form of short-term energy.
    b) They are hydrophobic at one end.
    c) They are hydrophilic at one end.
    d) They are a major constituent of cell membranes.
    e) They contain glycerol linked to fatty acids.

15. Proteins are an essential component of a healthy diet for humans (and other animals). Their most common purpose is to serve as:
    a) raw material for growth.
    b) fuel for running the body.
    c) organic precursors for enzyme construction.
    d) long-term energy storage.
    e) inorganic precursors for enzyme construction.

16. Dietary proteins:
    a) are considered "complete" only if they contain the eight essential amino acids required by humans.
    b) consist of all 20 amino acids required in the human body.
    c) are considered "complete" only if they contain the 12 non-essential amino acids required by humans.
    d) are nutritionally identical, since all are broken down into their constituent amino acids in the digestive system.
    e) can be obtained from animal sources but not plant sources.

17. The primary structure of proteins is often described as amino acids connected like beads on a string. In this same vein, which of the following images best describes a protein's quaternary structure?
    a) threads in a cloth
    b) needles in a haystack
    c) rungs on a ladder
    d) links on a chain
    e) coils in a spring

18. Which of the following statements about enzymes is incorrect?
    a) Enzymes can initiate chemical reactions.
    b) Enzymes speed up chemical reactions.
    c) Enzymes often induce conformational changes in the substrates that they bind.
    d) Enzymes contain an active site for binding of particular substrates.
    e) Enzymes undergo a permanent change during the reactions they promote.

19. Which of the following nucleotide bases are present in equal amounts in DNA?
    a) adenine and cytosine
    b) thymine and guanine
    c) adenine and guanine
    d) thymine and cytosine
    e) adenine and thymine

20. Which type of macromolecule contains an organism's genetic information?
    a) polysaccharide
    b) monosaccharide
    c) fatty acid
    d) DNA
    e) phospholipid

21. All of the following are features of RNA except:
    a) a sugar-phosphate-sugar-phosphate backbone.
    b) a coiled double-stranded structure.
    c) a different type of sugar than is found in DNA.
    d) an ability to direct protein production.
    e) a different type of base than is found in DNA.

SHORT-ANSWER QUESTIONS

1. An atom of sodium has an atomic number of 11 and an atom of chlorine has an atomic number of 17.
    a) Indicate the number of electrons that are present in the outermost electron shell of each atom.
    b) Predict what type of bond would form between these atoms, and explain why.

2. Explain how hydrogen bonding plays a part in each of the unique properties of water and, in essence, allows for life on earth.

3. There are many cleaning products on the market that advertise their ability to get rid of stubborn, oily dirt. Why is water alone not sufficient for removing oily dirt?

4. Some who are watching what they eat may opt for a salad when they are dining out. A dinner salad may include lettuce, celery, strawberries, walnuts, chicken, and a salad dressing of oil and vinegar. Explain which category of major macromolecules each of these individual salad components falls into. Then explain the general purpose or function of each major macromolecule.

See Appendix for answers. For additional study questions, go to www.prep-u.com.

3

Cells

The smallest part of you

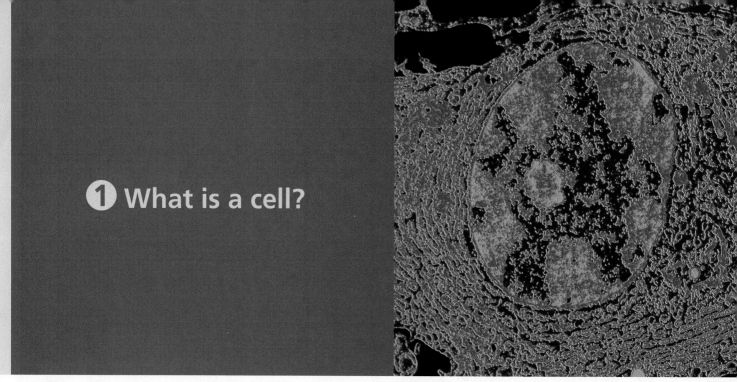

① What is a cell?

Human cell, packed with organelles.

3·1

All organisms are made of cells.

Where do we begin if we want to understand how organisms work? Given their complexity, this task can be daunting. Fortunately, as with most complex things, a strategy of divide and conquer comes in handy. In the case of organisms, whether we are studying a creature as small as a flea or as large as an elephant or giant sequoia, they can be broken down into smaller units that are more easily studied and understood (**FIGURE 3-1**). The most basic unit of any organism is the **cell,** the smallest unit of life that can function independently and perform all the necessary functions of life, including reproducing itself. Understanding cell structure and function is the basis for our understanding of how complex organisms are organized.

The term "cell" was first used in the mid-1600s by Robert Hooke, a British scientist also known for his contributions to philosophy, physics, and architecture. When he was made Curator of Experiments for the Royal Society of London, Hooke suddenly had access to many of the first microscopes available, and he began to examine everything he could get his hands on. Because Hooke thought the close-up views of a very thin piece of cork resembled a mass of small, empty rooms, he named these compartments *cellulae,* Latin for "small rooms."

Today, we know that a cell is a three-dimensional structure, like a fluid-filled balloon, in which many of the essential chemical reactions of life take place (such as the breakdown of carbohydrates for energy, the modification of cholesterol to

create testosterone and estrogen, and the translation of the genetic code into protein production). Generally, these reaction involve transporting raw materials and fuel into the cell and exporting finished materials and waste products out of the cell. In addition, nearly all cells contain DNA (deoxyribonucleic acid), a molecule that contains the information that directs the chemical reactions in a cell, the formation of various cellular products within the cell, and the cell's ability to reproduce itself (A few types of cells, including mammalian red blood cells and cells called "sieve tube elements" that form part of the plant circulatory system, lose their nuclei after they are created and ar unable to divide.) We explore all of these features of cell functioning in this and the next three chapters.

To see a cell, you don't have to work in a lab or use a microscope. Just open your refrigerator. Chances are you've got a dozen or so visible cells in there: eggs. Although most cells are to small to see with the naked eye, there are a few exceptions, including hens' eggs from the supermarket. As long as they are unfertilized, which most store-bought hens' eggs are, each egg tends to contain just one cell. The ostrich egg, weighing about three pounds, contains the largest of all animal cells. (It should be noted, however, that by the time the ostrich lays a fertilized egg, the embryo inside has already gone through multiple divisions.) In addition to being among the largest cells around, eggs are also the most valuable. Almas caviar, eggs from the beluga sturgeon, sells for nearly $700 per ounce. This value is exceeded only by th

The Cell   Cell Membranes   Crossing the Membrane   Cell Connections

FIGURE 3-1 What do these diverse organisms have in common? Cells.

of human eggs, which currently fetch as much as $25,000 for a dozen or so eggs on the open market (**FIGURE 3-2**). (Human sperm cells command only about a penny per 20,000 cells!)

Most cells are much smaller than hens' eggs and ostrich eggs. Consider that, at this very moment, there are probably more than seven billion bacteria in your mouth—even if you just brushed your teeth! This is more than the number of people on earth. It is possible to squeeze so many bacteria in there because most cells (not just bacteria) are really, really tiny—so tiny that 2,000 red blood cells, lined up end to end, would just extend across a dime.

After sufficient improvements were made to early microscopes in the 19th century, the central role of the cell in biology could be understood. As scientists began putting everything they studied under their microscopes, the importance and universality of the cell finally dawned on them. By the 1830s, scientists realized that all plants and animals were made entirely from cells. Subsequent studies revealed that every cell seemed to arise from the division of another cell. You, for example, are made up of at least 60 trillion cells, all of which came from just one cell: the single fertilized egg produced when an egg cell from your mother was fertilized by a sperm cell from your father.

The facts that (1) all living organisms are made up of one or more cells and (2) all cells arise from other, pre-existing cells are the foundations of **cell theory,** one of the unifying theories in biology, and one that is universally accepted by all biologists. As we will see in Chapter 10, the origin of life on earth was a one-time deviation from cell theory: the first cells on earth probably originated from free-floating molecules in the oceans early in the earth's history (about 3.5 billion years ago). Since that time, however, all cells and thus all life have been produced as a continuous line of cells, originating from these initial cells.

In this chapter, we investigate the two different kinds of cells that make up all of the organisms on earth, the processes by which cells control how materials move into and out of the cell, and how cells communicate with each other. We also explore some of the important landmarks found in many cells. We look, too, at the specialized roles these structures play in a variety of cellular functions and learn about some of the health consequences that occur when they malfunction.

TAKE-HOME MESSAGE 3·1

The most basic unit of any organism is the cell, the smallest unit of life that can function independently and perform all of the necessary functions of life, including reproducing itself. All living organisms are made up of one or more cells, and all cells arise from other, pre-existing cells.

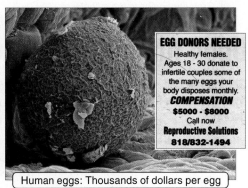

Hummingbird egg: 0.02 ounce
Elephant bird (extinct) egg: two gallons

Beluga sturgeon eggs: $700 per ounce

Human eggs: Thousands of dollars per egg

FIGURE 3-2 Not all cells are tiny. And some cells are extremely valuable!

Eggs are the largest and most expensive cells in the world!

Prokaryotic cells are structurally simple, but there are many types of them.

Although there are millions of diverse species on earth, billions of unique organisms alive at any time, and trillions of different cells in many of those organisms, every cell on earth falls into one of two basic categories.

A **eukaryotic cell** (from the Greek for "good" and "kernel") has a central control structure called a nucleus, which contains the cell's DNA. Organisms composed of eukaryotic cells are called **eukaryotes.**

A **prokaryotic cell** (from the Greek for "before" and "kernel") does not have a nucleus; its DNA simply resides in the middle of the cell. An organism consisting of a prokaryotic cell is called a **prokaryote.**

We begin our study of the cell by exploring the prokaryotes. Prokaryotes were the first cells on earth, making their appearance about 3.5 billion years ago, and, for a long time (1.5 billion years), they had the planet to themselves.

All prokaryotes are one-celled organisms and are thus invisible to the naked eye. Prokaryotes have four basic structural features (**FIGURE 3-3**).

1. A **plasma membrane** encompasses the cell (and is sometimes simply called the "cell membrane"). For this reason, anything inside the plasma membrane is referred to as "intracellular," and everything outside the plasma membrane is "extracellular."

2. The **cytoplasm** is the jelly-like fluid that fills the inside of the cell.

3. **Ribosomes** are little granular bodies where proteins are made; thousands of them are scattered throughout the cytoplasm.

4. Each prokaryote has one or more circular loops or linear strands of DNA.

In addition to the characteristics common to all prokaryotes, some prokaryotes have additional, unique features. Many have a rigid **cell wall,** for example, that protects and gives shape to the cell. Some have a slimy, sugary capsule as their outermost layer. This sticky outer coat provides protection and enhances the prokaryotes' ability to anchor themselves in place when necessary.

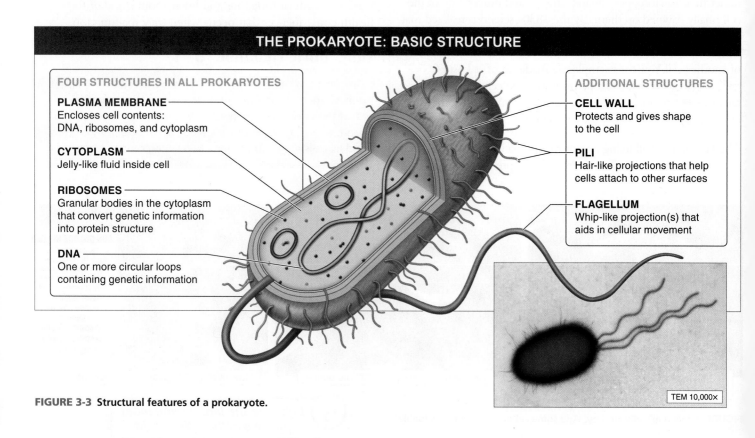

THE PROKARYOTE: BASIC STRUCTURE

FOUR STRUCTURES IN ALL PROKARYOTES

PLASMA MEMBRANE
Encloses cell contents:
DNA, ribosomes, and cytoplasm

CYTOPLASM
Jelly-like fluid inside cell

RIBOSOMES
Granular bodies in the cytoplasm
that convert genetic information
into protein structure

DNA
One or more circular loops
containing genetic information

ADDITIONAL STRUCTURES

CELL WALL
Protects and gives shape
to the cell

PILI
Hair-like projections that help
cells attach to other surfaces

FLAGELLUM
Whip-like projection(s) that
aids in cellular movement

TEM 10,000×

FIGURE 3-3 Structural features of a prokaryote.

The Cell   Cell Membranes   Crossing the Membrane   Cell Connections

Many prokaryotes have a **flagellum** (*pl.* **flagella**), a long, thin, whip-like projection that rotates like a propeller and moves the cell through the medium in which it lives. Other appendages include **pili** (*sing.* **pilus**), much thinner, hair-like projections that help prokaryotes attach to surfaces.

From our human perspective, it is easy to underestimate the prokaryotes. Although they are smaller, evolutionarily older, and structurally more simple than eukaryotes, prokaryotes are fantastically diverse metabolically (i.e., in the way they break down and build up molecules). Among many other innovations, bacteria can fuel their activities in the presence or absence of oxygen, using almost any energy source on earth, depending on the type of bacteria—from the sulfur in deep-sea hydrothermal vents to hydrogen to the sun.

You may think you've never encountered a prokaryote, but you are already familiar with the largest group of prokaryotes: the bacteria. All bacteria are prokaryotes, from those such as *Escherichia coli* (*E. coli*), which live in your intestine and help your body make some essential vitamins, to those responsible for illness, such as *Streptococcus pyogenes,* which causes strep throat. Another recently discovered group of organisms, the archaea, are also prokaryotes.

TAKE-HOME MESSAGE 3·2

Every cell on earth is either a eukaryotic or a prokaryotic cell. Prokaryotes, which have no nucleus, were the first cells on earth. They are all single-celled organisms. Prokaryotes include the bacteria and archaea and, as a group, are characterized by tremendous metabolic diversity.

3·3

Eukaryotic cells have compartments with specialized functions.

Eukaryotes showed up about 1.5 billion years after prokaryotes, and in the 2 billion years that they have been on earth, they have evolved into some of the most dramatic and interesting creatures, such as platypuses, dolphins, giant sequoias, and the Venus fly trap. Because all prokaryotes are single-celled and thus invisible to the naked eye, every organism that we see around us is a eukaryotic organism. (**FIGURE 3-4**). All fungi, plants, and animals are eukaryotes, for

FIGURE 3-4 Diversity of the eukaryotes. Every organism that we can see without magnification is a eukaryotic organism.

EUKARYOTES vs. PROKARYOTES

TYPICAL EUKARYOTIC CELL FEATURES
• DNA contained in nucleus
• Internal structures organized into compartments
• Larger than prokaryotes—usually 10 times bigger
• Cytoplasm contains specialized structures called organelles

Compartments   Nucleus   Organelles

TEM 6,000×

TYPICAL PROKARYOTIC CELL FEATURES
• No nucleus—DNA is in the cytoplasm
• Internal structures not organized into compartments
• Much smaller than eukaryotes

TEM 10,000×

FIGURE 3-5 Comparison of eukaryotic and prokaryotic cells.

instance. Not all eukaryotes are multicellular, however. There is a huge group of eukaryotes, called the Protista (or protists), nearly all of which are single-celled organisms visible only with a microscope.

The chief distinguishing feature of eukaryotic cells is the presence of a **nucleus,** a membrane-enclosed structure that contains linear strands of DNA. In addition to a nucleus, eukaryotic cells usually contain in their cytoplasm several other specialized structures, called **organelles,** many of which are enclosed separately within their own lipid membranes. Eukaryotic cells are also about 10 times larger than prokaryotes. All of these physical differences make it easy to distinguish eukaryotes from prokaryotes under a microscope (**FIGURE 3-5**).

Organelles enable eukaryotic cells to do many things that a prokaryotic cell cannot do. Most important, the creation of physically separate compartments means that there can be distinct areas within the same cell in which different chemical reactions can occur simultaneously. In the non-compartmentalized interior of a prokaryotic cell, random molecular movements quickly blend the chemicals throughout the cell, reducing the ease with which different reactions can occur simultaneously.

FIGURE 3-6 illustrates a generalized animal cell and a generalized plant cell. Because they share a common,

eukaryotic ancestor, they have much in common. Both can have a plasma membrane, nucleus, cytoskeleton, and ribosomes, and a host of organelles, including rough and smooth endoplasmic membranes, Golgi apparatus, and mitochondria. Animal cells have centrioles, which are not present in most plant cells. Plant cells have a rigid cell wall (as do fungi and many protists) and chloroplasts (also found in some protists). Plants also have a vacuole, a large central chamber (only occasionally found in animal cells). We explore each of these plant and animal organelles in detail later in this chapter.

When you compare a complex eukaryotic cell with the structurally simple prokaryotic cell, it's hard not to wonder how eukaryotic cells came about. How did they get filled up with so many organelles? We can't go back 2 billion years to watch the initial evolution of eukaryotic cells, but we can speculate about how it might have occurred. One very appealing idea, called the **endosymbiosis theory,** has been developed to explain the presence of two organelles in eukaryotes: chloroplasts in plants and algae, and mitochondria in plants and animals. Chloroplasts help plants and algae convert sunlight into a more usable form of energy. Mitochondria help plants and animals harness the energy stored in food molecules. (Chapter 4, on energy, explains the details of both of these processes.)

According to the theory of endosymbiosis, two different types of prokaryotes may have set up close partnerships with each

The Cell   Cell Membranes   Crossing the Membrane   Cell Connections

STRUCTURES FOUND IN BOTH CELLS

Nucleus
Plasma membrane
Ribosomes
Mitochondria
Rough endoplasmic reticulum
Smooth endoplasmic reticulum
Cytoplasm
Cytoskeleton
Golgi apparatus
Lysosome

STRUCTURE NOT FOUND IN PLANT CELLS

Centriole

STRUCTURES NOT FOUND IN ANIMAL CELLS

Chloroplast
Cell wall
Vacuole (occasionally found in animal cells)

TEM 3,500×

TEM 1,500×

FIGURE 3-6 Structures found in animal and plant cells.

other. For example, some small prokaryotes capable of performing photosynthesis (the process by which plant cells capture light energy from the sun and transform it into the chemical energy stored in food molecules) may have come to live inside a larger "host" prokaryote. The photosynthetic "boarder" may have made some of the energy from its photosynthesis available to the host.

After a long while, the two cells may have become more and more dependent on each other until neither cell could live without the other (they became "symbiotic"), and they became a single, more complex organism. Eventually, the photosynthetic prokaryote evolved into a **chloroplast,** the organelle in plant cells in which photosynthesis occurs. A similar scenario might explain how a prokaryote unusually efficient at converting food and oxygen into easily usable energy took up residence inside another, host prokaryote and evolved into a **mitochondrion,** the organelle in plant and

Q Humans, deep down, may be part bacteria. How can that be?

animal cells that converts the energy stored in food into a form usable by the cell (**FIGURE 3-7**).

The idea of endosymbiosis is supported by several observations.

1. Chloroplasts and mitochondria are similar in size to prokaryotic cells.

2. Chloroplasts and mitochondria have small amounts of circular DNA, similar to the circular DNA in prokaryotes and in contrast to the linear DNA strands found in a eukaryote's nucleus.

3. Chloroplasts and mitochondria divide by splitting (fission), just like prokaryotes.

4. Chloroplasts and mitochondria have internal structures called ribosomes that are similar to those found in bacteria.

In addition to the theory of endosymbiosis as an explanation for the existence of chloroplasts and mitochondria, another

ENDOSYMBIOSIS

ANCESTRAL EUKARYOTE

ANCESTRAL PROKARYOTE proficient at converting food and oxygen into energy

1 Ancestral eukaryote engulfs prokaryote.

2 Ancestral eukaryote and prokaryote merge.

Mitochondrion

3 Over time, the engulfed prokaryote evolves into an organelle, such as a mitochondrion or a chloroplast.

INVAGINATION

ANCESTRAL EUKARYOTE
DNA
Plasma membrane

1 Plasma membrane folds in on itself.

Nucleus

Rough endoplasmic reticulum

2 Inner compartments (organelles) are formed.

Organelles may have developed by endosymbiosis or invagination or a combination of the two.

FIGURE 3-7 How did eukaryotic cells become so structurally complex? Two theories.

theory about the origin of organelles in eukaryotes is the idea that the plasma membrane around the cell may have folded in on itself (a process called **invagination**) to create the inner compartments, which subsequently became modified and specialized (see Figure 3-7). It may turn out that organelles arose from both processes. Perhaps mitochondria and chloroplasts originated from endosymbiosis, and all of the other organelles arose from plasma membrane invagination. We just don't know.

TAKE-HOME MESSAGE 3·3

Eukaryotes are single-celled or multicellular organisms consisting of cells with a nucleus that contains linear strands of genetic material. The cells also commonly have organelles throughout their cytoplasm; these organelles may have originated evolutionarily through endosymbiosis or invagination, or both.

The Cell   Cell Membranes   Crossing the Membrane   Cell Connections

❷ Cell membranes are gatekeepers.

Cell membranes control the movement of material into and out of the cell.

3·4

Every cell is bordered by a plasma membrane.

Just as skin covers our bodies, every cell of every living thing on earth, whether a prokaryote or a eukaryote, is enclosed by a plasma membrane, a two-layered membrane that holds the contents of a cell in place and regulates what enters and leaves the cell. Plasma membranes are thin (a stack of a thousand would be only as thick as a single hair) and flexible, and in photos or diagrams the membranes often resemble simple plastic bags, holding the cell contents in place. This image is a gross oversimplification, however. Membranes are indeed thin and flexible, but they are far from simple: a close look at a plasma membrane will reveal that its surface is filled with pores, outcroppings, channels, and complex molecules floating around within the two layers of the membrane itself (**FIGURE 3-8**).

Why are plasma membranes such complex structures? It's because they perform several critical functions beyond simply acting as the boundary for a cell's interior contents. Cells, after all, are perpetually interacting with their external

environment. They take in food and nutrients and dispose of waste products. They take in water. They build and export molecules needed elsewhere in the body. Sometimes they absorb heat from the outside environment, whereas at other times they dissipate excess heat generated by cell activities. Like the booths or checkpoints at a country's borders that control the flow of people into and out of the country, plasma membranes serve as gatekeepers that control the flow of molecules into and out of the cell.

The foundation of all plasma membranes is a layer of lipid molecules all packed together. These are a special type of lipid, called **phospholipids,** which, as you may recall from Chapter 2, have what appear to be a head and two long tails. The head consists of a molecule of **glycerol** linked to a molecule containing phosphorus (**FIGURE 3-9**). This head region is said to be **polar,** because it has an electrical charge. As you may also recall from Chapter 2, water is also a polar molecule and, for this reason, other polar molecules mix easily with water.

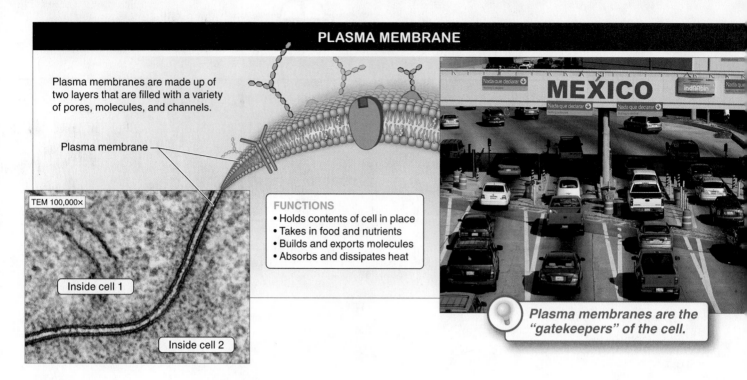

PLASMA MEMBRANE

Plasma membranes are made up of two layers that are filled with a variety of pores, molecules, and channels.

Plasma membrane

TEM 100,000×

Inside cell 1

Inside cell 2

FUNCTIONS
- Holds contents of cell in place
- Takes in food and nutrients
- Builds and exports molecules
- Absorbs and dissipates heat

MEXICO

Plasma membranes are the "gatekeepers" of the cell.

FIGURE 3-8 More than just an outer layer. The plasma membrane performs several critical functions beyond simply enclosing a cell's interior contents.

Molecules that can mix with water are described as **hydrophilic** ("water-loving") molecules. The two tails of the phospholipid are long chains of carbon and hydrogen atoms. Because they have no electrical charge, the carbon–hydrogen chains are **non-polar.** And because they are non-polar, these tails do not mix with water and are said to be **hydrophobic** ("water-fearing"). The chemical structure of phospholipids gives them a sort of split personality: their hydrophilic head

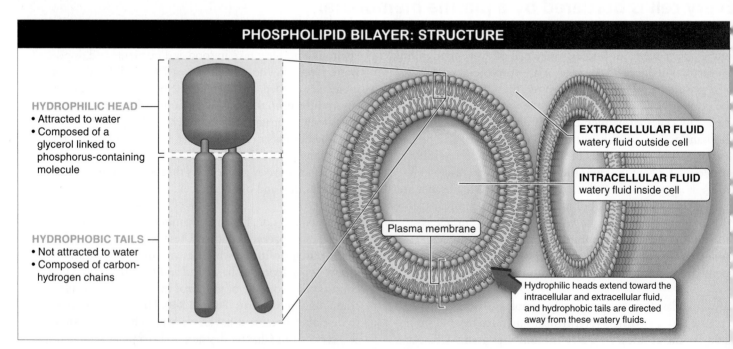

PHOSPHOLIPID BILAYER: STRUCTURE

HYDROPHILIC HEAD
- Attracted to water
- Composed of a glycerol linked to phosphorus-containing molecule

HYDROPHOBIC TAILS
- Not attracted to water
- Composed of carbon-hydrogen chains

EXTRACELLULAR FLUID
watery fluid outside cell

INTRACELLULAR FLUID
watery fluid inside cell

Plasma membrane

Hydrophilic heads extend toward the intracellular and extracellular fluid, and hydrophobic tails are directed away from these watery fluids.

FIGURE 3-9 Good membrane material. The phospholipid bilayer of the plasma membrane prevents fluid from leaking out of the cell.

The Cell   Cell Membranes   Crossing the Membrane   Cell Connections

region mixes easily with water, while their hydrophobic tail region does not mix with water.

The split personality of phospholipids makes them good membrane material. Once a large number of phospholipids are packed together with all of their heads facing one way and their tails the other, we have a sheet with one side that is hydrophilic and one that is hydrophobic. In a cell's plasma membrane, two of these sheets of phospholipids are arranged so that the hydrophobic tails are all in contact with one another and the hydrophilic heads are in contact with the watery solution outside and inside the cell (see Figure 3-9). This arrangement gives us another way to describe the structure of the plasma membrane: as a **phospholipid bilayer.**

The phospholipids are not locked in place in the plasma membrane; they just float around in their side of the bilayer. They cannot pop out of the membrane, or flop from one side to the other, because their hydrophobic tails always line up away from any watery solution. Just as similarly charged sides of two magnets push away from each other, so do the hydrophobic tails in the center of the membrane push away from and avoid coming into contact with water molecules. Because the center part of the bilayer membrane is made up of hydrophobic lipids, the solution on one side of the membrane cannot leak across into the solution on the other side. In this way, the plasma membrane forms a boundary around the cell's contents.

TAKE-HOME MESSAGE 3·4

Every cell of every living organism is enclosed by a plasma membrane, a two-layered membrane that holds the contents of a cell in place and regulates what enters and leaves the cell.

3·5

Molecules embedded in the plasma membrane help it perform its functions.

While the plasma membrane's phospholipid bilayer construction forms the cell's basic boundary with its environment, there is much more to a plasma membrane. Embedded within or attached to the phospholipid bilayer are different types of protein, carbohydrate, and lipid molecules (**FIGURE 3-10**).

The proteins found in the plasma membrane enable it to carry out most of its gatekeeping functions. For every 50 to 100 phospholipids in the membrane, there is one protein molecule. Some of these proteins, called **transmembrane proteins,** penetrate right through the lipid bilayer, from one side to the other. Others, called **surface proteins,** reside primarily on the inner or outer surface of the membrane.

What determines whether a protein resides on the surface or extends through the bilayer? Its tertiary structure. Remember from Chapter 2 that all the amino acids that make up each protein have side chains that differ from one another chemically. Some of these side chains are hydrophobic, others are hydrophilic, and as a protein is assembled into its final shape, these side chains can cause parts of the protein to be attracted to hydrophobic or hydrophilic regions. Because a

MOLECULES WITHIN THE PLASMA MEMBRANE

Extracellular fluid

☐ Hydrophilic region
☐ Hydrophobic region

Carbohydrates

Plasma membrane

Transmembrane protein

Lipid

Surface proteins

Intracellular fluid

Hydrophobic and hydrophilic forces determine the orientation of proteins in the plasma membrane.

FIGURE 3-10 Protein and carbohydrate molecules are embedded in the plasma membrane.

FUNCTION OF PLASMA MEMBRANE MOLECULES

Extracellular fluid

CARBOHYDRATE CHAINS
Provide a "fingerprint" for the cell, so it can be recognized by other cells

CHOLESTEROL
Helps the membrane retain its flexibility

REACTIONS

Intracellular fluid

REACTIONS

RECEPTOR PROTEINS
Bind to external chemicals in order to regulate processes within the cell

RECOGNITION PROTEINS
Provide a "fingerprint" for the cell, so it can be recognized by other cells

TRANSPORT PROTEINS
Provide a passageway for molecules to travel into and out of the cell

ENZYMATIC PROTEINS
Accelerate intracellular and extracellular reactions on the plasma membrane

FIGURE 3-11 Plasma membrane molecules serve diverse roles.

transmembrane protein has both hydrophobic and hydrophilic regions, part of the protein can be positioned in the hydrophobic region in the center of the membrane while the other part resides in the hydrophilic regions. Peripheral membrane proteins, on the other hand, reside on the membrane surface and have an entirely hydrophilic structure and so can bind only to the head regions of the phospholipids. As a consequence, they can be positioned on either the outer or the inner side of the membrane.

Once membrane proteins are in place, the hydrophobic and hydrophilic forces keep them properly oriented. Because all of the components of the plasma membrane are held in the membrane in this manner, they can float around without ever popping out.

There are four primary types of membrane proteins, each of which performs a different function (**FIGURE 3-11**).

1. Receptor proteins bind to chemicals in the cell's external environment and, by doing so, regulate certain processes within the cell. Cells in the heart, for example, have receptor proteins that bind to adrenaline, a chemical released into the bloodstream in times of extreme stress or fright. When adrenaline binds to these heart cells, the cells increase the heart's rate of contraction to pump blood through the body more quickly. You have experienced this reaction if you've ever been startled and felt your heart start to pound.

2. Recognition proteins give each cell a "fingerprint" that makes it possible for the body's immune system (which

fights off infections) to distinguish the cells that belong inside your body from those that are invaders and need to be attacked. (Note that carbohydrates also play a role in recognition.) Recognition proteins also can help cells bind to or adhere to other cells or molecules.

3. Transport proteins are transmembrane proteins that help large and/or strongly charged molecules pass through the plasma membrane. Transport proteins come in a variety of shapes and sizes, making it possible for a wide variety of molecules to be transported.

4. Enzymatic proteins (enzymes) accelerate chemical reactions on the plasma membrane's surface (a variety of enzymatic proteins exist, with some accelerating reactions on the inside of the plasma membrane and others accelerating reactions on the outside of the plasma membrane).

In addition to the various kinds of membrane proteins, two other types of molecules can be incorporated in a cell's plasma membrane.

1. Short, branched carbohydrate chains that are attached to proteins or to phospholipid heads on the outside of the cell membrane serve as part of a membrane's fingerprint, along with recognition proteins. This fingerprint allows the cell to be recognized by other cells, such as those of the immune system.

2. The plasma membrane also can contain **cholesterol,** a lipid that helps the membrane maintain its flexibility. It prevents the membrane from becoming too fluid or

The Cell | Cell Membranes | Crossing the Membrane | Cell Connections

floppy at moderate temperatures and acts as a sort of antifreeze, preventing the membrane from becoming too rigid at freezing temperatures. The membranes of some cells are about 25% cholesterol; other plasma membranes, such as those of most bacteria and plants, have no cholesterol at all.

As we've seen, the plasma membrane is made up from several different types of molecules, like a mosaic, and many of those molecules float around, held in a proper orientation by hydrophobic and hydrophilic forces, but not always anchored in place. For these reasons, the plasma membrane is often described as a **fluid mosaic.**

TAKE-HOME MESSAGE 3·5

The plasma membrane is a fluid mosaic of proteins, lipids, and carbohydrates. Proteins found in the plasma membrane enable it to carry out most of its gatekeeping functions. The proteins act as receptors, help molecules gain entry into and out of the cell, and catalyze reactions on the inner and outer cell surfaces. In conjunction with carbohydrates, some plasma membrane proteins identify the cell to other cells. And, in addition to the phospholipids that make up most of the plasma membrane, cholesterol is an important lipid in some membranes, influencing fluidity.

3·6

Faulty membranes can cause disease.

With all the complexity of plasma membranes, it's not surprising that there are many ways in which they can malfunction. One disease that results from an improperly functioning membrane is cystic fibrosis, the single most common fatal inherited disease in the United States. At any given time, about 30,000 people in the United States have cystic fibrosis.

Cystic fibrosis occurs when an individual inherits from both parents incorrect genetic instructions for producing one type of transmembrane protein. This protein occurs primarily in the membranes of cells in the lungs and digestive tract. When functioning normally, the protein serves as a passageway that allows one type of molecule—chloride ions—to get into and out of cells.

There are more than a thousand different ways in which these genetic instructions can be defective, but in every case the result is the same: the lack of properly working chloride passageways in a cell's membrane. This defect leads to gradual accumulation of chloride ions within cells. Although it is not clear exactly how the chloride ion accumulation leads to the symptoms of cystic fibrosis, in nearly all cases two primary effects occur: an improper salt balance in the cells and a buildup of thick, sticky mucus—particularly in the lungs. Normal mucus helps to protect the lungs by trapping dust and bacteria. This mucus is then moved out of the lungs (helped along by coughing). The mucus produced by someone with cystic fibrosis, however, is too thick and sticky to be moved out of the lungs, so it collects there, where it impairs lung function and increases the risk of bacterial infection. Because of the improper cellular salt balance, one way to test for cystic fibrosis is to measure the concentration of salt in the sweat—

abnormally high concentrations indicate that the person has the disease.

Although many high-tech treatments have been promised for the sufferers of cystic fibrosis and a great deal of research is being done on this disease, one of the most common treatments is decidedly low-tech. Parents help their children with cystic fibrosis clear the mucus out of their lungs by holding them on a steep slant, almost upside down, and vigorously patting or thumping their chest and back to shake loose the mucus in their lungs and move it to a place where they can cough it up. With careful treatment, the life expectancy of someone with cystic fibrosis can be 35—40 years or longer (**FIGURE 3-12**).

FIGURE 3-12 Moving mucus manually, or through an inhalation vest. The thick and sticky mucus produced by someone with cystic fibrosis collects in the lungs, impairing lung function and increasing the risk of bacterial infection. Thumping on the chest and back can loosen the mucus. The vest, by inflating and deflating rapidly, can have a similar effect in the course of a 20-minute session.

Kidney Adrenal gland

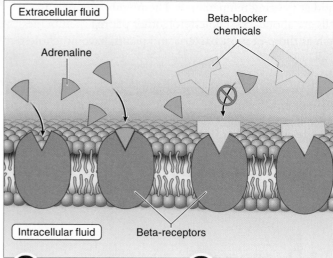

Extracellular fluid

Adrenaline

Beta-blocker chemicals

Intracellular fluid Beta-receptors

1 In stressful situations, the adrenal glands pump out adrenaline.

2 Adrenaline binds with beta-receptors on cells, causing a faster heartbeat and increased blood pressure.

3 Beta-blocker chemicals bind to receptors and prevent adrenaline from binding to the cell.

By binding to adrenaline receptors, beta-blockers reduce anxiety symptoms.

FIGURE 3-13 Reducing anxiety through beta-blockers.

While faulty membranes can cause a disorder as serious as cystic fibrosis, pharmaceutical tinkering with cell membranes can alter cellular function in ways that have beneficial effects. For example, a group of drugs called "beta-blockers" is extremely effective at reducing anxiety. This effect was discovered almost accidentally—the drugs were actually developed as a treatment for high blood pressure.

Q Why do "beta-blockers" reduce anxiety?

Here's how beta-blockers work. Many cells in your body, particularly the cells of the heart, have receptor proteins on their plasma membranes that can bind to *adrenaline,* a chemical manufactured in the adrenal glands (located atop the kidneys) that helps your body cope with stressful situations. These receptor proteins are called "beta-receptors." In stressful situations, your adrenal glands pump out adrenaline (**FIGURE 3-13**). On reaching cells in your heart (among other locations in your body) and binding to beta-receptors, the adrenaline promptly causes your heart to beat faster and more forcefully, increasing your blood pressure in the process. This reaction is fine in a short-term fight-or-flight situation, but it is not healthy over the long run

because the increased pressure can damage blood vessels. Depending on its severity, this reaction can also be problematic if you are giving a presentation or taking a test, or if you're in any other anxiety-producing situation.

When you take a beta-blocker pill, the pill dissolves and the chemicals travel throughout your body until they encounter the beta-receptors. They bind to the receptors, hold on, and block the adrenaline from doing its job. This outcome slows your heart rate, causes a reduction in blood pressure, and can bring great relief to those suffering from the sweating and trembling associated with anxiety.

TAKE-HOME MESSAGE 3•6

Normal cell functioning can be disrupted when cell membranes—particularly the proteins embedded in them—do not function properly. Such malfunctions can cause health problems, such as cystic fibrosis. But disruption of normal cell membrane function can also have beneficial, therapeutic effects, such as in the treatment of high blood pressure and anxiety.

The Cell   Cell Membranes   Crossing the Membrane   Cell Connections

Membrane surfaces have a "fingerprint" that identifies the cell.

As mentioned earlier, every cell in your body has a "fingerprint" made from a variety of molecules on the outside-facing surface of the cell membrane. Some of these membrane molecules vary, depending on the specific function of the cell. Others are common to all of your cells and convey to your immune system: "I belong here." Cells with an improper fingerprint are recognized as foreign and are attacked by your body's defenses.

Throughout our evolutionary history, this system has been tremendously valuable in helping our bodies fight infection. In some cases, however, this vigilance is a problem, like a car alarm that goes off even when you don't want it to. Suppose you receive a liver (or any other organ) transplant. Even if the donor is a close relative, the molecular fingerprint on the cells of the donated liver is not identical to your own. Consequently, your body sees the new organ as a foreign object and puts up a fight against it (**FIGURE 3-14**). Because your body will naturally try to reject the new organ, doctors must administer drugs that suppress your immune system. Immune suppression helps you tolerate the new liver, but, as you can imagine, it leaves you without some of the defenses to fight off other foreign invaders, such as bacteria that may cause infection. The presence or absence of certain molecular markers on plasma membranes is also responsible for a person's blood type and can lead to problems with simple blood transfusions.

Q Why is it extremely unlikely that a person will catch HIV from casual contact—such as shaking hands— with an infected individual?

The AIDS-causing virus, HIV, uses the molecular markers on plasma membranes to infect an individual's cells. These same molecular markers are also the reason that it is extremely unlikely that you can catch an HIV infection from casual contact with an infected individual, such as shaking his or her hand. The specific molecular markers involved in infection by HIV belong to a group of identifying markers called "clusters of differentiation." Abbreviated as "CD markers" and having names such as CD1, CD2, and CD3, these marker molecules are proteins embedded in the plasma membrane that enable a cell to bind to outside molecules and, sometimes, transport them into the cell.

One CD marker, called the CD4 marker, is found only on cells deep within the body and in the bloodstream, such as immune system cells and some nerve cells. It is the CD4 marker, in conjunction with another receptor, that is targeted by HIV. If the virus can find a cell with a CD4 marker, it can infect you, and because the CD4 markers *never* occur on the surface of your skin cells, casual contact such as touching is very unlikely

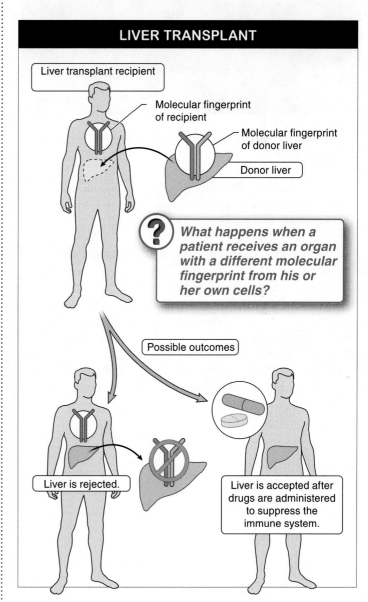

LIVER TRANSPLANT

Liver transplant recipient

Molecular fingerprint of recipient

Molecular fingerprint of donor liver

Donor liver

? *What happens when a patient receives an organ with a different molecular fingerprint from his or her own cells?*

Possible outcomes

Liver is rejected.

Liver is accepted after drugs are administered to suppress the immune system.

FIGURE 3-14 Mismatched molecular fingerprints can cause difficulty in organ transplantation.

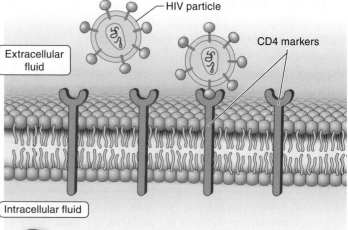

Cells within the human body, and not those on the surface, have CD4 markers. HIV infects the body by binding to the CD4 markers on these cells.

HIV particle

Extracellular fluid

CD4 markers

Intracellular fluid

 HIV is not spread through casual contact; the virus cannot bind to skin cells because they do not have CD4 markers.

FIGURE 3-15 HIV is not transmitted through casual contact.

to transmit the virus (**FIGURE 3-15**). Even if millions of HIV particles are present on a person's hands, they just can't gain access into any of the other person's surface cells.

How does HIV get transmitted? Far and away, the most common methods of transmission involve the transfer of blood, semen, vaginal fluid, or breast milk from one individual to another. Particles of the virus are present in these fluids, as are cells already infected by the virus. As a consequence, the chief routes of transmission are from an infected mother to her child in breast milk, from an infected mother to her baby at birth, the use of contaminated needles, and unprotected sexual intercourse. Because an open sore or

cut might expose some of the cells in your bloodstream to the outside world, however, it is not impossible for casual transmission of HIV to occur.

TAKE-HOME MESSAGE 3·7

Every cell in your body has a "fingerprint" made from a variety of molecules on the outside-facing surface of the cell membrane. This molecular fingerprint is key to the function of your immune system.

The Cell   Cell Membranes   Crossing the Membrane   Cell Connections

❸ Molecules move across membranes in several ways.

Passage of proteins between cells can be tracked (junctions between these human cancer cells are stained red and green).

3·8

Passive transport is the spontaneous diffusion of molecules across a membrane.

To function properly, cells must take in food and/or other necessary materials and must move out metabolic waste and molecules produced for use elsewhere in the body. In some cases, this movement of molecules requires energy and is called active transport. (We cover active transport later in this chapter.) In other cases, the molecular movement occurs spontaneously, without the input of energy, and is called **passive transport.** There are two types of passive transport: diffusion and osmosis. (Osmosis is the topic of the next section.)

Diffusion is passive transport in which a particle, called a **solute,** is dissolved in a gas or liquid (a **solvent**) and moves from an area of high solute concentration to an area of lower concentration (**FIGURE 3-16**). (When we are talking about cells, "diffusion" usually refers to the situation in which the solute moves across a membrane.) In the absence of other forces, molecules of a substance will always tend to move from

FIGURE 3-16 Diffusion: a form of passive transport that results in an even distribution of molecules.

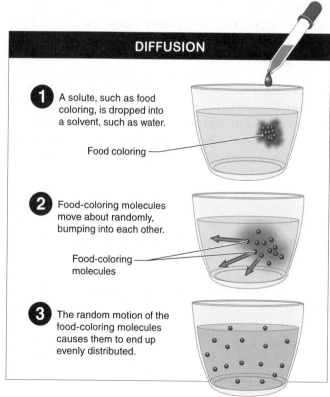

DIFFUSION

1 A solute, such as food coloring, is dropped into a solvent, such as water.

Food coloring

2 Food-coloring molecules move about randomly, bumping into each other.

Food-coloring molecules

3 The random motion of the food-coloring molecules causes them to end up evenly distributed.

93

where they are more concentrated to where they are less concentrated. This movement occurs because molecules move randomly and are equally likely to move in any direction. And when certain molecules are highly concentrated, they keep bumping into each other and eventually end up evenly distributed. For this reason, we say that molecules tend to *move down their concentration gradient*. For a simple illustration, drop a tiny bit of food coloring into a bowl of water and wait for a few minutes. The molecules of dye are initially clustered together in a very high concentration. Gradually, they disperse down their concentration gradient until the color is equally spread throughout the bowl.

Molecules such as oxygen (O_2) and carbon dioxide (CO_2) that are small and carry no charge can pass directly through the phospholipid bilayer of the membrane without the assistance of any other molecules, in a process called **simple diffusion.** Each time you take a breath, for example, there is a high concentration of O_2 molecules in the air you pull into your lungs. That oxygen diffuses across the plasma membranes of the lung cells and into your bloodstream, where red blood cells pick it up and deliver it to parts of your body where it is needed. Similarly, because CO_2 in your bloodstream is at a higher concentration than in the air in your lungs, it diffuses from your blood into your lungs and is released to the atmosphere when you exhale (**FIGURE 3-17**).

Most molecules, however, can't get through plasma membranes on their own. They may be electrically charged (polar) and, hence, repelled by the hydrophobic middle region of the phospholipid bilayer. Or the molecules may be too big to squeeze through the membrane. Nonetheless, when there is a concentration gradient from one side of the membrane to the other, these molecules may still be able to diffuse across the membrane, down their concentration gradient, with the help of a carrier molecule—one of the transport proteins, which we discussed in Section 3-5. Often, this transport protein spans the membrane and functions like a revolving door. When spontaneous diffusion across a plasma membrane requires a transport protein, it is called **facilitated diffusion** (see Figure 3-17).

Defects in transport proteins can reduce facilitated diffusion or even bring it to a complete stop, with serious health consequences. Many genetic diseases are the result of inheriting incorrect genetic instructions for building transport proteins. In the disease cystinuria, for example, incorrect genetic instructions result in a malformed transport protein in the plasma membrane. When structured and functioning properly, this transport protein facilitates the diffusion of some amino acids (including cystine, from which the disease gets its name) out of the kidneys. When the proteins are malformed, they

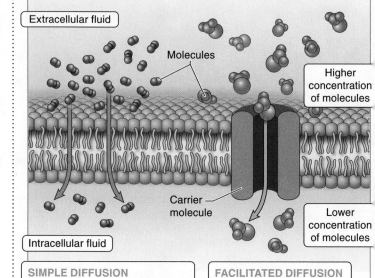

PASSIVE TRANSPORT

Passive transport occurs when molecules move across a membrane without energy input. Molecules move down their concentration gradients.

Extracellular fluid

Molecules

Higher concentration of molecules

Carrier molecule

Intracellular fluid

Lower concentration of molecules

SIMPLE DIFFUSION
Molecules pass directly through the plasma membrane without the assistance of another molecule.

FACILITATED DIFFUSION
Molecules move across the plasma membrane with the help of a carrier molecule.

FIGURE 3-17 Simple and facilitated diffusion.

cannot facilitate this diffusion and these amino acids build up in the kidneys, forming painful and dangerous kidney stones.

Diffusion across membranes doesn't just occur in animals, we see it in all organisms on earth. As we'll see in Chapter 4, one of the most important biological processes on earth is the diffusion of CO_2 from the atmosphere (an area of relatively high concentration) into the leaf cells of plants (areas of relatively low concentration), where it can be attached to other molecules, forming sugars through photosynthesis. At the same time, O_2 diffuses out of the leaves and into the atmosphere.

TAKE-HOME MESSAGE 3·8

For proper functioning, cells must acquire food molecules and/or other necessary materials from outside the cell. Similarly, metabolic waste molecules and molecules produced for use elsewhere in the body must move out of the cell. In passive transport—which includes simple and facilitated diffusion and osmosis—the molecular movement occurs spontaneously, without the input of energy. This generally occurs as molecules move down their concentration gradient.

The Cell   Cell Membranes   ▼ Crossing the Membrane   Cell Connections

3·9

Osmosis is the passive diffusion of water across a membrane.

Just as solute molecules will passively diffuse down their concentration gradients, water molecules will also move from areas of high concentration to areas of low concentration to equalize the concentration of water inside and outside the cell. The diffusion of water across a membrane is a special type of

passive transport called **osmosis** (**FIGURE 3-18**). As solute molecules diffuse across a plasma membrane, molecules of water also move across the membrane, equalizing the water concentration inside and outside the cell.

Osmosis can have some dramatic effects on cells. It turns out that many molecules just can't move across a cell membrane. They may be too big or too charged, or there may not be any carrier molecules in the membrane that can move them. Let's imagine, for instance, that there is a high concentration of a large molecule inside a cell and that it can't pass through the cell membrane. Although the molecule can't move out of the cell and down its concentration gradient, water can move into the cell down *its* concentration gradient. As water diffuses into the cell, the cell will get larger.

When a cell is in a solution, we describe the concentration of solutes outside the cell relative to that inside the cell as the **tonicity** of the solution (see Figure 3-18). A **hypertonic** solution has a greater concentration of solutes than the solution inside the cell. As a consequence, if the cell membrane is not permeable to the solutes, water will move out of the cell into the surrounding solution, equalizing the solute concentration inside and out, and the cell shrivels. A **hypotonic** solution has a lower solute concentration than the solution inside the cell. If the cell membrane is not permeable to the solutes, water will move into the cell and it will swell. In an **isotonic** solution, the concentration of solutes is the same inside and outside the cell.

You can see osmosis in action in your own kitchen (**FIGURE 3-19**). Take a stalk of celery and leave it on the counter for a couple of hours. As water evaporates from the cells of the celery stalk, it will shrink and become limp. You can make it crisp again by placing it in a solution of distilled water. Why distilled water? Because it contains very few dissolved molecules—it is a hypotonic solution. The cells in the celery stalk, on the other hand, contain many dissolved molecules, such as salt. Because those dissolved molecules can't easily pass across the plasma membrane of the celery stalk cells, the water molecules move into the cells (moving from the pool of distilled water where they are at super-high concentration to the interior of the celery cells where water is scarcer). Would the celery regain its crispness if you placed it in concentrated salt water? No, because in the hypertonic salt solution there are more dissolved molecules (and fewer water molecules) outside the celery cells, so what little water remains in the celery cells actually moves, via osmosis, out of the celery, causing it to shrivel even more.

OSMOSIS

Osmosis is a type of passive transport by which water diffuses across a membrane, in order to equalize the concentration of water inside and outside the cell. The direction of osmosis is determined by the total amount of solutes on either side of the membrane. Water will always move toward the side that has a greater concentration of solutes.

Extracellular fluid — **PLANT CELL**   **ANIMAL CELL (RED BLOOD CELL)**

HYPERTONIC SOLUTION
- Solute concentrations are higher in the extracellular fluid.
- Water diffuses out of cells.

HYPOTONIC SOLUTION
- Solute concentrations are lower in the extracellular fluid.
- Water diffuses into cells.

ISOTONIC SOLUTION
- Solute concentrations are balanced.
- Water movement is balanced.

 Unlike animal cells, plant cells generally do not explode in hypotonic solutions, because their rigid cell walls limit cellular expansion.

FIGURE 3-18 Osmosis overview.

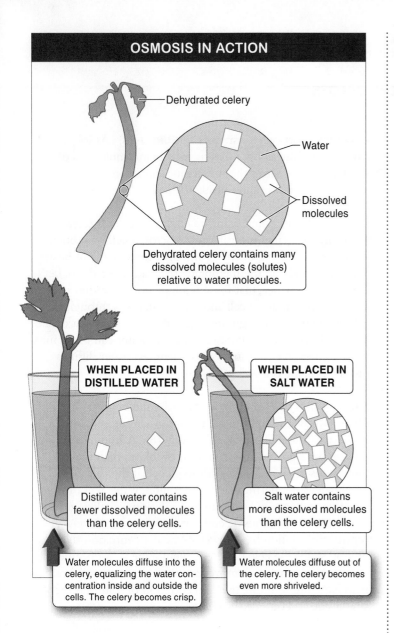

OSMOSIS IN ACTION

Dehydrated celery

Water

Dissolved molecules

Dehydrated celery contains many dissolved molecules (solutes) relative to water molecules.

WHEN PLACED IN DISTILLED WATER

WHEN PLACED IN SALT WATER

Distilled water contains fewer dissolved molecules than the celery cells.

Salt water contains more dissolved molecules than the celery cells.

Water molecules diffuse into the celery, equalizing the water concentration inside and outside the cells. The celery becomes crisp.

Water molecules diffuse out of the celery. The celery becomes even more shriveled.

FIGURE 3-19 Osmosis in your kitchen.

Q How do laxatives relieve constipation?

A more practical use of osmosis is seen with the laxative Milk of Magnesia. This product contains magnesium salts, which are poorly absorbed from the digestive tract. As a consequence, after a dose of the laxative, water moves via osmosis from the surrounding cells into the intestines. The water softens the feces in the intestines and increases the fecal volume, thereby relieving constipation.

It's important to note that the direction of osmosis is determined only by a difference in the *total concentration* of all the molecules dissolved in the water: it does not matter what the solutes are, only how many molecules of solutes there are. To determine which way the water molecules will move, you need to determine the total amount of "dissolved stuff" on either side of the membrane. The water will move toward the side with more stuff dissolved in it. For this reason, even small increases in the salinity of lakes can have disastrous consequences for the organisms living there, from fish to bacteria. Conversely, putting animal cells—such as red blood cells—in distilled water will cause them to explode, because water will diffuse into the cell (which contains more solutes) and the cell will swell and burst. This will not generally happen to plant cells because (as we will see later in this chapter) the plant cell plasma membrane is surrounded by a rigid cell wall that limits the amount of cell expansion possible when water moves in by osmosis.

TAKE-HOME MESSAGE 3·9

The diffusion of water across a membrane is a special type of passive transport called osmosis. Water molecules move across the membrane until the concentration of water inside and outside the cell is equalized.

3·10

In active transport, cells use energy to move small molecules into and out of the cell.

Molecules can't always move spontaneously and effortlessly in and out of cells. Sometimes their transport needs energy, in which case the process is called **active transport.** Such energy expenditures may be necessary if the molecules to be

moved are very large or if they are being moved *against* their concentration gradient. In all active transport, proteins embedded in the membrane act like motorized revolving doors, pushing molecules into the cell regardless of the

The Cell

Cell Membranes

Crossing the Membrane

Cell Connections

Active transport occurs when the movement of molecules into and out of a cell requires the input of energy. For example, in response to eating, the cells lining your stomach use ATP to pump large numbers of H+ ions into the stomach.

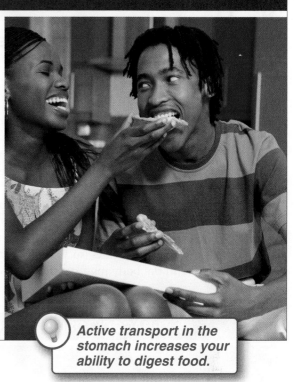

Active transport in the stomach increases your ability to digest food.

FIGURE 3-20 Active transport. Some energy expenditure is required to move molecules into and out of cells when the molecules are very large or are being moved against their concentration gradient.

concentration of those molecules on either side of the membrane. There are two distinct types of active transport, primary and secondary, which differ only in the source of the fuel that keeps the revolving doors spinning.

Every time you eat a meal, you start the motors that spin the revolving-door transport proteins in your stomach (**FIGURE 3-20**). To help break down the food into more digestible bits, the cells lining your stomach create an acidic environment by pumping large numbers of H+ ions (also called protons) into the stomach contents, against their concentration gradient. (That is, there are more H+ ions in the stomach contents than there are inside the cells lining the stomach.) All of this H+ pumping increases your ability to digest the food but comes at a great energetic cost—in the form of usage of the high-energy molecule ATP—because the protons would not normally flow into a region against their concentration gradient. When active transport uses energy directly from ATP to fuel the revolving door, the process is called **primary active transport.** (We explore ATP in more detail in Chapter 4.)

Many transporter proteins use an indirect method of fueling their activities rather than using energy released directly from ATP. In the process of **secondary active transport,** the transport protein simultaneously moves one molecule against its concentration gradient while letting another flow down its concentration gradient. Although no ATP is used directly in this process, at some other time and in some other location, energy from ATP was used to pump one of the types of molecule involved in the secondary transport process against its concentration gradient. The process is a bit like using energy to pump water up to the top of a high water tower. Later, the water can be allowed to run out of the tower over a water wheel, which can, in turn, power a process such as grinding wheat into flour. Our bodies frequently use the energy from one reaction that occurs spontaneously to fuel another reaction that requires energy.

TAKE-HOME MESSAGE 3·10

In active transport, moving molecules across a membrane requires energy. Active transport is necessary if the molecules to be moved are very large or if they are being moved against their concentration gradient. Proteins embedded in the plasma membrane act like motorized revolving doors to actively transport (pump) the molecules.

Endocytosis and exocytosis are used for bulk transport of particles.

Many molecules needed by cells are just too big to get into a cell by passive or active transport. After all, a protein embedded in a thin plasma membrane can only be so big, and some cells in your immune system, for example, must even ingest (and destroy) entire bacterial cells that are invading your body. To absorb such large particles, cells engulf them with their plasma membrane in a process called **endocytosis.** Cells also have another method besides passive and active transport for moving molecules out of the cell. Cells that manufacture molecules (such as digestive enzymes) for use elsewhere in the body must get those molecules out

of the cell, and they often use the process of **exocytosis** to do this.

There are three types of endocytosis: phagocytosis, pinocytosis, and receptor-mediated endocytosis. All three involve the basic process of the plasma membrane oozing around an object that is outside the cell, surrounding it, forming a little pocket called a **vesicle,** and then pinching off the vesicle so that it is inside the cell but separated from the rest of the cell contents.

Phagocytosis and Pinocytosis
Phagocytosis is the process by which relatively large particles are engulfed by cells (**FIGURE 3-21**). Amoebas and other unicellular protists, as well as white blood cells, use phagocytosis to consume entire organisms either as food or as their way of defending against pathogens (disease-causing organisms or substances). Whereas "phagocytosis" comes from the Greek for "eat" and "container," the term **pinocytosis** comes from the Greek for "drink" and "container" and describes the process of cells taking in dissolved particles and liquids. The two processes are largely the same, except that the vesicles formed during pinocytosis are generally much smaller than those formed during phagocytosis.

Receptor-Mediated Endocytosis
The third type of endocytosis, **receptor-mediated endocytosis,** is much more specific than either phagocytosis or pinocytosis. In this process, receptor molecules on the surface of a cell sit waiting until the one type of molecule they recognize bumps into them. For one receptor it might be insulin, for another it might be cholesterol. Many receptors of the same type are often clustered together in a cell's plasma membrane. When the appropriate molecule binds to each of the receptor proteins, the membrane begins to fold inward, first forming a little pit and then completely engulfing the molecules, which are still attached to their receptors.

One of the most important examples of receptor-mediated endocytosis involves cholesterol (**FIGURE 3-22**). Most cholesterol that circulates in the bloodstream is in the form of particles called low-density lipoproteins, or LDL. Each molecule of LDL is a cholesterol globule coated by phospholipids. Proteins embedded within the LDL's phospholipid coat are recognized by receptor proteins built into the plasma membranes of liver cells. Once bound to the receptors, the LDL molecule is consumed by the cell via endocytosis. Inside the cell, the

PHAGOCYTOSIS

TEM 4,700×

Phagocytosis is a type of endocytosis by which cells engulf large particles.

Plasma membrane

Large particle

Extracellular fluid

Intracellular fluid

1 The plasma membrane forms a pocket-like vesicle around a large particle.

Vesicle

2 The particle is transported into the cell in a vesicle.

FIGURE 3-21 Through phagocytosis, amoebas and other unicellular protists, as well as white blood cells, consume other organisms for food or for defense.

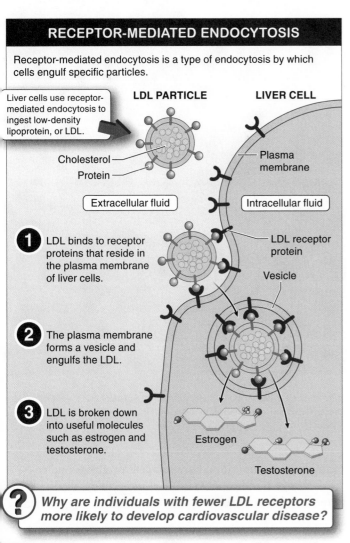

RECEPTOR-MEDIATED ENDOCYTOSIS

Receptor-mediated endocytosis is a type of endocytosis by which cells engulf specific particles.

Liver cells use receptor-mediated endocytosis to ingest low-density lipoprotein, or LDL.

LDL PARTICLE **LIVER CELL**

Cholesterol
Protein
Plasma membrane

Extracellular fluid   Intracellular fluid

1 LDL binds to receptor proteins that reside in the plasma membrane of liver cells.

LDL receptor protein

Vesicle

2 The plasma membrane forms a vesicle and engulfs the LDL.

3 LDL is broken down into useful molecules such as estrogen and testosterone.

Estrogen

Testosterone

? *Why are individuals with fewer LDL receptors more likely to develop cardiovascular disease?*

FIGURE 3-22 Receptor proteins aid in endocytosis. This process is important in the ability of your liver to remove cholesterol from your bloodstream.

---

cholesterol is broken down and used to make a variety of other useful molecules, such as the hormones estrogen and testosterone.

Circulating cholesterol often builds up on the walls of arteries, reducing the area (that is, the diameter of the blood vessel) available for blood flow and causing the artery to harden. Because too much circulating cholesterol in LDL molecules can lead to cardiovascular disease and death (**FIGURE 3-23**), it's good to remove as much cholesterol from your bloodstream as quickly as possible. Individuals lucky enough to have large numbers of LDL receptors on the plasma membranes of their liver cells have a significantly lower risk of cardiovascular disease.

Conversely, individuals who consume food laden with too much cholesterol (such as egg yolks, cheese, and sausages), or those who have the misfortune of inheriting genes that code for faulty liver cell membranes that have only a few LDL receptors, can have a heavy load of circulating blood cholesterol. This outcome can result in the early onset of cardiovascular disease. In the extreme case where an individual is born with no LDL receptors at all (a disorder called familial hypercholesterolemia), circulating cholesterol accumulates in the arteries so rapidly that cardiovascular disease begins to develop even before puberty, and death from a heart attack can occur before the age of 30.

Q *Faulty cell membranes are a primary cause of cardiovascular disease. What modification to these membranes might be an effective treatment?*

HEART DISEASE

Healthy artery

Plaque

Partially blocked artery

Plaque

Blocked artery

💡 *LDL receptors bind to LDL molecules, removing cholesterol from the bloodstream and reducing the risk of cardiovascular disease.*

FIGURE 3-23 Comparison of a healthy artery and arteries choked by the buildup of cholesterol.

Exocytosis Cells in the pancreas produce a chemical called insulin that moves throughout the circulatory system, informing body cells that there is glucose in the bloodstream that ought to be taken in and utilized for energy. The insulin molecule is much too large to pass out through the plasma membranes of the cells in which it is manufactured. As a result, after molecules of insulin are produced, they are coated with a phospholipid membrane to form a vesicle. The insulin-carrying vesicle then moves through the cytoplasm to the inner surface of the cell's plasma membrane. Once there, the phospholipid membrane surrounding the insulin and the phospholipid membrane of the cell fuse together, dumping the contents of the vesicle out of the cell and into the bloodstream (**FIGURE 3-24**).

Exocytosis, the movement of molecules out of a cell, occurs throughout the body and is not restricted to large molecules. In the brain and other parts of the nervous system, for

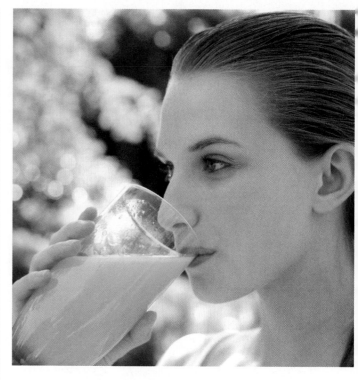

After drinking a glass of orange juice, your blood concentrations of glucose increase, causing the cells of your pancreas to secrete insulin through exocytosis.

example, communication between cells occurs as one cell releases large numbers of very small molecules, called neurotransmitters, via exocytosis.

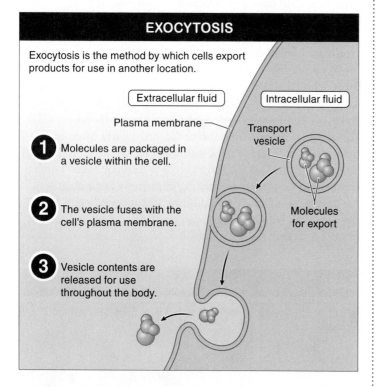

EXOCYTOSIS

Exocytosis is the method by which cells export products for use in another location.

Extracellular fluid | Intracellular fluid

Plasma membrane

Transport vesicle

1 Molecules are packaged in a vesicle within the cell.

2 The vesicle fuses with the cell's plasma membrane.

Molecules for export

3 Vesicle contents are released for use throughout the body.

FIGURE 3-24 Exocytosis moves molecules out of the cell. This is how insulin is exported from the cells where it is synthesized.

TAKE-HOME MESSAGE 3·11

When materials cannot get into a cell via diffusion or a pump (for example, when the molecules are too big), cells can engulf the molecules or particles with their plasma membrane in a process called endocytosis. Similarly, molecules can be moved out of a cell via exocytosis. In both processes, the plasma membrane moves to surround the molecules or particles and forms a little vesicle that is pinched off inside the cell (endocytosis) or fuses with the plasma membrane and dumps its contents outside the cell (exocytosis).

The Cell | Cell Membranes | Crossing the Membrane | Cell Connections

4 Cells are connected and communicate with each other.

Cells reach out and connect; no telephone lines required.

3·12

Connections between cells hold them in place and enable them to communicate with each other.

So far in this chapter we have examined the cell as a free-living and independent entity. The majority of cells in any multicellular organism, however, are connected to other cells. Let's consider how they are connected and how they communicate with each other. There is a variety of methods by which cells adhere to other cells, involving numerous types of protein and glycoprotein adhesion molecules. We examine three primary types of connections between animal cells: (1) tight junctions, (2) desmosomes, and (3) gap junctions (**FIGURE 3-25**); and one type of connection between plant cells: plasmodesmata.

Tight junctions form continuous, water-tight seals around cells and also anchor cells in place. Much like the caulking around a tub or sink that keeps water from leaking into the surrounding walls, tight junctions prevent fluid flow between cells. Tight junctions are particularly important in the small intestine, where digestion occurs. Cells lining the small intestine absorb nutrients from the watery fluid moving through your gut. If the fluid—and the resident bacteria—inside the intestine were to leak between the cells and into your body cavity, you would not be able to extract sufficient energy and nutrients

from your food, and the bacteria would make you sick. The tight junctions instead force fluid to pass *into* the cells that line the intestine, where the nutrients can be utilized.

Desmosomes are like spot welds or rivets that fasten cells together into strong sheets. They occur at irregular intervals and function like fastened Velcro: they hold cells together but are not water-tight, allowing fluid to pass around them. Desmosomes are found in much of the tissue that lines the cavities of animal bodies. They also are found in muscle tissue, holding fibers together. Genetic disorders that reduce cells' ability to form desmosome proteins or lead to destruction of desmosomes by the immune system result in the formation of blisters, where layers of skin separate from each other.

Finally, **gap junctions** are pores surrounded by special proteins that form open channels between two cells (see Figure 3-25). Functioning like secret passageways, these junctions are large enough for salts, sugars, amino acids, and the chemicals that carry electrical signals to pass through, but are too small for the passage of organelles or very large molecules such as proteins and nucleic acids. Gap junctions

1 TIGHT JUNCTIONS
Form a water-tight seal between cells, like caulking around a tub

2 DESMOSOMES
Act like Velcro and fasten cells together

3 GAP JUNCTIONS
Act like secret passageways and allow materials to pass between cells

Cell 1

Cell 2

TEM 38,000×

TEM 70,000×

TEM 36,000×

FIGURE 3-25 Cell connections: tight junctions, desmosomes, and gap junctions.

are an important mechanism for cell-to-cell communication. In the heart, for example, the electrical signal telling muscle cells to contract is passed from cell to cell through gap junctions. Gap junctions are also important in allowing a cell to recognize that it has bumped up against another cell; chemicals flowing from one cell to the next can signal the body to stop producing cells of a particular type.

Q How can a lack of communication between cells lead to cancer?

Normal cells generally stop dividing when they bump up against other cells, a phenomenon called **contact inhibition.** Cancer cells, however, do not have this feature. Instead, they divide continuously, eventually forming a mass of cells, called a tumor, which can cause serious health problems. Cancer cells differ from other cells in several important ways; one of these ways is that they usually have reduced numbers of gap junctions. With fewer of these "secret passageways" of communication, it may be harder for a cell to detect that it has bumped up against other cells, in which case the cell is more likely to continue dividing, possibly contributing to its eventually becoming a tumorous mass of dividing cells.

In most plants, the cells have anywhere from 1,000 to 100,000 microscopic tube-like channels, called **plasmodesmata** (*sing.* **plasmodesma**) (see Figure 3-36), connecting the cells to each other and enabling communication and transport between them. In fact, because so many of the cells are connected to one another, sharing cytoplasm and other molecules, some biologists have wondered whether we should consider a plant as just one big cell. How would you respond to that idea?

TAKE-HOME MESSAGE 3·12

In multicellular organisms, most cells are connected to other cells. The connections can form a water-tight seal between the cells (tight junctions), can hold sheets of cells together while allowing fluid to pass between the cells (desmosomes), or can function like secret passageways, allowing the movement of cytoplasm, molecules, and other signals between cells (gap junctions). In plants, plasmodesmata connect cells and enable communication and transport between them.

The Cell   Cell Membranes   Crossing the Membrane   Cell Connections

❺ Nine important landmarks distinguish eukaryotic cells.

Cell of the voodoo lily. How many different organelles can you spot in this plant cell?

3·13 --

The nucleus is the cell's genetic control center.

As we have seen, all cells are surrounded by a complex plasma membrane that actively regulates what materials get into and out of a cell. Now it's time to look at the cellular contents surrounded by the plasma membrane in eukaryotic cells.

The nucleus is the largest and most prominent organelle in most eukaryotic cells. In fact, the nucleus is generally larger than any prokaryotic cell. If a cell were the size of a large lecture hall or movie theater, the nucleus would be the size of a big-rig 18-wheeler truck parked in the front rows. The nucleus has two primary functions, both related to the fact that most of the cell's DNA resides in the nucleus. First, the nucleus is the genetic control center, directing most cellular activities by controlling which molecules are produced, and in what quantity. Second, the nucleus is the storehouse for hereditary information.

Three important structural components stand out in the nucleus (**FIGURE 3-26**). First is the **nuclear membrane,** sometimes called the nuclear envelope, which surrounds the nucleus and separates it from the cytoplasm. Unlike most plasma membranes, however, the nuclear membrane consists of *two* bilayers, one on top of the other, much like the double-bagging of groceries at the market. The nuclear membrane is not a sack, though. It is perforated, covered with tiny pores made from multiple proteins embedded in the phospholipid membranes and spanning both bilayers. These pores enable large molecules to pass from the nucleus to the cytoplasm and from the cytoplasm to the nucleus.

The second prominent structure in the nucleus is the **chromatin,** a mass of long, thin fibers consisting of DNA with some proteins attached to it that keep it from getting impossibly tangled. Most of the time, as the DNA directs cellular activities, the chromatin resembles a plate of spaghetti. When it's time for cell division (a process described in detail in Chapter 6), the chromatin coils up and the threads become shorter and thicker until they become visible as chromosomes, the compacted, linear DNA molecules on which all of the organism's hereditary information is carried.

103

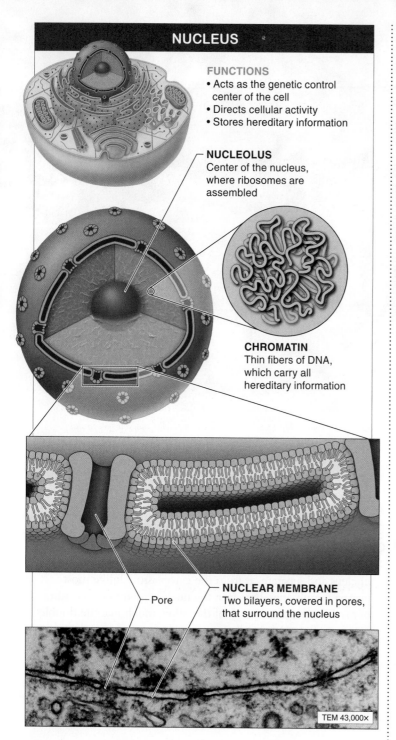

NUCLEUS

FUNCTIONS
- Acts as the genetic control center of the cell
- Directs cellular activity
- Stores hereditary information

NUCLEOLUS
Center of the nucleus, where ribosomes are assembled

CHROMATIN
Thin fibers of DNA, which carry all hereditary information

NUCLEAR MEMBRANE
Two bilayers, covered in pores, that surround the nucleus

Pore

TEM 43,000×

FIGURE 3-26 The nucleus: the cell's genetic control center.

The nucleus holds the genetic information that makes it possible to build organisms. (That's why identical twins, carrying the same genetic information, look so similar.)

A third structure in the nucleus is the **nucleolus,** an area near the center of the nucleus where subunits of the ribosomes, a critical part of the cellular machinery, are assembled. Ribosomes are like little factories that copy bits of the information stored in the DNA and use them to construct proteins, including enzymes and the proteins that make up tissues such as the bark of trees or the bone of vertebrates. The ribosomes are built in the nucleolus but pass through the nuclear pores and into the cytoplasm before starting their protein-production work.

TAKE-HOME MESSAGE 3·13

The nucleus is usually the largest and most prominent organelle in the eukaryotic cell. It directs most cellular activities by controlling which molecules are produced and in what quantity. The nucleus is also the storehouse for all hereditary information.

The Cell   Cell Membranes   Crossing the Membrane   Cell Connections

3·14

Cytoplasm and the cytoskeleton form the cell's internal environment, provide its physical support, and can generate movement.

If you imagine yourself inside a cell the size of a big lecture hall, it might come as a surprise that you can barely see that big rig of a nucleus parked in the front rows. Visibility is almost zero, not only because the room is filled with jelly-like cytoplasm, but also because there is a dense web of thick and thin, straight and branched, ropes, strings, and scaffolding, running every which way throughout the room.

This inner scaffolding of the cell, which is made from proteins, is the **cytoskeleton** (**FIGURE 3-27**). It has three chief purposes. First, it gives animal cells shape and support—making red blood cells look like little round doughnuts (without the hole in the middle) and giving neurons their very long, thread-like appearance. Plant cells are shaped primarily by their cell wall (a structure we discuss later in the chapter), but they also have a cytoskeleton. Second, the cytoskeleton controls the intracellular traffic flow, serving as a series of tracks on which a variety of organelles and molecules are guided across and around the inside of the cell. And third, because the elaborate scaffolding of the cytoskeleton is dynamic and can generate force, it gives all cells some ability to control their movement.

The cytoskeleton also plays a more direct and obvious role in helping some cells to move—whether moving the cell through its environment, or moving stuff in the environment over the cell surface. **Cilia** (*sing.* **cilium**) are short projections that often occur in large numbers on a single cell (**FIGURE 3-28**). Cilia beat

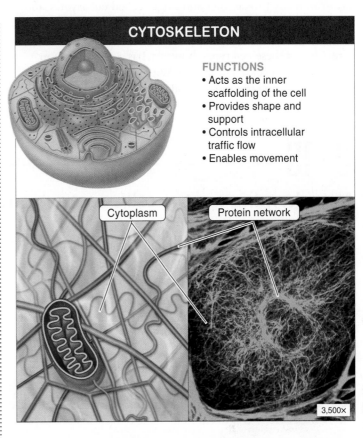

CYTOSKELETON

FUNCTIONS
• Acts as the inner scaffolding of the cell
• Provides shape and support
• Controls intracellular traffic flow
• Enables movement

Cytoplasm

Protein network

3,500×

FIGURE 3-27 The cytoskeleton: the cell's inner scaffolding.

CELLULAR MOVEMENT

With gentle beating, cilia can move fluid past cells, whereas flagella, with whip-like motions, can move the cells themselves.

FIGURE 3-28 Cilia and flagella assist the cell with movement.

Nine Cell Landmarks

swiftly, often in unison and in ways that resemble blades of grass in a field, blowing in the wind. Cilia can move fluid along and past a cell. This movement can accomplish many important tasks, including sweeping the airways to our lungs to clear them of debris (such as dust) in the air we breathe.

Flagella (*sing.* **flagellum**) are much longer than cilia. Flagella occur in many prokaryotes and single-celled eukaryotes, and many algae and plants have cells with one or more flagella. But in animals, cell types with one or more flagella are very rare. One of these cell types, however, has a critical role in every animal species: sperm cells. With a flagellum for a tail, sperm are among the most mobile of all animal cells. Some

spermicidal birth control methods prevent conception by disabling the flagellum and immobilizing the sperm cells.

TAKE-HOME MESSAGE 3·14

The inner scaffolding of the cell, which is made from proteins, is the cytoskeleton. It gives animal cells their shape and support, gives cells some ability to control their movement, and serves as a series of tracks on which organelles and molecules are guided across and around the inside of the cell.

3·15

Mitochondria are the cell's energy converters.

Cars have it easy: we generally put only a single type of fuel in them, and it is exactly the same fuel every time. With human bodies it's a different story. During some meals we put in meat and potatoes. Other times, it's juice and fruits. Still others, bread or vegetables, popcorn and gummy bears, pizza and ice cream. Yet no matter what we eat, we expect our body to utilize the energy in these various foods to power all the

reactions in our bodies that make it possible for us to breathe, move, and think. The mitochondria are the organelles that make this possible (**FIGURE 3-29**).

Mitochondria (*sing.* **mitochondrion**) are the cell's all-purpose energy converters, and they are present in virtually all plant cells, animal cells, and every other eukaryotic cell.

MITOCHONDRIA

FUNCTIONS
• Act as all-purpose energy converters
• Harvest energy to be used for cellular functions

DNA
Matrix
Outer membrane
Inner membrane
Intermembrane space

TEM 73,000×

Cells such as muscle and liver cells, which use a lot of energy, can have up to 2,000 mitochondria!

FIGURE 3-29 Mitochondria: the cell's all-purpose energy converters.

The Cell   Cell Membranes   Crossing the Membrane   Cell Connections

Although we consume a variety of foods, our mitochondria allow us to convert the energy contained in the chemical bonds of the carbohydrates, fats, and proteins in the food into carbon dioxide, water, and ATP—the molecule that is the energy source all cells use to fuel all their functions and activities. (ATP and how it works are described in detail in Chapter 4.) Because this energy conversion requires a significant amount of oxygen, organisms' mitochondria consume most of the oxygen used by each cell. In humans, for example, our mitochondria consume as much as 80% of the oxygen we breathe. They give a significant return on this investment by producing about 90% of the energy our cells need to function.

As with so many aspects of our bodies, form follows function. Cells that are not very metabolically active, such as fat cells in humans, have very few mitochondria. Other cells, such as muscle, liver, and sperm cells in animals and fast-growing root cells in plants—all of which have large energy requirements—are packed densely with mitochondria. Some of these cells have as many at 2,000 mitochondria!

To visualize the structure of a mitochondrion, imagine a plastic sandwich bag. Now take another, bigger plastic bag and stuff it inside the sandwich bag. That's the structure of mitochondria: there is a smooth outer membrane and a scrunched up inner membrane. This construction creates two separate compartments within the mitochondrion: a region outside the inner plastic bag (called the **intermembrane space**) and another region, called the **matrix,** inside the inner plastic bag. This bag-within-a-bag structure has important implications for energy conversion. And having a heavily folded inner membrane that is much larger than the outer membrane provides a huge amount of surface area on which to conduct chemical reactions. (We discuss the details of mitochondrial energy conversion and the role of mitochondrial structure in Chapter 4.)

As we learned in our earlier discussion of endosymbiosis, mitochondria may very well have existed, billions of years ago, as separate single-celled bacteria-like organisms. They are similar to bacteria in size and shape, and may have originated when symbiotic bacteria took up permanent residence within other cells. Perhaps the strongest evidence for this is that mitochondria have their own DNA. Mixed in among the approximately 3,000 proteins in each mitochondrion, there are anywhere from 2 to 10 copies of its own little ring-shaped DNA. This DNA carries the instructions for making 13 important mitochondrial proteins necessary for metabolism and energy production.

We're always taught that our mothers and fathers contribute equally to our genetic composition, but this isn't quite true: the mitochondria in every one of your cells (and the DNA that comes with them) come from the mitochondria that were initially present in your mother's egg, which, when fertilized by your father's sperm, developed into you. In other words: all of your mitochondria are descended from your mother's mitochondria. The tiny sperm contributes DNA, but no cytoplasm and, hence, no mitochondria. Consequently, mitochondrial DNA is something that we inherit exclusively from our mothers. This is true not only in humans but in most multicellular eukaryotes. As the fertilized egg develops into a two-celled, then four-celled, embryo, the mitochondria split themselves by a process called fission, the same process of division and DNA duplication used by bacteria—so there are always a sufficient number of mitochondria for the newly produced cells. This similarity between mitochondria and bacteria is another characteristic that supports the theory that mitochondria were originally symbiotic bacteria.

Given the central role of mitochondria in converting the energy in food molecules into a form that is usable by cells, you won't be surprised to learn that mitochondrial malfunctions can have serious consequences. Recent research has focused on possible links between defective mitochondria and diseases characterized by fatigue and muscle pain. It seems, for instance, that many cases of "exercise intolerance"—extreme fatigue or cramps after only slight exertion—may be related to defective mitochondrial DNA.

> **Q** We all have more DNA from one parent than the other. Who is the bigger contributor: mom or dad? Why?

TAKE-HOME MESSAGE 3·15

In mitochondria, which are found in virtually all eukaryotic cells, the energy contained in the chemical bonds of carbohydrate, fat, and protein molecules is converted into carbon dioxide, water, and ATP, the energy source for all cellular functions and activities. Mitochondria may have their evolutionary origins as symbiotic bacteria living inside other cells.

Lysosomes are the cell's garbage disposals.

Garbage. What does a cell do with all the garbage it generates? Mitochondria wear out after about 10 days of intensive activity, for starters. And white blood cells constantly track down and consume bacterial invaders, which they then have to dispose of. Similarly, the thousands of ongoing reactions of cellular metabolism produce many waste macromolecules that cells must digest and recycle. Many eukaryotic cells deal with this garbage by maintaining hundreds of versatile floating "garbage disposals" called lysosomes (**FIGURE 3-30**).

Lysosomes are round, membrane-enclosed, acid-filled vesicles that function as garbage disposals. Lysosomes are filled with about 50 different digestive enzymes and a super-acidic fluid, a corrosive broth so powerful that if a lysosome were to burst, it would almost immediately kill the cell by rapidly digesting all of its component parts. The selection of enzymes in the lysosome represents a broad spectrum of chemicals designed for dismantling macromolecules that are no longer needed by cells or are generated as by-products of cellular metabolism. Some of the enzymes break down lipids, others

Q Why is Tay-Sachs disease like a strike by trash collectors?

carbohydrates, others proteins, and still others nucleic acids. Consequently, lysosomes are frequently also a first step when, via phagocytosis, a cell consumes and begins digesting a particle of food or even an invading bacterium. And, ever the efficient system, the cell releases most of the component parts of molecules that are digested, such as amino acids, back into its cytoplasm, where they can be reused by the cell as raw materials.

With 50 different enzymes necessary for lysosomes to carry out their metabolic salvaging act, malfunctions sometimes occur. A common genetic disorder called Tay-Sachs disease is the result of just such a genetic mishap. In Tay-Sachs disease, an individual inherits an inability to produce a critical lipid-digesting enzyme. Even though the lysosomes cannot digest certain lipids, the cells continue to send lipids to the lysosomes, where they accumulate, undigested. This leads to a sort of lysosome constipation. The lysosome swells until it bursts and digests the whole cell or until it chokes the cell to death. Within the first few years of life, this process occurs in large numbers of cells and eventually leads to the child's death.

LYSOSOMES

FUNCTION
• Act as floating garbage disposals for the cells digesting and recycling cellular waste products and consumed material

Membrane

Digestive enzymes and acid

Partially digested organelle

TEM 59,500x

FIGURE 3-30 Lysosomes: digestion and recycling of the cell's waste products.

The Cell   Cell Membranes   Crossing the Membrane   Cell Connections

Although it has long been debated among biologists, it does seem that plant cells contain lysosomes, compartments with similar digestive broths that carry out the same digestive processes. Among animals, some immune system cells tend to have particularly large numbers of lysosomes, most likely because of their great need for disposing of the by-products of disease-causing bacteria.

3·17

The endoplasmic reticulum is the site where cells build proteins and disarm toxins.

The information for how to construct the molecules essential to a cell's smooth functioning and survival is stored in the DNA found in the cell's nucleus. The energy used to construct these molecules and to run cellular functions comes primarily from the mitochondria. The actual production and modification of biological molecules, however, occurs in a system of organelles called the **endomembrane system** (**FIGURE 3-31**). This mass of interrelated membranes spreads out from and surrounds the nucleus, forming chambers within the cell that contain their own mixture of chemicals. The endomembrane system takes up as much as one-fifth of the cell's volume and is responsible for many of the fundamental functions of the cell.

Lipids are produced within these membrane-enclosed compartments, products for export to other parts of the body are modified and packaged here, polypeptide chains are assembled into functional proteins here, and many of the toxic chemicals that find their way into our bodies—from recreational drugs to antibiotics—are broken down and neutralized in the endomembrane system.

Because the process of protein production follows a somewhat linear path, we explore the endomembrane system sequentially, beginning just outside the nucleus with the endoplasmic reticulum.

OVERVIEW OF THE ENDOMEMBRANE SYSTEM

FUNCTIONS
• Produces and modifies molecules to be exported to other parts of the organism
• Breaks down toxic chemicals and cellular by-products

Rough endoplasmic reticulum

Smooth endoplasmic reticulum

Golgi apparatus

FIGURE 3-31 The endomembrane system: the smooth endoplasmic reticulum, rough endoplasmic reticulum, and Golgi apparatus.

ROUGH ENDOPLASMIC RETICULUM

FUNCTION
• Modifies proteins that will be shipped elsewhere in the organism

Ribosomes

Rough ER is covered in ribosomes. Ribosomes are protein-making machines.

TEM 56,500×

FIGURE 3-32 **The rough endoplasmic reticulum is studded with ribosomes.**

Rough Endoplasmic Reticulum Perhaps the organelle with the most cumbersome name, the **rough endoplasmic reticulum,** or **rough ER** ("endoplasmic reticulum" is derived from the Greek for "within" and "anything molded" and the Latin for "small net"), is a large series of interconnected, flattened sacs that look like a stack of pancakes. These sacs are connected directly to the nuclear envelope. In most eukaryotic cells, the rough ER almost completely surrounds the nucleus (**FIGURE 3-32**). It is called "rough" because its surface is studded with little bumps. These bumps are ribosomes, the cell's protein-making machines, and generally cells with high rates of protein production have large numbers of ribosomes We cover the details of ribosome structure and protein production in Chapter 5.

The primary function of the rough ER is to fold and package proteins that will be shipped elsewhere in the organism. Poisonous frogs, for example, package their poison in rough ER of the cells where it is produced before transporting it to the poison glands on their skin. Proteins that are used within the cell itself are generally produced on free-floating ribosomes in the cytoplasm.

Smooth Endoplasmic Reticulum As its name advertises, the **smooth endoplasmic reticulum** is part of the endomembrane network that is smooth because there are no ribosomes bound to it (**FIGURE 3-33**). Although it is connected to the rough ER, it is farther from the nucleus and, besides lacking ribosomes, differs slightly in appearance. Whereas the rough ER looks like stacks of pancakes, the smooth ER sometimes looks like a collection of branched tubes.

The smooth surface gives us the first hint that smooth ER has a different job than rough ER. Because ribosomes are absolutely essential for protein production, we can be certain that, without them, the smooth ER is not involved in folding or packaging proteins. It isn't. Instead, it synthesizes lipids such as fatty acids, phospholipids, and steroids. Exactly which lipids are produced varies throughout the organism and across plant and animal species. Inside the smooth ER of mammalian ovaries and testes, for example, the hormones estrogen and testosterone are produced. Inside the smooth ER of liver and fat cells, lipids are produced. As in the rough ER, following their production these lipids are packaged in transport vesicles and are then sent to other parts of the cell or to the plasma membrane for export.

Another critical responsibility of the smooth ER—particularly the smooth ER in human liver cells—is to help protect us from the many dangerous molecules that get into our bodies. Alcohol, antibiotics, barbiturates, amphetamines or other

The Cell   Cell Membranes   Crossing the Membrane   Cell Connections

SMOOTH ENDOPLASMIC RETICULUM

FUNCTIONS
- Synthesizes lipids such as fatty acids, phospholipids, and steroids
- Detoxifies molecules such as alcohol, drugs, and metabolic waste products

Smooth ER is called "smooth" because it has no ribosomes on its surface.

TEM 7,700×

Liver cells are packed with huge amounts of smooth ER, because the liver is the primary site for detoxifying harmful molecules.

FIGURE 3-33 In the smooth endoplasmic reticulum, lipids are synthesized and alcohol, antibiotics, and other drugs are detoxified.

stimulants that we may consume, along with many toxic metabolic waste products formed in our bodies, are made less harmful by the detoxifying enzymes in the smooth ER. And just as a body builder's muscles get bigger and bigger in response to weightlifting, our smooth ER proliferates in cells that are exposed to large amounts of particular drugs. This proliferation can be beneficial because it increases the capacity for detoxification. But as the cells become more and more efficient at detoxification, our tolerances to the very drugs the smooth ER is trying to destroy can increase.

As we see over and over in living organisms, form follows function. Not surprisingly, then, just as cells with high rates of protein production have large numbers of ribosomes, we find huge amounts of smooth ER in liver cells because they are the primary sites of molecular detoxification. Other cells that are packed with ER (both rough and smooth) include plasma cells in the blood that produce immune system proteins for export, and pancreas cells that secrete large amounts of digestive enzymes. On the other hand, there is relatively little smooth ER in cells such as fat-storage cells, which produce little or no protein for export.

Q How can long-term use of one drug increase your resistance to another, different drug that you have never encountered?

Chronic exposure to many drugs (from antibiotics to heroin) can induce a proliferation of smooth ER, particularly in the liver, and the smooth ER's associated detoxification enzymes. This proliferation in turn increases tolerance to the drugs, necessitating higher doses to achieve the same effect. Moreover, the increased detoxification capacity of the cells often enables them to better detoxify other compounds, even if the person has never been exposed to these chemicals. This increased detoxification capacity can lead to problems. An individual who has been exposed to large amounts of certain drugs, for example, may end up responding less well to antibiotics.

TAKE-HOME MESSAGE 3·17

The production and modification of biological molecules in eukaryotic cells occurs in a system of organelles called the endomembrane system, which includes, among other organelles, the rough and smooth endoplasmic reticulum. In rough ER, proteins that will be shipped elsewhere in the body are folded and packaged. In the smooth ER, lipids are synthesized and alcohol, antibiotics, and other drugs are detoxified.

Nine Cell Landmarks

The Golgi apparatus is the site where the cell processes products for delivery throughout the body.

Moving farther outward from the nucleus, we encounter another organelle within the endomembrane system: the Golgi (GOHL-jee) apparatus (**FIGURE 3-34**). The **Golgi apparatus** processes molecules synthesized in the cell— primarily proteins and lipids—and packages those that are destined for use elsewhere in the body. The Golgi apparatus is also a site of carbohydrate synthesis, including the complex polysaccharides found in many plasma membranes. The Golgi apparatus, which is not connected to the endoplasmic reticulum, is a flattened stack of membranes (each of which is called a Golgi body) that are *not* interconnected.

After transport vesicles bud from the endoplasmic reticulum, they move through the cytoplasm until they reach the Golgi apparatus. Here, the vesicles fuse with the Golgi apparatus membrane and dump their contents into a Golgi body. There are about four successive Golgi body chambers to be visited, and the molecules get passed from one to the next. In each Golgi body, enzymes make slight modifications to the molecule (such as the addition or removal of phosphate groups or sugars). The processing that occurs in the Golgi

apparatus often involves tagging molecules (much like adding a postal address or tracking number) to direct them to some other part of the organism. After they are processed, the molecules bud off from the Golgi apparatus in a vesicle, which then moves into the cytoplasm. If the molecules are destined for delivery and use elsewhere in the body, the transport vesicle eventually fuses with the cell's plasma membrane and dumps the molecules into the bloodstream via exocytosis.

FIGURE 3-35 shows how the various parts of the endomembrane system work to produce, modify, and package molecules within a cell.

TAKE-HOME MESSAGE 3•18

The Golgi apparatus—another organelle within the endomembrane system—processes molecules synthesized in a cell and packages those that are destined for use elsewhere in the body.

GOLGI APPARATUS

FUNCTION
• Processes and packages proteins, lipids, and other molecules for export to other parts of the organism

Transport vesicles

TEM 62,500×

FIGURE 3-34 Golgi apparatus: processing of molecules synthesized in the cell and packaging of those molecules destined for use elsewhere in the body.

The Cell   Cell Membranes   Crossing the Membrane   Cell Connections

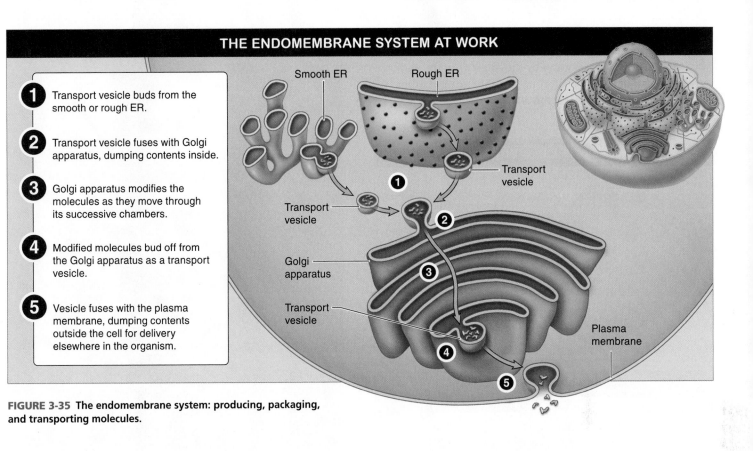

THE ENDOMEMBRANE SYSTEM AT WORK

Smooth ER　　　　Rough ER

1 Transport vesicle buds from the smooth or rough ER.

2 Transport vesicle fuses with Golgi apparatus, dumping contents inside.

3 Golgi apparatus modifies the molecules as they move through its successive chambers.

4 Modified molecules bud off from the Golgi apparatus as a transport vesicle.

5 Vesicle fuses with the plasma membrane, dumping contents outside the cell for delivery elsewhere in the organism.

Transport vesicle

Transport vesicle

Golgi apparatus

Transport vesicle

Plasma membrane

FIGURE 3-35 The endomembrane system: producing, packaging, and transporting molecules.

3·19

The cell wall provides additional protection and support for plant cells.

Up until now, we've discussed organelles and structures that are common to both plants and animals. Now we're going to look at several structures that are not found in all eukaryotic cells. Because plants are stuck in the ground, unable to move, they have several special needs beyond those of animals. In particular, they can't outrun or outmaneuver their competitors to get more food. Nor can they outrun organisms that want to eat them. If they want more sunshine, they have few options beyond simply growing larger or taller. And if they want to resist plant-eating animals, they must simply grow tougher outer layers.

One organelle that helps plants achieve both of these goals is the cell wall, a structure that surrounds the plasma membrane. The cell wall is made from polysaccharides in which another carbohydrate, called cellulose, is embedded. Note that although animal cells do not have cell walls, some non-plants

such as archaea, bacteria, protists, and fungi also have cell walls, but the chemical composition of their cell walls differs from that found in plants.

In plants, cell wall production can be a multistage process. Initially, when the cell is still growing, a primary cell wall is laid down, along with some glue that helps adjacent cells adhere to each other. Sometime later in life, a secondary cell wall is laid down. This secondary cell wall usually contains a complex molecule called lignin, which gives the wall much of its strength and rigidity. Oddly, this strength remains even after the plant cell dies—hence wood's great value to humans as a construction material, among other things.

The cell wall is nearly 100 times thicker than the plasma membrane, and the tremendous structural strength it confers on plant cells enables some plants to grow several hundred feet tall. Cell walls also help to make plants more water-tight—an important feature in organisms that cannot reduce water loss through evaporation by moving out of the hot sun—and provide some protection from insects and other animals that might eat them (**FIGURE 3-36**).

PLANT CELL WALL

FUNCTIONS
- Provides the cell with structural strength
- Gives the cell increased water resistance
- Provides some protection from insects and other animals that might eat plant parts

Plasmodesmata allow water and other molecules to pass between adjacent cells.

Cell 1
Cell 2
Cell 3

Primary cell wall | Secondary cell wall | Plasmodesma | Plasma membrane

TEM 440x

FIGURE 3-36 The plant cell wall: providing strength.

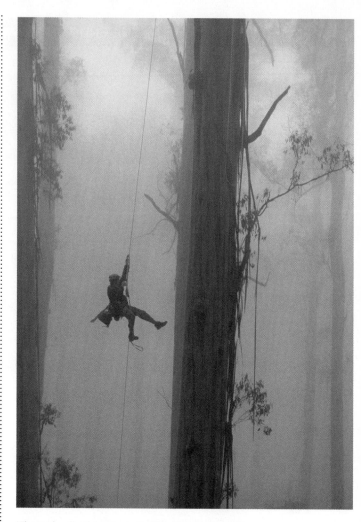

The rigid walls of the plant cell allow plants to grow tall.

Surprisingly, despite its great strength, the cell wall does not completely seal off plant cells from one another. Rather, it is porous, allowing water and solutes to reach the plasma membrane. It also has plasmodesmata, the channels connecting adjacent cells (as described in Section 3-12) and allowing the passage of some molecules between them.

TAKE-HOME MESSAGE 3·19

The cell wall is an organelle found in plants (and in some other non-animal organisms). It is made primarily from the carbohydrate cellulose and it surrounds the plasma membrane of the cell. The cell wall confers tremendous structural strength on plant cells, gives plants increased resistance to water loss, and provides some protection from insects and other animals that might eat them.

The Cell | Cell Membranes | Crossing the Membrane | Cell Connections

Vacuoles are multipurpose storage sacs for cells.

VACUOLE

FUNCTIONS
• Stores nutrients
• Retains and degrades waste products
• Accumulates poisonous materials
• Contains pigments, enabling plants to attract birds and insects that help the plant reproduce
• Provides physical support

— Vacuole

TEM 5,000×

FIGURE 3-37 The vacuole: multipurpose storage.

If you look at a mature plant cell through a microscope, one organelle, the **central vacuole,** usually stands out more than all the others because it is so huge and appears empty (**FIGURE 3-37**). Although it may look like an empty sac, the central vacuole is anything but. Surrounded by a membrane, filled with fluid, and occupying from 50% to 90% of a plant cell's interior space, the central vacuole can play an important role in five different areas of plant life. (Vacuoles are also found in some other eukaryotes, including some protists, fungi, and animals, but they tend to be particularly prominent in plant cells.)

1. **Nutrient storage**—the vacuole stores hundreds of dissolved substances, including amino acids, sugars, and ions.

2. **Waste management**—the vacuole retains waste products and degrades them with digestive enzymes, much like the lysosome in animal cells.

3. **Predator deterrence**—the poisonous, nasty-tasting materials that accumulate inside the vacuoles of some plants make a powerful deterrent to animals that might try to eat parts of the plant.

4. **Sexual reproduction**—the vacuole may contain pigments that give some flowers their red, blue, purple, or other colors, enabling them to attract birds and insects that help the plant reproduce by transferring pollen.

5. **Physical support**—high concentrations of dissolved substances in the vacuole can cause water to rush into the cells through the process of osmosis. The increased fluid pressure inside the vacuole can cause the cell to enlarge a bit and push out the cell wall. This process is responsible for the pressure (called **turgor pressure**) that allows stems, flowers, and other plant parts to stand upright. The ability of non-woody plants to stand upright is due primarily to turgor pressure. Wilting is the result of a loss of turgor pressure.

TAKE-HOME MESSAGE 3·20

In plants, vacuoles can occupy most of the interior space of the cell. Vacuoles are also present in some other eukaryotic species. They function as storage spaces and play a role in nutrition, waste management, predator deterrence, reproduction, and physical support.

3·21

Chloroplasts are the plant cell's power plant.

It would be hard to choose the "most important organelle" in a cell, but if we had to, the chloroplast would be a top contender. The chloroplast, an organelle found in all plants and eukaryotic algae, is the site of photosynthesis—the conversion of light energy into the chemical energy of food molecules, with oxygen as a by-product. Because all photosynthesis in plants and algae takes place in chloroplasts, these organelles are directly or indirectly responsible for everything we eat and for the oxygen we breathe. Life on

Life on earth would be vastly different without the chloroplasts found in photosynthetic plants.

earth would be vastly different without the chloroplast (**FIGURE 3-38**).

In a green leaf, each cell has about 40–50 chloroplasts. This means there are about 500,000 chloroplasts per square millimeter of leaf surface (that's more than 200 million chloroplasts in an area the size of a small postage stamp). Chloroplasts are oval, somewhat flattened objects. On the outside, the chloroplast is encircled by two distinct layers of membranes (similar to the structure of mitochondria). The fluid in the inside compartment, called the **stroma,** contains some DNA and much protein-making machinery.

With a simple light microscope, it is possible to see little spots of green within the chloroplasts. Up close, these spots look like stacks of pancakes. Each stack consists of numerous, interconnected little flattened sacs called **thylakoids,** and it is on the membranes of the thylakoids that the light-collecting for photosynthesis occurs. (In Chapter 4, we discuss the details

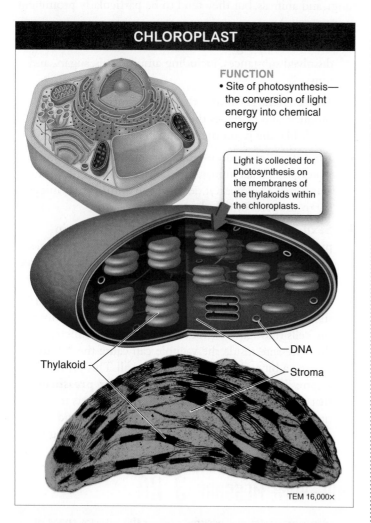

CHLOROPLAST

FUNCTION
• Site of photosynthesis—the conversion of light energy into chemical energy

Light is collected for photosynthesis on the membranes of the thylakoids within the chloroplasts.

DNA

Thylakoid

Stroma

TEM 16,000×

FIGURE 3-38 The chloroplast: location of photosynthesis.

The Cell   Cell Membranes   Crossing the Membrane   Cell Connections

ORGANELLE REVIEW

STRUCTURE	ANIMALS	PLANTS	FUNCTION
Nucleus	Yes	Yes	Directs cellular activity and stores hereditary information
Cytoskeleton	Yes	Yes	Provides structural shape and support and enables cellular movement
Mitochondrion	Yes	Yes	Harvests energy for cellular functions
Lysosomes	Yes	Yes	Digests and recycles cellular waste products and consumed material
Rough ER	Yes	Yes	Modifies proteins that will be shipped elsewhere in the organism
Smooth ER	Yes	Yes	Synthesizes lipids and detoxifies molecules
Golgi apparatus	Yes	Yes	Processes and packages proteins, lipids, and other molecules
Cell wall	No	Yes	Provides structural strength, protection, and increased resistance to water loss
Vacuole	Sometimes	Yes	Stores nutrients, degrades waste products, provides pigments and structural support
Chloroplast	No	Yes	Performs photosynthesis

Nine Cell Landmarks

of how chloroplasts convert the energy in sunlight into the chemical energy stored in sugar molecules.)

A peculiar feature of chloroplasts, mentioned in Section 3-3, is that they resemble photosynthetic bacteria, particularly with their circular DNA (which contains many of the genes essential for photosynthesis). Also, the dual outer membrane of the chloroplast is consistent with the idea that, long ago, a cell engulfed a photosynthetic bacterium, enveloping it with its plasma membrane in endocytosis. These features have given rise to the belief that chloroplasts might have originally been bacteria that were engulfed by a predatory cell. According to the endosymbiosis theory (see Section 3-3), the bacteria remained alive and, rather than becoming a meal, became the cell's meal ticket, providing food for the cell in exchange for protection.

FIGURE 3-39 summarizes all of the parts of a cell, in animals and plants, and their functions.

TAKE-HOME MESSAGE 3·21

The chloroplast is the organelle in plants and algae that is the site of photosynthesis—the conversion of light energy into chemical energy, with oxygen as a by-product. Chloroplasts may have originally been bacteria that were engulfed by a predatory cell by endosymbiosis.

FIGURE 3-39 Review of the structures and functions of cellular organelles.

Knowledge You Can Use

Did you know? Drinking too much water can be dangerous!

People have long understood the risks of becoming dehydrated, particularly during activities such as marathon running in which a great deal of fluid can be lost through sweating. Only recently, however, has it been recognized that too much water—called "water intoxication"—can also be dangerous. In 2007, a 28-year-old woman competing in a water-drinking contest died just a few hours after consuming about two gallons of water without urinating. Similarly, the death of a runner during the 2002 Boston marathon was attributed to water intoxication.

Q: When people sweat, what do they lose? Sweat consists of water and some dissolved solids, primarily salt. As the sweat evaporates, the body is cooled.

Q: How do people respond to nausea and dizziness, the warning signs of dehydration? By drinking water. Because the water they drink lacks salt and other solutes, this can lead to sodium imbalances in the body, particularly in the bloodstream and the fluid around cells (extracellular fluid).

Q: What is osmosis? Osmosis is the diffusion of water across a membrane toward areas where there is a greater concentration of solutes and, consequently, a lower concentration of water molecules.

Q: If you drink lots of water (two gallons or more)—which has few or no solutes—where is it going to move once it gets into your bloodstream and extracellular fluid? It moves by osmosis into your cells, where there is a higher concentration of solutes (primarily sodium) and a lower concentration of water molecules.

Q: What happens to your cells if they absorb too much water? They swell, sometimes to the point of rupturing. Such swelling and rupturing in the enclosed brain cavity can cause vomiting and confusion. Disastrously, these symptoms are often mistaken for the symptoms of dehydration and so the consumption of water is recommended, making the situation worse. Further swelling can lead to seizures, coma, and even death. (The reverse situation occurs when people drink too much seawater. Their bloodstream and extracellular fluid gain in solutes, particularly salt, so water flows out of cells by osmosis. Cell dehydration and death can occur—usually from a shrinkage of brain cells.)

What should you do? Many marathon organizers have been reducing the number of water stops they offer runners during the race and testing symptomatic runners' sodium levels in medical tents along the course. Consuming salt tablets and salty snacks helps keep blood sodium levels in a healthy range. Also, when possible, runners should weigh themselves during a race to make sure they are only replacing the fluid they have lost through sweating and are not gaining weight.

① What is a cell?

The most basic unit of any organism is the cell, the smallest unit of life that can function independently and perform all of the necessary activities of life, including reproducing itself. All living organisms are made up of one or more cells, and all cells arise from other, pre-existing cells. Every cell on earth is either a eukaryote or a prokaryote. Prokaryotes, which have no nucleus and are single-celled, were the first cells on earth. Eukaryotes are single-celled or multicellular organisms whose cells have a nucleus that contains linear strands of genetic material.

② Cell membranes are gatekeepers.

Every cell of every living organism is enclosed by a plasma membrane, a two-layered membrane that holds the contents of a cell in place and regulates what enters and leaves the cell. The plasma membrane is a fluid mosaic of proteins, lipids, and carbohydrates. Every cell in your body has a "fingerprint" made from a variety of molecules on the outside-facing surface of the cell membrane that is key to the functioning of your immune system.

③ Molecules move across membranes in several ways.

Cells must acquire food molecules and other necessary materials from outside the cell. Similarly, metabolic waste molecules and molecules produced for use elsewhere must move out of the cell. In passive transport the molecular movement occurs spontaneously, without the input of energy. The diffusion of water across a membrane is a special type of passive transport called osmosis. Active transport is necessary if the molecules to be moved are very large or if they are being moved against their concentration gradient. It relies on proteins embedded in the plasma membrane which act like motorized revolving doors. Cells can also engulf particles with their plasma membrane in a process called endocytosis. Similarly, molecules can be moved out of a cell via exocytosis.

④ Cells are connected and communicate with each other.

In multicellular organisms, most cells are connected to other cells. The connections can form a water-tight seal between the cells (tight junctions), can hold sheets of cells together while allowing fluid to pass between the cells (desmosomes), or can function like secret passageways between cells (gap junctions). In plants, plasmodesmata connect cells and enable communication and transport between them.

⑤ Nine important landmarks distinguish eukaryotic cells.

Eukaryotic cells contain many distinct structures, each of which performs a specific life-sustaining function. The nucleus directs all protein production and is also the storehouse for all hereditary information. The cytoskeleton gives animal cells shape and support. In mitochondria, energy from macromolecules is converted into usable energy in the form of ATP. Lysosomes are like garbage disposals for dismantling waste and bacterial pathogens. The production and modification of molecules, including drug detoxification, occurs in the rough and smooth endoplasmic reticulum, and the Golgi apparatus processes molecules synthesized in the cell and packages those destined for use elsewhere in the body. In plants, the cell wall confers structural strength, herbivore protection, and resistance to water loss. Vacuoles function as storage spaces, and chloroplasts are the site of photosynthesis, the conversion of light energy into food molecules.

KEY TERMS

active transport, p. 96
cell, p. 78
cell theory, p. 79
cell wall, p. 80
chloroplast, p. 83
cholesterol, p. 88
chromatin, p. 103
cilium (pl. cilia), p. 105
contact inhibition, p. 102
cytoplasm, p. 80
cytoskeleton, p. 105
desmosome, p. 101
diffusion, p. 93
endocytosis, p. 98
endomembrane system, p. 109
endosymbiosis theory, p. 82

enzymatic proteins, p. 88
eukaryote, p. 80
eukaryotic cell, p. 80
exocytosis, p. 98
facilitated diffusion, p. 94
flagellum (pl. flagella), pp. 81, 106
fluid mosaic, p. 89
gap junction, p. 101
glycerol, p. 85
Golgi apparatus, p. 112
hydrophilic, p. 86
hydrophobic, p. 86
hypertonic, p. 95
hypotonic, p. 95
intermembrane space, p. 107
invagination, p. 84

isotonic, p. 95
lysosome, p. 108
matrix, p. 107
mitochondrion (pl. mitochondria), pp. 83. 106
non-polar, p. 86
nuclear membrane, p. 103
nucleolus, p. 104
nucleus, p. 82
organelle, p. 82
osmosis, p. 95
passive transport, p. 93
phagocytosis, p. 98
phospholipid, p. 85
phospholipid bilayer, p. 87
pilus (pl. pili), p. 81
pinocytosis, p. 98

plasma membrane, p. 80
plasmodesma (pl. plasmodesmata), p. 102
polar, p. 85
primary active transport, p. 97
prokaryote, p. 80
prokaryotic cell, p. 80
receptor protein, p. 88
receptor-mediated endocytosis, p. 98
recognition protein, p. 88
ribosome, p. 80
rough endoplasmic reticulum, p. 110
secondary active transport, p. 97

simple diffusion, p. 94
smooth endoplasmic reticulum, p. 110
solute, p. 93
solvent, p. 93
stroma, p. 116
surface protein, p. 87
thylakoid, p. 116
tight junction, p. 101
tonicity, p. 95
transmembrane protein, p. 87
transport protein, p. 88
turgor pressure, p. 115
vacuole (central), p. 115
vesicle, p. 98

1. Which of the following statements about the cell theory is correct?
   a) All living organisms are made up of one or more cells.
   b) All cells arise from other, pre-existing cells
   c) All eukaryotic cells contain symbiotic prokaryotes.
   d) All prokaryotic cells contain symbiotic eukaryotes.
   e) Both a) and b) are correct.

2. Which of the following statements about prokaryotes is incorrect?
   a) Prokaryotes appeared on earth before eukaryotes.
   b) Prokaryotes have circular pieces of DNA within their nuclei.
   c) Prokaryotes contain cytoplasm.
   d) Prokaryotes contain ribosomes.
   e) Some prokaryotes can conduct photosynthesis.

3. Which of the following facts supports the claim that mitochondria developed from bacteria that, long ago, were incorporated into eukaryotic cells by the process of phagocytosis?
   a) Mitochondria have flagella for motion.
   b) Mitochondria have proteins for the synthesis of ATP.
   c) Mitochondria are the "powerhouses" of the cell.
   d) Mitochondria are small and easily transported across cell membranes.
   e) Mitochondria have their own DNA.

4. Hydrophobic molecules can pass freely through the plasma membrane, but molecules with electrical charges (such as ions and polar molecules) are impeded by the hydrophobic core. For this reason, plasma membranes can be considered:
   a) partially permeable.
   b) impermeable.
   c) hydrophobic.
   d) hydrophilic.
   e) None of these terms properly describe plasma membranes.

5. Drugs called beta-blockers do all of the following except:
   a) reduce high blood pressure.
   b) block signaling through adrenaline receptors.
   c) reduce outward symptoms of anxiety.
   d) bind to the cytoplasmic side of a receptor protein.
   e) reduce the effects of adrenaline on the heart.

6. Cellular "fingerprints":
   a) are exposed on the cytoplasmic side of the membrane.
   b) are made from cholesterol.
   c) are "erased" by the HIV virus.
   d) can help the immune system distinguish "self" from "non-self."
   e) All of the above are correct.

7. The movement of molecules across a membrane from an area of high concentration to one of low concentration is best described as:
   a) active transport.
   b) inactivated transport.
   c) passive transport.
   d) channel-mediated diffusion.
   e) electron transport.

8. The transport of water across a membrane from a solution of lower solute concentration to a solution of higher solute concentration is best describe as:
   a) osmosis.
   b) facilitated diffusion.
   c) receptor-mediated transport.
   d) active transport.
   e) general diffusion.

9. In an experiment, you measure the concentration of a polar molecule inside and outside a cell. You find that the concentration is high and gradually increasing inside the cell. You also measure the ATP concentration inside the cell and find that it is dropping. What is your best hypothesis for the process you are observing?
   a) facilitated diffusion
   b) passive transport
   c) simple diffusion
   d) active transport
   e) endocytosis

10. Which of the following allows the passage of small molecules between animal cells?
   a) nucleoli
   b) tight junctions
   c) desmosomes
   d) gap junctions
   e) black holes

11. The largest structure in a eukaryotic cell is the _____ and it is surrounded by _____ membrane(s).
   a) nucleus; one
   b) nucleus; two
   c) Golgi apparatus; one
   d) mitochondrion; two
   e) mitochondrion; one

12. The cytoskeleton:
   a) is a viscous fluid found in all cells.
   b) fills a cell's nucleus but not the other organelles.
   c) gives an animal cell shape and support, but cannot control movement.
   d) helps to coordinate intracellular movement of organelles and molecules.
   e) All of the above are correct.

13. Which of the following statements about mitochondria is correct?
    a) Mitochondria are found in both eukaryotes and prokaryotes.
    b) There tend to be more mitochondria in fat cells than in liver cells.
    c) Most plant cells contain mitochondria.
    d) Mitochondria may have originated evolutionarily as photosynthetic bacteria.
    e) All of the above are correct.

14. Which of the following organelles is not present in animal cells?
    a) lysosome
    b) Golgi apparatus
    c) rough endoplasmic reticulum
    d) mitochondrion
    e) chloroplast

15. Given that a cell's structure reflects its function, what function would you predict for a cell with a large Golgi apparatus?
    a) movement
    b) secretion of digestive enzymes
    c) transport of chemical signals
    d) rapid replication of genetic material and coordination of cell division
    e) attachment to bone tissue.

16. Cell walls:
    a) only occur in plant cells.
    b) are not completely solid, having many small pores.
    c) confer less structural support than the plasma membrane.
    d) dissolve when a plant dies.
    e) are made primarily from phospholipids.

17. Which one of the following organelles is not found in both plant and animal cells?
    a) nucleus
    b) rough endoplasmic reticulum
    c) mitochondrion
    d) smooth endoplasmic reticulum
    e) central vacuole

18. In plant cells, chloroplasts:
    a) serve the same purpose that mitochondria serve in animal cells.
    b) are the site of conversion of light energy into chemical energy.
    c) play an important role in the breakdown of plant toxins.
    d) have their own linear strands of DNA.
    e) Both a) and b) are correct..

SHORT-ANSWER QUESTION

1. Name and note the function of the organelles shown in the diagram.

See Appendix for answers. For additional study questions, go to www.prep-u.com.

ORGANELLE:
FUNCTION:

4

Energy

From the sun to you
in just two steps

① Energy flows from the sun and through all life on earth.

Sunlight filters through the northern California redwoods.

4•1

Cars that run on french fry oil? Organisms and machines need energy to work.

Imagine that you are on a long road trip. The fuel gauge of your car is nearing empty, so you pull off the highway. Instead of driving into a gas station, however, you head to a fast-food restaurant. You drive around to the back where the restaurant stores used cooking materials and fill your car's fuel tank with recycled cooking grease. You head back to the highway, ready to drive several hundred miles before needing another pit stop.

Q Humans can get energy from food. Can machines?

Fast food for your car? Yes! The idea isn't as far-fetched as it sounds. In fact, on the roads of America today many vehicles run on **biofuels,** fuels produced from plant and animal products (**FIGURE 4-1**). Most vehicles, however, run on **fossil fuels** such as gasoline. These fuels (which also include oil, natural gas, and coal) are produced from the decayed remains of ancient plants and animals modified over the course of millions of years by heat, pressure, and bacterial processes.

It turns out that biofuels, fossil fuels, and the food fuels that supply energy to most living organisms are chemically similar. This fact is not surprising because energy from the sun is the source of the energy stored in the chemical bonds between the atoms in all these fuels. Let's investigate how fuels provide energy.

When we burn gasoline, long chains of carbon and hydrogen atoms separate, releasing carbon dioxide (CO_2), water, and a lot of energy that was stored in the chemical bonds holding each gasoline molecule together. (An interesting fact: the energy released in burning one gallon of gas is equivalent to the caloric content of 15 large cheese pizzas.) In an automobile engine, some of this released energy is harnessed to push pistons, spin a crankshaft, turn wheels, and move the car.

Animal fats and the oils in many plants—such as those used to cook french fries—share an important chemical feature with

The Nature of Energy　　　Photosynthesis　　　Cellular Respiration　　　Alternative Pathways

FIGURE 4-1 Biofuel technology. Biofuels are chemically similar to fossil fuels.

gasoline. Like gasoline, these fats and oils contain chains of carbon and hydrogen atoms bound together, and just as with gasoline, breaking these bonds releases large amounts of energy (and water and CO_2). If this released energy can be captured efficiently, it, too, can be used to push pistons and turn car wheels.

Cars that run on biofuels are more than just a technological trick. The production of biofuels requires only the plant or animal source, sunlight, air, water, and a relatively short amount of time—a few months or years, depending on the source. On the other hand, the production of fossil fuels such as coal or crude oil requires plant and animal remains and millions of years. This difference gives biofuels an important advantage over fossil fuels: they are a renewable resource. For this reason, they point the way toward a future of reduced dependence on fossil fuels, the supplies of which are dwindling and the combustion of which has many harmful consequences, such as increasing global warming and the release of cancer-causing particles into the atmosphere. Are we at the point yet where all our cars can run on biofuels? Not quite: there are several significant drawbacks to the increased use of biofuels, chief among them the destruction of forests, wetlands, and other ecologically important habitats from the increased use of land to grow these fuels. This is why the search for better fuels continues.

In this chapter we explore how plant, animal, and other living "machines" run on energy stored in chemical bonds. Just as the forward motion of a car is fueled by breaking the chemical bonds in gasoline and harnessing the released energy, the activities of living organisms are fueled by breaking the chemical bonds in food molecules and harnessing the released energy.

All life depends on capturing energy from the sun and converting it into a form that living organisms can use. This

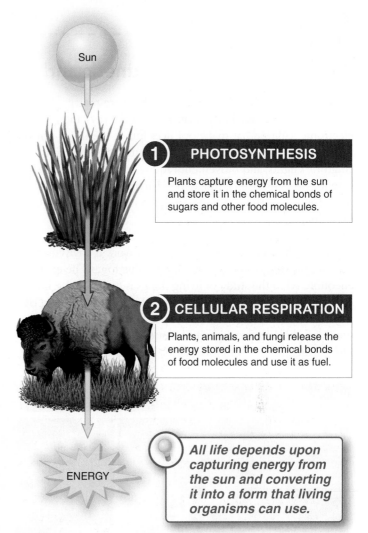

1 PHOTOSYNTHESIS

Plants capture energy from the sun and store it in the chemical bonds of sugars and other food molecules.

2 CELLULAR RESPIRATION

Plants, animals, and fungi release the energy stored in the chemical bonds of food molecules and use it as fuel.

ENERGY

All life depends upon capturing energy from the sun and converting it into a form that living organisms can use.

FIGURE 4-2 Photosynthesis and cellular respiration.

energy capture and conversion occurs in two important processes that mirror each other: (1) **photosynthesis,** the process by which plants capture energy from the sun and store it in the chemical bonds of sugars and other food molecules they make, and (2) **cellular respiration,** the process by which all living organisms release the energy stored in the chemical bonds of food molecules and use it to fuel their lives (**FIGURE 4-2**). The sun to you in just two steps!

TAKE-HOME MESSAGE 4·1

The sun is the source of the energy that powers all living organisms and other "machines." The energy from sunlight is stored in the chemical bonds of molecules. When these bonds are broken, energy is released regardless of whether the bond is in a molecule of food, a fossil fuel, or a biofuel like the oil in which french fries are cooked.

4·2 ------------------------------

Energy has two forms: kinetic and potential.

"Batteries not included." For a child, those are pretty depressing words. We know that many of the toys and electronic gadgets that make our lives fun or useful (or both) need energy—usually in the form of batteries. Generating ringtones, lights, and movement requires energy. The same is true for humans, plants, and all other living organisms: they need energy for their activities, from thinking to moving to reproducing.

Energy is the capacity to do work. And work is anything that involves moving matter against an opposing force. The energy encountered in the study of living things is of two types: kinetic energy and potential energy. **Kinetic energy** is the energy of moving objects. Legs pushing bike pedals and the flapping wings of a bird are examples of kinetic energy (**FIGURE 4-3**). Heat, which results from lots of molecules moving rapidly, is

another form of kinetic energy. Because it comes from the movement of high-energy particles, light is also a form of kinetic energy—probably the most important form of kinetic energy on earth. (We explore the nature of sunlight and how it is harnessed for the work of producing food molecules when we look at photosynthesis later in this chapter.)

An object does not have to be moving to have the capacity to do work; it may have **potential energy,** which is stored energy or the capacity to do work that results from an object's location or position. Water behind a dam, for example, has potential energy. If a hole in the dam is opened, the water can flow through, and perhaps spin a water wheel or turbine. A concentration gradient, which we discussed in Chapter 3, also has potential energy: if the molecules in an area of high concentration move toward an area of lower concentration,

FIGURE 4-3 Kinetic and potential energy. Kinetic energy is the energy of motion; potential energy is energy stored in an object, such as water trapped behind a dam.

The Nature of Energy   Photosynthesis   Cellular Respiration   Alternative Pathways

the potential energy of the gradient is converted to the kinetic energy of molecular movement, and this kinetic energy can do work. And **chemical energy,** the storage of energy in chemical bonds, is also a type of potential energy.

Because potential energy doesn't involve movement, it is a less obvious form of energy than kinetic energy. An apple has potential energy, as does any other type of food (**FIGURE 4-4**). Why? Because the chemical energy stored in the chemical bonds making up the food can be broken and the energy released during cellular respiration, enabling you to run, play, and work. We explore cellular respiration, the energy-releasing breakdown of molecules, later in this chapter. But first we need to know more about the nature of energy.

TAKE-HOME MESSAGE 4·2

Energy, the capacity to do work, comes in two forms. Kinetic energy is the energy of moving objects, while potential energy, such as chemical energy, is stored energy or the capacity to do work that results from the position or location of an object.

Food is a form of chemical energy!

Glucose $C_6H_{12}O_6$

CHEMICAL ENERGY

A form of potential energy stored in chemical bonds

ENERGY

FIGURE 4-4 **Chemical energy.** The chemical bonds in food molecules are a form of potential energy.

4·3

As energy is captured and converted, the amount of energy available to do work decreases.

Every minute of every day—even on cloudy ones—the sun shines brightly, releasing tremendous amounts of energy. Organisms on earth cannot capture every single bit of energy released by the sun; indeed, most plants capture only about 1% of the available energy. What happens to the other 99%? This unused energy does not simply disappear. Accountants would

love to monitor the flow of energy because, as in a good accounting ledger, all of the energy numbers add up perfectly. All energy from the sun can be accounted for: some (probably less than 1%) is captured and transformed into usable chemical energy by organisms through photosynthesis (**FIGURE 4-5**). The rest of the energy from the sun is reflected back into

Energy lost in the form of HEAT

Light energy from the sun

Chemical energy stored in plants

Energy lost in the form of HEAT

Kinetic energy of forward motion

Energy lost in the form of HEAT

Kinetic energy of forward motion

FIGURE 4-5 **Energy efficiency and heat loss.** As energy is converted to do work, some energy is released as heat.

space (probably about 30%) or absorbed by land, the oceans, and the atmosphere (about 70%), and mostly transformed into heat. Heat is not easily harnessed to do work, however, and is therefore a much less useful form of energy than the energy transformed into chemical energy in plants. The same accounting also exists on a smaller level. If you eat a bowl of rice, some portion of the chemical energy stored in the bonds of the molecules that make up the rice grains is transformed into usable energy that can fuel your cells' activities. All the rest is transformed into heat and is ultimately lost into the atmosphere.

The fact that energy can change form but never disappear is an important feature of energy in the universe, whether we are looking at the sun and the earth or a human and her rice bowl. Just as energy can never disappear or be destroyed, energy can never be created. All the energy now present in the universe has been there since the universe began, and everything that has happened since then has occurred by the transformation of one form of energy into another. In all our eating and growing, driving and sleeping, we are simply transforming energy. The study of the transformation of energy from one type to another, such as from potential energy to kinetic energy, is called **thermodynamics,** and the **first law of thermodynamics** states that energy can never be created or destroyed. It can only change from one form to another.

Because plants capture less than 1% of the sun's energy, it might seem like they are particularly inefficient. But we humans are also rather inefficient at extracting the chemical energy of plants when we eat them. These inefficiencies occur because every time energy is converted from one form to another some of the energy is always converted to heat. When a human converts the chemical energy in a plate of spaghetti into the kinetic energy of running a marathon or when a car transforms the chemical energy of gasoline into the kinetic energy of forward motion, in both cases some energy is converted to heat, the least usable form of kinetic energy. In automobiles, for example, about three-quarters of the energy in gasoline is lost as heat. Thus, for every $10 spent on gas, only about $2.50 goes toward moving the car!

The **second law of thermodynamics** states that every conversion of energy is not perfectly efficient and invariably includes the transformation of some energy into heat. Although heat is certainly a form of energy, because it is not easily harnessed to do work it is almost completely useless to living organisms for fueling their cellular activity. Put another way, the second law of thermodynamics tells us that although the quantity of energy in the universe is not changing, its quality is. Little by little, the amount of energy that is available to do work decreases. Now that we understand that organisms on earth cannot capture every single bit of energy released by the sun—and that energy conversions are inefficient—we can look at the chief energy currency of the cell: ATP.

TAKE-HOME MESSAGE 4·3

Energy is neither created nor destroyed but can change forms. Each conversion of energy is inefficient and some of the usable energy is converted to less useful heat energy.

4·4 -

ATP molecules are like free-floating rechargeable batteries in all living cells.

Much of the work that cells do requires energy. But even though light energy from the sun carries energy, as do molecules of sugar, fat, and protein, none of this energy can be used directly to fuel chemical reactions in organisms' cells. First it must be captured in the bonds of a molecule called **adenosine triphosphate (ATP),** a free-floating molecule found in cells that acts like a rechargeable battery that temporarily stores energy that can then be used for cellular work in plants, animals, bacteria, and all the other organisms on earth. The use of ATP solves an important timing and coordination problem for living cells: a supply of ATP guarantees that the energy required for energy-consuming reactions will be available when it's needed.

ATP is a simple molecule with three components (**FIGURE 4-6**). At the center of the ATP molecule are two of these components: a small sugar molecule attached to a molecule called adenine. But it is the third component that makes ATP so effective in carrying and storing energy for a short time: attached to the sugar and adenine is a chain of three negatively charged phosphate molecule groups (hence the "tri" in "triphosphate"). Because the bonds between these three phosphate groups must hold the groups together in the face of the three electrical charges that all repel one another, each of these bonds contains a large amount of energy and is stressed and unstable. The instability of these high-energy bonds makes the three phosphate groups like a tightly coiled

Adenine

Phosphate groups

Ribose (sugar)

High-energy bonds

P_i Separate phosphate group

ENERGY

ATP Symbol for ATP used in this book

The green halo represents ATP's potential energy.

Adenine

Phosphate groups

Ribose (sugar)

ADP Symbol for ADP used in this book

FIGURE 4-6 **The structure of ATP and ADP.** When ATP ejects one of its phosphate groups, energy is released as ATP becomes ADP.

spring or a twig that is bent almost to the point of breaking. With the slightest push, one of the phosphate groups will pop off, releasing a little burst of energy that the cell can use.

It is precisely because each molecule of ATP is always on the brink of ejecting one of its phosphate groups that ATP is such an effective energy source inside a cell. As long as plenty of ATP molecules are around, they can energize the chemical reactions that make it possible for the cell to carry out reactions that require work, such as building muscle tissue, repairing a wound, or growing roots. Each time a cell expends one of its ATP molecules to pay for an energetically expensive reaction, a phosphate is broken off and energy is released. What is left is a molecule with two phosphates, called ADP (adenosine *di*phosphate), and a separate phosphate group (labeled P_i).

An organism can then use ADP, a free-floating phosphate, and an input of kinetic energy to rebuild its ATP stocks

(**FIGURE 4-7**). The kinetic energy is converted to potential energy when the free phosphate group attaches to the ADP molecule and makes ATP. In this manner, ATP functions like a rechargeable battery. Where does the input of energy for recharging ATP come from? When we discuss photosynthesis, we'll see that plants, algae, and some bacteria directly use light energy from the sun to make ATP from ADP and free-floating phosphate groups. Animals use the energy contained in the bonds of their food molecules. In either case, the energy is used to re-create the unstable bond in the triphosphate chain. When energy is needed, the organism can again release it by breaking the bond holding the phosphate group to the rest of the molecule. Our bodies recycle ATP molecules in this way tens of thousands of times a day.

Here's the ATP story in a nutshell. Breaking down a molecule of sugar—in a glass of orange juice, for example—leads to a miniature burst of energy in your body. The energy from the mini-explosion is put to work building the unstable high-energy bonds that attach phosphate groups to ADP molecules, creating new molecules of ATP. Later—perhaps only a fraction of a second later—when an energy-consuming reaction is needed, your cells can release the energy stored in the new ATP molecules.

TAKE-HOME MESSAGE 4·4

Cells temporarily store energy in the bonds of ATP molecules. This potential energy can be converted to kinetic energy and used to fuel life-sustaining chemical reactions. At other times, inputs of kinetic energy are converted to the potential energy of the energy-rich but unstable bonds in the ATP molecule.

ATP

ENERGY

ENERGY

Energy released from the breakdown of food

Energy to do work

ADP + P_i

ATP can be used and recycled hundreds of thousands of times!

FIGURE 4-7 **ATP is like a rechargeable battery.**

❷ Photosynthesis uses energy from sunlight to make food.

Sunflowers capture light energy and convert it to organic matter (including tasty seed

4·5

Where does plant matter come from? Photosynthesis: the big picture.

Watching a plant grow over the course of a few years can seem like watching a miracle, or at least a very subtle magic trick. Of course it's neither, but the process is nonetheless amazing. Consider that in five years a tree in a big planter can increase its weight by 150 pounds (68 kg) as it grows (**FIGURE 4-8**). Where does that 68 kg of new tree come from?

Our first guess might be the soil. Could that be it? It's easy enough to weigh the soil in the pot when first planting the tree and again 5 years later. After 5 years, though, we find that the soil in our planter has lost less than a pound, nowhere near enough to explain the massive increase in the amount of plant material. Perhaps the new growth comes from the water? Wrong again. Although the older and much larger tree holds more water in its many cells, the water provided to the plant does not come close to accounting for the increase in the dry weight of the plant.

FIGURE 4-8 Where does a plant come from?

? *When plants grow, where does the new tissue come from? From water? From the dirt? From thin air?*

5 LB. → 5 years → 155 LB.

The Nature of Energy   Photosynthesis   Cellular Respiration   Alternative Pathways

When humans grow, the new tissue comes from food we eat. When plants grow, where does the new tissue come from?

The amazing truth is that most of the new material comes from an invisible gas in the air. In the process of photosynthesis, plants capture carbon dioxide gas (CO_2) from the air and, using energy they get from sunlight, along with water and small amounts of chemicals usually found in soil, they produce solid, visible (and often tasty) sugars and other organic matter that are used to make plant structures such as leaves, roots, stems, flowers, fruits, and seeds. In the process, the plants give off oxygen (O_2), a by-product that happens to make all animal life possible.

Although plants are the most visible organisms that have evolved the ability to capture light energy and convert it to organic matter, they are not the only organisms capable of photosynthesis. Some bacteria and many other unicellular organisms are also capable of using the energy in sunlight to produce organic materials (**FIGURE 4-9**).

There are three inputs to the process of photosynthesis (**FIGURE 4-10**): light energy (from the sun), carbon dioxide (from the atmosphere), and water (from the ground). From these three inputs, the plant produces sugar and oxygen. As we will see, photosynthesis is best understood as two separate events: a "photo" segment, during which light is captured, and a "synthesis" segment, during which sugar is synthesized.

FIGURE 4-10 Photosynthesis: the big picture.

In the "photo" reactions, light energy is captured and temporarily stored in energy-storage molecules. During this process, water molecules split and produce oxygen. In the "synthesis" reactions, the energy in the energy-storage molecules is used to build sugar molecules from carbon dioxide in the air.

FIGURE 4-9 Plants aren't the only photosynthesizers. Some bacteria and single-celled organisms are capable of photosynthesis.

Cyanobacterium (magnified 660×)

Euglena (magnified 125×)

Dinoflagellate (magnified 80×)

TAKE-HOME MESSAGE 4·5

Through photosynthesis, plants use water, the energy of sunlight, and carbon dioxide gas from the air to produce sugars and other organic materials. In the process, photosynthesizing organisms also produce oxygen, which makes all animal life possible.

Photosynthesis takes place in the chloroplasts.

The best way to know which parts of a plant are photosynthetic is simply to look for the green bits. Leaves are green because the cells near the surface are packed full of **chloroplasts,** light-harvesting organelles found in plant cells, which make it possible for the plant to use the energy from sunlight to make sugars (their food) and other plant tissue (much of which animals use for food) (**FIGURE 4-11**). Other plant parts, such as stems, may also contain chloroplasts (in which case they, too, are capable of photosynthesis), but most chloroplasts are located within the cells in a plant's leaves.

Let's take a closer look at chloroplasts (**FIGURE 4-12**). The sac-shaped organelle is filled with a fluid called the **stroma.** Floating in the stroma is an elaborate system of interconnected membranous structures called **thylakoids,** which often look like stacks of pancakes. Once inside the chloroplast, you can be in one of two places: in the stroma or inside the thylakoids. The conversion of light energy to

CHLOROPLAST

TEM 16,000×

Stroma

Thylakoid

Chlorophyll

THYLAKOID

Location of "photo" reaction, where light energy is converted into chemical energy.

STROMA

Location of "synthesis" reaction, where chemical energy is synthesized into sugar.

FIGURE 4-12 The chloroplast. The chloroplast is where photosynthesis takes place in a plant.

chemical energy—the "photo" part of photosynthesis—occurs inside the thylakoids. The production of sugars—which are made in the "synthesis" part of photosynthesis—occurs within the stroma.

We examine both the "photo" and the "synthesis" processes in greater detail later in this chapter. First, however, we examine the nature of light energy and of **chlorophyll,** the special molecule found in chloroplasts that makes the capture of light energy possible.

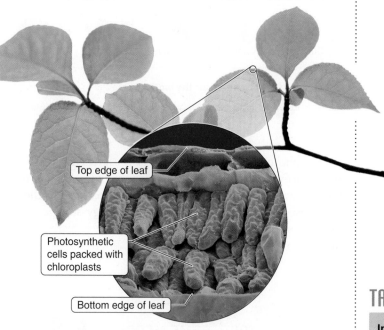

Top edge of leaf

Photosynthetic cells packed with chloroplasts

Bottom edge of leaf

FIGURE 4-11 Photosynthesis factories. Cells near the leaf's surface are packed with photosynthetic chloroplasts.

TAKE-HOME MESSAGE 4·6

In plants, photosynthesis occurs in chloroplasts, green organelles packed in cells near the plants' surfaces.

The Nature of Energy   Photosynthesis   Cellular Respiration   Alternative Pathways

4•7 ----------

Light energy travels in waves: plant pigments absorb specific wavelengths.

You can't eat sunlight. That's because sunlight is *light* energy rather than the *chemical* energy found in the bonds of food molecules. Photosynthesis is powered by **light energy,** a type of kinetic energy made up of little energy packets called **photons,** which are organized into waves. Photons can do work as they bombard surfaces such as your face (heating it) or a leaf (enabling it to build sugar from carbon dioxide and water).

Photons have various amounts of energy, and the length of the wave in which they travel corresponds to the amount of energy carried by the photon. The shorter the wavelength, the more energy the light carries. Within a ray of light, there are super-high-energy packets of photons (those with short wavelengths), relatively low-energy packets (those with longer wavelengths), and everything in between. This range, which is called the **electromagnetic spectrum,** extends from extremely short high-energy gamma rays and X rays, with wavelengths as short as 1 nanometer (a human hair is about 50,000 nanometers in diameter), to very long low-energy radio waves, with wavelengths as long as a mile (**FIGURE 4-13**).

Just as we can't hear some super-high-pitched frequencies of sound (even though many dogs can), there are some wavelengths of light that are too short or too long for us to see. The light that we can see, visible light, spans all the colors of the rainbow. Humans (and some other animals) can see colors because our eyes contain light-absorbing molecules called **pigments.** These pigments absorb wavelengths of light within the visible range. The energy in these light waves excites electrons in the pigments, which in turn stimulate nerves in our eyes. These nerves then transmit electrical signals to our brains. We perceive different wavelengths within the visible spectrum as different colors. The pigments in the human eye absorb many different wavelengths pretty well: that's why we can see so many colors. When plants use sunlight's energy to make sugar during photosynthesis, they also use the visible portion of the electromagnetic spectrum. Unlike our eyes, however, plant pigments (the energy-capturing parts of a plant) absorb and use only a portion of visible light wavelengths.

Chlorophyll is the pigment molecule in plants that absorbs light energy from the sun. Chlorophyll molecules are

FIGURE 4-13 A spectrum of energy. A ray of light emits high-energy photons, low-energy photons, and everything in between. Plants use only a fraction of the light's available energy.

embedded in the thylakoid membrane of chloroplasts, which are found primarily in plants' leaves. Just as light energy excites electrons in the pigments responsible for color vision in humans, electrons in a plant's chlorophyll can become excited by certain wavelengths of light and can capture a bit of this light energy.

Plants produce several different light-absorbing pigments (**FIGURE 4-14**). The primary photosynthetic pigment, called **chlorophyll *a*,** efficiently absorbs blue-violet and red wavelengths of light. Every other wavelength generally travels through or bounces off this pigment. Because chlorophyll *a* cannot efficiently absorb green light and instead reflects those wavelengths, our eyes and brain perceive the reflected light waves as green, and so the pigment (and the leaves in which it is found) appears green. Another pigment, **chlorophyll *b*,** is similar in structure but absorbs blue and red-orange wavelengths. Chlorophyll *b* reflects yellow-green wavelengths. A related group of pigments called **carotenoids** absorbs blue-violet and blue-green wavelengths and reflects yellow, orange, and red wavelengths.

FIGURE 4-14 **Plant pigments.** Each photosynthetic pigment absorbs and reflects specific wavelengths.

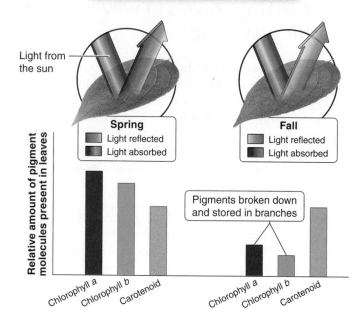

In the late summer, cooler temperatures cause some trees to prepare for the winter by shutting down chlorophyll production and reducing their photosynthesis rates, and they go into a state that

Q *Why do the leaves of some trees turn beautiful colors each fall?*

resembles an animal's hibernation. Gradually, the chlorophyll *a* and *b* molecules present in the leaves are broken down and their chemical components are stored in the branches. As the amounts of chlorophyll *a* and *b* in the leaves decrease relative to the remaining carotenoids, the striking colors of the fall

foliage are revealed (see Figure 4-14). During the rest of the year, chlorophyll *a* and *b* are so abundant in leaves that green masks the colors of the other pigments.

TAKE-HOME MESSAGE 4·7

Photosynthesis is powered by light energy, a type of kinetic energy made of energy packets called photons. Photons hit chlorophyll and other light-absorbing molecules near the green surfaces of plants. These molecules capture the light energy and harness it to build sugar from carbon dioxide and water.

4·8

Photons cause electrons in chlorophyll to enter an excited state.

An organism can use energy from the sun only if it can convert the light energy of the sun into the chemical energy in the bonds between atoms. The most important molecule in this conversion is the pigment chlorophyll (**FIGURE 4-15**). When chlorophyll is hit by photons of certain wavelengths,

the light energy bumps an electron (e^-) in the chlorophyll molecule to a higher energy level, an *excited* state. Upon absorbing the photon, the electron briefly gains energy, and the potential energy in the chlorophyll molecule increases.

The Nature of Energy   Photosynthesis   Cellular Respiration   Alternative Pathways

ENERGY MOVEMENT THROUGH CHLOROPHYLL

1 Light energy bumps an electron in the chlorophyll molecule to a higher, excited energy level.

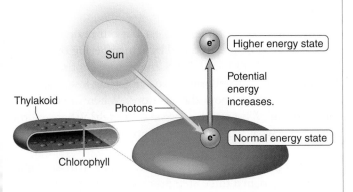

2 The excited electron generally has one of two different fates:

Some energy is transferred to a nearby molecule, where it excites another electron.

ENERGY

or

The excited electron is transferred to a nearby molecule.

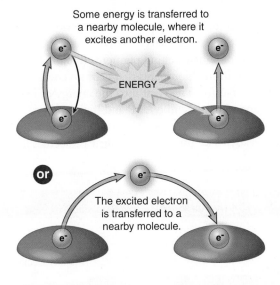

FIGURE 4-15 Capturing light energy with excited electrons. Chlorophyll electrons are excited to a higher energy state by light energy.

An electron in a photosynthetic pigment that is excited to a higher energy state generally has one of two fates: (1) the electron returns to its resting, unexcited state and, in the process, energy is released, some of which may be transferred to a nearby molecule, bumping electrons in that molecule to a higher energy state (and the rest of the energy is dissipated as heat), or (2) the excited electron itself is passed to another molecule.

The passing of electrons from molecule to molecule is one of the chief ways that energy moves through cells. Many molecules carry or accept electrons during cellular activities. All that is required is that the acceptor have a greater attraction for electrons than the molecule from which it accepts them. This receiver molecule, in turn, hands off electrons to another acceptor with an even greater attraction for them. A molecule that gains electrons always carries greater energy than it did before receiving the electron(s). For this reason, the passing of electrons from one molecule to another can be viewed as a passing of potential energy. In this way, energy moves through cells.

This transfer of electrons is one of the first steps of photosynthesis, the process that enables a plant to harness light energy from the sun efficiently and convert it to the more readily usable chemical energy. As we see later in this chapter, the dismantling of food molecules such as glucose to generate energy is also a story of breaking and rearranging chemical bonds as electrons pass from one atom or molecule to another.

Q *Suppose a large meteor hit the earth. How could smoke and soot in the atmosphere wipe out life far beyond the area of direct impact?*

Because any particles in the atmosphere can block the light from the sun and reduce the excitation of electrons in chlorophyll molecules, photosynthesis depends on a relatively clean atmosphere. Any reduction in the available sunlight can have serious effects on plants. Scientists believe that if a large meteor hit the earth—as one did when the dinosaurs were wiped out 65 million years ago—smoke, soot, and dust in the atmosphere could block sunlight to such an extent that plants in the region, or even possibly all of the plants on earth, could not conduct photosynthesis at high enough levels to survive. And when plants die off, all of the animals and other species that rely on them for energy die as well. All life on earth is completely dependent on the continued excitation of electrons by sunlight.

TAKE-HOME MESSAGE 4·8

When chlorophyll is hit by photons, the light energy excites an electron in the chlorophyll molecule, increasing the chlorophyll's potential energy. The excited electrons can be passed to other molecules, moving the potential energy through the cell.

4·9

Photosynthesis in detail: the energy of sunlight is captured as chemical energy.

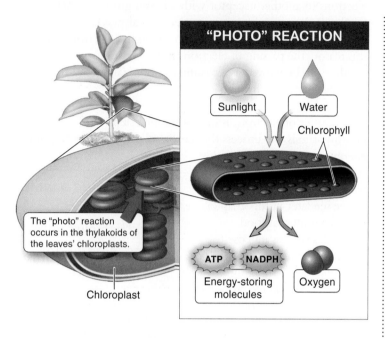

FIGURE 4-16 Overview of the "photo" portion of photosynthesis. Light energy is captured in the "photo" portion of photosynthesis. It is later used to power the building of sugar molecules.

Photosynthesis is a complex process, but our understanding of this process can be greatly aided by remembering one phrase: FOLLOW THE ELECTRONS. In the passages that follow, if you feel that you are losing focus or getting lost, just remember to think about the electrons: Where are they coming from? What are they passing through? Where are they going? And what will happen to them when they get there?

In the first part of photosynthesis, the "photo" part, sunlight hits a plant and, in a three-step process, the energy in this sunlight is ultimately captured and stored in an ATP molecule and in another molecule (called NADPH) that stores energy by accepting high-energy electrons (**FIGURE 4-16**).

The energy-capturing process occurs in a series of steps that are carried out in two **photosystems.** These photosystems are arrangements of light-catching pigments (including chlorophyll) within chloroplasts that capture energy from sunlight and transform it—first into the energy of excited electrons and ultimately into ATP and high-energy electron carriers. After these transformations, the captured energy is ready to be used to make sugar molecules in the

FIGURE 4-17 The water-splitting photosystem. Splitting water provides electrons for photosynthesis.

The Nature of Energy   Photosynthesis   Cellular Respiration   Alternative Pathways

"synthesis" part of photosynthesis. We begin following electrons as sunlight hits a leaf and the chloroplasts in it (**FIGURE 4-17**).

The chloroplasts in a leaf convert light energy from the sun into chemical energy. This conversion begins in a collection of chlorophyll molecules and other light-absorbing pigments arranged within a chloroplast's thylakoid membrane. As these pigments absorb photons from the sunlight that hits the leaves, electrons in the pigments become excited and then return to their resting state. As the electrons return to their resting state, energy (but not the electrons) is transferred to neighboring pigment molecules. This process continues until the transferred energy from many pigment molecules excites the electrons in a chlorophyll *a* molecule at the center of the photosystem (see Figure 4-17). This is where the electron journey begins.

Each energy burst boosts chlorophyll's electrons to an excited state, but the chlorophyll *a* molecule at the center of the photosystem is special, differing from the other pigment molecules in one key feature. When its electrons are boosted to an excited state they do not return to their resting, unexcited state. Instead, the special chlorophyll *a* continually loses its excited electrons to a nearby molecule, called the **primary electron acceptor,** which acts like an electron vacuum.

As electrons keep getting taken away from the special chlorophyll *a* molecule, the electrons must be replaced. The

Q Why must plants get water for photosynthesis to occur?

replacement electrons come from water. As long as photosynthesis is occurring, a constant supply of replacement electrons is required. Molecules of water inside the thylakoid are continuously split in the chloroplast, near the special chlorophyll *a* molecule in the thylakoid membrane. This split causes electrons from the water to fly off the water molecule and replenish chlorophyll *a*'s electron supply. A convenient and life-sustaining by-product of the splitting of water in photosynthesis is the oxygen that is released from the cell. Only a by-product—but a by-product essential for all animal life.

Once the primary electron acceptor gets hold of the high-energy electrons from chlorophyll *a,* it passes them like hot potatoes to another molecule, which passes them to another, which in turn passes them to yet another in what is called an **electron transport chain** (**FIGURE 4-18**). At each step in the electron transport chain's sequence of electron handoffs, the electrons fall to a lower energy state and a little bit of energy is released. These bits of energy are harnessed to power pumps in the thylakoid membrane that move protons (H^+ ions) from the stroma to the inside of the thylakoid. These pumps pack the protons inside the thylakoid sac at higher and higher concentrations. Think of a pump pushing water into an elevated tank, creating a store of potential energy that can gush out of the tank with great force and kinetic energy. Similarly, the protons eventually rush out of

THE ELECTRON TRANSPORT CHAIN

1 Electrons move through the electron transport chain, releasing a little energy and falling to a lower energy state.

2 The released energy powers proton pumps that move hydrogen ions from the stroma and pack them inside the thylakoid.

3 Protons rush out of the thylakoid with great kinetic energy, which can be used to build ATP.

Electron passed from the primary electron acceptor

Stroma

Proton pumps

Thylakoid

ADP ATP

To NADPH-producing photosystem

Chloroplast

Thylakoid

AREA OF DETAIL

FIGURE 4-18 The electron transport chain. Electrons are passed from the primary electron acceptor to a chain of molecules embedded within the thylakoid membrane, called the electron transport chain.

1 WATER-SPLITTING PHOTOSYSTEM
Light energy is used to transfer electrons to the primary electron acceptor. Electrons are donated by water releasing oxygen and hydrogen as by-products.

2 1st ELECTRON TRANSPORT CHAIN
High-energy electrons are used to pump hydrogen ions into the thylakoid. The kinetic energy from the release of these ions is used to build ATP.

3 NADPH-PRODUCING PHOTOSYSTEM
The NADPH-producing photosystem is identical to the water-splitting photosystem, except that electrons are donated by the electron transport chain.

4 2nd ELECTRON TRANSPORT CHAIN
High-energy electrons are passed to NADP+, creating NADPH, a high-energy electron carrier.

Sun — e⁻

ATP — ADP

H⁺ ions

Sun — e⁻

NADP⁺ — e⁻ — NADPH

Follow the electrons.

Water — Oxygen

H⁺ ions

AREA ENLARGED ABOVE

Thylakoid

FIGURE 4-19 Summary of the "photo" reactions.

the thylakoid sacs with great force—and that force is harnessed to build energy-storing ATP molecules, one of the two products of the "photo" portion of photosynthesis.

Recall that the energy-capturing and transforming process of the "photo" reactions occurs in two photosystems (arrangements of chlorophyll and other light-catching molecules). The electron transport chain physically links the first photosystem to the second. As the traveling electrons continue their journey, they fill electron vacancies in the reaction center of a second photosystem, right next to the first photosystem (**FIGURE 4-19**). Like the first photosystem, the second photosystem also has numerous pigments that harness photons from the sun and pass the light energy to another special chlorophyll *a* molecule. The special chlorophyll *a* molecule at the center of this second photosystem has electron vacancies because, as in the first photosystem, when electrons in the special chlorophyll *a* molecule are boosted to an excited state, they are whisked away from the chlorophyll molecule by another primary electron acceptor. This electron acceptor then passes the electrons to a second electron transport chain. At the end of this second electron transport chain, the electrons are passed to a molecule called NADP+, creating **NADPH,** a high-

energy electron carrier. NADPH is the second important product of the "photo" portion of photosynthesis.

With the electrons' passage through the second photosystem and arrival in NADPH, we now have the final products of the "photo" part of photosynthesis (which are also called the light-dependent reactions): we've captured light energy from the sun and converted it to the chemical energy of ATP and the high-energy electron carrier, NADPH (see Figure 4-19). But we haven't made any food yet. In the next section, we cover the "synthesis" part of photosynthesis and see how plants use the energy in ATP and NADPH to produce sugar from carbon dioxide.

TAKE-HOME MESSAGE 4·9

There are two parts to photosynthesis. The first is the "photo" part, in which light energy is transformed into chemical energy, while splitting water molecules and producing oxygen. Sunlight's energy is first captured when an electron in chlorophyll is excited. As this electron is passed from one molecule to another, energy is released at each transfer, some of which is used to build the energy-storage molecules ATP and NADPH.

Photosynthesis in detail: the captured energy of sunlight is used to make food.

The "synthesis" part of photosynthesis takes place in a series of chemical reactions called the **Calvin cycle.** All the Calvin cycle reactions occur in the stroma of the leaves' chloroplasts, outside the thylakoids. Plants carry out these reactions using the energy stored in the ATP and NADPH molecules that are built in the "photo" portion of photosynthesis. This dependency links the light-gathering ("photo") reactions with the sugar-building ("synthesis") reactions (**FIGURE 4-20**).

If there is any part of photosynthesis that appears magical, it is the Calvin cycle. Just as a magician seems to make a rabbit appear from thin air, the Calvin cycle takes invisible molecules of CO_2 from the air and uses them to assemble visible—even edible—molecules of sugar. The processes in the Calvin cycle occur in three steps (**FIGURE 4-21**).

1. *Fixation.* First, using an enzyme called **rubisco,** plants pluck molecules of carbon from the air where they occur in the form of carbon dioxide and then attach, or "fix," them to a visible organic (carbon-containing) molecule within the chloroplast. Not surprisingly, given its role as the critical chemical that enables plants to build food molecules, rubisco is the most abundant protein on earth.

FIGURE 4-20 Overview of the "synthesis" reactions of photosynthesis.

2. *Sugar creation.* Next, the newly built molecule is chemically modified: a phosphate from ATP is added to it and it also receives some high-energy electrons from

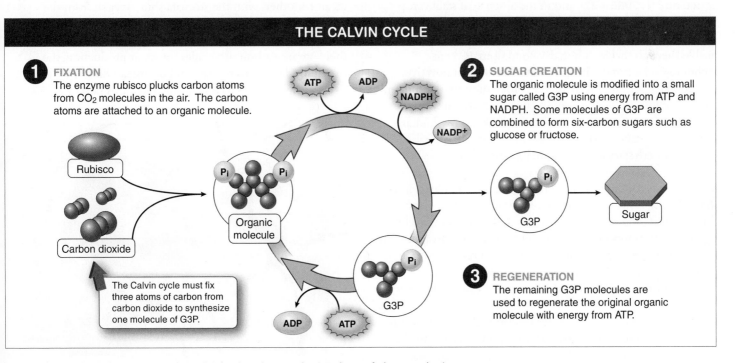

FIGURE 4-21 **The Calvin cycle.** In the Calvin cycle—the "synthesis" phase of photosynthesis—sugars are produced.

NADPH. This product of the Calvin cycle is a small sugar called glyceraldehyde 3-phosphate (G3P). To synthesize one molecule of the three-carbon sugar G3P, the Calvin cycle must fix three molecules of carbon from carbon dioxide to the initial organic molecule.

Some G3P molecules are combined to make the six-carbon sugars glucose and fructose. These sugars can be used as fuel by the plant, enabling it to grow. These sugars can also be used as fuel by animals that eat the plant.

3. *Regeneration.* Not all G3P molecules are used to produce sugars. In the third and final phase of the Calvin cycle, some G3P molecules are used to regenerate the original molecule in the chloroplast to which the carbon from CO_2 is attached. This regeneration process requires energy from ATP produced in the "photo" reactions of photosynthesis. With this regeneration, the Calvin cycle can continue to fix carbon and produce molecules of G3P.

Ultimately, to synthesize one molecule of G3P, the Calvin cycle must fix three molecules of carbon from carbon dioxide; this process consumes nine molecules of ATP and six molecules of NADPH generated in the "photo" reactions of photosynthesis.

TAKE-HOME MESSAGE 4·10

The second part, or "synthesis" part, of photosynthesis is the Calvin cycle, which occurs in the stroma of the chloroplast. During this phase, carbon from CO_2 in the atmosphere is attached (fixed) to molecules in chloroplasts, sugars are built, and molecules are regenerated to be used again in the Calvin cycle. The fixation, building, and regeneration processes consume energy from ATP and NADPH (the products of the "photo" part of photosynthesis).

4·11

The battle against world hunger can use plants adapted to water scarcity.

The Sudan. Ethiopia. India. Somalia. Many of the world's regions with the highest rates of starvation also are places with the hottest, driest climates. This is not a coincidence. These climate conditions present difficult challenges for sustaining agriculture (**FIGURE 4-22**), and in the absence of stable crop yields, food production is unpredictable and the risk of starvation high. But evolutionary adaptations in some plants enable them to thrive in hot, dry conditions. Recent technological advances in agriculture use these innovative evolutionary solutions to battle the problem of world hunger. In this section, we discuss some adaptations that allow plants to thrive when water is scarce. We also look at how humans use these adaptations to grow food in the dry, inhospitable climates where starvation rates are highest.

When it gets too hot and dry, animals can seek coolness in the shade. Plants, however, are anchored in place and do not have this option. Consequently, plants in hot, dry climates can lose significant amounts of water through evaporation. Evaporation is a problem for plants because water is essential to photosynthesis, growth, and the transport of nutrients throughout the plant. Without water, plants cannot live long.

One method of combating water loss through evaporation is for plants to close their **stomata,** small pores usually on the underside of leaves (**FIGURE 4-23**). These openings are the primary sites for gas exchange in plants: carbon dioxide for photosynthesis enters through these openings and oxygen

generated as a by-product in photosynthesis exits through them. When open, the stomata also allow water to evaporate from the plant. Closing their stomata, however, solves one problem for plants (too much water evaporation) while it creates another: with the stomata shut, oxygen from the "photo" reactions of photosynthesis cannot be released from the chloroplasts, and carbon dioxide cannot enter them. If there are no carbon molecules for sugar production, the Calvin cycle tries to fix carbon but instead finds only oxygen. Plant growth comes to a standstill and crops fail.

FIGURE 4-22 Nowhere to hide. Plants that lose too much water can't always survive in extremely hot, dry weather.

The Nature of Energy   Photosynthesis   Cellular Respiration   Alternative Pathways

Stoma open

Stoma closed

FIGURE 4-23 Plant stomata. Carbon dioxide enters a plant through stomata (*sing.* stoma), but water can be lost through the same openings.

Some plants, including corn and sugarcane, have evolved a process that minimizes water loss but still enables them to make sugar when the weather is hot and dry. In the process called **C4 photosynthesis,** these plants add an extra set of steps to the usual process of photosynthesis (**FIGURE 4-24**). In these steps, the plants produce an enzyme that functions like the ultimate "CO$_2$-sticky tape." This enzyme has a tremendously strong attraction for carbon dioxide; it can find

C3 PHOTOSYNTHESIS

Carbon dioxide

Day

CALVIN CYCLE

Stomata open

Sugar

ADVANTAGE
• energy efficient

DISADVANTAGE
• water lost to evaporation in hot climates

Common ivy

C4 PHOTOSYNTHESIS

Carbon dioxide

Day

ATP

CARBON UPTAKE

Stomata slightly open

CALVIN CYCLE

Sugar

ADVANTAGE
• water loss is minimized in warm climates

DISADVANTAGE
• requires more energy

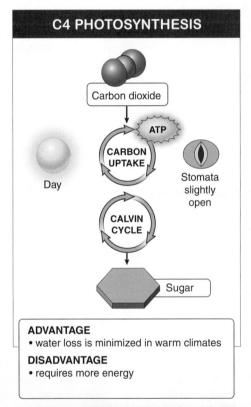

Corn

CAM PHOTOSYNTHESIS

Carbon dioxide

Night

ATP

CARBON UPTAKE

Stomata open

Day

CALVIN CYCLE

Stomata closed

Sugar

ADVANTAGE
• water loss is minimized in hot climates

DISADVANTAGES
• requires more energy
• slow growth

Saguaro cactus

FIGURE 4-24 C3, C4, and CAM photosynthesis.

and bind carbon even when CO_2 concentration is very low. (In contrast, rubisco, the usual enzyme that plants use to pluck carbon from the atmosphere, functions poorly when CO_2 is scarce.) As a consequence, stomata can be opened just a tiny bit, and let in just a little CO_2. Having the stomata closed also reduces evaporation and conserves water for the plant.

This seems like such a good solution that we would expect all plants to use it. There is a catch, though. The extra steps in C4 photosynthesis require the plant to expend additional energy. Specifically, every time the plant generates a molecule of the "CO_2-sticky tape" enzyme, it uses one molecule of ATP. It is acceptable to pay this energy cost only when the climate is so hot and dry that the plant would otherwise have to close its stomata and completely shut down all sugar production. If the climate is mild, however, plants conducting the more energetically expensive C4 photosynthesis will be out-competed by the more efficient plants conducting standard photosynthesis (called C3 photosynthesis). Not surprisingly, we see few C4 plants in the temperate regions of the world or among photosynthetic organisms living in the oceans. In hot, dry regions, however, they are the dominant plants and displace the C3 plants wherever both occur (**FIGURE 4-25**). With global warming, many scientists expect to see a gradual expansion of the geographic ranges over which C4 plants occur and believe that non–C4 plants will be pushed farther and farther away from the equator.

A third and similar method of carbon fixation, called **CAM** (for "crassulacean acid metabolism"), is also found in hot, dry areas. In this method, used by many cacti, pineapples, and other fleshy, juicy plants, the plants close their stomata during the hot, dry days. At night, they open the stomata and let CO_2 into the leaves, where it binds temporarily to a holding molecule. During the day, when a carbon source is needed to make sugars in the Calvin cycle, the CO_2 is gradually released from the holding molecule, enabling photosynthesis to proceed while keeping the stomata closed to reduce water loss (see Figure 4-24). A disadvantage of CAM photosynthesis is that by completely closing their stomata during the day, CAM plants significantly reduce the total amount of CO_2 they can take in. As a consequence, they have much slower growth rates and cannot compete well with non-CAM plants under any conditions other than extreme dryness.

DISTRIBUTION OF PHOTOSYNTHESIS METHODS

Equator

C3 plants dominant
C4 plants dominant

FIGURE 4-25 Map of C3 and C4 photosynthesis.

C4 and CAM photosynthesis originally evolved because they made it possible for plants to grow better in the world's hot and dry regions. Researchers are now using these adaptations to fight world hunger. Specifically, they have introduced from corn into rice several genes that code for the C4 photosynthesis enzymes. Once in the rice, these genes increase the rice plant's ability to photosynthesize, thus leading to higher growth rates and food yields. The experiments are still in early stages, and whether the addition of C4 photosynthesis enzymes will make it possible to grow new crops on a large scale in previously inhospitable environments is not certain. Early results suggest, however, that this is a promising approach.

TAKE-HOME MESSAGE 4·11

C4 and CAM photosynthesis are evolutionary adaptations at the biochemical level that, although being more energetically expensive than regular (C3) photosynthesis, allow plants in hot, dry climates to close their stomata and conserve water without shutting down photosynthesis.

The Nature of Energy · Photosynthesis · Cellular Respiration · Alternative Pathways

❸ Cellular respiration converts food molecules into ATP, a universal source of energy for living organisms.

Hamburger powered! We extract energy from all the foods we eat.

4·12

How do living organisms fuel their actions? Cellular respiration: the big picture.

Food is fuel. And all of the activities of life—growing, moving, reproducing—require fuel. Plants, most algae, and some bacteria obtain their fuel directly from the energy of sunlight, which they harness through photosynthesis. Less self-sufficient organisms, such as humans, alligators, and insects, must extract the energy they need from the food they eat.

This energy comes from photosynthetic organisms either directly (from eating plants) or indirectly (from eating animals that eat plants) **(FIGURE 4-26)**.

All living organisms extract energy from the chemical bonds of molecules (which can be considered "food") through a

FIGURE 4-26 Living organisms require fuel.

CELLULAR RESPIRATION

High-energy bonds of food molecules are broken down, releasing energy.

Carbon dioxide

Water

ATP

Oxygen

Sugar

INPUT	OUTPUT
Oxygen + Sugar	Carbon dioxide + Water + ATP Energy

FIGURE 4-27 Cellular respiration: the big picture.

process called cellular respiration (**FIGURE 4-27**). This process is a bit like photosynthesis in reverse. In photosynthesis, the energy of the sun is captured and used to build molecules of sugars, such as glucose. In cellular respiration, plants and animals break down the chemical bonds of sugar and other

energy-rich food molecules (such as fats and proteins) to release the energy that went into creating them. (Don't confuse cellular respiration with the act of breathing, which is also called *respiration*.) As energy is released by these reactions, cells capture it and store it in the bonds of ATP molecules. This plentiful, readily available stored energy can then be tapped as needed to fuel the work of the life-sustaining activities and processes of all living organisms.

In humans and other animals, cellular respiration starts after we eat food, digest it, absorb the nutrient molecules into the bloodstream, and deliver them to the cells of our bodies. At this point, our cells begin to extract some of the energy stored in the bonds of the food molecules. We focus here on the breakdown of glucose, but later in this chapter we'll see that the process is similar for the breakdown of fats or lipids. Ultimately, when a food molecule has been completely processed, the cell has used the food molecule's stored energy (along with oxygen) to create a large number of high-energy-storing ATP molecules (which supply energy to power the cell's activities), water, and carbon dioxide (which is exhaled into the atmosphere).

TAKE-HOME MESSAGE 4·12

Living organisms extract energy through a process called cellular respiration, in which the high-energy bonds of sugar and other energy-rich molecules are broken, releasing the energy that went into creating them. The cell captures the food molecules' stored energy in the bonds of ATP molecules. This process requires fuel molecules and oxygen and it yields ATP molecules, water, and carbon dioxide.

4·13

The first step of cellular respiration: glycolysis is the universal energy-releasing pathway.

To generate energy, fuels such as glucose and other carbohydrates and proteins and fats are broken down in three steps: (1) glycolysis, (2) the Krebs cycle, and (3) the electron transport chain. **Glycolysis** means the splitting (*lysis*) of sugar (*glyco-*) and it is the first step all organisms on the planet take in breaking down food molecules; for many single-celled organisms, this one step is sufficient to provide all of the energy they need (**FIGURE 4-28**).

As **FIGURE 4-29** illustrates, glycolysis is a sequence of chemical reactions (there are 10 in all) through which glucose is broken down to yield two molecules of a substance called **pyruvate.** Glycolysis has two distinct phases: an "uphill" preparatory phase and a "downhill" payoff phase.

Just as you sometimes have to spend money to make money, before any energy can be extracted from glucose, some

The Nature of Energy   Photosynthesis   Cellular Respiration   Alternative Pathways

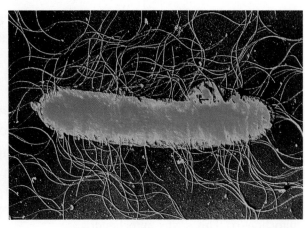

FIGURE 4-28 Plants, animals, bacteria, and all other organisms undergo glycolysis.

energy must be added to the molecule. This addition occurs during the "uphill" phase. The additional energy (which comes from ATP) makes the glucose molecule less stable and ripe for chemical breakdown. Once the glucose has been destabilized, it can be broken down chemically, and the energy stored in its bonds can be harnessed as the bonds are broken.

Three of the 10 steps in glycolysis yield energy. In two of these three, as bonds from the sugar are broken, the energy released is quickly harnessed by the attachment of phosphate groups to molecules of ADP to create energy-rich ATP molecules. In the third energy-yielding step of glycolysis, electrons originally from the glucose are transferred to NAD^+ to become the high-energy electron carrier NADH. Later (in the electron transport chain) this energy will be converted to ATP. The net result of glycolysis is that each glucose molecule is broken down into two molecules of pyruvate. During this breakdown, some of the released energy is captured in the production of energy-rich ATP molecules and molecules of the high-energy electron carrier NADH. Two molecules of water are also produced during glycolysis.

In the absence of oxygen and in many yeasts and bacteria, glycolysis is the only game in town for fueling activity. Because single-celled organisms have much lower energy needs, they can function solely on the yields of glycolysis. For many organisms (including humans), however, glycolysis is a springboard to further energy extraction. The additional energy payoffs come from the Krebs cycle and the electron transport chain.

GLYCOLYSIS

1 PREPARATORY PHASE

ATP (2)

Unstable molecule prepared to be broken down

Glucose

−2 ATP

Gycolysis takes place in the cell's cytoplasm.

2 PAYOFF PHASE

P_i P_i

ATP (4)

NADH (2)

Water

Pyruvate (2)

+4 ATP +2 NADH

FIGURE 4-29 Glycolysis up close.

TAKE-HOME MESSAGE 4·13

Glycolysis is the initial phase in the process by which all living organisms harness energy from food molecules. Glycolysis occurs in a cell's cytoplasm and uses the energy released from breaking chemical bonds in food molecules to produce high-energy molecules, ATP and NADH.

The second step of cellular respiration: the Krebs cycle extracts energy from sugar.

Cells could stop extracting energy when glycolysis ends, but they rarely do because that would be like leaving most of your meal on your plate. This is because in glycolysis only a small fraction of the energy stored in sugar molecules is recovered and converted to ATP and NADH. Cells get much more of an "energy bang" for their "food buck" in the steps following glycolysis, which occur in the mitochondria. This is why mitochondria are considered ATP "factories." In the mitochondria, the molecules produced from the breakdown of glucose during glycolysis are broken down further, during two steps that are dramatically more efficient at capturing the energy in food molecules: the Krebs cycle (the subject of this section) and the electron transport chain (the subject of the next section). In breaking down the products of glycolysis, the **Krebs cycle** produces some additional molecules of ATP and, more important, captures a huge amount of chemical energy by producing high-energy electron carriers.

Before the Krebs cycle can begin, however, the end products of glycolysis—two molecules of pyruvate for every molecule of glucose used—must be modified. To start this modification process, the pyruvate molecules move from the cytoplasm into the mitochondria. Once in the mitochondria, the pyruvate molecules undergo three quick modifications that prepare them to be broken down in the Krebs cycle (**FIGURE 4-30**):

Modification 1. Each pyruvate molecule passes some of its high-energy electrons to the energy-accepting molecule NAD$^+$, building two molecules of NADH.

Modification 2. Next, a carbon atom and two oxygen atoms are removed from each pyruvate molecule and released as carbon dioxide. The CO_2 molecules diffuse out of the cell and, eventually, out of the organism. In humans, for example, these CO_2 molecules pass into the bloodstream and are transported to the lungs, from which they are eventually exhaled.

Modification 3. In the final step in the preparation for the Krebs cycle, a giant compound known as coenzyme A attaches itself to the remains of each pyruvate molecule, producing two molecules called acetyl-CoA. Each acetyl-CoA molecule is now ready to enter the Krebs cycle.

> **Q** Aerobic training can cause our bodies to produce more mitochondria in cells. Why is this beneficial?

There are eight separate steps in the Krebs cycle, but our emphasis here is on its three general outcomes (**FIGURE 4-31**):

Outcome 1. *A new molecule is formed.* Acetyl-CoA adds its two-carbon acetyl group to a molecule of the starting material of the Krebs cycle, a four-carbon molecule called oxaloacetate. This process creates a six-carbon molecule.

Outcome 2. *High-energy electron carriers (NADH) are made and carbon dioxide is exhaled.* The six-carbon molecule then gives electrons to NAD$^+$ to make the high-energy electron carrier NADH. The six-carbon molecule releases two carbon atoms along with four oxygen atoms to form two carbon dioxide molecules. This CO_2 is carried by the bloodstream to the lungs from which it is exhaled into the atmosphere.

ACETYL-CoA PRODUCTION

Glucose → Pyruvate = Molecular model of pyruvate

1 Each pyruvate molecule passes a high-energy electron to NAD$^+$, creating NADH.

2 A carbon and two oxygen atoms are released as carbon dioxide.

3 Coenzyme A attaches itself to the remaining molecule, creating acetyl-CoA.

NAD$^+$ → NADH

Carbon dioxide

+ Coenzyme A

Acetyl-CoA

to Krebs cycle

Modifications of pyruvate take place in the cell's mitochondria.

FIGURE 4-30 Preparation of pyruvate. In the mitochondria, pyruvate must be modified before it can be broken down in the Krebs cycle.

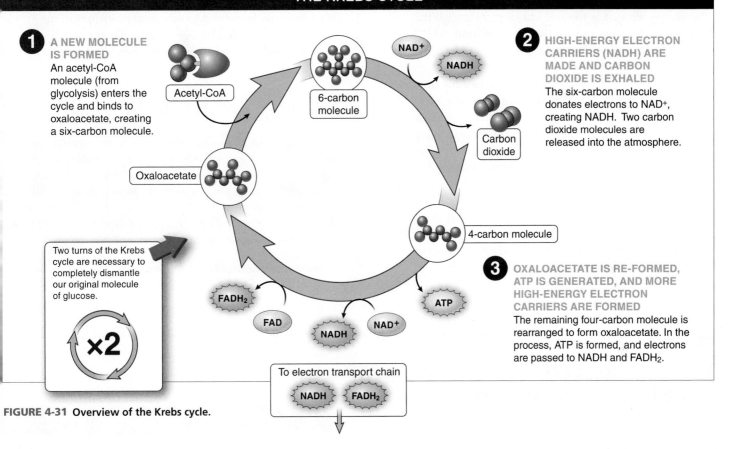

1 **A NEW MOLECULE IS FORMED**
An acetyl-CoA molecule (from glycolysis) enters the cycle and binds to oxaloacetate, creating a six-carbon molecule.

Acetyl-CoA

6-carbon molecule

Oxaloacetate

NAD+

NADH

Carbon dioxide

4-carbon molecule

2 **HIGH-ENERGY ELECTRON CARRIERS (NADH) ARE MADE AND CARBON DIOXIDE IS EXHALED**
The six-carbon molecule donates electrons to NAD+, creating NADH. Two carbon dioxide molecules are released into the atmosphere.

3 **OXALOACETATE IS RE-FORMED, ATP IS GENERATED, AND MORE HIGH-ENERGY ELECTRON CARRIERS ARE FORMED**
The remaining four-carbon molecule is rearranged to form oxaloacetate. In the process, ATP is formed, and electrons are passed to NADH and $FADH_2$.

Two turns of the Krebs cycle are necessary to completely dismantle our original molecule of glucose.

×2

$FADH_2$

FAD

NADH

NAD+

ATP

To electron transport chain

NADH $FADH_2$

FIGURE 4-31 Overview of the Krebs cycle.

Outcome 3. *The starting material of the Krebs cycle is re-formed, ATP is generated, and more high-energy electron carriers are formed.* After the CO_2 is released, the four-carbon molecule that remains from the original pyruvate-oxaloacetate molecule formed in Outcome 1 is modified and rearranged to once again form oxaloacetate, the starting material of the Krebs cycle. In the process of this reorganization, one ATP molecule is generated and more electrons are passed to one familiar high-energy electron carrier, NADH, and a new one, $FADH_2$. The formation of these high-energy electron carriers increases the energy yield of the Krebs cycle. One oxaloacetate is re-formed, and the cycle is ready to break down the second molecule of acetyl-CoA. Two turns of the cycle are necessary to completely dismantle our original molecule of glucose.

We started this process of cellular respiration with a molecule of glucose, and now that we have seen the Krebs cycle in its entirety, let's trace the path of the original six carbons in that glucose molecule.

1. Glycolysis: the six-carbon starting point. Glucose is broken down into two molecules of pyruvate. No carbons are removed.

2. Preparation for the Krebs cycle: two carbons are released. Two pyruvate molecules are modified to enter the Krebs cycle and they each lose a carbon atom, in the form of two molecules of carbon dioxide.

3. Krebs cycle: the last four carbons are released. A total of four carbon molecules enter the Krebs cycle in the form of acetyl Co-A. For each turn of the Krebs cycle, two molecules of carbon dioxide are released. So the two final carbons are released into the atmosphere during the second turn of the wheel. Poof! The six carbon atoms that were originally present in our single molecule of glucose are no longer present.

In a sense, the carbon atoms that were first plucked from the atmosphere to make sugar during photosynthesis have been exhaled back into the atmosphere as six molecules of carbon dioxide. At this point, we've come full circle. In photosynthesis, carbon atoms from the air were used to build sugar molecules, which had energy stored in the bonds between their carbon, hydrogen and oxygen atoms. In cellular respiration, the energy previously stored in the bonds of the sugar is converted to molecules of ATP, NADH, and $FADH_2$. Carbon atoms from sugar are exhaled back into the air as CO_2 and water is produced. What happens to the high-energy electron carriers, NADH and FADH$_2$? They eventually give up their high-energy electrons to the electron transport chain. The energy released as those electrons pass through the transport chain is captured in the bonds of more ATP molecules. We explore that process in the next section.

Q Why might mitochondria malfunctions play a role in lethargy or fatigue?

As we explore the important roles of the Krebs cycle and electron transport chain in generating usable energy for organisms, it's important to note that mitochondria malfunctions have serious consequences for health. More than a hundred genetic mitochondrial disorders have been identified, all of which can lead to energy shortage, including muscle weakness, fatigue, and muscle pain. It

appears, for instance, that many cases of "exercise intolerance"—extreme fatigue or cramps after only slight exertion—may be related to inherited mutations in the mitochondrial DNA. Damage to our cellular powerhouses, not surprisingly, can create personal energy crises.

TAKE-HOME MESSAGE 4·14

A huge amount of additional energy can be harvested by cells after glycolysis. First the end product of glycolysis, pyruvate, is chemically modified. Then, in the Krebs cycle, the modified pyruvate is broken down step by step. This breakdown releases carbon molecules to the atmosphere as bonds are broken and captures some of the released energy in two ATP molecules and numerous high-energy electron carriers.

4·15

The third step of cellular respiration: ATP is built in the electron transport chain.

How do we finally get a big payoff of usable energy from our glucose molecule? Glycolysis and the Krebs cycle produce a few molecules of ATP for each molecule of glucose broken down, but it is the energy held in the high-energy electron carriers NADH and FADH$_2$ generated in these processes that ultimately generates the largest amount of usable energy in the form of ATP. In fact, almost 90% of the energy payoff from a molecule of glucose is harvested in the final step of cellular respiration when the electrons from NADH and FADH$_2$ move along the electron transport chain. This process, like the Krebs cycle, takes place in the mitochondria.

In a manner that is similar to that seen in the chloroplast during photosynthesis, mitochondria convert kinetic energy (from electrons) into potential energy (a concentration gradient of protons). Two structural features of mitochondria are essential to their impressive ability to harness energy from molecules.

Feature 1. Mitochondria have a "bag-within-a-bag" structure that makes it possible to harness the potential energy in the bonds of NADH and FADH$_2$ molecules to produce ATP (**FIGURE 4-32**). Material inside the mitochondrion can lie in one of two spaces: (1) the

MITOCHONDRIA: A CLOSER LOOK AT STRUCTURE

1 **"BAG-WITHIN-A-BAG"**
Inside the mitochondrion, material can lie in one of two places:

Intermembrane space

Mitochondrial matrix

2 **INNER "BAG" STUDDED WITH MOLECULES**
These molecules create an electron transport chain that enables ATP production.

Plane of cross section

FIGURE 4-32 "A bag within a bag." The structure of mitochondria makes possible their impressive ability to harness energy from food molecules.

The Nature of Energy Photosynthesis Cellular Respiration Alternative Pathways

intermembrane space, which is outside the inner bag, or (2) the **mitochondrial matrix,** which is inside the inner bag.

With two distinct regions separated by a membrane, the mitochondrion can create higher concentrations of molecules in one area or the other. And because a concentration gradient is a form of potential energy—molecules move from the high-concentration area to the low-concentration area the way water rushes down a hill—once a gradient is created, the energy released as the gradient equalizes itself can be used to do work. In the electron transport chain, this energy is used to build the energy-rich molecule ATP.

Feature 2. The inner bag of the mitochondria is studded with molecules. These molecules, mostly electron carriers, are sequentially arranged within the inner membrane of the mitochondrion, hence their description as a "chain." This arrangement makes it possible for the molecules to hand off electrons in an orderly sequence.

Now let's explore how these features of mitochondria make it possible to harness energy from high-energy electron carriers (**FIGURE 4-33**).

Q Over-the-counter NADH pills provide energy to sufferers of chronic fatigue syndrome. Why might this be?

Step 1 of the electron transport chain begins with NADH and $FADH_2$ in the mitochondrial matrix (inside the inner bag) moving to the inner mitochondrial membrane. There, the high-energy electrons they carry are transferred to molecules embedded within the membrane. After they donate their electrons, the molecules that remain, NAD^+ and FAD^+, are recycled back to the Krebs cycle.

The embedded molecules pass the electrons to the next carrier, which passes the electrons to the next, and so on. At each handoff, a bit of energy is released. Thus, as electrons move from one carrier to another through the electron transport chain, they lose energy at each handoff.

At the end of the chain (step 2), the lower-energy electrons are handed off to oxygen, which then combines with free H^+ ions in the mitochondrial fluid to form water.

As shown in step 3 of Figure 4-33, most of the energy released at each handoff from one electron carrier to another in the electron transport chain is used to pump protons (H^+ ions) from the mitochondrial matrix across the membrane and into the intermembrane space. As more and more protons are pumped across the membrane and packed in the

THE MITOCHONDRIAL ELECTRON TRANSPORT CHAIN

High-energy electrons are passed from the carriers NADH and $FADH_2$ to a series of molecules embedded in the inner mitochondrial membrane called the electron transport chain.

1 At each step in the electron transport chain's sequence of handoffs, the electrons fall to a lower energy state, releasing a little bit of energy.

2 At the end of the chain, the lower-energy electrons are handed off to oxygen, which then combines with free H^+ ions to form water.

3 The energy is used to power proton pumps, which pack hydrogen ions from the mitochondrial matrix into the intermembrane space.

4 The protons rush back into the mitochondrial matrix with great kinetic energy, which can be used to build ATP.

Mitochondrial matrix · NADH · e^- · NAD^+ · H^+ · $FADH_2$ · e^- · FAD · H^+ · H^+ · e^- · e^- · Water · Oxygen · H^+ · ADP · ATP · Inner mitochondrial membrane · Intermembrane space

FIGURE 4-33 The big energy payoff. Most of the energy harvested during cellular respiration is generated by the electron transport chain in the mitochondria.

SUMMARY OF CELLULAR RESPIRATION

1 GLYCOLYSIS

Glucose

Pyruvate

ATP

Cytoplasm

Mitochondria

2 ACETYL-CoA PRODUCTION

Pyruvate

Carbon dioxide

Acetyl-CoA

3 KREBS CYCLE

Carbon dioxide

ATP

NADH   FADH₂

4 ELECTRON TRANSPORT CHAIN

e⁻

e⁻

Oxygen

Water

ATP

Each step in the break-down of food increases the amount of usable energy that is generated!

FIGURE 4-34 The steps of cellular respiration: from glucose to usable energy.

intermembrane space, a concentration gradient is created. This gradient represents a significant source of potential energy.

If this description seems familiar, it is. In chloroplasts, during photosynthesis, great numbers of protons are pumped from the stroma outside the thylakoid sacs to the inside of the thylakoids. We likened this potential energy to the potential energy of water in an elevated tower, which can be released with great force. Similarly, in step 4 of the mitochondrial electron transport chain, the protons pumped into the intermembrane space rush back to the inner mitochondrial matrix through channels in the inner mitochondrial membrane. And as the protons pass through, the force of their flow fuels the attachment of free-floating phosphate groups to ADP to produce ATP.

In the end, the number of ATP molecules generated from the complete dismantling of one molecule of glucose is about 36, most of which are produced with the energy harnessed from high-energy electron carriers as they pass their electrons down the electron transport chain (**FIGURE 4-34**).

Given the central role of the electron transport chain in the generation of usable energy from the breakdown of food molecules, any interference in its functioning has dire consequences. And in fact, murder by cyanide poisoning, an old tradition in detective stories, is just such an interference. When cyanide gets into the mitochondria, it binds to a molecule in the electron transport chain, preventing it from accepting electrons. This halts the transfer of electrons and the pumping of protons across the mitochondrial membrane. As a consequence, the production of ATP that would occur when protons rush back across the membrane down their concentration gradient ceases. Halting the production of ATP removes a cell's energy source, starving it very quickly. For this reason, cyanide poisoning can cause death within minutes.

Q *Cyanide blocks the passage of electrons to oxygen in the electron transport chain. Why does this make it a toxic poison?*

TAKE-HOME MESSAGE 4·15

The largest energy payoff of cellular respiration comes as electrons from NADH and FADH₂ produced during glycolysis and the Krebs cycle move along the electron transport chain. The electrons are passed from one carrier to another and energy is released, pumping protons into the intermembrane space. As the protons rush back to the inner mitochondrial matrix, the force of their flow fuels the production of large amounts of ATP.

The Nature of Energy   Photosynthesis   Cellular Respiration   Alternative Pathways

❹ There are alternative pathways to energy acquisition.

Unlike cars, living organisms (such as this cheetah) can use multiple different types of fuel.

4·16

Beer, wine, and spirits are by-products of cellular metabolism in the absence of oxygen.

Every beer brewery, the entire wine industry, and all distilleries of whiskey, vodka, tequila, and other alcoholic beverages owe their existence to microscopic yeast cells scrambling to break down their food for energy under stressful conditions. To better understand how yeast metabolism produces the alcohol we drink, it helps to investigate first what happens when humans and other animals try to metabolize energy from sugar molecules under some stressful conditions.

FIGURE 4-35 Energy production without oxygen. Organisms have a backup method for breaking down sugar when oxygen is not present.

If you run or swim as fast as you can, you soon feel a burning sensation in your muscles. What is happening? Your muscle cells are suddenly becoming very acidic. This acid buildup occurs when we demand of our bodies bursts of energy beyond that which they can sustain (**FIGURE 4-35**). (The next-day muscle soreness is not due to acid buildup, which goes away in a matter of minutes or hours; it is caused by damage to the muscle fibers. They break down a bit before growing stronger.)

With rapid, strenuous exertion, our bodies soon fall behind in delivering oxygen from the lungs to the bloodstream to the cells and finally to the mitochondria. Oxygen deficiency then limits the rate at which the mitochondria can break down fuel and produce ATP (**FIGURE 4-36**). This slowdown in ATP production occurs because the electron transport chain requires oxygen as the final acceptor of all the electrons that are generated during glycolysis and the Krebs cycle. If oxygen is in short supply, the electrons from NADH (and $FADH_2$) have nowhere to go. Consequently, the regeneration of NAD^+ (and FAD^+) in the electron transport chain is halted, leaving no recipient for the high-energy electrons harvested from the breakdown of glucose and pyruvate, and the whole process of cellular respiration can grind to a stop. Organisms don't let this interruption last long, though; most have a backup method for breaking down sugar.

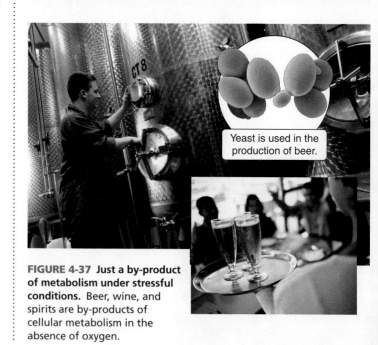

FIGURE 4-36 Energy production compared: with and without oxygen. Energy production without oxygen (anaerobic) is also called fermentation.

Among animals, there is one willing acceptor for the NADH electrons in the absence of oxygen: pyruvate, the end product of glycolysis. When pyruvate accepts the electrons, it forms lactic acid (see Figure 4-36). Once the NADH gives up its electrons, NAD^+ is generated, and glycolysis can continue. But as lactic acid builds up, it causes a burning feeling in our muscles. It's not an ideal situation, but if you are trying to escape a predator or are otherwise engaged in strenuous activity, the two ATP molecules generated from each glucose molecule during glycolysis are better than nothing.

Like humans, yeast normally use oxygen during their breakdown of food. And like humans, they have a backup method when oxygen is not available. But yeast make use of a different electron acceptor than do humans when oxygen isn't available, and the resulting reaction leads to the production of all drinking alcohol.

In these single-celled organisms, after glycolysis pyruvate is usually converted to a molecule called *acetaldehyde,* generating bubbles of CO_2 (which, when yeast is used in baking, allows bread to rise). In the absence of oxygen, this molecule accepts the electrons released from NADH, allowing glycolysis to resume. Acetaldehyde's acceptance of NADH's electrons results in the production of **ethanol,** the molecule that gives

beer, wine, and spirits their kick. Ethanol can also be used as a fuel source because it can be combusted in much the same way as the biofuels generated from animal fats and plant oils described earlier in this chapter.

The process by which glycolysis occurs in the absence of oxygen, in which alternative molecules are used as electron acceptors, is called **fermentation.** Interestingly, although ethanol is always the alcohol produced by fermentation, the flavor of the output of fermentation depends on the type of sugar metabolized by the yeast. Fruits, vegetables, and grains all give different results. If the sugar comes from grapes, wine is produced. If the sugar comes from a germinating barley plant, beer is produced. Potatoes, on the other hand, are the sugar source usually used to produce vodka.

Because yeast prefer the more efficient process of aerobic respiration, they produce alcohol only in the absence of oxygen. That is why the fermentation tanks used in producing wine, beer, and other spirits are built specifically to keep oxygen out (**FIGURE 4-37**). Only in this circumstance will yeast be forced to use their backup respiratory pathway of fermentation.

TAKE-HOME MESSAGE 4·16

Oxygen deficiency limits the breakdown of fuel because the electron transport chain requires oxygen as the final acceptor of the electrons generated during glycolysis and the Krebs cycle. When oxygen is unavailable, yeast resort to fermentation, in which they use a different electron acceptor, pyruvate, generating in the process ethanol, the alcohol in beer, wine, and spirits.

Yeast is used in the production of beer.

FIGURE 4-37 Just a by-product of metabolism under stressful conditions. Beer, wine, and spirits are by-products of cellular metabolism in the absence of oxygen.

Eating a complete diet: cells can run on protein and fat as well as on glucose.

Most automobiles can run on only one type of fuel, gasoline. If you run out of fuel and cannot get to a gas station, you are out of luck. In this chapter, we have examined the steps by which plants, animals, and other organisms use glucose as fuel. But living organisms are more flexible than autos when it comes to fuel sources. They also have more complex needs than an automobile because their fuel must also provide raw materials for growth.

Evolution has built humans and other organisms with the metabolic machinery that allows them to extract energy and other valuable chemicals from proteins, fats, and a variety of carbohydrates (**FIGURE 4-38**). For that reason, we are able to consume and efficiently utilize meals comprising various combinations of molecules.

Sugars. In the case of dietary sugars, many are polysaccharides—multiple simple sugars linked together—rather than solely the simple sugar glucose. Before they can be broken down by cellular respiration, the polysaccharides must first be separated by enzymes into glucose or related simple sugars that can be broken down by cellular respiration.

Lipids. Dietary lipids are broken down into their two constituent parts: a glycerol molecule and fatty acids. The glycerol is chemically modified into one of the molecules produced during one of the 10 steps of glycolysis. It then enters glycolysis at that step in the process and is broken down to yield energy. The fatty acids, meanwhile, are chemically modified into acetyl-CoA, at which point they enter the Krebs cycle.

Proteins. Proteins are chains of amino acids. Upon consumption they are broken down chemically into their constituent amino acids. Once that is done, each amino acid is broken down into (1) an amino group that may be used in the production of tissue or excreted in the urine and (2) a carbon compound that is converted to one of the intermediate compounds in glycolysis or the Krebs cycle, allowing the energy stored in its chemical bonds to be harnessed.

In the end, humans (indeed, all animals) are able to harvest energy from a variety of food sources beyond simple glucose. Whether a meal contains carbohydrates, lipids, proteins, or some combination thereof, the nutrients are chemically modified in some preliminary steps and are then

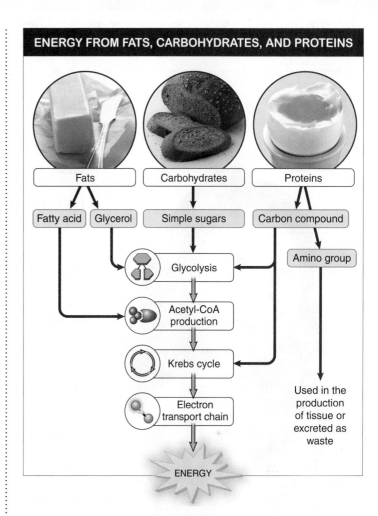

ENERGY FROM FATS, CARBOHYDRATES, AND PROTEINS

FIGURE 4-38 "More flexible than autos." Animals are able to harvest energy from proteins, carbohydrates, and lipids.

fed into one of the intermediate steps in glycolysis or the Krebs cycle to furnish usable energy for the organism (see Figure 4-38).

TAKE-HOME MESSAGE 4·17

Humans and other organisms have metabolic machinery that allows them to extract energy and other valuable chemicals from proteins, fats, and carbohydrates in addition to the simple sugar, glucose.

Knowledge You Can Use

Did you know? If you feed and protect your flowers in a vase, they'll last longer.

Fact: Like animals, plants require fuel for the cellular activities that keep them alive.

Q: How do plants get the energy they need to stay alive? Plants use photosynthesis to harness light energy, converting it to sugar molecules that serve as their food.

Q: Can plants still photosynthesize once they're in a vase in your house? Yes, but humans don't make it easy. Once cut, plants generally cannot produce sufficient sugar through photosynthesis. **Light levels in houses tend to be a bit too low, and the loss of many or most plant leaves reduces the number of chloroplasts in which photosynthesis can occur.** So they're starving to death.

Q: Can you slow their demise? Yes. **Plants are able to take up sugar in the vase water and use it as an energy source** for cell activities. So adding a bit of sugar is like putting fuel in their tank.

Q: Is it that easy? No. Putting sugar—a molecule with lots of energy stored within its chemical bonds—in the vase is like offering a free lunch. And many, many organisms are looking for a free lunch. Unfortunately, **when you add sugar, bacteria on the stems can grow rapidly, blocking the water-conducting tubes in flower stems.** This slows the flow not just of sugar, but of water as well.

Q: What should you do? With the addition to vase water of both sugar and an antibacterial chemical such as chlorine bleach, you can feed and protect your flowers, significantly increasing their longevity in vases.

Conclusion: Here's a useful summary from Martha Stewart (www .marthastewart.com): "Flowers last longer if their stems are cut under water. Use a sharp knife, and cut the stem on a slant so it can absorb as much water as possible. Next, place [the flowers] in a flask filled with 2 inches of warm water (no hotter than 110 degrees); this expedites the flow of water into the flower. Add either cut-flower food or a teaspoon of sugar and a couple drops of liquid bleach to a vase filled with cool water up to the point where the flower foliage will hit. After 5 minutes, transfer [the flowers] to the vase."

❶ Energy flows from the sun and through all life on earth.

Energy is neither created nor destroyed but can change forms. Energy from the sun fuels all life on earth as it is converted to different forms. Each conversion is inefficient and some of the usable energy is converted to less useful heat energy. Cells temporarily store energy in the bonds of ATP molecules. This potential energy can be converted to kinetic energy and used to fuel life-sustaining chemical reactions.

❷ Photosynthesis uses energy from sunlight to make food.

In the "photo" part of photosynthesis, chloroplasts transform light energy into the chemical energy of ATP and NADPH, while splitting water molecules and producing oxygen. In the Calvin cycle, the "synthesis" part of photosynthesis, carbon from CO_2 in the atmosphere is attached to molecules in chloroplasts to build sugars. This production of sugars consumes ATP and NADPH generated in the "photo" part of photosynthesis. C4 and CAM photosynthesis are evolutionary adaptations at the biochemical level that, although having competitive drawbacks, allow plants in hot, dry climates to close their stomata and conserve water without shutting down photosynthesis.

❸ Cellular respiration converts food molecules into ATP, a universal source of energy for living organisms.

In cellular respiration, glucose and oxygen are converted to carbon dioxide, water, and energy that is stored in the high-energy bonds of ATP molecules. In the electron transport chain, high-energy electrons from NADH and $FADH_2$ pass from carrier to carrier, releasing energy with each step. This energy fuels the creation of a proton concentration gradient. The energy released as the protons move back down their concentration gradient is used to produce ATP. Overall, the cellular respiration of one glucose molecule yields about 36 molecules of ATP.

❹ There are alternative pathways to energy acquisition.

Organisms are built with multiple systems for acquiring energy. They can generate ATP even when oxygen is lacking or when organic molecules other than glucose, such as lipids, proteins, and polysaccharides, are consumed.

KEY TERMS

adenosine triphosphate (ATP), p. 128
biofuel, p. 124
C4 photosynthesis, p. 141
Calvin cycle, p. 139
CAM (crassulacean acid metabolism), p. 142
carotenoid, p. 133
cellular respiration, p. 125
chemical energy, p. 127
chlorophyll, p. 132
chlorophyll *a*, p. 133

chlorophyll *b*, p. 133
chloroplast, p. 132
electromagnetic spectrum, p. 133
electron transport chain, p. 137
energy, p. 126
ethanol, p. 152
fermentation, p. 152
first law of thermodynamics, p. 128
fossil fuel, p. 124

glycolysis, p. 144
kinetic energy, p. 126
Krebs cycle, p. 146
light energy, p. 133
mitochondrial matrix, p. 149
NADPH, p. 138
photon, p. 133
photosynthesis, p. 125
photosystem, p. 136
pigment, p. 133
potential energy, p. 126

primary electron acceptor, p. 137
pyruvate, p. 144
rubisco, p. 139
second law of thermodynamics, p. 128
stoma (*pl.* stomata), p. 140
stroma, p. 132
thermodynamics, p. 128
thylakoid, p. 132

1. Animal fats and plant oils are sometimes used as sources of fuel for automobile engines. How is energy harvested from these molecules?
   a) They contain long chains of hydrogen and carbon that, when broken, release the energy stored in the bonds linking the atoms together.
   b) They contain hydrogen and carbon tails linked by disulfide bridges that, when broken, release chemical energy.
   c) They contain multiple phosphate groups that each release energy when "liberated" from the molecule chemically.
   d) They contain long hydrophobic regions that, when mixed with water, generate explosive resistances.
   e) They contain long carbon tails and each atom has unpaired electrons that are released on exposure to extreme heat and pressure.

2. A cyclist rides her bike up a very steep hill. Pick from the following choices the statement that properly describes this example in energetic terms.
   a) Potential energy in food is converted to kinetic energy as the cyclist's muscles push her up the hill.
   b) Kinetic energy is highest when the cyclist is at the crest of the hill.
   c) The cyclist produces the most potential energy as she cruises down the hill's steep slope.
   d) Potential energy is greatest when the cyclist is at the top of the hill.
   e) Both a) and d) are correct.

3. Every time a source of energy is converted from one form to another:
   a) the potential energy of the system increases.
   b) heat is required.
   c) the second law of thermodynamics is violated.
   d) the total amount of energy in the universe is reduced by a tiny amount.
   e) some of the energy is converted to heat, which is not a very usable form of kinetic energy.

4. In your body, when energy is released from the breakdown of a molecule such as glucose:
   a) adenosine monophosphate is created.
   b) adenosine diphosphate is created.
   c) some of the energy may be harnessed by building the unstable high-energy bonds that attach phosphate groups to ADP.
   d) molecules of ATP are required to capture and absorb the heat generated by the reaction.
   e) all of the energy is lost as heat.

5. A green plant can carry out photosynthesis if given nothing more than:
   a) water, light, and carbon dioxide.
   b) water, light, and oxygen.
   c) carbon dioxide.
   d) oxygen.
   e) oxygen and carbon dioxide.

6. The actual production of sugars during photosynthesis takes place:
   a) within the outer membrane of the chloroplast.
   b) within the stroma, inside the thylakoids of the chloroplast.
   c) within the stroma, outside the thylakoid, but still inside the chloroplast.
   d) just outside the chloroplast, within the mitochondria.
   e) within the thylakoid membrane of the chloroplast.

7. The leaves of plants can be thought of as "eating" sunlight. From an energetic perspective this makes sense because:
   a) light energy, like chemical energy released when the bonds of food molecules are broken, is a type of kinetic energy.
   b) both light energy and food energy can be converted to kinetic energy without the loss of heat.
   c) the carbon-oxygen bonds within a photon of light release energy when broken by the enzymes in chloroplasts.
   d) the carbon-hydrogen bonds within a photon of light release energy when broken by the enzymes in chloroplasts.
   e) photons are linked together by hydrogen bonds, which release energy when striking the surface of a leaf.

8. A molecule of chlorophyll increases in potential energy:
   a) when it binds to a photon.
   b) when one of its electrons is boosted to a higher-energy excited state on being struck by a photon of light.
   c) when it loses an electron.
   d) only in the presence of oxygen.
   e) None of the above. The potential energy of a molecule cannot change.

9. Photosynthesizing plants rely on water:
   a) to provide the protons necessary to produce chlorophyll.
   b) to concentrate the beams of light hitting a leaf, focusing them on the reaction center.
   c) to replenish oxygen molecules that are lost during photosynthesis.
   d) to replace electrons that are excited by light energy and pass from molecule to molecule down an electron transport chain.
   e) to serve as a high-energy electron carrier.

10. During photosynthesis, which step is most responsible for a plant's acquisition of new organic material?
    a) the "building" of NADPH during the Calvin cycle
    b) the excitation of chlorophyll molecules by photons of light
    c) the "plucking" of carbon molecules from the air and fixing of them to organic molecules within the chloroplast
    d) the loss of water through evaporation
    e) the production of ATP during the light reactions

11. During C4 photosynthesis:
    a) plants use less ATP when producing sugar.
    b) plants are able to continue producing sugars even when they must close their stomata to reduce water loss on hot days.
    c) plants are able to generate water molecules to cool their leaves.
    d) plants are able to reduce water loss by producing more rubisco.
    e) plants are able to produce sugars without any input of carbon dioxide.

12. Cellular respiration is the process by which:
    a) oxygen is used to transport chemical energy throughout the body.
    b) oxygen is produced during metabolic activity.
    c) light energy is converted to kinetic energy.
    d) ATP molecules are converted to water and sugar.
    e) energy from the chemical bonds of food molecules is captured by an organism.

13. During cellular respiration, most of the energy contained within the bonds of food molecules is captured in:
    a) the conversion of the kinetic energy of food to the potential energy of ATP.
    b) the Krebs cycle and electron transport chain.
    c) digestion.
    d) glycolysis.
    e) None of the above. Energy is lost, not gained, during cellular respiration.

14. Which of the following energy-generating processes is the only one that occurs in all living organisms?
    a) the Krebs cycle
    b) glycolysis
    c) combustion
    d) photosynthesis
    e) None of the above. There are no energy-generating processes that occur in all living organisms.

15. During the Krebs cycle:
    a) the products of glycolysis are further broken down, generating additional ATP and the high-energy electron carrier NADH.
    b) high-energy electron carriers pass their energy to molecules of sugar, which store them as potential energy.
    c) the products of glycolysis are further broken down, generating additional ATP and the high-energy electron carrier NADPH.
    d) cellular respiration can continue even in the absence of oxygen.
    e) the products of glycolysis are converted to acetyl-CoA.

16. Mitochondria have a "bag within a bag" structure. This structure is necessary in order to:
    a) create two distinct regions with a concentration gradient, a form of potential energy.
    b) keep molecules of ADP in close proximity to molecules of the ATP-synthesizing enzyme.
    c) allow light-reactive accessory pigments to be embedded within the membranes.
    d) segregate the most toxic digestive enzymes from molecules of ATP and NADP$^+$.
    e) None of the above.

17. All alcoholic beverages are produced as the result of:
    a) cellular respiration by bacteria that occurs in the absence of oxygen.
    b) cellular respiration by bacteria that occurs in the absence of free electrons.
    c) cellular respiration by yeast that occurs in the absence of free electrons.
    d) cellular respiration that occurs in the absence of sugar.
    e) cellular respiration by yeast that occurs in the absence of oxygen.

18. In harvesting the chemical energy of the molecules in food:
    a) all macromolecules must first be converted to glucose.
    b) all macromolecules must first be converted to their hydrocarbon chains.
    c) all macromolecules must first be converted to glucose or another simple sugar.
    d) organisms can use sugars, lipids, and proteins.
    e) all macromolecules must first be converted to proteins or free-form amino acids.

Short-Answer Questions

1. A plant and a mouse are placed in a sealed container with a watering system. For a period of time, both will survive. Explain what the two organisms can provide for each other in order to allow them to survive temporarily.

2. It is possible to measure the rate of the "photo" reactions in plants by measuring O_2 levels produced by chloroplasts. If bicarbonate solution, a source of CO_2, is provided to the plants, the rate of the "photo" reactions increases.

   a) Explain why measuring O_2 levels provides an indication of the rate of the "photo" reactions.

   b) Being as specific as possible, describe how the plants will use the CO_2 provided by the bicarbonate solution.

   c) Propose an explanation of how increasing the CO_2 source for the plants will affect the rate of the "photo" reactions.

3. Some plants grow much more quickly than others. For a plant that is growing at a rapid rate, propose a hypothesis as to whether cellular respiration or photosynthesis is occurring at a faster rate. Justify your hypothesis.

See Appendix for answers. For additional study questions, go to www.prep-u.com.

5

DNA, Gene Expression, and Biotechnology

What is the
code and how
is it harnessed?

① DNA: What is it and what does it do?

DNA microarrays measure the expression levels of many genes simultaneously.

5·1

"The DNA 200"—knowledge about DNA is increasing justice in the world.

In 1981, Julius Ruffin, a 27-year-old maintenance worker at Eastern Virginia Medical School, got onto an elevator and lost more than 20 years of his life. Several weeks earlier, a nursing student at the school had been raped by an attacker who broke into her apartment. When Ruffin got on the elevator, the student thought she recognized him as her attacker and called the police, who immediately arrested him.

Ruffin's girlfriend testified that he was with her at the time of the attack, but on the basis of the victim's eyewitness testimony, a jury found Ruffin guilty and sentenced him to life in prison. Ruffin maintained his innocence, to no avail, until 2003. At that time, the state's Division of Forensic Science performed a DNA analysis on a swab of evidence that remained from the investigation. The analysis revealed that Ruffin was not the

Q What is the most common reason why DNA analyses overturn incorrect criminal convictions?

attacker. Rather, the analysis showed that the DNA perfectly matched that of a man who was already in a Virginia prison, serving time for rape. Ruffin was freed, but only after having served more than two decades in prison (**FIGURE 5-1**).

Julius Ruffin's case is tragic, but it is not unusual. He is one of a group of 200 people in the United States who have been freed from prison as a result of DNA analyses. Called "the DNA 200," these unjustly imprisoned people spent an average of 12 years behind bars. Eighty percent had been convicted of sexual assault, 28% had been convicted of murder. In more than three-quarters of the cases, inaccurate eyewitness testimony played an important role in the guilty verdict. (Recall, from Chapter 1, the experiments that revealed the unreliability of eyewitness identification.)

What Is DNA?   Building Organisms   Genetic Damage   Biotechnology and Health

FIGURE 5-1 **Vindicated by DNA evidence.** Julius Ruffin was released from prison after two decades of wrongful incarceration.

In this chapter, we take a close look at DNA, the molecule responsible for Julius Ruffin's exoneration and the deferred justice served to the DNA 200. It is a molecule that all living organisms—people, plants, animals, bacteria, and otherwise—carry in almost every cell in their body (with just a few exceptions, such as red blood cells). Like a social security number, DNA is unique in virtually every person. In addition to being contained in our living cells, our DNA exists in what we leave behind. It is in our saliva, hair, blood, and even the dead skin cells that fall from our bodies. This is why DNA can serve as an individual identifier, a trail we all leave that is increasingly being used to ensure greater justice in our society.

The importance of DNA goes far beyond its function as an individual identifier, however. The information carried within this molecule, which is organized into individual units called genes, is among the most important of all biological knowledge. And, as witnessed by the following excerpts, it is often in the news.

"Selfish dictators may owe their behaviour partly to their genes, according to a study that claims to have found a genetic link to ruthlessness."
—*Nature,* April 2008

"Whether a man has one type of gene versus another could help decide whether he's good 'husband material,' a new study suggests."
—*Washington Post,* September 2008

By all accounts, we live in the "Age of the Gene." It's nearly impossible to open a newspaper or watch a news report these

FIGURE 5-2 **Genetics issues are in the news.**

days without being informed that yet another complex human characteristic or trait has been linked to a newly discovered gene (**FIGURE 5-2**). But what does that actually mean? What is this entity that apparently exerts influence over everything from our marriage readiness to our ruthlessness? We explore these issues and more in this chapter, beginning with a look at the structure of DNA itself and how it contains the information for producing organisms. In later sections of the chapter, we learn how modern manipulations of DNA are having far-reaching implications not just for human health but for agriculture as well.

TAKE-HOME MESSAGE 5·1

DNA is a molecule that all living organisms carry in every cell in their body. Because every person's DNA is unique and because we leave a trail of DNA behind us as we go about our lives, DNA can serve as an individual identifier. This fact is the basis of the DNA analysis that is being used increasingly to ensure greater justice in our society, such as by establishing the innocence of individuals wrongly convicted of crimes.

The DNA molecule contains instructions for the development and functioning of all living organisms.

Beginning in the 1900s and continuing through the early 1950s, a series of experiments revealed two important features of DNA. First, molecules of DNA are passed down from parent to offspring. Second, the instructions on how to create a body and control its growth and development are encoded in the DNA molecule.

Once scientists knew that DNA encoded instructions and that these instructions were passed on from one generation to the next, DNA became something of a celebrity molecule. Given that it must be able to hold the instructions for how to produce every possible type of structure in every living organism, scientists were crazed to learn all they could about it. There was a spirited race to determine the chemical structure of DNA and to understand how the molecule was assembled and shaped so that it could hold and transmit so much information.

Many formidable scientists rose to the challenge of determining the structure of DNA. American Linus Pauling had already won a Nobel prize in chemistry for his work on elucidating the structure of molecules when he began investigating the structure of DNA. Simultaneously, Maurice Wilkins and Rosalind Franklin in England devoted their research to this task as well, and produced X-ray pictures of DNA that were critical to decoding its shape. But it was Englishman Francis Crick and American James Watson, working in Cambridge, England, who happened to put all the pieces together and deduce the exact structure of DNA (**FIGURE 5-3**). As we will see later in this chapter, their discovery was more than just a description of a molecule. As soon as they figured out DNA's structure, the answers to several other thorny problems in biology—such as how DNA might be able to duplicate itself—became apparent immediately. We explore that process later in this chapter, but first we need to examine the structure of DNA in more detail.

DNA (deoxyribonucleic acid) is a **nucleic acid,** a macromolecule that stores information. It consists of individual units called **nucleotides,** which have three components: a molecule of sugar, a phosphate group (containing four oxygen atoms bound to a phosphorus atom), and a nitrogen-containing molecule called a **base.** The physical structure of DNA is frequently described as a "double helix." What exactly is a double helix? Picture a long ladder twisted around like a spiral staircase and you'll have a good idea of what a DNA molecule looks like (**FIGURE 5-4**). The molecule has two distinct strands, like the vertical sides of a ladder. These are the "backbones" of the DNA molecule, and each is made from two alternating

FIGURE 5-3 Watson and Crick. James Watson and Francis Crick figured out the exact structure of DNA. The first sketch of the double helix (lower right) was rendered by Crick's wife, Odile.

molecules: a sugar, then a phosphate, then a sugar, then a phosphate, and so on. The sugar is always deoxyribose and the phosphate molecule is always the same, too. It is the shapes of the backbones that cause the DNA "ladder" to twist.

The alternating sugars and phosphates hold everything in place, but they play only a supporting role. The rungs of the ladder are where things get interesting. Attached to each sugar, and protruding like half of a rung on the ladder, is one of the nitrogen-containing bases. Each sugar always has a base attached to it, and there are four different kinds of bases—adenine, thymine, cytosine, and guanine. When discussing DNA, these bases are usually referred to by their first letter: A, T, C, and G.

Both backbones of the ladder have a base protruding from each sugar. The base on one side of the ladder binds, via hydrogen bonds, to a base on the other side, and together these **base pairs** form the rungs of the ladder. They don't just pair up at random, though. Every time a C protrudes from one side, it forms hydrogen bonds with a G on the other side (and

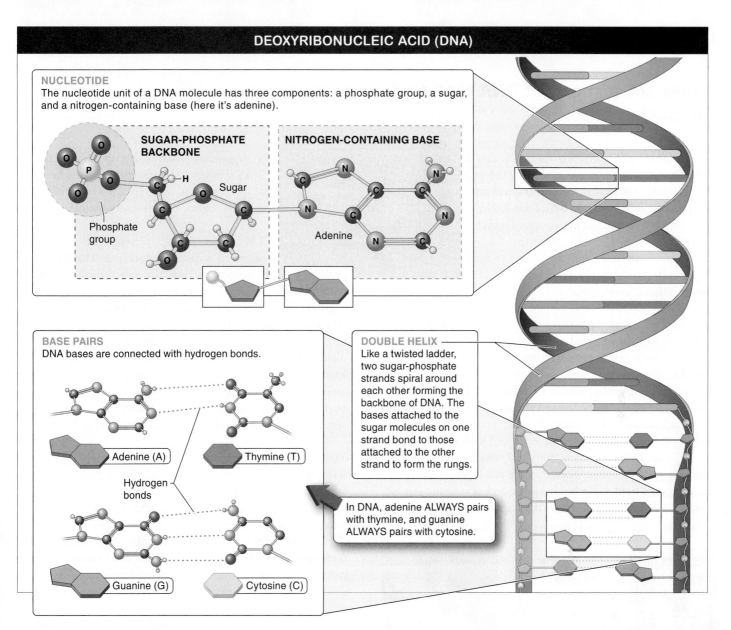

NUCLEOTIDE
The nucleotide unit of a DNA molecule has three components: a phosphate group, a sugar, and a nitrogen-containing base (here it's adenine).

SUGAR-PHOSPHATE BACKBONE

Phosphate group

Sugar

NITROGEN-CONTAINING BASE

Adenine

BASE PAIRS
DNA bases are connected with hydrogen bonds.

Adenine (A)

Thymine (T)

Hydrogen bonds

Guanine (G)

Cytosine (C)

DOUBLE HELIX
Like a twisted ladder, two sugar-phosphate strands spiral around each other forming the backbone of DNA. The bases attached to the sugar molecules on one strand bond to those attached to the other strand to form the rungs.

In DNA, adenine ALWAYS pairs with thymine, and guanine ALWAYS pairs with cytosine.

FIGURE 5-4 Overview of the structure of DNA.

vice versa: a G always bonds to a C). Similarly, every time a T protrudes from one side, it forms hydrogen bonds with an A on the other side (and vice versa). For this reason, each DNA molecule always has the same number of Gs and Cs, and the same numbers of As and Ts. Because of these base-pairing rules, it also is true that if we know the base sequence for one of the strands in a DNA molecule, we know the sequence in the other. For this reason, a DNA sequence is described by writing the sequence of bases on only one of the strands.

If our DNA molecule were really a spiraled ladder, it would be a very, very long one. One molecule of DNA can have as many as 200 million base pairs, or rungs. This length would make it difficult to squeeze the molecule into the cell. But the rungs are small and the twisting of the molecule—twists upon

twists—shortens it considerably: think about how, if you repeatedly twist your shoe lace around and around, it becomes shorter and shorter. That's what happens with DNA. Let's now investigate how DNA's structure—the rungs of the ladder, in particular—enables it to carry information.

TAKE-HOME MESSAGE 5·2

DNA is a nucleic acid, a macromolecule that stores information. It consists of individual units called nucleotides: a sugar, a phosphate group, and a nitrogen-containing base. DNA's structure resembles a twisted ladder, with the sugar and phosphate groups serving as the backbones of the molecule and base pairs serving as the rungs.

5·3

Genes are sections of DNA that contain instructions for making proteins.

One of DNA's most amazing features is that it embodies the instructions for building the cells and structures for virtually every single living organism on earth (**FIGURE 5-5**). Thus, DNA is like a universal language, the letters of which are the bases A, T, C, and G. (Note that the sugar-phosphate backbone only serves to hold the bases in sequence, like the binding of a book. It does not convey genetic information.)

> **Q** Why is DNA considered the universal code for all life on earth?

You can think of an organism's DNA as a cookbook. Just as a cookbook contains detailed instructions on how to make a variety of foods (such as french toast, macaroni and cheese, or chocolate chip cookies), an organism's DNA carries the detailed instructions to build an organism and keep it running. And just as a book can be viewed as a sequence of letters, with the book's meaning determined by which letters are strung together and in what order, a molecule of DNA can be viewed as a sequence of bases. Letters don't have much meaning on their own, of course, but when they are put together into words and sentences, their order holds a great deal of information. Similarly, the sequence in which bases appear in a molecule of

an organism's DNA makes up a "code" that holds the detailed instructions for the building of the organism, whether it is a one-celled amoeba, a giant oak tree, or a biology student.

The full set of DNA present in an individual organism is called its **genome** (**FIGURE 5-6**). In prokaryotes, including all bacteria, the information is contained within circular pieces of DNA. In eukaryotes, including humans, this information is laid out in long linear strands of DNA in the nucleus. Rather than being one super-long DNA strand, eukaryotic DNA exists as many smaller, more manageable pieces, called **chromosomes.** Humans, for example, have three billion base pairs, divided into 23 unique pieces of DNA (and we have two copies of each piece, one from our mother and one from our father, for a total of 46 chromosomes and six billion base pairs in every cell).

The number of chromosomes varies from species to species, but is not related to how simple or complex an organism is. Corn, for example, has 10 unique chromosomes and fruit flies have only 4. Dogs and chickens have 39 different chromosomes, while goldfish put most other animal species to shame with 50 different chromosomes. As in humans, individuals in each of these species inherit one copy of each chromosome from each parent, so the total number of chromosomes in a cell is doubled— a dog, for example, has 78 chromosomes in each cell. Chromosomes vary in length, too. In humans, the longest chromosome has more than 200 million base pairs and the shortest has fewer than 50 million.

Within the long sequences of bases are relatively short sequences, on average about 3,000 bases long, that are the actual genes. "Gene" may seem like an impossibly nebulous concept because the word is often used casually in the media as if it were some magical, irresistible, and mysterious force that controls our bodies and behavior. Beyond these vague descriptions, though, the word has a literal meaning. A **gene** is a sequence of bases (strictly, as we've noted, base pairs) in a DNA molecule that carries the information necessary for producing a functional product, usually a protein or RNA molecule. Nothing more, nothing less.

Remember that a DNA molecule is like a ladder in which half of each rung is any one of the four bases— A, T, G, or C. Strung together, a segment might be read as "AAAGGCTAGGC . . ." continuing on for another

DNA provides the instructions for building virtually every organism on earth!

FIGURE 5-5 DNA is the universal code for all life on earth.

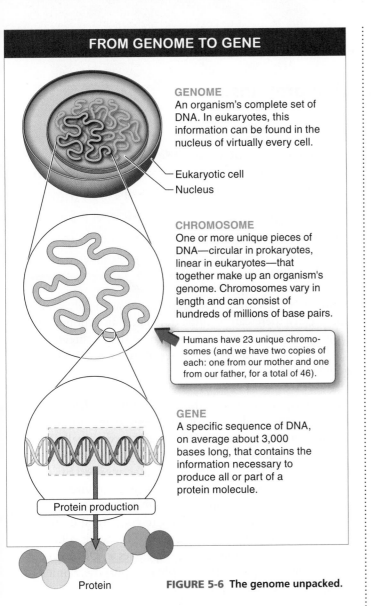

GENOME
An organism's complete set of DNA. In eukaryotes, this information can be found in the nucleus of virtually every cell.

— Eukaryotic cell
— Nucleus

CHROMOSOME
One or more unique pieces of DNA—circular in prokaryotes, linear in eukaryotes—that together make up an organism's genome. Chromosomes vary in length and can consist of hundreds of millions of base pairs.

Humans have 23 unique chromosomes (and we have two copies of each: one from our mother and one from our father, for a total of 46).

GENE
A specific sequence of DNA, on average about 3,000 bases long, that contains the information necessary to produce all or part of a protein molecule.

Protein production

Protein

FIGURE 5-6 The genome unpacked.

3,000 or so bases. Returning to our cookbook analogy, this segment can be thought of as a recipe, which is also a series of letters. And just as a particular sequence of letters in a cookbook may be read and understood as the directions for baking chocolate chip cookies, the sequence of bases in DNA also carries information. Perhaps the sequence spells out part of the instructions for producing a red blood cell, for constructing the keratin that will form part of a curly strand of hair, or for assembling a chemical that alters your brain chemistry so that you exhibit a mood disorder or suicidal behavior.

Each gene is the instruction set for producing one particular molecule, usually a protein. For example, there is a gene in silk moths that codes for fibroin, the chief component of silk. And, there is a gene in humans that codes for triglyceride lipase, an enzyme that breaks down dietary fat. Within a species, individuals sometimes have slightly different instruction sets for a given protein, and these instructions can result in a different version of the same characteristic. These alternative versions of a gene that

ALLELES

Within a species, individuals sometimes have alternate versions of a gene for a given protein. These instructions can result in a different version of the same trait.

ALLELE
Alternate versions of a gene that code for the same trait

ALLELE 1   ALLELE 2   ALLELE 3

Protein production   Protein production   Protein production

The protein, influenced by the environment and in some cases other genes, then produces the trait.

FIGURE 5-7 "Different versions of the same thing." Alleles are alternative versions of a gene.

code for the same feature are called **alleles** (**FIGURE 5-7**). And any single characteristic or feature of an organism is referred to as a **trait**. A simple hypothetical example will clarify the meaning of these terms. The color of a daisy's petals is a trait. The instructions for producing this trait are found in a gene that controls petal color. However, this gene may have many different alleles; one allele may specify the trait of red petals, another may specify white petals, and yet another may specify yellow petals. Similarly, one allele for eye color in fruit flies may carry the instructions for producing a red eye, while another, slightly different allele may have instructions for brown eyes. (Ultimately, the trait may be influenced not just by the genes an individual carries but the way those genes interact with the environment, too.)

TAKE-HOME MESSAGE 5·3

DNA is a universal language that provides the instructions for building all the structures in all living organisms. The full set of DNA an organism carries is called its genome. In prokaryotes, the DNA occurs in circular pieces. In eukaryotes, the genome is divided among smaller, linear strands of DNA called chromosomes. A gene is a sequence of bases in a DNA molecule that carries the information necessary for producing a functional product, usually a protein or RNA molecule.

Not all DNA contains instructions for making proteins.

It is debatable whether humans are the most complex species on the planet, but surely we must be more complex than an onion. "Complexity" is somewhat subjective and can be assessed in a variety of ways, such as by counting the number of different cell types in the organism. But if we measured complexity simply as the amount of DNA an organism has, we'd have to say an onion is more complex—it has more than five times as much DNA as a human (**FIGURE 5-8**)! We don't fare any better when compared with some other seemingly simple organisms, either. The salamander species *Amphiuma means,* for example, has about 25 times as much DNA as we do, and one species of amoeba—a single-celled organism—has almost 200 times as much!

Comparing the amount of DNA present in various species, in terms of both numbers of chromosomes and numbers of base pairs, reveals a paradox: there does not seem to be any relationship between the size of an organism's genome and the organism's complexity. Moreover, among species of seemingly similar complexity, there can be huge differences in genome size (among fish, for example, there is more than a threefold difference among different species of sturgeon). What is going on?

> **Q** An onion has five times as much DNA as a human. Why doesn't that make onions more complex than us?

The description earlier in this chapter about what DNA is and how genes code for proteins is logical and tidy, but it doesn't completely explain what we observe in cells. In humans, for example, genes make up less than 5% of the DNA (**FIGURE 5-9**). In many species, the proportion of the DNA that consists of genes is even smaller. In virtually all eukaryotic species, the amount of DNA present far exceeds the amount necessary to code for all of the proteins in the organism. The fact is, a huge proportion of base sequences in DNA do not code for anything and have no obvious purpose. Some biologists even call it "junk DNA."

In what types of organisms do we find the most "junk DNA"? Bacteria and viruses tend to have very little non-coding DNA; genes make up 90% or more of their DNA. It is in the eukaryotes (with the exception of yeasts) that we see an explosion in the amount of non-coding DNA, about 25% of which occurs within genes and 75% between genes (**FIGURE 5-10**).

Non-coding regions of DNA sometimes take the form of short sequences that are repeated thousands (or even hundreds of thousands) of times. Other times, the non-coding regions are slightly longer repeated sequences. Occasionally, the non-coding DNA consists of gene fragments, duplicate versions of genes, and pseudogenes (sequences very similar to actual genes but with a few slight alterations that make them lose their protein-coding ability). Non-coding regions occur both within genes—in which case they are called **introns**—and between genes.

GENOME SIZES OF VARIOUS ORGANISMS

Human (*Homo sapiens*) — 3,400

Newt (*Amphiuma means*) — 84,000

Fruit fly (*Drosophila melanogaster*) — 180

Onion (*Allium cepa*) — 18,000

Amoeba (*Amoeba dubia*) — 670,000

Estimated genome size (millions of base pairs)

> 💡 An onion has more than five times as much DNA in every cell as a human does! A newt and an amoeba have even more.

FIGURE 5-8 Is the size of an organism's genome related to its complexity?

What Is DNA?   Building Organisms   Genetic Damage   Biotechnology and Health

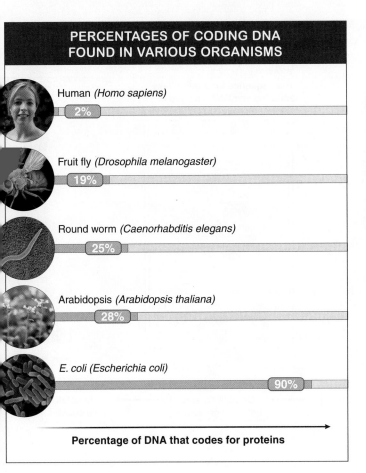

PERCENTAGES OF CODING DNA FOUND IN VARIOUS ORGANISMS

Human (*Homo sapiens*)
2%

Fruit fly (*Drosophila melanogaster*)
19%

Round worm (*Caenorhabditis elegans*)
25%

Arabidopsis (*Arabidopsis thaliana*)
28%

E. coli (*Escherichia coli*)
90%

Percentage of DNA that codes for proteins

FIGURE 5-9 **"Junk DNA"?** The proportion of DNA that codes for proteins or RNA varies greatly among species. Which species seems to have the least "junk DNA"?

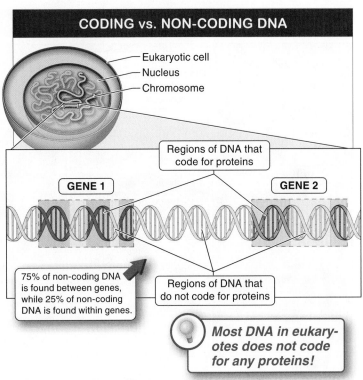

CODING vs. NON-CODING DNA

Eukaryotic cell
Nucleus
Chromosome

Regions of DNA that code for proteins

GENE 1   GENE 2

75% of non-coding DNA is found between genes, while 25% of non-coding DNA is found within genes.

Regions of DNA that do not code for proteins

Most DNA in eukaryotes does not code for any proteins!

FIGURE 5-10 **Non-coding regions of DNA.** These regions are found both between and within genes.

In the end, the presence of all this non-coding DNA remains a big mystery. All the extra DNA may serve some purpose. Perhaps it is a reservoir of potentially useful sequences. Or it may have some function in regulating when genes are turned on or off. Because we are not certain what non-coding DNA does, the label "junk DNA" is probably a bad description for it. The jury is still out and it is too early to assume that it has no function.

TAKE-HOME MESSAGE 5•4

Only a small fraction of the DNA in eukaryotic species is in genes, coding for proteins or RNA; the function of the rest is still a mystery.

5•5

How do genes work? An overview.

Just as having a recipe for chocolate chip cookies is not the same thing as having the actual cookies, having a wealth of hereditary information about how to build muscle cells or root cells or leaf cells is not sufficient to produce an organism. Think about it: every cell in an organism contains all of the information needed to manufacture every protein in its body. This means that the skin cells on your arm contain the genes

for producing proteins only found in liver cells or red blood cells or muscle tissue—but they don't produce them. Having the instructions is not the same as having the products.

The genes in strands of DNA are a storehouse of information, an instruction book, but they are only one part of the process by which an organism is built. If the genes that an organism

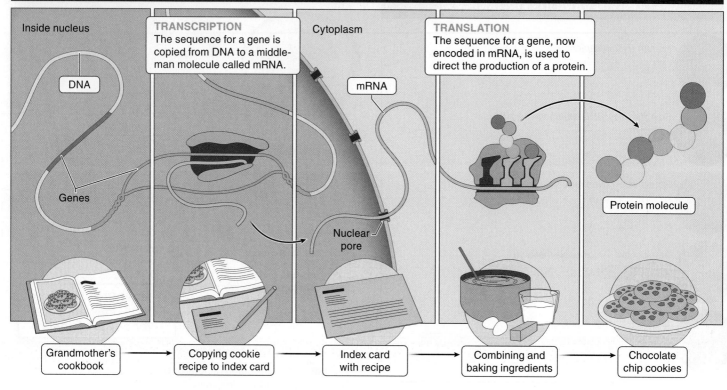

FIGURE 5-11 Overview of the steps from gene to protein.

carries for a particular trait—its **genotype**—are like a recipe in a cookbook, the physical manifestation of the instructions—the organism's **phenotype**—is the cookie, the macaroni and cheese, the french toast, or any of the other foods described by the recipes. And, just as you have to assemble ingredients, mix them, then bake the dough to get a cookie, there are several steps in the production of the molecules, tissues, and even behaviors that make up a phenotype.

How does a gene (a sequence of bases in a section of DNA) affect a flower's color or the shape of a nose or the texture of a dog's fur (the phenotype)? The process occurs in two main steps: **transcription,** in which a copy of a gene's base sequence is made, and **translation,** in which that copy is used to direct the production of a protein.

FIGURE 5-11 presents an overview of the processes of transcription and translation. In transcription, which in

eukaryotes occurs in the nucleus, the gene's base sequence or **code** is copied into a middleman molecule called **messenger RNA (mRNA)**. This is like copying the information for the chocolate chip cookie recipe out of the cookbook and onto an index card. In translation, the mRNA moves out of the nucleus and into the cytoplasm of the cell, where the messages encoded in the mRNA molecules are used to build proteins.

TAKE-HOME MESSAGE 5·5

The genes in strands of DNA are a storehouse of information, an instruction book. The process by which this information is used to build an organism occurs in two main steps: transcription, in which a copy of a gene's base sequence is made, and translation, in which that copy is used to direct the production of a protein.

❷ Building organisms: through gene expression, information in the DNA directs the production of the molecules that make up an organism.

Transcription and translation are a bit like copying a cookie recipe, then baking the cookies.

5·6

In transcription, the information coded in DNA is copied into mRNA.

If DNA is like a cookbook filled with recipes, transcription and translation are like cooking. In cooking, you use information about how to make chocolate chip cookies to actually produce the cookies. In an organism, the information about putting together proteins is used to build the proteins the organism needs in order to function. In this section, we examine transcription, the first step in the two-step process by which DNA regulates a cell's activity and its synthesis of proteins (see Figure 5-11). In transcription, a single copy of one specific gene within the DNA is made. Continuing our cookbook analogy, transcription is like copying a single recipe from the cookbook onto an index card. It happens in four steps (**FIGURE 5-12**).

Step 1. Recognize and bind. To start the transcription process, a large molecule, the enzyme RNA polymerase, recognizes a **promoter site,** a part of the DNA molecule that indicates the start of a gene, and, in effect, tells the RNA polymerase, "Start here." RNA polymerase binds to the DNA molecule at the promoter site and unwinds it just a bit, so that only one strand of the DNA can be read. Then, like a court reporter transcribing everything that is said in a courtroom, RNA polymerase begins to read the gene's message.

Step 2. Transcribe. As the DNA strand is processed through the RNA polymerase, the RNA polymerase builds a copy—called a "transcript"—of the gene from the DNA molecule. This copy is called messenger RNA (mRNA) because, once this copy of the gene is created, it can move elsewhere in the cell and its message can be translated into a protein. Throughout transcription, DNA is unwound ahead of the RNA polymerase so that a single strand of the DNA can be read, and is rewound after the polymerase passes.

The mRNA transcript is constructed from four different molecules called ribonucleotides (which are almost identical to DNA nucleotides, consisting of a sugar-phosphate complex with a nitrogen-containing base attached). Each

TRANSCRIPTION

1 RECOGNIZE and BIND
Once RNA polymerase recognizes a promoter site, it binds to one strand of the DNA and begins reading the gene's message.

RNA polymerase

Promoter site

DNA

2 TRANSCRIBE
As the DNA strand is processed through the RNA polymerase, the RNA polymerase builds a single-strand copy of the gene, called the mRNA transcript.

RNA polymerase

mRNA transcript

3 TERMINATE
When the RNA polymerase encounters a code signaling the end of the gene, it stops transcription and releases the mRNA transcript.

RNA polymerase

Termination site

mRNA transcript

UNWIND and REWIND
As the RNA polymerase moves down the strand of DNA, the helix unwinds so that the DNA can be read. At the same time, the DNA that has already been transcribed rewinds back to its original double-helix form.

Helix unwinds

Helix rewinds

Cap

Tail

Non-protein-coding regions of mRNA

4 CAPPING and EDITING
Before the mRNA transcript can be translated into a protein, a cap and tail are often added for protection and to promote recognition, and non-coding sections are removed.

mRNA transcript leaves nucleus to be translated into a protein.

FIGURE 5-12 Transcription: copying the base sequence of a gene. The first step in a two-step process by which DNA regulates a cell's activity and synthesis of proteins.

ribonucleotide pairs up with an exposed base on the now unwound and separated DNA, following these rules:

If the DNA strand has a thymine (T), an adenine (A) is added to the mRNA.

If the DNA strand has an adenine (A), a uracil (U) is added to the mRNA.

If the DNA strand has a guanine (G), a cytosine (C) is added to the mRNA.

If the DNA strand has a cytosine (C), a guanine (G) is added to the mRNA.

Because our court reporter (RNA polymerase) transcribes a specific sequence of DNA letters (the gene), the mRNA transcript carries this specific bit of the DNA's information. And because it is separate from the DNA, the mRNA transcript can move throughout the cell, to the places where the information is needed, while leaving the original information within the DNA.

Step 3. Terminate. When the RNA polymerase encounters a sequence of bases on the DNA at the end of the gene (called a termination sequence), it stops creating the transcript and detaches from the DNA molecule. After termination, the mRNA molecule is released as a free-floating, single-strand copy of the gene.

Step 4. Capping and editing. In prokaryotic cells, once the mRNA transcript separates from the DNA it is ready to be translated into a protein (it doesn't have a nuclear membrane to cross). In most eukaryotes, however, the transcript must first be edited in several ways. First, a cap and a tail may be added at the beginning and end of the transcript. Like a front and back cover to a book, these serve to protect the mRNA from damage and help the protein-making machinery recognize the mRNA. Second, because (as we saw earlier in the chapter) there may have been non-coding bits of DNA transcribed into mRNA, those sections—the introns—are snipped out. Once the mRNA transcript has been edited, it is ready to leave the nucleus for the cytoplasm, where it will be translated into a protein.

TAKE-HOME MESSAGE 5·6

Transcription is the first step in the two-step process by which DNA directs the synthesis of proteins. In transcription (occurring in the nucleus in eukaryotic cells), a single copy of one specific gene in the DNA is made, in the form of a molecule of mRNA, and this moves to the cytoplasm where it can be translated into a protein.

5·7

In translation, information from DNA is used to build functional molecules.

Once the mRNA molecule moves out of the cell's nucleus and into the cytoplasm, the translation process begins. In translation, the information carried by the mRNA is read and ingredients present in the cytoplasm are used to produce a protein (see Figure 5-11). The process of translation is like the combining and baking of the ingredients listed in our chocolate chip cookie recipe to produce a cookie.

Several ingredients must be present in the cytoplasm for translation to occur. First, there must be large numbers of free amino acids floating around. Recall from Chapter 2 that amino acids are the raw materials for building proteins and an essential component of our diet. Second, there must be molecules called **ribosomal subunits,** the protein-production factories where amino acids are linked together in the proper order to produce the protein. Finally, there must also be molecules that can read the mRNA code and translate it from a sequence of bases into a protein. These molecules, called **transfer RNA (tRNA),** interpret the mRNA code and link specific base sequences on the mRNA with specific amino acids (**FIGURE 5-13**). Because tRNAs play such a central role in translation, we examine them more closely.

Human translators can hear one a word in one language and say the same word in a different language. Transfer RNA molecules function in a similar manner. Picture a two-sided

TRANSFER RNA (tRNA)

Transfer RNA (tRNA) molecules translate the mRNA code, linking specific bases on the mRNA with specific amino acids that will be used to build a protein.

Amino acid

tRNA

Attachment site

Attachment sites consist of a three-base sequence that matches up with a three-base sequence on the mRNA transcript. Each three-base sequence in mRNA—called a codon— always matches with a tRNA that carries one particular amino acid.

Codon

mRNA

FIGURE 5-13 Each transfer RNA attaches a particular amino acid to the mRNA.

TRANSLATION

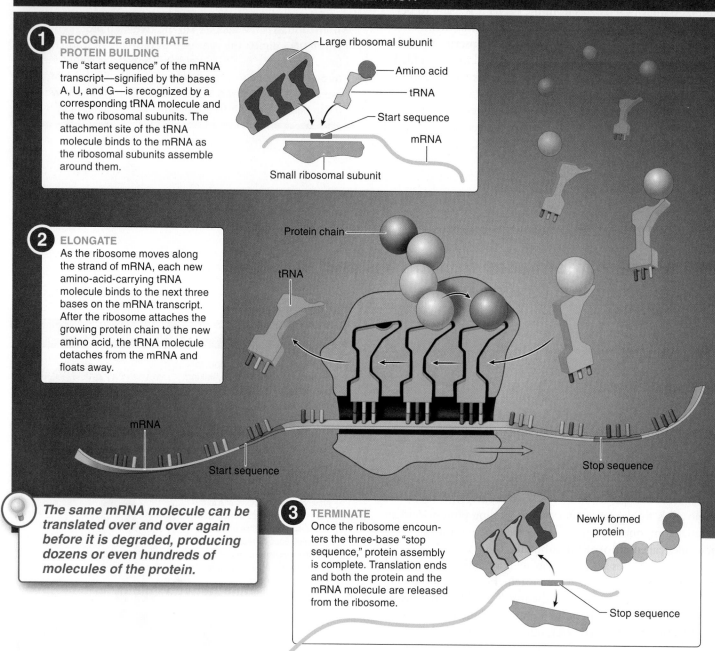

1 **RECOGNIZE and INITIATE PROTEIN BUILDING**
The "start sequence" of the mRNA transcript—signified by the bases A, U, and G—is recognized by a corresponding tRNA molecule and the two ribosomal subunits. The attachment site of the tRNA molecule binds to the mRNA as the ribosomal subunits assemble around them.

Large ribosomal subunit

Amino acid

tRNA

Start sequence

mRNA

Small ribosomal subunit

2 **ELONGATE**
As the ribosome moves along the strand of mRNA, each new amino-acid-carrying tRNA molecule binds to the next three bases on the mRNA transcript. After the ribosome attaches the growing protein chain to the new amino acid, the tRNA molecule detaches from the mRNA and floats away.

Protein chain

tRNA

mRNA

Start sequence

Stop sequence

The same mRNA molecule can be translated over and over again before it is degraded, producing dozens or even hundreds of molecules of the protein.

3 **TERMINATE**
Once the ribosome encounters the three-base "stop sequence," protein assembly is complete. Translation ends and both the protein and the mRNA molecule are released from the ribosome.

Newly formed protein

Stop sequence

FIGURE 5-14 Translation: reading a sequence of nucleotides and producing protein. The second step in a two-step process by which DNA regulates a cell's activity and synthesis of proteins.

What Is DNA?   Building Organisms   Genetic Damage   Biotechnology and Health

molecule. On one side a particular amino acid is attached. This amino acid can be any one of the 20 different amino acids that make up proteins. In other words, there are different tRNA molecules for each of the 20 different amino acid molecules, which are floating around in the cytoplasm in great numbers. On the other side of the two-sided tRNA molecule is an attachment site, consisting of a three-base sequence that matches up with a three-base sequence on the mRNA transcript. (Each three-base sequence in mRNA—called a **codon**—always matches with a tRNA that carries one particular amino acid.) This matchup enables the tRNA molecule to attach to the mRNA. Thus, the tRNA translates the code on the mRNA into an amino acid that will be used to build a protein. Translation occurs in three steps (**FIGURE 5-14**).

Step 1. Recognize and initiate protein building. Translation begins in the cell's cytoplasm when the subunits of a ribosome, essentially a two-piece protein-building factory, recognizes and assembles around a "start sequence" on the mRNA transcript. This start sequence is always the sequence A, U, and G (AUG). As the ribosomal subunits assemble themselves into a ribosome, one side of a tRNA molecule also recognizes the start sequence on the mRNA and binds to it. This initiator tRNA has the amino acid methionine bound to its other side. This will be the first amino acid in the protein that is to be produced (although occasionally, in eukaryotes, it is eventually "edited out").

Step 2. Elongate. After the mRNA start sequence (AUG), the next three bases on the mRNA specify which amino acid–carrying tRNA molecule should bind to the mRNA. If the next three bases on the mRNA transcript are GUU, for example, a tRNA molecule that recognizes that sequence, and carrying its particular amino acid, will attach to the mRNA at that point. The ribosome then facilitates the connection of this second amino acid to the first. After the amino acid carried by a tRNA molecule is attached to the preceding amino acid, the tRNA molecule detaches from the mRNA and floats away.

As this process continues, the protein grows. The next three bases on the mRNA specify the next amino acid to be added to the first two. And the three bases after that specify the fourth amino acid, and so on. This process is called **protein synthesis** because all proteins are chains of amino acids, like beads on a string.

The mRNA continues to be "threaded" through the ribosome, with the ribosome moving down the mRNA strand reading and translating its message in little three-base chunks. Each three-base sequence specifies the next amino acid, lengthening the growing amino acid strand.

Step 3. Terminate. Eventually, the ribosome arrives at the three-base sequence on the mRNA that signals the end of translation. Once the ribosome encounters this stop sequence, the assembly of the protein is complete. Translation ends, and the amino acid strand and mRNA molecule are released from the ribosome. As it is produced, the amino acid sequence folds and bends, based on the chemical features in the amino acid side chains (as we saw in Chapter 2), acquiring a three-dimensional structure. The completed protein—such as a membrane protein or insulin or a digestive enzyme—may be used within the cell or packaged for delivery via the bloodstream to somewhere else in the body where it is needed.

Following the completion of translation, the mRNA strand may remain in the cytoplasm to serve as the template for producing another molecule of the same protein. In bacteria, an mRNA strand may last from a few seconds to more than an hour; in mammals, mRNA may last several days. Depending on how long it lasts, the same mRNA strand may be translated hundreds of times. Eventually, it is broken down by enzymes in the cytoplasm.

TAKE-HOME MESSAGE 5·7

Translation is the second step in the two-step process by which DNA directs the synthesis of proteins. In translation, the information from a gene that has been encoded in the nucleotide sequence of an mRNA is read and ingredients present in the cell's cytoplasm are used to produce a protein.

❸ Damage to the genetic code has a variety of causes and effects.

Damage to the genetic code can interfere with normal development.

5·8

What causes a mutation and what are its effects?

Through the two-step process of transcription and translation, an organism converts the information held in its genes into the proteins necessary for life. But the process is only as good as the organism's underlying genetic information. Sometimes, however, something occurs to alter the sequence of bases in an organism's DNA. Such an alteration is called a **mutation,** and it can lead to changes in the structure and function of the proteins produced. Mutations can have a range of effects. Sometimes they result in a serious, even deadly, problem for an organism. Sometimes they have little or no detrimental effect. And, occasionally—but very rarely—they may even turn out to be beneficial to the organism.

As an example of how mutations can affect organisms, consider the case of breast cancer in humans. When two human genes, called BRCA1 and BRCA2, are functioning properly, they help to prevent breast cancer by deterring cells from dividing uncontrollably. If the DNA sequence of either of these genes is altered through mutation and the gene's normal function is lost, the person carrying the gene has a significantly increased risk of developing breast cancer. (Because a variety of other factors, including environmental variables, are involved in development of cancer, it's impossible to know for certain whether these individuals will definitely develop breast cancer.) Currently, more than 200 different changes in the DNA sequences of these genes have been detected, each of which results in an increased risk of developing breast cancer.

Given the havoc they can cause for an organism, it's not surprising that mutations have a bad reputation. After all, because they can change the protein produced, they tend to disrupt normal processes and usually harm the individual (**FIGURE 5-15**). Fortunately, mutations are very, very rare. More surprising, though, is the paradoxical fact that mutations are essential to evolution. Those mutations that don't kill an organism, or reduce its ability to survive and reproduce, can be beneficial. Every genetic feature in every organism was, initially, the result of a mutation. In Chapter 8, we will explore the relationship between mutation and evolution.

What Is DNA?   Building Organisms   Genetic Damage   Biotechnology and Health

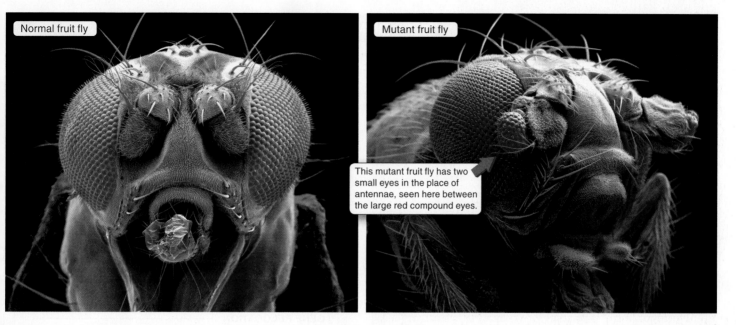

Normal fruit fly

Mutant fruit fly

This mutant fruit fly has two small eyes in the place of antennae, seen here between the large red compound eyes.

FIGURE 5-15 Wreaking havoc. Mutations can change the protein produced by the altered gene, with disastrous consequences.

It's important to note that mutations can occur in an organism's gamete-producing cells (that is, cells that produce sperm or eggs) as well as in its non-sex cells (such as skin cells or cells in the lungs). Mutations in the non-sex cells generally have bad health consequences for the person carrying them. Many forms of cancer, such as lung cancer or skin cancer, result from such mutations. On the upside, though, non-sex-cell mutations are not passed on to your children. Mutations in the sex cells (gametes), on the other hand, do not have any adverse health effects on the person carrying them, but they can be passed on to offspring, with terrible effects such as the induction of a miscarriage or the occurrence of birth defects. Individuals inheriting certain mutations from a parent—because the mutation occurred in the parent's sex cells or the parent inherited the mutation from his or her parent—can be at increased risk for certain diseases such as breast cancer or cardiovascular disease.

Mutations generally fall into two types: point mutations and chromosomal aberrations (**FIGURE 5-16**). In point mutations, one base pair is changed, whereas in chromosomal aberrations, entire sections of a chromosome are altered.

Point mutations are mutations in which one nucleotide base pair in the DNA is replaced with another, or a base pair is inserted or deleted. Insertions and deletions can be much more harmful than substitutions because the amino acid sequence of a protein is determined by reading the three-base sequence (codon) on an mRNA molecule and attaching the particular amino acid specified by that sequence. If a single base is added

or removed, the three-base groupings get thrown off and the sequence of amino acids stipulated "downstream" from that point will be all wrong—the reading frame is shifted. It's almost like putting your hands on a computer keyboard, but offset by one key to the left or right, and then typing what should be a normal sentence. It comes out as gibberish.

Chromosomal aberrations are changes to the overall organization of the genes on a chromosome. Chromosomal aberrations are like the manipulation of large chunks of text when you are working on a paper. They can involve the complete deletion of an entire section of DNA, the moving of a gene from one part of a chromosome to elsewhere on the same chromosome or to a different chromosome, or the duplication of a gene, with the new copy inserted elsewhere on the chromosome or on a different chromosome. Whatever the type of aberration, a gene's expression—the production of the protein that the gene's sequence codes for—can be altered when it is moved, as can the expression of the genes around it.

Given the potentially hazardous health consequences of mutations, it is advisable to minimize their occurrence. Can this be done? Yes and no. There are three chief causes of mutation and, although one of them is beyond our control, the other two can be significantly reduced (**FIGURE 5-17**).

1. Spontaneous mutations. Some mutations arise by accident as long strands of DNA are duplicating themselves—at the rate of more than a thousand bases a minute in humans—when cells are dividing (you'll read more details on this process

175

TYPES OF MUTATIONS

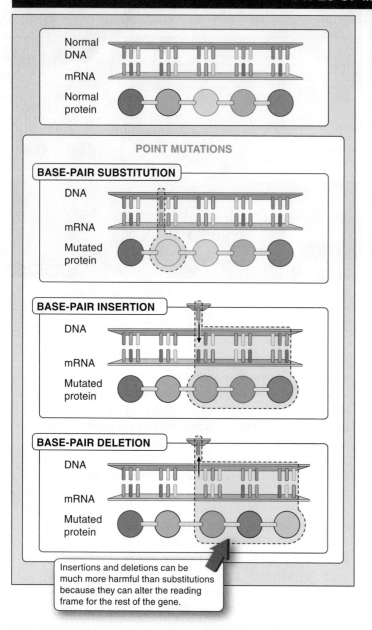

POINT MUTATIONS

Normal DNA
mRNA
Normal protein

BASE-PAIR SUBSTITUTION
DNA
mRNA
Mutated protein

BASE-PAIR INSERTION
DNA
mRNA
Mutated protein

BASE-PAIR DELETION
DNA
mRNA
Mutated protein

Insertions and deletions can be much more harmful than substitutions because they can alter the reading frame for the rest of the gene.

Normal chromosome
Gene 1   Gene 2   Gene 3

CHROMOSOMAL ABERRATIONS

GENE DELETION
Gene 1   Gene 2 **DELETED**   Gene 3

GENE RELOCATION
Gene 2   Gene 3
Gene 1 **RELOCATED** to a different chromosome

GENE DUPLICATION
Gene 1 **DUPLICATED**   Gene 2   Gene 3

In point mutations, one base pair is changed, whereas in chromosomal aberrations, entire sections of a chromosome are altered.

FIGURE 5-16 Point mutations and chromosomal aberrations.

in Chapter 6). Most errors are repaired by DNA repair enzymes, but some still slip by and there's not much we can do about them.

2. *Radiation-induced mutations.* Ionizing radiation is radiation with enough energy to disrupt atomic structure—even breaking apart chromosomes—by removing tightly bound electrons. Sources of ionizing radiation include X rays and the ultraviolet (UV) rays of the sun. When you lie in the sun, for example, its ultraviolet rays can induce a mutation in

Q Why do dentists put a heavy apron over you when they X-ray your teeth?

one of your skin cells that can transform the cell into a cancer cell. This is why long–term sun exposure can contribute to the development of skin cancer. Because ionizing rays cannot pass through lead, the lead apron a doctor or dentist puts over you when you get an X ray protects your body from the ionizing radiation.

Another source of dangerous radiation is found in the core of nuclear power plants, where radioactive atoms are used and

What Is DNA?   Building Organisms   Genetic Damage   Biotechnology and Health

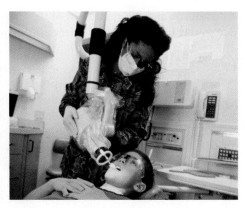

FIGURE 5-17 Gambling with mutation-inducing activities? You can increase or decrease your risk of mutations with your behavior: smoking, sun worshipping, and radiation (but notice the protective lead apron).

Q **Why is it dangerous to be near the core of a nuclear power plant?**

produced in energy-generating reactions. While it is the high energy of the radioactivity that fuels the production of usable energy, this radioactivity is potentially harmful because it can pass through your body and disrupt your DNA, causing point mutations. Radioactivity can also cause larger-scale chromosomal aberrations. With the proper safety precautions, however, nuclear power plant workers can minimize their exposure to harmful radiation.

3. *Chemical-induced mutations.* Many chemicals, such as those found in cigarette smoke and in exhaust from internal combustion engines, can also react with the atoms in DNA molecules and induce mutations.

In the next section, we examine how even tiny changes in the sequence of bases in DNA can lead to errors in protein production and profound health problems.

TAKE-HOME MESSAGE 5·8

Mutations are alterations in a single base or changes in large segments of DNA that include several genes. They are rare, but when they do occur in a gene this usually disrupts normal physiological functioning. Mutations play an important role in evolution.

5·9

Faulty genes, coding for faulty enzymes, can lead to sickness.

Isabella joins her friends in sipping wine during a dinner party. As the meal progresses, her companions become tipsy. Their conversations turn racy, their moods relaxed. They refill their glasses, reveling in a little buzz. Not so for Isabella. Before her first glass is empty, she experiences a "fast-flush" response: her face turns crimson, her heart begins to race, and her head starts to pound. Worse still, she soon feels the need to vomit.

How can people respond so differently to alcohol? It comes down to a difference in a single base pair in their DNA, a single difference that can influence dramatically a person's behavior, digestion, respiration, and general ability to function. The base-pair change leads to the production of a non-functional enzyme, and the lack of a functional version of this enzyme leads to physical illness. Let's look at the details.

When we consume alcohol, our bodies start a two-step process to convert the alcohol molecules from their intoxicating form into innocuous molecules. Each of the two steps is made possible by a specific enzyme, whose assembly instructions are coded in the DNA of most people.

Fast-flushers like Isabella complete the first step of breaking down alcohol, but cannot complete the breakdown because they carry defective genetic instructions for making aldehyde dehydrogenase, the enzyme that makes possible the second step of the process. A poisonous substance subsequently accumulates, and the symptoms of the "fast-flush" reaction are due to this substance's toxic effects in the body.

Q Why *do many* Asians have unpleasant experiences associated with alcohol consumption?

Approximately half of the people living in Asia carry a non-functional form of the gene for aldehyde dehydrogenase, a mutation that may confer a greater benefit than harm. In a study of 1,300 alcoholics in Japan, not a single one was a fast-flusher, even though half of all Japanese people are fast-flushers. The minor change in the genetic code that makes alcohol consumption an unpleasant experience may be responsible for the lower incidence of alcoholism among Japanese and other Asian people.

In many other cases—perhaps in the majority of genetic diseases—the link between a particular defective DNA sequence and physical illness is equally direct. Recall from Chapter 3 the case of Tay-Sachs disease. In Tay-Sachs disease, an individual inherits genes with a mutation that causes an inability to produce a critical lipid-digesting enzyme in their lysosomes, the cellular garbage disposals. Because these organelles cannot digest certain lipids, the lipids accumulate, undigested. The lysosomes swell until they eventually choke the cell to death. This occurs in numerous cells in the first few years of life, and ultimately leads to the child's death.

Although the details differ from case to case, the overall picture is the same for many, if not most, inherited diseases. The pathway from mutation to illness includes just four short steps (**FIGURE 5-18**).

1. A mutated gene codes for a non-functioning protein, commonly an enzyme.

2. The non-functioning enzyme can't catalyze the reaction as it normally would, bringing the reaction to a halt.

3. The molecule with which the enzyme would have reacted accumulates, just as half-made products would pile up on a blocked assembly line.

4. The accumulating chemical causes sickness and/or death.

The fact that most genetic diseases involve illnesses brought about by faulty enzymes suggests some strategies for treatment. These include administering medications that contain the normal-functioning version of the enzyme. For instance, lactose-intolerant individuals can consume the enzyme lactase, which for a short while gives them the ability to digest lactose. Alternatively, lactose-intolerant individuals can reduce their consumption of lactose-containing foods to keep the chemical from accumulating, thus reducing the problems that come from its overabundance.

FROM MUTATION TO ILLNESS

1 A mutated gene codes for a non-functioning protein, commonly an enzyme.

DNA

mRNA

Functioning enzyme should look like this:

Non-functioning enzyme

2 The non-functioning enzyme can't catalyze the reaction as it normally would.

3 The molecule it would have reacted with accumulates.

4 The accumulating chemical causes sickness (fast-flushing, for example) or death (Tay-Sachs disease, for example).

FIGURE 5-18 Faulty enzymes can interfere with metabolism.

TAKE-HOME MESSAGE 5·9

Most genetic diseases result from mutations that cause a gene to produce a non-functioning enzyme, which in turn blocks the functioning of a metabolic pathway.

❹ Biotechnology has the potential for improving human health.

A visual representation of the human genome. (Each color represents a different nucleotide.)

5·10

What is biotechnology?

Understanding a phenomenon is nice, but controlling it takes the satisfaction to an entirely new level. This may explain why there is so much excitement surrounding the field of **biotechnology**, in which organisms, cells, and their molecules are modified to achieve practical benefits. As we have seen in this chapter, the structure and function of DNA are pretty well understood. Biotechnology uses this knowledge to develop medicines for fighting viral infections, produce more nutritious food while reducing reliance on pesticides, and analyze forensic evidence as part of criminal investigations.

The modern emphasis in biotechnology is on **genetic engineering**, the manipulation of organisms' genetic material by adding, deleting, or transplanting genes from one organism to another. Such manipulation may create a better-tasting tomato or improve the treatment of a human disease.

This section introduces the most important tools and techniques used in biotechnology. We then explore the two primary areas in which biotechnology is applied: human health and agriculture. Biotech advances in human health fall into three categories: (1) producing medicines to treat diseases, (2) curing diseases, and (3) preventing diseases from

occurring in the first place. In agriculture, biotechnology is used to create more nutritious and healthful food as well as to increase the efficiency and reduce the ecological impact of farming (**FIGURE 5-19**).

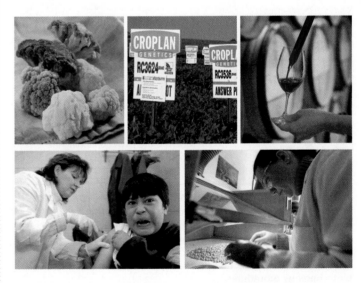

FIGURE 5-19 Biotechnology in agriculture and human health.

179

How would you create a plant resistant to being eaten by insects? Or a colony of bacteria that can produce human insulin? Although there are many different uses of biotechnology, it employs a surprisingly small number of processes and tools. Each of these applications, for example, would use a similar sequence of steps and applications (**FIGURE 5-20**).

1. **Chop** up the DNA from a donor organism that exhibits the trait of interest.

2. **Amplify** the small amount of DNA into more useful quantities.

3. **Insert** the different DNA pieces into bacterial cells or viruses.

4. **Grow** separate colonies of the bacteria or viruses, each of which contains a different inserted piece of donor DNA.

5. **Identify** the colonies that have received the DNA containing the trait of interest.

THE 5 STEPS OF BIOTECHNOLOGY

1 CHOP up the DNA from a donor species that exhibits the trait of interest.

2 AMPLIFY the small amount of DNA into more useful quantities.

3 INSERT the different DNA pieces into bacterial cells.

4 GROW separate bacterial colonies, each containing a different inserted piece of donor DNA.

5 IDENTIFY the bacterial colonies that have received the DNA containing the gene of interest.

Not all of the steps are used in all biotechnology applications—some applications utilize only one or a few of these techniques.

FIGURE 5-20 Five important tools and techniques of most biotechnology procedures.

In other words, we can reduce decades of complex research down to five steps: Chop, Amplify, Insert, Grow, and Identify. Then we're ready to utilize the products. This may be as simple as harvesting a product of interest or may require inserting the gene into another species, possibly a crop plant or maybe a sick human. To be sure, it's easier said than done, but these steps capture the essence of most modern biotechnology. Not all of the steps are used in all biotech applications—some use only one or a few of these techniques—nonetheless, they all are mainstays of today's biotechnology world. Now let's explore each step in more detail.

Step 1. Chopping up DNA from a donor organism. To begin, researchers select an organism that has a trait they want to make use of. For example, they might want to produce human growth hormone in large amounts. Their first step would be to obtain a sample of human DNA and cut it into smaller pieces. Cutting DNA into small pieces requires the use of **restriction enzymes** (**FIGURE 5-21**).

Restriction enzymes have a single function: when they encounter DNA, they cut it up into small pieces. These enzymes evolved to protect bacteria from attack by viruses. Immediately upon encountering DNA from an invading virus, a restriction enzyme recognizes and binds to a particular sequence of four to eight bases and cuts the DNA there, thus making it impossible for the virus to reproduce within the bacterial cell. Dozens of different restriction enzymes exist, each of which recognizes a different sequence of bases and cuts the DNA molecule at a different location.

Restriction enzymes are one of the key tools in biotechnology because the first step of nearly all biotech applications involves cutting the DNA from a donor species that has a gene or genes of interest into shorter lengths (without actually cutting anywhere *within* the gene of interest).

Step 2. Amplifying DNA pieces into more useful quantities. In many situations, only a small amount of DNA will be available for analysis or for some other biotechnology use. The **polymerase chain reaction** (**PCR**) is a laboratory technique that allows a tiny piece of DNA (perhaps one that has been cut from a larger piece by restriction enzymes, or one that has been recovered from a crime scene) to be duplicated repeatedly, producing virtually unlimited amounts of that piece of DNA. PCR is especially useful in forensics, because investigators often find only small amounts of DNA at crime scenes, which must then be amplified before they can be analyzed by using the technique of DNA fingerprinting (which we discuss below).

In the first step of PCR, the DNA of interest is heated, which separates the double-stranded DNA into separate, single strands (**FIGURE 5-22**). Next, the DNA is cooled and an

RESTRICTION ENZYMES

1 The gene of interest is located on a section of DNA from the donor species.

Gene of interest

Source DNA

2 Restriction enzymes that target a particular base-pair sequence on either side of the gene are introduced.

Restriction enzymes

In this example, the restriction enzymes recognize the sequence ATCGAT and cut between the first A and T.

3 The restriction enzymes bind to their target base-pair sequence and cut the strand of DNA.

4 The gene of interest has now been separated from the donor's DNA.

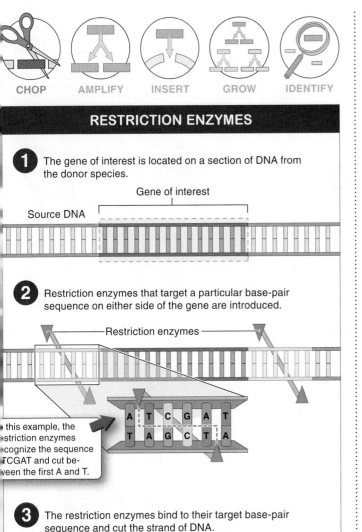

FIGURE 5-21 Restriction enzymes are used to isolate a gene of interest.

POLYMERASE CHAIN REACTION (PCR)

1 A solution containing an isolated segment of DNA is heated, separating the double-stranded DNA into two single strands.

Heat

2 The enzyme DNA polymerase is added along with a large number of free nucleotides, and the solution containing the segments is cooled.

Cool

DNA polymerase

Free nucleotides

3 DNA polymerase adds complementary bases to each single strand.

4 The result is two identical copies of the original segment of DNA.

This process can be repeated again and again until there are billions of identical copies of the target sequence.

FIGURE 5-22 The polymerase chain reaction can duplicate a small strand of DNA into billions of copies.

enzyme called DNA polymerase and a large number of free nucleotides are added to the DNA mixture. DNA polymerase uses one of the two strands of DNA as a template to build a complementary strand, using the free nucleotides as building blocks. This makes each of the single strands double-stranded again, resulting in two complete copies of the DNA of interest. This process of heating and cooling can be repeated

again and again until there are billions of identical copies of the target sequence. Depending on the experiment, PCR can be done so that it will only amplify a DNA fragment with a specific sequence, for example the gene for human growth hormone, which can later be separated from the original DNA. In other experiments, scientists want to amplify all the available DNA fragments so they can be surveyed later on.

181

Step 3. Inserting foreign DNA into the target organism. Most modern biotechnology applications involve the transfer of genes from one species to another, creating **transgenic organisms** that contain DNA from the donor species. In the human growth hormone example mentioned above, the researchers might want to transfer the human growth hormone gene into the bacterium *E. coli,* with the goal of having the bacteria produce human growth hormone.

To create a transgenic organism, researchers have to physically deliver the DNA of interest, isolated from a donor species, into the recipient organism. This delivery is often accomplished by using **plasmids,** circular pieces of DNA that can be incorporated into a bacterium's genome. This is an effective strategy because, following certain chemical treatments, researchers can construct plasmids that readily take up DNA that has been cut with restriction enzymes (**FIGURE 5-23**). Genes on the plasmid can then be expressed in the bacterial cell. The gene of interest is also replicated whenever the cell divides, so both of the new cells contain the plasmid. In some cases, rather than in plasmids, genes are incorporated into viruses, which can then be used to infect organisms and thus transfer the genes of interest to those species.

Step 4. Growing bacterial colonies that carry the DNA of interest: cloning. Once the DNA of interest has been transferred to the bacterial cell, every time the bacterium divides, it creates a **clone,** a genetically identical cell that contains the DNA of interest. The term **cloning** describes the production of genetically identical cells, organisms, or DNA molecules, a process that occurs each time a bacterium divides. As a consequence, with numerous rounds of cell division, it is possible to produce a huge number of clones, all transcribing and translating the gene of interest.

In a typical experiment, a large amount of DNA may be chopped up with restriction enzymes. Each of the pieces is incorporated into a plasmid that is introduced into the target organism, a bacterial cell. Then, all of the bacterial cells are allowed to divide repeatedly, each producing a clone of the foreign DNA fragment they carry. Together, all of the different bacterial cells containing all of the different fragments of the original DNA are called a **clone library** or a **gene library** (**FIGURE 5-24**).

Step 5. Identifying bacterial colonies that have received the gene of interest. Although a clone library contains a huge amount of potentially useful genetic information, the information is in no particular order, much like a library of books, uncatalogued and in complete disarray. If a researcher is interested in working with bacterial cells that contain the one human gene that produces human growth hormone, how can the bacteria

CHOP   AMPLIFY   INSERT   GROW   IDENTIFY

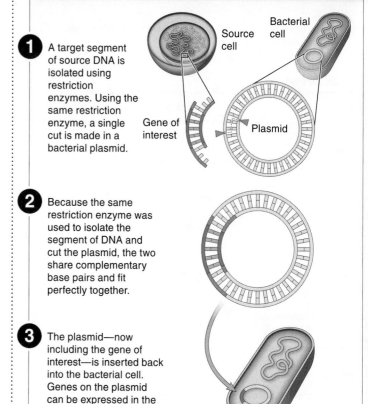

INSERTING DNA BY USING PLASMIDS

1 A target segment of source DNA is isolated using restriction enzymes. Using the same restriction enzyme, a single cut is made in a bacterial plasmid.

Source cell

Bacterial cell

Gene of interest

Plasmid

2 Because the same restriction enzyme was used to isolate the segment of DNA and cut the plasmid, the two share complementary base pairs and fit perfectly together.

3 The plasmid—now including the gene of interest—is inserted back into the bacterial cell. Genes on the plasmid can be expressed in the bacterial cell and are replicated whenever the cell divides.

FIGURE 5-23 A gene shuttle. Plasmids can be used to transfer DNA from one species to another.

containing that one particular piece of DNA be identified and separated from the millions of other clones in the library?

The gene of interest is usually found by using a method called **hybridization** (**FIGURE 5-25**). Hybridization requires the use of a **DNA probe,** a short sequence of single-stranded DNA that (1) contains a small part of the sequence of the gene of interest and (2) has had some of its nucleotides modified so that they carry radioactive elements. Bacteria that may carry the gene of interest are washed with a chemical that separates

CHOP   **AMPLIFY**   **INSERT**   **GROW**   **IDENTIFY**

CHOP   **AMPLIFY**   **INSERT**   **GROW**   **IDENTIFY**

CREATING A GENE LIBRARY

1 To create a gene library, a large amount of DNA is chopped up using restriction enzymes. **2** Each piece is inserted into a plasmid that is then introduced into a bacterial cell. **3** The bacteria are allowed to divide repeatedly, each producing a clone of the foreign DNA fragment it carries. **4** Together, all of the different bacterial cells contain all of the different fragments of the original DNA.

FIGURE 5-24 DNA collection. A gene library (or clone library) is a collection of cloned DNA fragments.

IDENTIFYING A GENE BY USING A DNA PROBE

1 To locate a gene of interest among the millions of clones in a gene library, the bacteria are washed with a chemical that breaks down the DNA, making it single-stranded.

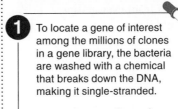

GENE LIBRARY

Gene of interest

2 A radioactive probe is then washed over the single-stranded DNA. The probe is a short length of DNA that contains a sequence of base pairs complementary to the gene of interest.

DNA probe

3 The DNA probe binds to the complementary base-pair sequence found in the gene of interest and glows with radioactivity, allowing the gene to be easily identified.

FIGURE 5-25 Finding the needle in a haystack. A DNA probe is used to locate the desired clone in a gene library.

---

the DNA strands, making single-stranded DNA. Then the radioactive probe is washed over the single-stranded DNA. Bacteria with DNA containing the sequence complementary to the probe will bind to the probe and glow with radioactivity. Once the desired clone in a library is identified, these cells can be grown in large numbers—for example, vats of *E. coli* that produce human growth hormone.

In the remainder of this chapter, we learn how these tools and techniques are being used to develop products. Keep in mind,

however, that even though biotechnology is frequently in the news and has had many important successes, the field is still in its infancy.

TAKE-HOME MESSAGE 5·10

Biotechnology is the use of technology to modify organisms, cells, and their molecules to achieve practical benefits. Modern molecular methods make it possible to cut and copy DNA from one organism and deliver it to another, not necessarily of the same species. With these methods, biotechnology has achieved some important successes in medicine, agriculture, and forensics, but the field is still in its infancy.

The treatment of diseases and production of medicines are improved with biotechnology.

You can't always get what you want. In the best of all worlds, biotechnology would *prevent* humans from ever getting debilitating diseases. Next best would be to *cure* diseases once and for all. But these noble goals are not always possible, so biotechnology often is directed at the more practical goal of *treating* diseases, usually by producing medicines more efficiently and more effectively than they can be produced with traditional methods. Biotechnology has had some notable successes in achieving this goal. The treatment of diabetes is one such success story.

Diabetes is a chronic disease in which the body cannot produce insulin, a chemical that allows cells to take up and break down sugar from the blood. Complications from diabetes can include vascular disease, kidney damage, and nerve damage. As recently as 1980, if you were one of the approximately 15 million Americans with diabetes, each day you would treat the disease by injecting yourself with insulin extracted from the pancreas of cattle or pigs that had been killed for meat. For most diabetics, the insulin injections kept the disease under control. But the traditional process of collecting insulin this way was difficult and costly. Moreover, cow and pig insulins differ slightly from human insulin in their structures, and about 5% of people with diabetes had negative reactions to the cow and pig insulin preparations.

Q Why do some bacteria produce human insulin?

Everything changed in 1982 when a 29-year-old entrepreneur, Bob Swanson, joined scientist Herbert Boyer to transform the potential of **recombinant DNA technology,** the combination of DNA from two or more sources, into a product. In doing so, they started the biotech revolution. Working with the scientist Stanley Cohen, Swanson and Boyer used restriction enzymes to snip out the human DNA sequence that codes for the production of insulin. They then inserted this sequence into the bacterium *E. coli.* After cloning the new, transgenic bacteria, the team was able to grow vats and vats of the bacteria, all of which churned out human insulin (**FIGURE 5-26**). The drug could be produced efficiently in huge quantities and made available for patients with diabetes. This was the first genetically engineered drug approved by the Food and Drug Administration and it continues to help millions of people every day.

FIGURE 5-26 Life-saving insulin. Human insulin is engineered through recombinant DNA technology.

Perhaps even more significant than providing a better source of insulin, Swanson, Boyer, and Cohen's application of biotechnology revealed a generalized process for genetic engineering. It instantly opened the door to a more effective method of producing many different medicines and treating diseases. Today, more than 1,500 companies work in the recombinant DNA technology industry, and their products generate more than $40 billion in revenues each year.

Several important achievements followed the development of insulin-producing bacteria. Here are just two examples.

1. *Human growth hormone (HGH).* Produced by the pituitary gland, human growth hormone has dramatic effects throughout the body. It stimulates protein synthesis, increases utilization of body fat for energy to fuel metabolism, and stimulates the growth of virtually every part of the body (**FIGURE 5-27**). Insufficient growth hormone production, usually due to pituitary malfunctioning, leads to dwarfism.

When treated with supplemental HGH, individuals with dwarfism experience additional growth. HGH is also used to combat weight loss in people with AIDS. Until 1994, HGH treatment was prohibitively expensive because the growth hormone could only be produced by extracting and purifying it from the pituitary glands of human cadavers. Through the creation of transgenic bacteria, using a technique similar to that used in the creation of insulin-producing bacteria, HGH can now be created in virtually unlimited supplies and made available to more people who need it.

The availability of HGH, which can increase strength and endurance, may be irresistibly tempting to some athletes—even at $7,500 for a month's supply. Recent sporting scandals suggest that the illegal use of HGH occurs frequently among elite swimmers, cyclists, and other athletes.

Q What is "blood doping"? How does it improve some athletes' performance?

2. *Erythropoietin.* Produced primarily by the kidneys, erythropoietin (also known as EPO) is a hormone that regulates the production of red blood cells. Numerous clinical conditions (nutritional deficiencies and lung disease, among others) and treatments (such as chemotherapy) can lead to anemia, a lower than normal number of red blood cells, which reduces an individual's ability to transport oxygen to tissues and cells.

Cloned in 1985, recombinant human erythropoietin (rhu-EPO) is now produced in large amounts in hamster ovaries. It is used to treat many forms of anemia. Worldwide sales of EPO exceeded $10 billion in 2004.

EPO has been at the center of several "blood doping" scandals in professional cycling. Why might a cyclist be interested in having elevated levels of this hormone? EPO increases the oxygen-carrying capacity of the blood, so some otherwise healthy athletes have used EPO to improve their athletic performance. It can be very dangerous, though. By increasing the number of red blood cells, the blood can become much thicker and this can strain the heart and increase the risk of heart attack.

Beyond these and other medicines currently produced via transgenic organisms, plans are under way to create a variety of other useful products—including potatoes that produce antibodies enabling more effective response to illnesses, and other food plants that fight tooth decay. Remember, however, that putting human genes in bacteria or other organisms makes it possible to harness the gene products to treat symptoms of diseases, but it doesn't cure or prevent the diseases. In the next section we examine the as yet less successful attempts to *cure* diseases through biotechnology.

TAKE-HOME MESSAGE 5·11

> Biotechnology has led to some notable successes in treating diseases, usually by producing medicines more efficiently and more effectively than they can be produced with traditional methods.

FIGURE 5-27 Bulking up with a little (illegal) help. Sylvester Stallone—age 61 in this photo—used human growth hormone (along with strength training) to develop larger muscles for a film role.

Gene therapy: the use of biotechnology to cure diseases is having limited success.

When it comes to curing a disease by using biotechnology, there is good news and bad news. The good news is that, in the 1990s, a handful of humans with a normally fatal genetic disease called severe combined immunodeficiency disease (SCID) were completely cured through the application of biotechnology. The bad news is that these promising techniques could not be applied to other diseases.

It's not for a lack of trying: there have been more than 500 other clinical trials for **gene therapies** designed to treat or cure a variety of diseases by inserting a functional gene into an individual's cells to replace a defective version of the gene. These trials have included attempts to cure cystic fibrosis, hemophilia, and an inherited form of heart disease, among many others. But there have been no clear successes. Not one. Moreover, recent evidence has even diminished the good news about the SCID treatment, which has been suspended following the deaths of two patients from illness related to their treatment.

The case of SCID is worth examining in some detail, however, because it proves that biotechnology can indeed be used to exchange working genes for malfunctioning disease-causing genes in a way that permanently cures a disease in a human individual.

SCID is a genetic disorder in which a baby is born with an immune system unable to properly produce a type of white blood cell, leaving the infant vulnerable to most infections. The disease usually causes death within the first year of life. It is sometimes called the "bubble boy" disease because in the 1970s, a boy suffering from SCID survived for 12 years by living in a sterile, germ-free bubble (**FIGURE 5-28**).

Researchers have been able to cure the disease in some individuals by using gene therapy that is simple in concept but difficult in practice. First, the researchers removed some cells from an affected baby's bone marrow. These were **stem cells,** cells that have the ability to develop into any type of cell in the body—a feature which makes them very useful in biotechnology. In bone marrow, they normally produce white blood cells, but in individuals with SCID, a malfunctioning gene disrupts normal white blood cell production. Next, in a test tube, the bone marrow stem

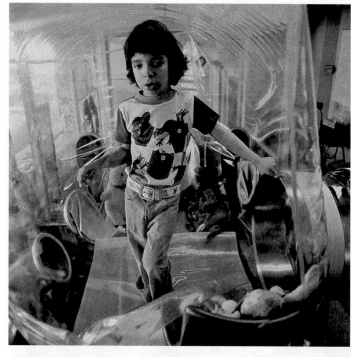

FIGURE 5-28 Protected by a bubble. This child with severe combined immunodeficiency lived 12 years in a protective bubble at Texas Children's Hospital.

Q Why has gene therapy had such a poor record of success in curing diseases?

cells were infected with a transgenic virus carrying the functioning gene. If all went well, the virus inserted the good gene into the DNA of the stem cells, which were then injected back into the baby's bone marrow. There, the cells could produce normal white blood cells, thereby permanently curing the disease.

Difficulties with gene therapy have been encountered in several different areas, usually related to the organism used to transfer the normal-functioning gene into the cells of a person with a genetic disease.

1. *Difficulty getting the working gene into the specific cells where it is needed.* For example, gene therapy for cystic fibrosis—a disease in which thick mucus accumulates in the lungs—attempts to use viruses like those responsible for the common cold to insert a normal gene into malfunctioning lung cells. Unfortunately, because the lungs have evolved to keep foreign objects out, the body is very effective at mounting immune responses against the viruses used to deliver the working gene to the lung cells.

2. *Difficulty getting the working gene into enough cells and at the right rate to have a physiological effect.* In the two deaths related to gene therapy for SCID, for example, the treatment apparently caused leukemia due to problems with the insertion of the gene disrupting normal functioning in white blood cells, triggering them to become cancerous.

3. *Problems with the transfer organism getting into unintended cells.* Viruses can cause serious side effects if they infect cells other than the target cells. Their delivery to target cells must therefore be precise.

Beyond these common problems, gene therapy faces additional difficulties because, for many diseases, the malfunctioning gene has not been identified or the disease is caused by more than one malfunctioning gene. And finally, it is important to keep in mind that gene therapy targets cells in the body other than sperm and eggs. Consequently, while the disease can, in theory, be cured in an individual, the techniques do not prevent those individuals from passing on the disease-causing gene(s) to their offspring. It's not clear what the future holds for gene therapy, but many scientists and patients remain hopeful and a great deal of research is still in progress.

TAKE-HOME MESSAGE 5·12

Gene therapy has had a poor record of success in curing human diseases. This stems primarily from technical difficulties in transferring normal-functioning genes into the cells of a person with a genetic disease.

5·13

Biotechnology can help prevent disease.

Would you want to know? Once, this was just a hypothetical question: if you carried a gene that meant you were likely to develop a particular disease later in your life, would you want to know about it? Or another question: would you want to know if there's a good chance that your future children will be born with a genetic disease? Now, for better or for worse, these are becoming real questions that we all must address. And there is more at stake than simply peace of mind. As biotechnology develops the tools to identify some of the genetic time-bombs that many of us carry, it also carries the danger that such information may become the basis for greater discrimination than we have ever known.

Intervening to prevent diseases by using biotechnology focuses on answering questions such as those posed above at three different points in time.

1. *Is a given set of parents likely to produce a baby with a genetic disease?* Many genetic diseases occur only if an individual inherits two copies of the disease-causing gene, one from each parent. This is true for Tay-Sachs disease, cystic fibrosis, and sickle-cell anemia, among others. Individuals with only a single copy of the disease-causing gene never fully show the disease, but they may pass on the disease gene to their children. Consequently, two healthy parents (that is, having no disease symptoms) may produce a child with the disease. In these cases, it can be beneficial for the parents to be screened

to determine whether they carry a disease-causing copy of the gene. Such screening, combined with genetic counseling and testing of embryos following fertilization, can reduce the incidence of the disease dramatically. This has been the case with Tay-Sachs disease, for example. Since screening began in 1969, the incidence of Tay-Sachs disease has been reduced by more than 75% (**FIGURE 5-29**).

Since screening began in 1969, the incidence of Tay-Sachs disease has been reduced by more than 75%!

FIGURE 5-29 Genetic screening can determine the presence of the Tay-Sachs gene.

Possessing mutations in the genes called BRCA1 and BRCA2 (short for breast cancer 1 and breast cancer 2) can make women more susceptible to breast cancer. A genetic screening for the gene is done with a simple blood test.

2. *Will a baby be born with a genetic disease?* Once fertilization has occurred, it is possible to test an embryo or developing fetus for numerous genetic problems. Prenatal genetic screening can detect cystic fibrosis, sickle-cell anemia, Down syndrome, and other disorders. The list of conditions that can be detected is growing quickly.

To screen the fetus, doctors must sample some of the fetal cells and/or the amniotic fluid, which carries many chemicals produced by the developing embryo. This is usually done via amniocentesis or chorionic villus sampling (CVS), techniques that we explore in detail in Chapter 6. Once collected, the cells can be analyzed by a variety of means.

3. *Is an individual likely to develop a genetic disease later in life?* DNA technology can also be used to detect disease-causing genes in individuals who are currently healthy but are at increased risk of developing an illness later. Early detection of many diseases, such as breast cancer, prostate cancer, and skin cancer, can greatly enhance the ability to treat the disease and reduce the risk of more severe illness or death.

While biotechnology may reduce suffering and the incidence of diseases, these potential benefits come with significant potential costs, including ethical dilemmas. People who have a gene that puts them at increased risk of developing a particular disease, for example, might be discriminated against, even though they are not currently sick and may never suffer from the particular disease for which they are at heightened risk. Although a federal Genetic Information Nondiscrimination Act was signed into law in 2008, the law does not cover all forms of genetic discrimination. It does not, for example, cover life insurance, disability insurance, and long-term care insurance. Insurance companies have already cancelled or denied such insurance coverage on discovering that an individual carries a gene that puts them at increased risk of disease. Additionally, parents who discover that their developing fetus will develop a painful, debilitating, or fatal disease soon after birth are confronted with the difficult question of how to proceed.

TAKE-HOME MESSAGE 5·13

Using biotechnology, many tools have been developed that enable us to identify whether a given set of parents is likely to produce a baby with a genetic disease, whether a baby is likely to be born with a genetic disease, and whether an individual carries certain disease-causing genes that may have their effect later in life. These tools can help us to reduce suffering and the incidence of diseases, but they also come with significant potential costs, particularly the risk of discrimination.

❺ Biotechnology is producing improvements in agriculture.

Genetically modified corn growing in a lab.

5·14

More nutritious and better foods are being produced with biotechnology.

Your breakfast cereal is probably fortified with vitamins and minerals. And for snacking you may have switched from candy bars to protein bars that have as much protein as a full chicken breast. It shouldn't come as a surprise, then, that farmers have begun using biotechnology to improve on the natural levels of vitamins, minerals, and other nutrients in the fruits, vegetables, and livestock they produce.

Using our knowledge of biology for agricultural improvements is nothing new. For thousands of years humans have been practicing a relatively crude and slow—but still very effective—form of genetic engineering by carefully selecting which plants or animals they use as the breeders for maintaining their crop or animal populations. Through this process of selecting plants or animals with certain desirable traits and breeding the organisms that have them, farmers and ranchers have improved virtually every product of agriculture, producing meatier turkeys, seedless watermelons, and big, juicy corn kernels (**FIGURE 5-30**). But what used to take many generations of breeding can now be accomplished in a fraction of the time, using recombinant DNA technology. Agriculture has entered into exciting but unknown territory.

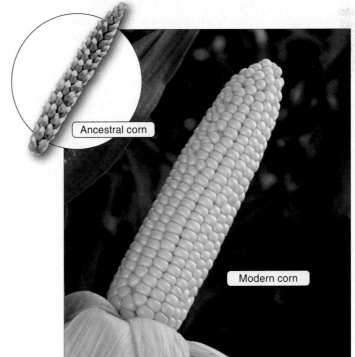

FIGURE 5-30 Ancestral corn and modern corn—selected for larger, juicier kernels—compared.

The process begins with the identification of a new characteristic, such as larger size or faster ripening time, that farmers would like in a particular crop. Traditionally, plant breeders would then search for an organism within the same species that had the desirable trait, breed it with their crop organisms, and hope that the offspring would express the trait in the desired way. With recombinant DNA technology, the desired trait can come from *any* species so the pool of organisms from which the trait can be taken becomes much larger. Organisms produced with recombinant DNA technology are referred to in the media as genetically modified organisms, or GMOs.

Although the rewards are potentially huge, in practice the process of creating transgenic species that are more nutritious or have other desirable traits turns out to be difficult. Nonetheless, the results so far hint at a rich and fruitful marriage of agriculture and technology.

Q How might a genetically modified plant help 500 million malnourished people?

Nutrient-Rich "Golden Rice." Almost 10% of the world's population suffers from vitamin A deficiency, which causes blindness in a quarter-million children each year and a host of other illnesses in people of all ages. These nutritional problems are especially severe in places such as southern Asia and sub-Saharan Africa, where rice is a staple of most diets. Addressing this global health issue, researchers have developed what may be the model for solving problems with biotechnology. It involves the creation of a new crop called "golden rice."

Mammals generally make vitamin A from beta-carotene, a substance found in abundance in most plants (it's what makes carrots orange). Beta-carotene is also found in rice plants, but not in the edible part of the rice grains. Researchers set out to change this by inserting into the rice genome three genes that code for the enzymes used in the production of beta-carotene: two genes from the daffodil plant and one bacterial gene (**FIGURE 5-31**). It's clear that the transplanted genes are working because the normally white rice grain takes on a golden color from the accumulated beta-carotene. The rice doesn't yet supply a full-day's requirement of vitamin A in one serving, but it does provide a significant amount. Since golden rice was first developed in 1999, new lines have been

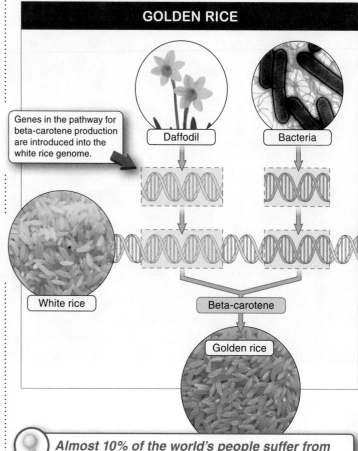

GOLDEN RICE

Genes in the pathway for beta-carotene production are introduced into the white rice genome.

Daffodil

Bacteria

White rice

Beta-carotene

Golden rice

Almost 10% of the world's people suffer from vitamin A deficiencies—leading to 250,00 cases of blindness each year. The addition of beta-carotene-producing genes to white rice has increased its vitamin A content almost 25-fold.

FIGURE 5-31 The potential to prevent blindness in 250,000 people each year. Engineering rice to prevent blindness by increasing its vitamin A content.

produced, now having only two transplanted genes, yet producing almost 25 times the vitamin A found in the original strains. Field tests of golden rice are still under way, so it is not yet being used widely. But this is viewed as one of the most promising applications yet of biotechnology.

TAKE-HOME MESSAGE 5·14

Biotechnology has led to important improvements in agriculture by using transgenic plants and animals to produce more nutritious food.

Farming can be made more efficient and eco-friendly through biotechnology.

> " Italians come to ruin most generally in three ways, women, gambling, and farming. My family chose the slowest one. "
>
> —Pope John XXIII

We are in the midst of a revolution—a green revolution—and few people are aware of it. The possibilities of biotechnology playing a role in treating, curing, and preventing human diseases may garner all the headlines, but the actual results pale in comparison with the current impact of biotechnology on agriculture. And although biotechnology can improve agriculture by making more nutritious food (as in the case of golden rice), the real revolution is the extent to which biotechnology has reduced the costs, both environmental and financial, of producing the plants and animals we eat.

The extent of biotechnology's success in the area of producing plants with built-in insecticides and genetically engineered resistance to herbicides is staggering. Currently, more than 170 million acres worldwide are planted with genetically modified crops, two-thirds of which are in the United States,

representing more than a fortyfold increase in the past 10 years. The financial benefits to farmers—at least in the short run—are so great that more and more of them are embracing the genetically modified crops.

The numbers are surprising: 45% of all corn grown in the United States—including corn grown in every single state in the continental United States—is genetically modified. Seventy-six percent of all cotton grown is genetically modified. And 85% of all soybeans grown is genetically modified (**FIGURE 5-32**). Two factors explain much of the rapid expansion and extensive adoption of genetically modified plants in U.S. agriculture. (1) Many plants have had insecticides and herbicide resistance engineered into them, which can reduce the amounts of insecticides and herbicides used in agriculture. (2) Because herbicide- and insect-resistant plants can reduce the amount of plowing required around crops to remove weeds,

> **Q** What genetically modified foods do most people in the U.S. consume (usually without knowing it)?

GENETICALLY MODIFIED CROPS IN THE UNITED STATES

Corn

55% | 45%

Cotton

24% | 76%

Soybeans

15% | 85%

☐ Proportion of crops that are not genetically modified
☐ Proportion of crops that are genetically modified

FIGURE 5-32 A significant portion of crops grown in the United States are genetically modified.

FIGURE 5-33 Competing with us for food. Insects can ravage crops.

a huge potential food resource for insects. Every year, about 40 million tons of corn are unmarketable as a consequence of insect damage. Increasingly, however, farmers have been enjoying greater success in their battles against insect pests, primarily through the use of genetically modified crops.

Farmers owe much of this success to soil-dwelling bacteria of the species *Bacillus thuringiensis*. These bacteria produce spores containing crystals that are highly poisonous to insects but harmless to the crop plants and to people. Within an hour of ingesting "Bt" crystals, the insects' feeding is disrupted. The toxic crystals cause pores to develop throughout the insects' digestive systems, paralyzing their gut and making them unable to feed. Within a few days the insects die from a combination of tissue damage and starvation.

genetically modified plants can reduce the costs of producing food and the loss of topsoil to erosion.

Several of the biggest successes of the application of recombinant DNA technology to agriculture are described below.

Insect Resistance Insect pests have a field day on agricultural crops (**FIGURE 5-33**). Crops that are planted at high densities and nurtured with ample water and fertilizer represent

Beginning in 1961, the toxic Bt crystals were included in the pesticides sprayed on crop plants. In 1995, however, recombinant DNA technology led to a huge reduction in the application of this toxic spray. The gene coding for the production of the Bt crystals was inserted directly into the DNA of many different crop plants, including corn, cotton, and potatoes, so that the plants themselves produced the crystals. As a consequence, it is no

Q How can genetically modifie plants lead to reduced pesticide use by farmers?

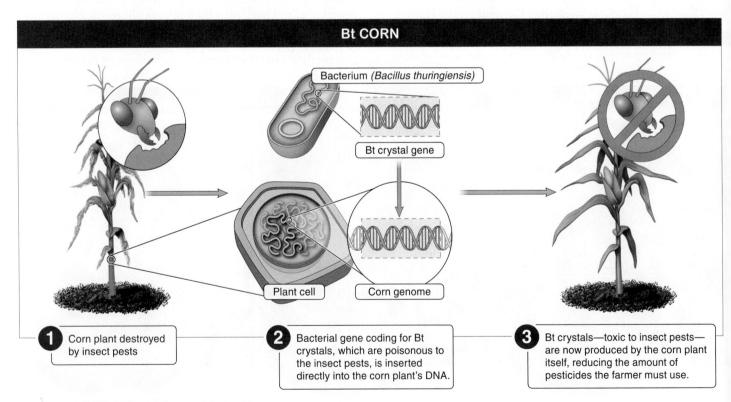

Bt CORN

Bacterium (*Bacillus thuringiensis*)

Bt crystal gene

Plant cell

Corn genome

1 Corn plant destroyed by insect pests

2 Bacterial gene coding for Bt crystals, which are poisonous to the insect pests, is inserted directly into the corn plant's DNA.

3 Bt crystals—toxic to insect pests— are now produced by the corn plant itself, reducing the amount of pesticides the farmer must use.

FIGURE 5-34 Help from bacteria in growing disease-resistant corn. Corn engineered to contain spores of the bacterium *Bacillus thuringiensis* (Bt) kills insect pests but does not harm humans.

What Is DNA?   Building Organisms   Genetic Damage   Biotechnology and Health

longer necessary for farmers to apply huge amounts of Bt-containing pesticides (**FIGURE 5-34**). Instead, the plants do that work themselves. The insects that try to eat the genetically modified plants ingest the toxin and soon die. There is no evidence that Bt crystals have any harmful effects on humans at all, even when they are exposed to very high levels. Because pesticides can be damaging to the environment, particularly when they flow from the farm and into the water supply as runoff, reduction in pesticide use can be beneficial for the environment.

Herbicide Resistance Bacteria have come to the aid of farmers in their fight against pests in another way, too. Consider a seemingly impossible challenge that farmers face when they attempt to kill weeds that harm crop plants by competing for light, water, and soil nutrients. Herbicides, chemicals that kill plants, can be applied to kill the weeds (**FIGURE 5-35**). These chemicals usually work by blocking the action of an enzyme that enables plants (as well as fungi and bacteria) to build three critical amino acids. Without these amino acids, the organisms soon die. The problem is that because herbicides affect *all* plants similarly, they are generally toxic to the crop plant as well as the weeds. This is where bacteria come in.

In the 1990s, researchers discovered bacteria that can resist the effect of herbicides. The gene that gives the bacteria resistance to herbicides was identified and introduced into crop plants. Integration of this gene into the plants' DNA gives them resistance to the herbicides and allows farmers to kill weeds

Herbicide-resistance genes from bacteria protect crop plants from the herbicides used to kill the weeds competing with them.

FIGURE 5-35 Crop duster. Herbicides like the one applied by this crop duster must kill weeds while leaving the crop unharmed.

FIGURE 5-36 Bigger salmon. The larger salmon carries a growth hormone gene that keeps it growing year-round rather than in the summer only.

with herbicides without harming the crop plants, greatly increasing yields.

Faster Growth and Bigger Bodies Agriculture includes the cultivation not just of plants but also of animals. Currently, researchers are developing transgenic salmon that grow significantly faster and reach a much larger size than normal salmon (**FIGURE 5-36**). These salmon carry a version of the growth hormone gene that functions year round, rather than primarily in the summer. It was isolated from a cold-water fish species, called arctic pout, and injected into the egg of a salmon with genetic engineering techniques. The super-fish can be raised much more quickly and using significantly less feed than normal salmon, reaching market size within 18 months rather than the usual 24–30 months. In taste tests, consumers cannot tell the difference between the transgenic and non-transgenic salmon.

Quite troubling, though, is the fact that researchers expected growth rate increases of about 25% but found that the genetically modified fish grew about 500% faster. Additionally, if the larger, faster-growing fish were to escape from their breeding nets back into their natural habitat—something that experts agree is inevitable—the fish might harm populations of other species because they can consume more resources and may grow too large to be consumed by their natural predators. It is unclear what the outcome would be.

TAKE-HOME MESSAGE 5·15

There has been a revolution in the extent to which biotechnology has reduced the environmental and financial costs of producing food, through the creation of herbicide-resistant and insect-resistant crops.

Biotechnology and Agriculture   DNA Sequences

Fears and risks: are genetically modified foods safe?

Chickens without feathers look ridiculous (**FIGURE 5-37**). But such a genetically modified breed was developed with a valuable purpose in mind: "naked" birds are easier and less expensive to prepare for market, benefiting farmers by lowering their costs and benefiting consumers by lowering prices. Such chickens, however, turned out to be unusually vulnerable to mosquito attacks, parasites, and disease, and ultra-sensitive to sunlight. They also have difficulty mating, because the males are unable to flap their wings. Researchers currently are working to address these problems.

These chickens teach us an important lesson about genetically modified plants and animals. Although the new breed of featherless chickens was produced by traditional animal husbandry methods—the cross-breeding of two different types of chickens—rather than by recombinant DNA technology, the new breed ended up having not just the desired trait of no feathers but also some unintended and undesirable traits. Now, as more genetically modified foods are

FIGURE 5-38 Consumer fears. Protesters voice opposition to the use of genetically modified organisms (GMOs).

created using modern methods of recombinant DNA technology, the same risks of unintended and potentially harmful traits occurring must be weighed. For these and other reasons—some legitimate and rational, others irrational—many people have concerns about the production and consumption of genetically modified foods (**FIGURE 5-38**).

Fear 1. Organisms that we want to kill may become invincible. Weed-resistant canola plants were cultivated in Canada, making it possible for farmers to apply herbicides freely to kill the weeds but not the canola plants. But the weed-resistant canola plants accidentally spread to neighboring farms and grew out of control, because traditional herbicides could not kill them. Similarly, there is the possibility that insect pests will develop resistance to the Bt that genetically modified crops produce, which will also make these pests resistant to Bt pesticides applied to crops that are not genetically modified.

Fear 2. Organisms that we don't want to kill may be killed inadvertently. Monarch butterflies feed on milkweed plants. Recent research has demonstrated that if pollen from plants genetically modified to contain the insect-killing Bt genes accidentally lands on milkweed plants and is consumed by monarch butterflies, the butterflies can be killed, which may significantly reduce their populations. Although such an incident has not occurred outside experimental fields, it illustrates a risk that may be hard to control.

Fear 3. Genetically modified crops are not tested or regulated adequately. It is impossible to ever really know whether a new

💡 *Featherless birds are cheaper for farmers and consumers. But there are unintended consequences, including vulnerability to mosquitoes and other parasites.*

FIGURE 5-37 "Naked" birds. The breeding of featherless chickens has benefited farmers but led to some unanticipated consequences.

technology has been tested adequately. Still, scientists and lawmakers have been working toward an organized and responsible set of policies designed to ensure sufficient safety testing is done. For example, laboratory procedures for working with recombinant DNA have been established, and researchers have developed techniques that make it impossible for most genetically engineered organisms to survive outside the specific conditions for which they are developed.

As an example of the degree of testing used in the field of genetically engineered foods, the Monsanto Company has had its strain of herbicide-resistant soybeans evaluated and approved by 31 different regulatory agencies in 17 different countries, including, in the United States, the Department of Agriculture, the Food and Drug Administration, and the Environmental Protection Agency. In a recent report on genetically modified animals, however, an expert committee from the U.S. National Academy of Sciences warned that genetically modified organisms still pose risks that the government is unable to evaluate. Technology is moving so fast that it is difficult to even know what the new risks might be.

> " And he gave it for his opinion, 'that whoever could make two ears of corn, or two blades of grass, to grow upon a spot of ground where only one grew before, would deserve better of mankind, and do more essential service to his country, than the whole race of politicians put together.'
>
> —Jonathan Swift, *Gulliver's Travels*, 1726 "

Fear 4. Eating genetically modified foods is dangerous. In the 1990s, a gene from Brazil nuts was used to improve the nutritional content of soybeans. The genetically modified soybeans had better nutritional content, but they also acquired some allergy-causing chemicals previously present in the Brazil nuts but not in soybeans. This outcome illustrates the risk that some unwanted features might be passed from species to species in the creation of transgenic organisms. In this case, all of the genetically modified soybeans were destroyed and this research program was suspended. To date, no evidence has appeared to suggest that consumption of any genetically modified foods is dangerous.

Fear 5. Loss of genetic diversity among crop plants is risky. As increasing numbers of farmers stop using non-genetically modified crops in favor of one or a few genetically modified strains of crops, there is a reduction in the genetic diversity of the crops. This can make them more vulnerable to environmental changes or pests. The Irish Potato Famine is an example of the value of genetic diversity in crops. In the mid-1800s, much of the population of Ireland depended on potatoes. Because most of the potato crops had been propagated from cuttings from the same plant, they were all genetically the same. When the crops were infected by a rot-causing mold, all of the potato plants were susceptible and most were wiped out, causing a famine responsible for the deaths of more than a million people.

Fear 6. Hidden costs may reduce the financial advantages of genetically modified crops. When seed companies create genetically modified seeds with crop traits desirable to farmers, the companies also engineer sterility into the seeds. As a consequence, the farmers must purchase new seeds for each generation of their crops. Such increases in the long-term costs and dependency on seed companies must be factored in by the farmers.

Among the less rational fears is that genetically modified foods are not "natural" and therefore must be harmful. This should not be a cause for concern. Smallpox, HIV, poison ivy, and cyanide, after all, are natural. The smallpox vaccine, on the other hand, is unnatural. Innumerable other valuable technological developments are equally unnatural. There simply is no value in knowing whether something is natural or unnatural when evaluating whether it is good and desirable or not.

In the end, we must compare the risks of producing genetically modified foods with the benefits. For example, farm workers will greatly benefit from spending less time applying pesticides to genetically modified, pest-resistant crops. The benefits of the workers' reduced pesticide exposure will be significantly greater in the less-developed countries, where safety regulations for pesticide use are more frequently ignored. The cost-benefit analyses will have to include the potential to reduce food costs and the ability to reduce environmental degradation from agriculture.

TAKE-HOME MESSAGE 5·16

More and more genetically modified foods are being created using modern methods of recombinant DNA technology. Some legitimate fears among the public remain, however, about the safety of these foods, given that their development relies on such new technology, and about the long-term financial advantages they offer.

With the cloning of a sheep, a new era in biotechnology began.

5·17

DNA is an individual identifier: the uses and abuses of DNA fingerprinting.

In another time, Colin Pitchfork, a murderer and rapist, would have walked free. But in 1987, he was captured and convicted, betrayed by his DNA, and is now serving two life sentences in prison. Pitchfork's downfall began when he raped and murdered two 15-year-old high-school girls in a small village in England in the 1980s. The police thought they had their perpetrator when a man confessed, but only to the second murder. He denied any involvement with the first murder, though, which perplexed the police because the details of the two crimes strongly suggested that the same person committed both.

At the time, British biologist Alec Jeffreys made the important discovery that there were small pieces of DNA in every person's chromosomes that were tremendously variable in their base sequences. In much the same way each person has a driver's license number or social security number that differs from everyone else's, these DNA fragments are so variable that it is extremely unlikely that two people would have identical sequences at these locations. Thus, a comparison between these regions in a person's DNA sample and in DNA-containing evidence left at a crime scene would enable police to determine whether the evidence came from that person.

Jeffreys analyzed DNA left by the murderer/rapist on the two victims and found that it did indeed come from a single person, and that that person was *not* the man who had confessed to one of the crimes. That original suspect was released and has the distinction of being the first person cleared of a crime through DNA fingerprinting. To track down the criminal, police then requested blood samples from all men in the area who were between 18 and 35 years old—a practice many viewed as an invasion of privacy—collecting and analyzing more than 5,000 blood samples. This led them to Colin Pitchfork, whose DNA matched perfectly the DNA left on both of the victims, and ultimately was the evidence responsible for his conviction. (He almost slipped through, having persuaded a friend to give a blood sample in his name.

What Is DNA?   Building Organisms   Genetic Damage   Biotechnology and Health

FIGURE 5-39 Betrayed by his DNA. Colin Pitchfork, the first criminal brought to justice with DNA fingerprinting.

But when the friend was overheard telling the story in a pub, police tracked down Pitchfork to get a blood sample.)

DNA fingerprinting is now used extensively in forensic investigations, in much the same way that regular fingerprints have been used for the past 100 years (**FIGURE 5-39**). But traditional fingerprinting is limited in its usefulness for many crimes because, often, no fingerprints are left behind. DNA fingerprinting, on the other hand, is not so limited because DNA samples more frequently are left behind, usually in the form of semen, blood, hair, skin, or other tissue. As a consequence, this technology has been directly responsible for bringing thousands of criminals to justice and, as we saw at the beginning of the chapter, for establishing the innocence of more than 200 people wrongly convicted of murder and other capital crimes. Let's examine how DNA fingerprinting is done, why it is such a powerful forensic tool, and why it is not foolproof.

The DNA from different humans is almost completely identical. More than 99.9% of the sequences of two individuals are the same because we are all from the same species and thus share a common evolutionary history. Even so, in a genome of three billion base pairs, even a tenth of a percent difference translates to about three million base-pair differences. These differences are responsible for the fact that all individuals have their own unique genome. (The lone exception? Identical twins, whose DNA is exactly the same.) Thus, when we are trying to evaluate whether the DNA from a crime scene matches that from a suspect, the analysis focuses on the parts of our DNA that differ. There are several dozen of these highly variable regions in the human genome.

Some of the most highly variable parts of the DNA are regions called **VNTR**s, because they contain a **v**ariable **n**umber of **t**andem **r**epeats. A VNTR region, we'll call it VNTR 1, might have a short sequence of 15 to 100 bases that repeats over and over again. Imagine that a person's genome is a book. The VNTR would be like the insertion of the word "green" over and over again on one of the pages. An individual—we'll call her Individual A—has two copies of each chromosome, one from her mother and one from her father, and the two copies of the VNTR 1 site that she carries are likely to differ from each other—maybe there are 14 repeats in one case and 3 repeats in the other. Individual B also has two copies of the VNTR 1 region, and the number of times the sequence repeats in those regions of Individual B's DNA might be 5 and 11 (**FIGURE 5-40**). Elsewhere in a person's genome are more than a dozen other VNTR regions that can be compared similarly.

Why are VNTRs so useful for forensic scientists? Because the existence of these regions means that forensic scientists don't need to look at all three billion bases in a person's entire DNA sequence. Instead, they only have to look at how many times a sequence is repeated in a suspect's two copies of VNTR 1, let's say 14 and 3 times. Then they look at how many times the VNTR 2 sequence is repeated in that person, let's say 7 and 34, and VNTR 3 might have 42 and 16 repeats. So the individual in question could be thought of as having a DNA fingerprint

CREATING DNA FINGERPRINTS BY USING VNTRs

A DNA fingerprint is created by counting the number of times that a repetitive sequence of base pairs occurs on an individual's chromosomes. Regions of repetitive base-pair sequences are called VNTRs because they contain a **V**ariable **N**umber of **T**andem **R**epeats.

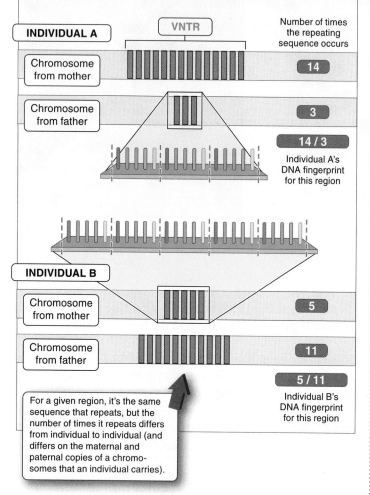

INDIVIDUAL A

VNTR

Number of times the repeating sequence occurs

Chromosome from mother — **14**

Chromosome from father — **3**

14 / 3
Individual A's DNA fingerprint for this region

INDIVIDUAL B

Chromosome from mother — **5**

Chromosome from father — **11**

5 / 11
Individual B's DNA fingerprint for this region

For a given region, it's the same sequence that repeats, but the number of times it repeats differs from individual to individual (and differs on the maternal and paternal copies of a chromosomes that an individual carries).

FIGURE 5-40 VNTRs in forensics. Forensic scientists use VNTRs to genetically link a person of interest with DNA-containing evidence left at a crime scene.

of 14/3, 7/34, 42/16. It's like checking whether two books are identical by looking at the first word on pages 16, 48, 123, and 200. It's a lot easier than comparing every word, but still can produce the correct answer. In the U.S., an individual's complete DNA fingerprint is generally built by sampling their DNA at more than ten different VNTR regions.

In court, DNA fingerprints are usually shown as photos of dark bands in a gel to demonstrate that the banding pattern of a suspect's DNA either does or doesn't match the banding pattern of DNA found at the crime scene (**FIGURE 5-41**).

Q What is a DNA fingerprint?

CREATING A DNA FINGERPRINT GEL

1 Using restriction enzymes, DNA samples are cut on either side of the repeating sequences. Only two VNTR regions are shown here. Actual DNA fingerprints are created by sampling up to eight regions.

INDIVIDUAL A

VNTR region #1

VNTR region #2

VNTR region

Restriction enzymes cut here

INDIVIDUAL B

VNTR region #1

VNTR region #2

2 The isolated DNA sequences are then poured into a gel and an electrical charge is applied. Because DNA is a negatively charged molecule, the pieces of DNA move toward the bottom of the gel. This process causes the pieces of DNA to be separated by size. Smaller pieces—those with a small number of repeats—move more quickly than larger pieces and are found closer to the bottom.

INDIVIDUAL A

INDIVIDUAL B

CRIME SCENE EVIDENCE

Electrical charge

Direction of DNA strand movement

Larger strands of DNA

These bands can be used to show that a suspect's DNA matches DNA found at a crime scene.

Smaller strands of DNA

FIGURE 5-41 Your unique identifier: a DNA fingerprint. DNA fingerprints are being used to match a suspect's DNA to DNA found at the scene of a crime.

How do we get from an entire genome to a simple photo of bands?

First, the DNA in an evidence sample is chopped with a restriction enzyme that makes cuts on either side of the area where the repeating sequence occurs. The DNA is then

What Is DNA? Building Organisms Genetic Damage Biotechnology and Health

poured into a gel and an electrical charge is applied to induce the DNA to migrate toward the bottom of the gel. Because smaller pieces move more quickly than larger pieces, this process causes different-size pieces of DNA to separate by size. The smaller pieces—those with a small number of repeats—are found closer to the bottom; the larger pieces—those with a large number of repeats—are found toward the top. At this point, because the DNA still is not visible, the repeating DNA sequence is stained with a radioactively labeled chemical and the gel is placed in contact with X-ray film. The film records dark bands at the point in the gel to which the DNA fragments have migrated.

DNA samples from different people will form different bands, whereas different samples of DNA from one person will have exactly the same pattern of dark bands.

In the end, despite universally accepted methods, DNA fingerprinting is not foolproof, because the possibility for human error remains. Even though we should not blindly draw conclusions solely from this one type of evidence, however, DNA fingerprinting is an increasingly valuable tool for law enforcement. The FBI, for example, has reported that nearly a third of their suspects are cleared immediately by DNA testing, and that many more criminals, because of DNA fingerprinting, now plead guilty to the crimes they have committed.

TAKE-HOME MESSAGE 5•17

Comparisons of highly variable DNA regions can be used to identify tissue specimens and determine the individual from whom they came.

5•18

DNA sequences reveal evolutionary relatedness.

It's hard to get somewhere new without a map. Just as explorers of the New World created maps to get the lay of the land, genetics researchers have been working since 1990 to map the genomes of humans and other species (**FIGURE 5-42**). Today, useful drafts of these sequences have been completed for more than 180 species, including humans and various species of bacteria, yeast, plants, worms, and fruit flies. The list is expected to top 1,000 species in a few years. Now that we have all of these data and are acquiring more, the big question is, what do we do with all of this information? Progress is

being made in numerous different directions. We'll touch on just two of them.

1. *Mapping genetic landscapes.* The **Human Genome Project** is a project to decode the three billion base pairs in the human genome and to identify all the genes present in it. The project neared completion in 2000, and subsequent efforts have focused on determining some basic information, including how many genes there are, where they are, and how they work. In fact, the first big surprise of the Human Genome Project was the discovery that the number of genes in human genetic material is much smaller than expected, falling somewhere between 20,000 and 25,000. This is not much different from the number of genes in the genomes of fruit flies (13,000) or nematode worms (19,000) or the small plant *Arabidopsis* (26,000). We saw earlier that the total amount of DNA an organism carries is not related to the organism's complexity. It seems that there also is no relationship between the number of genes an organism has and its complexity, either.

2. *Building earth's family tree.* Humans crave order. To organize our cities we use address systems, to manage our digital information we use folders, subfolders, and files on our computers, and to keep track of our books we use the Library of Congress cataloging system. Not surprisingly, humans desire order when it comes to the billions of living organisms on earth. For this, we create **phylogenetic trees,** a way of grouping organisms in a hierarchical system that reflects the evolutionary history and relatedness of all

FIGURE 5-42 The Human Genome Project: mapping the genetic landscape.

organisms. Phylogenetic trees are a useful organizational system that helps us understand the diversity of life on earth and the nature of how species are related to one another.

Traditionally, phylogenetic trees were built on the basis of similarities among organisms' physical structures and embryological development. We'll examine the details of how this was done in Chapter 10, but the net result was a system of six kingdoms—bacteria, archaea, protists, plants, animals, and fungi—that reflected reasonably well the consensus hypothesis about the evolutionary history of the different groups of organisms. Today, however, DNA sequences are being analyzed as a feature that can be traced over time, and this analysis is revolutionizing the construction of phylogenetic trees. The new DNA-sequence-based phylogenetic trees reflect much more accurately the branching patterns of different groups of organisms as they evolved (**FIGURE 5-43**).

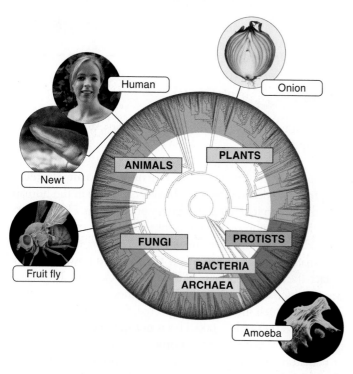

FIGURE 5-43 The tree of life. Our understanding of the evolutionary relationships among species is made more accurate through analysis and comparison of DNA sequences.

The rationale behind constructing phylogenies based on DNA sequences is straightforward. Organisms inherit DNA from their ancestors. As species evolve in their own unique ways, their DNA sequences diverge, becoming increasingly different. The more time that passes following the splitting off of one species from another, the greater the difference between their DNA sequences. Phylogenies are then constructed that place species in positions that reflect their relative genetic similarity.

Measures of overall DNA similarity between chimps and humans reveal that 96% of our base pairs are the same. (This is actually a comparison with only one chimp, a male named Clint, from the Yerkes Primate Research Center in Atlanta.) This is a greater similarity than humans share with any other species and indicates that chimps are our closest living relatives. Although most DNA doesn't code for proteins, when comparing only the sequences that code for proteins, we find that 29% of the genes code for the same exact proteins in chimps and humans.

> **Q** When we say humans and chimps are genetically 96% identical, what do we mean?

For the purpose of comparison:

1. The difference between human DNA and mouse DNA is 60 times greater than the human-chimp difference.

2. The difference between mouse and rat DNA is 10 times greater than the human-chimp difference.

3. The difference between human and chimp DNA is 10 times greater than the average difference in DNA between two humans.

TAKE-HOME MESSAGE 5·18

Comparisons of DNA sequence similarities across species reveal their evolutionary relatedness and make it possible to construct detailed evolutionary trees.

What Is DNA?   Building Organisms   Genetic Damage   Biotechnology and Health

5•19

Cloning—from organs to individuals—offers both promise and perils.

Cloning. Perhaps no scientific word more readily conjures horrifying images of the intersection of curiosity and scientific achievement. But is fear the appropriate emotion to feel about this burgeoning technology? Perhaps not.

For starters, let's clarify what the word means. "Cloning" actually refers to a variety of different techniques. To be sure, cloning can refer to the creation of new individuals that have exactly the same genome as the donor individual—a process called "whole organism cloning." That is, a clone is like an identical twin, except that it may differ in age by years or even decades. It is also possible to clone tissues (such as skin) and entire organs from an individual's cells. And, as we have already seen in this chapter, it is possible to clone genes.

Cloning took center stage in the public imagination in 1997 when Ian Wilmut, a British scientist, and his colleagues first reported that they had cloned a sheep, named Dolly. Their research was based on ideas that went back to 1938, when Hans Spemann first proposed the experiment of removing the nucleus from an unfertilized egg and replacing it with the nucleus from the cell of a different individual. Although the process used by Wilmut and his research group was difficult and inefficient, it was surprisingly simple in concept (**FIGURE 5-44**). They removed a cell from the mammary gland of a grown sheep, put its nucleus into another sheep's egg from which the nucleus had been removed, induced the egg to divide, and transplanted it into the womb of a surrogate mother sheep. Out of 272 tries, they achieved one success. But that was enough to show that the cloning of an adult was possible.

Shortly after news of Dolly's birth, teams set about cloning a variety of other species, including mice, cows, pigs, and cats (**FIGURE 5-45**). Not all of this work was driven by simple curiosity. For farmers, cloning could have real value. It can take a long time to produce animals with desirable traits from an agricultural perspective—such as increased milk production in cows. And with each successive generation of breeding, it can be difficult to maintain these traits in the population. But through the process of transgenic techniques and whole-animal cloning, large numbers of valuable animals with such traits can be produced and maintained.

FIGURE 5-44 No longer science fiction. The steps used in the cloning of Dolly the sheep.

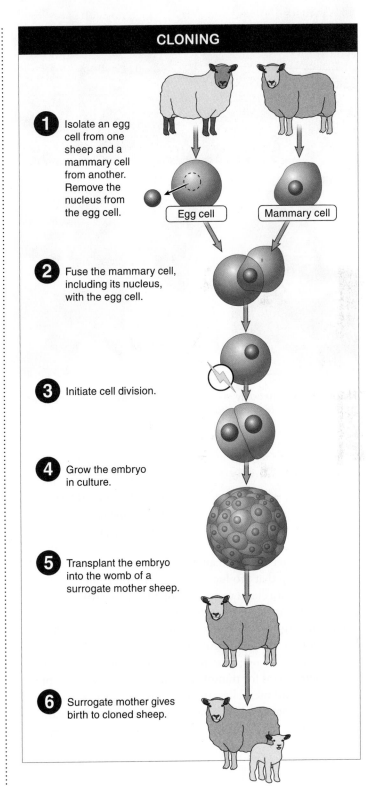

CLONING

1. Isolate an egg cell from one sheep and a mammary cell from another. Remove the nucleus from the egg cell.

Egg cell | Mammary cell

2. Fuse the mammary cell, including its nucleus, with the egg cell.

3. Initiate cell division.

4. Grow the embryo in culture.

5. Transplant the embryo into the womb of a surrogate mother sheep.

6. Surrogate mother gives birth to cloned sheep.

FIGURE 5-45 Genetically identical cloned animals. The cloning of animals can maintain desirable traits from generation to generation.

Q Are there any medical justifications for cloning?

Medical researchers, too, see much to gain from cloning. In particular, transgenic animals containing human genes—such as those discussed earlier in this chapter—can be very valuable. For instance, sheep that produce the human protein alpha-1 antitrypsin that is used to treat cystic fibrosis, or hamsters that produce human erythropoietin to treat kidney disease, are needed in large numbers. By cloning the transgenic animals, large colonies of pharmaceutical-drug-producing animals can be created. Pig clones, too, are being created with the hope of using their organs for transplantation into humans. Such pigs are unusual and useful because they have had genes inactivated that would normally cause their tissue to be rejected by the immune systems of human recipients.

Q Is it possible to clone a dinosaur? How could it be done?

Movies have raised the question of whether it is possible to clone a dinosaur (**FIGURE 5-46**). While the short answer is *yes,* that is in theory only. Several practical steps would be necessary, each of which might prove impossible. The first step would be retrieving the DNA of the dinosaur to be cloned. The most likely route would be to salvage fossilized DNA from the stomach of a mosquito, preserved since the time when dinosaurs lived. Mosquitoes from those days have actually been found, preserved in amber, a hardened, fossilized tree sap, but no ingested blood has been recovered from them. Then the dinosaur DNA would have to be extracted from the blood—assuming the mosquito had bitten a dinosaur. The biggest problem at this step is that it would be necessary to extract

What Is DNA?   Building Organisms   Genetic Damage   Biotechnology and Health

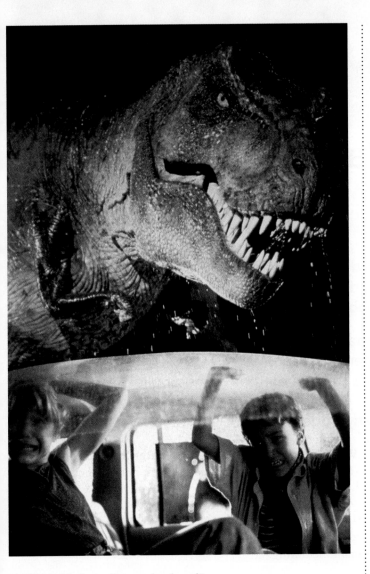

FIGURE 5-46 Can a dinosaur be cloned?

and isolate all of the dinosaur's DNA, not just a few fragments. In the unlikely event that this could be done, this DNA would need to be inserted into the egg from a living organism, perhaps a crocodile, to create an embryo. At this point the embryo would have to be put in some sort of artificial egg where it could be incubated and fed as it grows, until it could finally hatch.

And if a dinosaur, why not a human? At this point, it is almost certain that the cloning of a human will be possible. Many people wonder, though, whether such an endeavor should be pursued. There is near unanimity among scientists that human cloning should not be attempted, and governments are struggling to develop wise regulations for this new world.

TAKE-HOME MESSAGE 5·19

Cloning of individuals has potential benefits in agriculture and medicine, but ethical questions linger.

Knowledge You Can Use

Did you know? Mixing aspirin and alcohol can lead to metabolic interference and unexpected inebriation.

Ethanol is the form of alcohol found in cocktails, beer, and wine. When you consume alcohol, the first step in your body's metabolic breakdown of the ethanol is carried out by the enzyme alcohol dehydrogenase.

Q: What happens to ethanol molecules *not* broken down? Any ethanol molecules in the bloodstream not broken down by alcohol dehydrogenase make their way to the brain. Once there, they cause you to feel a bit inebriated—or drunk, if the amount of ethanol is sufficiently large. Aspirin has the unintended side effect of disabling alcohol dehydrogenase, thus interfering with its normal functioning.

Q: What do you think happens to someone who takes two aspirin and then drinks several alcoholic beverages? By blocking the activity of alcohol dehydrogenase, aspirin interferes with a person's ability to break down ethanol. As a consequence, the ethanol remains in the body longer and has a more pronounced effect on the brain, producing greater inebriation (26% greater, according to one study).

What can you conclude? Medications, even over-the-counter products, can have unexpected (and unintended) physiological consequences, particularly when mixed with alcohol consumption. Exercise great caution when taking them.

❶ DNA: What is it and what does it do?

DNA, the genetic material for all living organisms, is a double-helix molecule consisting of two "backbone" chains of sugar and phosphate molecules linked by pairs of nucleotide bases. Genes are sequences of bases in DNA that contain the code for the construction of protein molecules. Only a small fraction of the DNA in eukaryotes codes for genes.

❷ Building organisms: through gene expression, information in the DNA directs the production of the molecules that make up an organism.

Information in the genes is transcribed into the sequences of mRNA molecules. These mRNA sequences then direct the construction of proteins.

❸ Damage to the genetic code has a variety of causes and effects.

Mutations are rare alterations in a single base or changes in large segments of DNA that include several genes. When they occur in a gene, normal physiological functioning is usually disrupted. Mutations play an important role in evolution. Most genetic diseases result from a mutation that causes a gene to produce a non-functioning enzyme, resulting in a blocked metabolic pathway.

❹ Biotechnology has the potential for improving human health.

Biotechnology is the use of technology to modify organisms, cells, and their molecules to achieve practical benefits. With modern molecular methods, researchers can cut and copy DNA and deliver it to new organisms, not necessarily of the same species. Biotechnology has had some notable successes in treating diseases, usually by producing medicines more efficiently and more effectively than with traditional methods. Gene therapy, however, has so far had a poor record of success in curing human diseases. With biotechnology, many tools have been developed that enable us to identify individuals carrying disease-causing genes. These tools can help reduce the symptoms and incidence of diseases, but come with significant potential costs, particularly the risk of discrimination.

❺ Biotechnology is producing improvements in agriculture.

Biotechnology has led to important advances in agriculture by using transgenic plants and animals to produce more nutritious food. Even more dramatic is the extent to which biotechnology has reduced the environmental and financial costs of producing food through the creation of herbicide- and insect-resistant crops. Some legitimate fears among the public remain, however, as to the safety of genetically modified foods

❻ Biotechnology today and tomorrow: DNA sequences are rich in information.

Advances in biotechnology have led to automated methods for analyzing DNA sequences. Comparisons of highly variable DNA regions have forensic value in identifying tissue specimens and determining the individual from whom they came. Comparisons of sequence similarities across species reveal evolutionary relatedness and allow construction of detailed evolutionary trees. Cloning of individuals has potential benefits in agriculture and medicine, but ethical questions linger.

KEY TERMS

allele, p. 165
base, p. 162
base pair, p. 162
biotechnology, p. 179
chromosomal aberration, p. 175
chromosome, p. 164
clone, p. 182
clone library, p. 182
cloning, p. 182
code, p. 168
codon, p. 173
deoxyribonucleic acid (DNA), p. 162

DNA probe, p. 182
gene, p. 164
gene library, p. 182
gene therapy, p. 186
genetic engineering, p. 179
genome, p. 164
genotype, p. 168
Human Genome Project, p. 199
hybridization, p. 182
intron, p. 166
messenger RNA (mRNA), p. 168

mutation, p. 174
nucleic acid, p. 162
nucleotide, p. 162
phenotype, p. 168
phylogenetic tree, p. 199
plasmid, p. 182
point mutation, p. 175
polymerase chain reaction (PCR), p. 180
promoter site, p. 169
protein synthesis, p. 173
recombinant DNA technology, p. 184

restriction enzymes, p. 180
ribosomal subunits, p. 171
stem cell, p. 186
trait, p. 165
transcription, p. 168
transfer RNA (tRNA), p. 171
transgenic organism, p. 182
translation, p. 168
VNTRs (variable number of tandem repeats), p. 197

1. A person's unique DNA is carried in:
   a) muscle cells.
   b) hair.
   c) saliva.
   d) skin cells.
   e) All of the above contain a person's DNA.

2. Which of the following are always the same in every DNA molecule?
   a) the sugar
   b) the base
   c) the phosphate group
   d) Only a) and b) are always the same.
   e) Only a) and c) are always the same.

3. The full set of an individual organism's DNA is called its:
   a) complement.
   b) genome.
   c) nucleosome.
   d) nucleotide.
   e) chromosome.

4. In humans, genes make up _____ of the DNA.
   a) about 75%
   b) 100%
   c) less than 5%
   d) about 10%
   e) about 50%

5. Genotype is to phenotype as:
   a) cookie is to oven.
   b) cookie is to recipe.
   c) cookbook is to cookie.
   d) recipe is to cookie.
   e) oven is to cookie.

6. To start the transcription process, a large molecule, _____, recognizes a _____.
   a) RNA polymerase; messenger RNA
   b) DNA polymerase; termination site
   c) DNA polymerase; promoter site
   d) RNA polymerase; promoter site
   e) DNA polymerase; messenger RNA

7. During transcription, at the point where the DNA strand being copied has an adenine, a(n) _____ is added to the _____.
   a) thymine; tRNA
   b) cytosine; DNA
   c) uracil; tRNA
   d) adenine; mRNA
   e) uracil; mRNA

8. There are different _____ molecules for each of the 20 different amino acids that are used in building proteins.
   a) ribosomal subunit   d) DNA
   b) tRNA   e) elongation
   c) mRNA

9. Deletions and substitutions are two types of point mutations. Which type is more likely to cause mistranslations of proteins?
   a) Substitutions, because they shift the reading frame and cause downstream amino acids to be changed.
   b) Substitutions, because one protein is substituted for another protein.
   c) Deletions, because they shift the reading frame and cause downstream amino acids to be changed.
   d) Deletions, because one protein is deleted.
   e) None of the above is correct.

10. Which of the following statements about the metabolism of ethanol (which is present in alcoholic beverages) is incorrect?
    a) Individuals who produce non-functioning aldehyde dehydrogenase exhibit "fast-flushing."
    b) The process requires two enzymes: alcohol dehydrogenase and isopropyl dehydrogenase.
    c) Individuals who are "fast-flushers" are less likely to become alcoholics.
    d) Aspirin interferes with the action of alcohol dehydrogenase.
    e) All of the above are correct.

11. The polymerase chain reaction (PCR):
    a) makes it possible to create huge numbers of copies of tiny pieces of DNA.
    b) enables researchers to determine the sequence of a complementary strand of DNA when they have only single-stranded DNA.
    c) utilizes RNA polymerase to build strands of DNA.
    d) can create messenger RNA molecules from small pieces of DNA.
    e) All of the above are correct.

12. Which of the following is not a difficulty that medicine has encountered in its attempts to cure human diseases through gene therapy?
    a) The transfer organism—usually a virus—may get into unintended cells and cause disease.
    b) It is difficult to get the working gene into the specific cells where it is needed.
    c) It is difficult to get the working gene into enough cells at the right rate to have a physiological effect.
    d) For many diseases, a malfunctioning gene has not been identified.
    e) All of the above are difficulties encountered in attempts to cure human diseases through gene therapy.

13. Golden rice:
    a) grows without a husk, thereby reducing the processing required before it can be consumed.
    b) can make vitamin A without beta-carotene.
    c) could help prevent blindness in the 250,000 children who lose their sight each year because of vitamin A deficiency.
    d) supplies more vitamin A in one serving than an individual needs in a full week.
    e) is one of the most recent developments in organic farming.

14. Which of the following statements about Bt crystals is correct?
    a) They are produced by soil-dwelling bacteria of the species *Bacillus thuringiensis.*
    b) The gene coding for the production of Bt crystals has been genetically engineered into the genome of dairy cows, increasing their milk production sixfold.
    c) They are produced by the polymerase chain reaction (PCR).
    d) They are produced by most weedy species of plants.
    e) All of the above are correct.

15. A VNTR is:
    a) a gene that codes for a biochemical trait, rather than a structural trait.
    b) used in biotechnology when creating a clone.
    c) produced when a mutation occurs in a non-sex cell.
    d) a highly variable section of an individual's DNA.
    e) produced when a mutation occurs in a sperm-producing or egg-producing cell.

16. Ninety-six percent of the base-pair sequences in chimps and humans are the same. This finding indicates that:
    a) humans are more closely related to chimps than any two mice are related to each other.
    b) 96% of the genes in humans have identical counterparts in chimps.
    c) humans are more closely related to chimps than to any other species on earth.
    d) 4% of the DNA we carry contains mutations.
    e) 96% of the proteins produced by chimps is identical to proteins produced by humans.

SHORT-ANSWER QUESTIONS

1. After sequencing a molecule of DNA, you discover that 20% of the bases are cytosine. What percentage of the bases would you expect to be thymine? Explain why.

2. A cell is in the process of transcription. The single strand of DNA that is being copied has the sequence ATC GAC GGA TCC. Indicate the mRNA strand that will be synthesized from this strand, listing the correct sequence of bases. Explain why this step is important in the process of producing protein.

3. What is being "translated" in translation? What is the role of transfer RNA molecules in this step?

4. The genetic disorder known as sickle-cell disease results in an altered form of the protein hemoglobin, which ultimately can affect the structure of red blood cells. A portion of the sequence for the normal hemoglobin allele is:

   CTG ACT CCT GAG GAG AAG TCT

   Individuals with the sickle-cell disorder have the following sequence:

   CTG ACT CCT GTG GAG AAG TCT

   Identify the type of mutation and explain how it would result in an altered (in this case non-functional) protein.

5. Describe three major applications of biotechnology and their impact on human health.

See Appendix for answers. For additional study questions, go to www.prep-u.com.

6

Chromosomes and Cell Division

Continuity and variety

❶ There are different types of cell division.

Bladder cancer cells in the final stage of cell division.

6·1 --

Immortal cells can spell trouble: cell division in sickness and in health.

Once you are fully grown, do you have just one set of cells that live as long as you do? The answer is *no:* your cells are continually dying off and the ones that remain divide and replace the cells you've lost, in an ongoing process. But how long can this last? Can it go on forever? And does a cell even know how old it is?

Actually, a cell does have a measure of how old it is. Just as a car comes with an odometer, which keeps track of how far the car has been driven, animal cells have a sort of counter that keeps track of how many times a cell has divided. This "counter" is a section of DNA called the **telomere,** which is located at each tip of every chromosome, right next to the genes that direct the processes that keep an organism alive. The telomere functions like a protective cap at the end of the DNA. Every time a cell divides, making an exact copy of itself, its DNA divides as well. However, each time the DNA divides, the telomere gets a bit shorter. Eventually, after some

critical number of cell divisions, the telomere can become so short that additional cell divisions cause the loss of functional, essential DNA, and that means almost certain death for the cell (**FIGURE 6-1**).

At birth, the telomeres in most human cells are long enough to support about 50 cell divisions. Occasionally, however, individuals are born with telomeres that are much shorter than normal. In these people, the normal functioning of many genes is disrupted, and their cells and tissues begin to appear aged very soon after birth (**FIGURE 6-2**). As a consequence, those born with this disorder rarely live beyond the age of 13.

Just as someone might think it's a good idea to disconnect his or her car's odometer, you might think that disconnecting the cellular odometer by continually rebuilding the telomere would be an effective strategy for allowing a cell and its descendants to function for a longer time than normal. Such

Types of Cell Division   Mitosis   Meiosis   Sex Differences

TELOMERES

Every time a cell divides, the telomere gets shorter. After a critical number of cell divisions, functional DNA is lost, which means almost certain death for the cell.

Animal cell

Nucleus

Chromosome

TELOMERE
A protective cap at the end of each chromosome

Functional DNA

Cell division

Cell division

Cell division

Cell death

At birth, telomeres in most human cells are long enough to support about 50 cell divisions!

FIGURE 6-1 A cellular "odometer." Telomeres limit cells to a fixed number of divisions.

a line of cells would never die—so you'd think that the continually rebuilding telomere would be like a fountain of youth. It's not. We know this because there *are* some cells with a sort of disconnected odometer. These cells rebuild their telomeres after each cell division, restoring the protective cap. Unfortunately, most cells that rebuild their telomeres with each cell division present a big problem: they don't know when to stop dividing. There is a word for such cells: cancer.

Because cancer is runaway cell division, discovering a cure for cancer will necessarily involve a deep understanding of cell division. In this chapter, we explore the processes that have evolved that enable cells to divide and create new cells.

FIGURE 6-2 Just a child. Individuals with the genetic condition Hutchinson-Gilford progeria syndrome are born with shorter-than-normal telomeres and appear to age at a rapid rate. The inset shows chromosomes (in blue), with the telomeres highlighted in yellow.

" Cancer cells are those which have forgotten how to die.

—Harold Pinter, playwright, from the poem "Cancer Cells," 2002 "

Prokaryotes have one method. It is called binary fission and it serves all of their needs. Eukaryotes, on the other hand, have two methods, mitosis and meiosis, each of which has a specific purpose. In addition to discussing what happens when cell division goes unchecked, we also will explore some of the difficulties that arise when cells wind up with too many or too few chromosomes after cell division.

TAKE-HOME MESSAGE 6·1

Within cells there is a protective section of DNA called the telomere that gets a bit shorter every time the cell divides. If a telomere becomes too short, additional cell divisions cause the loss of essential DNA and cell death. Cells that rebuild the telomere with each division can become cancerous.

Some chromosomes are circular, others are linear.

As a method for storing genetic information, DNA has complete market saturation. All life on earth uses it. This is pretty remarkable considering the tremendous diversity of life that exists on earth—from bacteria to plants and animals. One way in which different organisms' DNA varies is in how it is organized into chromosomes.

In most bacteria and the other prokaryotes, the genetic information is carried in a single, circular chromosome, a strand of DNA that is attached at one site to the cell membrane (**FIGURE 6-3**). Eukaryotes, on the other hand, have much more DNA than do bacteria and organize it into free-floating linear chromosomes within the nucleus. As we saw in Chapter 5, a eukaryotic organism may have as few as 2 chromosomes or as many as 1,000. For plants and animals, the number is usually between 10 and 50.

The most important part of a eukaryotic chromosome is the DNA molecule, which carries information about how to carry out the processes needed to support the life of the organism. But eukaryotic chromosomes (and some prokaryotic chromosomes) are made of more than just DNA. The long, linear strand is wrapped around proteins called **histones,** which keep the DNA from getting tangled and enable an orderly, tight, and efficient packing of the DNA inside the cell (see Figure 6-3). In the next sections we examine the behavior of prokaryotic and eukaryotic chromosomes during cell division.

TAKE-HOME MESSAGE 6·2

In most bacteria and the other prokaryotes, the genetic information is carried in a single, circular chromosome, a strand of DNA that is attached at one site to the cell membrane. Eukaryotes have much more DNA than do bacteria and organize it into free-floating linear chromosomes within the nucleus.

PROKARYOTIC AND EUKARYOTIC CHROMOSOMES

PROKARYOTIC CELL

Chromosome

Attachment site

DNA

EUKARYOTIC CELL

Chromosome

Nucleus

Histones

FIGURE 6-3 Chromosomes compared. Prokaryotic cells have a single circular chromosome attached to the cell membrane. Eukaryotic cells contain free-floating linear chromosomes within a nucleus.

Types of Cell Division · Mitosis · Meiosis · Sex Differences

Prokaryotes divide by binary fission.

When it is time for bacteria and the other prokaryotes to reproduce, they use a method called **binary fission,** which means "division in two" (**FIGURE 6-4**). This process begins with **replication,** the process by which a cell's DNA duplicates itself. Replication begins as the double-stranded DNA molecule unwinds from its coiled-up configuration. Once the strands are uncoiled, they split apart like a zipper. As the double-stranded molecule unzips, free-floating nucleotide bases attach to the bases exposed on each of the two separated, single-stranded circular molecules of DNA, matching A to T and G to C to create two identical double-stranded DNA molecules. The newly created circular chromosomes of DNA attach to the inside of the plasma membrane at a different spot than the original. The original cell, called the **parent cell,** then pinches into two new cells, called **daughter cells,** so each of the daughter cells has an exact and precise two-stranded copy of the original two-stranded circular chromosome.

In some prokaryotes, such as the *E. coli* that live in our digestive system, the complete process of binary fission can occur very quickly—often in as little as 20 minutes. Binary fission is considered **asexual reproduction** because the daughter cells inherit their DNA from a single parental cell. In **sexual reproduction,** a combination of DNA from two separate individuals is passed on to offspring, resulting in offspring that are genetically different both from one another and from their parents. We will discuss sexual reproduction in more detail later in this chapter.

TAKE-HOME MESSAGE 6•3

> Bacteria divide by a type of asexual reproduction called binary fission: first the circular chromosome duplicates itself and then the cell splits into two identical new cells.

FIGURE 6-4 "Dividing in two." Asexually reproducing prokaryotes reproduce rapidly through binary fission.

PROKARYOTIC CELL DIVISION: BINARY FISSION

Prokaryotic parent cell — Double-stranded DNA

REPLICATION
An exact copy of the cell's DNA is created.

Cell elongates and begins to pinch in two.

Daughter cells are formed.

Binary fission results in two genetically identical daughter cells.

There is a time for everything in the cell cycle.

In life, we often go through phases that are defined by the focus of our interests and activities. For many years we go to school. For a while we may tend to our career. Then, for a spell, our personal life may take center stage. Most eukaryotic cells do this, too. They may spend a long period of time occupied with activities relating solely to growth of the cell and then suspend those activities as they segue into a period devoted exclusively to reproducing themselves. This alternation of activities between processes related to cell division and processes related to growth is called the **cell cycle** (**FIGURE 6-5**).

Before we go any further in discussing the cell cycle, we need to note an important distinction among the cells of the body. All of the cells of a multicellular eukaryotic organism can be divided into two types: **somatic cells** are the cells

forming the body of the organism; **reproductive cells** are the sex cells, or **gametes.** The processes of cell division by which somatic cells and reproductive cells are produced differ from each other. In this section, we focus on somatic cells. Later in the chapter, we examine cell division leading to the production of sex cells.

The cell cycle describes the series of phases that leads to somatic cell division. There are two main phases in the cell cycle: **interphase,** during which the cell grows and prepares to divide, and the **mitotic phase** (or **M phase**), during which first the nucleus and genetic material within the cell divides, and then the rest of the cellular contents divides. Interphase is further divided into three distinct subphases, described below. A eukaryotic somatic cell moves through the phases in precise order and, at any given moment, a somatic

EUKARYOTIC CELL CYCLE

INTERPHASE

1 GAP 1
The cell's primary growth phase. Normal cellular functions (making proteins, getting rid of waste, etc.) take place.

2 DNA SYNTHESIS
The cell begins preparations for division. Every chromosome creates an exact duplicate of itself in a process called replication.

3 GAP 2
Second period of growth and preparation for cell division.

4 MITOSIS
The cell's nucleus duplicates, then divides.

5 CYTOKINESIS
The cell then duplicates, forming two separate cells.

2 DNA synthesis

INTERPHASE

1 Gap 1

MITOTIC PHASE

3 Gap 2

5 Cytokinesis

4 Mitosis

FIGURE 6-5 The cycle of cellular activity. The eukaryotic cell cycle is the series of events that results in the division of somatic cells (cells that make up the body of an organism).

Types of Cell Division   Mitosis   Meiosis   Sex Differences

cell is at some point in this cycle. The phases and subphases can be summarized as follows.

Interphase

Gap 1. During this period, a cell grows and performs all cellular functions (making proteins, getting rid of waste, and so on). Cells that divide infrequently, such as most neurons and heart muscle cells, spend most of their time in the Gap 1 phase.

DNA synthesis. During this phase, the cell begins to prepare for cell division. Every chromosome creates an exact duplicate of itself by replication. Before replication, each chromosome is a long linear strand of genetic material. After replication, each chromosome has become a pair of identical long linear strands, held together near the center; this region, where the chromosomes are in contact, is called the **centromere.**

Gap 2. In this phase, the cell continues to grow and prepare for cellular division. This phase differs from Gap 1 because the genetic material has now been duplicated. Gap 2 is usually much shorter than Gap 1.

Mitotic phase

This phase begins with **mitosis,** a process in which the nucleus of the parent cell duplicates. Mitosis is generally followed by **cytokinesis,** during which the cytoplasm, organelles, and the rest of the materials in the cell duplicate and the cell separates into two daughter cells, each of which has a complete set of the parent cell's DNA and other cellular structures. (Note that each daughter cell becomes a parent cell in the next cell cycle.) The mitotic phase is usually the shortest period in the eukaryotic cell cycle.

The transition from one phase to the next is triggered by specific events. For instance, a cell moves from the Gap 1 phase (denoted G_1) to DNA synthesis only if environmental conditions outside the cell are favorable for cell division. Until conditions are favorable, the cell remains in G_1. Likewise, a cell begins mitosis only when the genetic material has been successfully duplicated. Later in this chapter we'll see that errors in this orderly, step-by-step process can lead to out-of-control cell division and cancer.

TAKE-HOME MESSAGE 6·4

Eukaryotic somatic cells alternate in a cycle between cell division and other cell activities. The cell division portion of the cycle is called the mitotic phase. The remainder of the cell cycle, called interphase, consists of two gap phases separated by a DNA synthesis phase during which the genetic material is replicated.

6·5

Cell division is preceded by replication.

In one of the great understatements in the scientific literature, James Watson and Francis Crick wrote the following sentence in their paper describing the structure of DNA: "It has not escaped our notice that the specific pairing we have postulated immediately suggests a possible copying mechanism for the genetic material." The researchers' ability to explain how DNA copied itself was a critical feature of their description of DNA's structure. After all, every single time any cell in any organism's body divides, that cell's DNA must first duplicate itself so that each of the two new cells has all of the genetic material of the original parent cell. The process of DNA duplication, as we've seen, is called replication.

What is it about DNA's structure that makes duplication so straightforward? Watson and Crick were referring to the feature of DNA called **complementarity,** the characteristic that in the double-stranded DNA molecule, the base on one strand always has the same pairing partner (called the **complementary base**) on the other strand: A pairs with T (and vice versa), and G pairs with C (and vice versa).

With this consistent pattern of pairing, when the DNA molecule separates into two strands, it is possible to perfectly reconstruct all the information on the missing half because one strand carries all the information needed to construct its complementary strand. Just before cells divide, the DNA molecule unwinds and "unzips" and each half of the unzipped molecule serves as a template on which the missing half is reconstructed. At the end of the process of reconstructing the missing halves, there are two DNA molecules, each identical to the original DNA molecule, one for each of the two new cells.

The process of DNA replication occurs in two steps: unwinding and rebuilding (**FIGURE 6-6**).

1. Unwinding. Replication begins when the coiled, double-stranded DNA molecule unwinds and separates into two strands, like a zipper unzipping.

2. Rebuilding. In the rebuilding process, each of the single strands becomes a double strand as an enzyme connects the appropriate complementary base to the exposed base. If an A is exposed, a T binds to it; if a C is exposed, a G binds to it.

The end result of replication is two double-stranded DNA molecules, each identical to the cell's original double-stranded DNA molecule. DNA replication occurs in all types of cells, somatic and reproductive, prior to cell division.

A variety of mutations (such as mismatched bases and added or deleted segments) can occur during replication, but many

This artist is carefully duplicating a painting. Similarly, DNA must be duplicated prior to cell division.

of these errors are caught and repaired after replication. If an error remains, however, the sequences in a replicated DNA molecule (including the genes) can be different from those in the parent molecule. A changed sequence may then produce a different mRNA sequence, which may in turn produce a different amino acid

> **Errors sometimes occur when DNA duplicates itself. Why might that be a good thing?**

sequence, and, hence, a different protein. In this way, new genes can enter a population and be acted on by evolution. We explore the relationship between mutation and evolution in more detail in Chapter 8.

TAKE-HOME MESSAGE 6·5

Every time a cell divides, that cell's DNA must first duplicate itself so that each of the two new cells has all the genetic material of the original parent cell. The process of DNA duplication is called replication. Errors in replication can lead to mutations, which are changes in the DNA sequence.

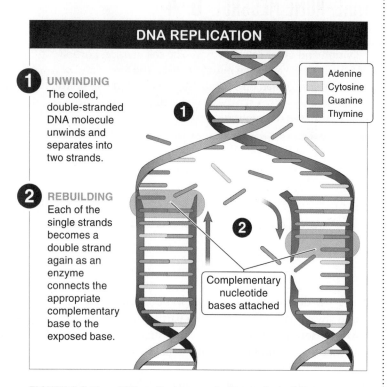

DNA REPLICATION

1 UNWINDING
The coiled, double-stranded DNA molecule unwinds and separates into two strands.

2 REBUILDING
Each of the single strands becomes a double strand again as an enzyme connects the appropriate complementary base to the exposed base.

Adenine
Cytosine
Guanine
Thymine

Complementary nucleotide bases attached

FIGURE 6-6 How DNA replicates: unwinding and rebuilding.

Types of Cell Division   Mitosis   Meiosis   Sex Differences

❷ Mitosis replaces worn-out old cells with fresh new duplicates.

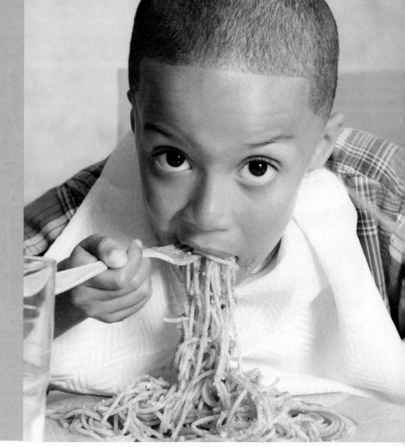

For most of the cell cycle, chromosomes resemble a plate of spaghetti more than the familiar condensed, replicated, X shape seen in photos.

6·6

Most cells are not immortal: mitosis generates replacements.

Look around your dorm room. Dust is everywhere. What is it? It is primarily dead skin cells. In fact, you (and your roommates) slough off millions of dead skin cells each day—yet your skin doesn't disappear. How can that be? Obviously, your body is replacing the sloughed-off cells. The cells have simply worn out, so your body creates replacements. It does this through the process of mitosis.

What is dust? Why is it your fault?

Mitosis has just one purpose: to enable existing cells to generate new, genetically identical cells. There are two different reasons for this need (**FIGURE 6-7**).

1. Growth. During development, organisms get bigger. Growth happens in part through the creation of new cells. In fact, if you want to see cell division in action, one surefire place to look is at the tip of a plant root: at a growth rate of about half an inch per day, the root is one of the fastest-growing parts of a plant.

2. Replacement. Cells must be replaced when they die. The wear and tear that come from living can physically damage cells. The daily act of shaving, for example, damages thousands of cells on a man's face. It's nothing to worry about, though. Microscopic views of human skin reveal several distinct layers, with the outermost layers—the layers under assault during shaving—made up primarily of dead cells. These cells help protect us from infection and also reduce the rate at which the underlying living cells dry out. The living cells that exist just below the layers of dead cells are being produced at a high rate by mitosis; they can also be harmed if you're not careful.

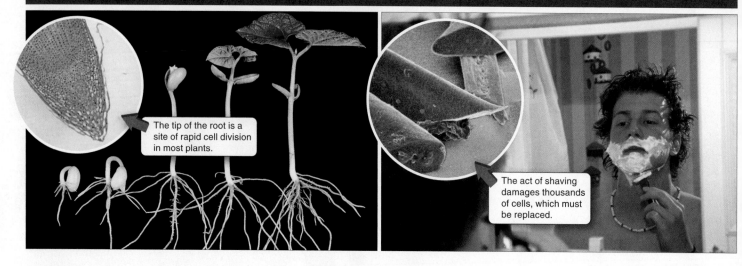

FIGURE 6-7 Reasons for mitosis. Mitosis is important in organism growth and the replacement of cells.

Some other cells that must be replaced actually die on purpose, in a planned process of cell suicide called **apoptosis.** This seemingly counterproductive strategy is employed in parts of the body where the cells are likely to accumulate significant genetic damage over time and are therefore at high risk of becoming cancer cells (a process described later in this chapter). Cells targeted for apoptosis include many of the cells lining the

digestive tract as well as those in the liver, two locations where cells are almost constantly in contact with harmful substances.

Every day, a huge number of cells in an individual must be replaced by mitosis. In humans this number is in the billions. Nearly all the somatic cells of the body—that is, everything other than sperm- and egg-producing cells—undergo mitosis. There are a few notable exceptions. Brain cells and heart muscle cells, in particular, do not seem to divide, or, if they do divide, they do so at very, very slow rates. (It is not known why this is so.)

The rate at which mitosis occurs varies dramatically for different types of cells. The most rapid cell division occurs in the blood and in the cells lining various tissues and organs. The average red blood cell, for example, is in circulation only for about two to four months and then must be replaced. The cells lining the intestines are replaced about every three weeks. Hair follicles, too, are among the most rapidly dividing cells.

The red blood cells in your body carry oxygen to the body's organs and tissues and are replaced about every 120 days.

TAKE-HOME MESSAGE 6·6

Mitosis enables existing cells to generate new, genetically identical cells. This makes it possible for organisms to grow and to replace cells that die.

Overview: mitosis leads to duplicate cells.

For mitosis to begin, the parent cell duplicates its DNA, creating a duplicate copy of each chromosome. Once this task is completed, the other materials in the cell duplicate and the cell divides into two new duplicate cells, the daughter cells.

Mitosis occurs in just four steps. It begins with the condensing of the chromosomes, which are all tangled during interphase. Next, all of the duplicated and condensed chromosomes move to the center of the cell. Each chromosome is then pulled apart from its duplicate. In the final step, new membranes form around each complete set of chromosomes to create the new nuclei, and the cytoplasm and rest of the cell duplicate as well. Where once there was one parent cell, now there are two daughter cells (**FIGURE 6-8**).

These two human embryonic stem cells have just completed mitosis.

TAKE-HOME MESSAGE 6•7

Mitosis is the process by which cells duplicate themselves. It occurs in just four steps, following the replication of chromosomes. It leads to the production of two daughter cells from one parent cell.

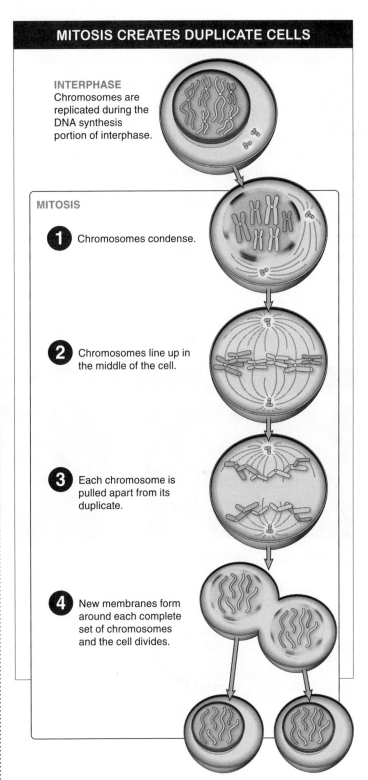

MITOSIS CREATES DUPLICATE CELLS

INTERPHASE
Chromosomes are replicated during the DNA synthesis portion of interphase.

MITOSIS

1 Chromosomes condense.

2 Chromosomes line up in the middle of the cell.

3 Each chromosome is pulled apart from its duplicate.

4 New membranes form around each complete set of chromosomes and the cell divides.

FIGURE 6-8 A simplified introduction to mitosis.

Deviation in Chromosome Numbers

The details: mitosis is a four-step process.

Let's look at the process of mitosis in a bit more detail, keeping in mind that the ultimate consequence of the process is the production of two cells with identical chromosomes.

Interphase: in preparation for mitosis, the chromosomes replicate

Processes essential to cell division take place even before the mitotic phase of the cell cycle begins. During the DNA synthesis part of interphase, every chromosome replicates itself. Recall from Section 6–5 that prior to replication, each chromosome is just a long, linear strand of genetic material; after replication, each chromosome is a *pair* of identical long, linear strands, held together at the center.

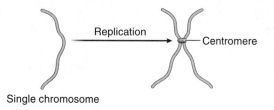

Mitosis The actual process of cell division occurs in four steps (**FIGURE 6-9**).

1. Prophase: the long, linear chromosomes that have replicated condense. When you look at a cell through a microscope, you generally won't see any chromosomes because the cells you're looking at are in some part of their interphase. At this point, the chromosomes are strung out so thin that they are not visible. Mitosis begins with prophase, when the chromosomes in the cell's nucleus become more and more tightly coiled. As they condense, they become thick enough to be seen through a light microscope.

At this point, in prophase, each chromosome looks like the letter X. This appearance is misleading for a couple of reasons. First, during all of the cell cycle except mitosis, chromosomes are uncoiled and spread out in a diffuse way like a mass of spaghetti. Because they are so stretched out, they are not dense

FIGURE 6-9 Mitosis: cell duplication, step by step.

Types of Cell Division   Mitosis   Meiosis   Sex Differences

enough to be visible. Second, chromosomes are not actually X-shaped. They are *linear*. Each X is really two identical linear DNA molecules: a chromosome and its identical replicated copy, joined at the centromere. (Each of the identical DNA molecules is called a **chromatid;** together, the pair are called **sister chromatids.**) The reason for the X shape in most photos of chromosomes is that the only time the chromosome is coiled tightly and thus thick enough to be seen is during cell division.

Because a lot of room is required for separation of the duplicated chromosomes, the membrane around the nucleus is dismantled and disappears near the end of this first stage of mitosis. At the same time, a structure called the **spindle** is assembled. The spindle, which is part of the cell's

Q Animal chromosomes are linear. So, in pictures, why do they look like the letter X?

cytoskeleton, can be thought of as a group of parallel threads stretching from one pole of the cell to the other. These threads (known as **spindle fibers**) pull the sister chromatids to the middle of the cells and will eventually be used to pull the chromatids apart as cell division proceeds.

2. Metaphase: the chromosomes congregate at the cell center. After condensing, the chromatids seem to move aimlessly around the cell, but eventually they line up at the cell's center, pulled by spindle fibers attached to the centromere. Metaphase can be considered the half-time of mitosis. At the end of metaphase, all the chromatids are lined up in an orderly fashion, straddling the center in a "single-file" congregation that is called the metaphase plate. The chromatids are at their most condensed during this part of mitosis.

3. Anaphase: the chromatids separate and move in opposite directions. In anaphase, the fibers attached to the centromeres begin pulling each chromatid in the sister chromatid pairs toward opposite poles of the cell. From each pair of sister chromatids, one strand of DNA is pulled

CYTOKINESIS

3 **ANAPHASE**
• The sister chromatid pairs are pulled apart by the spindle fibers. One full set of chromosomes goes to one side of the cell and another identical set goes to the other.

4 **TELOPHASE**
• The chromosomes begin to uncoil as the nuclear membrane is reassembled around them.
• The cell begins to pinch in two.

CYTOKINESIS
• Cytoplasm and organelles duplicate and are divided into approximately equal parts. The cell splits in two.

in one direction and the other, identical strand is pulled in the opposite direction. At the end of anaphase one full set of chromosomes is at one end of the cell and another identical full set is at the other end. These chromosome sets will eventually reside in the nucleus of each of the two new daughter cells that result from the cell division.

4. Telophase: new nuclear membranes form around the two complete chromosome sets. With two full, identical sets of chromosomes collected at either end of the cell, the cell is prepared to divide into two genetically identical cells. In this last step, called telophase, the chromosomes begin to uncoil and fade from view, nuclear membranes reassemble, and the cell begins to pinch into two.

The process of mitosis, the division of a cell's nucleus into two identical sets, is generally followed by cytokinesis, during which the cell's cytoplasm is also divided into approximately equal parts, with some of the organelles going to each of the two new cells. Only when cytokinesis is complete do the two new daughter cells, each with an identical nucleus containing identical genetic material, enter interphase and begin the business of being cells.

TAKE-HOME MESSAGE 6·8

The ultimate consequence of mitosis and cytokinesis is the production of two genetically identical cells.

6·9

Cell division out of control means cancer.

Too much of a good thing can be bad. This is especially true when cell division runs amok, a situation that can lead to cancer. **Cancer** is defined as unrestrained cell growth and division and can cause serious health problems. Cancer is the second leading cause of death in the United States, responsible for more than 20% of all deaths. Only heart disease causes more deaths.

Cancer occurs when some disruption of the DNA in a normal cell interferes with the cell's ability to regulate cell division. DNA disruption can be caused by chemicals that mutate DNA or by sources of high energy such as X rays, the sun, or nuclear radiation. Cancer can even be caused by some viruses. However it begins, once a cell loses control over its cell cycle, cell division can proceed unrestrained (**FIGURE 6-10**).

Cancer cells have several features that distinguish them from normal cells; the two most significant differences are:

1. *They lose their "contact inhibition."* Most normal cells divide until they bump up against other cells or collections of cells. At that point, they stop dividing. Cancer cells, however, ignore the signal that they are at high density and continue to divide.

2. *Cancer cells can divide indefinitely.* As we saw in Section 6-1, normal cells can divide approximately 50 times. After that point, they may continue living but they lose the ability

to divide. Cancer cells, on the other hand, never lose their ability to divide and continue to do so indefinitely, even in the presence of conditions that normally would halt the cell cycle before cell division. (The ability of cancer cells to divide indefinitely is made possible because they rebuild their telomeres following each cell division.)

Tumors caused by excessive cell growth and division are of two very different types: benign and malignant. Benign tumors, such as many moles, are just masses of normal cells that do not spread. They can usually be removed safely without any lasting consequences. Malignant tumors, on the other hand, are the result of unrestrained growth of cancerous cells. They grow continuously and shed cells (**FIGURE 6-11**). The shedding of cancer cells from malignant tumors is how cancer spreads, a process called metastasis (meh-TASS-tuh-siss). In this process, cancer cells separate from a tumor and invade the circulatory system, which spreads them to different parts of the body where they can cause the growth of additional tumors.

Q What is cancer? How does it usually cause death?

How does cancer actually cause death? Somewhat surprisingly, it's not because of some chemical or genetic property of the cancer cells. It's simpler than that. As a tumor gets larger, it takes up more and more space, pressing against neighboring cells and tissue (**FIGURE 6-12**). Eventually, the tumor may block other cells and tissue from carrying out their normal functions and even kill them. This cell dysfunction or cell death can

Types of Cell Division   Mitosis   Meiosis   Sex Differences

CANCER CELLS

Cancer cells have several features that distinguish them from normal cells.

CANCER CELLS HAVE NO CONTACT INHIBITION

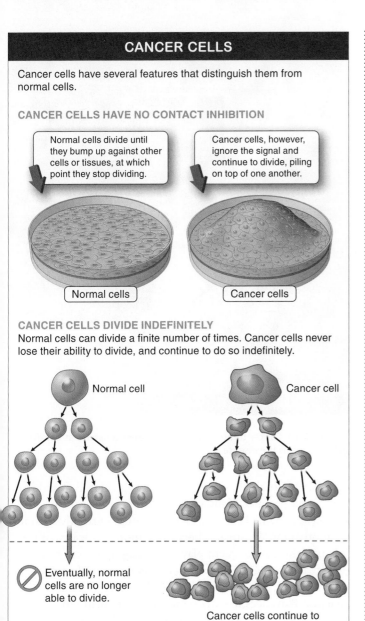

Normal cells divide until they bump up against other cells or tissues, at which point they stop dividing.

Cancer cells, however, ignore the signal and continue to divide, piling on top of one another.

Normal cells

Cancer cells

CANCER CELLS DIVIDE INDEFINITELY

Normal cells can divide a finite number of times. Cancer cells never lose their ability to divide, and continue to do so indefinitely.

Normal cell

Cancer cell

Eventually, normal cells are no longer able to divide.

Cancer cells continue to divide indefinitely.

FIGURE 6-10 Uncontrolled cell division. Cancer occurs when there is a disruption in cells' ability to regulate cell division.

have disastrous consequences when the affected normal tissue controls processes critical to life, such as breathing, heart function, or the detoxification processes in the liver.

To treat cancer, the rapidly dividing cells must be removed surgically, killed, or their division at least slowed down. Currently, the killing and slowing down are done in two ways: by chemotherapy and by radiation. In chemotherapy, drugs that interfere with cell division are administered, slowing down the growth of tumors. Because these drugs interfere with rapidly dividing cells throughout the body (not just the rapidly dividing

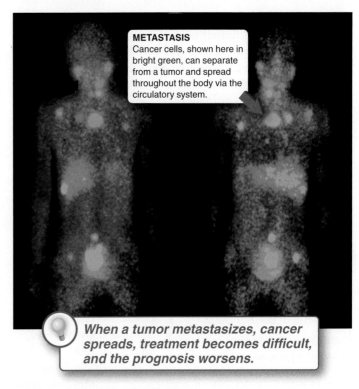

METASTASIS
Cancer cells, shown here in bright green, can separate from a tumor and spread throughout the body via the circulatory system.

When a tumor metastasizes, cancer spreads, treatment becomes difficult, and the prognosis worsens.

FIGURE 6-11 Multiple tumors. Metastasis spreads cancer cells throughout the body.

THE DANGER OF CANCER CELLS

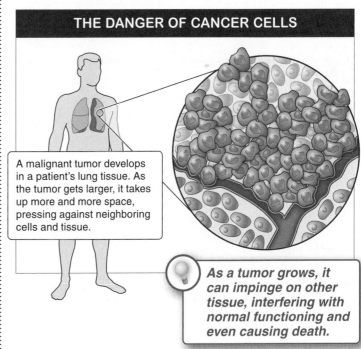

A malignant tumor develops in a patient's lung tissue. As the tumor gets larger, it takes up more and more space, pressing against neighboring cells and tissue.

As a tumor grows, it can impinge on other tissue, interfering with normal functioning and even causing death.

FIGURE 6-12 Cancer's effects. Cancer cells harm the body by crowding and disrupting normal cells.

Deviation in Chromosome Numbers

cancer cells), they can have terrible side effects. In particular, chemotherapy drugs disrupt normal systems that rely on the rapid and constant production of new cells. For instance, chemotherapy often causes extreme fatigue and shortness of breath because it reduces the rate at which red blood cells are produced, limiting the amount of oxygen that can be transported throughout the body. By interfering with the division of bone marrow stem cells, chemotherapy also reduces the production of platelets and white blood cells and thus increases bruising and bleeding, and increases susceptibility to infection. Another location of rapidly dividing cells commonly affected by chemotherapy and radiation is the hair follicle. Many people lose their hair when undergoing chemotherapy (it usually grows back when treatments stop).

Q Why is the treatment for cancer often considered as bad as the disease?

Like chemotherapy, radiation works by disrupting cell division. Unlike the drugs used in chemotherapy, however, which circulate throughout the entire body, radiation therapy directs high-energy radiation only at the part of the body where a tumor is located. Like chemotherapy, the radiation process is not perfect and nearby tissue is often harmed as well. The significant negative effects of chemotherapy and radiation treatment on normal tissue and the suffering this leads to has caused some patients to comment that the treatment for cancer is worse than the disease itself—especially because patients may be asymptomatic at the time of treatment (**FIGURE 6-13**).

> " Bitterness is like cancer. It eats upon the host. But anger is like fire. It burns it all clean. "
>
> —Maya Angelou, U.S. poet and writer

Is there hope for a complete cure soon? Not yet. Nonetheless, many potentially successful therapies for cancer treatment and prevention are on the horizon. Extensive research is being conducted on the mechanisms by which genes controlling the cell cycle are damaged, for example, and how such damage might be prevented or reversed.

In addition, there is a rapidly growing field of research into cancer-inhibiting chemicals that have evolved in many plant

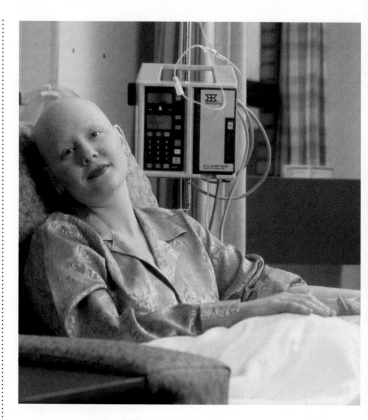

FIGURE 6-13 Cancer treatments. The treatments can be as painful and difficult as the disease.

species. One such chemical is resveratrol, which is found in grapes and peanuts. Many of these naturally occurring chemicals may be less harsh than the drugs currently used in chemotherapy. We are also becoming more conscious of the role that the environment plays in increasing cancer risk; our greater awareness is leading to changes in industrial processes and, on the individual level, to dietary or lifestyle changes. Advances in early screening, particularly in identifying cancer prior to metastasis, continue to have significant benefits as well.

TAKE-HOME MESSAGE 6·9

Cancer is unrestrained cell growth and division, leading to large masses of cells called malignant tumors that can cause serious health problems. Treatment focuses on killing or slowing down the fast-growing and dividing cells, usually using chemotherapy and/or radiation.

❸ Meiosis generates sperm and eggs and a great deal of variation.

Human gametes: sperm attempting to fertilize an egg.

6 • 10

Overview: sexual reproduction requires special cells made by meiosis.

There are two ways in which an organism can reproduce. Many organisms, including bacteria, fungi, and even some plants and animals, undergo asexual reproduction, in which a single parent produces identical offspring. Other organisms, including most animals and plants, undergo sexual reproduction, in which offspring are produced by the fusion of two reproductive cells in the process of **fertilization.**

Sexually reproducing organisms, humans included, have a problem to solve when it comes to cell division. When offspring are created, they carry the genetic material from two individuals. But think about the difficulties this presents. If reproductive cells were produced through mitosis, both parents would contribute a full set of genes—that is, 23 pairs of chromosomes in humans—to create a new individual, and the new offspring would inherit 46 pairs of chromosomes in all. And when that individual reproduced, if he or she contributed 46 pairs of chromosomes and his or her mate also contributed 46 pairs, their offspring would have 92 pairs of

chromosomes. Where would it end? The genome would double in size every generation. That wouldn't work at all. At the very least, within a few generations cells would be so overloaded with chromosomes that they would explode.

Sexually reproducing organisms have evolved a way to avoid chromosome overload. The solution is **meiosis,** a process that enables organisms, prior to fertilization, to make special reproductive cells, the gametes, which have only half as many chromosomes as the rest of the cells in the organism's body. In other words, in anticipation of combining one individual's genome with another's, meiosis reduces each individual's genome by half in the gametes. In humans, for example, gamete cells have only one set of 23 chromosomes, rather than two sets. In genetics, the term **diploid** refers to cells that have two copies of each chromosome, and the term **haploid** refers to cells that have one copy of each chromosome. Thus, somatic cells are diploid and gametes, the cells produced in meiosis, are haploid. At fertilization, two haploid

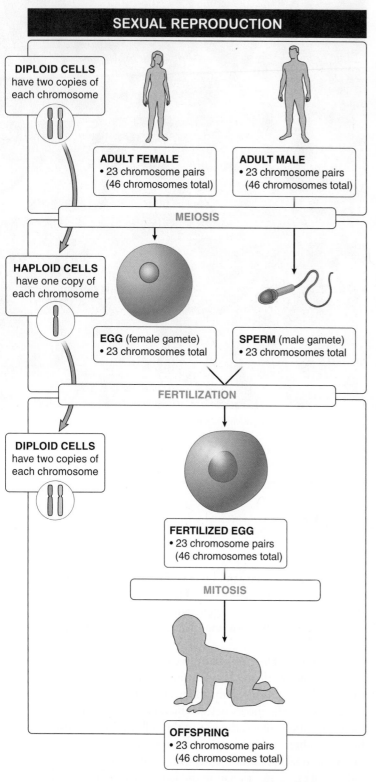

SEXUAL REPRODUCTION

DIPLOID CELLS
have two copies of
each chromosome

ADULT FEMALE
• 23 chromosome pairs
  (46 chromosomes total)

ADULT MALE
• 23 chromosome pairs
  (46 chromosomes total)

MEIOSIS

HAPLOID CELLS
have one copy of
each chromosome

EGG (female gamete)
• 23 chromosomes total

SPERM (male gamete)
• 23 chromosomes total

FERTILIZATION

DIPLOID CELLS
have two copies of
each chromosome

FERTILIZED EGG
• 23 chromosome pairs
  (46 chromosomes total)

MITOSIS

OFFSPRING
• 23 chromosome pairs
  (46 chromosomes total)

FIGURE 6-14 Sexual reproduction. Diploid organisms produce haploid gametes that fuse at fertilization and return to the diploid state.

cells, each with one set of 23 chromosomes, merge and create a new individual with the proper diploid human genome of 46 chromosomes. And when the time comes to reproduce, this new individual also will produce haploid gametes through meiosis that have only a single set of 23 chromosomes. With sexual reproduction, then, diploid organisms produce haploid gametes that fuse at fertilization to restore the diploid state (**FIGURE 6-14**). This process repeats perpetually and maintains a stable genome size in a species.

Although there are some variations on this pattern of alternation between the haploid and diploid states, most multicellular animals produce simple haploid cells for reproduction. And after two of those gametes come together to form a diploid fertilized egg, multiple cell divisions via mitosis again produce a diploid multicellular animal.

Meiosis achieves more than just a reduction in the amount of genetic material in gametes. As a diploid individual, you have two copies of every gene in every somatic cell: one from your mother and one from your father. When making haploid cells from cells that are diploid, an individual creates cells that have one allele for each trait rather than two. Which of these two alleles is included in each gamete cannot be predicted.

Each egg or sperm is produced with a varied combination of maternal and paternal alleles so that all of the gametes an individual makes carry a unique set of alleles. As a consequence, each offspring inherits a slightly different assemblage of that parent's alleles. All offspring resemble their parents, yet none resembles them in exactly the same way. This variation among offspring can be seen among three of the Kennedy brothers in the photo that opens this chapter (pages 208–209). Edward Kennedy is in the middle, with Robert on the left and John on the right.

In all, meiosis has two important outcomes:

1. It reduces the amount of genetic material in gametes.

2. It produces gametes that differ from one another with respect to the combinations of alleles they carry.

In the next sections, we examine the exact steps by which these outcomes occur and investigate the consequences of all the variation that meiosis and sexual reproduction generate.

TAKE-HOME MESSAGE 6·10

Meiosis is the process by which gametes are produced in sexually reproducing organisms. It results in gametes that have only half as much genetic material as the parent cell and that differ from one another with respect to the combinations of alleles they carry.

Types of Cell Division   Mitosis   Meiosis   Sex Differences

Sperm and egg are produced by meiosis: the details, step by step.

Mitosis is an all-purpose process for cell division. It occurs all over the body, all the time. Meiosis, on the other hand, is a special-purpose process. It occurs in just a single place: the **gonads** (the ovaries and testes in sexually reproducing animals). And it occurs for just a single reason: the production of gametes (reproductive cells). To better understand meiosis, let's examine in detail the steps by which a diploid cell creates haploid cells, each of which is different from the other.

Meiosis starts with a diploid cell—not just any diploid cell, but one of the specialized diploid cells, found in the gonads, that is capable of undergoing meiosis. Thus, for humans, meiosis starts with a cell that has 46 chromosomes: a maternal copy and a paternal copy of each of the 23 human chromosomes. Together, the maternal and paternal copies of a chromosome are called a **homologous pair,** or **homologues.** This means that there 23 homologous pairs in a diploid human cell (**FIGURE 6-15**).

Before meiosis can occur (and just as we saw with mitosis), all of these 46 chromosomes are duplicated. So now, instead of having just a maternal and paternal copy of chromosome 1, we have two copies of the maternal copy of chromosome 1, bound together as sister chromatids, and a pair of sister chromatids for the paternal copy of chromosome 1. This means that when meiosis begins, we have 92 (2 × 46) strands of DNA after replication. Remember that this duplication of the chromosomes occurs during the interphase portion of the cell cycle, before actual cell division has begun.

Unlike mitosis, which has only one cell division, cells undergoing meiosis divide twice. In the first division, the homologues separate. In other words, for each of the 23 chromosome pairs, the maternal sister chromatids and the paternal sister chromatids separate into two new cells. In the second division, each of the two new cells divides again, and the sister chromatids separate from each other into two newer cells. At the end of meiosis, there are four new cells, each of which has 23 strands of DNA—that is, 23 chromosomes (**FIGURE 6-16**).

HOMOLOGUES AND SISTER CHROMATIDS

Homologues are the maternal and paternal copies of a chromosome. A sister chromatid is a chromosome and its identical duplicated version held together at a centromere.

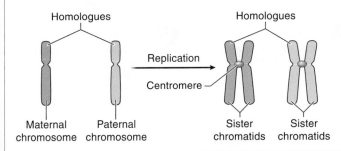

Homologues

Homologues

Replication

Centromere

Maternal chromosome Paternal chromosome

Sister chromatids Sister chromatids

FIGURE 6-15 Chromosome vocabulary: homologues and sister chromatids.

MEIOSIS: REDUCING THE GENOME BY HALF

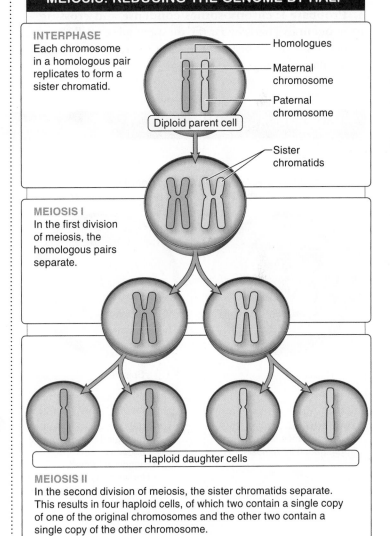

INTERPHASE
Each chromosome in a homologous pair replicates to form a sister chromatid.

Homologues

Maternal chromosome

Paternal chromosome

Diploid parent cell

Sister chromatids

MEIOSIS I
In the first division of meiosis, the homologous pairs separate.

Haploid daughter cells

MEIOSIS II
In the second division of meiosis, the sister chromatids separate. This results in four haploid cells, of which two contain a single copy of one of the original chromosomes and the other two contain a single copy of the other chromosome.

FIGURE 6-16 Meiosis reduces the genome by half in anticipation of combining it with another genome.

Interphase: in preparation for meiosis, the chromosomes replicate

Meiosis is a one-way process: cells undergoing meiosis produce gametes that do not themselves undergo meiosis, so the cells that undergo meiosis do not have a cell cycle. Before meiosis occurs, however, preparations for cell division occur that are similar to those occurring in interphase of the mitotic cell cycle. In particular, there is a DNA synthesis phase during which every chromosome creates an exact duplicate of itself by replicating. As in mitosis, before replication each chromosome is a long, linear strand of genetic material, while after replication each chromosome is a *pair* of identical long, linear strands, held together at the centromere.

Meiosis begins following replication and occurs in eight steps (**FIGURE 6-17**).

Meiosis division I: the homologues separate

1. Prophase I: chromosomes condense and crossing over occurs. This is by far the most complex of all the phases of meiosis. It begins with all of the replicated genetic material condensing.

As the sister chromatids become shorter and thicker, the homologous chromosomes come together. That is, the maternal and paternal sets of sister chromatids for chromosome 1 come together so there are four versions of this chromosome lined up together. The maternal and paternal sets of chromosome 2, 3, 4, and so on, also line up. Under a microscope, the two pairs of sister chromatids appear as pairs of X's lying on top of each other.

At this point, the sister chromatids that are next to each other do something that makes every sperm or egg cell genetically unique: they swap little segments. In other words, when this is happening inside of you, some of the genes that you inherited from your mother get swapped onto the strand of DNA you inherited from your father, and the corresponding bit from your father is inserted into the DNA strand from your mother. This event is called **recombination** or **crossing over,** and it can take place at several (up to dozens) of spots. As a result of crossing over, every sister chromatid ends up having a unique mixture of the genetic material that you received from your two parents. Note that crossing over occurs only during the production of gametes, in meiosis. It does not occur during

| INTERPHASE | MEIOSIS DIVISION 1: HOMOLOGUES SEPARATE |

INTERPHASE
- Chromosomes replicate in preparation for meiosis.

1 PROPHASE I
- Replicated chromosomes condense.
- Spindle is formed.
- Homologous pairs of sister chromatids come together and cross over.
- Nuclear membrane disintegrates.

2 METAPHASE I
- Homologues move toward the center of the cell and line up.

3 ANAPHASE I
- Homologues separate and are pulled to opposite poles. Sister chromatids going to each side are a mix of maternal and paternal genetic material.

FIGURE 6-17 Meiosis: generating reproductive cells, step by step.

Types of Cell Division   Mitosis   Meiosis   Sex Differences

mitosis. Following crossing over, the nuclear membrane disintegrates.

We explore crossing over in more detail in Section 6-13. The remaining steps of meiosis are relatively straightforward.

2. Metaphase I: chromosomes all line up at the center of the cell.
After crossing over has occurred, each pair of homologous chromosomes (that is, the pairs of X's lying on top of each other) moves to the center of the cell, pulled by the spindle fibers to form the arrangement called the metaphase plate. Remember that each pair of homologous chromosomes includes the maternal and paternal version of the chromosome *and* the replicated copy of each—four strands in all.

3. Anaphase I: homologues are pulled to either side of the cell.
This is the beginning of the first cell division that occurs during meiosis. In this phase, the homologues are pulled apart toward opposite sides of the cell. One of the homologues (consisting of two sister chromatids) goes to the top pole, the other to the bottom. At this point, something else occurs that contributes, along with crossing over, to making all the products

of meiosis genetically unique. The maternal and paternal sister chromatids are pulled to the ends of the cell in a random fashion. As a result, the sister chromatids gathered at each pole are a mix of maternal and paternal sister chromatids. Imagine all the different combinations that can occur in a species with 23 pairs of chromosomes. For chromosome pair 1, perhaps the maternal homologue goes to the "top" pole and the paternal to the "bottom" pole. And for pair 2, perhaps the maternal homologue also goes to the top and the paternal to the bottom. But maybe for pair 3 it is the paternal homologue that goes to the top and the maternal homologue to the bottom. For each of the 23 pairs, you cannot predict which will go to the top and which will go to the bottom. There is a *huge* number of possible combinations. (Can you figure out how many? Here's a hint: if there were 2 chromosome pairs, the answer would be 4; if there were 3 chromosome pairs, the answer would be 8…)

4. Telophase I and cytokinesis: nuclear membrane reassembles around sister chromatids and two daughter cells form.
After the chromatids arrive at the two poles of the cell, the nuclear membrane re-forms, then cytokinesis occurs and the cytoplasm divides, and the cell membrane pinches the cell into two daughter cells, each with its own nucleus,

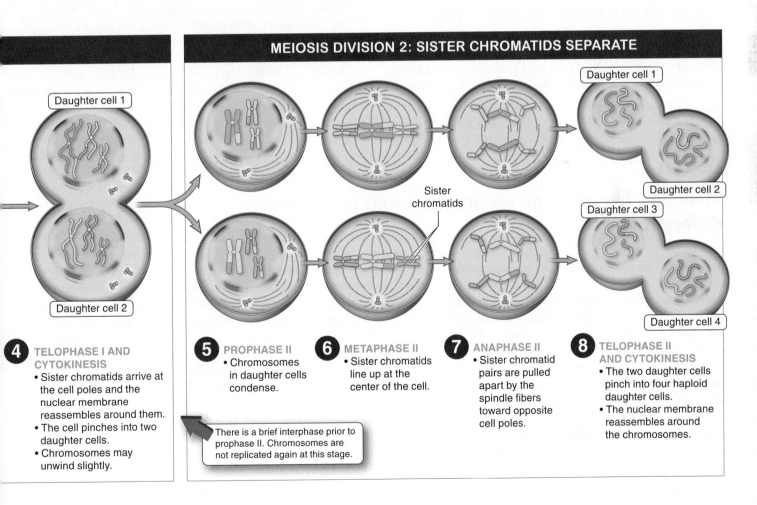

MEIOSIS DIVISION 2: SISTER CHROMATIDS SEPARATE

Daughter cell 1

Daughter cell 2

Daughter cell 1

Daughter cell 2

Sister chromatids

Daughter cell 3

Daughter cell 4

4 **TELOPHASE I AND CYTOKINESIS**
- Sister chromatids arrive at the cell poles and the nuclear membrane reassembles around them.
- The cell pinches into two daughter cells.
- Chromosomes may unwind slightly.

There is a brief interphase prior to prophase II. Chromosomes are not replicated again at this stage.

5 **PROPHASE II**
- Chromosomes in daughter cells condense.

6 **METAPHASE II**
- Sister chromatids line up at the center of the cell.

7 **ANAPHASE II**
- Sister chromatid pairs are pulled apart by the spindle fibers toward opposite cell poles.

8 **TELOPHASE II AND CYTOKINESIS**
- The two daughter cells pinch into four haploid daughter cells.
- The nuclear membrane reassembles around the chromosomes.

Deviation in Chromosome Numbers

containing the genetic material—two sister chromatids for each of the 23 chromosomes in humans.

Meiosis division II: separating the sister chromatids
There is a brief interphase after the first division of meiosis. In some organisms, the DNA molecules (now in the form of chromatids) briefly uncoil and fade from view. In others, the second part of meiosis begins immediately. *It is important to note that in the brief interphase prior to prophase II, there is no replication of any of the chromosomes.*

5. Prophase II: chromosomes re-condense. The second part of meiosis, like the first division of meiosis, is a four-phase process. It begins with prophase II. In this phase, the genetic material in each of the two daughter cells once again coils tightly, making the chromatids visible under the microscope.

6. Metaphase II: sister chromatids line up at the center of the cell. In each of the two daughter cells, the sister chromatids (each appearing as an X) move to the center of the cell, pulled by spindle fibers attached to the centromere, where the sister chromatids are held together. The congregation of all the genetic material in the center of each daughter cell is visible as a flat metaphase plate.

7. Anaphase II: sister chromatids are pulled to opposite sides of the cell. This phase starts with 46 pieces of DNA in each cell created by meiosis I: 23 sister chromatid pairs. During this phase, the fibers attached to the centromere begin pulling

each chromatid in the 23 sister chromatid pairs toward opposite poles of each daughter cell. When anaphase II is finished, each of what will become the four daughter cells (you could think of them as granddaughter cells) has one single copy of each of the 23 chromosomes.

8. Telophase II and cytokinesis: nuclear membranes reassemble and the two daughter cells pinch into four haploid gametes. Finally, the sister chromatids for all 23 chromosomes have been pulled to opposite poles. The cytoplasm then divides, the cell membrane pinches the cell into two new daughter cells, nuclear membranes begin to re-form, and the process comes to a close.

In humans, the outcome of one diploid cell undergoing meiosis is the creation of four haploid daughter cells, each with just one set of 23 chromosomes. These chromosomes contain a combination of traits from the individual's diploid set of chromosomes.

TAKE-HOME MESSAGE 6·11

Meiosis occurs only in gamete-producing cells. It is preceded by DNA replication and consists of two rounds of cellular division, one in which homologous pairs of sister chromatids separate and a second in which the sister chromatids separate. The final product of meiosis in a diploid organism is four haploid gametes.

6·12

Male and female gametes are produced in slightly different ways.

No matter how small or large they are, no matter whether they're plants or animals, there is just one way to distinguish males from females in all sexually reproducing organisms. Regardless of the species, the defining feature is always the same (and if you're thinking of anything visible to the naked eye, you're wrong). When there are two sexes—as there are in nearly every sexually reproducing plant and animal species— the females are the sex that produces the larger gamete, and the males produce the smaller, more motile, gamete (**FIGURE 6-18**). Because gametes are all produced through meiosis, it is a slight variation in how meiosis works in males and females that leads to this difference.

How do you distinguish a male from a female?

The size difference between the male gamete and the female gamete (sperm and eggs in animals) all comes down to the fact that sperm cells have very little cytoplasm, while eggs have a huge amount. During the production of sperm, the two divisions occur just as described in Section 6-11, resulting in four evenly sized cells that become sperm. During the production of eggs, things are a bit different. The first division occurs just as described in Section 6-11, except that in telophase I, as the cell divides, instead of forming two cells of the same size, the division is lopsided. The genetic material is evenly divided, but nearly all of the cytoplasm goes to one of the cells and almost none goes to the other. Then, in the second meiotic division of the

Types of Cell Division   Mitosis   Meiosis   Sex Differences

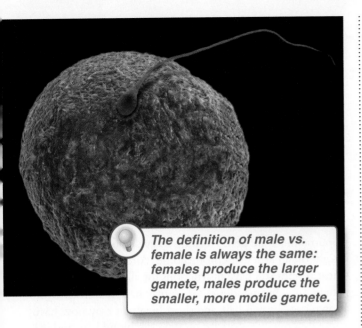

> The definition of male vs. female is always the same: females produce the larger gamete, males produce the smaller, more motile gamete.

FIGURE 6-18 Egg and sperm. In sexually reproducing organisms, the female produces the larger gamete.

larger cell, there is again an unequal division of cytoplasm. As in the first division, one of the cells gets nearly all of the cytoplasm and the other gets almost none. The net result of meiosis in the production of eggs is one large egg with lots of cytoplasm and three small cells with very little cytoplasm. These small cells degrade almost immediately and never function as gametes (**FIGURE 6-19**).

Ultimately, whether it is eggs or sperm that are being produced through meiosis, each gamete ends up with just one copy of each chromosome. That way, the fertilized egg that results from the fusion of sperm and egg carries two complete sets of chromosomes, so the developing individual will be diploid. The extra cytoplasm carried by the egg contains a large supply of nutrients and other chemical resources to help with the initial development of the organism following fertilization.

TAKE-HOME MESSAGE 6·12

In species with two sexes—including nearly every sexually reproducing plant and animal species—females are the sex that produces the larger gamete, and males produce the smaller gamete. Whether it is male or female gametes that are being produced, each gamete ends up with just one copy of each chromosome.

FEMALE GAMETE DEVELOPMENT

Diploid female cell

Replication

MEIOSIS I
(Telophase I)

Genetic material is divided evenly, but nearly all of the cytoplasm goes to just one of the cells.

MEIOSIS II
(Telophase II)

Functional female gamete
(haploid cell)

As in the first division, one cell gets nearly all of the cytoplasm. The net result is one large egg and smaller cells that degrade almost immediately.

FIGURE 6-19 Unequal distribution of cytoplasm results in one large egg.

Crossing over and meiosis are important sources of variation.

Genetically speaking, there are two ways to create unique individuals. The obvious way is for an organism to carry an allele that is not present in any other individuals. Alternatively—and equally successful in creating uniqueness—an individual can carry a *collection* of alleles, no single one of which is unique, that has never before occurred in the same individual. Both types of novelty introduce important variation into a population of organisms. The process of crossing over (**FIGURE 6-20**), which occurs during prophase I in meiosis, creates a significant amount of the second type of variation.

As we saw in Section 6-11, during the first prophase of meiosis, the sister chromatids of homologous chromosomes all come together. That previous sentence is a mouthful! Let's review exactly what it means. Let's look at just one of your 23 homologous pairs of chromosomes, the homologous pair of chromosome 15. When we refer to the "homologous pair" of chromosome 15, remember that this pair includes two copies of chromosome 15: one copy from your mother (which you inherited from the egg that was fertilized to create you) and one copy from your father (which you inherited from the sperm that fertilized the egg). Each chromosome in the pair carries the same genes, but because they came from different people, they don't necessarily have the same alleles.

Once the sister chromatids of the homologous chromosomes line up, regions that are close together can swap segments. A piece of one of the maternal chromatids—perhaps including the first 100 genes on the strand of DNA—may swap places with the same segment in a paternal chromatid. Elsewhere, a stretch of 20 genes in the middle may be swapped from the

other maternal chromatid with one of the paternal chromatids. Every time a swap of DNA segments occurs, an identical amount of genetic material is exchanged, so all four chromatids still contain the complete set of genes that make up the chromosome. The *combination* of alleles on each chromatid, though, is now different.

Suppose there are genes relating to eye color, hair color, and height on a particular chromosome. After crossing over, the linear strands still have instructions for all of those traits. But where one chromatid previously may have had instructions for brown eyes, brown hair, and short height, it may now have some differences—perhaps brown eyes, blond hair, and tall height. All of the alleles from your parents are still carried on one DNA molecule or another. But the *combination of traits* that are linked together on a single chromatid is new. And when a gamete, let's say it's an egg, carrying a new combination of alleles is fertilized by a sperm, the developing individual will carry a completely novel set of alleles. And so without creating any new traits (perhaps yellow eyes or purple hair), crossing over still creates gametes with collections of alleles that may never have existed together. In Chapter 8, we will see that this variation is tremendously important for evolution.

TAKE-HOME MESSAGE 6·13

Although it doesn't create any new traits, crossing over during the first prophase of meiosis creates gametes with collections of traits that may never have existed before; this variation is important for evolution.

CROSSING OVER

Homologous chromosomes

Sister chromatids

Maternal copy Paternal copy

Crossing over between the sister chromatids of the homologous chromosomes

Homologous chromosomes after the exchange of genetic information

Each of these 4 chromatids gets packaged into a haploid gamete (sperm or egg cell).

Chromatids with recombined DNA

Crossing over doesn't create new alleles but it does create new combinations of alleles on a chromatid.

FIGURE 6-20 Swapping DNA. Crossing over creates new combinations of alleles on each chromatid.

What are the costs and benefits of sexual reproduction?

There are two fundamentally different ways by which cells and organisms can reproduce. On the one hand there is mitosis and asexual reproduction via binary fission. On the other hand there is meiosis and sexual reproduction. Is one method better than the other? It depends. In fact, the more appropriate question is, what are the advantages and disadvantages of each method and under what conditions do the benefits outweigh the costs?

What are the advantages of sexual reproduction? Sexual reproduction leads to offspring that are all genetically different from one another and from either parent, through three different routes (**FIGURE 6-21**).

1. *Crossing over during the production of gametes.* As we saw, crossing over during prophase I of meiosis causes every chromosome in a gamete to carry a mixture of that individual's maternal and paternal genetic material.

2. *Shuffling and reassortment of homologues during meiosis.* Recall that as the homologues for each chromosome are pulled to opposite poles of the cell during the first division of meiosis, maternal and paternal homologues are randomly pulled to each pole. This means that there is an extremely large number of different combinations of maternal and paternal homologues that might end up in each gamete.

3. *Combining alleles from two parents at fertilization.* First and foremost, with sexual reproduction a new individual comes from the fusion of gametes from two different people. Each of these parents comes with his or her own unique set of genetic material.

Q Bacteria reproduce asexually, whereas most plants and animals reproduce sexually. Which is the better method?

The variability among the offspring produced by sexual reproduction enables populations of organisms to cope better with changes in their environment. After all, if the environment is gradually changing from one generation to the next, individuals producing many offspring increase the likelihood that one of their offspring will carry a set of genes particularly suited to the new environment. Over time, populations of sexually reproducing organisms can quickly adapt to changing environments. It's like buying lottery tickets—the more different tickets you buy, the more likely it is that one of them will be a winner.

SOURCES OF GENETIC VARIATION

There are multiple reasons why offspring are genetically different from their parents and one another.

CROSSING OVER
Crossing over during meiosis produces a mixture of maternal and paternal genetic material on each chromatid.

REASSORTMENT OF HOMOLOGUES
The homologues and sister chromatids distributed to each daughter cell during meiosis are a random mix of maternal and paternal genetic material.

ALLELES COME FROM TWO PARENTS
Each parent donates his or her own set of genetic material.

FIGURE 6-21 Crossing over and meiosis: creating many different combinations of alleles. As a result of crossing over and meiosis, each individual born from a separate fertilized egg is genetically unique.

What are the disadvantages of sexual reproduction? In the yellow dung fly (*Scathophaga stercoraria*), males sometimes wrestle each other for mating access to a female (**FIGURE 6-22**). The female awaits the outcome of the battle in a pile of dung. Occasionally, females drown in the dung pile as they wait. Dangers associated with mating are just one of the downsides to sexual reproduction. There are several others. First, when one parent reproduces, only half of its offsprings' alleles will come from that organism.

FIGURE 6-22 Drowning in dung. A downside to sexual reproduction.

Some bacteria can divide every 20 minutes!

FIGURE 6-23 Pluses and minuses. This asexually reproducing bacterial colony can reproduce quickly and efficiently, but because each new cell is an exact duplicate of the parent genome, there is no genetic variety to enable adaptation should the environment change.

The other half will come from the other parent. With asexual reproduction, parents produce nearly identical offspring, so there is a very efficient transfer of genetic information from one generation to the next. Also, with sexual reproduction it takes time and energy to find a partner. This is energy that asexual organisms can devote to additional reproduction. Moreover, as we see with the dung flies, sex can be a risky proposition because organisms make themselves vulnerable to predation, disease, and other calamities during reproduction. And finally, as we will see later in this chapter, the complex cellular division required for sexual reproduction offers opportunities for mistakes, sometimes leading to chromosomal disorders.

What are the advantages of asexual reproduction?
With asexual reproduction, the advantages and disadvantages are more or less reversed. Because asexual reproduction involves only a single individual, it can be fast and easy. Some bacteria can divide, forming a new generation, every 20 minutes (**FIGURE 6-23**). And for organisms in isolated habitats or when establishing new populations, asexual reproduction can be advantageous as well. Asexual reproduction is efficient, too. Offspring carry all of the genes that their parent carried—they are genetically identical. If the environment is stable, it is beneficial for organisms to produce offspring as similar to themselves as possible.

What are the disadvantages of asexual reproduction? The downside to asexual reproduction is

that the more closely an offspring's genome resembles its parent's, the less likely it is that the offspring will be suited to the environment when it changes.

In the end, we still see large numbers of species using asexual reproduction and large numbers, including the vast majority of animals and plants, that reproduce sexually. It seems that conditions favoring each occur in the great diversity of habitats of the world. That we see both sexual and asexual reproduction also highlights the recurring theme in biology that there often is more than one way to solve a problem.

TAKE-HOME MESSAGE 6·14

There are two fundamentally different ways that cells and organisms can reproduce: (1) mitosis and asexual reproduction via binary fission, and (2) meiosis and sexual reproduction. Asexual reproduction can be fast and efficient, but leads to genetically identical offspring that carry all of the genes that their parent carried. Sexual reproduction leads to offspring that are all genetically different from one another and from either parent, but takes more time and energy and can be risky.

Types of Cell Division   Mitosis   Meiosis   Sex Differences

4 There are sex differences in the chromosomes.

XX and XY: Only one of the 23 chromosome pairs determines sex in humans.

6·15

How is sex determined in humans?

In humans the sex of a baby is determined by its father. The complex sequence of events involved in sex determination is instigated by one special pair of chromosomes called the sex chromosomes. The sex chromosomes carry information that directs a growing fetus to develop as a male or as a female. An individual's sex depends on the sex chromosome inherited from his or her father.

Q Which parent determines a baby's sex? Why?

Let's take a closer look at the sex chromosomes. In humans, we noted that there are 23 pairs of chromosomes in every somatic cell. These can be divided into two different types: there is one pair of sex chromosomes and there are 22 pairs of non-sex chromosomes. The human sex chromosomes are called the **X and Y chromosomes** (**FIGURE 6-24**).

How do the X and Y chromosomes differ from the other chromosomes? As we described earlier, all of the genetic information is stored on the chromosomes in all cells of an organism's body. But most of this information is not sex specific—that is, if you are building an eye or a neuron

or a skin cell or a digestive enzyme, it doesn't matter whether it is for a male or for a female; the instructions are the same for both sexes. Some genetic information, however, instructs the body to develop into one sex or the other. That information—which *does* differ dramatically depending on whether it is the genetic information for building a female or a male—is found on the sex chromosomes.

An individual has two copies of all of the non-sex chromosomes. One copy is inherited from the mother, one from the father. Individuals also have two copies of the sex chromosomes, but not always two copies of the same kind. Males have one copy of the X chromosome and one copy of the Y chromosome. Females, on the other hand, don't have a Y chromosome but instead have two copies of the X chromosome.

So how does the father determine the sex of the baby? During meiosis in females, the gametes that are produced carry only one copy of each chromosome. This is true for

235

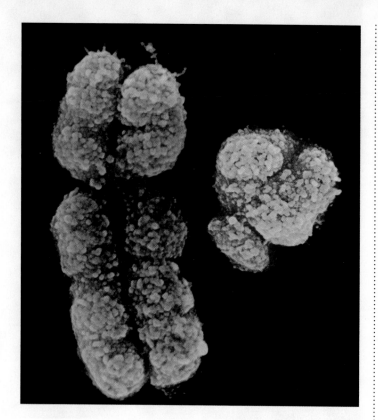

FIGURE 6-24 X and Y: the human sex chromosomes.

Individuals have two copies of the sex chromosomes in every cell.

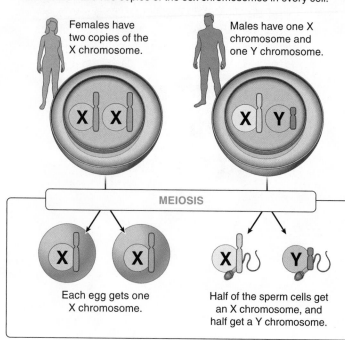

Females have two copies of the X chromosome.

Males have one X chromosome and one Y chromosome.

MEIOSIS

Each egg gets one X chromosome.

Half of the sperm cells get an X chromosome, and half get a Y chromosome.

FERTILIZATION

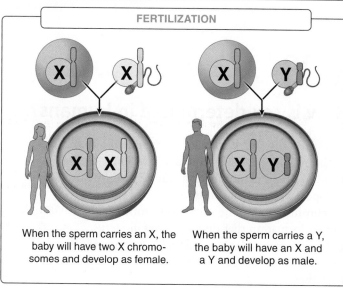

When the sperm carries an X, the baby will have two X chromosomes and develop as female.

When the sperm carries a Y, the baby will have an X and a Y and develop as male.

FIGURE 6-25 Sex determination in humans. The sex of offspring is determined by the father.

the sex chromosomes, too. So from the two copies of the X chromosome carried by females, half of the gametes end up with a copy of one of those X chromosomes while the rest of the gametes inherit the other X chromosome. Thus, every egg has an X for its one sex chromosome. During meiosis in males, the sperm that are produced also carry one copy of each chromosome, including the sex chromosomes, but in this case, half of the sperm produced inherit the X chromosome and the other half inherit the Y chromosome. At fertilization, an egg bearing a single X chromosome (and one copy of all the non–sex chromosomes) is fertilized by a sperm bearing one copy of all the non–sex chromosomes and *either* an X chromosome or a Y chromosome. When the sperm carries an X, the baby will have two X chromosomes and will develop as a female. When the sperm carries a Y, the baby will have an X and a Y and so will develop as a male (**FIGURE 6-25**).

Given the distribution of X and Y chromosomes into males and females, it must be true that there is no essential genetic information carried on the Y chromosome. Why?

Q Why can we be certain that there is no essential genetic information carried on the Y chromosome?

Because females don't have a Y chromosome in any of their cells, yet they are able to develop and live normal, healthy lives. For this reason, we know that nothing on the Y chromosome is absolutely necessary.

Physically, the X and Y chromosome look very different from each other. The X chromosome is relatively large and carries a great deal of genetic information relating to a large

Types of Cell Division   Mitosis   Meiosis   Sex Differences

number of non–sex-related traits. The Y chromosome, on the other hand, is tiny and carries genetic information only about a very small number of traits. The small set of genetic instructions on the Y chromosome instructs the fetal gonads to develop as testes rather than ovaries. Once this is done, very little additional genetic input from the Y chromosome is necessary. Instead, the hormones produced by the testes or ovaries generally direct the rest of the body to develop as a male or female. In the next sections we investigate some of the ramifications of males having two different sex chromosomes and look at some of the systems for sex determination that have evolved in other groups of organisms.

TAKE-HOME MESSAGE 6·15

In humans, the sex chromosomes carry information that directs a growing fetus to develop as either a male (if a Y chromosome is present) or a female (if no Y chromosome is present). The determination depends on the sex chromosomes inherited from the parents.

6·16

The sex of offspring is determined in a variety of ways in non-human species.

For something as fundamental to a species as sex determination, you might imagine that one method evolved and all species use it. The world is more diverse than that. In most plants there aren't even distinct males and females. In corn, for example, every individual produces both male and female gametes. All earthworms and garden snails are also capable of producing both male and female gametes. Such organisms are called **hermaphrodites** (from the names of the Greek god Hermes and goddess Aphrodite) because both male and female gametes are produced by an individual. But even among the species with separate males and females there are several different methods of sex determination. The human method, in which having both an X and a Y chromosome makes you male and having two X chromosomes makes you female, is common among eukaryotes and is seen in all mammals. But it is only one of at least four different methods used by organisms for determining sex. We'll examine the three others, used by different groups, here (**FIGURE 6-26**).

SEX DETERMINATION IN VARIOUS OTHER SPECIES

BIRDS
In birds, the mother determines the sex in a way that is similar to how fathers determine sex in humans.

FEMALE W Z   MALE Z Z

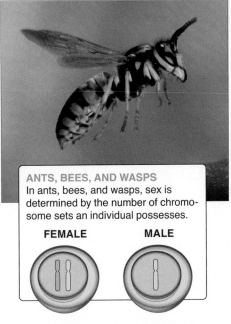

ANTS, BEES, AND WASPS
In ants, bees, and wasps, sex is determined by the number of chromosome sets an individual possesses.

FEMALE   MALE

TURTLES
In most turtles, sex is determined by the temperature at which the eggs are incubated.

FEMALE   MALE

FIGURE 6-26 Other methods of sex determination. In some species, sex is determined by the type of chromosomes, the number of chromosomes, or incubation temperature of the eggs.

Some biologists are concerned that global warming will harm turtles, like this loggerhead sea turtle. Since the sex of the animal is determined by the temperature of the incubating eggs, a warming of the nesting beaches could result in all female offspring.

Birds In birds, the mother determines the sex in a way that is similar to the way fathers determine sex in humans. Females have one copy of two different sex chromosomes, called the Z and the W chromosomes. Males, on the other hand, have only one type, carrying two copies of the Z chromosome. Consequently, the sex of bird offspring is determined by the mother rather than the father. This method is also found in some fish and butterfly species.

Ants, bees, and wasps In these insects, sex is determined by the number of chromosome sets an individual possesses.

Males are haploid, having only a single set of chromosomes, and females are diploid, carrying two full sets of chromosomes. In this unusual method, females produce haploid eggs by meiosis. They then mate with males and store the sperm in a sac. As each egg is produced, the female can allow it to be fertilized by some of the sperm she has stored, in which case the offspring will be diploid and female. Alternatively, she can lay the unfertilized egg, which can develop into a haploid, male individual. Just think, in these species, males don't have a father, yet they do have a grandfather!

Turtles In some species, sex determination is controlled by the environment rather than by the number or types of chromosomes an organism has. In most turtles, for example, offspring sex is determined by the temperature at which the eggs are kept. Eggs that are kept relatively hot during incubation become females, while the eggs incubated at slightly cooler temperatures become males. The sex of some lizards and crocodiles is also determined by the temperature at which the eggs are incubated.

TAKE-HOME MESSAGE 6·16

A variety of methods are used for sex determination across the world of plant and animal species. These include the presence or absence of sex chromosomes, the number of chromosome sets, and environmental factors such as incubation temperature.

Types of Cell Division   Mitosis   Meiosis   Sex Differences

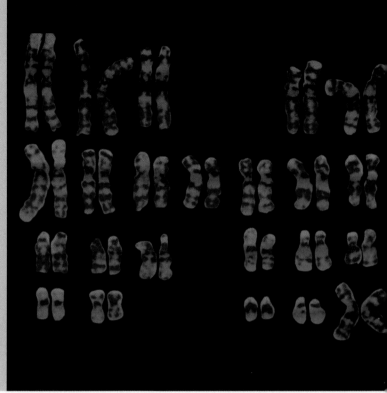

⑤ Deviations from the normal chromosome number lead to problems.

Karyotype displaying the chromosome pairs of a normal human female.

6 · 17

Down syndrome can be detected before birth: karyotypes reveal an individual's entire chromosome set.

It becomes riskier for women to have children as they become older. Increasingly, their gametes contain incorrect numbers of chromosomes or chromosomes that have been damaged. These problems can lead to effects that range from minor to fatal.

To find out if their offspring may have some disorders associated with incorrect numbers of chromosomes, parents can request a quick test for some common genetic problems even before their baby is born. This information is available from an analysis of an individual's **karyotype,** a visual display of a complete set of chromosomes. A karyotype can be made for adults or children, but it is most commonly done for a fetus. A karyotype is a useful diagnostic tool because it can be prepared very early in the fetus's development to assess whether there is an abnormality in the number of chromosomes or in their structure. And because it shows all of the chromosomes, even the sex chromosomes, it also reveals the sex of the individual.

Preparing a karyotype takes five steps. (1) First it is necessary to obtain some cells from the individual. (2) The cells are then encouraged to divide by culturing them in a test tube with nutrients. (3) After a few days to two weeks of cell division, the cells are treated with a chemical that stops them exactly midway through cell division—a time when the chromosomes are coiled thickly and more visible than usual. (4) Then the cells are placed on a microscope slide and a stain is added that binds to the chromosomes, making them visible. (5) And finally, the chromosomes are arranged by size and shape and displayed on a monitor or in a photograph (**FIGURE 6-27**).

The first step—obtaining cells to prepare a karyotype from— is relatively easy in an adult or child. Usually cells are collected from a small blood sample. Collecting cells from a fetus, on the other hand, poses a special problem. Two different methods for collecting cells have been developed.

1. *Amniocentesis.* This procedure can be done approximately three to four months into a pregnancy (**FIGURE 6-28**). In one quick motion (and without using anesthetic), a 3- to 4-inch needle is pushed through the abdomen, through the amniotic sac, and into the amniotic fluid that surrounds and protects the fetus. Using ultrasound for guidance, the doctor

FIGURE 6-27 **A human karyotype.** A visual display of a complete set of chromosomes.

FIGURE 6-28 **Amniocentesis.** Fluid surrounding a fetus (containing some of its cells) is extracted and analyzed to determine the genetic composition of the developing fetus.

aims for a small pocket of fluid as far as possible from the fetus and withdraws about 2 tablespoons of fluid. This fluid contains many cells from the fetus, which can then be used for karyotype analysis. Any chromosomal abnormalities in the fetus will be present in these cells.

2. *Chorionic villus sampling (CVS).* In this procedure, rather than sampling cells from the amniotic fluid, a small bit of tissue is removed from the **placenta,** the temporary organ that allows the transfer of gases, nutrients, and waste products between a mother and fetus. A needle is inserted either through the abdomen or through the vagina and cervix, again using ultrasound for guidance. Then a small piece of the finger-like projections from the placenta are removed via the syringe. Because the fetus and placenta both develop

from the same fertilized egg, their cells contain the same genetic composition. The chief advantage of CVS over amniocentesis is that it can be done several weeks earlier in the pregnancy, usually between the 10th and 12th weeks.

The resulting karyotype, whether from amniocentesis or CVS, will reveal whether the fetus carries an extra copy of any of the chromosomes or lacks a copy of one or more chromosomes. Of all the chromosomal disorders detected by karyotyping, Down syndrome is the most commonly observed. Named after John Langdon Down, the doctor who first described it in 1866, the syndrome is revealed by the presence of an extra copy of chromosome 21 (**FIGURE 6-29**). (For this reason, the condition that causes Down syndrome is called "trisomy 21.") Striking about 1 of every 1,000 children born, Down syndrome is

FIGURE 6-29 **Trisomy 21.** An extra copy of chromosome 21 causes Down syndrome.

Types of Cell Division   Mitosis   Meiosis   Sex Differences

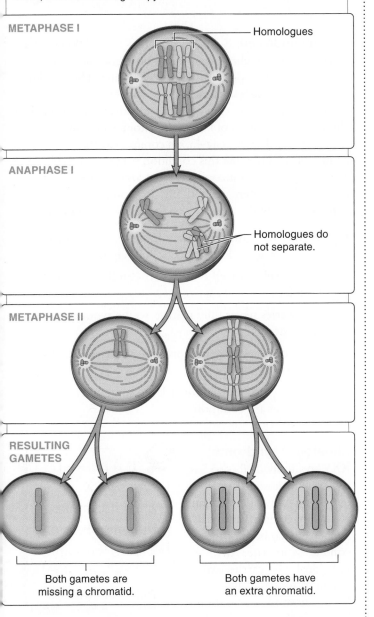

NONDISJUNCTION

Nondisjunction is the unequal distribution of chromosomes during meiosis. The resulting gametes have zero or two copies of a chromosome, rather than a single copy.

METAPHASE I

Homologues

ANAPHASE I

Homologues do not separate.

METAPHASE II

RESULTING GAMETES

Both gametes are missing a chromatid.

Both gametes have an extra chromatid.

FIGURE 6-30 Nondisjunction: forming gametes with too many or too few chromosomes.

characterized by a suite of physical and mental characteristics that includes learning disabilities, a flat facial profile, heart defects, and increased susceptibility to respiratory difficulties.

Down syndrome and other disorders caused by a missing chromosome or an extra copy of a chromosome are a consequence of **nondisjunction,** the unequal distribution of

chromosomes during meiosis. Nondisjunction can occur at two different points in meiosis: homologues can fail to separate during meiosis I or sister chromatids can fail to separate during meiosis II (**FIGURE 6-30**). In both cases, nondisjunction results in an egg or sperm with zero or two copies of a chromosome rather than a single copy. Each of the chromosomes is approximately equally likely to fail to separate during cell division, but the ramifications of trisomy (having an extra copy of one chromosome in every cell) are greater for chromosomes with larger numbers of genes. When trisomy occurs for chromosomes with greater numbers of genes, the likelihood that the developing embryo survives to birth is reduced. Consequently, we tend to see cases of trisomy that involve only the chromosomes with the fewest genes, such as chromosomes 13, 15, 18, 21, and 22. In fact, actual observations show that trisomy 1 is never seen (all such fertilized eggs die before implantation in the uterus), trisomy 13 occurs in 1 in 20,000 newborns (and most die soon after birth), while trisomy 21 occurs in 1 in 1,000 newborns (many of whom live long lives).

As we mentioned at the beginning of this section, it becomes riskier for women to have children as they become older. Older women, for example, have more babies with Down syndrome. Why does the risk of having a baby with Down syndrome or some other disorder that results from trisomy increase with increasing age for women but not for men? As women age, their gametes tend to have more errors. The problem is that those eggs *began* meiosis near the time the woman was born and they may not complete it until she is 40 or more years old. During those decades, the cells may accumulate impairments that interfere with normal cell division. In men, the cells that are undergoing meiosis are relatively young because new sperm-producing cells are produced every couple of weeks after puberty.

Q *Why do older women have more babies with Down syndrome?*

Whereas lacking a non-sex chromosome or having an extra chromosome usually has serious consequences for health, we'll see in the next section that lacking or having an extra X or Y chromosome has consequences that are much less severe.

TAKE-HOME MESSAGE 6·17

A karyotype is a visual display of a complete set of chromosomes. A karyotype is a useful diagnostic tool because it can be prepared very early in the fetus's development to assess whether there is an abnormality in the number of chromosomes or in their structure, such as in the case of Down syndrome. Down syndrome is caused by having an extra copy of chromosome 21.

Life is possible with too many or too few sex chromosomes.

It is usually fatal to have one too many or one too few of the non-sex chromosomes. When it comes to the sex chromosomes, however, the situation is less extreme. Many individuals are born lacking one of the sex chromosomes or with an additional X or Y chromosome, and they usually survive. We can get a glimpse into the role of the sex chromosomes by looking at the physical and mental consequences of having an abnormal number of sex chromosomes. In each of the cases below, the condition is caused by nondisjunction during the production of sperm or eggs (**FIGURE 6-31**).

TOO MANY OR TOO FEW SEX CHROMOSOMES

GAMETE GENOTYPE	OFFSPRING GENOTYPE	SYNDROME CHARACTERISTICS
X / — and — / X	X —	**TURNER SYNDROME** • Short height • Web of skin between neck and shoulders • Underdeveloped ovaries; often sterile • Some learning difficulties
X X / Y and X / X Y	X X Y	**KLINEFELTER SYNDROME** • Underdeveloped testes • Lower testosterone levels; usually infertile • Development of some female features • Long limbs and slightly taller than average
X / Y Y	X Y Y	**"SUPER MALES"** • Taller than average • Moderate to severe acne • Intelligence may be slightly lower than average
X X / X	X X X	**"METAFEMALES"** • May be sterile • No obvious physical or mental problems

FIGURE 6-31 Characteristics of individuals with too many or too few sex chromosomes.

Turner syndrome: X_ Approximately 1 in 5,000 females carry only one X chromosome and no Y chromosome, exhibiting a condition called Turner syndrome. This condition, denoted as X_ (or sometimes XO), is the only condition in humans in which a person can survive without one of a pair of chromosomes. Instead of having 46 chromosomes in every cell, these individuals have only 45. As common as Turner syndrome is, 98% of the time that this condition occurs in a fertilized egg, the egg is spontaneously aborted long before a fetus can come to term. There are both physical and mental consequences of the absence of a second sex chromosome.

• Women with Turner syndrome are usually relatively short, averaging 4 feet 8 inches in height.

• They develop a web of skin between the neck and shoulders.

• The ovaries never fully mature, so the women are almost always sterile.

• The breasts and other secondary sex characteristics develop incompletely.

• Intelligence is usually normal, but some learning difficulties are common.

Klinefelter syndrome: XXY An individual who has two X chromosomes is female; an individual with an X and a Y is male. But what happens when both of those conditions are true? An individual who carries two X chromosomes *and* a Y chromosome, a condition known as Klinefelter syndrome, develops as male. This is because, as we saw earlier, the Y chromosome carries genetic instructions that, if present, cause fetal gonads to develop as testes; if absent, the fetal gonads develop as ovaries. The extra X chromosome, however, does cause Klinefelter males to be somewhat feminized, although this effect can be reduced through treatments such as testosterone supplementation. Approximately 1 in 1,000 males have the genotype XXY, making this one of the most common genetic abnormalities in humans. Klinefelter syndrome has physical and mental consequences:

> **Q** If a person has two X chromosomes but also has a Y chromosome, is the individual male or female?

| Types of Cell Division | Mitosis | Meiosis | Sex Differences |

- Affected individuals have testes, but they are smaller than average. Because the testes are small, levels of testosterone are low and the individuals are almost always infertile.

- They develop some female features, including reduced facial and chest hair, and some breast development.

- They have long limbs and are slightly taller than average (about 6 feet on average).

- They learn to speak at a later age than average and tend to have language impairments.

- Sometimes individuals have further additional X chromosomes, exhibiting the karyotypes XXXY or even XXXXY. These individuals also exhibit Klinefelter syndrome but more frequently have mental retardation.

Q Do human hermaphrodites exist?

A hermaphrodite is an individual with functioning male and female reproductive organs capable of producing both male and female gametes. Often it is mistakenly assumed that a person with Klinefelter syndrome must be a hermaphrodite because he has both two X chromosomes (which would usually make an individual a female) and an X and a Y chromosome (usually making the individual a male). But although hermaphroditism is common among invertebrates and occurs in some fish and other vertebrates, contrary to urban legends, human hermaphrodites do not exist. Although some men with Klinefelter syndrome may have some features of the opposite sex, they do not produce female gametes and so are not hermaphrodites.

XYY males There is no official name for the condition in which an individual has one X chromosome and two Y chromosomes, although they are sometimes referred to as "super males." This chromosomal abnormality occurs in approximately 1 in 1,000 males (and in about 1 in 325 males who are 6 feet or taller). There are no distinguishing features at birth to indicate that an individual carries an extra Y chromosome, and the vast majority live their lives normally without knowing they have an extra chromosome in every cell. Several consequences of the XYY condition have been well documented.

- XYY males are relatively tall (about 6 feet 2 inches on average).

- They tend to have moderate to severe acne.

- Their intelligence usually falls within the same range as that of XY males, although the average may be slightly lower.

Because in the United States about 20 times as many XYY males are found in prisons as in the population as a whole, there has been tremendous controversy over whether the extra Y chromosome predisposes individuals to criminal behavior. Because these observations were not part of randomized, controlled, double-blind experiments, however, they are open to numerous alternative interpretations. One large study, for example, concluded that the increased representation of XYY males in prison was more likely due to the fact that taller males and males of lower intelligence are more likely to be apprehended, regardless of which chromosomes they carry. The controversy remains unresolved, and the majority of XYY males are *not* in prison.

Although an error during meiosis in either the father *or* the mother causes Klinefelter or Turner syndrome, it is only an error in meiosis in a male that gives rise to an XYY child. Why? Because only males carry Y chromosomes. Consequently, an XYY child must receive both of his Y chromosomes from his father. This means that the father's sperm cell must have contained two copies of the Y, a result of nondisjunction during meiosis in the father.

XXX females Sometimes called "metafemales," individuals with three X chromosomes occur at a frequency of about 1 in 1,000 women. Very few studies of this condition have been completed, although initial observations suggest that some XXX females are sterile but otherwise have no obvious physical or mental problems.

TAKE-HOME MESSAGE 6·18

Although it is usually fatal to have one too many or one too few of the non-sex chromosomes, individuals born lacking one of the sex chromosomes or with an additional X or Y chromosome usually survive, though usually with physical and/or physiological problems.

Knowledge You Can Use

Can you select the sex of your baby? (Would you want to?)

Some fertility clinics now promise that for about $200 they can allow a couple to choose the sex of their baby.

Q: **Given our knowledge of the behavior of the X and Y chromosomes, is it more likely that these sex-selection techniques involve manipulations of sperm or of eggs? Why?** Because all eggs have X chromosomes, the X chromosome doesn't play a role in determining the sex of a baby. Instead, the fertility clinics must somehow sort and separate sperm cells based on whether or not they carry an X or a Y chromosome (men produce approximately equal numbers of each).

Q: **What feature of sperm must be used in separating them?** This process must be based on distinguishing between sperm carrying an X chromosome and sperm carrying a Y chromosome. After the two types of sperm are distinguished, they must then be separated.

Q: **What techniques might make this possible?** One method involves determining, by weighing sperm, which cells have more DNA. The heavier sperm must be carrying the X rather than the Y chromosome because the X is so much larger. Another method is to add a fluorescent dye to sperm that temporarily attaches to DNA. Because sperm with an X chromosome have more DNA, more of the dye attaches to them and they are more fluorescent. A machine then sorts the sperm one by one, and at ovulation, insemination is performed using the sperm with the desired sex chromosome.

Q: **Does it work?** The technique is still fairly new, but initial results suggest that the procedures have a success rate of 70% to 90%.

Concerns for you to ponder.
What are the ethical concerns raised by selecting the sex of one's baby? Are there some circumstances in which such a selection would be more acceptable than in others?

1 **There are different types of cell division.**

Telomeres are protective sections of DNA that get shorter every time a cell divides. If a telomere gets too short, additional cell divisions cause loss of essential DNA and cell death. Cells that rebuild telomeres with each division can become cancerous. In most prokaryotes, genetic information is carried in a single, circular DNA strand (chromosome). Eukaryotes have much more DNA, organized into linear chromosomes in the nucleus. Bacteria divide by a type of asexual reproduction, binary fission. In the cell cycle, eukaryotic somatic cells alternate between division, called the mitotic phase, and other cell activities, called interphase, consisting of two gap phases separated by a DNA synthesis phase. Every time a cell divides, its DNA must first replicate so that each of the two new cells has all the genetic material of the parent cell.

2 **Mitosis replaces worn-out old cells with fresh new duplicates.**

In mitosis, cells generate new, genetically identical cells, enabling organisms to grow and to replace cells that die. Mitosis occurs in four steps, following replication of the chromosomes, to produce two genetically identical daughter cells from one parent cell. Cancer is unrestrained cell growth and division, leading to large masses of cells (tumors). Treatment focuses on killing or slowing down cell growth and division, by chemotherapy and/or radiation.

3 **Meiosis generates sperm and eggs and a great deal of variation.**

Meiosis occurs only in gamete-producing cells of sexually reproducing organisms. Gametes have only half as much genetic material as the parent cell and they differ from one another in the combinations of alleles they carry. Meiosis is preceded by DNA replication and consists of two rounds of cell division: separation of homologous pairs of sister chromatids, then separation of the sister chromatids. The final product in a diploid organism is four haploid gametes. In species with two sexes, the female is the sex producing the larger gamete, while males produce the smaller gamete. Every gamete has just one copy of each chromosome. Crossing over during the first prophase of meiosis creates gametes with collections of alleles that may never have existed together before; this variation is important for evolution. Cells and organisms can reproduce by mitosis and asexual reproduction via binary fission or by meiosis and sexual reproduction.

4 **There are sex differences in the chromosomes.**

In humans, the sex chromosomes carry information that directs a fetus to develop as male (if a Y chromosome is present) or female (no Y present). The sex is determined by the sex chromosome inherited from the parents. Methods for sex determination in plant and animal species include the presence or absence of sex chromosomes, the number of chromosome sets, and environmental factors such as incubation temperature.

5 **Deviations from the normal chromosome number lead to problems.**

A karyotype, a visual display of a complete set of chromosomes, is a useful diagnostic tool. It can be prepared very early in fetal development to detect abnormalities in the number or structure of chromosomes. Having one too many or one too few non-sex chromosomes is usually fatal, but individuals born lacking one of the sex chromosomes or with an additional X or Y usually survive, but often with physical and/or physiological problems.

KEY TERMS

1. Which of the following statements about telomeres is incorrect?
   a) They function like a counter, keeping track of how many times a cell has divided.
   b) At birth, they are long enough to permit approximately 50 cell divisions in most cells.
   c) They are slightly shorter in prokaryotic cells than in eukaryotic cells.
   d) They function like a protective cap on chromosomes.
   e) They contain no critical genes.

2. Prokaryotic cells can divide via:
   a) mitosis.
   b) binary fission.
   c) meiosis.
   d) both mitosis and binary fission.
   e) None of the above.

3. In multicellular organisms, cells that undergo mitotic division but not meiotic division are called _____ cells.
   a) somosis
   b) skin
   c) interphase
   d) somatic
   e) germ

4. The _____ marks the break in the cell cycle between the end of mitosis and beginning of the DNA synthesis stage.
   a) mitotic phase
   b) synthesis phase
   c) Gap 2 phase
   d) Gap 1 phase
   e) None of the above.

5. Mitosis results in:
   a) daughter cells with twice as much genetic material as the parent cell and a unique collection of alleles.
   b) eight daughter cells.
   c) daughter cells with the same number and composition of chromosomes.
   d) gametes.
   e) daughter cells with the same number of chromosomes but different combinations of alleles.

6. Using a light microscope, it is easiest to see chromosomes:
   a) during mitosis and meiosis, because the condensed chromosomes are thicker and therefore more prominent.
   b) during interphase, when they are concentrated in the nucleus.
   c) in the mitochondria, because the chromosomes are circular.
   d) during asexual reproduction.
   e) during interphase, because they are uncoiled and have a more linear structure.

7. The division of the cytoplasm during cell division is referred to as
   a) cytoplasm splicing.
   b) cytokinesis.
   c) vegetative growth.
   d) cytodivision.
   e) hybridization.

8. Which of the following statements about tumors is incorrect?
   a) Benign tumors pose less of a health risk than do malignant tumors.
   b) Malignant tumors shed cancer cells that can spread to other parts of the body.
   c) Tumors are caused by excessive cell growth and division.
   d) Cancer cells from malignant tumors can travel to other parts of the body in a process called metastasis.
   e) They contain cells with abnormally high contact inhibition.

9. During meiosis but not during mitosis:
   a) haploid gametes are produced that are all identical in their allelic composition.
   b) division of the cytoplasm occurs.
   c) chromosomes line up in the center of the cell during metaphase.
   d) genetic variation among the daughter cells is increased.
   e) two identical daughter cells are produced.

10. Sister chromatids are:
    a) the result of crossing over.
    b) identical molecules of DNA resulting from replication.
    c) homologous chromosomes.
    d) produced in meiosis but not in mitosis.
    e) single-stranded.

11. Which of the following events does not occur during prophase I of meiosis?
    a) Spindle fibers form.
    b) Homologous pairs of chromosomes align at the metaphase plate.
    c) Homologues come very close together.
    d) Crossing over occurs between sister chromatids.
    e) Chromosomes condense.

12. Which of the following is the best way to distinguish male from female?
    a) Males are larger.
    b) Males are more brightly colored.
    c) Males produce motile gametes.
    d) Males are more aggressive.
    e) All of the above statements are correct.

13. A potential disadvantage of asexual reproduction is that:
    a) it increases the time required to find a mate.
    b) it allows perpetuation of a population even when the members are isolated.
    c) it allows population size to increase rapidly.
    d) it produces genetically uniform populations.
    e) it requires additional rounds of meiosis, which is energetically much more costly than mitosis.

14. Which of the following is not a method of chromosomal sex determination that occurs in nature?
    a) In birds, the mother's sex chromosomes determine the sex of the offspring.
    b) In sea turtles, eggs laid in hot sand become females and eggs laid in cooler sand become males.
    c) In humans, the presence of a Y chromosome makes an individual male, even if he also possesses two X chromosomes.
    d) In bees, the eggs that the queen allows to be fertilized become females and the eggs she doesn't fertilize become males.
    e) All of the above are naturally occurring examples of sex determination.

15. A karyotype reveals:
    a) the shape of the spindle.
    b) 23 pairs of chromosomes.
    c) the number, shapes, and sizes of chromosomes in an individual cell.
    d) the sex chromosomes but not the non-sex chromosomes.
    e) the non-sex chromosomes but not the sex chromosomes.

16. What type of chromosomal abnormality leads to the phenotype known as Down syndrome?
    a) trisomy 21
    b) monosomy 21
    c) monosomy 22
    d) trisomy 22
    e) disomy 21

17. Nondisjunction:
    a) is the unequal division of the genetic material during cell division.
    b) occurs during meiosis but not mitosis.
    c) occurs in males but not females among mammals, and in females but not males among birds.
    d) leads to a missing chromosome or extra chromosome.
    e) Both a) and d) are correct.

18. Of all the varying types of sex chromosome abnormalities, one possibility—that of an individual having one Y but no X—has never been reported. Which of the following statements is the most likely reason that medical researchers have yet to report a person having a karyotype with one Y and no X?
    a) There is no meiotic event that could produce an egg that does not have an X chromosome.
    b) Individuals are probably born with this karyotype; however, because the phenotypic abnormalities caused are so slight, they live out their lives normally and are unaware of this genetic anomaly.
    c) The Y chromosome needs the X chromosome to be present in the cell in order for its genes to be expressed.
    d) The X chromosome contains genes that are unrelated to sex determination and are essential for life.
    e) Our current technology for karyotyping would not reveal such an abnormality.

SHORT-ANSWER QUESTIONS

1. Seventy to ninety percent of the genetic material in a sperm or egg cell made in your body could be inherited from your mother. Why isn't there a 50/50 split (half from your mother and half from your father)? Is the reverse situation (more genetic material from your father than from your mother) possible?

2. Healthy individuals may have just one sex chromosome, as long as it is an X chromosome. Why can't a person survive with a Y chromosome and no X chromosome?

3. Some organisms can switch between sexual and asexual reproduction. Under what conditions would you expect them to reproduce sexually? What conditions would be more conducive to asexual reproduction? How would you test your hypotheses under laboratory conditions?

See Appendix for answers. For additional study questions, go to www.prep-u.com.

7

Mendelian Inheritance

Family resemblance:
how traits are
inherited

① Why do offspring resemble their parents?

Identical twins inherit the same genetic material. (These twins were not told what to do with their hands when the photographer took the photo. Note the similarities in their hand positions.)

7•1

Family resemblance: your mother and father each contribute to your genetic makeup.

Can a gene be cruel? Of course not. But if one could, consider this candidate: in humans, there is a gene for an enzyme called FMO3 (flavin-containing mono–oxygenase–3), which breaks down a chemical in our bodies that smells like rotting fish. Some unfortunate individuals inherit a defective FMO3 gene and can't break down the noxious chemical. Instead, their urine, sweat, and breath excrete it, causing them to smell like rotting fish. Worst of all, because the odor comes from within their bodies, they cannot wash it away no matter how hard they try. Called "fish odor syndrome," this disorder often causes those afflicted by it to suffer ridicule, social isolation, and depression.

For individuals born with this malady, beyond their own suffering there looms a scary question: "Will I pass this condition on to my children?" They might also wonder how

Q How can a single bad gene make you smell like a rotten fish?

they came to have the disorder, particularly if neither of their parents suffered from it.

Fortunately, most of us do not have to worry about fish odor syndrome, but we do wonder about many other inherited traits that we may or may not pass down to our children. Who do I blame for my straight hair (or curly hair or big feet)? Hearing a new baby described as having "his father's nose" and "his grandmother's lips" could make someone think that we're all cobbled together from a bunch of used parts. Where do we begin and our parents end (**FIGURE 7-1**)?

In many cases, the answers to questions about heredity are simple. Fish odor syndrome, for example, is just such a case. Recall from Chapter 6 that sexually reproducing organisms generally carry two copies of every chromosome in every cell (except their sex cells), because they inherit one copy of each chromosome from each parent. Humans, for example, have 23 pairs of chromosomes (46 individual chromosomes). At each location on the two chromosomes of a pair is the same gene: one copy from the mother and one from the father (**FIGURE 7-2**). As we noted in Chapter 5, each of the two copies of the gene is call an **allele.** The gene for FMO3 is on chromosome 1. There is a normal version—or allele—of the gene for FMO3, which most people carry, and there is a rare, defective version that is responsible for fish odor syndrome. As long as a person has at least one normal version of the FMO3 gene, he or she will produce enough of the enzyme to break down the fishy chemical. But if a person inherits two copies of the defective version of the fish odor gene, one from each parent, that person will inherit the disorder (**FIGURE 7-3**).

When it comes to having children, there is a bright side, at least. Although individuals with fish odor syndrome carry two defective copies of the allele and will pass on one set of the bad instructions in every sperm or egg cell that they make, their children won't necessarily inherit the disease. As long as the other parent supplies a normal version of the FMO3 gene, the child will not have fish odor syndrome. The unaffected children, though, will carry a silent copy of the fish odor allele,

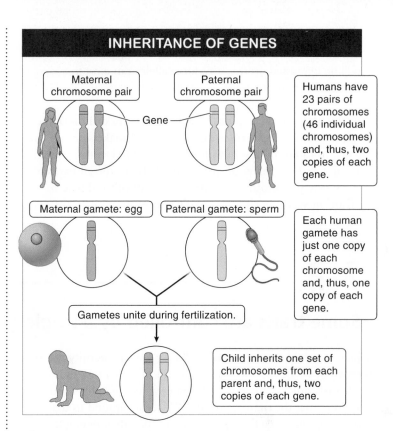

FIGURE 7-2 **How we inherit our genes.** Each human offspring inherits one maternal set of 23 chromosomes and one paternal set.

FIGURE 7-1 **Where do we begin and our parents end?** Family resemblances reveal that many traits are inherited.

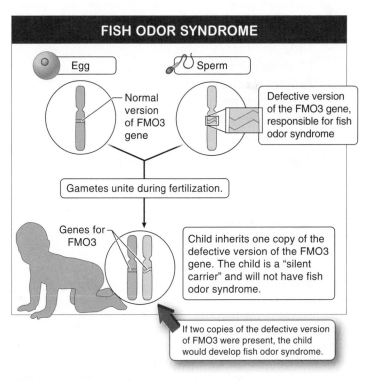

FIGURE 7-3 **Unlucky catch.** A baby inheriting two copies of the defective FMO3 gene will develop fish odor syndrome.

and if, when they have children, it comes together with a defective FMO3 allele from another person, the fish odor trait will be expressed. In this way, some alleles can exist in a population without always revealing themselves.

In this chapter, we explore how heredity works. Inheritance follows some simple rules that allow us to make sense of the patterns of family resemblance we see, and even to predict accurately how many offspring are likely to inherit particular traits—or, put another way, predict the likelihood that an offspring will inherit a trait. We'll also examine why the behavior of some traits is easy to predict while many other traits have less straightforward patterns of inheritance, yet still can be studied experimentally and yield predictable patterns.

TAKE-HOME MESSAGE 7·1

Offspring resemble their parents because they inherit genes—instruction sets for biochemical, physical, and behavioral traits, some of which are responsible for diseases—from their parents.

7·2

Some traits are controlled by a single gene.

Like father, like son. No one will ever seek a paternity test to prove that Michael Douglas is the son of Kirk Douglas. All it takes is a quick look at their legendary dimpled chins and we are sure that the men are related. We see all around us that offspring resemble their parents more than they resemble other random individuals in the population—a consequence of the passing of characteristics from parents to offspring through their genes. This is **heredity.**

HEREDITY

> I AM the family face;
> Flesh perishes, I live on,
> Projecting trait and trace
> Through time to times anon,
> And leaping from place to place
> Over oblivion.
>
> The ears-heired feature that can
> In curve and voice and eye
> Despise the human span
> Of durance—that is I;
> The eternal think in man,
> That heeds no call to die.
>
> —Thomas Hardy, *Moments of Vision and Miscellaneous Verses*, 1917

Observing heredity is easy. Elucidating how it works is not. For thousands of years before the mechanisms of heredity were discovered and understood, plant and animal breeders recognized that there is a connection from parents to offspring across generations. In ancient Greece, for example, the poet Homer extolled the tremendous benefits to society that came

Once breeders recognized the existence of heredity, selective breeding—such as for increased body size in cattle—became possible.

FIGURE 7-4 Have a cow! Selective breeding was used to produce this steer.

from the skillful breeding of horses. The awareness of beneficial breeding practices enabled farmers to systematically create strains of crops, livestock, and even pets with desirable traits (**FIGURE 7-4**). From flocks of sheep and herds of reindeer to litters of puppies and fields of wheat, the similarity among relatives is clear. Once breeders recognized the existence of heredity, they began selecting individual plants or animals with the desired traits to breed with each other, in the hope that their offspring would also have the desirable traits. And since then, it has been possible to create a rich world of sweeter corn, loyal dogs, docile livestock, beautiful flowers, and more.

EXAMPLES OF SINGLE-GENE TRAITS

Cleft chin | Non-cleft chin

Unattached earlobes | Attached earlobes

Widow's peak | Straight hairline

FIGURE 7-5 Chins, ears, and hairlines: single-gene traits. Some traits are determined by the instructions a person carries on one gene.

And these breeders did it all without ever really understanding how heredity works.

Practical successes were many, but people didn't understand exactly how the outcomes were achieved. They knew the result of selective breeding, but why and how it worked, or didn't always work, was a mystery. Patterns of similarity among related individuals are impossible to make sense of without an underlying understanding of *how* heredity works. This is the province of the field of genetics.

Mechanisms of heredity are like a puzzle, and they become a bit easier to grasp when we focus on aspects of family resemblances that are commonplace. Virtually everyone with a cleft chin, for instance, has a similarly dimpled parent. Everyone who has earlobes that hang from their ears rather than being attached directly to their head has at least one parent with the same feature. Everyone who has a widow's peak has a parent with the same hairline. Everyone who is farsighted has a similarly farsighted parent. The list goes on and on. In fact, there are more than 9,000 human traits that exhibit these straightforward patterns of inheritance. Traits that are determined by the instructions a person carries on one gene are called **single-gene traits** (**FIGURE 7-5**).

Q Are any human traits determined by a single gene?

How single-gene traits such as the cleft chin pass from parent to child is the easiest pattern of inheritance to decipher. For this reason, we first explore the mechanisms by which single-gene traits are inherited. Then we investigate how to expand our model of heritability to account for the passing on of more complex traits.

TAKE-HOME MESSAGE 7·2

More than 9,000 human traits are determined by the instructions a person carries on a single gene, and the traits exhibit straightforward patterns of inheritance.

Mendel learned about heredity by conducting experiments.

What do parents "give" their offspring that confers similarity? In other words, how is it that a physical entity is inherited—that is, how is it passed from parent to offspring? It wasn't until the mid-1800s that any real headway was made on these questions. At that time, Gregor Mendel, a monk living in what is now the Czech Republic, began some studies that not only shed light on these questions but practically answered them completely. Mendel understood the essence of the genetics puzzle and set out to piece it all together.

When Mendel turned to these questions about heredity, there were no obvious answers and the prevailing state was confusion. There were a couple of existing ideas, but they had obvious problems. One postulated that perhaps an entire, pre-made human—albeit a very, very tiny one—was contained in every sperm cell (**FIGURE 7-6**). That idea had been popular since the late 1600s. It doesn't take much imagination to see why it ran into difficulty, though, because children resemble both their mothers and their fathers, not just their fathers. Another popular idea was that offspring reflect a simple blending of their two parents' traits via the blood. But this couldn't explain how brown-eyed parents could give birth to

Q Individuals who share common ancestry are called "blood relatives," yet they don't actually share any blood. How might the phrase "blood relatives" be a reflection of early conceptions of inheritance?

blue-eyed children. Or why one tall and one short parent sometimes produced a tall child, rather than always producing children of intermediate height.

Sometimes scientific breakthroughs are made because an innovative new technique is invented or a lucky, chance observation is made. Neither played a role in Mendel's success. He didn't do anything radically new, but simply applied the tried and true methodical experimentation and scientific thinking (as described in Chapter 1) that had been a boon to chemists and physicists. Three features of Mendel's research, in particular, were critical to its success (**FIGURE 7-7**).

1. He chose a good organism to study: the garden pea. It's not that Mendel had a particular fondness for vegetables. In fact, his goals were to understand inheritance in all organisms, not just plants. Pea plants were simply the right tool. Cats and dogs or even mice wouldn't have served his purposes very well, because they would have been too hard to take care of in the large numbers—thousands and thousands of individuals—that Mendel required. Humans, too, would have made a terrible study organism. We take too long to breed (and won't produce offspring on command). Pea plants, on the other hand, have a lot going for them as experimental organisms. They are relatively easy to fertilize manually by "pollen dusting." It is easy to collect dozens or even hundreds of offspring from a single **cross,** in which male pollen is used to fertilize female eggs. And, on top of all this, pea plants are fast enough breeders that Mendel could conduct experiments that lasted for multiple generations.

2. Mendel chose to focus on easily categorized traits. For instance, shape: all peas of the variety that Mendel studied are either round or wrinkled in shape, with nothing in between. In addition, all peas are either yellow or green in color, never any intermediate shade. In all, Mendel looked at seven different traits but, for each trait, only two variants ever appeared, so he and his research assistants could easily observe and unambiguously identify them.

3. Mendel began his studies by first repeatedly breeding together similar plants until he had many distinct populations, each of which was unvarying for a particular

The mistaken idea that a tiny, pre-made human existed in every sperm cell was introduced in the 1600s. This theory remained popular through the 1800s.

FIGURE 7-6 The "pre-made human." Tiny humans in every sperm cell? Why would children have any resemblance to their mothers?

Family Resemblance   Genetics and Chance   Translation of Genotypes   Gene Linkage

MENDEL'S RESEARCH APPROACH

Gregor Mendel
(1822–1884)

Three features of Mendel's methodical research were critical to its success.

1 **Pea plant:** The ideal study organism

Qualities:
- Easy to maintain
- Easy to breed
- Quick reproduction; multiple generations can be observed

2 **Numerous easily categorized traits with two variants each**

TRAIT	VARIANTS	
Flower color	Purple	White
Pea shape	Round	Wrinkled
Pea color	Green	Yellow

3 **Distinct populations established**

True-breeding purple-flower plants

True-breeding white-flower plants

FIGURE 7-7 Mendel's notebook. Careful planning and a well-selected study organism contributed to the success of Mendel's experiments.

trait. He described these plants as **true-breeding** for that trait because they always produced offspring with the same variant of the trait as the parents. True-breeding round-pea plants always produced plants with round peas when they were crossed together. True-breeding purple-flowered pea plants always produced purple-flowered offspring, while true-breeding white-flowered pea plants always produced white-flowered offspring. It took a lot of prep work to establish these populations, but once Mendel had them, he was in a position to set up all of the different crosses that enabled him to piece together the genetics puzzle.

Once he had obtained his groups of true-breeding plants, Mendel began a straightforward process of experimentation. He crossed plants with different traits—for example, he crossed plants with green peas and plants with yellow peas—and observed large numbers of their offspring, counting the numbers of green peas and yellow peas produced. (This cross, written as "green × yellow cross," always resulted in plants with nothing but yellow peas.) Mendel devised a hypothesis that would explain his observations and generate predictions about the outcome of further crosses. Then he conducted

those crosses to see whether the predictions generated by his hypothesis were borne out.

There was a simple elegance to Mendel's work: his predictions were always in the form of simple questions that could be answered by his experiments. His crosses would come out either one way or the other. Everything was black and white. This process of performing well thought out, rigorous experiments was a radical innovation for biology. In the end, Mendel's patience, perseverance, and cleverness paid off. As we explore his results in the next section, we see that they allowed a definitive interpretation.

TAKE-HOME MESSAGE 7·3

In the mid-1800s, Gregor Mendel conducted studies that helped us understand how traits are inherited. He applied methodical experimentation and rigorous hypothesis testing, focusing on easily observed and categorized traits in garden peas.

Segregation: you've got two copies of each gene but put only one copy in each sperm or egg.

One odd and recurring result spurred Mendel to figure out the mechanism by which traits could be passed from parent to offspring. Just as brown-eyed parents can have blue-eyed children, sometimes traits that weren't present in either parent pea plant would show up in their offspring. Crosses that entailed the fertilization of plants with purple flowers by pollen from other plants with purple flowers produced *mostly* purple-flowered offspring, for instance, but *sometimes* they produced plants with white flowers. How was that possible? Where did the whiteness come from?

Here's where Mendel's meticulous and methodical experiments paid off. First, he started with some true-breeding white-flowered plants. Then he got some true-breeding purple-flowered plants. He wondered: which color wins out when a white-flowered plant is crossed with a purple-flowered plant? The answer was definitive: purple wins (**FIGURE 7-8**). All of the offspring from these crosses were purple, every time. For this reason, Mendel called the purple-flower trait **dominant,** and he considered the white-flower trait to be the **recessive** trait. In general, a dominant trait masks the effect of a recessive trait when an individual carries both the dominant and the recessive versions of the instructions for the trait.

Things got a bit more interesting when Mendel took the purple-flowered plants that came from the cross between true-breeding purple- and white-flowered plants and bred these purple offspring with each other. He found that these mixed-parentage plants were no longer true-breeding. Occasionally, they would produce white-flowered offspring. (To be exact, of the 929 plants Mendel examined, 705 had purple flowers, and 224 had white flowers.) Apparently, the directions for building white flowers—last seen in one of their grandparents—were still lurking inside the purple-flowered parent plants. The existence of traits that could disappear for a generation and then show up again was quite perplexing. Mendel devised a simple and perfect hypothesis to explain these observations (**FIGURE 7-9**).

Mendel's hypothesis for explaining this pattern of inheritance incorporated three ideas that then helped him (and now help us) make predictions about crosses he hadn't yet done.

1. Rather than passing on the trait itself, **each parent puts into every sperm or egg it makes a single set of instructions for building the trait.** Today, we call that instruction set a *gene.*

DOMINANT AND RECESSIVE TRAITS

1 Mendel crossed true-breeding purple-flower plants with true-breeding white-flower plants.

True-breeding purple-flower plant ✕ **True-breeding white-flower plant**

All offspring have purple flowers.

The purple-colored flower is the dominant trait, while the white-colored flower is a recessive trait.

2 Then, Mendel crossed two of the purple-flower offspring.

Most offspring have purple flowers, but some have white flowers.

The recessive trait for the white-colored flower must have been lurking in the previous generation, even though it is not visible.

FIGURE 7-8 White or purple? By careful and repeated crosses among pea plants, Mendel determined that there were "dominant" and "recessive" traits.

2. Offspring receive two copies of the instructions for any trait. Often, both sets of instructions are identical and the offspring produce the traits according to those instructions. Other times, though, each parent contributes a slightly different set of instructions—that is, a different

MENDEL'S LAW OF SEGREGATION

According to Mendel's law of segregation, only one of the two alleles for a gene is put into a gamete. At fertilization, offspring receive from each parent one allele for each gene.

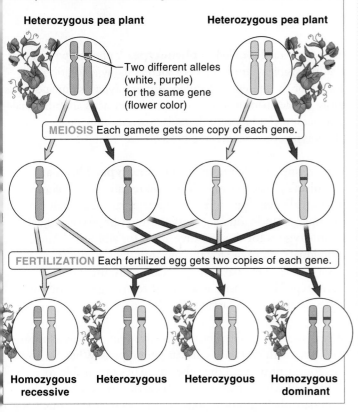

Heterozygous pea plant   **Heterozygous pea plant**

Two different alleles (white, purple) for the same gene (flower color)

MEIOSIS Each gamete gets one copy of each gene.

FERTILIZATION Each fertilized egg gets two copies of each gene.

Homozygous recessive   **Heterozygous**   **Heterozygous**   **Homozygous dominant**

FIGURE 7-9 Mendel's law of segregation. Organisms have two copies of each gene but place only one copy into each gamete during the process of meiosis (as described in Chapter 6).

allele—for the trait. So, for example, in pea plants there are two alleles for flower color: a purple-flower allele and a white-flower allele. Each is a different allele, but because both specify instructions for producing flowers, they are both genes for flower color. Same gene (flower-color gene), different alleles (purple and white).

3. The trait observed in an individual depends on the *two* copies of the gene it inherits from its parents. When

an individual inherits the same two alleles for this gene, the individual's genotype for that gene is said to be **homozygous** and the individual shows the trait specified by the instructions embodied in those alleles. When an individual inherits a different allele from each parent, the individual's genotype for that gene is said to be **heterozygous.** Dominant and recessive alleles are defined by their action when they are in the heterozygous state: if one of the alleles is fully apparent in the individual while the other is not, the first is called the dominant allele and is said to "mask" the effect of the other allele, which is called the recessive allele.

> ❝ 'There were no questions.'
>
> —Entry in the meeting notes following Mendel's first public presentation of his ideas on how heredity works. (*No one in the audience of scientists had any idea what he was talking about. It was about 40 years before the world understood his discoveries.*) ❞

Later, when the offspring grows up and gets ready to have its own offspring, it only gets to contribute one of its two copies of the gene to its offspring. The other parent will contribute the other allele. So, when sperm and eggs are made, each sex cell gets only one copy of the gene—as opposed to the two copies present in every other cell in the body. For a male who is heterozygous, for example, it means that half of the sperm he produces will have one of the alleles and half will have the other. The idea that, of the two copies of each gene everyone carries, only one of the two alleles gets put into each gamete is significant and important enough that it is called **Mendel's law of segregation.**

TAKE-HOME MESSAGE 7·4

Each parent puts into every sperm or egg it makes a single set of instructions for building a particular trait. This instruction set is what today we call a gene. The trait observed in an individual depends on the two copies (alleles) of the gene it inherits from its parents.

Observing an individual's phenotype is not sufficient for determining its genotype.

Things are not always as they appear. Take skin coloration, for example. Humans and many other mammals have a gene that contains the information for producing melanin, one of the chemicals responsible for giving our skin its coloring (**FIGURE 7-10**). Unfortunately, there is also a defective, non-functioning version of the melanin gene that is passed along through some families. An individual who inherits two copies of the defective version of the gene cannot produce pigment and has a condition known as albinism, a disorder characterized by little or no pigment in the eyes, hair, and skin. But it is impossible to tell whether a normally pigmented individual carries one of these defective alleles just by looking at his or her appearance—we would need to get a genetic analysis done to discover this information.

The inability to deduce an individual's genetic makeup through simple observation is a general problem in genetics: physical appearances don't always exactly reflect the underlying genes. A normally pigmented individual may have two copies of the pigment-producing allele or may have only one copy. In either case, the individual will look the same. The outward appearance

of an individual is called its **phenotype.** A phenotype includes features visible to the naked eye such as flashy coloration, height, or the presence of antlers. A phenotype also includes less easily visible characteristics such as the chemicals an individual produces to clot blood or digest lactose. An individual's phenotype even includes the behaviors it exhibits.

Underlying the phenotype is the **genotype.** This is an organism's genetic composition. We usually speak of an individual's genotype in reference to a particular trait. For example, an individual's genotype might be described as "homozygous for the recessive allele for albinism." Another individual's genotype for the melanin gene might be described as "heterozygous." Occasionally, the word "genotype" is also used as a way of referring to *all* of the genes an individual carries.

When an organism exhibits a recessive trait, such as albinism, we know with certainty what its genotype is. When it shows the dominant trait, on the other hand, it's impossible to distinguish whether the organism carries two copies of the dominant allele (homozygous dominant) or carries one copy of the dominant allele and one of the recessive (heterozygous). Because it's not possible to discern the genotypes of two individuals with the same phenotype just by looking at them, much of genetic analysis must make use of clever experiments and careful record-keeping to determine organisms' genotypes. Let's explore a useful method of analyzing the relationships between genotypes and phenotypes.

How do we analyze and predict the outcome of crosses? First, we must assign symbols to represent the different variants of a gene. Generally we use an upper-case letter for the dominant allele and lower-case letter for the recessive allele. In the case of the albino giraffe, we represent the albino individual as *aa,* because it must carry two copies of the recessive allele, *a.* A giraffe that is pigmented must have the genotype *AA* or *Aa.* If we don't know which of the two possible genotypes the pigmented individual is, we can write *A_,* where _ is a placeholder for the unknown second allele, whose identity we aren't certain of.

We can trace the possible outcomes of a cross between two individuals using a handy tool called the **Punnett square.** In **FIGURE 7-11** we illustrate the cross between a true-breeding

PHENOTYPE: Little or no pigment in the eyes, hair, and skin
GENOTYPE: Homozygous for the recessive allele for albinism

FIGURE 7-10 An albino deer stands out from its peers. Carrying two non-functioning versions of the gene that produces the pigment melanin causes albinism.

PUNNETT SQUARE: ALBINISM

A Punnett square is a useful tool for determining the possible outcomes of a cross between two individuals.

Cross 1

MOTHER
albino
homozygous
aa

FATHER
pigmented
homozygous
AA

GAMETES: *a* *a*

GAMETES: *A* *A*

Offspring: *Aa*, *Aa*, *Aa*, *Aa*

OFFSPRING	Genotype	Phenotype
	All heterozygous *Aa*	All pigmented

Cross 2

MOTHER
pigmented
heterozygous
Aa

FATHER
pigmented
heterozygous
Aa

GAMETES: *A* *a*

GAMETES: *A* *a*

Offspring: *AA*, *Aa*, *Aa*, *aa*

OFFSPRING	Genotype	Phenotype
	1/4 homozygous dominant *AA*	3/4 pigmented
	2/4 heterozygous *Aa*	
	1/4 homozygous recessive *aa*	1/4 albino

FIGURE 7-11 Predicting the outcome of crosses. A Punnett square helps in determining the likelihood of inheriting albinism.

pigmented individual, *AA*, and an albino, *aa*. Along the top of the square we list, individually, the two alleles that one of the parents produces, and along the left side of the square we list the two alleles that the other parent produces. We split up an individual's two alleles in this way because, although the individual carries two alleles, only one of the alleles is contained in each sperm or egg cell that it produces.

In the four cells of the Punnett square, we enter the genotypes of all the possible offspring resulting from our cross—a cell contains the allele given at the head of the column, which is one parent's contribution, and the allele at the left of the row, which is the other parent's contribution. The two gametes that come together at fertilization produce the genotype of the offspring. In Cross 1 illustrated in Figure 7-11, every possible offspring would be heterozygous and would be normally pigmented, because it receives a dominant allele from the pigmented parent and a recessive allele from the albino parent.

In the bottom half of Figure 7-11 (Cross 2), we trace the cross between two heterozygous individuals. Note that each parent produces two kinds of gametes, one with the dominant allele and one with the recessive allele. This cross has four possible outcomes: one-quarter of the time the offspring will be homozygous dominant (*AA*), one-quarter of the time the offspring will be homozygous recessive (*aa*), and the remaining half of the time the offspring will be heterozygous (*Aa*). Phenotypically, three-quarters of the offspring will be normally pigmented (*AA* or *Aa*) and one-quarter will be albino (*aa*).

TAKE-HOME MESSAGE 7·5

It is not always possible to determine an individual's genetic makeup, known as its genotype, by observation of the organism's outward appearance, known as its phenotype. For a particular trait, an individual may carry a recessive allele whose phenotypic effect is masked by the presence of a dominant allele. Much genetic analysis therefore makes use of clever experiments and careful record-keeping, using Punnett squares, to determine organisms' genotypes.

❷ Probability and chance play central roles in genetics.

Because of the role of chance in genetics, we cannot always predict the exact outcome of a genetic cross.

7·6

Chance is important in genetics.

Sometimes genetics is a bit like gambling. Even with perfect information, it can still be impossible to know the genetic outcome with certainty. It's like flipping a coin: you can know every last detail about the coin, but you still can't know whether the coin will land on heads or tails. The best you can do is define the probability of each possible outcome.

The rules of probability (the same ones that govern coin tosses and the rolling of dice) have a central role in genetics, for two reasons. The first is a consequence of segregation, the process Mendel described, in which each gamete an individual produces receives only one of the two copies of each gene that the individual carries in most of its other cells. As a result, it is equally likely that the haploid gamete—the sperm or egg—will include one or the other of the two alleles that the individual carries. It is impossible to know which allele it will be. The second reason probability plays a central role in genetics is that fertilization, too, is a chance event. All of the sperm or eggs produced by an individual are different from one another, and any one of those gametes may be the gamete

involved in fertilization. Thus, knowing everything about the alleles a parent carries is not enough to be able to determine with certainty which alleles his or her offspring will carry.

> ❝ Chaos umpire sits,
> And by decision more embroils the fray
> By which he reigns: next him high arbiter
> Chance governs all. ❞
>
> —John Milton, *Paradise Lost*, 1667

Let's explore how we can make predictions in games of chance, as well as in matings, based on probabilities. As with the probability of getting heads in a coin flip, any gamete produced by an individual heterozygous for a trait has a 50% probability of carrying the dominant allele and a 50% probability of carrying the recessive allele. If an individual is homozygous for a trait, 100% of his or her gametes will carry that allele. Let's use these probabilities in an example.

Family Resemblance   Genetics and Chance   Translation of Genotypes   Gene Linkage

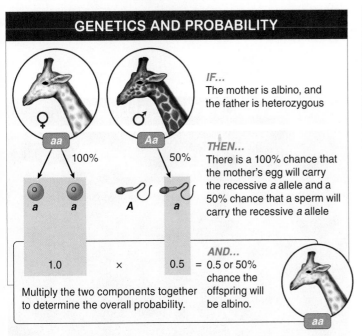

IF...
The mother is albino, and the father is heterozygous

THEN...
There is a 100% chance that the mother's egg will carry the recessive *a* allele and a 50% chance that a sperm will carry the recessive *a* allele

AND...
= 0.5 or 50% chance the offspring will be albino.

Multiply the two components together to determine the overall probability.

FIGURE 7-12 Using probability to determine the chance of inheriting albinism.

IF...
Parents are heterozygous for Tay-Sachs

THEN...
There is a 50% chance that a gamete will carry the recessive *t* allele

AND...
= 0.25 or 25% chance the child will be homozygous for Tay-Sachs.

Multiply the two components together to determine the overall probability.

FIGURE 7-13 The chance of inheriting Tay-Sachs disease. The probability that a child inherits Tay-Sachs disease from two heterozygous parents is 25%.

If a male is heterozygous for albinism (*Aa*) and a female is albino (*aa*), what is the probability that their child will be homozygous for albinism (*aa*)? In order to get the *aa* outcome, two events must occur. First, the father's gamete must carry the recessive allele (*a*) and, second, the mother's gamete must carry the recessive allele (*a*). In this case, the probability of a homozygous recessive offspring is 0.5 (the probability that the father's gamete carries *a*) times 1.0 (the probability that the mother's gamete carries *a*), for a probability of 0.5. This is a general rule when determining the likelihood of a complex event occurring: if you know the probability of each component that must occur, you simply multiply all the probabilities together to get the overall probability of that complex event occurring (**FIGURE 7-12**).

Consider another example, involving Tay-Sachs disease. As described in Chapter 3, Tay-Sachs is a disease caused by malfunctioning lysosomes that do not digest cellular waste properly. It leads to death in early childhood. Tay-Sachs occurs if a child inherits two recessive alleles for the Tay-Sachs gene. If each parent is heterozygous for the Tay-Sachs gene, what is the probability that their child will have Tay-Sachs disease?

To solve this, just break down the event of the child having Tay-Sachs into two separate events: first, it must inherit a recessive allele from its heterozygous father. The probability of that is 0.5. Second, it must also inherit a recessive allele from its heterozygous mother. The probability of that is also 0.5. So the overall probability of the child having Tay-Sachs disease is 0.5 × 0.5 = 0.25, or 1 in 4 (**FIGURE 7-13**). Of course, if the couple has only one child, we can't predict with certainty whether this child will have Tay-Sachs. Mathematicians, on the other hand, might be satisfied just to be able to say that if the couple had an infinite number of children, we could be certain that one-fourth of them would have Tay-Sachs. Still, this is not much help for heterozygous couples trying to decide whether to have a child or not.

TAKE-HOME MESSAGE 7·6

Probability plays a central role in genetics. In segregation, each gamete that an individual produces receives only one of the two copies of each gene the individual carries in its other cells, but it is impossible to know which allele goes into the gamete. Chance plays a role in fertilization, too: all of the sperm or eggs produced by an individual are different from one another, and any one of those gametes may be the gamete involved in fertilization.

7·7

A test-cross enables us to figure out which alleles an individual carries.

How can you see something that is invisible to the naked eye? When it comes to genetics, this is a practical issue that has been causing problems for as long as humans have been breeding plants and animals for food or other purposes. Genes are too small to be seen, and so determining an individual's genotype requires indirect methods. Suppose you are in charge of the alligators at a zoo. Some of your alligators come from a population in which white, albino alligators have occasionally occurred, although none of your alligators are white. Because white alligators —those having two recessive pigmentation alleles, *mm* ("m" for melanin)—are popular with zoo visitors, you would like to produce some at your zoo through a mating program.

The problem is that you cannot be certain of the genotype of your alligators. They might be homozygous dominant, *MM*, or they might be heterozygous, *Mm*. In either case, their phenotype is normal coloration. How can you figure out which of these two possibilities is the genotype of a particular alligator? This is a challenge to animal breeders, but not an insurmountable one. Genes may be invisible, but their identity can be revealed by a simple tool called the **test-cross.**

In the test-cross, you take an individual exhibiting a dominant trait but whose genotype is unknown. You cross (i.e., mate) that individual with an individual that is homozygous recessive and look at the phenotypes of their offspring. In the case of your breeding program for albino alligators, you could borrow an albino alligator from another zoo and breed your unknown-genotype alligator (genotype: *M_*) with that albino alligator (genotype: *mm*). There are two possible outcomes, and they will reveal the genotype of your unknown-genotype alligator (**FIGURE 7-14**). If your alligator is homozygous dominant (*MM*), it will contribute a dominant allele, *M*, to every offspring. Even though the albino alligator will contribute the recessive allele, *m*, to all its offspring, all the offspring will be heterozygous, *Mm*, and none of them will be albino.

If, on the other hand, your unknown-genotype alligator is heterozygous, *Mm*, half of the time it will contribute a recessive allele, *m*, to the offspring. In every one of those cases, the

FIGURE 7-14 A test-cross can reveal an unknown genotype. In this test-cross, a homozygous white female alligator is bred with a normally colored male of unknown genotype. The color of their offspring will help identify whether the male is homozygous dominant or heterozygous.

TEST-CROSS: WHITE ALLIGATORS

Test-cross

MOTHER
white
homozygous
mm

FATHER
pigmented
unknown genotype
*M_*
(*MM* or *Mm*)

GAMETES — *m*   *m*

GAMETES
M — *Mm* *Mm*
M — *Mm* *Mm*
m — *mm* *mm*

Unknown allele could be *M* or *m*.

OFFSPRING (if unknown genotype is *MM*)

	Genotype	Phenotype
	All heterozygous *Mm*	All pigmented

OFFSPRING (if unknown genotype is *Mm*)

	Genotype	Phenotype
	2/4 heterozygous *Mm*	2/4 pigmented
	2/4 homozygous recessive *mm*	2/4 white

offspring will be homozygous recessive and thus albino. So the cleverness of the test-cross is that when you cross your unknown-genotype organism with an individual showing the recessive trait, if it sometimes produces offspring with the recessive trait (and if it does, it will do so half the time, on average), its genotype must be heterozygous. If it never produces offspring with the recessive trait, it must be homozygous for the dominant allele. In order to be confident in concluding that the unknown-genotype alligator has the *MM* genotype, though, you'd have to observe as many offspring as possible. After all, even if its genotype is *Mm,* quite a few offspring in a row might be normally pigmented, with the genotype *Mm.* Eventually, however, a heterozygous individual is likely to produce an offspring with the homozygous recessive genotype, *mm,* and the albino phenotype.

TAKE-HOME MESSAGE 7·7

In a test-cross, an individual that exhibits a dominant trait but has an unknown genotype is mated with an individual that is homozygous recessive. The phenotypes of the offspring reveal whether the unknown-genotype individual is homozygous dominant (all of the offspring exhibit the dominant trait) or heterozygous (half of the offspring show the dominant trait and half show the recessive trait).

7·8
We use pedigrees to decipher and predict the inheritance patterns of genes.

People want to know things about the future, such as: what is the likelihood that I will have a child with a particular genetic disease, say hemophilia? Or what is my own risk of developing a genetic disease, such as Huntington's disease, later in my life? Geneticists who study these and other diseases want to know other things: how is a particular disease inherited? Is it recessive or dominant? Is it carried on the sex chromosomes or on one of the other chromosomes? A **pedigree** is a type of family tree that can help answer these questions.

In a pedigree, information is gathered from as many related individuals as possible across multiple generations (**FIGURE 7-15**). Starting from the bottom, each row in the chart represents a generation, listing all of the children in their order of birth and whether or not they express a particular trait. Working up the pedigree, their parents are indicated and, above them, their parents' parents, for as far back as data are available. Squares represent males and circles represent females, and these shapes are shaded to indicate that an individual exhibits the trait of interest. Sometimes the genotype (as much of it as is known) is also listed for each individual.

By analyzing which individuals manifest the trait and which do not, it may be possible to deduce the pattern of inheritance for the trait—or, at least, rule out certain patterns. For example, if an individual exhibits a trait that neither of his or her parents exhibits, the trait is recessive. For dominant traits, all affected individuals must have at least one parent who exhibits the trait. In contrast, an individual can exhibit a recessive trait even if both parents are unaffected (i.e., do not exhibit the trait). In this case, the individual's parents must be heterozygous for that trait, each carrying one dominant and one recessive allele. Similarly, it is sometimes possible to determine whether a trait is carried on the sex chromosomes (X or Y, which we discuss in Section 7-13) or on one of the non-sex chromosomes (also called "autosomes"). Traits that are controlled by genes on the sex chromosomes are called **sex-linked traits.** Recessive sex-linked traits, for example, appear more frequently in males than females, whereas dominant sex-linked traits appear more frequently in females. These patterns may become obvious only on inspection of a large pedigree.

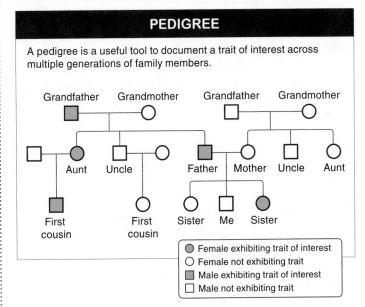

PEDIGREE

A pedigree is a useful tool to document a trait of interest across multiple generations of family members.

● Female exhibiting trait of interest
○ Female not exhibiting trait
■ Male exhibiting trait of interest
□ Male not exhibiting trait

FIGURE 7-15 Family tree. A pedigree maps the occurrence of a trait in a family.

Anury is a condition in dogs and other animals in which they are born without a tail. The condition is inherited as a recessive trait.

? *Can you figure out the genotype of the individual labeled 1?*

IF...
A dog has no tail, but his father was normal

THEN...
The normal-looking mother (1) of the tailless dog must be heterozygous.

PEDIGREE

① ——— □

■ ○ ■

?

Female with anury
Female not exhibiting anury
Male with anury
Male not exhibiting anury

? *Can you now determine the probability of this puppy having anury?*

FIGURE 7-16 Pedigree puzzle: tracing the occurrence of anury in a family of dogs.

An example of how pedigrees can help determine how traits are inherited is given in **FIGURE 7-16**. Anury is a condition seen in dogs and some other animals in which the animal has no tail. The pedigree reveals that anury is inherited as a recessive trait, because unaffected parents can have offspring with the disorder.

Can you figure out the genotype of the individual labeled "1"? That female must be heterozygous (*Aa*) for anury. (An individual who carries one allele for a recessive trait, and so does not exhibit the trait but can have offspring that do, is referred to as **carrier** of the trait.) The same is true for her mate. On the same pedigree, note that two individuals in the second generation have a puppy (indicated by "?"). What is the probability that this puppy has anury? Examine the pedigree carefully and see if you can come up with the answer; the next paragraph will guide you through if you get stuck.

Q *Why do breeders value "pedigreed" horses and dogs so much?*

In the cross producing the mystery puppy, the father has anury and so must be homozygous recessive; he will definitely pass on one *a* to the son. The mother's genotype can be *AA, Aa,* or *aA,* given that both of her parents are heterozygous. Consequently, she has a ⅔ (2 in 3) probability of carrying the *a* allele. If she does, then there is a 1 in 2 (50%) chance that she will pass it on to her offspring and he will have anury. The probability, therefore, is ⅔ × ½ = ⅓—or a 1 in 3 chance that the puppy will have anury.

As we will discuss in later sections of this chapter, some traits may not show complete dominance and many traits are also influenced by the environment, so it is not always completely obvious what a trait's mode of inheritance is. In such cases, the more individuals we can include in the pedigree, the more accurate the analysis. Some human pedigrees contain thousands of individuals and stretch back six or more generations. With some other species it is possible to analyze tens of thousands of individuals per generation for a dozen or more generations. This is why plants and small insects (among other organisms) are excellent for studying inheritance patterns.

Dog and horse breeders often speak of "pedigreed" animals, a feature that adds tremendous value to the animals. This is because, with knowledge of an animal's family tree or complete lineage, it is much less likely that any genetic surprises will occur as the animal develops and reproduces.

Once you have an idea about how a trait is inherited, it is possible to make informed predictions about a couple's risk of having a child with a particular disorder. This makes earlier prenatal testing and treatment possible. It also enables the identification of individuals who are "carriers" of a recessive trait.

TAKE-HOME MESSAGE 7·8

Pedigrees help scientists, doctors, animal and plant breeders, and prospective parents determine the genes that individuals carry and the likelihood that the offspring of two individuals will exhibit a given trait.

Family Resemblance   Genetics and Chance   Translation of Genotypes   Gene Linkage

❸ The translation of genotypes into phenotypes is not a black box.

Phenotypic diversity has multiple sources and is all around us. (The photo shows schoolchildren from London.)

7·9

Incomplete dominance and codominance: the effects of both alleles in a genotype can show up in the phenotype.

As Mendel saw it, the world of genetics was straightforward and simple. We should be so lucky. Unfortunately, the world in which each trait is coded for by a single gene with two alleles—one completely dominant and one recessive—and with no environmental effects at all doesn't quite capture the complexity of the world beyond Mendel's pea plants. So, here and in the next sections, we'll build up a more complex model of how genes influence the building of bodies. We begin with the observation that, sometimes, the phenotype of heterozygous individuals differs from that of either of the homozygotes, and instead reflects the influence of both alleles rather than a clearly dominant allele.

One situation in which complete dominance is not observed is called **incomplete dominance,** in which the heterozygote appears to be intermediate between the two homozygotes. The quintessential example of incomplete dominance is the flower color of snapdragons (**FIGURE 7-17**). We can obtain true-breeding (homozygous) lines of snapdragons with red flowers, and true-breeding (homozygous) lines that produce

only white flowers. When plants from these two populations are crossed, we would expect—if one allele were dominant over the other—either all red or all white flowers. Instead, such crosses always produce plants with pink flowers. Interestingly, when we cross two plants with pink flowers, we get ¼ red-flowered plants, ½ pink-flowered plants, and ¼ white-flowered plants.

How can we interpret this cross? It seems that the plants with white flowers have the genotype $C^W C^W$ and produce no pigment. At the other extreme, the plants with red flowers have the genotype $C^R C^R$ and produce a great deal of pigment. The letter "C" refers to the fact that the gene codes for **c**olor, and the superscript "W" or "R" refers to an allele producing no pigment (**w**hite) or **r**ed pigment. We use these designations for the genotypes because it isn't clear that either white or red is dominant over the other, and so neither should be upper-case or lower-case. The pink flowers receive one of the pigment-producing C^R alleles and one of the no-pigment-producing C^W alleles, and so produce an intermediate amount

265

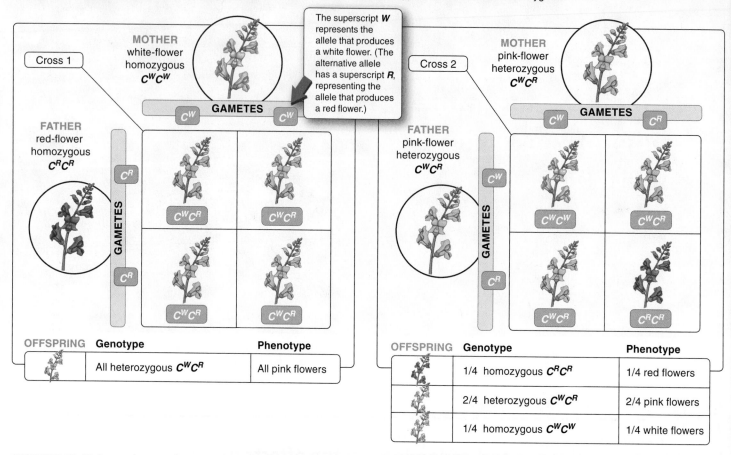

INCOMPLETE DOMINANCE: SNAPDRAGONS

Incomplete dominance occurs when a heterozygote exhibits an intermediate phenotype between the two homozygotes.

The superscript **W** represents the allele that produces a white flower. (The alternative allele has a superscript **R**, representing the allele that produces a red flower.)

Cross 1

MOTHER
white-flower
homozygous
$C^W C^W$

GAMETES: C^W | C^W

FATHER
red-flower
homozygous
$C^R C^R$

GAMETES: C^R | C^R

| | $C^W C^R$ | $C^W C^R$ |
| | $C^W C^R$ | $C^W C^R$ |

OFFSPRING	Genotype	Phenotype
	All heterozygous $C^W C^R$	All pink flowers

Cross 2

MOTHER
pink-flower
heterozygous
$C^W C^R$

GAMETES: C^W | C^R

FATHER
pink-flower
heterozygous
$C^W C^R$

GAMETES: C^W | C^R

| | $C^W C^W$ | $C^W C^R$ |
| | $C^W C^R$ | $C^R C^R$ |

OFFSPRING	Genotype	Phenotype
	1/4 homozygous $C^R C^R$	1/4 red flowers
	2/4 heterozygous $C^W C^R$	2/4 pink flowers
	1/4 homozygous $C^W C^W$	1/4 white flowers

FIGURE 7-17 Pink snapdragons demonstrate incomplete dominance. When true-breeding white and red snapdragons are crossed, offspring have pink flowers.

CODOMINANCE: SICKLE-CELL DISEASE

Codominance occurs when a heterozygote displays characteristics of both homozygous parents.

$Hb^A Hb^A$
Homozygote

Individual does not have sickle-cell disease.

$Hb^S Hb^A$
Heterozygote

Individual carries a defective allele and has an intermediate condition. Some cells become sickled under extreme conditions.

$Hb^S Hb^S$
Homozygote

Individual has two copies of the defective hemoglobin allele and has sickle-cell disease.

FIGURE 7-18 With codominance, a heterozygous individual shows features of both alleles.

Family Resemblance   Genetics and Chance   Translation of Genotypes   Gene Linkage

of pigment. Ultimately, the intensity of pigmentation just depends on the amount of pigment chemical made by the flower-color gene.

A second situation in which complete dominance is not observed is called **codominance,** in which the heterozygote displays characteristics of both homozygotes. In this situation, the alleles can be thought of as codominant because neither masks the effect of the other. An example of codominance occurs with sickle-cell disease (**FIGURE 7-18**), a condition in which individuals produce defective red blood cells that change their shape, becoming sickle-shaped, when they lose the oxygen they carry. The defective blood cells cannot effectively transport oxygen to tissues, and they accumulate in blood vessels, causing extreme pain. Individuals with sickle-cell disease suffer shortness of breath and numerous other problems that lead to a significantly reduced lifespan.

Sickle-cell disease seems, at first inspection, to be a condition seen only in individuals with two copies of the sickle-cell

allele for hemoglobin, Hb^S; recall that hemoglobin is the oxygen-carrying molecule in red blood cells. Individuals with two copies of the normal hemoglobin allele, $Hb^A Hb^A$, and those who are heterozygous, $Hb^S Hb^A$, seem to be normal. However, closer observation reveals that heterozygotes—who are described as having "sickle-cell trait"—carry many red blood cells that become sickled under extreme conditions of physical exertion or low atmospheric oxygen. In other words, heterozygous individuals show an intermediate phenotype between the two homozygotes.

TAKE-HOME MESSAGE 7·9

Sometimes the effects of both alleles in a heterozygous genotype are evident in the phenotype. With incomplete dominance, a heterozygote appears to be intermediate between the two homozygotes. With codominance, a heterozygote displays characteristics of both homozygotes.

7·10

What's your blood type? Some genes have more than two alleles.

What is your blood type? It can be O, A, B, or AB. Each of these different blood types indicates something about the physical characteristics of your red blood cells and has implications for blood transfusions—both giving and receiving blood. The blood groups are also interesting from a genetic perspective, because they illustrate a case of **multiple allelism,** in which a single gene has more than two alleles. Each individual still carries only two alleles—one from the mother and one from the father. But if you survey all of the alleles present in the population, you will find more than just two alleles.

Inheritance of the ABO blood groups provides the simplest example of multiple allelism, because there are only three alleles. We can call these alleles *A, B,* and *O.* The *A* and *B* alleles are both completely dominant to *O,* so individuals are considered to have blood type A whether they have the genotype *AA* or *AO* (**FIGURE 7-19**). Similarly, an individual with the genotype *BB* or *BO* is considered to have blood type B. If you carry two copies of the *O* allele, you are blood type B.

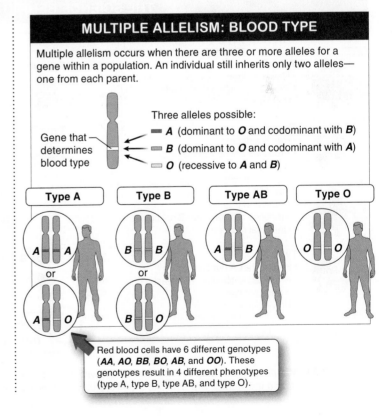

MULTIPLE ALLELISM: BLOOD TYPE

Multiple allelism occurs when there are three or more alleles for a gene within a population. An individual still inherits only two alleles—one from each parent.

Gene that determines blood type

Three alleles possible:
- **A** (dominant to **O** and codominant with **B**)
- **B** (dominant to **O** and codominant with **A**)
- **O** (recessive to **A** and **B**)

| Type A | Type B | Type AB | Type O |

A A or *A O*   *B B* or *B O*   *A B*   *O O*

Red blood cells have 6 different genotypes (*AA, AO, BB, BO, AB,* and *OO*). These genotypes result in 4 different phenotypes (type A, type B, type AB, and type O).

FIGURE 7-19 Multiple allelism. There are three different alleles—*A, B,* and *O*—for blood type.

BLOOD TYPE, ANTIGENS, AND ANTIBODIES

Antigens are chemicals on the surface of some cells. They act as signposts that tell the immune system whether the cell belongs in the body. Antibodies are immune system molecules that attack cells with foreign antigens.

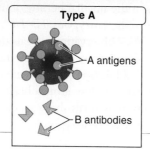

Type A
— A antigens
— B antibodies

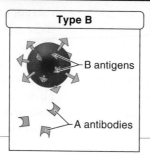

Type B
— B antigens
— A antibodies

Type AB
— A and B antigens
Neither A nor B antibodies

Type O
— Neither A nor B antigens
— A and B antibodies

FIGURE 7-20 Friend or foe? Antigens are signposts that tell the immune system whether or not a cell belongs in the body.

O. The *A* and *B* alleles are codominant with each other, so the genotype *AB* gives rise to blood type AB. Consequently, with these three alleles in the population, individuals can be one of four different blood types: A, B, AB, and O.

What are the phenotypes of these alleles? An individual's blood type alleles carry instructions that direct construction of a specific set of chemicals, called *antigens,* that protrude from every red blood cell. Antigens are proteins that jut from the surface of a cell and can "turn on" its defenses against foreign invaders. The *A* allele directs the production of A antigens all over the surface of red blood cells. Similarly, the *B* allele directs

the production of B antigens on all red blood cells. The *O* allele does not code for either type of antigen. This means that individuals with blood type AB have red blood cells with both A and B antigens, while individuals with blood type O have red blood cells with a "smoother" surface because they produce no A or B antigens (**FIGURE 7-20**).

Antigens on red blood cells play a role in the body's disease-fighting immune system. Antigens are like signposts, telling the immune system whether a cell belongs in the body or not. If a red blood cell with the wrong antigens were to enter your bloodstream, your immune system would recognize it as a

THE SCIENCE BEHIND BLOOD DONATION

BLOOD TYPE	CAN DONATE TO	CAN RECEIVE FROM
Type A • Has A antigens • Produces antibodies that attack B antigens	Type A Type AB	Type A Type O
Type B • Has B antigens • Produces antibodies that attack A antigens	Type B Type AB	Type B Type O
Type AB • Has A and B antigens • Produces neither A nor B antibodies • Universal recipient	Type AB	Type A Type B Type AB Type O
Type O • Has neither A nor B antigens • Produces antibodies that attack A and B antigens • Universal donor	Type A Type B Type AB Type O	Type O

Individuals with type O blood are universal donors. Individuals with type AB are universal recipients.

FIGURE 7-21 Mapping blood compatibility. Individuals with type O blood are said to be universal donors, and individuals with type AB blood are universal recipients.

Family Resemblance   Genetics and Chance   Translation of Genotypes   Gene Linkage

foreign invader and destroy it. Such an attack is initiated by molecules in the bloodstream called *antibodies,* which attack only foreign antigens. Individuals with only A antigens on their red blood cells produce antibodies that attack B antigens. If they encounter a red blood cell with B antigens, they attack it. Such an immune response can lead to destruction of red blood cells, low blood pressure, and even death. Under normal circumstances, antibodies would not encounter a red blood cell with foreign antigens—unless, that is, red blood cells with foreign antigens are accidentally injected into the person's bloodstream in a transfusion.

Q Why are people with type O blood considered "universal donors"? Why are those with type AB considered "universal acceptors"?

Individuals with only B antigens on their red blood cells produce antibodies that attack A antigens. Individuals with blood type O, who have neither A nor B antigens on their red blood cells, produce antibodies that attack both A and B antigens.

Individuals with blood type AB don't produce either type of antibody (or else they would have antibodies that attacked their own blood cells). From this information, we can deduce which blood types can be used in transfusions. This is shown in **FIGURE 7-21.**

Another marker on the surface of red blood cells is the Rh blood group marker. This marker results from the effects of a single gene with two alleles. Individuals' red blood cells carry the Rh cell surface marker if they have one or two copies of the dominant Rh marker allele. This is then noted in their blood type as a "+," or "positive," in addition to their ABO blood type, as in "O-positive" or "B-negative." Individuals who have two copies of the recessive allele for this gene do not have any Rh markers, and they are described as "negative," as in "O-negative" or "A-negative." If individuals who are Rh-negative are exposed to Rh-positive blood, their immune system attacks the Rh antigens as foreign invaders—an immune response that can vary from mild, and passing unnoticed, to severe, which can lead to death. Thus, the Rh marker further restricts whose blood a person can receive in a transfusion.

Beyond the ABO and the Rh marker groups, there are many, many genes with multiple alleles—a dozen or even more alleles in some cases. In fact, one gene for eye color in fruit flies has more than 1,000 different alleles!

TAKE-HOME MESSAGE 7·10

In multiple allelism, a single gene has more than two alleles. Each individual still carries only two alleles, but in the population, more than just two alleles occur. This is the case for the ABO blood groups in humans.

7·11

Multigene traits: how are continuously varying traits such as height influenced by genes?

When babies are born, the parents are often curious about how tall their child will grow to be. Old wives' tales suggest a couple of ways for predicting height. If the baby is a boy, they say to add 5 inches to the mother's height and average that with the father's height. If it is a girl, subtract 5 inches from the father's height and average that with the mother's height. Alternatively, the lore says, just take the child's height at two years of age and double it.

While these methods can be surprisingly accurate at making predictions, they don't really help us understand the underlying reason *why* height can be predicted so well. The reason these methods work is that genes play a strong role in influencing height, and so offspring do resemble their parents in measurable ways. But unlike the simple case of Mendel's

peas, where a single gene with two alleles determines the height of the plant, for humans and most animals, adult height is influenced by many different genes. Such a trait is said to be **polygenic.**

Recent research has identified two genes that help determine height in humans. Individuals with the "tall" allele for both genes are taller than those with the tall allele for only one. Individuals with one tall allele, in turn, are taller than people who do not have a tall allele for either gene. The term **additive effects** describes what happens when the effects of alleles from multiple genes all contribute to the ultimate phenotype. Traits such as skin color in humans also work this way. In the case of height genes, one of the genes is on chromosome 15 and codes for an enzyme that converts testosterone to estrogen. This enzyme influences height because estrogen helps bones to fuse at their ends and thus stop growing. In all, the two height genes identified in humans account for only about 2 inches of a person's height, but they exemplify how multiple genes can influence a single characteristic. The variety of heights from very short to very tall, with every height in between, reflects that height is a trait influenced by contributions from multiple genes as well as the environment (**FIGURE 7-22**).

Many other physical traits are influenced by multiple genes, including eye color and skin color in humans. Eye color, long believed to be controlled by a single gene with a dominant brown-eye allele and a recessive blue-eye allele, now seems to be the result of the interactions of at least two genes and possibly more—a situation that makes more sense, given the

Q Why might computer nerds be more likely to have autistic children?

significant continuous variation in eye color seen among adults.

Many behavioral traits are influenced by multiple genes. The developmental disorder known as autism, for example, seems to be the result of alterations in numerous—perhaps as many as 10 or even 20—different genes. Individuals with autism have difficulty interacting with others, particularly in making emotional connections. Autistic individuals also tend to have narrowly focused and repetitive interests. Autism is notoriously difficult to study, though, because its symptoms are varied, as is their intensity. It turns out that this may be because different combinations of the many genes involved in autism cause different variations of the disorder, much as different alleles for several height genes may work together to produce a variety of heights.

Interestingly, the genes responsible for autism may also influence some desirable characteristics. Behaviors that cause problems when manifest in the extreme may turn out to be beneficial when less extreme, such as unusual abilities of perception, analytical skills, and focus. This idea—called the "geek theory of autism"—was first suspected when an upsurge in cases of autism in children was noticed in areas with large numbers of high-tech workers, including Silicon Valley in California and near Cambridge, England, in the heart of the United Kingdom's high-technology industry. Perhaps alleles for genes that contribute to making individuals good at computer programming and solving complex technology problems may produce autism when an individual carries too many of them.

POLYGENIC TRAITS

FIGURE 7-22 From many genes, one trait. Height and skin color are multigene traits.

TAKE-HOME MESSAGE 7·11

Many traits, including continuously varying traits such as height, eye color, and skin color, are influenced by multiple genes.

Family Resemblance   Genetics and Chance   Translation of Genotypes   Gene Linkage

7·12

Sometimes one gene influences multiple traits.

What is the benefit of "almost" having sickle-cell disease?

Just as multiple genes can influence one trait, some individual genes can influence multiple unrelated traits, a phenomenon called **pleiotropy.** In fact, this may be true of nearly all genes. For example, earlier we described the sickle-cell allele for hemoglobin production. This allele causes sickle-cell disease when in the homozygous state, but in the heterozygous state it has the effect of conferring resistance to the parasite that causes malaria. The resistance is due to the fact that the malarial parasite—which lives in red blood cells—cannot survive well in cells that carry the defective version of the hemoglobin gene. Because individuals who are heterozygous for sickle-cell anemia have a significant number of such red blood cells, their bloodstream is just not a hospitable environment for the malarial parasite (**FIGURE 7-23**).

Another example of pleiotropy is the SRY gene. Named for "**s**ex-determining **r**egion on the **Y** chromosome," this gene causes fetal gonads to develop as testes shortly after fertilization. Following the gonads' secretion of testosterone, a cascade of other developmental changes then occurs, such as development of the internal and external male reproductive structures. Ultimately, the SRY gene is responsible for numerous behavioral characteristics as well. These are described further in Chapter 9.

TAKE-HOME MESSAGE 7·12

In pleiotropy, one gene influences multiple unrelated traits. Most, if not all, genes may be pleiotropic.

PLEIOTROPY: ONE GENE, MANY EFFECTS

Pleiotropy occurs when one gene influences multiple, different traits.

Heterozygote for the sickle-cell trait

An allele that causes cells to sickle has two effects:

1 It disrupts red blood cells' oxygen delivery.

2 It causes red blood cells to be inhospitable to malarial parasites.

Someone with no sickled cells does not have sickle-cell anemia but is susceptible to malaria.

Malarial parasite infecting a red blood cell

FIGURE 7-23 From one gene, multiple traits. The allele for sickle-cell disease is pleiotropic: it causes red blood cells to form an unusual, sickled shape, and it also provides resistance to malaria.

7·13

Why are more men than women color-blind? Sex-linked traits differ in their patterns of expression in males and females.

The patterns of inheritance of most traits do not differ between males and females. When a gene is on an autosome (one of the non-sex chromosomes), both males and females inherit two copies of the gene, one from their mother and one from their father. The likelihood that an individual inherits one genotype versus another does not differ between males and females.

Traits coded for by the sex chromosomes, on the other hand, have different patterns of expression in males and females. One of the most easily observed examples of this phenomenon is red-green color-blindness. On the X chromosome in humans, there is a gene that carries the instructions for producing light-sensitive proteins in the eye that, when produced normally, respond differently to red wavelengths and green wavelengths of light. These proteins make it possible to distinguish between the colors red and green. As long as an individual has at least one functioning copy of the gene carrying the instructions for production of these light-sensitive proteins, he or she produces sufficient amounts of the protein to have normal color vision.

There is a rare allele for this gene, however, that produces a non-functioning version of the protein. Having some of this

non-functioning protein is not a problem as long as the person also carries another, normal version of the gene and produces some of the functioning protein. But this poses a problem for men, because they have only one X chromosome. In contrast, females inherit two X chromosomes.

Here's the problem: men only get one chance to inherit the normal version of the gene that codes for red-green color vision. It must be on the X chromosome they inherit from their mother. Women get two chances. Although a woman may inherit the defective allele from one parent, she can still inherit the normal allele from the other parent. As long as she inherits the normal gene from one parent, she will have normal color vision. As we would predict, then, the frequency of red-green color-blindness is significantly greater in males than in females (**FIGURE 7-24**). Approximately 7% to 10% of men exhibit red-green color-blindness, while fewer than 1% of women are red-green color-blind.

While males exhibit sex-linked recessive traits more frequently than do women, the situation is reversed for sex-linked dominant traits. In these cases, because females have two chances to inherit the allele that causes the trait, they are more likely to have the allele and thus exhibit the trait than are males, who have only one chance to inherit the allele.

Q If a man is color-blind, did he inherit this condition from his mother, his father, or both parents?

SEX-LINKED TRAITS: COLOR-BLINDNESS

A sex-linked trait is carried on the X chromosome. Women carry two copies of the X chromosome, while men carry an X chromosome and a Y chromosome.

Gene with instructions for light-sensitive proteins within the eye

Two alleles possible:
- **R** (produces functioning light-sensitive proteins)
- **r** (produces defective light-sensitive proteins)

TO BE COLOR-BLIND

Male must inherit color-blindness allele (**r**) from his mother.

Female must inherit color-blindness allele (**r**) from both parents.

TO HAVE NORMAL VISION

Male must inherit normal color-vision allele (**R**) from his mother.

Female can inherit normal color-vision allele (**R**) from either her mother or her father.

FIGURE 7-24 Sex-linked traits such as color-blindness are not expressed equally among males and females.

TAKE-HOME MESSAGE 7·13

The patterns of inheritance of most traits do not differ between males and females. However, when a trait is coded for by a gene on a sex chromosome, such as color vision on the X chromosome, the pattern of expression differs for males and females.

Family Resemblance   Genetics and Chance   Translation of Genotypes   Gene Linkage

7·14

Environmental effects: identical twins are not identical.

It is a very serious warning, in boldfaced capital letters: **"PHENYLKETONURICS: CONTAINS PHENYLALANINE."** But it's not next to a skull and crossbones on a glass bottle in a chemistry lab, it's on cans of diet soda intended for human consumption (**FIGURE 7-25**). Most of us either don't notice the warning or ignore it. Still, it's always there, and to some people it's a matter of life and death. What does it mean?

Q *Drinking diet soda can be deadly if you carry a single bad gene. What gene is it and why is it so deadly?*

At the most fundamental level, this warning is on products with phenylalanine because an organism's phenotype is a product of its genes in combination with the environment. Put another way, nature and nurture interact to produce bodies. In this case, the interaction is related to how humans metabolize a particular chemical called phenylalanine, one of the amino acids. Sometimes our bodies use phenylalanine directly to build proteins, adding it to a growing amino acid chain. At other times, phenylalanine is chemically converted into another amino acid, called tyrosine. Tyrosine is then used to build proteins and in a variety of other ways by the body.

The problem is this: at birth, some people carry two copies of a mutant version of the gene that is supposed to produce the enzyme that converts phenylalanine into tyrosine. The mutant gene produces a malfunctioning enzyme, and none of the body's phenylalanine is converted into tyrosine. Perhaps this doesn't seem as though it should be a big problem, but it is. Little by little, as these individuals consume phenylalanine, it builds up in their bodies because none of it is converted into tyrosine. Eventually, so much accumulates that it reaches toxic levels and poisons the brain, leading to mental retardation and death. The disease is called phenylketonuria, or PKU.

Here's where the warning label comes in. By limiting the amount of phenylalanine in their diet (from diet soda and other sources), individuals with the two mutant alleles for processing phenylalanine can avoid the toxic buildup of the amino acid in their brain. In essence, they modify their environment so that it contains little or no phenylalanine. And in that environment, the PKU mutant alleles are harmless. This example highlights the fact that genes by themselves do not "code" for physical characteristics. Rather, genes interact with the environment to produce physical characteristics. Unless you have information about both the genes *and* the environment, it is not usually possible to know what the phenotype will be.

A less life-threatening illustration of the interaction of genes with the environment can be seen at a pet shop. Siamese cats (as well as the Himalayan rabbit) carry genes that produce dark pigmentation. These genes interact strongly with the environment and are heat-sensitive. Dark pigment is produced only in relatively cold areas of the animal's body, while warm areas remain very light in color. This is why the fur on the coldest parts of the body—the ears, paws, tail, and tip of the face—becomes the darkest, while the fur on the rest of the body remains cream-colored or white (**FIGURE 7-26**). For Siamese cats living in cold climates that spend a lot of time outside, it's interesting to notice that they become significantly darker in color during the winter months. Those that lounge indoors all winter remain lighter in color.

Q *Could you create a temporarily spotted Siamese cat with an ice pack? Why?*

There are thousands of other cases in which genes' interactions with the environment influence their ultimate effects in the body. The very fact that identical twins—who inherit exactly the same set of alleles at the time of

FIGURE 7-25 Change the environment, "cure" the disease. The ingestion of phenylalanine in diet soda can be fatal to individuals with the inherited condition phenylketonuria (PKU).

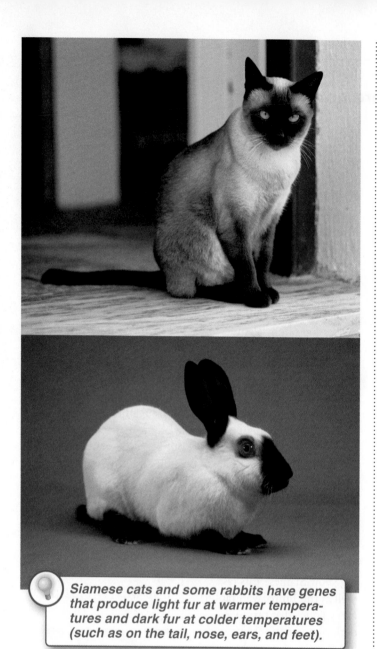

Siamese cats and some rabbits have genes that produce light fur at warmer temperatures and dark fur at colder temperatures (such as on the tail, nose, ears, and feet).

FIGURE 7-26 Heat-sensitive fur color. Some pigment-producing genes produce dark fur only under cold conditions. That's why these animals have darker patches of fur on their extremities.

fertilization—don't die on the same day at the same moment and from the same cause, for example, reveals that environmental variation influences the expression of genes. The scope of environmental influences ranges from traits with large and obvious environmental effects, such as body weight and its relationship with caloric intake, to traits such as eye color that are barely influenced by environmental effects, to traits with complex and subtle interactions with the environment, such as intelligence or personality.

Because of the role of environmental factors in influencing phenotypes, DNA is not like a blueprint for a house. This metaphor, though frequently used, is inappropriate, because there is nearly always a significant interaction between the genotype and the environment that influences the exact phenotype produced. The use of this metaphor might even be considered irresponsible, to the extent that it suggests that the phenotype is determined solely by the genotype. If that were the case, there would be no reason to invest in better schools, physical fitness regimens, nutritional monitoring, self-help efforts, or any other process by which individuals or societies try to improve people's lives (i.e., alter phenotypes) by enriching their environment.

Q James Watson, the co-discoverer of DNA, once wrote that when we completed the Human Genome Project, we would have "the complete genetic blueprint of man." Why was he wrong?

TAKE-HOME MESSAGE 7·14

Genotypes are not like blueprints that specify phenotypes. Phenotypes are generally a product of the genotype in combination with the environment.

Family Resemblance | Genetics and Chance | Translation of Genotypes | Gene Linkage

Different genes influence red hair and freckles, so why are they often inherited together?

4 Some genes are linked together.

7·15 --

Most traits are passed on as independent features: Mendel's law of independent assortment.

Sometimes you can be right about something for the wrong reason. This happened to Gregor Mendel. He didn't know that genes were carried on chromosomes. He believed that the units of heredity were just free-floating entities within cells. Given this perspective, it made sense to him that the inheritance pattern of one trait wouldn't influence the inheritance of any other trait. He believed that all genes behaved independently.

It helps to consider an example. Earlier in this chapter we saw that the characteristic of having a dimpled chin is caused by a single dominant gene. Imagine that you had a true-breeding population of people with dimpled chins (remember, "true-breeding" for a trait means that all offspring always manifest the trait; in the case of dimples, all have the genotype *DD*). Now suppose that an individual in this population had children with someone from a population of true-breeding, non-dimple-chinned people (everyone has the genotype *dd*). In this case, all of their children would have dimpled chins, but they would be heterozygous (*Dd*), getting a dominant allele from their dimple-chinned parent and a recessive allele from the other parent. If two of those heterozygotes then had children together, they would produce three-quarters dimpled

and one-quarter non-dimpled children, with genotypes in the ratio of ¼ *DD*, ½ *Dd*, and ¼ *dd*. That is just what Mendel observed for traits in pea plants.

But what if we concurrently observed another characteristic of these people? Suppose the original true-breeding population of dimpled-chin people (*DD*) was also true-breeding for albinism (all *aa*), a disorder caused by carrying two recessive alleles for a single gene. And suppose that individuals from the normal-chinned population (*dd*) were also true-breeding for normal pigmentation (all *AA*). The question is, do the alleles an individual inherits for the dimpled-chin trait influence which alleles that individual inherits for pigmentation? And the answer is that, in most cases, they do not (**FIGURE 7-27**). Rather, the first cross of a dimple-chinned albino with a normal-chinned, normally pigmented individual would result in a child heterozygous for both traits, expressing each of the dominant traits. Phenotypically, this and all subsequent offspring would be dimple-chinned and normally pigmented. Then, in a mating between two of these doubly heterozygous individuals, three-quarters of their children would have the dominant trait and one-quarter would have the recessive trait,

Mendel's law of independent assortment states that one trait does not influence the inheritance of another trait.

FIGURE 7-27 Independent assortment of genes.

regardless of which trait you are tallying. In other words, neither trait influences the inheritance pattern for the other trait; all traits are inherited independent of each other. This is known as **Mendel's law of independent assortment.**

In the next section we'll see that, despite Mendel's correct understanding that separate traits are inherited independently, his belief that this happened because all genes just float freely around in the cell was not correct. The genes, as we now know,

are carried on chromosomes. And this fact leads occasionally to some situations in which independent assortment does *not* occur.

TAKE-HOME MESSAGE 7·15

Genes tend to behave independently, such that the inheritance pattern of one trait doesn't usually influence the inheritance of any other trait.

7·16

Red hair and freckles: genes on the same chromosome are sometimes inherited together.

Most redheads have pale skin and freckles. This simple observation is problematic for the law of independent assortment as Mendel imagined it. After all, in his law, he asserted that the

inheritance of one trait does not influence the inheritance of another. But clearly that doesn't happen in this case. Having one of the traits, such as red hair, seems to influence the presence of

FIGURE 7-28
Violating the law of independent assortment. Red hair and freckles are often inherited as a package deal.

another trait, pale skin (**FIGURE 7-28**). Strictly speaking, Mendel's second law is not true for *every* pair of traits. Sometimes the alleles for two genes are inherited together and expressed almost as a package deal. Let's investigate why that is so.

Q *Why do most redheads have pale skin?*

For starters, how many traits make up an individual? Of course, this depends on the species. Nonetheless, the number will almost always extend into the thousands, if not tens of thousands. In the case of humans, for example, there are about 25,000 genes in our genome. Yet we have only 23 unique chromosomes (two copies of each). Thus, genes influencing some different traits must be on the same chromosome, maybe even right next to each other. When they are close together, we say that they are **linked genes.** One 2008 study, for example, demonstrated a link between human genes that influence hair color and skin pigmentation.

Why are linked genes inherited together? To answer this, we must revisit the behavior of chromosomes during the

production of gametes, discussed in Chapter 6. Imagine that you have a child. Let's focus on your gamete that took part in the fertilization to produce that child. When you made that sperm or egg by meiosis, only one of the two copies of each of your chromosomes ended up in the gamete. It may have been the one from your mother or it may have been the one from your father. In either case, all of the alleles that were on the chromosome from that one parent were passed on as a group to the child that resulted from the fertilization involving that gamete. This process continues generation after generation. The linked alleles never get split up unless, during meiosis, recombination occurs between them, moving one or more to the other chromosome in the pair so that they now become linked with the alleles on that chromosome (**FIGURE 7-29**).

> **❝** Four be the things I'd been better without: Love, curiosity, freckles, and doubt. **❞**
>
> —Dorothy Parker, *Inventory,* 1926

When alleles are linked closely on the same chromosome, Mendel's second law doesn't hold true. It is very surprising—and was fortunate for Mendel—that of the seven pea traits he studied, none of them were close together on the same chromosome. For this reason they all behaved as if they weren't linked, and in his crosses of different pea plants Mendel never noticed any linked genes.

TAKE-HOME MESSAGE 7·16

Sometimes, having one trait, such as red hair, influences the presence of another trait, such as pale skin. This is because the alleles for two genes are inherited and expressed almost as a package deal when the genes are located close together on the same chromosome.

LINKED GENES

Homologous chromosomes

Linked genes

Maternal copy   Paternal copy

When crossing over occurs, linked genes usually stay together.

Homologous chromosomes after the exchange of genetic information

If this gamete is fertilized, the linked genes will be passed on to the offspring together as a group.

Each of the four chromatids gets packaged into a gamete.

FIGURE 7-29 Gene linkage. Alleles that are closely linked on the same chromosome will be passed on to offspring in one bundle.

If genes are far apart on a chromosome or are on different chromosomes, the inheritance of one does not influence the inheritance of another.

Knowledge You Can Use

Where did you come from? Where are you going (to dinner)? World migrations, novelty-seeking, and a single gene that influences both.

On human chromosome 11 there is a gene called D4DR. This gene carries the instructions for building a protein embedded in the membranes of many of your brain cells. The protein is a receptor for the brain chemical dopamine, which is active in several areas of the brain called "pleasure centers" and influences initiative and motivation.

Although all humans have some form of the D4DR gene, there are several different alleles that a person might carry (though only two per person, of course). Each type of allele can be described by the length of the sequence of bases that makes up its DNA: some sequences are short, others are long.

Q: Can a single gene influence your personality? Several studies have reported that individuals carrying one or two long alleles of the D4DR gene, as opposed to two short alleles, are more likely to exhibit certain personality traits, including novelty-seeking and engaging in impulsive behaviors. On personality questionnaires, several differences emerge:

People carrying two short alleles are slightly more likely to be:	People carrying one or more long alleles are slightly more likely to be:
Reflective	Impulsive
Rigid	Exploratory
Stoic	Excitable
Slow-tempered	Quick-tempered
Frugal	Extravagant

Individuals carrying the long alleles even show a preference for spicy foods!

Q: Can a single gene explain why some people are willing to migrate over long distances and others remain rooted in one location? A study of 39 populations from around the world reported a strong relationship between D4DR allele length and how likely a population was to migrate or to remain stationary. Populations in which the long alleles were more common tended to migrate long distances, while those in which the short alleles were more common tended to stay put.

Population	Frequency of the long allele
Chinese and Japanese	5%
African	16%
European	20%
North American	32%
Central American	42%
South American	69%

Q: Do you want to know which alleles you carry for the D4DR gene? As more and more companies offer personalized genetic testing, it may soon be possible for you to learn which alleles you carry for the D4DR gene. Would you want to know? What would you do with this information?

Q: Do you want your employers or insurance companies to know which alleles you carry for the D4DR gene? Carrying one or more long alleles has also been linked with increased use and abuse of alcohol and other drugs. Information about your genotype could put you at risk for genetic discrimination. Moreover, the personality differences influenced by D4DR are relatively slight, they seem to be influenced by numerous other genes, and there is a tremendous variation in personality traits that is unrelated to the D4DR gene. So it's just not clear what it means for you to have short or long D4DR allele.

What can you conclude? Possessing the long D4DR alleles does not necessarily mean you will want to go sky-diving or feel an urge to move out of the country. Conversely, possessing the short D4DR alleles may not discourage you from climbing K2. **But knowledge about the makeup of your D4DR gene might place you at risk for employment or insurance discrimination.**

❶ Why do offspring resemble their parents?

Offspring resemble their parents because they inherit genes—instruction sets for biochemical, physical, and behavioral traits, some of which are responsible for diseases—from their parents. Gregor Mendel conducted studies in garden peas that helped us understand how traits are inherited, by applying methodical experimentation and rigorous hypothesis testing and focusing on easily observed and categorized traits in the pea plants. Each parent puts into every sperm or egg it makes a single set of instructions for building a particular trait. The trait observed in an individual depends on the two copies of the gene that it inherits from its parents. It is not always possible to determine an individual's genotype through observation of its phenotype. Much genetic analysis therefore makes use of clever experiments and careful record-keeping to determine organisms' genotypes.

❷ Probability and chance play central roles in genetics.

Probability plays a central role in genetics. In segregation, each gamete an individual produces receives only one of the two copies of each gene the individual carries in its other cells; it is impossible to know which allele it will be. Chance plays a role in fertilization, too: all of the sperm or eggs produced by an individual are different from one another, and any one of those gametes may be the gamete involved in fertilization. Test-crosses and pedigrees help scientists, doctors, plant and animal breeders, and prospective parents determine which genes individuals carry and the likelihood that the offspring of two individuals will exhibit a given trait.

❸ The translation of genotypes into phenotypes is not a black box.

Sometimes the effects of both alleles in a heterozygous genotype are seen in the phenotype. Many traits are influenced by multiple genes, and many genes may influence multiple unrelated traits. When a trait is coded for by a gene on the sex chromosomes, the pattern of expression differs for males and females. Genotypes are not like blueprints that specify phenotypes. Rather, phenotypes are a product of the genotype in combination with the environment.

❹ Some genes are linked together.

Many genes tend to behave independently, such that the inheritance pattern of one trait doesn't usually influence the inheritance of any other trait. When genes are located close together on the same chromosome, however, the alleles for two genes are inherited and expressed almost as a package deal.

KEY TERMS

additive effects, p. 269
allele, p. 251
carrier, p. 264
cross, p. 254
codominance, p. 267
dominant, p. 256
genotype, p. 258

heredity, p. 252
heterozygous, p. 257
homozygous, p. 257
incomplete dominance, p. 265
linked gene, p. 277
Mendel's law of independent assortment, p. 276

Mendel's law of segregation, p. 257
multiple allelism, p. 267
pedigree, p. 263
phenotype, p. 258
pleiotropy, p. 271
polygenic, p. 269

Punnett square, p. 258
recessive, p. 256
sex-linked trait, p. 263
single-gene trait, p. 253
test-cross, p. 262
true-breeding, p. 255

1. Most genes come in alternative forms called:
   a) alleles.   d) chromosomes.
   b) heterozygotes.   e) homozygotes.
   c) gametes.

2. Traits that are determined by a single gene:
   a) occur in single-celled organisms, but not in humans.
   b) are common in humans.
   c) must occur on the X chromosome, because males have only a single X and so the gene must be able to function in the absence of its homologous allele.
   d) include eye color and skin color.
   e) can have only two alleles.

3. Pea plants were well suited for Mendel's breeding experiments for all of the following reasons except:
   a) Peas exhibit variations in a number of observable characteristics, such as flower color and seed shape.
   b) Mendel and his staff could control the pollination between different pea plants.
   c) It is easy to obtain large numbers of offspring from any given cross.
   d) Many of the characteristics that vary in pea plants are not linked closely on the same chromosome.
   e) Peas have a particularly long generation time.

4. The law of segregation states that:
   a) the transmission of genetic diseases within families is always recessive.
   b) an allele on one chromosome will always segregate from an allele on a different chromosome.
   c) gametes cannot be separate and equal.
   d) the number of chromosomes in a cell is always divisible by 2.
   e) each of two alleles for a given trait segregate into different gametes.

5. In pea plants, purple flower color is dominant to white flower color. If two pea plants that are true-breeding for purple flowers are crossed, in the offspring:
   a) all of the flowers will be purple.
   b) three-quarters of the flowers will be purple and one-quarter will be white.
   c) half of the flowers will be purple and one-quarter will be white.
   d) one-quarter of the flowers will be purple and three-quarters will be white.
   e) all of the flowers will be white.

6. Pea flowers may be purple (*P*) or white (*p*). Pea seeds may be round (*R*) or wrinkled (*r*). What proportion of the offspring from a cross between purple-flowered, round-seeded individuals will have both white flowers and round seeds?
   a) $\frac{1}{16}$ d) $\frac{3}{4}$
   b) $\frac{1}{2}$ e) $\frac{9}{16}$
   c) $\frac{3}{16}$

7. The test-cross:
   a) makes it possible to determine the genotype of an individual of unknown genotype that exhibits the dominant version of a trait.
   b) is a cross between an individual whose genotype for a trait is not known and an individual homozygous recessive for the trait.
   c) sometimes requires the production of multiple offspring to reveal the genotype of an individual whose genotype is unknown (but who exhibits the dominant phenotype).
   d) Only a) and b) are correct.
   e) Choices a), b), and c) are correct.

8. Which of the following statements is correct regarding pedigree analysis?
   a) Darkened squares or circles always represent individuals with the trait being traced.
   b) White squares or circles always represent heterozygous individuals.
   c) Horizontal lines connect siblings.
   d) The length of the vertical lines is dependent on the relatedness between two individuals.
   e) Squares represent females, and circles represent males.

9. All of the offspring of a black hen and a white rooster are gray. The simplest explanation for this pattern of inheritance is:
   a) multiple alleles.
   b) codominance.
   c) incomplete dominance.
   d) incomplete heterozygosity.
   e) sex linkage.

10. A woman with type B blood and a man with type A blood could have children with which of the following phenotypes?
    a) AB only
    b) AB or O only
    c) A, B, or O only
    d) A or B only
    e) A, B, AB, or O

11. Which of the following traits shows a polygenic method of inheritance?
    a) flower color in snapdragons
    b) blood type in humans
    c) seed color in peas
    d) sickle-cell disease in humans
    e) skin color in humans

12. The impact of a single gene on more than one characteristic is called:
    a) incomplete dominance.
    b) environmentalism.
    c) balanced polymorphism.
    d) pleiotropy.
    e) codominance.

13. A rare, X-linked dominant condition in humans, congenital generalized hypertrichosis, is marked by excessive hair growth all over a person's body. Which of the following statements about this condition is incorrect?
    a) The son of a woman with this disease has just slightly more than a 50% chance of having this condition.
    b) The daughter of a man with this condition has a 100% chance of having this condition.
    c) The daughter of a woman with this disease has just slightly more than a 50% chance of having this condition.
    d) The son of a woman with this disorder has a 100% chance of having this condition.
    e) Males with this condition almost always have a more severe phenotype, because women usually have at least one normal allele that dilutes the effect of the mutated allele.

14. Individuals carrying two non-functioning alleles for the gene producing the enzyme that converts phenylalanine into tyrosine:
    a) will develop phenylketonuria (PKU).
    b) may or may not develop phenylketonuria, because the environment (diet, in this case) also plays a role in determining their phenotype.
    c) will develop both PKU and Tay-Sachs disease, because the genes causing the two traits are on the same chromosome.
    d) will develop both PKU and Tay-Sachs disease, because one pleiotropic gene influences both traits.
    e) do not need to worry about their phenylalanine consumption, because PKU depends on both genes and the environment.

15. Because of Mendel's law of independent assortment:
    a) individuals with red hair are more likely to have freckles.
    b) skin color and hair texture tend to be inherited together.
    c) we can deduce that genes cannot exist as free-floating entities within a cell but must be carried on chromosomes.
    d) the alleles coding for one trait do not usually influence the inheritance pattern for another trait.
    e) Both a) and b) are correct.

16. Thousands (or even tens of thousands) of different traits make up an individual. For this reason:
    a) in a species with 23 different chromosomes, some traits must be coded for by genes on the same chromosome.
    b) the environment must influence more than half of our traits.
    c) all (or nearly all) genes must be pleiotropic.
    d) knowing an individual's phenotype is not sufficient for determining the person's genotype.
    e) All of the above are correct.

SHORT-ANSWER QUESTIONS

1. Two healthy parents have two children, both of whom have a degenerative muscular disorder called SMA (spinal muscular atrophy).

    a) Explain how SMA must be inherited and what the genotype of the parents must be.

    b) The parents wish to have a third child and are contemplating adopting versus having a biological child. They seek the guidance of a genetic counselor and ask what the probability of having another child with SMA would be. What does the genetic counselor tell them? Explain.

2. Mackenzie's favorite flower is the hydrangea. She plants a large hydrangea bush in her yard and enjoys the big purple blossoms. Her sister, Anna, would like some hydrangeas for her yard as well, so they transplant a small portion of the large bush to Anna's yard. Anna is surprised when, the first time the plant in her yard blooms, the blossoms are pink instead of purple. If the genotype of this plant has not changed, what might have influenced a change in the phenotype?

3. Your friend explains to you that her father has hemophilia, a genetic disorder that affects the process of blood clotting, but her mother does not.

    a) Knowing that the inheritance pattern for this disorder is sex-linked, explain to your friend why it is more common for males to inherit a sex-linked trait.

    b) Using a Punnett square, indicate the probability that a brother of your friend would have hemophilia, assuming that her mother carries two functional copies of the gene involved in this sex-linked recessive disorder. Explain your answer.

See Appendix for answers. For additional study questions, go to www.prep-u.com.

20

Introduction to Animal Physiology

Principles of animal organization and function

❶ Animals have an internal environment.

Heat radiates from warm bodies in cold weather.

20·1

Our bodies function best within a narrow range of internal conditions.

Following an extremely rigorous practice in the summer of 2001, 27-year-old Minnesota Vikings football player Korey Stringer walked into an air-conditioned tent to recover. Almost immediately, however, the 6 foot 4 inch, 335-pound all-pro player began to feel weak and dizzy; his breathing became rapid and his blood pressure dropped. He was rushed to the hospital, but as a consequence of his body temperature allegedly reaching 108.8° F (42.7° C), many of his organs failed, and he died that night.

Normal body temperature is approximately 98.6° F (37° C). **Hyperthermia** occurs when too much heat is produced or when high environmental temperature and humidity overwhelm the body's ability to dissipate heat. (It is unlike a fever, in which the body sets its core temperature slightly higher in response to an infection by pathogens.) Korey Stringer's death is an example of the disastrous consequences that can result from extreme cases of hyperthermia, called

Q What is heat stroke? Why is it dangerous?

heat stroke, and illustrates the danger when organisms fail to maintain an internal environment within a safe range.

Although the environmental temperature range you experience every day may involve a 20°, 30°, or even 40° F difference between high and low, humans cannot tolerate such large internal temperature swings. Even deviations of less than 10° F can lead to a cascade of biochemical problems with serious health implications. For mammals, the risks of getting too hot include reduced enzyme activity and, at extreme temperatures, the complete breakdown of enzymes. Excessive water loss, too, can occur, leading to numerous problems—including organ failure. For these reasons, heat stroke can be life-threatening (**FIGURE 20-1**).

At the other extreme, **hypothermia,** or extremely low body temperature, can cause difficulties in coordination and movement, along with disorientation and confusion, irregular heartbeat, and, ultimately, death. Similarly disastrous

The Internal Environment   How Does Homeostasis Work?   Form Reflects Function

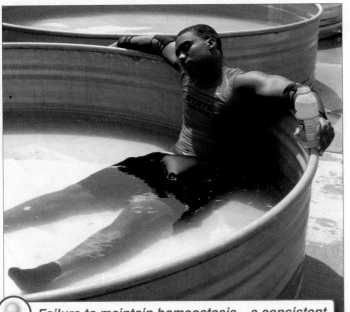

Failure to maintain homeostasis—a consistent internal environment—can lead to multiple problems in the normal functioning of cells, tissues, and organs, and can result in death.

consequences can occur as a result of the failure to maintain a consistent internal environment in other ways, including in blood sugar levels, blood pH, and tissue concentrations of oxygen and carbon dioxide.

In this chapter, we explore a fundamental characteristic of organism function, **homeostasis,** the body's use of physical and chemical processes to maintain a consistent internal environment, even in the face of changing external and internal environmental forces. We also examine the forms behind those functions—cells, tissues, organs, and organ systems.

TAKE-HOME MESSAGE 20·1

Failure to maintain a consistent internal physical and chemical environment can lead to multiple problems in the normal functioning of cells, tissues, and organs, and can result in death.

20·2

Animals regulate their internal environment through homeostasis.

When it comes to **physiology**—the functions and activities of an organism—taking care of business is straightforward in single-celled organisms. Food and other necessary materials for life do not have far to go to get into the cell—all they have to do is cross a plasma membrane. Moving waste products out of the cell is similarly simple. Such are the advantages to living close to the external environment. But direct contact with the external environment has its costs, too. Perhaps most important among these costs is that the cell is, to a large extent, at the mercy of its external environment. Changes in the environment—such as in temperature or pH—can have a great impact on the cell itself.

Like single-celled organisms, multicellular animals also must acquire food and other materials, as well as get rid of waste. These tasks become increasingly complex as organisms become more complex and more of their cells are not in direct contact with the external environment. On the other hand, when it's not in direct contact with the external

environment, a cell can be protected from harsh or changing environmental conditions. To most cells in a multicellular organism, the more important environment is the "internal environment."

With multicellularity and increasing size, then, an animal's internal environment takes on greater importance than the external environment in influencing cell functioning. In vertebrates, this internal environment consists of the **extracellular fluid** that fills the space between cells (also called the **interstitial fluid**), bathing the cells. This fluid is primarily water, but also contains nutrients and raw materials for growth and development, as well as waste products that have diffused out of or been removed from cells. The volume of interstitial fluid is not insignificant. In fact, one-third of the water in the human body is outside the body's cells, with more than two and a half gallons (10 liters)—picture five 2-liter soda bottles!—surrounding and bathing the cells.

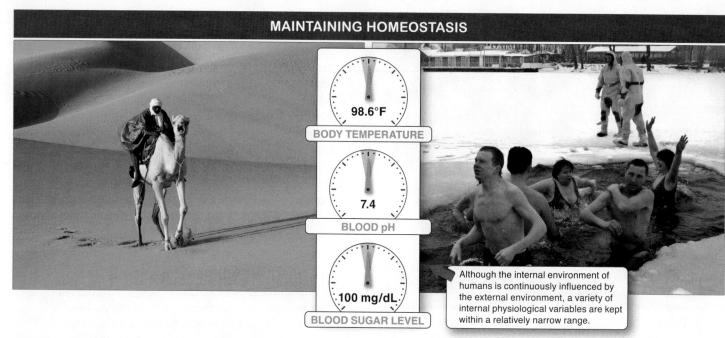

MAINTAINING HOMEOSTASIS

98.6°F
BODY TEMPERATURE

7.4
BLOOD pH

100 mg/dL
BLOOD SUGAR LEVEL

Although the internal environment of humans is continuously influenced by the external environment, a variety of internal physiological variables are kept within a relatively narrow range.

FIGURE 20-2 Homeostasis: maintaining a stable internal environment.

The internal environment of multicellular animals is continuously influenced by their external environment as well as by the cellular activities that add and remove materials. One of the hallmarks of animal physiology, however, is that organisms generally maintain homeostasis, or the ability to return to a narrow range of physical and chemical conditions, even in the face of changing external environmental forces. In this relatively constant, steady internal environment, variables such as temperature, water-solute balances, pH, blood sugar levels, and O_2 and CO_2 concentrations in blood and other tissues are maintained within narrow ranges by the activities of cells within the organism's tissues, organs, and systems (**FIGURE 20-2**).

Homeostasis is of huge value to the organism. Cellular functioning (from DNA replication to protein production to intercellular communication) depends, in large part, on the activities of enzymes. In turn, an enzyme's activity depends critically on the temperature and other characteristics of its immediate environment. Even slight changes in these variables can disrupt, reduce, or even stop enzyme functioning. And this can have catastrophic consequences, such as in the case of heat stroke described above.

Enzyme activity is just one of many facets of cell function influenced by temperature and other physical features of the cell's internal environment: membrane permeability and the rates at which materials diffuse across membranes also respond to changes in the environment. Through homeostasis, organisms maintain optimum metabolic functioning—the processes by which organisms take up nutrients from their environment and use them for growth, movement, reproduction, and all the other actions necessary for life. In the next section, we explore how homeostasis is maintained.

TAKE-HOME MESSAGE 20·2

Although the internal environment of multicellular animals is continuously influenced by their external environment, many animals maintain homeostasis: they keep a variety of internal physiological variables—including temperature, water-solute balances, pH, blood sugar levels, and blood gas concentrations—within a relatively constant range.

The Internal Environment   How Does Homeostasis Work?   Form Reflects Function

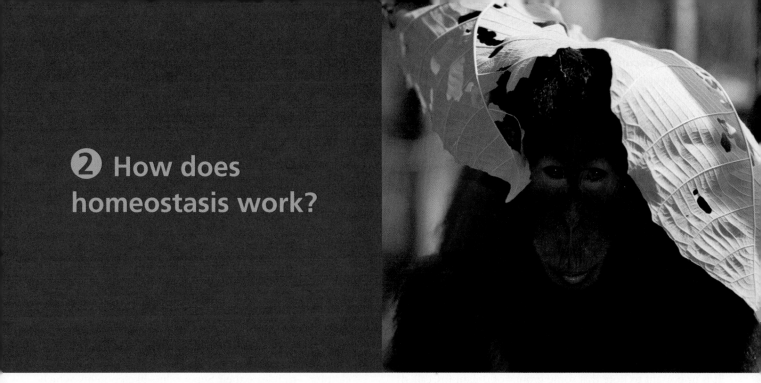

❷ How does homeostasis work?

Relief from heat: A young orangutan seeks shelter under a leaf.

20•3

Negative and positive feedback systems influence homeostasis.

For animals to maintain homeostasis with regard to a particular physiological variable, that variable must have a **set point,** a target value or range to which the organism can return. Most vertebrates have set points for a variety of physiological variables, including body temperature, water-solute balances, blood sugar levels, blood pH, and tissue O_2 and CO_2 concentrations.

In the face of changes in its external environment, how does an organism maintain its homeostasis, its constant internal environment? The most common method involves the phenomenon of **negative feedback,** in which sensors detect a change in the internal environment and trigger structures called **effectors** to oppose or reduce the change. This cycle of detection, response, and change is called a negative feedback loop (**FIGURE 20-3**).

An example of a negative feedback loop that we encounter in everyday life is the regulation of room temperature in a house, which involves a sensor (the thermostat) and two effectors (a furnace and an air conditioner). Within the thermostat is a sensor that detects the temperature in the

NEGATIVE FEEDBACK LOOP

In a negative feedback loop, sensors detect changes in the internal environment and trigger effectors to oppose or reduce the change.

EFFECTOR: AIR CONDITIONER Decreases temperature

TOO HOT

SENSOR: THERMOSTAT Detects temperature

DESIRED TEMPERATURE

TOO COLD

EFFECTOR: FURNACE Increases temperature

In animals, negative feedback systems are the most common method used to maintain the internal environment within a narrow range.

FIGURE 20-3 **A negative feedback loop restores the internal environment to a set point.**

house. If the temperature drops too low, the thermostat triggers an effector—the furnace—to turn on, bringing the room temperature back up to the desired level. Once the temperature reaches a specified level, the thermostat tells the furnace to shut off. Similarly, if the temperature gets too high, the thermostat can trigger the air conditioning to turn on, which brings the temperature back down to the desired level, after which it shuts off. In both cases, a negative feedback system senses a change in the temperature, triggers events that reverse the change, and restores the house's internal environment to its desired level.

In the human body, negative feedback systems are the most common method used to maintain the internal environment within a narrow range. These systems include those that maintain body temperature, regulate levels of sugar in the bloodstream, and control levels of salt and other solutes in body fluids. We explore these systems in detail later in this chapter.

It is important to note that some groups of organisms, called **regulators,** maintain homeostasis for a certain variable (as we've just described for temperature), while other organisms, called **conformers,** may have no set point for that variable at all and the variable may fluctuate with external changes. Animals vary in the traits for which they are regulators and conformers. Most fishes, for example, conform to the

temperature of the water but regulate closely the concentration of salt in their blood and tissues, independent of the salt concentration in the water (**FIGURE 20-4**).

In addition to negative feedback systems, organisms also have a small number of **positive feedback** systems, in which deviations from conditions normally found in the internal environment cause an increase or acceleration of the change, in the same direction. Such systems push the body away from homeostasis and often initiate cascading processes that increase the rate at which the system deviates from the normal range. For this reason, positive feedback systems, if unchecked, can become highly unstable.

An example of a positive feedback system is the blood-clotting process (**FIGURE 20-5**). Injury to a blood vessel causes platelets—cellular fragments involved in clotting—to release their Super Glue–like contents, which begin to seal any rip or tear in the blood vessel (see Section 21-6). Within the bloodstream, the contents released from a platelet have another effect as well: they cause other platelets to release their contents. This is a positive feedback system, because the release of some blood-clotting molecules into the bloodstream causes the release of more, which causes the release

Q Why don't we bleed to death when we get a cut?

RESPONDING TO ENVIRONMENTAL CHANGE

REGULATE
For some physiological variables, an organism has a set point and maintains the variable within a consistent range around that point.

WHEN SALT CONCENTRATION OF WATER IS LOW

WHEN SALT CONCENTRATION OF WATER IS HIGH

Salt concentration within body remains constant

CONFORM
For some physiological variables, an organism has no set point and the variable fluctuates with changes in the external environment.

WHEN WATER TEMPERATURE IS LOW

WHEN WATER TEMPERATURE IS HIGH

Body temperature decreases

Body temperature increases

Organisms may regulate their internal environment around a consistent set point for some variables, while conforming to their external environment—often varying widely—for other variables.

FIGURE 20-4 Regulate or conform? Two strategies to cope with a changing environment.

The Internal Environment   How Does Homeostasis Work?   Form Reflects Function

In positive feedback systems, such as the blood-clotting process, a change away from conditions normally found in the body causes an increase or acceleration of the change.

- Platelets
- Injured blood vessel
- Clot

An injured blood vessel triggers platelets to form a clot.

The release of blood-clotting molecules into the bloodstream causes the release of more, which causes the release of still more such molecules to aid in forming the clot.

Positive feedback is generally part a of larger, negative feedback system; after a period of positive feedback, the variable is brought back within its typical range.

FIGURE 20-5   Patching a tear. The blood clot that forms after an injury is a result of a positive feedback system.

of still more. The result is that a dangerous situation, injury to a blood vessel, is quickly remedied.

Generally, positive feedback systems are part of larger, negative feedback systems, which, after a short period of positive feedback, bring the variable (and the organism) back to within its original, normal range of internal environmental conditions. After blood clotting has stopped the loss of blood from a damaged vessel, other chemical signals interrupt the positive feedback loop, stop the further release of blood-clotting molecules, and even begin to break down blood clots that no longer serve a function.

TAKE-HOME MESSAGE 20·3

For animals to maintain homeostasis with regard to a particular physiological variable, that variable must have a set point to which the organism can return. Through negative feedback, sensors detect a change in the internal environment and trigger effectors to oppose or reduce the change. Positive feedback systems, much less common, oppose homeostasis in response to a change, pushing the body away from normal conditions and increasing change in the same direction.

20·4

Temperature control is a component of homeostasis.

As we saw in the case of Korey Stringer, one of the most important environmental factors that affect animals is temperature. And for many animal species, the control of temperature, called **thermoregulation,** is an important component of homeostasis.

When it comes to thermoregulation, the biggest distinction among animal species is in how they generate their body heat. **Endotherms** (sometimes described as "warm-blooded") generate their heat internally, within their own bodies. Most mammals and birds are endotherms. **Ectotherms** (sometimes described as "cold-blooded") get their heat primarily from the environment, usually the sun. Invertebrates, fishes, amphibians, and reptiles are all ectotherms. While these groups are often distinguished as

Q Why do some cold-blooded animals have "hot" blood and some warm-blooded animals have "cold" blood?

"warm-blooded" and "cold-blooded" (**FIGURE 20-6**), closer investigation reveals that such terms do not always accurately describe the two groups. Some animals, including numerous mammalian species, **hibernate,** going into a state of reduced metabolic activity for days or weeks, during which their body temperature can drop considerably. The body temperature of some hibernating ground squirrels, for example, can drop below freezing for more than three weeks. Some hibernating mammals can become quite cold, while some lizards basking in the sun can get very warm.

These observations highlight another important aspect of thermoregulation. Some organisms (such as humans) are **homeotherms,** meaning that they maintain a relatively

GENERATING BODY HEAT

ENDOTHERMS
• Animals that generate body heat internally
• Sometimes described as "warm-blooded"
• Include most mammals and birds

ECTOTHERMS
• Animals that get their heat primarily from the environment
• Sometimes described as "cold-blooded"
• Include invertebrates, fishes, amphibians, and reptiles

FIGURE 20-6 Strategies to heat the body.

constant body temperature. Other organisms (such as the lizards and hibernating mammals) are **heterotherms,** and their body temperatures, at times, fluctuate as the environmental temperature changes (**FIGURE 20-7**). As a consequence, animals are most accurately categorized by describing their source of heat (internal or external) *and* the degree to which they maintain a constant temperature or have a temperature that fluctuates.

Whether or not an animal generates its own heat and maintains a constant body temperature, all animals exchange heat with the environment. Ultimately, an organism's body temperature is a function of the heat it produces in conjunction with the heat that is transferred from the environment to its body or from its body to the environment. This heat exchange can occur in four ways (**FIGURE 20-8**), and these four mechanisms sometimes make it challenging for organisms to acquire heat, and sometimes make it challenging to dissipate heat.

1. *Conduction* is the transfer of heat that occurs when two objects at different temperatures come in contact. Holding an ice cube or sitting on a hot car seat dramatically reveals conduction in action.

2. *Convection* is the transfer of heat from an object to a medium such as water or air as it passes next to the object. This is particularly noticeable to us when a cold breeze blows.

3. *Radiation* is the transfer of heat, without direct contact, from a warmer object to a colder object. You are experiencing radiant heat when you feel the warmth of the sun on your face or the heat from a fireplace on your feet.

4. *Evaporation* is the loss of heat that occurs as a liquid substance, such as liquid water, turns to a gas. When you sweat and the sweat evaporates, it cools you off.

MAINTAINING BODY TEMPERATURE

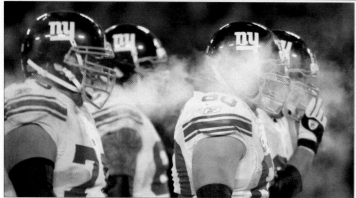

HOMEOTHERMS
Body temperature remains relatively constant.

Reptiles can often be found on the edges of roads in the afternoon and early evening, using the warmth of the road to elevate their body temperature.

HETEROTHERMS
Body temperature fluctuates as environmental temperatures change.

FIGURE 20-7 Stable body temperature versus variable body temperature.

The Internal Environment   How Does Homeostasis Work?   Form Reflects Function

EXCHANGING BODY HEAT WITH THE ENVIRONMENT

Animals exchange heat with the environment in four ways.

CONDUCTION
The transfer of heat that occurs when two objects at different temperatures come in contact.

CONVECTION
The transfer of heat to a medium such as water or air as it passes next to an object.

RADIATION
The transfer of heat, without direct contact, from a warmer object to a colder object.

EVAPORATION
The loss of heat that occurs as a substance such as liquid water turns to a gas.

An organism's temperature depends on the heat that it gains or loses to the environment, in conjunction with the heat the organism produces.

FIGURE 20-8 How organisms acquire or dissipate heat.

We'll find further examples of each of these mechanisms as we look at four of the methods—physical, behavioral, physiological, and cellular—by which animals regulate body temperature (**FIGURE 20-9**).

Numerous physical features have evolved in organisms that influence the organism's body temperature. These include the organism's body size, surface area, and levels of insulation. The thick lipid-rich coat of blubber in walruses, whales, and many other marine mammals, for example, can account for up to 50% of the body weight of some animals and provides effective insulation, helping them to maintain a constant body temperature.

An organism can also use behavioral strategies to regulate its body temperature. Most lizards, for example, bask in the sun during the early morning hours, increasing their body temperature. Later, when the day is at its hottest, they may retreat to a burrow to reduce their body temperature. Many large mammals that cannot get to shade orient their bodies to minimize the angle at which the sun strikes them. The African ground squirrel even shades itself with its tail as it forages.

Animals also employ many physiological methods of thermoregulation. One specific example of this occurs as cells maintain concentration gradients of various ions, such as potassium (K^+) and sodium (Na^+). Many cell membranes are somewhat permeable to K^+ and Na^+ ions. The ions "leak" across the membrane, requiring active transport to restore and maintain the concentration gradients necessary for some cellular processes. Because the reactions involved in active transport are not perfectly efficient in their use of energy,

---

METHODS FOR REGULATING BODY TEMPERATURE

PHYSICAL METHODS
The walrus has a thick coat of blubber that provides insulation from the external environment.

BEHAVIORAL METHODS
The African ground squirrel shades itself with its tail while foraging, to minimize heat from the sun.

PHYSIOLOGICAL METHODS
By panting, dingos make use of the efficient loss of heat due to evaporation.

CELLULAR METHODS
Human infants have a special type of fat that produces heat, rather than ATP, when broken down.

FIGURE 20-9 Adaptations that aid in temperature regulation.

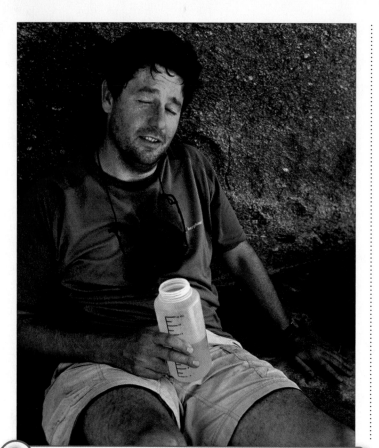

Most organisms must maintain water and solute concentrations within a narrow range. Imbalances can lead to serious health problems and even death.

FIGURE 20-10   Heat exchange. Sweating can help cool us off through evaporation. By leaning up against a cool rock wall, we can also lose some heat through conduction.

some energy is released as heat with each reaction. This heat can help maintain an organism's body temperature. Interestingly, as it turns out, cell membranes in endotherms, such as humans, are leakier than the cell membranes in ectotherms, such as fishes, suggesting that such "leakiness" is an adaptation that helps endotherms generate heat internally. It is also likely that it's because mitochondria are the sites of greatest heat generation that endotherms have, on average, three to four times as many mitochondria per cell as ectotherms.

Another physiological method by which animals—both ectotherms and endotherms—can regulate their body heat is by controlling the flow of blood to the skin. To lose heat, such as during periods of extreme exertion or at extremely high external temperatures, they increase blood flow to the skin, allowing greater heat loss by convection. Through panting and sweating, too, many animals make use of the efficient loss of heat due to evaporation (**FIGURE 20-10**). Alternatively, in cold environments, the loss of heat can be reduced by reducing the flow of blood to the skin and by shivering, through which animals can increase their heat production.

One cellular method of temperature regulation is particularly important to human babies. It takes place in a special type of connective tissue called "brown fat." Unlike the cells of "white fat," or adipose tissue (most of the fat in adult's bodies), in which there are few mitochondria, the cells of brown fat have a high density of mitochondria along with the stored fat. When brown fat cells oxidize their fat, however, they don't generate ATP. Instead, a special protein causes protons to leak directly across the mitochondrial membrane, rather than passing through the enzyme that synthesizes ATP (see Section 4-15), causing the production of heat rather than ATP from the fat breakdown. Human infants have significantly more brown fat than adults. This probably evolved because their small body size gives them a large surface-area-to-volume ratio, which results in a relatively large surface area over which they can lose heat and a relatively small body mass in which they can generate heat.

Q *Why does "baby fat," unlike regular fat, act like a built-in heating pad?*

TAKE-HOME MESSAGE 20·4

The control of body temperature, called thermoregulation, is an important component of homeostasis. Body temperature is a function of internal heat production and heat transfer between an organism and its environment. Heat transfer to and from the environment is regulated physically, behaviorally, physiologically, and at the cellular level.

The Internal Environment   How Does Homeostasis Work?   Form Reflects Function

Animals must balance their water content within a narrow range.

Organisms, whether they live in the water or on land, require water. But they can't take in too much or they will burst. And they can't lose too much or they will shrivel up and die. **Osmoregulation,** an important component of homeostasis in animals, is the regulation of water content and of the concentrations of dissolved solutes that influence osmosis. The most abundant solutes in animal fluids are sodium, chloride, potassium, magnesium, and calcium.

Although a variety of mechanisms of water regulation have evolved in animals, there are just four ways that animals get water: by drinking it, by eating foods that contain it, by absorbing it through osmosis, and as a by-product of cellular respiration. Similarly, there are four ways that animals lose water: urination, defecation, evaporation (including panting, breathing, and sweating), and osmosis.

Osmoregulation revolves around controlling and regulating these mechanisms of water loss and gain. Through osmosis, water flows from areas of low solute concentration to areas of high solute concentration. Thus organisms often control their water content indirectly by regulating their solute content. They generally balance the total amount of solutes—which influences the direction and magnitude of osmosis—and the concentration of each solute individually. Imbalances in the concentrations of certain solutes can cause serious health

problems, from muscle spasms to confusion to paralysis, and even death.

Because animals live in such a wide range of habitats, they encounter a similarly wide range of osmoregulation challenges. The challenges are very different for aquatic organisms than for terrestrial organisms, for example. And among the aquatic organisms, the challenges facing organisms living in saltwater habitats are very different from—almost the opposite of—those faced by organisms living in fresh water.

Different strategies have evolved for coping with such diverse osmoregulation challenges. Most invertebrates that live in salt water are **osmoconformers,** meaning that they let the solute concentration of their body fluids reflect that of their environment. Most vertebrates, on the other hand, are **osmoregulators,** maintaining their fluids and solute concentrations within narrow ranges that differ from those of their environment (**FIGURE 20-11**).

A variety of structures have evolved that enable animals to regulate their water balance. In insects, for example, very small tubes branch off the digestive tract, near its end at the rectum. These extensions from the gut, called Malpighian tubules, function as the animals' chief excretory organs. Using active transport (see Section 3-10), an animal moves potassium ions

---

OSMOREGULATION STRATEGIES

OSMOCONFORMERS
Osmoconformers are organisms that let the composition of their body fluids reflect that of their environment.

External environment · Body fluid

OSMOREGULATORS
Osmoregulators are organisms that maintain their fluids and solute concentrations within narrow ranges that differ from those of their environment.

Excess solutes · Circulatory system · Digestive tract · Waste

Excess solutes · Waste · Kidneys · Excess water · Waste

MALPIGHIAN TUBULES
These small tubes regulate osmotic balance in insects by removing excess solutes from the circulatory system.

KIDNEYS
These complex organs regulate osmotic balance in vertebrates by removing either excess solutes or excess water from the circulatory system, depending on the organism's external environment.

FIGURE 20-11 Two strategies for regulating the amount of salt and water in the body.

(K^+) and cellular waste products from its body cavity—where its blood is—into the Malpighian tubules. As a consequence of the increase in solutes in the tubules, water moves into them by osmosis. The K^+ ions, water, and waste products move down the digestive tract until, near its end, the K^+ ions and water are mostly reabsorbed into the circulatory system. This is a very effective system for conserving water, leaving mostly waste products to be excreted as feces.

Do fish drink water?

Another osmoregulatory structure is the vertebrate kidney. The kidney, as we shall see, is a complex organ that filters blood, removing metabolic waste products— particularly excess nitrogen from the breakdown of proteins and nucleic acids—and other ions while regulating the organism's water balance. The specific details of kidney function vary across the different groups of vertebrates. Let's consider, for example, the challenges faced by two groups of aquatic vertebrates: freshwater and saltwater fishes. A freshwater fish faces the problems of high concentrations of water entering its body and solutes leaving its body. A saltwater fish, on the other hand, tends to lose water to its environment while taking in high concentrations of solutes from the environmental water. As a consequence, vertebrate kidneys—depending on the type of animal—may function either to conserve water or to remove it. (This explains why a freshwater fish does not drink water, but a saltwater fish drinks large amounts.)

In the next section, we examine the details of kidney functioning, focusing specifically on the human kidney and how it is able to produce urine that has a solute concentration more than four times that of blood, and how it is able to eliminate the many potentially harmful molecules contained within the food and drink consumed in the diet.

TAKE-HOME MESSAGE 20·5

Many organisms maintain their water content within a narrow range. To maintain osmotic balance, organisms must be able to take up water and get rid of water, and they must be able to regulate concentrations of ions in their body fluids. Various mechanisms and strategies have evolved for coping with these challenges.

20·6

In humans, the kidney is the chief excretory organ.

The kidney is an organ in vertebrates that helps maintain homeostasis by regulating water balance and solute concentration in body fluids. It accomplishes this by filtering blood and reabsorbing water and other substances needed by the body. Blood flows into capillaries within each kidney via a renal artery and leaves the kidney via a renal vein. From the kidneys, waste products and water removed from the bloodstream pass to the bladder, and from there are excreted as urine (**FIGURE 20-12**).

A human has two kidneys, each about the size of a fist, located on either side of the spine, just above the waist. Each kidney is made up of approximately one million nephrons. A **nephron** consists of two basic components: a nephron tubule and a mass of blood vessels that work together to accomplish the tasks of filtration, reabsorption, and excretion (**FIGURE 20-13**). The blood-filtering unit of the nephron is a mass of capillaries called a **glomerulus,** and the ball-like structure that surrounds it is called **Bowman's capsule.** Each Bowman's

FIGURE 20-12 Structure of the kidney. Human kidneys filter blood, reabsorb water and solutes, and excrete waste.

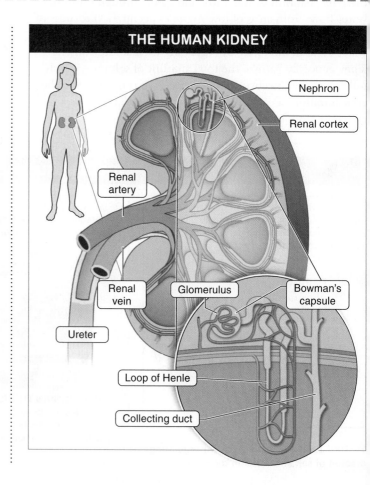

THE HUMAN KIDNEY

Nephron

Renal cortex

Renal artery

Renal vein

Glomerulus

Bowman's capsule

Ureter

Loop of Henle

Collecting duct

726   CHAPTER 20 • INTRODUCTION TO ANIMAL PHYSIOLOGY

The Internal Environment   How Does Homeostasis Work?   Form Reflects Function

Glomerulus

Bowman's capsule

2a

Na⁺

Cl⁻

Water

Filtrate

2c

Na⁺

Cl⁻

1 FILTRATION
Blood pressure forces water and small molecules out of the capillaries in the glomerulus. The filtrate accumulates in Bowman's capsule.

2 REABSORPTION
As the filtrate moves from Bowman's capsule through the long tubule of the nephron, a majority of the water and dissolved solutes are reabsorbed.

2a Sodium ions are moved out of the tubule by active transport, which causes water and chloride ions to move out of the tubule by passive transport.

2b As the filtrate moves down the loop of Henle, the solute concentration outside the tubule increases, causing more water to move out of the tubule.

2c As the filtrate moves back up toward the cortex, additional salt is reabsorbed as sodium and chloride ions move out of the tubule through diffusion and active transport.

2d The tubule exits into the collecting duct, which passes back through the increased solute concentration of the inner kidney, drawing more water out.

2b

Water

2d

Collecting duct

Water

Loop of Henle

Urine

3 EXCRETION
The collecting duct merges with the collecting ducts from other nephrons, forming the ureter, which empties into the urinary bladder.

To urinary bladder

FIGURE 20-13 The nephron is the fundamental unit of the human kidney. One million nephrons enable the human kidney to regulate water balance and solute concentration in body fluids while producing urine.

capsule is connected to a single, long, urine–producing tube that excretes its filtered fluid into a collecting duct.

The capillaries in the glomerulus are porous, and blood pressure forces out water and small molecules and ions (but not blood cells or most proteins) through the capillary walls. Fluid that accumulates in Bowman's capsule, called **filtrate,** contains salts, sugars, amino acids, vitamins, and many other molecules, all at the same concentration as in the blood.

As the filtrate moves from Bowman's capsule through the urine-collecting tubule of the nephron, the vast majority of the water and dissolved solutes must be reabsorbed. In fact, up to 2,000 liters of blood (about 275 times the total volume of blood in your body) passes through the kidneys each day, but only about 1.5 liters of urine is produced and excreted.

Reabsorption in the long tubule of the nephron is a complex process. It begins with the active transport of sodium ions out of the tubule, which causes water and chloride ions to follow, moving out of the tubule by passive transport.

The tubule (and the filtrate it contains) then loops from the outer part of the kidney, called the cortex (see Figure 20-13), down into the innermost part of the kidney and back again, in a path called the loop of Henle. As the tubule passes to the innermost part of the kidney, the solute concentration of the interstitial fluid, outside the tube, increases. This causes more and more water to move out of the tubule, from the filtrate and into the interstitial fluid. As the filtrate moves up toward the kidney cortex again, more salt is lost, through diffusion and active transport. From the cortex, the tubule passes into the collecting duct, which passes through the innermost part of the kidney again, returning additional water to the interstitial fluid and further concentrating the urine for excretion. The collecting duct eventually merges with collecting ducts from other nephrons, forming the ureter, which empties into the urinary bladder. From the bladder, urine passes through the urethra and is excreted from the body.

> **Q** Why do some desert mammals never need to drink water?

Filtering the blood and producing urine not only follows a complicated path but is very energetically expensive. Considerable amounts of energy are expended in the active transport of solutes that leads to the recovery of water. Nonetheless, some animals, such as kangaroo rats, are so efficient at reabsorbing water that they can recover nearly all of the water filtered by their kidneys. They never have to drink water at all; the water contained in their food and the water generated as a by-product during cellular metabolism is sufficient.

Among the most important of the metabolic waste products that must be filtered and removed from the blood by the kidneys are those containing nitrogen. Produced from the breakdown of proteins and nucleic acids, this nitrogen tends to be in the form of ammonia, which is generally very toxic to organisms. Some organisms—mostly aquatic organisms—are able to rid their bodies of excess nitrogen by simply excreting the ammonia. Terrestrial animals (and many marine animals), however, cannot consume sufficient water to keep ammonia diluted enough so that it is not toxic. These organisms instead combine ammonia with carbon dioxide, producing urea, which can be stored for longer periods of time and at higher concentrations (thereby requiring much less water). There is a cost to this system, however; the production of urea from ammonia and carbon dioxide is energetically expensive. Besides ammonia and urea, there is a third form in which nitrogenous wastes can be excreted, as a paste called uric acid. This method requires even less water than urea excretion, but is even more energetically expensive. It is used by insects, terrestrial snails, birds, and many reptiles.

The kidneys are so effective at filtering blood and concentrating the many waste products of metabolism in urine that it is possible to detect the use of many drugs

FIGURE 20-14 Detectible remainders. Drugs break down into metabolites, chemicals that sometimes linger in the body and urine. Here an individual tends to marijuana plants grown for medicinal purposes.

through urinalysis. Most drug-screening urinalysis does not actually involve testing for the presence of the drugs themselves, which may remain in the body for only a short time. Instead, the tests look for the presence of chemicals, called metabolites, that result from the breakdown of the drugs (**FIGURE 20-14**). Metabolites have been identified for many drugs, including Ecstasy, cocaine, methamphetamines, and marijuana. In the case of marijuana, the metabolites are fat-soluble. This means that they are stored in fat cells indefinitely, and released only when fat from those cells is metabolized for energy. As a consequence, marijuana can be detected a month or longer after the last use.

> **Q** How can some drugs be detected by urinalysis even month after the last intake?

TAKE-HOME MESSAGE 20·6

The kidney is the organ in vertebrates that helps maintain homeostasis by regulating water balance and solute concentrations in body fluids, filtering blood, and removing potentially harmful ions and metabolic waste products, excreting them in urine.

The Internal Environment   How Does Homeostasis Work?   Form Reflects Function

❸ Form reflects function: animal anatomy.

An elephant uses its trunk to forage for tree-top leaves.

20·7

Most animal bodies are organized into cells, tissues, organs, and organ systems.

Form follows function. This simple statement captures one of the most universal relationships in the living world. For example, fast-swimming organisms, from penguins to tuna to sharks, share a common streamlined body shape (**FIGURE 20-15**). If a structure is adaptive—the product of natural selection—then its physical features closely reflect its function. And just as form follows function for large animal structures, so, too, does the relationship hold true for molecules, organelles, and cells. In this section we examine the levels of organization in animal bodies and see how form fits function in each.

Animals are multicellular organisms. And multicellularity makes it possible for animals to attain much larger sizes and much greater physiological complexity than single-celled organisms. Increased size and complexity bring many benefits, including a reduction in the number of potential predators, an increase in the number of potential prey, and, more generally, a

FORM FOLLOWS FUNCTION

If a structure is the product of natural selection, the structure commonly reflects closely its function. For example, fast-swimming organisms have streamlined body shapes.

FIGURE 20-15 Adapted for swimming: the streamlined body of the penguin.

729

ORGANIZATION OF ANIMAL BODIES

One of the fundamental features of the organization of the animal body is that it is hierarchical, containing four levels of organization.

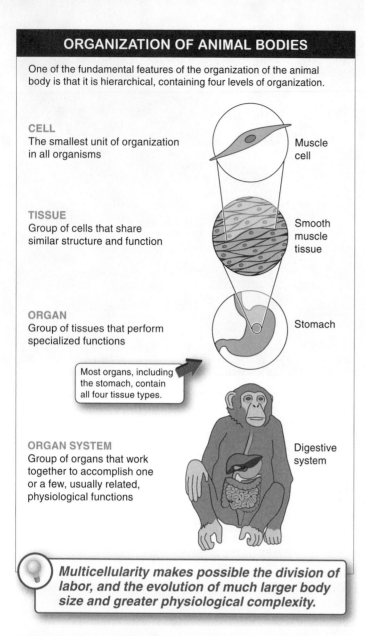

CELL
The smallest unit of organization in all organisms

Muscle cell

TISSUE
Group of cells that share similar structure and function

Smooth muscle tissue

ORGAN
Group of tissues that perform specialized functions

Stomach

Most organs, including the stomach, contain all four tissue types.

ORGAN SYSTEM
Group of organs that work together to accomplish one or a few, usually related, physiological functions

Digestive system

Multicellularity makes possible the division of labor, and the evolution of much larger body size and greater physiological complexity.

FIGURE 20-16 From cells to organ systems.

reduction in the influence of the external environment. For these reasons, among others, the transition from a single-celled to a multicellular body is one of the most important evolutionary transitions.

Possibly the chief benefit of multicellularity is that it makes possible a division of labor and specialization at the cellular level. No longer is it necessary for each cell to carry out every single physiological process (such as generating movement, detoxifying harmful chemicals, digesting macromolecules, and sensing and responding to environmental changes). Instead, cells can be organized into groups, and groups organized into larger groups, to carry out specific life-sustaining functions such as exchanging gases between the organism and its

environment, thinking and feeling, and fighting pathogens (**FIGURE 20-16**).

One of the fundamental features of the organization of the animal body is that it is hierarchical. Cells, as you'll recall from Chapter 3, are the smallest unit of organization in all organisms. Sponges, structurally the simplest of all animals, have cells specialized to perform a few distinct tasks. For example, some cells form the covering of the sponge's body, and others obtain food to provide nutrition and energy to sustain the sponge's activities. At the other end of the spectrum are humans—with 210 different cell types.

In most animals, groups of cells with similar structure, along with some products of those cells, form **tissues,** in which the cells act together to perform specific functions in the body. Adult animals generally have four main types of tissue (**FIGURE 20-17**), which we'll discuss in more detail in Sections 20-8 through 20-11.

Connective tissue consists of cells embedded in a large amount of extracellular material, called **matrix,** which together contribute to body structure and support. Found throughout the human body, connective tissue can also serve to anchor cells, regulate communication between cells, and influence growth and wound healing. Some of the most important structures formed from connective tissue include tendons, cartilage, blood, adipose, and bone.

Epithelial tissue covers and lines most exterior and interior surfaces of the body. Skin is an epithelial tissue, as are the tissues that line the nose, throat, lungs, blood vessels, and digestive tract.

From the circulatory and respiratory systems that deliver oxygen and remove carbon dioxide, to the muscle tissue that generates the flapping of wings, to the neurons in the eyes that detect prey, to the epithelial tissue across which nutrients from food are absorbed, the working together of cells, tissues, organs, and organ systems make many complex actions of organisms possible—such as flight in these red-and-green macaws in Peru.

The Internal Environment   How Does Homeostasis Work?   Form Reflects Function

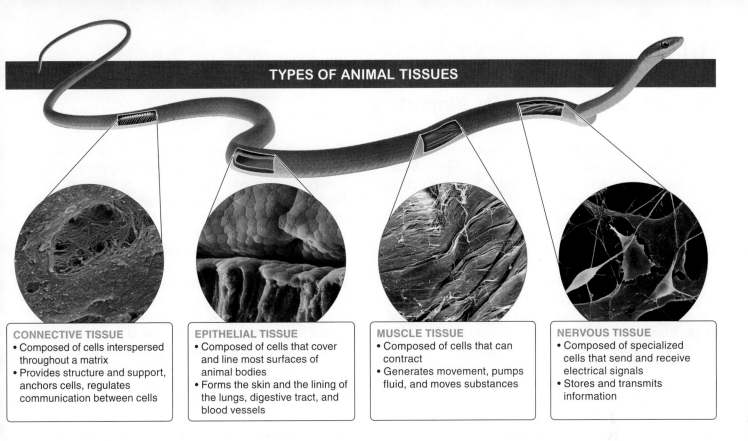

TYPES OF ANIMAL TISSUES

CONNECTIVE TISSUE
- Composed of cells interspersed throughout a matrix
- Provides structure and support, anchors cells, regulates communication between cells

EPITHELIAL TISSUE
- Composed of cells that cover and line most surfaces of animal bodies
- Forms the skin and the lining of the lungs, digestive tract, and blood vessels

MUSCLE TISSUE
- Composed of cells that can contract
- Generates movement, pumps fluid, and moves substances

NERVOUS TISSUE
- Composed of specialized cells that send and receive electrical signals
- Stores and transmits information

FIGURE 20-17 Tissues perform specific functions in the body.

Muscle tissue is made up of cells that can contract. This characteristic gives muscle tissue the ability to generate movement or pump fluids through the body.

Nervous tissue, found throughout the human body, is specialized to send and receive electrical signals and, in doing so, can store and transmit information. The brain and spinal cord are made up of large amounts of nervous tissue.

Just as cells with similar functions are grouped into tissues, so tissues are often grouped into organs or organ systems. **Organs** are structures that serve specialized functions, and they usually contain several types of tissue. The heart, liver, kidneys, and brain are examples of organs in the human body. Most organs—including the stomach and the small intestine, for example—have all four types of tissue. **Organ systems** are groups of organs that work together to accomplish one or a few, usually related, physiological functions. The circulatory system, for example, includes the heart, blood vessels, and blood.

In the remaining chapters of the book, we explore the complex functions carried out by each of the organ systems in animals. We describe the structures that are part of each system, how they function, and how they have evolved. As we do this, we see that an organism is greater than the sum of its parts. The working together of cells to form tissues, and of tissues to form organs and organ systems, gives multicellular organisms the abilities to reproduce, defend themselves, and communicate (among many other abilities), in ways that are not possible for a single cell or a single type of tissue.

TAKE-HOME MESSAGE 20·7

Animal bodies are highly organized, and at all levels of organization, the physical features are closely related to function. In most animals, cells with similar structure and function are organized into tissues. There are four types of tissue: connective tissue, epithelial tissue, muscle tissue, and nervous tissue. Tissues are often organized into organs, which serve specialized functions and can contain several types of tissue. In turn, organs can be organized into organ systems that accomplish highly complex tasks.

20•8

Connective tissue provides support.

Connective tissue is usually the most abundant type of tissue in an animal. Connective tissue is sometimes called "cellular glue," because it holds cells together and, as bone and cartilage, for example, gives shape, structure, and support to other tissues, structures, and organs throughout the body. Connective tissue, however, isn't restricted to supporting roles; it also includes tissues such as fat cells and blood.

Regardless of the function it performs or the form it takes, all connective tissue consists of cells that are embedded in matrix—a mass of non-living extracellular material (**FIGURE 20-18**). Matrix, in vertebrates, consists chiefly of polysaccharides and protein (and some minerals, in the case of bone), which are produced and secreted by various cells within the matrix. The matrix can be liquid, jelly-like, or solid. With the exception of blood, all connective tissue contains cells called *fibroblasts,* which produce and secrete the matrix proteins **collagen** and **elastin.** So common is connective tissue that collagen, which often forms a sort of net surrounding organs, is the most abundant protein in humans and other mammals.

CONNECTIVE TISSUE STRUCTURE

Connective tissue is a collection of cells arranged within an extracellular matrix that gives shape, structure, and support to other body tissues.

FIBROBLASTS
Cells that produce and secrete the proteins collagen and elastin (present in every type of connective tissue except blood)

MATRIX
A non-living, extracellular mass of protein fibers and surrounding liquid, jelly-like, or solid material
• Collagen protein
• Elastin protein
• Surrounding material

FIGURE 20-18 Connective tissues consist of cells embedded in an extracellular matrix.

Connective tissue proper functions much like packing material. It can be loose or dense. In loose connective tissue, the cells are in a semi-fluid, flexible matrix that generally has many fibers, usually collagen, embedded in it (**FIGURE 20-19**). Loose connective tissue includes the soft padding under your skin, the tissue surrounding most organs, and adipose (fat) tissue, which aids in cushioning, lubricating, and insulating other tissues. Dense connective tissue is stronger than loose connective tissue. It also has collagen as its chief matrix element, but it has many more, tightly packed collagen fibers than loose connective tissue. Examples of dense connective tissue include **tendons,** which connect muscle to bone, and **ligaments,** which bind bone to bone. A sprained ankle is a common injury in which a twisting of the ankle overstretches and tears part of a ligament in the foot.

What is a sprained ankle?

The second type of connective tissue, called **special connective tissue,** includes bone, cartilage, and blood (see Figure 20-19). In these tissues, the matrix differs from that of connective tissue proper in that it is rigid or liquid. In **bone,** the mineral calcium is incorporated into the extracellular matrix, which then hardens into a solid material. Bones can give significant protection to organisms (the skull protects the brain, ribs protect the lungs and heart) or can provide structural support, as the backbone does. **Cartilage,** a dense connective tissue with an extracellular matrix rich in collagen, elastin, and proteins bound to long carbohydrate chains, has a hardness between that of bone and of tendons. Strong, but also flexible, cartilage is found in the ears and tip of the nose in humans, and it cushions the bones in joints throughout the body. In some organisms, including sharks, the entire skeleton is made of cartilage. **Blood** is unique among the connective tissues because it has a liquid extracellular matrix. This liquid matrix, called plasma, is made up mostly of water, but also contains dissolved proteins, sugars, and other molecules. Blood cells, including red blood cells and white blood cells, and the cellular fragments called platelets (see Chapter 21), are suspended within plasma as they transport gases and other substances throughout the body.

All connective tissues in the body, as we've seen, have essentially the same structure: cells embedded within an extracellular matrix that may be solid, soft and flexible, or

The Internal Environment | How Does Homeostasis Work? | Form Reflects Function

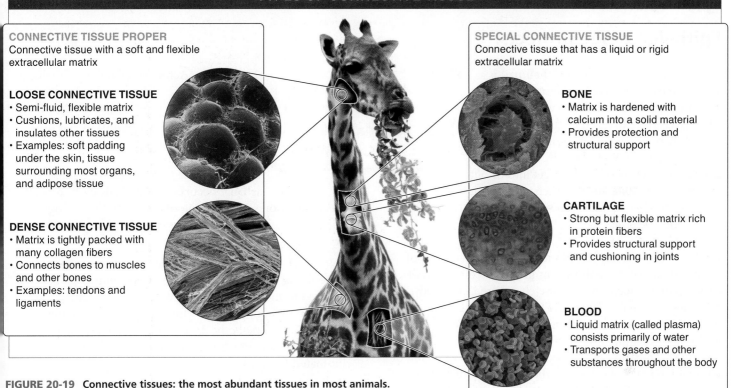

CONNECTIVE TISSUE PROPER
Connective tissue with a soft and flexible extracellular matrix

LOOSE CONNECTIVE TISSUE
- Semi-fluid, flexible matrix
- Cushions, lubricates, and insulates other tissues
- Examples: soft padding under the skin, tissue surrounding most organs, and adipose tissue

DENSE CONNECTIVE TISSUE
- Matrix is tightly packed with many collagen fibers
- Connects bones to muscles and other bones
- Examples: tendons and ligaments

SPECIAL CONNECTIVE TISSUE
Connective tissue that has a liquid or rigid extracellular matrix

BONE
- Matrix is hardened with calcium into a solid material
- Provides protection and structural support

CARTILAGE
- Strong but flexible matrix rich in protein fibers
- Provides structural support and cushioning in joints

BLOOD
- Liquid matrix (called plasma) consists primarily of water
- Transports gases and other substances throughout the body

FIGURE 20-19 Connective tissues: the most abundant tissues in most animals.

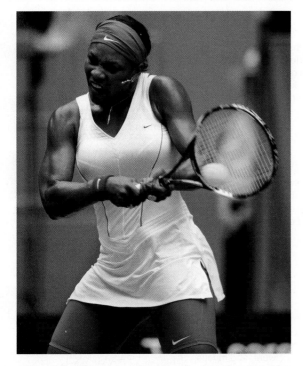

Most activities rely heavily on connective tissue, often in conjunction with muscle tissue. Playing tennis, for example, relies on blood to deliver oxygen to muscle, tendons that connect muscles to bones, and cartilage, cushioning the joints. (Collagen from the intestines of cows is even used as a material for producing the strings in some tennis rackets!)

fluid. An inflammation or weakness in any of the types of connective tissue, particularly problems with the maintenance of collagen, is the cause of many diseases with widespread effects, including scleroderma and Marfan syndrome. The most common type of arthritis, osteoarthritis, results from the breakdown of connective tissue, usually the cartilage, around joints. The reduced cushioning often leads to inflammation of tissue around the joint, with stiffness and pain, and is commonly treated with anti-inflammatory drugs including aspirin and ibuprofen.

Q The most common form of arthritis is called "wear and tear" arthritis. Why?

TAKE-HOME MESSAGE 20·8

The most abundant type of tissue in most animals is connective tissue. Connective tissue is a collection of cells arranged within an extracellular matrix, usually containing collagen, that holds the cells together and gives shape, structure, and support to other body tissues. Examples of connective tissue include tendons, ligaments, fat, blood, bone, and cartilage.

Epithelial tissue protects.

Epithelial tissue (also called **epithelium**) is a sheet-like tissue that covers the surfaces of an animal's body. It is made up of a single layer or a few layers of cells, called epithelial cells, that are tightly bound together so that fluids and gases must pass through the cells, rather than around or between the cells, to get into or out of the body (**FIGURE 20-20**). When you look at a vertebrate, most of what you see is epithelium, because skin is an epithelial tissue.

Epithelial tissue is not just found on the outer surfaces of organisms, however. It also forms **glands**—collections of cells producing secretions for use elsewhere in the body—and lines the internal tubes and cavities of the body, such as the stomach and intestine, lungs, and blood vessels. In each location, epithelium always has two distinctive sides. The "outside" can be in contact with the outside of the body or with an internal cavity such as the stomach, where it plays a protective role. The "inside" (or underside) faces away from the surface and is generally secured to underlying tissues. Epithelium plays multiple roles in organisms. Three of its most important functions are protection, transport, and secretion (**FIGURE 20-21**).

> **Q** Damage to the lining of the stomach can have painful consequences. Why?

1. *Protection.* Acting as a barrier, epithelial cells are linked closely by tight junctions and desmosomes (see Section 3–12), which keep fluids from leaking into or out of tissue. If the strong acids in the stomach, for example, were to leak out, they would seriously damage surrounding tissue. This is what occurs in individuals with stomach ulcers, open sores in the lining of the stomach. The tight fit between epithelial cells is also why the skin of terrestrial vertebrates is usually waterproof.

2. *Transport.* Epithelium forms small finger-like projections in the lining of the small intestine, where nutrients are absorbed from digested food into the bloodstream. In blood vessels, epithelium controls which molecules can enter other tissues of the body. And in the kidneys, epithelium helps to regulate which molecules from the bloodstream are eliminated with urine.

EPITHELIAL TISSUE

Epithelial tissue covers the surfaces of an animal's body. It consists of a single layer or a few layers of cells that are tightly bound together, and acts as a barrier between the inside and outside of an organism, and around body cavities and organs.

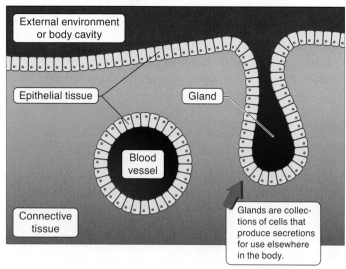

- External environment or body cavity
- Epithelial tissue
- Gland
- Blood vessel
- Connective tissue
- Glands are collections of cells that produce secretions for use elsewhere in the body.

FIGURE 20-20 Epithelial tissue forms with two distinct sides.

FUNCTIONS OF EPITHELIAL TISSUE

PROTECTION
Epithelial tissue acts as a barrier between the inside and outside of an organism and keeps fluids from leaking into or out of tissue.

- Inside stomach
- Stomach acid
- Surrounding tissue

TRANSPORT
Epithelial tissue regulates the movement of nutrients and other molecules into and out of body tissues.

- Blood vessel
- Oxygen
- Carbon dioxide
- Muscle tissue

SECRETION
Epithelial tissue can form exocrine glands, which secrete products such as saliva, sweat, and mucus, and endocrine glands, which secrete hormones.

- Saliva
- Salivary gland

FIGURE 20-21 The multiple roles of epithelial tissue.

The Internal Environment   How Does Homeostasis Work?   ▼ Form Reflects Function

3. *Secretion.* Epithelium can also form glands. **Exocrine glands** generally secrete products—including earwax, sweat, saliva, milk, mucus, and, in the case of some frogs, toxic poisons—onto the surface of the epithelium. **Endocrine glands,** on the other hand, produce hormones, chemical messengers that affect cells elsewhere in the body, which are released into the fluid surrounding the glands and usually enter the bloodstream for distribution to other parts of the body.

Because epithelial cells are often in contact with a large variety of materials, they tend to experience more damage than other tissues. For this reason, they tend not to last long and are replaced frequently. Human skin cells, for example, are replaced approximately every two weeks. (Dandruff is mostly dead skin cells.) Cells lining the digestive tract have an even shorter life span, lasting only about five days. Liver epithelium experiences slightly less wear and tear, lasting a year or two before replacement.

TAKE-HOME MESSAGE 20·9

Epithelium is a very thin, sheet-like tissue that covers most of the exterior and interior surfaces of an animal's body. Made up of a single layer or a few layers of cells that are tightly bound together, epithelium acts as a barrier between the inside and outside of an organism. It also can be specialized to aid in the secretion and transport of molecules.

20·10

Muscle tissue enables movement.

Most animals move. And muscle tissue, made up of elongated cells capable of generating force by contracting, is responsible for much of that movement. Most muscle tissue cells are packed with protein filaments that slide together as they break down ATP, causing the entire cell to shorten and thus the muscle to contract. The action of muscle cells, which is usually stimulated by nerve cells, enables organisms to generate force and motion. There are three types of muscle tissue: skeletal, cardiac, and smooth muscles (**FIGURE 20-22**).

Skeletal muscle (sometimes called voluntary muscle) is usually attached to bones and is responsible for generating most movement we see in animals, including facial expressions and breathing. Muscles account for about 40% of human body

TYPES OF MUSCLE TISSUE

SKELETAL MUSCLE
• Generates most of the movement seen in animals
• Under both conscious and unconscious control

CARDIAC MUSCLE
• Muscle in the heart that pumps blood through the body
• Under unconscious control

SMOOTH MUSCLE
• Generates slow, rhythmic contractions that can gradually move blood, food, or other substances through the body
• Under unconscious control and can generate contractions without nervous stimulation

FIGURE 20-22 Muscle tissues are made up of elongated cells capable of generating force when they contract.

weight. Individual skeletal muscle cells, called **muscle fibers,** are very long and contain multiple nuclei, and the repeating units of protein filaments in the cells give the fibers a striped, or striated, appearance. Skeletal muscles are controlled by the nervous system, and the individual nerve cells (neurons) attached to each muscle fiber stimulate its contraction. Skeletal muscles can be under conscious control, such as when you choose to flex your biceps, or unconscious control, such as those that control breathing or moving your eyes around.

Cardiac muscle, as the name indicates, is located only in the heart, and it causes the heart to pump blood through the body. Take a look at the large colorized photo that opens this chapter. You will see capillaries passing among the muscle fibers of the heart. Because of the tremendous amount of energy that cardiac muscles use, contracting incessantly throughout our life, the cells contain many more mitochondria than other types of muscle cells. The cells of heart muscle are fused together and connected by gap junctions (see Section 3-12). The electrical signals that initiate each contraction of the cardiac muscle pass through these gap junctions. Cardiac muscle tissue is not under conscious control.

Smooth muscle is found in the walls surrounding blood vessels, the stomach and intestines, bladder, and many other organs and inner "tubes" within the body. Smooth muscle generates slow, rhythmic contractions that can gradually move blood, food, or other substances through the tube. Not under conscious control, smooth muscle is regulated by other physiological systems and can generate contractions without nervous stimulation.

TAKE-HOME MESSAGE 20·10

Muscle tissue consists of elongated cells capable of generating force when they contract. Skeletal muscle is responsible for generating most of the movement we see in animals. Cardiac muscle causes the heart to pump blood through the body. And smooth muscle, surrounding blood vessels and many internal organs, generates slower contractions that can gradually move blood, food, or other substances.

20·11

Nervous tissue transmits information.

The fourth type of animal tissue is nervous tissue, specialized to store and transmit information. It is responsible for much of the communication that occurs within an animal's body. Nervous tissue enables animals to sense and respond to stimuli such as the smell of food, the sight, smell, or sounds of a predator or a potential mate, or the heat of a fire.

There are two types of nervous tissue cells: neurons and glial cells (**FIGURE 20-23**). **Neurons** are the "excitable" cells that receive and transmit a signal. Neurons have three distinctive elements: dendrites, a cell body, and an axon. **Dendrites** are a bit like an antenna system, specialized for receiving signals from the external environment or from other neurons. The **cell body** contains the nucleus and other cellular machinery found in eukaryotic cells. And the **axon** is a single projection that transmits impulses away from the cell body and can extend over very long distances—sometimes 3 feet (1 m) or more!

Glial cells, also called **neuroglia,** are like the support staff to neurons. They do not carry signals but assist and nourish neurons. There are numerous types of glial cells, and they vastly outnumber neurons. Together, the various types of glial cells produce insulation for neurons, protect and regulate the chemical environment around neurons, hold

STRUCTURE OF NERVOUS TISSUE

Nerve tissue is responsible for much of the communication that occurs within an animal. There are two types of nervous tissue: neurons and glial cells.

— External signal

NEURONS
Cells that can receive and transmit signals. They are composed of three distinct elements:

• **DENDRITES**
Receive signals from the external environment or from other neurons

• **CELL BODY**
Contains the nucleus and other cellular machinery

• **AXON**
A single projection from the cell body that transmits impulses away from the cell body

GLIAL CELLS (NEUROGLIA)
Assist neurons by insulating, protecting, and regulating their chemical environment, holding them in place, destroying pathogens, and providing nutrients and oxygen

FIGURE 20-23 Neuron and glial cells.

The Internal Environment　　　How Does Homeostasis Work?　　　Form Reflects Function

In vertebrates, the nervous system is divided into the central nervous system and the peripheral nervous system.

CENTRAL NERVOUS SYSTEM
Composed of cells (including neurons) of the brain and spinal cord.

PERIPHERAL NERVOUS SYSTEM
Composed of sensory and motor neurons and associated glial cells.

Brain

Spinal cord

Neurons

FIGURE 20-24 **The vertebrate nervous system: brain, spinal cord, and neurons.**

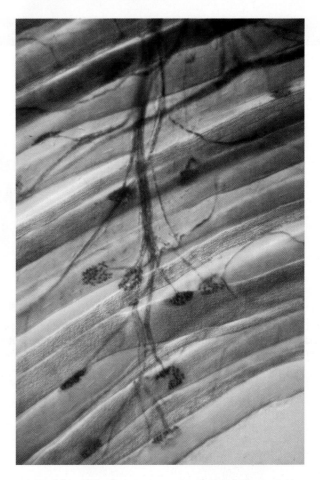

Motor neurons of the peripheral nervous system convey signals that can initiate contractions (and movement) in muscle cells.

the neurons in place, destroy pathogens, and provide nutrients and oxygen.

All of the nervous tissue of an organism makes up its nervous system (**FIGURE 20-24**). In vertebrates, the nervous system is divided into the **central nervous system,** which includes the brain and spinal cord, and the **peripheral nervous system,** which includes the sensory neurons that detect a stimulus and the neurons that transmit signals to the muscles and glands of an organism in response to that stimulus. (The nervous system is discussed in detail in Chapter 23.)

TAKE-HOME MESSAGE 20·11

Nervous tissue is specialized to store and transmit information. There are two types of nervous tissue cells: neurons, which can receive and transmit a signal, and glial cells, which assist and provide nutrients for neurons.

20·12

Each organ system performs special tasks.

With the exception of sponges and some cnidarians, all animals have some tissues that are organized into organs—structures such as the heart, brain, lungs, and liver—that serve specialized functions and consist of multiple tissue types. And just as cells make up tissues and tissues make up organs, organs, too, are part of larger functional units, the organ systems, which carry out the various physiological

processes necessary for the growth, development, maintenance, and reproduction of organisms.

We briefly describe 11 animal organ systems in **FIGURE 20-25**, and we'll discuss them in greater detail in Chapters 21–26. It's important to keep in mind that these systems do not operate in isolation: in carrying out its tasks, each system not only

DIGESTIVE SYSTEM
Disassembles and absorbs food so the body
can acquire the nutrients it needs to function

CIRCULATORY SYSTEM
Transports nutrients and respiratory gases to the
tissues and eliminates wastes from the tissues

RESPIRATORY SYSTEM
Provides a site for gas exchange between
the external environment and an organism's
circulatory system

REPRODUCTIVE SYSTEM (MALE)
Produces sperm and delivers it to the female
reproductive system, where fertilization may
occur

REPRODUCTIVE SYSTEM (FEMALE)
Produces eggs and provides an environment
that can nurture a developing embryo and
fetus, if fertilization occurs

NERVOUS SYSTEM
Acts as the control center of the body and
interprets, stores, and transmits information
using electrical impulses and chemical signals

FIGURE 20-25 The major organ systems of animals.

depends on the proper functioning of one or more of the
other systems, but often influences the functioning of other
systems. The act of running, for example, might be initiated
when the *nervous system* detects a threat and sends impulses to
the *musculoskeletal system* (which causes the body to move), to
the *respiratory system* (which increases the rate of oxygen
consumption), and to the *circulatory system* (which increases
the rate at which the heart pumps blood and thus increases
the oxygen available to muscle tissue). Even though these
11 systems constantly add, modify, and remove substances in
the body, the body maintains a consistent internal
environment through homeostasis.

The Internal Environment   How Does Homeostasis Work?   Form Reflects Function

IMMUNE AND LYMPHATIC SYSTEM
Attacks pathogens that threaten the body and plays a supporting role in circulation by recycling fluid that leaks from the circulatory system

URINARY/EXCRETORY SYSTEM
Purifies the blood by filtering out wastes and transports wastes out of the body

ENDOCRINE SYSTEM
Regulates body activities by releasing hormones that travel through vessels in the circulatory system to reach target cells

Hair
Skin
Nails

INTEGUMENTARY SYSTEM
Provides protection by forming a barrier between the inside and outside of an organism and can aid in the secretion and transport of molecules

SKELETAL SYSTEM
Supports and protects the body and internal organs, manufactures blood cells, and provides a surface for muscle attachment, creating a foundation for movement

MUSCULAR SYSTEM
Generates force through contraction, which enables movement of the body and of blood, food, and other substances throughout the body

As we explore organ systems in more detail in the following chapters, we will pay particular attention to the ways in which the form and function of the systems' components are intimately related and what this relationship reveals about how these systems (and the organisms of which they are a part) evolved.

TAKE-HOME MESSAGE 20·12

In nearly all animals, some tissues are organized into organs (such as the heart, brain, lungs, and liver) that serve specialized functions and consist of multiple tissue types, and into organ systems (such as the circulatory system) that carry out the various physiological processes necessary for the growth, development, maintenance, and reproduction of the organism.

streetBio

Knowledge You Can Use

Your body sometimes deliberately upsets homeostasis. (And you might not want to fight it.)

Q: What do you usually do when you have a fever? At the first sign of fever, many people take aspirin, Tylenol, Advil, or Motrin.

Q: What is the result? Aspirin, acetaminophen (Tylenol), and ibuprofen (Advil and Motrin) quickly reduce a fever.

Q: Why did you have a fever? Generally, fever is not itself an illness. Rather, it is your body's response to cues that there is a bacterial or viral infection. In response to infection, your temperature set point is raised, because pathogens are more easily brought under control by the body's defenses at higher temperatures. (Ectotherms use a similar strategy, moving to warmer areas when they have an infection!)

Q: How does reducing a fever interfere with your body's defenses? Blocking a fever by taking aspirin or other medication may reduce your body's ability to fight infection. A recent well-controlled study demonstrated, for example, that chicken pox lasts longer, on average, when aspirin is used to treat it, compared with placebo.

Q: Is the lesson here about more than fever? Yes. There are other "symptoms" of infection that, as defenses rather than part of the illness itself, maybe shouldn't be fought. For example: (1) *Coughing:* the use of codeine to block coughing after surgery increases the risk of pneumonia; the coughing is *helpful.* (2) *Diarrhea:* anti-diarrhea medications delay recovery and slow the eradication of bacteria from the digestive tract; the diarrhea is *helpful.* (3) *Vomiting* and *inflammation,* too, appear to be important parts of our evolved defenses and, as such, blocking them can have serious health consequences.

What can you conclude? Is this the dawn of Darwinian medicine? This new perspective on when to treat and when not to treat symptoms is called "Darwinian medicine." It represents a newfound appreciation for the fact that organisms have evolved many protective responses that may be useful. Of course, suffering is not always the solution. There can be real costs to vomiting, diarrhea, coughing, fever, and other body defenses. Opting not to treat them isn't necessarily the best solution if, for example, antibiotics can bring an infection under control easily. Either way, bringing an evolutionary perspective to medical decision making can be valuable.

1 Animals have an internal environment.

Failure to maintain a consistent internal environment can lead to multiple problems in the normal functioning of cells, tissues, and organs, and can result in death. Organisms maintain a variety of internal physiological variables, including temperature, water-solute balances, pH, blood sugar levels, and blood gas concentrations, within relatively constant ranges. The process of maintaining an organism's internal environment is called homeostasis.

2 How does homeostasis work?

Organisms generally maintain homeostasis through negative feedback, in which sensors detect a change in the internal environment and trigger structures, called effectors, to oppose or reduce the change. For animals to maintain homeostasis, the variable must have a set point, a target value or range to which the organism can return. Methods for controlling temperature, blood sugar levels, and water and solute concentrations, among many other variables, are important components of homeostasis. To maintain osmotic balance, organisms must be able to take up water and get rid of water, and must also be able to regulate concentrations of ions in their fluids. The kidney is the organ in vertebrates that helps maintain homeostasis by regulating water balance and solute concentration in body fluids, filtering blood, and enabling the removal of potentially harmful ions and metabolic waste products in urine.

3 Form reflects function: animal anatomy.

At all levels of animal organization, from molecules to whole organisms, the physical features of a structure are closely related to its function. Cells with similar structure and function are organized into groups, called tissues, that work together. There are four types of tissue: connective tissue, epithelial tissue, muscle tissue, and nervous tissue. In nearly all animals, some tissues are organized into organs that serve specialized functions and consist of multiple tissue types, and into organ systems that carry out the various physiological processes necessary for the growth, development, maintenance, and reproduction of organisms.

KEY TERMS

1. The term "homeostasis" describes:
   a) the body's use of physical and chemical processes to maintain a consistent internal environment.
   b) the biochemical processes associated with the maintenance of body temperature.
   c) the metabolic patterns of active (versus stationary) animals.
   d) the metabolic patterns of stationary (versus active) animals.
   e) the health benefits of a sedentary lifestyle.

2. Interstitial fluid:
   a) is found exclusively within the spinal cord, surrounding the nerve bundles.
   b) is found exclusively within the skull, surrounding the brain.
   c) is mostly water.
   d) is found exclusively within the skull and spinal cord, surrounding nervous tissue.
   e) occurs within the organelles of all eukaryotic cells.

3. Negative feedback loops:
   a) generally lead to highly unstable internal physiological conditions.
   b) cause internal conditions to deviate from the normal range.
   c) are part of larger, positive feedback systems.
   d) rely on sensors to trigger effectors to alter an organism's internal environment.
   e) None of the above.

4. A set point:
   a) is the target value or range for a physiological variable, to which it generally returns following perturbation.
   b) is a physiological state that occurs in animals called "conformers," but not in "regulators."
   c) can occur in fishes but not in terrestrial animals.
   d) is the target value or range for a physiological variable regulated through positive feedback, but not negative feedback.
   e) Both a) and c) are correct.

5. It is not necessarily accurate to refer to endotherms as "warm-blooded," because:
   a) some endotherms allow their body temperature to drop significantly during hibernation.
   b) on average, their body temperature is colder than that of "cold-blooded" animals.
   c) they generate their heat primarily from within their own bodies.
   d) most do not actually have blood in their bodies.
   e) some are homeotherms rather than heterotherms.

6. "Form follows function" refers to the fact that:
   a) organisms' physical structures often are adaptations, shaped by natural selection, and so reflect their physiological functions.
   b) organisms' physical structures generally come to reflect their physiological function only *after* that function has been fine-tuned by evolution.
   c) natural selection can produce adaptations in physical structures but not in physiological processes.
   d) natural selection can produce adaptations in physiological processes but not in physical structures.
   e) all structures that have the same function also have the same structure.

7. Which of the following is not a type of connective tissue?
   a) bone   d) collagen
   b) cartilage   e) ligament
   c) blood

8. Epithelium plays all of the following roles in organisms except:
   a) secretion.
   b) transport.
   c) protection.
   d) preventing fluids from leaking from an organ system into surrounding tissue.
   e) cushioning, lubricating, and insulating other tissue.

9. Smooth muscle:
   a) is usually attached to bones.
   b) generates slow, rhythmic contractions.
   c) is usually under conscious control.
   d) generally contains more mitochondria than cardiac or skeletal muscle.
   e) All of the above are correct.

10. Neurons generally have all of the following components except:
   a) dendrites.
   b) a cell body.
   c) an axon.
   d) glial processes.
   e) a nucleus.

11. With the exception of _____, all animals have some tissues organized into organs.
   a) sponges and some cnidarians
   b) insects
   c) roundworms and flatworms
   d) sponges and insects
   e) amphibians

Short-Answer Questions

1. What is homeostasis? How does hyperthermia illustrate the failure of the body to maintain homeostasis? What are the potential consequences of this failure?

2. What is the hierarchical organization of cells in a multicellular organism? Name the four types of tissue they form and note their general functions.

3. What are the two kinds of connective tissue? What are their general characteristics?

4. What are the three types of muscle tissue? What are their general characteristics?

See Appendix for answers. For additional study questions, go to www.prep-u.com.

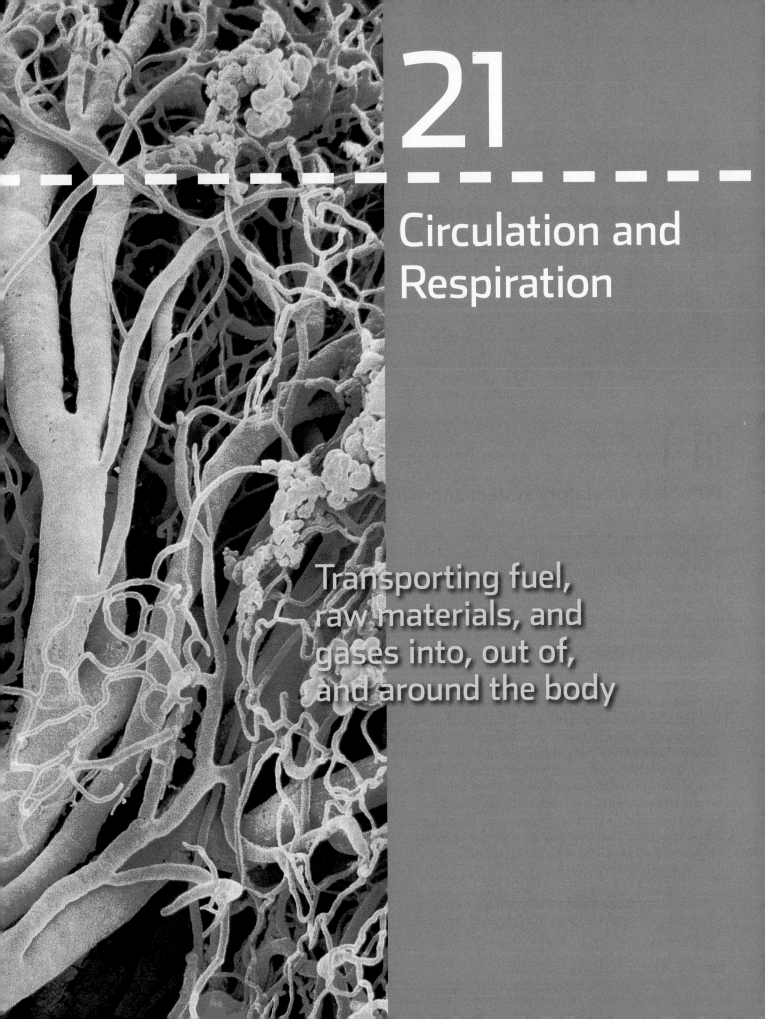

21

Circulation and Respiration

Transporting fuel,
raw materials, and
gases into, out of,
and around the body

① The circulatory system is the chief route of distribution in animals.

The swiftness of the hare and greyhound depend on efficient circulatory systems.

21•1

What is a circulatory system and why is one needed?

Size matters. When life first arose on earth, the tiny, single-celled organisms were small enough to acquire the fuel and raw materials they needed in a straightforward way: those materials could simply diffuse across the cell membrane and be used as needed. Similarly, metabolic waste products could diffuse out of the cell. Today, single-celled organisms and small multicellular organisms in which all cells are in contact with (or just a few cells away from) the external environment acquire raw materials and dispose of metabolic waste in this same way.

The evolution of large body sizes opened up a world of new niches in which organisms could exist. Physiologically, however, large body sizes created a host of new challenges. Many of these challenges resulted from the fact that with increasing size, most of an animal's cells are no longer in direct contact with the outside world, the environment from which the animal obtains oxygen, nutrients, water, and other substances it needs to survive. Consequently, these substances can no longer just diffuse in, and the waste an animal generates can no longer diffuse out. As body size increased, dedicated delivery and removal systems became a necessity.

In animals, the primary distribution system is the circulatory system. Like a system of highways for delivering important goods and removing garbage, the circulatory system reaches all tissues of the body. In vertebrates, circulatory systems have three principal functions: transport, body temperature regulation, and protection (**FIGURE 21-1**).

1. Transport. The circulatory system transports oxygen, nutrients, waste products, hormones, and immune system cells in the blood throughout the body.

- In vertebrates, blood vessels take oxygen from the lungs or gills and deliver it to the tissues for energy-releasing cellular respiration. Blood that comes from the lungs or gills is loaded with oxygen and is said to be oxygenated or oxygen-rich.

- Simultaneously, blood vessels whisk away carbon dioxide and other metabolic wastes that are produced in cellular respiration and other cell processes and must be removed from the body. Blood that carries a lot of carbon dioxide is said to be deoxygenated or oxygen-poor.

- Once food particles are digested, the nutrients must be absorbed and delivered to all the tissues of the body, for activity, growth, and reproduction.

Circulatory Systems   Human Circulation   Gas Exchange   Hemoglobin and Myoglobin

FUNCTIONS OF THE CIRCULATORY SYSTEM

Among vertebrates, circulatory systems have three principal functions.

TRANSPORT
The circulatory system transports oxygen, nutrients, waste products, immune system cells, and hormones in the blood throughout the body.

TEMPERATURE REGULATION
The circulatory system helps to maintain body temperature within the optimum range for metabolic functioning.

PROTECTION
The circulatory system contains a variety of cells and chemicals that contribute to the individual's defenses against infection by pathogens.

FIGURE 21-1 Like a set of highways for the body. Circulatory system functions: transport, temperature regulation and protection.

- The circulatory system delivers hormones (chemicals produced throughout the body by glands and other tissues) to target tissues to regulate growth, development, and reproduction.

2. Body temperature regulation. By expanding or contracting the blood vessels closest to the exterior of the body, animals can absorb or release heat, a process that helps them maintain their body temperature within the optimum range for metabolism.

3. Protection. A variety of cells and chemicals contribute to the individual's defenses against infection by pathogens. White blood cells, or leukocytes, have the ability to engulf and destroy many disease-causing microorganisms. Platelets and certain chemicals in the blood also provide protection by limiting blood loss and infection when the skin or other tissues are damaged.

TAKE-HOME MESSAGE 21·1

In animals, the circulatory system is the chief distribution system. It transports gases, nutrients, waste products, hormones, and immune system cells throughout the body. The circulatory system also helps animals regulate their body temperature and plays a protective role against infection.

21·2

Circulatory systems can be open or closed.

There's more than one way to build a circulatory system. And, in fact, not all multicellular organisms even need a circulatory system. In spite of their relatively large size and multicellularity, for example, flatworms, as well as jellyfish and other cnidarians, have a body plan that gives every cell easy access to oxygen and nutrients through simple diffusion (**FIGURE 21-2**). This access is possible because every cell is close to the external surface of the cnidarian's body or to its internal gastrovascular cavity. Although the gastrovascular cavity is not a true circulatory system, it serves many digestive ("gastro") and circulatory ("vascular") functions by directing water into the central mouth and through an elaborate system of channels. Cells lining the mouth and the channels can absorb nutrients and exchange gases by diffusion. The nutrients then diffuse to other cells, none of which are very far away. Once nutrients have been extracted (and waste

products picked up), fluid in the gastrovascular cavity is flushed back out of the mouth, and the process is repeated.

Among other multicellular animals, there are two distinct types of circulatory systems: open and closed (**FIGURE 21-3**). Open circulatory systems are found in insects and most molluscs, while closed circulatory systems are found in all vertebrates. The defining feature of an **open circulatory system** is that it has one fluid, called **hemolymph,** that both circulates to transport nutrients, gases, and waste products and also surrounds each cell in the body. In other words, there is no clear distinction between the circulating fluid and the interstitial fluid, the fluid that is outside the cells and bathes all the tissue of the body. There is a heart (or sometimes many hearts!) that pumps the hemolymph, but it essentially squirts the fluid throughout the extracellular spaces. Large collecting

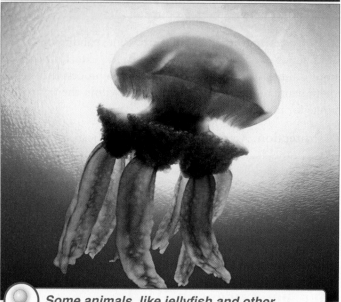

> Some animals, like jellyfish and other cnidarians, do not have circulatory systems. Instead, they obtain oxygen and nutrients, and eliminate waste, through diffusion.

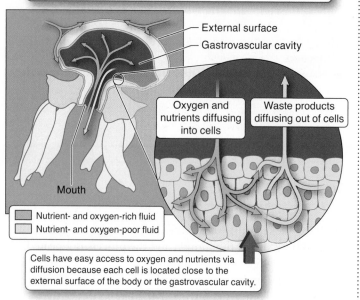

External surface
Gastrovascular cavity

Oxygen and nutrients diffusing into cells

Waste products diffusing out of cells

Mouth

Nutrient- and oxygen-rich fluid
Nutrient- and oxygen-poor fluid

Cells have easy access to oxygen and nutrients via diffusion because each cell is located close to the external surface of the body or the gastrovascular cavity.

FIGURE 21-2 No circulatory system required. The cells of jellyfish and other cnidarians can acquire nutrients and oxygen from the environment through direct diffusion.

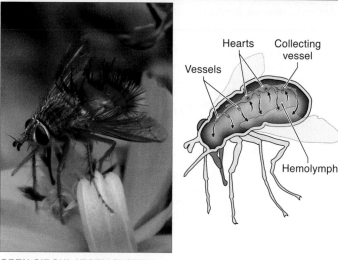

Hearts   Collecting vessel
Vessels

Hemolymph

OPEN CIRCULATORY SYSTEM
- No clear distinction between the circulating fluid and interstitial fluid
- Heart(s) pump the fluid mixture—called hemolymph—throughout the extracellular spaces inside the body
- Occurs in insects and most molluscs

Vessels

Heart

CLOSED CIRCULATORY SYSTEM
- Blood is contained within vessels that separate it from interstitial fluid
- Muscular heart propels blood through vessels to tissues throughout the body
- Occurs in all vertebrates

FIGURE 21-3 There are open and closed circulatory systems.

vessels then channel the hemolymph back to the heart, where it can be pumped throughout the body again. These collecting vessels have little valves that close when the heart pumps to prevent the hemolymph from being pumped back through the same vessel from which it was collected. This one-way collection system gives some order to the circulation of the hemolymph fluid throughout the organism's body.

In **closed circulatory systems,** the circulating fluid—called **blood**—is always contained in a vessel as it is pumped throughout the animal's body, and it is physically and chemically separated from the interstitial fluid that bathes each cell. A muscular **heart** serves as a pump, and with each contraction it propels blood at high pressure through vessels called **arteries.** Like a highway system with numerous exits

Circulatory Systems   Human Circulation   Gas Exchange   Hemoglobin and Myoglobin

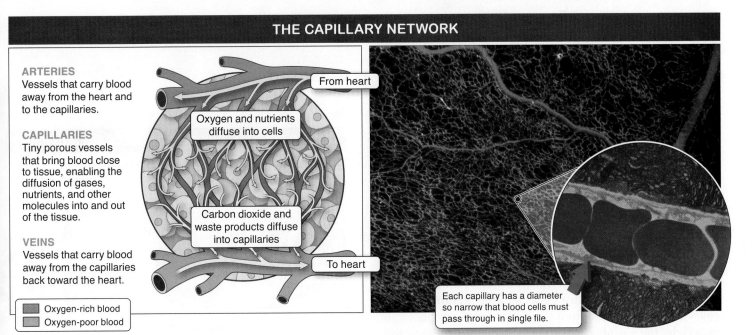

THE CAPILLARY NETWORK

ARTERIES
Vessels that carry blood away from the heart and to the capillaries.

CAPILLARIES
Tiny porous vessels that bring blood close to tissue, enabling the diffusion of gases, nutrients, and other molecules into and out of the tissue.

VEINS
Vessels that carry blood away from the capillaries back toward the heart.

- Oxygen-rich blood
- Oxygen-poor blood

From heart

Oxygen and nutrients diffuse into cells

Carbon dioxide and waste products diffuse into capillaries

To heart

Each capillary has a diameter so narrow that blood cells must pass through in single file.

FIGURE 21-4 Arteries, capillaries, and veins: the three types of blood vessels in a closed circulatory system.

and connecting roads, the arteries branch extensively so that blood can be delivered to all the tissues of the body.

At the organs and tissues, arteries branch into thousands upon thousands of ever-smaller vessels, first the arterioles and then, as they become much narrower and thinner-walled, the **capillaries.** Each capillary has an inner diameter so narrow that blood cells must pass through in single file. The capillary wall is thin—just one layer of wall cells—and somewhat porous, so the diffusion of gases, nutrients, and other molecules into and out of the tissue, down their concentration gradients, readily occurs (**FIGURE 21-4**).

The network of capillaries in an organism is staggeringly large—more than 50,000 miles in an adult human! And this number is constantly in flux: gaining a single pound of fat, for example, is accompanied by the addition of more than a mile of new capillaries.

Capillaries are the last branch of the circulatory system to carry nutrients and oxygen-rich blood to cells of the body, but they are also the first branch to carry nutrient-poor, carbon-dioxide-rich, and waste-product-rich blood back from cells of the body toward the heart. After passing through the capillaries, blood returns to the heart in vessels called **veins.**

The pressure of blood in the veins is significantly less than that in the arteries. This reduced pressure occurs because, in the

Q Is it more dangerous to cut the carotid artery or the jugular vein? Why?

capillaries, an increasing proportion of the blood is in direct contact with the inside surface of the capillary wall. This contact increases the friction and slows the blood flow. As the capillaries merge to form veins, the pressure as blood moves through these larger vessels is further reduced. In fact, in most animals, blood will spurt and gush when an artery is cut, but will only trickle out of cut veins. It is not surprising, then, that most arteries are not as close to the skin as are veins. It would be too risky to put them there. This is why people who cut their wrists when attempting suicide rarely die. They generally cut only the veins in their wrists, which are closer to the surface, and rarely bleed enough to cause death.

TAKE-HOME MESSAGE 21·2

Animals that can acquire all the nutrients and oxygen they need by diffusion (such as flatworms and cnidarians) do not have circulatory systems. Among animals that do have circulatory systems, the system can be open, with no clear distinction between circulating fluid and the interstitial fluid that bathes tissues, or closed, with a clear distinction. In closed circulatory systems, tiny blood vessels called capillaries bring blood close enough to tissues that diffusion can move the necessary molecules from the blood into the cells and from the cells into the blood.

Respiratory Adaptations

21·3

Vertebrates have several different types of closed circulatory systems.

Among the vertebrates, there are several variations of the closed circulatory system. These variations evolved in concert with numerous dramatic adaptations that accompanied and made possible the transition from life in the seas to life on land. As some vertebrates developed lungs and the ability to extract oxygen from the air rather than water, their circulatory systems increased in complexity.

In fishes, the flow of blood follows a circular path (**FIGURE 21-5 FISH**). In tracing its flow, we can begin with the two-chambered heart. Blood first passes into the **atrium**, the collecting chamber, and from there is pumped into the **ventricle**, the chamber from which blood is pumped to the gills. Blood flows through the capillary beds of the gills, where it picks up oxygen. From there, the blood travels to the tissues of the body, delivering the oxygen. After passing through the capillary beds of the body tissues, the oxygen-poor blood flows back to the heart, and the cycle begins again as that blood is pumped to the gills.

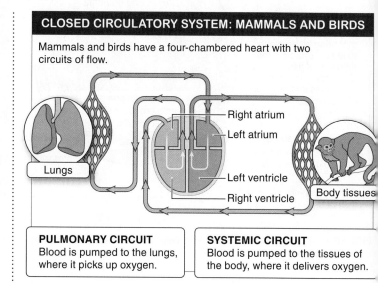

CLOSED CIRCULATORY SYSTEM: MAMMALS AND BIRDS

Mammals and birds have a four-chambered heart with two circuits of flow.

Lungs

Right atrium
Left atrium
Left ventricle
Right ventricle

Body tissues

PULMONARY CIRCUIT
Blood is pumped to the lungs, where it picks up oxygen.

SYSTEMIC CIRCUIT
Blood is pumped to the tissues of the body, where it delivers oxygen.

FIGURE 21-5 MAMMALS AND BIRDS **Blood flow in mammals and birds.** Note that the right side of the animal's heart is on the left side in the diagram, and the left side is on the right. This is because drawings of the heart are made as if the animal is facing you.

In contrast to the two-chambered heart of fishes, birds and mammals have a four-chambered heart: two atria and two ventricles (**FIGURE 21-5 MAMMALS AND BIRDS**). Twice as many chambers are required because, rather than having a single circuit of flow, birds and mammals have two circuits of flow. The two circuits can be visualized as a figure 8: blood flows into the right atrium and through to the right ventricle (see Figure 21-5). From there it is pumped out to the capillaries of the lungs, and then it returns to the heart. This first circuit of flow is called the **pulmonary circuit.** The blood returning to the heart from the lungs collects in the left atrium. It immediately passes into the left ventricle and from there is pumped to the rest of the body. After passing through the body capillaries, it completes its second circuit, called the **systemic circuit,** and collects in the right atrium, where the cycle begins again.

CLOSED CIRCULATORY SYSTEM: FISH

Fishes have a two-chambered heart with a single circuit of flow.

Oxygen-rich blood
Oxygen-poor blood

Ventricle Atrium

Gills

Body tissues

FIGURE 21-5 FISH **Blood flow in fish.**

This single-circuit flow of blood in fishes has a limitation. By passing through the numerous tiny blood vessels that make up the gill capillaries, the newly oxygenated blood slows its flow greatly, losing most of the pressure it gained following the contraction of the heart. It flows—or, more accurately, trickles—at a relatively low velocity to the oxygen-depleted parts of the body, limiting the rate at which oxygen can be delivered to the tissues. The blood is helped along through the arteries by contractions of muscles around the blood vessels as the fish swims, but the blood flow never reaches the velocity it had just after being pumped out of the ventricle.

Mammals and birds vary widely in the size of their hearts—from tiny hummingbird hearts no bigger than a pencil eraser all the way up to the heart of a blue whale, bigger than a small car, that pumps 25 gallons with every beat—but they all share the same basic layout. And almost

Q The left side of mammalian and bird hearts always bigger th the right. Why?

Circulatory Systems | Human Circulation | Gas Exchange | Hemoglobin and Myoglobin

always, because the left ventricle has to pump blood to the entire body rather than just to the lungs, the left ventricle becomes much larger and more muscular than the right ventricle.

With two circuits of flow, mammalian and bird hearts are better than fish hearts at delivering oxygen to body tissues. In fishes, as we've seen, all the oxygenated blood flowing to the body has low pressure and velocity because it passes first through the gill capillaries. With two circuits of flow in birds and mammals, all the oxygenated blood flowing to body tissues is at higher pressure because it is pumped straight from the left ventricle and does not first pass through the pressure-robbing capillaries of the lungs. This makes it possible for bird and mammal hearts to sustain greater levels of activity with greater amounts of oxygen delivered to the muscles and organs. The single-circuit system of fishes is like trying to put out a big fire with a low-pressure garden hose, while the two-circuit system of birds and mammals is more akin to using a high-pressure fire hose. Nonetheless, the large number and diversity of fishes on earth suggests that they are able to thrive with their single-circuit system.

Amphibians have circulatory systems that appear similar, but not identical, to the mammalian and bird plan (**FIGURE 21-5 AMPHIBIANS**). They have two circuits of flow, but have hearts with only three chambers rather than four. Blood is collected from the lungs and from the rest of the body in the left and right atria, respectively, but it then flows into a single ventricle. Surprisingly, though, little mixing of the oxygenated blood from the lungs and deoxygenated blood from the rest of the body occurs in the ventricle. Rather, the two types of blood flow side by side and are pumped into vessels that direct the oxygenated blood to the body capillaries and the deoxygenated blood to the lungs.

With the exception of birds, most reptiles also have three-chambered hearts, although the ventricle is partially divided in two. In one group of reptiles (the crocodilians), however, the division is complete; they also have an extra little artery that

CLOSED CIRCULATORY SYSTEM: AMPHIBIANS

Amphibians (and most reptiles) have a three-chambered heart with two circuits of flow.

Right atrium
Left atrium
Ventricle
Lungs
Body tissues

PULMONARY CIRCUIT
Blood is pumped to the lungs, where it picks up oxygen.

SYSTEMIC CIRCUIT
Blood is pumped to the tissues of the body, where it delivers oxygen.

FIGURE 21-5 AMPHIBIANS Blood flow in amphibians.

allows blood to be pumped from the right ventricle to the rest of the body rather than to the lungs. This extra artery is an adaptation allowing the crocodile to bypass sending blood to the lungs when the animal is underwater. There is no sense in pumping blood to the lungs if there is no oxygen to be picked up there. Instead, the blood is sent back to the body, where the remaining oxygen in the blood can be utilized.

TAKE-HOME MESSAGE 21·3

Vertebrates' circulatory systems vary in structure. Fishes have two-chambered hearts, with one circuit of flow: from the heart through the gills through the body and back to the heart. Birds and mammals have four-chambered hearts and two circuits of flow: from the heart to the lungs and back to the heart, then from the heart to the body and back to the heart. This enables blood to be pumped to the body at higher pressure. Amphibians and most reptiles have a three-chambered heart and two circuits of blood flow.

❷ The heart is at the center of the human circulatory system.

Red blood cells flow in a single file through capillaries.

21·4

Blood flows through the four chambers of the human heart.

Clench your fist. That is the size of your heart. Now clench it and relax it a hundred thousand times. That is what you require your heart to do, every day, for 70 or more years. The human heart, at the center of our circulatory system, is one of the most durable and reliable pumps ever produced (**FIGURE 21-6**).

As we saw above, the four-chambered heart sends blood on a figure 8, two-cycle path through the body, sending all blood first to the lungs for loading up on oxygen and, on its second circuit, to the tissues and organs. Let's explore the workings of this heart, tracing the flow of blood as it cycles through the heart, lungs, and tissues of the body (**FIGURE 21-7**). We'll start with the arrival of oxygen-depleted blood from the organs and tissues.

1. Deoxygenated blood from the organs and tissues enters the right atrium. The blood arriving from the lower half of the body enters through the inferior vena cava, and blood arriving from the head and arms enters through the superior vena cava.

2. Most of the blood passes directly through the right atrium into the right ventricle. A contraction pushes the

FIGURE 21-6 Heart and blood vessels. An overview of the human circulatory system.

THE HUMAN CIRCULATORY SYSTEM

The human circulatory system is composed of a fist-sized heart and an intricate system of blood vessels that transport respiratory gases, nutrients, and waste products throughout the body.

Heart
Vein
Artery

THE HUMAN HEART

Superior vena cava
Aorta
Right atrium
Left atrium
Right ventricle
Left ventricle
Inferior vena cava

FLOW OF BLOOD THROUGH THE HUMAN CIRCULATORY SYSTEM

1 Deoxygenated blood from the organs and tissues enters the right atrium. The blood arriving from the lower half of the body enters through the inferior vena cava, and blood arriving from the head and arms enters through the superior vena cava.

2 Most of the blood passes directly through the right atrium into the right ventricle. A contraction pushes the remainder of the blood in the right atrium down and into the right ventricle.

3 The contraction continues, pumping the blood out of the ventricle through the pulmonary artery. This large artery immediately forks, sending half of the blood to the left lung and half to the right lung.

4 Passing through the pulmonary capillaries in the lungs, the blood picks up oxygen and loses carbon dioxide.

5 The oxygenated blood then returns to the heart, arriving in the left atrium via the left and right pulmonary veins.

6 Most of the blood passes directly through the left atrium and into the left ventricle. A contraction pushes the remaining blood from the left atrium into the left ventricle.

7 As the contraction continues, the blood is pumped up and out of the ventricle through the largest artery in the body, the aorta. After making a sharp turn, the aorta splits, sending some blood to the capillaries of the arms and head and the remainder to the capillaries of the trunk and legs.

8 Depleted of oxygen after passing through the capillary beds of the head, trunk, and legs, the blood trickles in veins back to the heart, and collects in the right atrium via the venae cavae.

Legend: ■ Oxygen-rich blood ■ Oxygen-poor blood

Labels: Capillaries of the head and arms; Superior vena cava; Aorta; Left atrium; Right atrium; Pulmonary capillaries; Right pulmonary vein; Inferior vena cava; Right ventricle; Left ventricle; Left pulmonary vein; Pulmonary capillaries; Capillaries of the trunk and legs

FIGURE 21-7 The path of blood flow in the human body.

---

remainder of the blood in the right atrium down and into the right ventricle.

3. The contraction continues, pumping the blood out of the ventricle through the pulmonary artery. This large artery immediately forks, sending half of the blood to the left lung and half to the right lung.

4. Passing through the pulmonary capillaries in the lungs, the blood picks up oxygen and loses carbon dioxide.

5. The oxygenated blood then returns to the heart, arriving in the left atrium via the left and right pulmonary veins.

6. Most of the blood passes directly through the left atrium and into the left ventricle. A contraction pushes the remaining blood from the left atrium into the left ventricle.

7. As the contraction continues, the blood is pumped up and out of the ventricle through the largest artery in the body, the aorta. After making a sharp turn, the aorta splits, sending some blood to the capillaries of the arms and head and the remainder to the capillaries of the trunk and legs.

8. Depleted of oxygen after passing through the capillary beds of the head, trunk, and legs, the blood trickles in veins back to the heart, and collects in the right atrium via the venae cavae.

If you place your ear on the center of another person's chest in a quiet room, you can hear the heart working. "Lub dup, lub dup, lub dup." Over and over, the same two sounds. These are the sounds that a doctor hears when using a stethoscope. What is the source? It's not the contraction of the heart. Surprisingly, the muscular contractions don't make much noise. Rather, the sounds come from two sets of valves that help keep blood flowing in the proper direction (**FIGURE 21-8**).

The first set of valves is the atrioventricular (or AV) valves. Located between the atrium and ventricle on each side of the heart, these two valves allow blood to flow from the atrium to the ventricle. But when the ventricle contracts, these flaps of tissue slam shut, preventing blood from being pushed back into the atria: "lub." With no other escape, the blood flows out through the pulmonary arteries on the right side and the aorta on the left. At these two primary exits from the heart are two more valves. These semilunar valves, so called because of their half-moon shape, close and prevent blood from flowing back into the ventricles. Like doors slamming shut, the valves make a noise that you can hear with your ear pressed to someone's chest: "dup."

> **Q** Sometimes a doctor will hear additional sounds besides the "lub" and "dup" of normal heart valve functioning. What is the source of such heart murmurs?

When the atrioventricular or semilunar valves do not completely close, some blood can squirt back through them, flowing in the wrong direction. The blood moving backward through the valve can be heard, with a stethoscope, making a buzzing or swishing noise.

> **?** Why does the heart make a "lub dup, lub dup" sound?

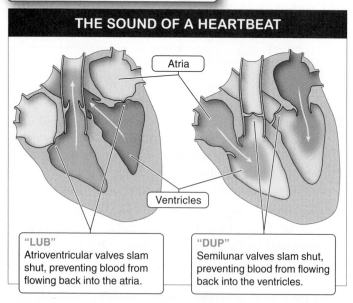

THE SOUND OF A HEARTBEAT

Atria

Ventricles

"LUB"
Atrioventricular valves slam shut, preventing blood from flowing back into the atria.

"DUP"
Semilunar valves slam shut, preventing blood from flowing back into the ventricles.

FIGURE 21-8 Audible heartbeats. Like doors slamming shut, the heart valves make noises that you can hear with your ear pressed to someone's chest.

Most heart murmurs are not life-threatening, and the individual suffers no ill effects.

The heart is not the only component of the circulatory system directing the flow of blood. Consider this: when you go out in very cold weather, your face or hands may get very cold and may even turn bluish in color. Why does this happen? Flow of blood in the capillaries is controlled by smooth muscle around the arterioles the smaller vessels that branch off arteries and lead to capillaries. When the muscles, called precapillary sphincters, contract, blood flow can be cut off to capillaries and shunted elsewhere in the body (**FIGURE 21-9**). As a consequence of these muscles, bodies can reduce blood flow (and the heat it brings) to parts such as the face or hands in situations where such blood flow could lead to excessive and energetically wasteful heat loss. Blushing is the opposite situation: precapillary sphincters relax and blood flow to the face and neck increases.

"Food coma," that feeling of lethargy following a large meal, results from a similar shunting of blood. In this case, more blood is allowed to flow through the capillaries surrounding the digestive tract while less flows to other parts of the body. Alternatively, during strenuous exercise, more blood is directed toward the skeletal muscles in use. This accounts for the feeling of being "pumped up" during and shortly after a weightlifting session. Surprisingly, the vast majority of the capillaries have little or no blood flowing through them at any given time, and the body is constantly directing blood flow to the tissues where it is most needed.

> **Q** What is "food coma"?

Veins, too, aid in the control of blood flow. After sitting for a very long time, such as on a long plane or car ride, you may notice that your feet become swollen and it is difficult to put your shoes back on. What is the cause of this? The answer has to do with the way that blood flows back to the heart after passing through capillary beds. Remember that capillaries, with their small diameter and thin, leaky walls, reduce the pressure and speed of flowing blood. By the time it begins collecting in veins, blood has very little pressure. It is able to "limp" back to the heart only with the assistance of two important features. First, as muscles surrounding veins contract and relax during normal movement, they squeeze the veins, pushing the blood through. And second, within veins, at regular intervals, are one-way valves. Similar in function to the atrioventricular and semilunar valves of the heart, these valves allow blood to flow in one direction—toward the heart—but not in the reverse direction (see Figure 21-9).

Regulating blood flow by means of valves in the veins and the contractions of muscles surrounding the veins usually works fine. As we've noted, though, you can encounter a problem if you sit on a plane for several hours. Blood pumped to your feet must somehow climb up your legs, yet in the absence of contractions of your calf and thigh muscles, this doesn't occur so well. Instead

Circulatory Systems   Human Circulation   Gas Exchange   Hemoglobin and Myoglobin

PRECAPILLARY SPHINCTERS
In the arterioles, precapillary sphincters can contract and cut off blood flow to the capillaries in order to shunt it elsewhere in the body.

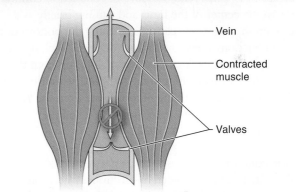

MUSCLE CONTRACTIONS AND VALVES
Contractions of muscles surrounding the veins push blood toward the heart. Valves within the veins keep the blood on course by preventing it from moving backward.

FIGURE 21-9 Controlling blood flow. Precapillary sphincters can reduce blood flow to hands or feet in cold weather, saving the blood's warmth for vital organs. When traveling on a long flight, it is helpful to move your feet and legs to help push blood back toward your heart.

Some individuals develop enlarged, twisted, and visible veins, a painful condition called varicose veins. Why might this occur?

the blood pools in your feet, causing them to get more swollen increasing the risk of blood clots. This is why it is good to get up and move around occasionally, or to exercise your leg muscles as you sit.

One serious circulatory problem is called varicose veins, a painful condition that occurs when the valves preventing backflow of blood malfunction and blood pools in the veins, stretching them. This can be caused or exacerbated by standing for long periods of time. Several methods are effective

for treating varicose veins, including laser surgery or injections that cause the veins to slowly fade and disappear, with deeper veins taking over the circulation in that region.

TAKE-HOME MESSAGE 21·4

The human heart, at the center of our circulatory system, is an extremely durable pump. It sends blood on a figure 8, two-circuit path through the body, first to the lungs for loading up with oxygen and, on its second circuit, to the tissues and organs of the body. Valves in the heart and veins keep blood flowing in one direction.

Electrical activity in the heart generates the heartbeat.

Vertebrate hearts have a small piece of modified muscle tissue, the sinoatrial (SA) node, that initiates the regular, rhythmic contractions of the heart. Unlike most muscular tissue, which must be stimulated by a nerve before it contracts, the sinoatrial node spontaneously fires an electrical impulse that initiates contractions in the heart muscle. It begins this spontaneous firing early in fetal development and continues to give rise to every heartbeat for your entire life. As the pacemaker of the heart, the SA node initiates a carefully choreographed contraction that results in an efficient blood pump.

Beginning just above the right atrium, the electrical impulse in the SA node quickly spreads to the left atrium as well. As the atria contract, blood is pushed into the ventricles. The atria then enter a "relaxation" phase, and the wave of contraction continues, passing down the center of the heart and pausing briefly as it passes between the two ventricles. On reaching the bottom of the heart, the contraction appears to almost "bounce" back upward, causing a deep contraction that pushes the blood up from the bottom of both ventricles and into the pulmonary arteries and aorta, much like squeezing a tube of toothpaste from the bottom up. The ventricles then enter a relaxation phase, and the SA node starts the contraction anew (**FIGURE 21-10**).

Because the contraction of muscle tissue is a powerful electrical event, it can be recorded by electrodes placed on the skin that detect the changing electrical charges as the heart beats. Called an electrocardiogram, or EKG (from the German *Elektrokardiogramm*), these readings allow quick and easy display and analysis of the cardiac cycle.

Q **What is an artificial pacemaker?**

In some individuals, the sinoatrial node does not function properly or may be damaged by infection. This malfunctioning can lead to a heartbeat that is too slow or erratic and can cause reduced blood flow, leading to problems such as fainting. An artificial pacemaker is a battery-operated electronic device that generates stimulation to the heart, causing a more regular heartbeat.

TAKE-HOME MESSAGE 21·5

The sinoatrial node, modified muscle tissue in the vertebrate heart, initiates regular, rhythmic contractions. A heart contraction begins with an electrical impulse in the SA node in the right atrium. The contraction quickly spreads to the left atrium, and passes down the center to the bottom of the heart, then moves upward, pushing blood from both ventricles out through the pulmonary arteries and aorta.

HEART CONTRACTION

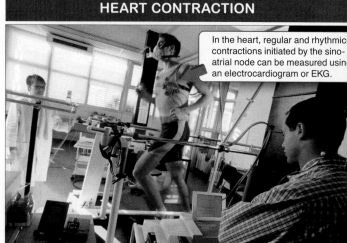

In the heart, regular and rhythmic contractions initiated by the sinoatrial node can be measured using an electrocardiogram or EKG.

1 Sinoatrial (SA) node fires and the contraction spreads to both atria.

Atria

SA node

EKG reading

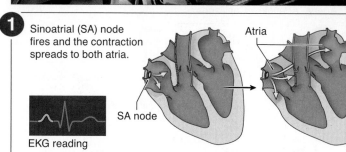

2 Wave of contraction passes down center of heart and bounces back up, causing the ventricles to contract.

Ventricles

EKG reading

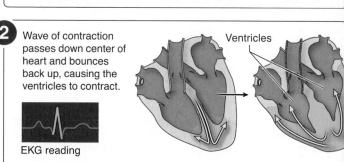

3 Ventricles relax and the process begins again.

EKG reading

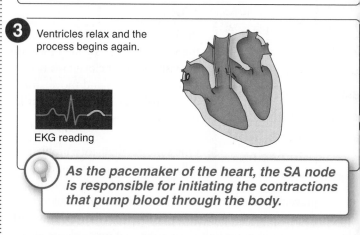

As the pacemaker of the heart, the SA node is responsible for initiating the contractions that pump blood through the body.

FIGURE 21-10 Rhythmic contractions of the heart.

21·6

Blood is a mixture of cells and fluid.

If circulatory systems are like highways throughout our bodies, transporting goods and garbage, then blood is the traffic. Endlessly circulating, this viscous fluid—its consistency is closer to that of motor oil than water—is a salty, protein-rich mixture of cells and fluid. The average human body has 4–5 quarts of blood, and the blood makes up just under 10% of our total body weight. Blood's functions revolve primarily around its transport and delivery capabilities, including the transport of (1) respiratory gases such as oxygen and carbon dioxide, (2) vitamins and minerals, (3) nutrients, (4) hormones, (5) cells of the immune system, and (6) metabolic wastes. Blood also helps to maintain body temperature and homeostasis (see Chapter 20).

Blood has several distinct components. Putting a small sample of blood in a test tube and spinning it rapidly in a centrifuge makes it possible to identify them (**FIGURE 21-11**). The lighter-weight part of the blood, the creamy yellow layer in the test tube, is the **plasma,** the liquid part of the blood. Plasma is 90% salty water. Dissolved within this water is a huge variety of molecules: metabolites and wastes, salts and ions, and hundreds of plasma proteins that serve to transport lipids, vitamins, and a host of other chemicals that need molecular escorts to the tissues where they are required. Most of the carbon dioxide produced in tissues as a by-product of cellular respiration is carried to the lungs dissolved in the plasma.

The heaviest components of blood get forced to the bottom of the test tube when spun in a centrifuge. This is a layer of packed cells, containing various types of blood cells, and is usually dark red in color. The proportion of the blood that consists of cells is called the **hematocrit.** In humans, a hematocrit of about 45% is normal. Individuals living at high altitudes for a few weeks or longer, however, have hematocrits of around 48% or 49%. Why? The increased hematocrit is a response to the reduced oxygen concentrations in the air at high altitudes. To continue to deliver enough oxygen to the body's tissues, there must be more blood cells to carry it.

Where do these blood cells come from? They are made in the bone marrow (the material that fills the interior of our bones) by specialized cells, called **stem cells,** that are able to develop into a diverse range of cell types. Stem cells throughout the bones in our body produce blood cells at a rate of about two million cells per second. There are two types of blood cells suspended in the plasma: red blood cells and white blood cells, as well as platelets, which are cellular fragments (**FIGURE 21-12**).

1. Red blood cells (also called **erythrocytes**). These workhorses of the circulatory system are the most common

CONSTITUENTS OF BLOOD

Putting a small sample of blood in a test tube and spinning it rapidly in a centrifuge makes it possible to identify the primary constituents of blood: plasma and packed cells.

PLASMA
- Salty water (generally 90% of plasma)
- Variety of molecules, including metabolites and wastes, salts and ions, and hundreds of plasma proteins

PACKED CELLS
- Red blood cells (generally more than 90% of the packed cells)
- White blood cells
- Platelets

55%

45%

The proportion of blood that is made up of packed cells is called a hematocrit reading, which is typically about 45% in humans.

FIGURE 21-11 What makes up blood?

blood cells. In a human being, about 95% of the blood cells circulating at any given time are red blood cells. They are oxygen-transporting specialists, and their structure maximizes their effectiveness. Externally, they are shaped like flexible disks, so they can squeeze through capillaries in single file. Internally, they have hardly any organelles; they have no nucleus, mitochondria, or protein-making machinery. What are they filled with? Each red blood cell contains about 250 million molecules of **hemoglobin,** an oxygen-carrying protein molecule. Because they lack almost all internal cellular machinery for repair and upkeep, red blood cells don't last long, remaining in circulation for about four months. During its short life, though, a red blood cell will travel about 900 miles, endlessly picking up oxygen in the lungs and releasing it to body cells that need it.

RED BLOOD CELLS (ERYTHROCYTES)
- Transport oxygen from the lungs to the rest of the body
- Flexible disks containing few organelles
- Packed full of hemoglobin

WHITE BLOOD CELLS (LEUKOCYTES)
- Destroy pathogens and foreign organisms in the bloodstream and interstitial fluid
- There are several types of white blood cells that differ in their methods of fighting disease and responding to foreign materials

PLATELETS
- Slow blood loss by initiating the constriction of blood vessels and the formation of a clot
- Composed of small pieces of cytoplasm
- Contain no organelles

FIGURE 21-12 Erythrocytes, leukocytes, and platelets.

2. White blood cells (also called **leukocytes**). White blood cells are the defenders of the body and are the primary components of the body's immune response system. Five different types of white blood cells can be found circulating: neutrophils, lymphocytes, monocytes, eosinophils, and basophils (see Chapter 26 for more on the roles of these white blood cells). Like red blood cells, white blood cells arise from stem cells in bone marrow. Once in the bloodstream, they patrol for **pathogens,** disease-causing foreign organisms circulating in the bloodstream. White blood cells also spend much of their time outside the circulatory system, diffusing out of the capillaries and moving about in the interstitial fluid between cells where many pathogens such as viruses and bacteria may be, and where they also can destroy cancerous body cells or body cells that have been infected by pathogens. The number of leukocytes circulating in an individual can vary greatly, depending on his or her health status. Under normal conditions, there is approximately one leukocyte for every thousand red blood cells, but the number of leukocytes increases as much as two- to threefold during an infection.

3. Platelets. With more than 50,000 miles of blood vessels in our bodies, it is inevitable that there will be occasional cuts or punctures (**FIGURE 21-13**). Fortunately, the platelets are ready to swing into action when this happens. **Platelets** are considered cellular fragments rather than full-fledged cells. In the bone marrow, large cells called megakaryocytes repeatedly pinch off little bits of cytoplasm that have no nuclei or other organelles. These cell fragments, the platelets,

are filled with critical enzymes and chemicals for patching damaged blood vessels. Hundreds of thousands of platelets circulate at any given time, with each platelet generally lasting about a week. You can envision platelets as fragile glass jars full of Super Glue. When they bump into the edge of a cut in a blood vessel, they shatter and release their cargo,

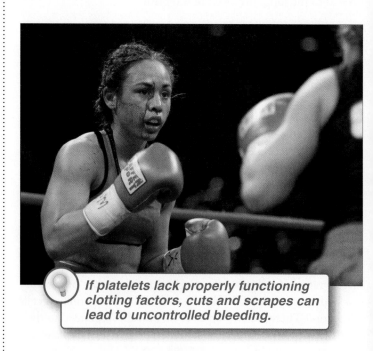

If platelets lack properly functioning clotting factors, cuts and scrapes can lead to uncontrolled bleeding.

FIGURE 21-13 Fighting blood loss. Platelets patch damaged blood vessels.

Circulatory Systems   Human Circulation   Gas Exchange   Hemoglobin and Myoglobin

Cooking in a cast iron skillet can increase significantly the iron content of foods!

initiating constriction of the blood vessel and the production of fibrin threads that form a blood clot to reduce blood loss.

Some individuals lack platelets with properly functioning clotting factors, and they experience uncontrolled bleeding from even minor cuts or scrapes. These problems can be due to an inherited malfunctioning gene (as in the condition of hemophilia). They can also be acquired, or environmental: if the liver—where many of the clotting enzymes are produced—is damaged by disease (such as cirrhosis, which can result from alcoholism), uncontrolled bleeding can occur. Conversely, problems of blood clotting *too* readily can also lead

to health problems. Thrombosis, for example, is the formation of clots of coagulated blood within a blood vessel. When such clots block circulation in these blood vessels that supply blood to the muscle tissue of the heart itself, a heart attack occurs.

Anemia occurs when an individual has too few red blood cells. Because red blood cells deliver oxygen to the body's cells, one consequence of anemia is a reduction in the oxygen available to cells, essentially suffocating them. This causes people with anemia to feel tired and run-down. A reduction in the number of red blood cells is also associated with an increased susceptibility to infection, apparently by weakening the immune system's ability to mount a response to pathogens. Iron deficiency is the most common cause of anemia. Iron is a critical element that enables oxygen to be carried by red blood cells. If iron is in short supply, red blood cells can't deliver sufficient oxygen to the tissues where it's needed. Both men and women can be anemic, but anemia affects women much more commonly, because of the blood loss during menstruation. The relationship between iron deficiency and anemia has been known for a long time. An old folk remedy for anemia—that actually worked(!)—was sipping liquid daily from a jug containing rusty iron nails and water.

Q What is anemia? Why are women more susceptible than men?

TAKE-HOME MESSAGE 21·6

Blood is a salty, protein-rich mixture of cells and fluid, important in the transport of (1) respiratory gases, (2) vitamins and minerals, (3) nutrients, (4) hormones, (5) components of the immune system, and (6) metabolic wastes. Blood also helps maintain a constant internal environment, including body temperature. Blood cells are produced throughout life by stem cells in bone marrow. There are two types of cells suspended in the plasma: red cells (oxygen transport), white cells (defense from infections), as well as cellular fragments, platelets (repair).

Blood pressure is a key measure of heart health.

Feel your pulse. With no fancy equipment at all, it is possible to get very useful information about the functioning of your heart. For some arteries, such as those on the underside of your wrist or on the side of your neck, you can feel with your fingers the pressure increase as a blood surge stretches the arteries with each contraction of the heart. Taking a person's pulse provides a quick and easy determination of the rate and rhythm of the heartbeats.

Additional information about heart health can be gained with measurement of **blood pressure,** which measures the force with which blood flows through a person's arteries. This force tells us the magnitude of each heart contraction and gives important clues about an individual's cardiovascular health. There are two different parts to a blood pressure reading (**FIGURE 21-14**). The first, called **systolic pressure,** is the pressure when the heart contracts. The powerful contraction pumps blood into the arteries, momentarily causing them to stretch as they accommodate the large pulse of blood. The second blood pressure reading is called **diastolic pressure.** This is a measure of the force that blood exerts on the artery walls while the heart is between beats. Because blood isn't being actively pumped at that moment, the diastolic pressure is always lower than the systolic pressure.

Blood pressure can be measured in four easy steps, using a blood pressure cuff.

1. The cuff is fastened around the upper arm and pumped up, clamping off the arteries in the arm so that no blood gets through.

2. Gradually, pressure on the cuff is released.

3. When the pulsing of blood getting pushed through the arteries under the cuff can first be heard with a stethoscope held to the arteries just below the cuff—heard as a little squirt—the pressure reading is noted. That is the systolic pressure. Each contraction of the heart is just strong enough to push blood through the barrier of that much pressure.

4. Additional pressure in the cuff is released until the squirting sound disappears. The pressure at that point is the diastolic pressure. Blood is flowing through the arteries with this amount of pressure between heart contractions.

If your blood pressure is "120 over 80," it means that the systolic pressure is 120 and the diastolic pressure is 80. This is

BLOOD PRESSURE

Blood pressure readings consist of two measurements:

SYSTOLIC PRESSURE
- The force that blood exerts on the artery walls when the heart contracts and pumps blood into the arteries
- Normal range is between 90 and 120 mmHg.

DIASTOLIC PRESSURE
- The force that blood exerts on the artery walls while the heart is between beats
- Normal range is between 60 and 90 mmHg.

 With elevated blood pressure, your heart must work harder at all times and your arteries can lose some of their elasticity. This increases your health risks.

FIGURE 21-14 Blood pressure readings can reveal heart health.

written as 120/80, and the units of measure are millimeters of mercury (mmHg), representing how high a column of mercury could be lifted by such pressure.

Blood pressure above 140/90 is considered high and a potential health hazard. What does this mean, and why is it cause for concern? Imagine a pair of shorts with an elastic waistband. If you were to stretch the waistband as far as possible and hold it in that position for a long time, what would happen? The waistband would lose its elasticity. This is similar to what

Circulatory Systems   Human Circulation   Gas Exchange   Hemoglobin and Myoglobin

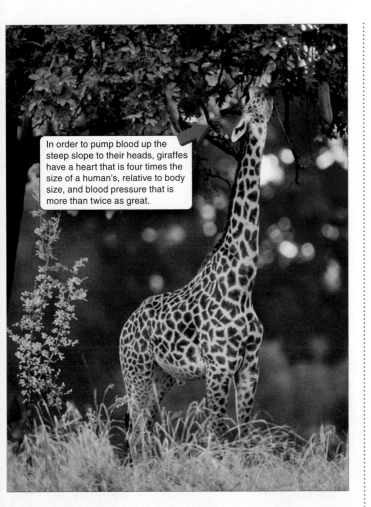

In order to pump blood up the steep slope to their heads, giraffes have a heart that is four times the size of a human's, relative to body size, and blood pressure that is more than twice as great.

FIGURE 21-15 Contents under pressure. The large heart of a giraffe pumps blood through its long neck all the way to its head.

happens to your arteries if they are stretched by high pressures for long periods of time. With high blood pressure, also called hypertension, not only must your heart work harder at all times, potentially weakening it, but your arteries have a reduced ability to expand and accommodate the increasing pulses of blood during times of exertion. Moreover, more cholesterol sticks to artery walls when they are rigid than when they are elastic, and as this narrows the diameter of the blood vessel, it further

reduces the efficiency of the circulatory system and taxes the heart. These problems all increase the risk of catastrophic heart attacks and strokes, which we discuss in Section 21.8. Although both systolic pressure and diastolic pressure are important, systolic blood pressure is more important in identifying and controlling hypertension.

Low blood pressure, or hypotension, at the other extreme, is defined as a pressure of 90/60 or lower and can cause symptoms such as dizziness, particularly just after a person stands up, due to inadequate blood flow to the brain. Sometimes caused by medications, low blood pressure can also be associated with weakness or depression. Most often it is not a problem, and it rarely has long-term risks.

Relative heart size and blood pressure are consistent among the mammals, with one notable exception: giraffes. With their necks stretching 8 feet (2.5 meters) or more, giraffes must pump blood up a pretty steep slope. Not surprisingly, their hearts are much bigger—about four times bigger (relative to body size)—than a human heart, and their blood pressure is more than twice as great. Scientists have begun studying giraffe circulation in the hope of learning physiological secrets to help humans cope with high blood pressure. Why, for example, with twice the blood pressure of a human, doesn't a giraffe's head explode when it lowers to drink from a pond (**FIGURE 21-15**)?

TAKE-HOME MESSAGE 21·7

Blood pressure measurement gives important clues about an individual's cardiovascular health. A blood pressure reading consists of two measures. The first, systolic pressure, is the force that blood exerts on the artery wall when the heart contracts and pumps blood into the arteries. The second, diastolic pressure, is the force that blood exerts on the artery wall while the heart is between beats. With high blood pressure, the heart must work harder at all times, the arteries can lose some of their elasticity, and health risks are increased.

Cardiovascular disease is a leading cause of death in the United States.

The heart is among the most neglected organs. Most people take it for granted. But every year heart attacks cause 20% of the deaths in the United States, more than any other single cause and among the most avoidable. Heart attacks are brought on by an interruption in the flow of blood through one of the **coronary arteries**—the blood vessels that deliver oxygen and nutrients to the heart muscle itself. When cells in the heart muscle are deprived of oxygen, the heart may beat irregularly or cease to beat, and the heart muscle cells deprived of oxygen die. This has serious and long-term implications, because heart cells are among the rare cells of the body that do not reproduce themselves. Once they are gone, they are really gone.

> " Broken heart. A pump after all, pumping thousands of gallons of blood every day. One fine day it gets bunged up and there you are. "
>
> —James Joyce, *Ulysses*

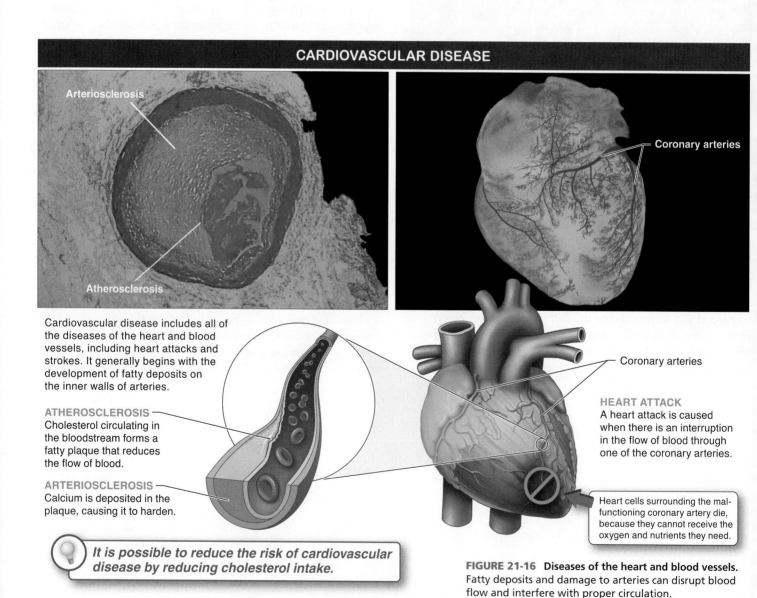

CARDIOVASCULAR DISEASE

Arteriosclerosis

Atherosclerosis

Coronary arteries

Cardiovascular disease includes all of the diseases of the heart and blood vessels, including heart attacks and strokes. It generally begins with the development of fatty deposits on the inner walls of arteries.

ATHEROSCLEROSIS Cholesterol circulating in the bloodstream forms a fatty plaque that reduces the flow of blood.

ARTERIOSCLEROSIS Calcium is deposited in the plaque, causing it to harden.

Coronary arteries

HEART ATTACK A heart attack is caused when there is an interruption in the flow of blood through one of the coronary arteries.

Heart cells surrounding the malfunctioning coronary artery die, because they cannot receive the oxygen and nutrients they need.

It is possible to reduce the risk of cardiovascular disease by reducing cholesterol intake.

FIGURE 21-16 Diseases of the heart and blood vessels. Fatty deposits and damage to arteries can disrupt blood flow and interfere with proper circulation.

Circulatory Systems   Human Circulation   Gas Exchange   Hemoglobin and Myoglobin

Contrary to appearances—and James Joyce's belief—heart attacks rarely strike out of the blue. Although the heart attack itself is a sudden event, it usually occurs after decades of progressive deterioration of the arteries and other degradations of the circulatory system, collectively called **cardiovascular disease** (FIGURE 21-16).

Cardiovascular disease includes all diseases of the heart and blood vessels and is ultimately responsible for close to half of all deaths in the United States. In addition to heart attacks, strokes are a common outcome of advanced cardiovascular disease. Caused by blocked arteries or blood clots in the brain, strokes also lead to cell death in the brain tissues starved of oxygen. There is, however, some cause for optimism: the death rate from heart disease has been declining steadily for the past 50 years, including a 25% drop in the past 20 years. These reductions have come not from advances in heart transplants and other surgical interventions, but rather from improvements in diet and exercise as well as advances in diagnosis and preventive medicine.

Cardiovascular disease generally begins with the development of fatty deposits called plaques on the inner walls of arteries. Plaques increase the risk of formation of blood clots and, by narrowing the artery, reduce the flow of blood. Called **atherosclerosis,** this narrowing of the arteries is often followed by the depositing of calcium at the plaques, causing them to harden in a process known as **arteriosclerosis.** The initial formation of plaques usually occurs as a consequence of circulating cholesterol in the bloodstream. Because most of this circulating cholesterol comes from cholesterol in our diet, we can reduce our risk of atherosclerosis by reducing our cholesterol intake.

Cholesterol is all the same, but you may hear references to "good" cholesterol and "bad" cholesterol. Why is this? As we discussed in Chapter 3, most cholesterol circulating in the bloodstream is packaged as LDL, or low-density lipoproteins. These molecules consist of thousands of molecules of cholesterol surrounded by a phospholipid coat. Because the LDL particles are sticky, they adhere to artery walls and can initiate the buildup of dangerous plaques. Other circulating particles, high-density lipoproteins (HDL), are considered "good" cholesterol. Less well-understood than LDL, these particles seem to remove cholesterol from arteries and deliver it to liver cells where it can be broken down. This process can actually reduce the progression of cardiovascular disease. By including in your diet fish and other foods that contain a specific type of fatty acids, called omega-3 fatty acids, you can increase your HDL levels.

Both nature and nurture play a role in cardiovascular disease. As we saw in Chapter 3, the tendency to develop cardiovascular disease is inherited. Individuals vary in the number of LDL receptors they produce on their liver cells, and the more receptors an individual has, the better that individual is able to remove atherosclerosis-causing cholesterol from circulation. You cannot alter the genes you inherit for LDL receptor production. But you *can* alter the amount of cholesterol or type of cholesterol (that is, LDL vs. HDL) that is circulating in the first place. Several different behavioral changes can reduce the level of circulating cholesterol and the risk of cardiovascular disease: in the first place by increasing aerobic exercise, not smoking, and eating a low-cholesterol, low-fat diet (FIGURE 21-17).

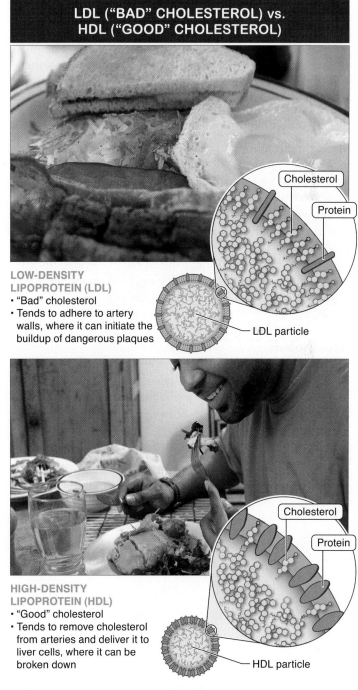

LDL ("BAD" CHOLESTEROL) vs. HDL ("GOOD" CHOLESTEROL)

Cholesterol
Protein

LOW-DENSITY LIPOPROTEIN (LDL)
- "Bad" cholesterol
- Tends to adhere to artery walls, where it can initiate the buildup of dangerous plaques

LDL particle

Cholesterol
Protein

HIGH-DENSITY LIPOPROTEIN (HDL)
- "Good" cholesterol
- Tends to remove cholesterol from arteries and deliver it to liver cells, where it can be broken down

HDL particle

FIGURE 21-17 Cholesterol can be helpful or harmful.

Respiratory Adaptations

Q **If exercising makes the heart work harder and if being overweight from eating fatty foods also makes the heart work harder, why does one lead to fitness and the other to disease?**

With aerobic training, such as running, the muscle fibers of the heart get bigger (in much the same way that skeletal muscle gets bigger when you lift weights), and cardiovascular health is improved. When people are sedentary, though, their hearts must work harder for reasons such as hypertension, poor diet, or increased blood pressure. The increased load on the heart causes the heart to get bigger, but in a pathological manner that increases the risk of heart failure, rather than in a manner that increases strength and efficiency.

Cardiovascular disease continues to be the most prevalent disease and leading cause of death in the United States. But, as we mentioned above, the situation has been improving over the past several decades. The onset and progression of Cardiovascular disease are strongly influenced by factors within your control, and with the proper dietary strategies and lifestyle changes most people can reduce their risk.

In summarizing their research-based recommendations for reducing risk factors for heart disease, heart attack, and stroke, the American Heart Association suggests a focus on "A, B, and C":

Avoid tobacco.
- Stop using any tobacco products and minimize exposure to tobacco smoke. Because cigarette smokers are two- to three-times more likely to die from heart disease, this behavioral change can lead to significant improvements to health and longevity.

Be more active.
- Participate in at least 30 minutes of moderate-intensity physical activity (i.e., brisk walking) on five or more days each week (or vigorous-intensity activity, such as jogging, on three or more days). Additionally, every adult should perform activities that increase or maintain muscle strength, including progressive weight training and/or stair climbing, on a minimum of two days each week.

Choose good nutrition.
- Eat a diet that balances energy intake with exercise to prevent weight gain. If you are overweight, take steps to increase physical activity and decrease energy intake to establish a healthy body weight (see Section 22-16).

- Chose a diet rich in vegetables, fruits, and whole grains, particularly those that are high in fiber.

- Limit intake of saturated fat, trans fat and cholesterol by choosing lean meats, vegetables, and low-fat dairy products. Read food labels to check for hydrogenated fats (see Section 2.13 for a refresher on hydrogenated fat and trans fats).

- Limit alcohol to one drink daily for women, and two drinks daily for men.

These behavioral changes are much easier said than done. Because they include the most effective strategies for reducing the risk of cardiovascular disease, however, the payoffs are significant.

TAKE-HOME MESSAGE 21·8

Cardiovascular disease includes all diseases of the heart and blood vessels, including heart attacks and strokes, and is the leading cause of death in the United States. It generally begins with the development of fatty deposits on the inner walls of arteries that increase the risk of blood clots and reduce the flow of blood in coronary vessels that supply oxygen to the heart (atherosclerosis). Because the hardening of arteries (arteriosclerosis) is usually initiated by circulating cholesterol, it is possible to reduce the risk of cardiovascular disease by reducing cholesterol intake.

Circulatory Systems   Human Circulation   Gas Exchange   Hemoglobin and Myoglobin

21·9

The lymphatic system plays a supporting role in circulation.

Our bodies have another circulatory system (**FIGURE 21-18**). In addition to the cardiovascular system, and running close to it throughout the body, is the lymphatic system. Why the seeming redundancy? The lymphatic system has a supporting role in the process of circulation. It has three important functions (**FIGURE 21-19**).

1. Recycling. As diffusion occurs between the capillaries and the interstitial fluid that surrounds cells, mopeouch fluid is lost from the blood. Here's where the lymphatic system comes in. Intertwined around blood vessels, lymphatic capillaries take in, by diffusion, fluid, proteins, and other substances that have leaked into the interstitial fluid from the blood. Once recovered, this fluid, now called **lymph,**

THE HUMAN LYMPHATIC SYSTEM

The lymphatic system runs close to the circulatory system throughout the body and plays a supporting role in the process of circulation.

Lymph node

Lymphatic capillary

Lymph vessel

Valve

FIGURE 21-18 The "other" circulatory system. An overview of the human lymphatic system.

FUNCTIONS OF THE LYMPHATIC SYSTEM

RECYCLING
The lymphatic system recycles fluid and proteins that diffuse from the blood capillaries during circulation back into the bloodstream.

FIGHTING ILLNESS
As lymph circulates through the body, white-blood-cell-packed lymph nodes remove dangerous materials, including bacteria, cancer cells, and viruses, from the body.

RETRIEVING NUTRIENTS
Little projections that extend into the small intestine absorb lipids from the digestive tract and shuttle them to the bloodstream.

FIGURE 21-19 The lymphatic system supports the circulatory system while fighting illness.

travels through progressively larger lymphatic vessels that eventually join up with veins in the shoulders. At this point, the recovered proteins and fluid (which amounts to several liters each day) are returned to the blood on its way back to the heart.

2. Fighting illness. As it moves through the lymphatic system, lymph passes through patches of connective tissue called **lymph nodes.** These compartmentalized sacs are filled with pathogen-fighting white blood cells that remove dangerous materials (including bacteria, cancer cells, and viruses) from the body. This is why your lymph nodes—including your tonsils, the largest lymph nodes of all—become swollen when your body is fighting an infection.

Q It's not necessarily a good idea to have your tonsils taken out, even if they are painfully swollen. Why?

Respiratory Adaptations

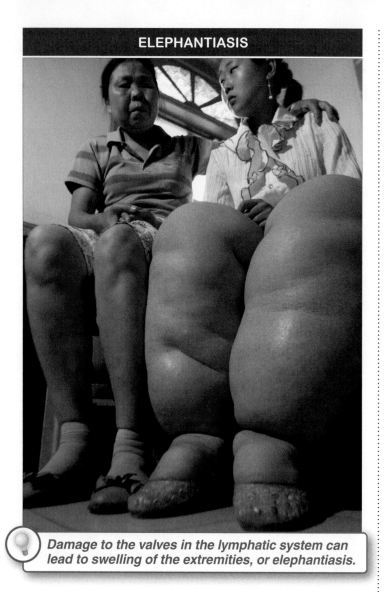

ELEPHANTIASIS

Damage to the valves in the lymphatic system can lead to swelling of the extremities, or elephantiasis.

FIGURE 21-20 A malfunctioning lymphatic system. When the lymphatic system is damaged, fluid builds up in the extremities.

3. Retrieving nutrients. The lymphatic system has numerous little projections that extend into the small intestine and absorb lipids from the food you have eaten and shuttle them from the digestive tract to the bloodstream.

In humans, the lymphatic system accomplishes these tasks without a pump. There is no "lymph heart." Rather, lymph is pushed through the system when muscles adjacent to lymph vessels contract and squeeze the fluid onward. Lymph vessels (like veins) have valves that keep the lymph flowing in one direction. When you sit for an extended period of time, lymph can accumulate in vessels. You can help move it along by contracting the muscles in your extremities and progressively contracting muscles closer and closer to your shoulders.

Infection by some parasitic worms can cause scarring of lymph vessels. Fluid recovered by the lymphatic system cannot be returned to the circulatory system, and elephantiasis, or a swelling of the extremities, results (**FIGURE 21-20**). Because the parasitic worms causing elephantiasis are transmitted by mosquitoes, the condition is most common in tropical regions. The condition can be treated with antibiotics that kill the symbiotic bacteria necessary for the parasitic worm to live.

TAKE-HOME MESSAGE 21·9

The lymphatic system runs close to the circulatory system throughout the body and plays a supporting role in the process of circulation, by performing three main functions: recycling fluid that leaks out of the capillaries of the circulatory system, marshaling white blood cells to help fight dangerous cells and pathogens, and absorbing nutrients from the digestive system.

21·10

The polygraph relies on cues from the cardiovascular system.

"Is your name John Doe? Do you have a driver's license? Did you stab Nick Eliot in the back?" Amazingly, measures of a person's respiratory and circulatory system functioning may help determine whether that person's answers to such radically unrelated questions are true. The **polygraph**—initially called the "lie detector" test—is a practical application of some of the physiological measures discussed above. Many law enforcement

agencies and other governmental bureaus, as well as numerous private organizations, use the polygraph to help them evaluate whether or not an individual is telling the truth.

Polygraph examiners make readings of three types of measures during an examination: (1) chest and abdominal movement during respiration, indicating breathing rate; (2) changes in

Circulatory Systems   Human Circulation   Gas Exchange   Hemoglobin and Myoglobin

skin conductance, indicating activity of sweat glands; and (3) heart rate and amplitude, and blood pressure (**FIGURE 21-21**). During the exam, the polygrapher asks a series of questions. Some of the questions are control questions for which the examiner knows the answer, such as: "Do you have a driver's license?" The questions of interest (such as the question about stabbing Nick Eliot), called relevant questions, are interspersed among the control questions.

In analyzing an individual's physiological responses to the interview questions, polygraphers are looking for evidence of the fight-or-flight response, an automatic set of responses to stress in an organism's environment. These take the form of increases in all three measurements during a relevant question—that is, in breathing rate, skin conductance, and heart rate—all of which are greater than when the respondent answers the control questions.

Interestingly, while the results of polygraph tests are not admissible in federal courts, law enforcement agencies such as the Federal Bureau of Investigation still find them to be of great value. Based on their assessments of a suspect's guilt or innocence after a polygraph test, investigators may then search for additional evidence to corroborate their belief in someone's guilt or to find another suspect when they believe, based on a polygraph, someone is innocent.

Some people have tried to develop techniques for "beating" the polygraph. These include behaviors such as putting a thumbtack in their shoe and leaning forward into it during the control questions, or biting the inside of their mouth so as to increase the magnitude of their respiration and sweating. Generally, these techniques increase the magnitude of some of the measures, but not all of them. And examiners are on the

> The polygraph can be an effective tool for evaluating whether or not an individual is telling the truth by looking for manifestations of the fight-or-flight response.

THREE TYPES OF POLYGRAPH MEASUREMENTS

Chest and abdominal movement during respiration, indicating breathing rate

Changes in skin conduction, indicating activity of the sweat glands

Heart rate and amplitude, and blood pressure

FIGURE 21-21 Telling the truth?

lookout for individuals' use of such attempts at deception and interpret them as signs of guilt. Does the machine enable polygraphers to detect lies? Analyses of in-the-field examinations and laboratory simulations of examinations indicate average accuracies of between 80% and 98%, but it depends greatly on the skills of the person administering the test and remains a controversial technique.

TAKE-HOME MESSAGE 21·10

> The polygraph can be an effective tool for evaluating whether or not an individual is telling the truth. A polygraph measures manifestations of the fight-or-flight response: (1) chest and abdominal movement during respiration, indicating breathing rate; (2) changes in skin conductance, indicating activity of sweat glands; and (3) heart rate and amplitude and blood pressure.

This polygraph tracing recorded Jack Ruby's physiological responses to questions about the murder of Lee Harvey Oswald.

❸ The respiratory system enables gas exchange in animals.

Humpback whales spouting (exhaling) while feeding in Alaska.

21·11

Oxygen and carbon dioxide must get into and out of the circulatory system.

As we've seen, circulatory systems are like trucking systems and the highways on which they move. Of the substances they transport, among the most important are the respiratory gases. After all, aerobic respiration requires cells to take up oxygen and release carbon dioxide. But how do these gases get into and out of the circulatory system? Where and how does gas exchange take place? In the remainder of this chapter, we investigate the structures where gas exchange occurs and the transport molecules that make it possible.

In single-celled and very small multicellular organisms, gas exchange can occur by direct diffusion. In larger multicellular organisms, however, gas exchange becomes a two-stage process (**FIGURE 21-22**). First comes the exchange between the external environment and the organism's circulatory system. Later comes the exchange between the circulatory system and the cells involved in cellular respiration.

The first of these two stages can occur in several different types of organs specialized for respiration, such as lungs or

GAS EXCHANGE IN ANIMALS

In large, multicellular organisms, gas exchange is a two-stage process.

1 Respiratory gases are exchanged between the external environment and the organism's circulatory system.

2 Respiratory gases are exchanged between the circulatory system and the cells involved in cellular respiration.

FIGURE 21-22 Overview of respiratory gas exchange in animals.

Circulatory Systems   Human Circulation   Gas Exchange   Hemoglobin and Myoglobin

DIVERSITY IN GAS EXCHANGE SYSTEMS

DIRECT DIFFUSION
- Gas exchange occurs directly between cells and the environment
- Occurs in single-celled organisms and small organisms with low metabolic demands

PROTRUDING RESPIRATORY SACS
- Balloon-like sacs that increase surface area for gas exchange
- Occur in sea stars and other echinoderms with low metabolic demands

GILLS
- Elaborate extensions of the body that exchange significant amounts of gases dissolved in water
- Occur in fishes and many marine invertebrates such as lobsters and clams

TRACHEAE
- Network of branching tubes connected to tiny openings on the body called spiracles
- Occur in most terrestrial insects

LUNGS
- Internal organs with highly branched, moist surfaces
- Occur in most land vertebrates

gills. In all cases, however, it requires a respiratory medium—air or water—that serves as a reservoir for the gases, and a moist respiratory surface on which the gas exchange can occur. The many different solutions for gas exchange that have evolved fall into five categories (**FIGURE 21-23**).

1. *Direct diffusion.* Single-celled organisms and many small multicellular organisms with low metabolic demands, such as marine flatworms, can accomplish respiration by direct diffusion between the cells and the environment.

2. *Protruding respiratory sacs.* Many slightly larger organisms also have low metabolic needs. Sea stars and other echinoderms have little balloon-like sacs that protrude from the skin—greatly increasing the surface area—and exchange gases between the body cavity and the environment.

3. *Gills.* Fishes and many aquatic invertebrates, such as lobsters and clams, have **gills.** These extensions of the body are tremendously elaborated structures in which the large surface area allows extensive exchange of gases between the water and the blood vessels of the circulatory system.

4. *Tracheae.* Although insect bodies look rather solid, they have a huge number of tiny openings—spiracles—that lead to tubes that branch extensively throughout the body. These inner tubes make it possible for gases in the air to come in direct contact with most of the organism's cells.

5. *Lungs.* Most land vertebrates have **lungs.** These are internal organs, characterized by highly branched, moist respiratory surfaces, across which gases in the air that is breathed in are exchanged with gases dissolved in the blood circulating through the lung tissue. Birds, reptiles, and mammals do virtually all of their respiration through their lungs, but amphibians (such as frogs) also exchange gases through their skin, which serves as a supplemental respiratory system. Their skin stays moist because of their largely aquatic lifestyle.

TAKE-HOME MESSAGE 21·11

In single-celled and very small multicellular organisms, gas exchange can occur by direct diffusion. In larger multicellular organisms, gas exchange is a two-stage process: (1) exchange between the external environment and the organism's circulatory system, which usually takes place in lungs, tracheae, or gills, and (2) exchange between the circulatory system and the cells involved in cellular respiration.

Gas exchange takes place in the gills of aquatic vertebrates.

Fishes have noses, but they don't use them for breathing. Respiration begins, instead, with a gulp. The fish opens its mouth and sucks in a mouthful of water. It then closes its mouth, opens small holes on either side of its head, and releases, or "exhales," the water. Unlike the air that humans and other mammals breathe in and out, water follows a one-way path into and out of the fish, never changing direction.

Gas exchange takes place as the water passes through the gills, complex structures adapted to extract as much O_2 as possible from water (**FIGURE 21-24**). This extraction is a difficult task, because water has only 5% of the oxygen concentration found in air. The gills generally consist of four bony or cartilaginous gill arches on either side of the head. Similar in appearance to the teeth of a comb, these arches give support to the gill. Long filaments of tissue extend like an accordion from each gill arch, spreading out and creating as much surface area as possible. The filaments are stacks of hundreds of disk-like structures, called **lamellae,** on which the gas

exchange takes place. Each membranous lamella is a semicircular disk of elaborately branched capillaries. As water rushes across the gills, it passes between the lamellae, coming in almost direct contact with the capillaries. Because the blood cells are so close to the water, dissolved O_2 can pass from the inhaled water to the blood by direct diffusion, and dissolved CO_2 can pass by direct diffusion from the blood to the exhaled water.

Blood circulation in gills is set up in a simple pattern that is highly efficient at extracting oxygen from the water. In each filament, the blood vessels are arranged so that the blood is moving in the opposite direction from the water flowing past the gills. Called a "countercurrent exchange system," this layout is dramatically more efficient than if the blood flowed in the same direction as the water. If the blood flowed in the same direction, the gills would extract a maximum of about 50% of the oxygen in the water; with the countercurrent system, the gills extract as much as 85% of the oxygen in the water.

GAS EXCHANGE IN FISHES

Gas exchange in fishes takes place in the gills—complex structures adapted to extract oxygen from water, generally consisting of four gill arches on either side of the head.

GILL ARCH
Cartilaginous structure that provides support for the filaments

LAMELLAE
Disk-like structures stacked along the filaments that contain the capillaries where gas exchange takes place

- Oxygen-rich blood
- Oxygen-poor blood

Gills

FILAMENTS
Thread-like structures—composed of hundreds of lamellae—that spread out and create as much surface area as possible

- Oxygen-rich water
- Oxygen-poor water

By orienting vessels so that the blood is flowing in the opposite direction to the water, gills make it possible to extract significantly more oxygen from the water than if vessels and water flowed in the same direction.

FIGURE 21-24 Gills. The remarkable structure of gills makes gas exchange possible in fishes.

Circulatory Systems   Human Circulation   Gas Exchange   Hemoglobin and Myoglobin

COUNTERCURRENT EXCHANGE

COUNTERCURRENT EXCHANGE:
BLOOD AND WATER FLOW IN OPPOSITE DIRECTIONS
In a countercurrent system, water always has slightly more oxygen than blood, so a continuous concentration gradient is maintained, extracting as much oxygen as possible.

BLOOD AND WATER FLOW IN THE SAME DIRECTION
If blood were to flow in the same direction as the water, it could only become 50% saturated with oxygen, because there is no longer a concentration gradient to enable more diffusion of oxygen.

The countercurrent exchange system is dramatically more efficient at extracting oxygen than if the blood flowed in the same direction as the water.

FIGURE 21-25 Improving gas exchange. In countercurrent exchange, the direction of blood flowing through the gills maximizes the uptake of oxygen.

The countercurrent system is so efficient because it maintains a concentration gradient (that is, a difference in concentration) between the water and the bloodstream for the entire time that the water and blood vessel are in close contact (and because the gas exchange is accomplished through diffusion, which is passive, no ATP is required) (**FIGURE 21-25**). Depleted of O_2 in the tissues of the body, blood moving into the lamella encounters water that has been next to capillaries for a considerable distance and has already lost most of its oxygen.

The water may only have, for example, 10% of the O_2 it contained when first taken into the fish's mouth. Still, because the blood next to the water has been almost totally depleted of oxygen, the water still has a greater concentration of oxygen and therefore O_2 will diffuse from the water to the blood. Further along through the lamella, the blood has slightly more oxygen. The water, however, also has slightly more oxygen. Consequently, O_2 continues to diffuse from the water to the blood. By the time the blood has traveled almost completely through the lamella, it is holding about 70% or 80% of the maximum amount of oxygen that it can hold. At this point, however, the blood is encountering water that has entered the lamella straight from the fish's mouth, and this water is as saturated with O_2 as it can be. And so, even at this point, there is a concentration gradient and the blood can pick up just a bit more oxygen before returning to the tissues in the fish where it is needed. Carbon dioxide is removed from the fish's circulatory system in the same, countercurrent exchange way.

> **Relationships are like sharks; they have to keep moving or they die.**
>
> —Woody Allen, *Annie Hall*

Fishes are not the only aquatic animals with gills. Many other groups of vertebrates and invertebrates have gills, including molluscs, such as clams, and arthropods, such as lobsters. Gills range from simple to complex, and there is a great deal of variation in the associated structures. Most sharks, for example, move water past the gills not in the manner described above, used by most fishes, but just by swimming forward all the time. If they stop moving forward, the oxygen in the water surrounding the gills is quickly depleted and the shark will suffocate. Consequently, they spend their whole lives moving forward.

TAKE-HOME MESSAGE 21·12

In aquatic vertebrates, respiration begins when an organism opens its mouth, takes in water, and moves the water out through its gills. Gas exchange takes place in the gills, which extract as much oxygen as possible from the water by maintaining an O_2 concentration gradient between the water and the blood flowing through the gills.

Respiratory systems of terrestrial vertebrates move oxygen-rich air into the lungs and carbon-dioxide-rich air out of the lungs.

Life on land is very different from life underwater, but the fundamental energetic needs remain. ATP is still the chemical that provides the energy for all the reactions necessary for life, and cells still need oxygen to produce ATP. And consequently, an organism must put air in contact with the cells that need it. Ultimately, oxygen must get into the cells and carbon dioxide must get out. These are universal challenges facing all terrestrial animals.

Terrestrial vertebrates have a general solution to these challenges. First, they suck in air through their mouth or nose. The air moves down a trachea, or windpipe, into lungs. In the lungs, O_2 diffuses from air to blood, while CO_2 diffuses from blood to air. Finally, the oxygen-depleted air is exhaled and the process begins again. The specific design of the lungs and respiratory system varies a bit from one taxon to another—we review the most notable distinctions below—but the general process is the same.

Mammalian respiration begins with a deep breath. Let's trace the air through the respiratory process (**FIGURE 21-26**). Air enters through the nose, filling the nasal cavity, where it becomes warm and moist. Additional air can be taken in through the mouth. In either case, these two entry points for air join together at the throat (also called the pharynx), in the back of the mouth. The air passes through the throat and moves through the voice box, or vocal cords—also called the larynx. The voice box can be seen as the bump on the front of your neck, called the "Adam's apple." From the larynx, the air moves into the trachea. The trachea is a long windpipe that takes the air into the chest cavity. Once there, the trachea splits, with a fork going to the left lung and a fork going to the right lung.

Lungs are like stretchy, elastic bags. Where the trachea splits, the two smaller tubes are called bronchi. These enter the lungs and branch again. And again. And again. With each successive branching, the bronchi get smaller. Under a certain size they are called bronchioles. And they all just keep branching and spreading out. Eventually, the bronchioles reach a dead end. These dead ends are tiny elastic sacs, the alveoli. Here is where the air meets the blood vessels (**FIGURE 21-27**).

There are about 300 million alveoli in each human lung, with a total surface area roughly the size of a movie screen. Alveoli are made up from the most delicate cells in our bodies and have ultra-thin walls. Completely surrounding the alveoli, the way

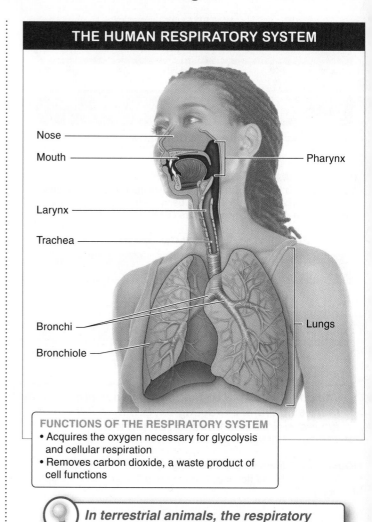

THE HUMAN RESPIRATORY SYSTEM

Nose
Mouth
Pharynx
Larynx
Trachea
Bronchi
Bronchiole
Lungs

FUNCTIONS OF THE RESPIRATORY SYSTEM
- Acquires the oxygen necessary for glycolysis and cellular respiration
- Removes carbon dioxide, a waste product of cell functions

In terrestrial animals, the respiratory system provides the route for inhaled air to meet the blood vessels of the body.

FIGURE 21-26 A terrestrial mammal. Overview of the human respiratory system.

your fingers might completely surround a small ball that you are grasping, are tiny capillaries. The capillaries have extremely thin walls, too. Oxygen in the alveoli dissolves in moisture on the cells lining them. It can then pass right through the two sets of thin membranes—alveolar and capillary—and get picked up by the bloodstream. Simultaneously, carbon dioxide can diffuse from the blood into the alveoli. In the short time you hold it in your lungs, the breath you inhaled is changed. When exhaled, it is depleted of O_2 and laden with CO_2.

Circulatory Systems | Human Circulation | Gas Exchange | Hemoglobin and Myoglobin

GAS EXCHANGE THROUGH ALVEOLI

Alveoli are the delicate, thin-walled elastic sacs at the end of bronchioles where air meets the blood vessels.

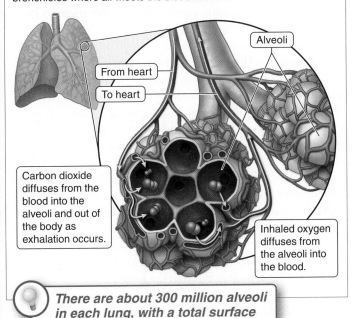

Carbon dioxide diffuses from the blood into the alveoli and out of the body as exhalation occurs.

Inhaled oxygen diffuses from the alveoli into the blood.

There are about 300 million alveoli in each lung, with a total surface area the size of a movie screen!

FIGURE 21-27 Alveoli in the lungs: where air meets blood vessels.

Amphibians and reptiles are almost identical to mammals when it comes to the respiratory system. The lungs of amphibians are a bit smaller, but amphibians make up for some of this reduced lung capacity by conducting a bit of gas exchange across their skin. This is why they must keep their skin moist at all times. Reptiles are generally too thick-skinned and scaly to achieve any respiration through their skin, but they have slightly larger lungs than amphibians to pick up the slack. Birds, among the terrestrial vertebrates, are the champions of respiratory efficiency. We explore some of their unique adaptations in Section 21.14.

Smoking introduces thousands of different chemicals into the respiratory system, many of which—such as formaldehyde, ammonia, and benzene—have powerfully destructive effects on its cells. Toxic particles in tobacco smoke can damage the cilia lining the trachea. This reduces the ability to filter out dirt and microorganisms from the air we breathe. The dangerous chemicals can also kill immune system cells that help fight off infections, further reducing our immune response to pathogens. The chemicals in smoke also trigger mucous secretions that can block airways and lead to other respiratory difficulties. After chronic exposure to smoke, the walls of the alveoli become brittle, reducing respiratory capacity. And perhaps most significantly, carcinogenic chemicals in tobacco smoke can trigger unrestrained cell multiplication in lung tissues, causing cancer (**FIGURE 21-28**).

Q How does smoking damage the lungs? Can the damage be reversed?

TWINS: SMOKER AND NON-SMOKER

DAMAGE CAUSED BY SMOKING
- Toxic particles damage the cilia lining the trachea.
- Chemicals can kill immune cells that help fight off infections.
- Chemicals trigger mucous secretions that can block the airways.
- Walls of alveoli become brittle, reducing respiratory capacity.
- Carcinogenic chemicals can trigger cancer.

Although smoking is destructive in numerous ways, stopping smoking at any point can begin the process of reversing some of the damage.

FIGURE 21-28 **Effects of smoking.** One of these identical twins is a smoker. Can you figure out which one?

Respiratory Adaptations

Although smoking is destructive in numerous ways, causing almost half a million deaths in the United States every year, stopping smoking at any point can begin the process of reversing some of the damage. By the end of the first year of nonsmoking, the risk of death from lung cancer and heart disease begins to decrease, and after 15 years of nonsmoking, the risk of death from these causes returns to the same levels as for individuals who have never smoked.

21·14

Birds have unusually efficient respiratory systems.

Birds take breathing to new heights. They often spend time in high-altitude, low-oxygen habitats, and they also fly for long periods of time, necessitating a great deal of oxygen (**FIGURE 21-29**). These extreme needs can be met by several key evolutionary adaptations that make it possible for birds to exchange gases much more efficiently than other terrestrial vertebrates.

Respiratory adaptations have evolved that enable birds to exchange gases with great efficiency—even at high altitudes where oxygen availability is low.

FIGURE 21-29 High-altitude respiration. Adaptations enable birds to function even when oxygen is in short supply.

For starters, birds' respiratory adaptations enable them to keep oxygen-rich air flowing through the lungs twice as long as in mammals. In mammals, air is inhaled and reaches a dead end at the alveoli. On the exhale, it changes direction and is breathed out. During the exhale, no new oxygen is reaching the lungs, a problematic situation during times of exertion. In birds, a more efficient system ensures that oxygen-containing air never runs into a dead end and the lungs never experience "stale" air. Here's how they do it (**FIGURE 21-30**).

When the bird inhales, some of the air passes through the lungs, where oxygen can diffuse into the blood. The rest of the air fills temporary holding structures called the posterior air sacs. Then, when the bird exhales, the posterior air sacs contract and push more oxygen-rich air through the lungs. With this system, even during exhales, when no "new" air is being breathed in, oxygen-rich air is passing through the lungs.

When a bird is inhaling, air moving through the lungs passes into other temporary holding structures, called anterior air sacs. Then, as the bird exhales, oxygen-poor air passing through the lungs *and* oxygen-poor air from the anterior air sacs together move into the trachea, and this mix is expelled from the bird's body.

With their circular system made possible by the air sacs and by the lungs' unique pass-through channels (called parabronchi), birds maintain a continuous and unidirectional flow of oxygen-rich air through the lungs. To increase the efficiency of the

Q How is bird breathing less like mammal breathing and more like fish "breathing"?

Circulatory Systems | Human Circulation | Gas Exchange | Hemoglobin and Myoglobin

CIRCULAR RESPIRATORY SYSTEMS IN BIRDS

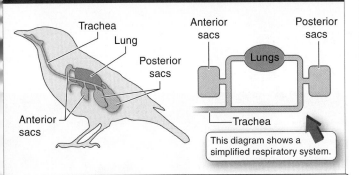

Trachea
Lung
Posterior sacs
Anterior sacs

Anterior sacs
Posterior sacs
Lungs
Trachea

This diagram shows a simplified respiratory system.

INHALATION
- Fresh, oxygen-rich air moves down the trachea, inflating the posterior "waiting room" sacs, as well as the lungs.
- At the same time, oxygen-poor air is expelled from the lungs, inflating the anterior sacs.

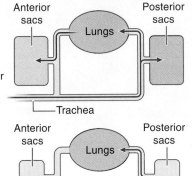

Anterior sacs
Posterior sacs
Lungs
Trachea

EXHALATION
- The posterior sacs deflate, pushing oxygen-rich air into the lungs.
- The anterior sacs deflate, pushing oxygen-poor air out of the trachea.

Anterior sacs
Posterior sacs
Lungs
Trachea

In birds, unlike in humans, air moves in one direction through the lungs. And during both inhalation and exhalation, fresh air continues flowing through the lungs.

FIGURE 21-30 Meeting extreme needs. The highly efficient gas-exchange system of birds supports the oxygen demands of flight.

Adaptations in the bird respiratory system make prolonged flight, even at low-oxygen altitudes, possible.

system even more, all the blood vessels in the lungs are oriented so that the blood is flowing at a 90° angle relative to the direction of the air flow. This use of "cross-current flow" further increases the diffusion of gases between the air and blood. In practical terms, these adaptations make it possible for geese to fly over Mount Everest, nearly six miles above sea level, while a mammal deposited at that height would pass out almost instantly from insufficient oxygen.

TAKE-HOME MESSAGE 21·14

Birds often spend time in high-altitude, low-oxygen habitats and may fly for long periods of time, both of which require a great deal of oxygen. These extreme needs are met by a circular system of air flow and cross-current blood flow in the lungs, which make it possible for birds to exchange gases more efficiently than other terrestrial vertebrates.

Muscles control the flow of air into and out of the lungs.

Breathe in. Breathe out. It all seems simple enough. You don't even have to think about it. But over the course of your life, this simple process will happen 500 million times without fail. How does it work?

In reptiles, birds, and mammals, breathing occurs in two steps: inhalation and exhalation (**FIGURE 21-31**). The chest cavity is bordered on the bottom by a large sheet of muscle called the

THE MECHANICS OF BREATHING

Breathing is made possible by the following structures in the chest cavity:

- Trachea
- Ribs
- Intercostal muscles
- Lung
- Diaphragm

In reptiles, birds, and mammals, breathing occurs in two steps.

1 **INHALATION**
- Diaphragm and intercostal muscles contract
- Diaphragm is pulled lower and rib cage expands
- Air is sucked into the lungs

2 **EXHALATION**
- Diaphragm and intercostal muscles relax
- Chest cavity returns to its original size
- Air is forced back out to the trachea

FIGURE 21-31 Body structures that make breathing possible.

The added buoyancy of lungs full of air makes it challenging to stay submerged under water.

diaphragm, which separates the chest cavity from the abdominal cavity. The rest of the chest cavity is surrounded by the rib cage and the intercostal muscles between the ribs. During inhalation, these two sets of muscles contract, pulling the diaphragm down and expanding the rib cage. This causes a rapid increase in the volume of the chest cavity and lungs, which causes air to be sucked into the lungs. When the diaphragm and intercostal muscles relax, the chest cavity returns to its original size. This reduction in the volume compresses the lungs and forces air back out of the trachea.

"I'm going to hold my breath until I die." As a child, you may have threatened your parents this way. It's actually not possible to do this, however. Although we can consciously control our breathing to some extent, chemical sensors in the body detect when carbon dioxide levels rise dangerously high, and our brain responds by sending signals to the muscles that control our breathing, spurring them to override our efforts to stop breathing.

TAKE-HOME MESSAGE 21·15

In reptiles, birds, and mammals, breathing occurs in two steps: inhalation and exhalation. During inhalation, muscles contract, pulling the diaphragm down, expanding the rib cage, and increasing the volume of the chest cavity and lungs, which causes air to be sucked into the lungs. When the muscles relax, the chest cavity returns to its original size and air is forced out of the lungs.

Some environments are more conducive to gas exchange than others.

Breathing is more difficult in some places than others. Because the diffusion of gases between the outside and inside of an animal depends on several physical factors, animals vary widely in their respiratory efficiency (**FIGURE 21-32**). The most important constraints on oxygen diffusion rates are temperature, viscosity, and pressure.

1. Temperature: cold versus hot. Keep some cans of beer or soda in a warm car all day and then open them. Why does the fluid fizz more than usual? As the temperature of water

CONSTRAINTS ON OXYGEN DIFFUSION RATES

Oxygen diffusion—and, hence, oxygen availability to body tissues—is influenced by features such as temperature, viscosity, and (shown here) pressure.

FIGURE 21-32 Gas exchange is more difficult in some environments than others.

(or air) goes up, its ability to hold gases goes down. Whether the respiratory medium is air or water, it doesn't hold as much oxygen when it gets warmer. This means that a fish must work harder to get enough oxygen in warmer water.

2. Viscosity (thickness): air versus water. From a breathing organism's perspective, air is much better than water. Air has much higher dissolved oxygen content than water, and oxygen diffuses from air into blood 8,000 times faster than from water into blood. It also takes less energy to move air than water.

3. Pressure: low versus high altitude. At high altitudes, much less oxygen is available. You don't even need to climb the Himalayas to experience this. A relatively short walk up a much smaller mountain will convince you. At 15,000 feet above sea level, for example, the air pressure is half of what it is at sea level. This is because there is less atmosphere above the air, pushing down on it. With lower pressure from above, less oxygen is squeezed into a given volume. This makes it hard to push air into lungs and to drive the oxygen across the alveoli and capillary membranes and into the blood. Mountain climbers often carry canisters of pressurized oxygen. In the lungs, the high-pressure oxygen can more easily diffuse into the bloodstream.

TAKE-HOME MESSAGE 21·16

The diffusion of gases between the outside and inside of an animal depends on several physical factors, including temperature, viscosity, and pressure, leading to variations among animals in their respiratory efficiency. The rate of gas exchange is higher in cold (vs. warm) temperatures, in air (vs. water), and at low (vs. high) altitudes.

Rowers strain to take in enough oxygen to fuel their high-intensity racing effort.

21·17

Hemoglobin is the molecule that transports oxygen.

Red blood cells are filled with hemoglobin. Hemoglobin is like an oxygen "shuttle bus," transporting oxygen around the body. In the lungs, it picks up O_2 and hangs on to it as the blood cell returns to the heart and is pumped to the body. Only when it reaches tissues, such as organs or muscles, that are in need of oxygen but are far from sources of the vital gas does the hemoglobin bus release its O_2 "passengers." The empty hemoglobin then returns to the lungs, where it can load up on oxygen again. It is the oxygen–carrying hemoglobin that gives our blood its red color. When it gives up its O_2, hemoglobin turns more of a purplish-maroonish color. That's why books often show oxygenated blood in arteries as red and deoxygenated blood in veins as blue.

Hemoglobin is a tiny molecule—so tiny that there are about 250 million copies of it in every single red blood cell. Built right inside the blood cell, it remains there for the cell's entire life. Each molecule of hemoglobin is a tangled mass of four polypeptide chains. Nestled within the molecule are four cozy compartments, each of which can carry one molecule of oxygen gas on a seat of iron. This iron attaches to the O_2 that diffuses into the red blood cell, temporarily making it part of the hemoglobin molecule (**FIGURE 21-33**). As we saw above, a shortage of iron in your diet can lead to anemia. This is because when iron is in short supply, less oxygen can be bound by hemoglobin and transported by each red blood cell, causing muscles and organs to be starved of oxygen and leading to feelings of fatigue and weakness.

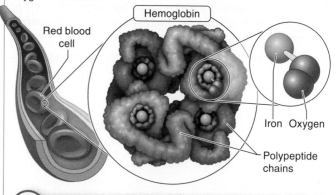

HEMOGLOBIN

Each molecule of hemoglobin is a tangled mass of four polypeptide chains with four molecules of iron that create four "seats" to which oxygen can attach.

Hemoglobin

Red blood cell

Iron Oxygen

Polypeptide chains

💡 *The hemoglobin molecule is like an oxygen "shuttle bus" that picks up oxygen in the lungs and transports it to tissues.*

FIGURE 21-33 Hemoglobin: the oxygen transporter.

Although it is banned by the Olympics and most sports organizations, "blood doping" has been used by some athletes to improve their performance. One method involves withdrawing red blood cells during the weeks and months leading up to a big competition, storing them, and re-injecting them in the few days just before the competition. Because red blood cells are filled with hemoglobin, the oxygen-carrying pigment, blood doping can increase the athlete's capacity for delivering O_2 to his or her tissues. In addition to being against the rules in most competitions, however, blood doping also carries some health risks, because it increases the viscosity of the blood. In the 1990s, dozens of apparently healthy, elite cyclists died inexplicably from heart failure. It was suspected that their blood had become so thick with red blood cells from blood doping that the burden on the heart to pump their sludge-like blood became too great.

Hemoglobin binds to oxygen, but doesn't hold on to it so tightly that it never lets go. Like Post-it notes, which are useful because they are sticky enough to attach to surfaces but not so sticky as to become permanently affixed, hemoglobin "knows" when to bind to O_2 and when to release it. This hinges on something called the partial pressure of the oxygen (denoted as Po_2), the force of oxygen particles in the air pressing against the body (**FIGURE 21-34**).

Where in a body might hemoglobin encounter relatively high or low partial pressures of oxygen? When you breathe air that

HIGH PARTIAL PRESSURE OF OXYGEN
When hemoglobin encounters a high partial pressure of oxygen, such as in inhaled air in the lungs, hemoglobin gets packed with oxygen.

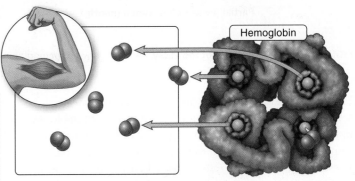

LOW PARTIAL PRESSURE OF OXYGEN
When hemoglobin encounters a low partial pressure of oxygen, such as in active muscle tissue in the body, hemoglobin releases oxygen.

FIGURE 21-35 Hemoglobin binds and releases oxygen, depending on the partial pressure of oxygen in the vicinity.

has a high concentration of oxygen, all four O_2 compartments in hemoglobin eagerly bind to oxygen molecules. Deep in the tissues of your body, though, oxygen is not in great supply—especially if you are exerting yourself and your muscles have been consuming oxygen as they contract. When these tissues become depleted of oxygen, any hemoglobin in the vicinity encounters a low partial pressure of oxygen (Po_2). And what does hemoglobin do when it encounters low Po_2? Because the oxygen it carries is not held too tightly, some of it is released (**FIGURE 21-35**). This oxygen is quickly soaked up by the tissue, which can then continue to generate ATP.

When you are sitting at your desk, the Po_2 in your tissues isn't very low. Your muscles aren't contracting, and your breathing rate isn't especially high. Much like a car coasting downhill, you aren't using much fuel. In these circumstances, hemoglobin only gives up about one of its four molecules of bound oxygen gas before returning to the lungs to load up again. Back and forth it cycles between getting packed with four oxygens in your lungs and being reduced to three oxygens in your tissues.

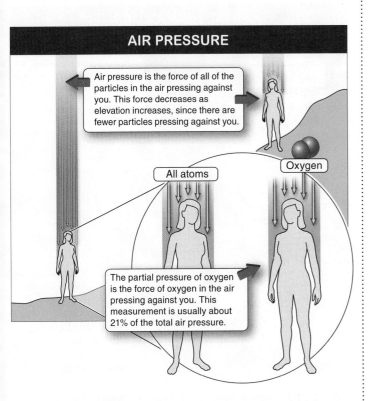

AIR PRESSURE

Air pressure is the force of all of the particles in the air pressing against you. This force decreases as elevation increases, since there are fewer particles pressing against you.

All atoms

Oxygen

The partial pressure of oxygen is the force of oxygen in the air pressing against you. This measurement is usually about 21% of the total air pressure.

FIGURE 21-34 The force of particles on you. Air pressure and the partial pressure of oxygen are reduced at higher altitudes.

OXYGEN BINDING CURVE FOR HEMOGLOBIN

OXYGEN DELIVERED DURING NORMAL METABOLISM
Hemoglobin only gives up one oxygen molecule in the body tissues before returning to the lungs.

OXYGEN DELIVERED DURING HIGH PHYSICAL EXERTION
Hemoglobin dips into its reserves, releasing two, three, or even all four of its oxygen molecules before returning to the lungs.

FIGURE 21-36 "Sticky, but not too sticky." A curve showing hemoglobin's affinity for oxygen.

This seems wasteful. If your hemoglobin usually oscillates between picking up a single molecule of oxygen in the lungs and dropping off that O_2 in the organs or muscles, what is the point of its carrying around the other three oxygen molecules? These are its emergency reserves for when you need a lot more oxygen to fuel some energetic activity. If you are exercising vigorously, for instance, the P_{O_2} in your tissues can drop so low that hemoglobin gives up another of its oxygen molecules. In extreme cases of exertion, it might give up three or even all four of the oxygens that it carries. **FIGURE 21-36** shows an oxygen binding curve for hemoglobin, illustrating the relationship between the P_{O_2} and the proportion of oxygen molecules that hemoglobin holds onto.

When a woman is pregnant, the growing fetus does not breathe air. This doesn't mean that the fetus doesn't need oxygen, however. During development, oxygen needs are actually very high. How does a fetus get the O_2 it needs? It has to scavenge oxygen molecules released by the mother's hemoglobin. Fetuses do this by producing their own special type of hemoglobin that is a bit stickier than normal adult hemoglobin. At a P_{O_2} that is low enough that the mother releases oxygen from her hemoglobin, the fetal hemoglobin—with its greater stickiness (or oxygen affinity)—binds to the oxygen. It can then deliver that oxygen to its own, fetal tissues (**FIGURE 21-37**).

If hemoglobin isn't put together exactly right, the health consequences can be serious and painful, as is seen in sickle-cell disease. A single change in the genetic instructions for building hemoglobin causes a malfunction in the hemoglobin molecules (see Chapter 7). When they lose their oxygen molecules—such as when an individual is exercising—the hemoglobin molecules

suddenly become misshapen and stick to each other, causing the entire red blood cell to collapse into a sharply pointed sickle. Once sickled, red blood cells cause a whole host of problems. Many break open, which can cause anemia if they aren't replaced promptly. Others clump together, often blocking

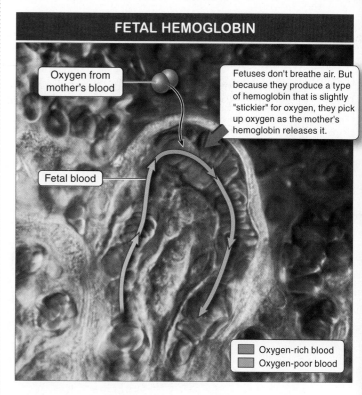

FETAL HEMOGLOBIN

Oxygen from mother's blood

Fetuses don't breathe air. But because they produce a type of hemoglobin that is slightly "stickier" for oxygen, they pick up oxygen as the mother's hemoglobin releases it.

Fetal blood

Oxygen-rich blood
Oxygen-poor blood

FIGURE 21-37 **How a fetus gets oxygen.** The fetus produces hemoglobin that binds oxygen released by the mother's hemoglobin.

Circulatory Systems   Human Circulation   Gas Exchange   Hemoglobin and Myoglobin

capillaries where, normally, they must pass through one at a time. This leads to intense pain, especially in the joints and muscles, and can cause strokes if it occurs in the brain. About 70,000 people in the United States live with sickle-cell disease. They are able to minimize the effects by avoiding strenuous activity or other situations in which the P_{O_2} in their muscles and other tissues drops too low.

What is carbon monoxide poisoning?

In an unfortunate coincidence, carbon monoxide (CO) also binds to hemoglobin, but with a higher affinity than oxygen does. In areas with high carbon monoxide concentrations— such as around a faulty furnace or a kerosene heater or lamp without adequate ventilation—the carbon monoxide will out-compete oxygen for hemoglobin's binding sites and it doesn't adhere like a Post-it note, rather, the binding is irreversible. Thus, when the hemoglobin travels to the body tissues, it has no oxygen to release and, in the absence of O_2, cellular respiration cannot generate the ATP the tissue needs (see Chapter 4). Consequently, the tissue is suffocated even as the person takes deeper and deeper breaths.

TAKE-HOME MESSAGE 21·17

Red blood cells are filled with hemoglobin, a molecule that picks up oxygen in the lungs and transports it around the body, releasing it in organs and tissues, such as muscles, where it is needed for cellular respiration.

21·18

Myoglobin in muscles holds a reservoir of oxygen for times of exertion.

Oxygen isn't the fuel that makes muscles contract, but it is an essential component of the process. You will quickly cramp up if your muscles try to work for long in the absence of oxygen. To increase the oxygen available beyond the amount delivered by hemoglobin, muscles have a trick for storing the valuable molecule. It's called **myoglobin,** and it is a protein embedded in the muscle cells themselves (**FIGURE 21-38**). Like hemoglobin,

What is the difference between white meat and dark meat?

myoglobin is an oxygen-binding molecule. It's a smaller, simpler molecule, though, and has only a single compartment for storing oxygen. And because of its structure, myoglobin has a higher affinity for O_2 than hemoglobin does. This means that at moderately low P_{O_2}, hemoglobin releases oxygen that can quickly be taken up by myoglobin. The myoglobin then just holds on tightly to the oxygen molecule, releasing it only under conditions of extremely low P_{O_2}. Think of it as a last gasp of air for an animal's muscles. As a rabbit runs full speed away from a lynx, its muscles must burn fuel at a very high rate; the value of just a tiny extra capacity can be the difference between life and death. Because myoglobin is a darkly pigmented protein, muscles with higher concentrations of myoglobin are darker. This is what distinguishes "white meat" from "dark meat," a distinction that generally reveals how metabolically active a particular muscle is. Turkeys hardly use their breast muscles, because they don't fly, but they do use their leg muscles all day. This is why breast meat is white and thigh meat is darker. We'll see later in the chapter that deep-diving marine mammals also make use of the O_2 stored in myoglobin during their long dives (as do long-distance migrating birds on their long flights).

TAKE-HOME MESSAGE 21·18

Myoglobin is an oxygen-binding protein embedded in muscle cells that can release one molecule of oxygen under conditions of extremely low P_{O_2}.

MYOGLOBIN

Myoglobin is a hemoglobin-like molecule within muscle tissue. It can hold a single oxygen molecule, which it releases only under extremely low-oxygen conditions—generally during exertion—when the muscles need it most.

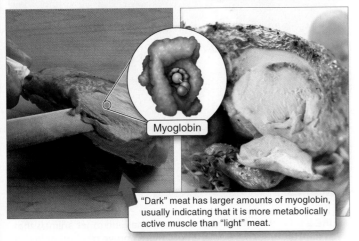

Myoglobin

"Dark" meat has larger amounts of myoglobin, usually indicating that it is more metabolically active muscle than "light" meat.

FIGURE 21-38 Oxygen reserves. Myoglobin is a protein in muscles that stores oxygen for times of extreme exertion.

5 Evolutionary adaptations maximize oxygen delivery.

Adapted to high altitudes, yaks are able to transport goods across mountain passes for farmers and Himalayan trekking expeditions.

21·19

Animals living at high altitude have special adaptations to the low-oxygen conditions.

As we saw above, because there is less atmosphere "pushing down" on air at high altitudes, the P_{O_2} is significantly reduced. It becomes hard to breathe, and activity is difficult. We struggle at high altitudes, because our hemoglobin isn't designed to pick up oxygen at such a low P_{O_2}; it isn't sticky enough. Mountain climbers can bring canisters of pressurized oxygen with them, but llamas and other animals living at high altitudes can't. How do they survive with less available oxygen? Their hemoglobin has a difficult task: it must pick up oxygen at very low pressure—precisely when hemoglobin is supposed to have a low affinity for oxygen—so that it can release it to muscles.

Living at altitudes of 5,000 meters, llamas have solved this problem by producing a slightly different form of hemoglobin, one that is adapted to low-oxygen conditions. At any given P_{O_2}, llama hemoglobin has a higher affinity for oxygen than human hemoglobin (**FIGURE 21-39**). It's stickier. This stickiness enables it to become saturated with four molecules of oxygen even when the llama breathes in

BREATHING AT HIGH ALTITUDES

Llamas can thrive in high-altitude, low-oxygen environments, because they produce a "stickier" form of hemoglobin that has a higher affinity for oxygen.

FIGURE 21-39 Built for high altitudes. Llamas and other animals that live at high altitudes have adaptations that improve respiration in low-oxygen environments.

Circulatory Systems   Human Circulation   Gas Exchange   Hemoglobin and Myoglobin

relatively "poor" air. Much like the oxygen binding curve of fetal hemoglobin, in llamas, the oxygen binding curve is shifted so that the hemoglobin is stickier for O_2, relative to adult human hemoglobin, at most Po_2 values. Because the Po_2 in llama tissues is even lower than in the air they breathe (because oxygen is being consumed by cellular respiration), the oxygen bound to the hemoglobin is still released to muscles to allow normal activity.

21·20

Humans become acclimated to low-oxygen conditions.

Is it just a coincidence that an unusually large percentage of the world's most accomplished mountain climbers are Sherpas, who live year-round in high-altitude Nepal? No. Although llamas may be built for high altitudes from the day they are born, humans acclimate well, and Sherpas are among the most impressively acclimated high-altitude dwellers (**FIGURE 21-40**).

You don't need to live on Mount Everest, however, to become physiologically acclimated to the low-oxygen conditions found at high altitudes. Athletes around the world have long known that they can increase their strength, speed, and

stamina by training at high altitudes. And, as with llamas, human acclimation to low-oxygen conditions comes from modifications (though they are acquired rather than inherited) to hemoglobin.

Training for three to five weeks at high altitudes—usually 6,000–7,000 feet in elevation—triggers several physiological changes, the process of acclimation. These changes include stimulating the production of additional red blood cells, increasing blood and capillary volume, and increasing the number of mitochondria. High-altitude training also causes an

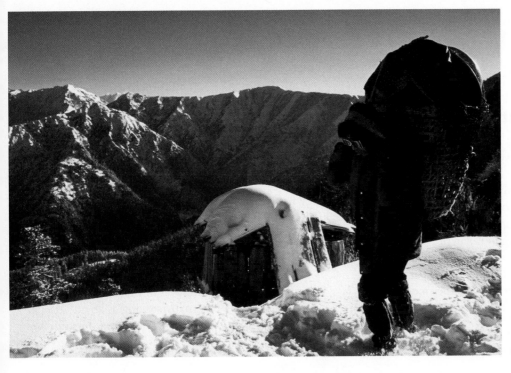

FIGURE 21-40 Humans acclimate to high-altitude living with improved respiratory efficiency.

Respiratory Adaptations

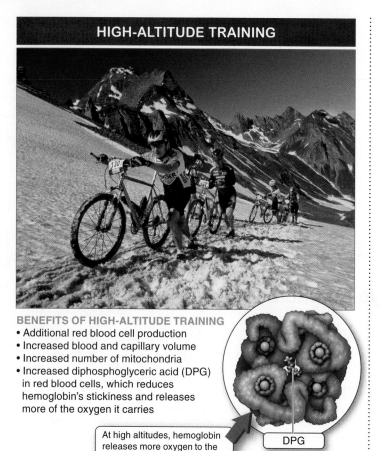

HIGH-ALTITUDE TRAINING

BENEFITS OF HIGH-ALTITUDE TRAINING
- Additional red blood cell production
- Increased blood and capillary volume
- Increased number of mitochondria
- Increased diphosphoglyceric acid (DPG) in red blood cells, which reduces hemoglobin's stickiness and releases more of the oxygen it carries

At high altitudes, hemoglobin releases more oxygen to the tissues at any P_{O_2}.

DPG

FIGURE 21-41 Improving athletic performance by training at high altitude.

increase in a chemical called diphosphoglyceric acid (DPG) in red blood cells. This acid combines with hemoglobin in the red blood cells and alters the protein's shape ever so slightly. In doing so, it reduces hemoglobin's stickiness, giving it a lower affinity for oxygen. With this reduced oxygen affinity, at any P_{O_2}, the DPG-modified hemoglobin releases more of the O_2 that it carries (**FIGURE 21-41**). Athletes who train at high altitudes find that with the additional oxygen released to their tissues, they can improve their performance by about 3%. This difference was manifested dramatically during the 1968 Olympics in Mexico City (altitude 7,500 feet) when the top five finishers in the 10,000-meter race were all year-round high-altitude residents. The benefits of high-altitude training remain after an athlete returns to sea level—increasing performance significantly. But just as humans become acclimated to high altitudes, we also become acclimated to low altitudes, and the DPG level (and the performance enhancement it can bring) is reduced about three to five weeks after returning to sea level.

TAKE-HOME MESSAGE 21·20

Humans living at high altitudes become acclimated to low-oxygen conditions over the course of three to five weeks. This acclimation includes increasing the production of diphosphoglyceric acid (DPG) in red blood cells and thereby reducing hemoglobin's affinity for oxygen, leading to release of higher levels of oxygen to muscles during exertion.

21·21

Deep-diving mammals are masters of efficient oxygen use.

How long can you hold your breath? If you're like most people, you can last just over a minute, or maybe 2 or 3 minutes at best. The world record is an amazing, but brain-choking, 11 minutes and 35 seconds held by Stéphan Mifsud of France, set in June 2009. Even this pales, though, when compared with the abilities of the Weddell seal (**FIGURE 21-42**). Living in Antarctica, these 900-pound mammals regularly make dives 200–500 meters deep in search of fish to eat. Usually staying underwater for 20 minutes, but sometimes for more than an hour, they are able to hold their breath for so long only as a consequence of numerous evolutionary adaptations.

Four critical respiratory and circulatory features make the seals' deep diving possible.

1. They have about double the volume of blood, per kilogram of body weight, that humans have. Much of it is stored in their unusually large spleen, which contracts during a dive, putting significantly more oxygen-carrying blood into circulation.

2. The myoglobin concentration in their muscles is about twice that in other mammals, serving as an additional storehouse of oxygen that can be utilized during dives.

Circulatory Systems   Human Circulation   Gas Exchange   Hemoglobin and Myoglobin

ADAPTATIONS IN WEDDELL SEALS

Several circulatory adaptations enable Weddell seals to hold their breath for an hour or more as they dive for fish to eat.

FIGURE 21-42 How long can you hold your breath? The deep-diving Weddell seal can swim underwater for long periods of time without surfacing for oxygen.

3. Not only do Weddell seals store more oxygen, but during dives they also use it more sparingly, lowering their heart rate from a normal 140 beats per minute to fewer than 30 beats per minute!

4. During dives, they become more efficient with their circulation, reducing metabolism by constricting the blood vessels in most tissues and sending blood only to those parts of the body that need it most, such as the brain, eyes, and spinal cord.

Much of this "diving reflex" of Weddell seals is also seen in other mammals. We experience a slight reduction in heart rate, for example, when we begin to hold our breath. Seals are just an extreme example of how physiological traits can reveal evolutionary adaptations.

TAKE-HOME MESSAGE 21·21

Deep-diving mammals can hold their breath for an hour or more by having double the volume of blood (per kilogram of body weight) and double the muscle myoglobin concentration relative to humans, by lowering their heart rate dramatically, and by constricting the blood vessels in most tissues, sending blood only where it is needed most.

Knowledge You Can Use

"Contents under pressure." Recognizing and avoiding the bends.

Q: What do scuba divers and bottles of champagne have in common? Under high pressure, large amounts of a gas can be dissolved in fluid. This is why champagne makers can load huge amounts of carbon dioxide into the bottle along with the champagne. It is also what happens to divers who, with tremendous water pressure on their bodies, must breathe highly pressurized air in order for oxygen to dissolve in their bloodstream.

Q: Why are bubbles bad news for divers? When a champagne bottle is uncorked, the pressure is suddenly released. Under low pressure, not nearly as much carbon dioxide can be held in the fluid, so it quickly bubbles out. Similarly, when a scuba diver returns too quickly to the surface, the pressure on the body is rapidly reduced, as is the capacity of the blood to hold gases. And like champagne after the cork is popped, many gases in the diver's blood—particularly nitrogen, which is the biggest component of air—quickly bubble out and can almost cause the diver to explode from within, in a condition known as "the bends." Something similar to the bends can occur if someone flies in an unpressurized plane and suddenly climbs very high, where the air pressure is lower. This was sometimes reported by pilots in World War II.

Q: What can you conclude about avoiding the bends? Just as the solution to opening a bottle of champagne without its bubbling over is to release the pressure very slowly by removing the cork slowly, a diver must reduce the pressure on his or her blood very slowly by rising gradually from the depths of the water. Alternatively, a diver can be placed in a chamber (called a hyperbaric chamber) to be gradually depressurized.

1 The circulatory system is the chief route of distribution in animals.

In animals, the circulatory system is the chief distribution system, with important functions in transport of gases, nutrients, waste products, immune system cells, and hormones, as well as maintenance of homeostasis. Circulatory systems can be open, with no clear distinction between circulating fluid and interstitial fluid, or closed, with a clear distinction. Fishes have two-chambered hearts and one circuit of blood flow; birds and mammals have four-chambered hearts and two circuits of flow, which enables them to pump blood to the body at higher pressure.

2 The heart is at the center of the human circulatory system.

The human heart is a muscular pump at the center of the circulatory system. It sends blood on a figure 8, two-cycle path through the body, first to the lungs and then, on its second circuit, to the tissues and organs. Blood is a salty, protein-rich mixture of cells and fluid, important in homeostasis and in the transport of respiratory gases, vitamins and minerals, nutrients, hormones, components of the immune system, and metabolic wastes. High blood pressure and cardiovascular disease impair circulatory system functioning. The lymphatic system has a supporting role in circulation: it recycles fluid from the circulatory system, moves white blood cells to help fight pathogens, and absorbs nutrients from the digestive system.

3 The respiratory system enables gas exchange in animals.

In very small organisms, gas exchange can occur by direct diffusion. In larger organisms, gas exchange is a two-stage process: exchange between the external environment and the organism's circulatory system, and exchange between the circulatory system and the cells involved in respiration. In aquatic vertebrates, gas exchange takes place as oxygen-carrying water passes through the gills. In terrestrial vertebrates, breathing occurs in two steps: inhalation and exhalation; O_2 diffuses across capillaries from the air to the blood, while CO_2 diffuses from blood to air.

4 Oxygen is transported and stored while bound to hemoglobin and myoglobin.

Red blood cells are filled with hemoglobin, which picks up oxygen in the lungs and transports it around the body, releasing it in organs and tissues for cellular respiration. Myoglobin is an oxygen-binding protein embedded in muscle cells that can release oxygen under conditions of extremely low P_{O_2}.

5 Evolutionary adaptations maximize oxygen delivery.

Some animals living at high altitudes cope with reduced P_{O_2} by producing hemoglobin that has a higher affinity for oxygen. Humans living at high altitudes become acclimated to the low-oxygen conditions by increasing production of diphosphoglyceric acid (DPG), thus reducing hemoglobin's affinity for oxygen. Adaptations in some deep-diving mammals include doubling of blood volume, doubling of muscle myoglobin, lowering of heart rate, and constriction of blood vessels to send blood only where it is needed most.

KEY TERMS

1. Which of the following is the name of the fluid in an insect's open circulatory system?
   a) blood
   b) hemoglobin
   c) lymph
   d) hemolymph
   e) tracheal lymph

2. How can flatworms, simple animals with a flat body shape, survive without a circulatory system?
   a) Flatworms do not have internal body fluids that need to be sectioned off and transported by vessels.
   b) Because all cells in flat-bodied animals are in direct contact with the external environment, direct diffusion is sufficient for all their respiratory needs.
   c) In flatworms, all cells are located near central body branches or near the body surface, so diffusion alone can transport important nutrients.
   d) Flatworms use the water currents in their aquatic environment to circulate the necessary nutrients throughout their body.
   e) Flatworms have multiple hearts and so can pump blood directly into tissues without needing a circulatory system.

3. Fishes have:
   a) a two-chambered heart.
   b) multiple hearts.
   c) an open circulatory system.
   d) a four-chambered heart.
   e) Both a) and c) are correct.

4. Blood pressure tends to fall with increasing distance from the heart. On the basis of this information, which of the following lists the types of blood vessel, in order, from highest blood pressure to lowest?
   a) veins, arteries, capillaries
   b) arteries, capillaries, veins
   c) veins, capillaries, arteries
   d) capillaries, veins, arteries
   e) arteries, veins, capillaries

5. The heartbeat in a vertebrate:
   a) is initiated by modified muscle tissue, the sinoatrial (SA) node, that contracts without nerve stimulation.
   b) is triggered by rhythmic stimulation from the cardiac nerve.
   c) begins at the bottom of the ventricles and moves upward through the heart.
   d) cannot be recorded by an EKG, but the neurons that control it can be.
   e) is initiated by the atrioventricular node.

6. Both red blood cells and white blood cells are derived from cells in:
   a) the heart.
   b) the liver.
   c) the spleen.
   d) the lungs.
   e) the bone marrow.

7. Which of the following components of human blood is a cell fragment?
   a) spiracle
   b) red blood cell
   c) white blood cell
   d) plasma
   e) platelet

8. How are the blood-circulation system and the lymphatic system related to each other?
   a) Blood carries nutrients to cells. The lymphatic system removes waste from the cells.
   b) Blood carries nutrients and oxygen to cells and removes their waste. The lymphatic system removes bacteria and debris from the blood.
   c) Blood carries nutrients and oxygen to cells and removes their waste. The lymphatic system takes the cellular waste to the kidneys.
   d) Blood carries oxygen to all the cells. The lymphatic system removes the carbon dioxide from the blood and carries it to the lungs.
   e) Blood carries carbon dioxide from tissues to the lungs. The lymphatic system carries oxygen from the lungs to the body tissues.

9. The polygraph, or "lie detector" test, functions by monitoring all of the following except:
   a) changes in skin conductance.
   b) changes in heart rate.
   c) changes in blood pressure.
   d) changes in chest and abdominal movement.
   e) changes in oxygen content of the blood.

10. Why do most fishes swim with their mouths open?
    a) They do this to take in any food particles suspended in the water.
    b) This is a cooling mechanism to help regulate body temperature.
    c) This allows a fish to swim faster.
    d) This helps prevent infection by mouth parasites.
    e) They do this to ventilate their gills.

11. Carbon dioxide transport differs from oxygen transport in the circulatory systems of mammals, because:
    a) CO_2 is transported mostly in the plasma, while O_2 is transported mostly in the red blood cells.
    b) CO_2 is transported mostly in the platelets, while O_2 is transported mostly in the red blood cells.
    c) CO_2 is transported mostly via the lymphatic system, while O_2 is transported mostly in the red blood cells.
    d) CO_2 is bound primarily to myoglobin, while O_2 is bound primarily to hemoglobin.
    e) CO_2 is transported mostly in the plasma, while O_2 is transported mostly in hemoglobin within the plasma.

12. Breathing in birds is more like "breathing" in fishes than in mammals, because:
    a) water and high-altitude air have similar viscosity.
    b) oxygen never runs into a dead end.
    c) both birds and fishes have gill arches.
    d) the blood vessels in bird lungs, like those in fish gills, are insulated with a fatty coating, reducing heat loss.
    e) in birds and fishes, but not mammals, the heart pumps in a two-circuit system of blood flow.

13. Which of the following are the main muscles used in breathing?
    a) back muscles and thoracic muscles
    b) intercostal muscles and pectoral muscles
    c) diaphragm and thoracic muscles
    d) diaphragm and back muscles
    e) intercostal muscles and diaphragm

14. With increasing temperatures:
    a) aquatic animals must exert more energy to obtain oxygen.
    b) aqueous environments contain more dissolved oxygen.
    c) aquatic animals require less oxygen.
    d) an aquatic animal's metabolism stabilizes.
    e) all of the above occur.

15. Under regular metabolic conditions, what percentage of oxygen is released from the blood to the tissues?
    a) 1%
    b) 75%
    c) 25%
    d) 100%
    e) 50%

16. Why is carbon monoxide (CO) so dangerous?
    a) CO prevents hemoglobin from binding to and transporting O_2 to the body tissues, resulting in oxygen starvation and death.
    b) CO prevents CO_2 from dissolving in the blood, and CO_2 builds up to toxic levels.
    c) CO modifies the structure of hemoglobin, making it more difficult for O_2 to be transported and released in the body.
    d) CO coats the inside of the alveoli, preventing diffusion of O_2 from the lungs into the blood.
    e) CO binds to myoglobin, so tissues cannot remove O_2 from the red blood cells and the tissue dies.

17. Myoglobin:
    a) is the chief O_2 carrier in mammalian circulatory systems.
    b) transports O_2 from the lungs to the body tissues.
    c) releases O_2 to the muscles when partial pressure is such that hemoglobin cannot do so.
    d) is a four-subunit protein containing iron.
    e) has a lower affinity for O_2 than hemoglobin does.

18. Which of the following has the highest binding affinity for oxygen?
    a) hemolymph
    b) human hemoglobin
    c) llama hemoglobin
    d) myoglobin
    e) All have equal binding affinity for oxygen.

19. Why does llama hemoglobin have a higher oxygen-binding affinity than human hemoglobin?
    a) Like humans, llama fetuses use a form of hemoglobin with a higher binding affinity than the mother's hemoglobin, but unlike humans, llamas continue to use this form of hemoglobin after birth.
    b) Because llamas are more active than humans, they require hemoglobin with a greater maximum oxygen saturation.
    c) Llama blood has a higher CO_2 concentration than human blood, resulting in a need for hemoglobin with a higher binding affinity.
    d) Llamas live at higher elevations than most humans and require a means to bind O_2 when oxygen is at a lower concentration in the air.
    e) Llamas lack myoglobin and need a way to ensure enough O_2 is available to their muscle tissues.

20. Diphosphoglyceric acid (DPG):
    a) causes the release of more O_2 to body tissues.
    b) makes it possible for blood to carry more CO_2.
    c) is the main reason that breathing is difficult at high altitudes.
    d) increases the binding affinity of adult hemoglobin for O_2.
    e) encourages the production of more hemoglobin.

21. Which of the following is not part of the "diving reflex" of the Weddell seal that allows seals to remain underwater for long periods of time?
    a) Weddell seals have double the muscle myoglobin concentration compared with other mammals.
    b) Weddell seals have double the blood volume (per kg of body weight) compared with other mammals.
    c) Weddell seals have an increased resting heart rate, causing more efficient oxygen usage.
    d) During dives, Weddell seals constrict blood vessels in most tissues, sending blood only to parts of the body that need it most.
    e) All of the above make deep diving possible by the Weddell seal.

SHORT-ANSWER QUESTIONS

1. Why has the evolution of multicellular organisms led to the development of circulatory systems? What characteristic distinguishes closed and open circulatory systems?

2. What is the difference between single- and double-circuit cardiovascular systems? Which would be better suited for a higher energy demand? Why?

3. Name the three main types of cells (or cell fragments) that are found in blood and describe their primary functions.

4. How is gas exchange accomplished in organisms with gills and in those with lungs?

See Appendix for answers. For additional study questions, go to www.prep-u.com.

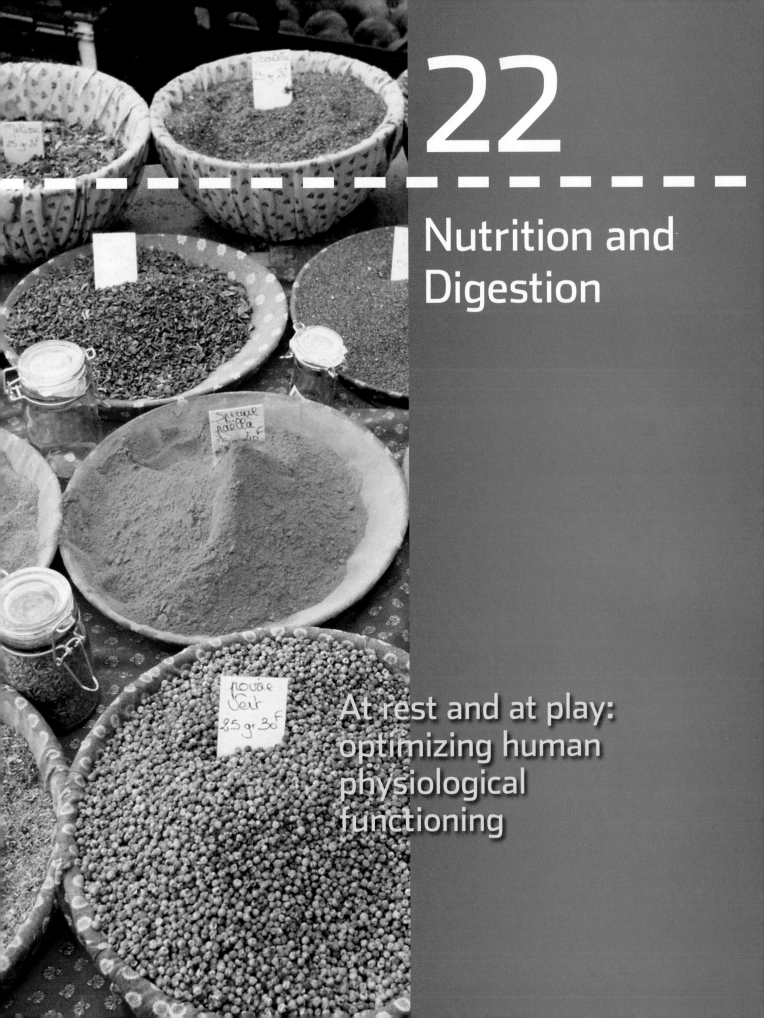

22

Nutrition and Digestion

At rest and at play: optimizing human physiological functioning

❶ Food provides the raw materials for growth and the fuel to make it happen.

Living organisms need raw materials and fuel to function.

22·1

Why do organisms need food?

Lamb roulade with leek basil stuffing and a red wine sauce. Chili fries. Lime-marinated tofu kabobs. A big vanilla milkshake. We dress food up in an almost infinite variety of combinations. We garnish it, we heap on condiments, we daydream about it, and we even write books about it. But despite all the fuss, it really boils down to two simple biological needs: raw materials and fuel. Just as a carpenter needs wood and a car needs fuel, living organisms need raw materials and fuel to function.

Here's why: every second of every day, chemical reactions are occurring inside us. We build complex molecules. We reproduce. We respond to stimuli. And just as a car won't roll uphill without a push, most of these chemical reactions won't occur spontaneously. With a little fuel in the motor, however, the car can easily be driven up a hill. So, too, can we, and all the other animals, do things that are energetically costly. Our need for fuel is one of the two reasons why we must eat:

building a body, moving around, reproducing, and just staying alive all require energy. Food provides that energy. And the other reason is that to grow and build the myriad complex molecules required for life, we need raw materials: molecules of carbon and nitrogen and phosphorus, to name just a few. Food provides these raw materials.

What exactly happens to the food we eat? We'll examine this question in detail throughout the chapter. In **FIGURE 22-1**, though, we can see that the food we eat is physically and chemically broken down into its fundamental macromolecular components in the process of **digestion.** Regardless of the form food takes when we eat it, our body quickly breaks it down and separates it into the usable and unusable. The usable materials are carbohydrates, lipids, proteins, vitamins, minerals, and water. These six groups of **nutrients** are the substances that are used for energy, raw materials, and maintenance of the body's systems. Anything we consume that doesn't fall into

▼

| Food for Energy and Growth | Nutrients | Digestion and Absorption | Diet and Health |

FOOD

DIGESTION

Food is physically and chemically broken down.

NUTRIENTS
Substances that are used for energy, raw materials, and maintenance of the body's systems

Carbohydrates   Lipids   Proteins

Vitamins   Minerals   Water

WASTE
Unusable material that is eliminated after passing through the digestive system

FIGURE 22-1 **Made possible by food.** Living organisms need raw materials and fuel to function.

one of these categories is unusable. You can't get nutrients from dirt or rocks. They just pass through the digestive system and are eliminated.

Ultimately, an organism's body weight represents the balance between the energy carried within the molecular bonds of the food it consumes and the energy that is burned in the process of living. Any surplus calories are stored, usually as fat or as glycogen (see Section 2-9), a form of carbohydrate stored primarily in muscle and liver tissue.

TAKE-HOME MESSAGE 22·1

Animals must eat for two reasons: to acquire the energy needed for all growth and activity, and to acquire the raw materials required for life.

22·2

What's on the menu? Organisms have a variety of diets.

All organisms need food. You've got two choices for how to get it. You can make it yourself, as plants and other photosynthetic organisms do through photosynthesis. Or you can eat another organism. Most animals eat the plants that make their own chemical energy, while some animals eat other animals (that eat plants). Some animals even eat animals that eat animals that eat animals (that eat plants)—but that's pretty rare (see Section 15-7). In every case, though, the choice is the same: capture solar energy to make food, or acquire that energy indirectly by consuming other organisms.

In the animal world, species fall into three groups based on their diets (**FIGURE 22-2**).

Carnivores The **carnivores** are predatory animals that consume only other animals. They include spiders and snakes; mammalian species such as wolves, seals, bats, and cats; as well as hawks, owls, and other birds of prey. Some carnivores don't actually kill their prey but instead just suck nutrient-rich fluids from them. Mosquitoes and ticks are carnivorous fluid-feeders.

Carnivory isn't just for animals. The Venus flytrap is a plant that captures and consumes insects. It does this with highly elastic, curved leaves. Water pressure inside the V-shaped leaf

Q Can plants be carnivorous?

causes it to expand into an unstable, stretched-open position that is on the verge of snapping closed. When an insect or spider lands on the leaf, it triggers an electrical signal that causes a brief, rapid change in the water pressure inside the leaf. The change in water pressure is enough to cause the leaf to snap shut, capturing the insect. The plant then releases digestive juices that break down the insect into its usable nutrients. Venus flytraps occur in places where the soil is poor and, especially, is low in nitrogen, which they are able to extract from the animal prey they capture. The green leaves and stems of Venus flytraps, however, should serve as a reminder that these plants are also photosynthetic, harnessing the energy in sunlight to build sugars.

Herbivores Food: easy to get, but hard to digest. That sums up life as a **herbivore,** an organism that consumes only plants. Because plants are plentiful in most habitats and can't run away, they are easy targets for predation. To protect themselves, however, plants tend to carry many toxic compounds that are difficult or impossible for animals to break down chemically. Nonetheless, many herbivores have developed digestive adaptations to overcome these difficulties. We'll explore a couple of them in detail in Section 22-14. Examples of herbivores include sea turtles and caterpillars. They also

CARNIVORES
Animals that consume only other animals. (Shown here: a rock python swallows a gazelle.)

HERBIVORES
Animals that consume only plants. (Shown here: a West-Indian manatee eating the plant hydrilla.)

OMNIVORES
Animals that consume both plants and animals. (Shown here: a young raccoon snacks on a plant; raccoons have a very broad diet that also includes insects, worms, fish, amphibians, and more.)

FIGURE 22-2 Animal diets: carnivores, herbivores, and omnivores.

include many species of seed-eating birds and nut-eating squirrels and a variety of large grazing mammals such as cows, horses, and deer. And just as there are fluid-feeding carnivores, there are fluid-feeding herbivores. Aphids, for example, pierce the surface of plants and suck their sugary sap.

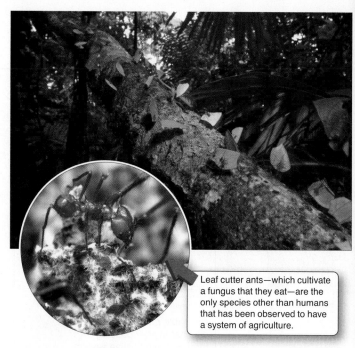

Leaf cutter ants—which cultivate a fungus that they eat—are the only species other than humans that has been observed to have a system of agriculture.

FIGURE 22-3 Fungus-farming ants. Leaf cutter ants harvest leaves in order to grow fungus, which they then consume.

Omnivores Most humans, as **omnivores,** eat plants and/or animals and can digest both efficiently. We share this diet with numerous other species, including cockroaches. Omnivores come in all sizes, from bears to raccoons, from chickens to flies and wasps.

Watching farmers cultivate plants and animals for food, it might seem reasonable to assume that humans are unique in this endeavor. Agriculture is not, however, limited to humans. Leaf cutter ants chop up leaves, but rather than eating them, spit out the mulch, mold it into a honeycomb shape, and then grow fungus on the mulch (**FIGURE 22-3**). They then eat the fungus at their leisure. These ants are the only species that scientists know of other than humans with a system of agriculture (and they've been doing it for significantly longer than humans have).

Q Humans grow and tend to plants and animals with t[h]e sole purpose o[f] eating them. A[re] there any othe[r] species with agriculture?

TAKE-HOME MESSAGE 22·2

All animals require food. Plants and other photosynthetic organisms produce food through photosynthesis, and animals have one of three types of diet. Carnivores consume only other animals. Herbivores consume only plants. And omnivores, including most humans, consume both plants and animals.

Food for Energy and Growth   Nutrients   Digestion and Absorption   Diet and Health

Calories count: organisms need sufficient energy.

Have you ever gone a whole day without eating? Or have you ever spent a few weeks trying to reduce your caloric intake? Living in a state of hunger can be torturous. In the early 1990s, eight human "guinea pigs" learned this the hard way. Living in the Biosphere 2 dome—a self-contained, 3.2-acre world filled with plants and animals that was designed to explore sustainable living with minimal environmental impact—they took part in an experiment on the effects of a low-calorie diet, among other things. The findings were dramatic but not surprising: all the participants lost weight, but they also became very unhappy. They argued constantly, got into ugly food spats, and frequently squabbled over dinner portions. After leaving what they dubbed "the hunger dome," one of the eight said, "If we ever all start talking to each other, that would be a major accomplishment" (**FIGURE 22-4**). In an earlier study, people were kept hungry for six months. Over time, study participants filled increasing hours with food fantasies. Recipes even displaced sex as the favorite topic of discussion. Put simply, humans (and all other living organisms) need a steady and sufficient flow of energy to function well.

Insufficient energy input for organisms always leads to the same outcome: death. As we saw in Section 8-1, when 27-year-old Bobby Sands went on a hunger strike in 1981, he gradually deteriorated and ultimately died after 66 days without food. In 2001, two prisoners in Turkey, Cafer Tayyar

Bektas and Huseyin Kayaci, also went on a hunger strike to protest the prison conditions. Because they started fasting at much higher initial body weights, they survived for much longer than Bobby Sands. The end result was the same, though. After 200 and 148 days respectively, both men died.

So what do we actually need to survive? And why isn't it the same for everyone? In this section, we examine the body's energy needs, and then the various nutrients necessary for growth and maintenance.

We measure the energetic value of food in very small amounts of energy called **calories,** where a single calorie is the energy required to raise the temperature of 1 gram of water by 1° C. However, the term can be a bit confusing: in discussing human consumption, the term "calorie" actually refers to a **kilocalorie** (**kcal**), which is 1,000 calories. So when the label on a package of cookies says that a cookie provides "100 calories," the cookie actually provides 100 *kilocalories* or 100,000 *calories*.

As we saw from the hunger strikers, there is tremendous variation in the amount of stored energy an individual carries. Similarly, there is much variation in how many calories an individual needs each day. To determine basic energy needs, we first factor out any variation due to differences in activity levels—searching for food, finding a mate, defending a territory—and instead assess the minimal energetic needs of an individual who is doing nothing more than the equivalent of sitting on a couch all day. This is called the **basal metabolic rate,** or **BMR,** and refers to the amount of energy expended at rest, with no food in the digestive tract, in a neutral-temperature environment. For humans, the BMR can be roughly approximated as 1 calorie per hour per gram of body weight, or about 1,400 kcal/day for a woman (weighing 120 pounds) and about 1,700 kcal/day for a man (weighing 160 pounds). The difference is mostly a function of the difference in body size; the male has more cells to power. The human BMR is approximately the energy needed to keep a 75-watt light bulb burning for 24 hours or to drive a small car one mile.

Basal metabolic rate allows easy comparisons across species because it is so clearly defined. From a biological perspective, though, it is almost meaningless. To realistically evaluate organisms' energy needs, we must have a sense of how active they are. Someone moving around and involved in physical exertion will require more energy than someone sitting at a desk all day, and a very large person will require more than a small person (**FIGURE 22-5**). In actuality, individuals need about

"If we ever all start talking to each other, that would be a major accomplishment."

– One of the eight participants of Biosphere 2

FIGURE 22-4 Hungry Biosphere 2 crew. Living on a low-calorie diet led to weight loss and a cranky disposition for Biosphere 2 participants.

COMPONENTS OF ENERGY EXPENDITURE

Average kcal/day to cover the minimal energetic needs of an organism at rest

Female | 1,400
Male | 1,700

BASAL METABOLIC RATE (BMR)
The minimal energy expenditure of an organism at rest.

Average kcal/day to cover all of the energetic needs of an organism (including all activity)

Female | 1,400
Male | 1,700

Individuals generally need about 50% to 100% more kilocalories per day than their BMR.

ACTUAL DAILY ENERGY EXPENDITURE
The basal metabolic rate *plus* the energy required for all activity.

FIGURE 22-5   How many calories do you need? Energy expenditure varies depending on body size and activity level.

50% to 100% more kilocalories per day than their BMR. A 120-pound woman requires 1,800–2,400 kcal/day, and a 160-pound man requires about 2,400–3,200 kcal/day.

Basal metabolic rates vary tremendously among different animal species. For the tiny shrew, for instance, BMR is about 35 times higher than for a human (**FIGURE 22-6**). The shrew's heart beats more than 500 times per minute *at rest*!

With the measurement of an animal's BMR, we can begin to estimate the animal's caloric needs. Let's estimate what a shrew needs to eat each day. If it weighs 5 grams and has a BMR of 35 calories per hour per gram, we can calculate as follows:

BMR varies tremendously among different animal species. The tiny shrew has a BMR about 35 times higher than that of a human, relative to weight.

FIGURE 22-6   Live fast. This tiny shrew must meet the high calorie demands of its fast-beating heart.

body weight	×	energy needed each hour	×	hours per day	=	animal's caloric needs
5 grams	×	35 cal/gram/hr	×	24 hr/day	=	4,200 cal/day

Thus, the shrew would need 4.2 kcal/day if it were at rest. But if it needed another 4 kcal/day for its normal activities, it would have to eat about 8 kcal/day. As we will see below, a pure source of carbohydrate or protein carries about 4 kcal/gram. Thus, every day, the shrew must find and consume at least 2 grams of food. This is no small challenge when you only weigh 5 grams. The task is equivalent to a 200-pound man finding and eating 80 pounds of food every day.

The shrew is not the only species with extreme caloric needs. Animals that fast or hibernate for long periods of time must prepare for the fast by consuming many kilocalories. Male elephant seals, for example, eat little or nothing during their 100-day breeding season, instead spending their time battling with other males for dominance and mating with females. During these 100 days, a large male who begins the season at 6,600 pounds (3,000 kg) may lose one-third of his body weight. Consequently, in the months leading up to the breeding season, the male seals' caloric requirements are dramatically higher than at other times.

TAKE-HOME MESSAGE 22·3

To function well, living organisms need sufficient energy, measured in kilocalories. The minimal energy needed by an individual not engaged in any activity is called its basal metabolic rate, or BMR.

Food for Energy and Growth   Nutrients   Digestion and Absorption   Diet and Health

❷ Nutrients are grouped into six categories.

A jaguar takes a drink at a watering hole in Belize.

22•4 -

Water is an essential nutrient.

We saw that a human could live 60 days or more without consuming food. The prognosis is much worse in the absence of water, perhaps the single most important component of a balanced diet. In the early 1900s, an Italian man sentenced to death reportedly volunteered to determine how long he could live without food or water. The fatal "experiment" lasted only 17 days before he died.

Water, which is considered an essential nutrient, constitutes about 60–65% of the body weight in most mammals. This water plays important roles in both the intracellular fluid and the extracellular fluids, including blood, in humans and other animals (**FIGURE 22-7**). Water in body fluids serves a variety of critical purposes, all of which can be impaired when the animal becomes dehydrated.

- Water transports nutrients and waste materials throughout the body.

- It takes part in chemical reactions.

- It serves as a solvent for many vitamins and minerals, amino acids, and sugars.

- It lubricates many joints, the spinal cord, and the eyes.

- It helps regulate body temperature.

A person expending about 2,000 kcal/day needs about 2–3 liters of water each day. This can come directly from

Water is an essential nutrient and plays important roles in both the intracellular fluid and the extracellular fluids, including blood.

FIGURE 22-7 Water is an essential component of the diet.

drinking water, but there are many other sources of water in our diet, including milk, which is about 90% water, juices, food, and water released as a by-product of many chemical reactions. It is essential that water intake offset the water lost in urine, feces, respiration, and sweating. It is important to remember, too, as we saw in the Chapter 3 StreetBio, that drinking too much water too quickly can also be dangerous. Water intoxication results from the consumption of too much water—which sometimes happens to marathon runners during a race. When coupled with the loss of salt through sweating, over-consumption of water can lead to severe sodium imbalance. This imbalance causes dizziness, nausea, confusion, and swelling of the extremities. And in serious cases, it can lead to swelling of the brain, which can cause death.

Q If water is so important, why are there some desert animals that never need to drink?

Water usage varies among some animal species. Some desert mammals, the kangaroo rat, for example, have evolved tremendous water efficiency, and some do not need to drink any water at all. Rather, they get all the water they need from their food and metabolic processes. Among the marine birds and reptiles, most are able to drink salt water. They can do this with the aid of salt glands that remove and excrete the excess salt they consume.

TAKE-HOME MESSAGE 22·4

Water is probably the single most important component of the diet. It constitutes 60-65% of the body weight of most mammals, transports nutrients and waste materials throughout the body, takes part in metabolic reactions, serves as a solvent, lubricates many body parts, and helps regulate body temperature.

22·5

Proteins in food are broken down to build proteins in the body.

When you are on the verge of starvation, any type of food can save you. So from that perspective, it's true that calories are all that matter. But for optimum health, organisms must consume many types of nutrients. In this section and the next, we investigate the chief nutritional features of the three types of calories: proteins, carbohydrates, and fats. We begin by investigating protein, a vital component of the diet and essential structural material in the body.

Protein: Raw Material for Growth

What are proteins, and what is their role in the diet? Protein in our diet is principally a building material. As described in detail in Sections 2-15 through 2-18, protein molecules are made of long chains of smaller molecules—amino acids—linked together, like beads on a string. Once eaten, protein molecules are broken down into the individual amino acids, much like removing the beads from the string one at a time. It's only in the form of individual amino acids that proteins can be absorbed by the digestive system. Our bodies can then reorder the beads, making proteins that are different from those we ate.

The process of protein digestion and protein rebuilding does seem a bit inefficient: we consume entire, intact proteins such as muscle cells or hemoglobin molecules, from chickens or fishes or other animals, which we then break down and may ultimately use to construct almost exactly the same types of protein molecules. Nonetheless, animal digestive systems are able to absorb only the simpler building blocks of proteins,

not entire proteins themselves, so we must first break down all the proteins we eat and later reassemble new ones.

Besides serving as building materials, proteins function as enzymes, catalyzing reactions throughout the body (see Section 2-18). They can also be broken down to release energy or to be stored as fat. Our bodies can use protein as fuel because we have variety of methods of converting one type of chemical to anothe to release or store energy (see Section 4-17). The breakdown of proteins for energy generates 4 kilocalories per gram. Protein breakdown generally happens only when we are consuming too few (or too many) calories to sustain necessary growth and activities. The reverse reaction—building proteins from fat or carbohydrates—however, cannot be done. All amino acids have elements—particularly nitrogen—that are not found in any sugar or fats that we consume. Only the proteins in our diet contain nitrogen. Thus, all of the proteins we build contain parts of proteins that we have consumed, and if a protein is broken down for energy, the nitrogen it carries is excreted in our urine.

There is a variety of sources of dietary protein, from both plants and animals (**FIGURE 22-8**). Animal sources include egg whites, shrimp, tuna, lobster, chicken, turkey, and all meat products. Plan sources of protein include grains, vegetables, nuts, seeds, and legumes, such as beans.

Try this. Put one can of Coke and one can of Diet Coke somewhere that they will get hot, and leave them for a few days. Then taste them. The Diet Coke will lose its flavor and taste

Food for Energy and Growth   Nutrients   Digestion and Absorption   Diet and Health

PROTEIN: RAW MATERIAL FOR GROWTH

4 kcal/gram

FUNCTION
Once proteins are broken down, the amino acids are used as the raw materials to build new complex proteins, such as hemoglobin and muscle.

SOURCE
• Animals: egg whites, shrimp, tuna, poultry, and meat
• Plants: grains and vegetables, such as beans

STORAGE
• Amino acids are usually stored for less than half a day before being reassembled into proteins throughout the body
• Can be converted to fat and stored in fat cells

FIGURE 22-8 Versatile proteins. Besides serving as building materials, proteins can be broken down to release energy or stored as fat.

Why does Diet Coke (but not regular Coke) taste bitter if you leave it in the sun for a few days?

bitter, even if you cool it down, while the Coke will taste fine. What's going on? Diet Coke, but not regular Coke, is sweetened with aspartame (NutraSweet is the brand name). Aspartame is made by linking together two amino acids, aspartic acid and phenylalanine—each of which tastes bitter by itself. When the two are joined as aspartame, however, the taste is very sweet. The reaction by which aspartic acid and phenylalanine are linked together can be reversed by heat. So if you leave a can of Diet Coke in a hot area, the aspartame decomposes to the bitter amino acids. They're not harmful, but they aren't very tasty either.

Are all proteins the same, or do they vary in important ways? All proteins are not created equal. Animals, including humans, require 20 different amino acids to make proteins. Most animals, however, can produce only about half of these amino acids

themselves. In the case of humans, we can't make 8 of the 20 amino acids. Because these 8 cannot be produced by our bodies, we must get them from the food we eat. For that reason, the amino acids we must consume in food are called the **essential amino acids,** and the remaining 12 are called **non–essential amino acids.**

Protein–containing animal products vary in their amino acid composition. All eight of the essential amino acids are found in milk, eggs, meat, poultry, cheese, and fish; these animal products have "complete" proteins (**FIGURE 22-9**). On the other hand, most proteins that we get from eating plants are not complete. Corn proteins, for example, have only six of the essential amino acids, as do beans (although they don't have the same six). In

COMPLETE PROTEINS
Proteins that contain all eight essential amino acids

INCOMPLETE PROTEINS
Proteins that do not contain all eight essential amino acids

 With the exception of soybeans, no single plant food has all eight essential amino acids.

FIGURE 22-9 Animal versus plant proteins. Animal proteins contain all eight of the essential amino acids. Plant foods contain varying amounts and types of essential amino acids.

fact, with the exception of soybeans, no single plant food has all eight. A healthy diet is one containing not just a sufficient *amount of protein* but a sufficient amount of each of the eight essential amino acids that we need to make proteins. Consequently, we must know more about the proteins we eat than the simple description on the food label of how many grams of protein the food contains.

> **Q** Why is it beneficial for vegetarians to eat beans and corn over the course of the same day?

How and where do we store proteins? Proteins and the amino acid pool they generate on digestion cannot be stored very long in our bodies, usually less than a day. By that point, they are broken down and the nitrogen is excreted. Because our bodies are making proteins constantly, it is important to take in all of the essential amino acids over the course of each day.

The recommended daily intake of protein is approximately 0.8 grams per kilogram of body weight. This translates to about 45 grams of protein for a 120-pound woman (and about 25 additional grams per day for pregnant or lactating women) and 60 grams for a 160-pound man. Exercising athletes can require double or even triple this amount, but it is important to remember that it is the exercise that generates the additional need. Protein on its own does nothing to stimulate muscle growth; it simply serves as the source for the raw materials.

TAKE-HOME MESSAGE 22·5

Animals consume three different types of macromolecules for calories: proteins, carbohydrates, and fats. Proteins provide raw materials for growth and for the production of enzymes. Food sources of protein vary in amino acid composition. Humans require 20 amino acids, and 8 of these, called essential amino acids, can only be supplied by the diet.

22·6

Carbohydrates and lipids provide bodies with energy and more.

Reading these words requires carbohydrates in your body, obtained from your diet, to fuel your brain—and your muscles as well, as they help you sit up and hold your book. Food fat, too, a subset of the group of macromolecular nutrients called lipids (see Sections 2-12–2-14), provides energy for your body's functioning and gives food delicious flavor (while contributing to weight gain and heart disease if consumed in too large a quantity). In this section, we evaluate the macromolecules carbohydrates and lipids. These two crucial nutrients supply nearly all the energy that fuels your daily activities.

Carbohydrates: Fuel for Living Machines

What are carbohydrates, and what is their role in the diet? Carbohydrates are the primary fuel on which animal bodies run. In humans, nearly all of the energy used by our brain every day comes from the simple carbohydrate glucose. As we saw in Chapter 2, all carbohydrates are made primarily from carbon, hydrogen, and oxygen. When the bonds between these atoms are broken, energy is released that can be captured by the body and used to fuel movement, growth, and all the other cellular activities that require energy.

We get the majority of our dietary carbohydrates from fruits, vegetables, and grains (**FIGURE 22-10**). And, as with proteins, the breakdown of carbohydrates for energy generates 4 kilocalories per gram.

Are all carbohydrates the same, or do they vary in important ways? Although, structurally, all carbohydrates are variations on a simple theme—molecules formed from carbon, hydrogen, and oxygen in the approximate proportions of CH_2O (see Figure 2-20)—they vary dramatically in their complexity. This variation has implications for their nutritional effects (**FIGURE 22-11**). From a dietary perspective, the most important distinctions are among simple sugars (monosaccharides), digestible complex sugars, and fiber (indigestible complex sugars).

Simple sugars: These include glucose and fructose. They are linear or ring structures with three to seven carbon atoms. Animals can break them down directly through the steps of glycolysis (see Section 4-13), rapidly releasing the stored energy from the bonds of the sugar.

Digestible complex sugars: Multiple simple sugars can bond together to form complex but digestible molecules. Some complex sugars, such as sucrose (table sugar), are just two simple sugars joined together. Others, such as starch and glycogen, are large molecules that may consist of

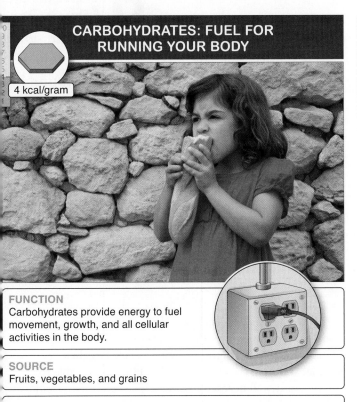

CARBOHYDRATES: FUEL FOR RUNNING YOUR BODY

4 kcal/gram

FUNCTION
Carbohydrates provide energy to fuel movement, growth, and all cellular activities in the body.

SOURCE
Fruits, vegetables, and grains

STORAGE
• Carbohydrates are stored in the liver and muscle cells as glycogen for about a day before being broken down to provide energy
• Can be converted to fat and stored in fat cells

FIGURE 22-10 Carbohydrate is the primary fuel on which animal bodies run.

hundreds or thousands of glucose molecules connected in dense branching patterns. In order for an animal to have access to the energy stored within the bonds of the individual simple sugars, it must first break the bonds that link those sugars together. As these bonds are broken, simple sugars become available for the energy-releasing reactions of glycolysis.

Fiber: This is a complex carbohydrate, such as cellulose, that forms the structural parts of plants. Fiber differs from starch and other digestible complex sugars by having a different bond connecting the simple sugars together. This bond cannot be broken by any human digestive enzyme, making fiber indigestible. As we'll see later in this chapter, although fiber isn't broken down for energy or other molecules used by the body, it still plays an important role in digestion and is necessary in the diet to maintain health.

How and where do we store carbohydrates? Carbohydrates in our body are stored mostly as glycogen in liver and muscle cells. At any given time, we can store only about one day's worth of energy. After we start exercising, or when our bodies need energy for an activity, a signal is sent causing the release of enzymes that break the bonds holding together the highly branched glycogen. This glycogen breakdown produces a flood of glucose into the bloodstream and at muscles where the energy is needed.

Large amounts of water are bound to stored glycogen: 4 pounds of water for every pound of glycogen. Consequently, as glycogen in your liver and muscles is used, the water bound to it is released from the tissue and lost as urine. This is why, as stores of glycogen are depleted in the initial stages of a diet, there is a dramatic initial weight loss from the loss of water that was bound to the glycogen. As your body starts utilizing stored fat, the rate of weight loss slows considerably.

TYPES OF CARBOHYDRATES

SIMPLE SUGARS
• Glucose, fructose
• Glycolysis reactions release energy rapidly

DIGESTIBLE COMPLEX SUGARS
• Simple sugars bonded together, such as sucrose (table sugar) or starch
• Bonds between simple sugars must be broken before the energy-releasing reactions of glycolysis occur

FIBER
• Complex carbohydrate that forms structural parts of plants
• Indigestible in humans, but has a significant role in digestion

FIGURE 22-11 Carbohydrate complexity. Some carbohydrates are readily broken down for fuel, but fiber passes through the human body undigested.

Fats: Long-Term Energy Storage Experts

What are fats, and what is their role in the diet? Dietary fats, described in detail in Chapter 2, function primarily as a dense source of energy that can be efficiently stored in the body (**FIGURE 22-12**). The average person has about four or five weeks' worth of stored energy in the form of fat. Compared with carbohydrates or proteins, a given amount of fat contains more than twice as much stored energy: 1 gram of fat produces 9 kilocalories. Another feature that makes fats particularly efficient as energy-storage molecules is the fact that, because they are hydrophobic, fats are stored without binding to water.

Because they also are poor conductors of heat, fats stored in a layer just beneath the skin help to keep the body warm. Penguins and walruses, for example, can maintain relatively high body temperatures despite living in very cold habitats, because of their thick layer of insulating fat.

Here's a perplexing fact: although the total amount of energy in a gram of fat is greater than that found in carbohydrates or proteins, fat isn't the optimum nutrient for most situations.

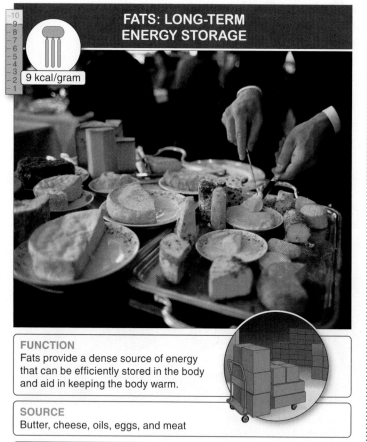

FATS: LONG-TERM ENERGY STORAGE

9 kcal/gram

FUNCTION
Fats provide a dense source of energy that can be efficiently stored in the body and aid in keeping the body warm.

SOURCE
Butter, cheese, oils, eggs, and meat

STORAGE
Fats are stored in fat cells throughout the body.

FIGURE 22-12 Energy-rich fats. At 9 kilocalories per gram, fats are rich in stored energy.

When it comes to exercise, for example, muscle cells need quick access to energy. The problem is that, in muscles, fat burns very slowly for energy. Remember from Chapter 4 that the universal source of chemical energy in the body is ATP. This means that the energy in fat or carbohydrate or protein must be captured as ATP before it is of use to muscle cells. It turns out to be much easier for the body to break down muscle glycogen and blood glucose to make ATP than to break down fat. In fact, the rate of ATP synthesis from carbohydrates is about double the rate from fats.

Are all fats the same nutritionally, or do they vary in important ways? With proteins, we saw that there were essential and non-essential amino acids. Similarly, with dietary fats, there are essential and non-essential fatty acids. Humans are able to produce nearly all necessary lipids. The essential fatty acids—including linoleic acid, a type of fatty acids called omega-6 fatty acids—must be consumed. Linoleic acid is essential as a building block for signaling molecules, such as some hormones; a deficiency can lead to infertility and difficulty lactating. Another essential fatty acid, important in a variety of metabolic processes, is linolenic acid, a type of fatty acids called omega-3 fatty acids. Linolenic acid is used by the body to make fatty acids that are essential for normal growth and development, especially in the eyes and brain.

Another important distinction among dietary fats is between saturated and unsaturated fats (**FIGURE 22-13**). In our diet, fats usually come in the form of fatty acids, long chains of carbon atoms with hydrogens attached. If each carbon within the chain is bonded to two hydrogen atoms, the molecule carries the maximum number of hydrogen atoms and is said to be saturated. (For a refresher, see Figure 2-31.) Conversely, if some of the carbons are bound to only a single hydrogen, the fatty acid is unsaturated.

When saturated, fatty acids are very straight and the fat molecules can be packed together tightly. This causes saturated fats to be solid at room temperature, like butter. When unsaturated, the fatty acids have kinks in the hydrocarbon tail and cannot be packed together as tightly. Consequently, unsaturated fats do not solidify so easily and tend to be liquid at room temperature, like vegetable oil. Because unsaturated fatty acids can accept one or more hydrogen atoms, they are a bit less stable and more reactive—that is, they will take part in a greater variety of chemical reactions—than saturated fatty acids, making them less likely to be stored as body fat.

Q If fats contain more than double the amount of energy found in the same amount of carbohydrates or proteins, why aren't fats a better fuel to consume before exercising?

Food for Energy and Growth   Nutrients   Digestion and Absorption   Diet and Health

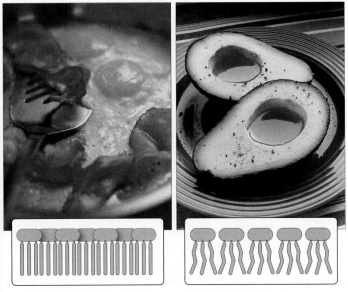

SATURATED FATS
- Fatty acids have straight tails and can be packed together tightly
- Tend to be solid at room temperature
- More likely to be stored as fat in the body

UNSATURATED FATS
- Fatty acids have kinked tails and cannot be packed together tightly
- Tend to be liquid at room temperature
- Less likely to be stored as fat in the body

FIGURE 22-13 Saturated and unsaturated fats compared.

Trans fats have been in the news because of their tendency when consumed to raise levels of low-density lipoprotein cholesterol, increasing the risk of coronary heart disease. Trans fat is made when hydrogen is added to vegetable oil—a process called hydrogenation (see Section 2-13 for a review of trans fat chemistry.) Trans fat often can be found in some of the same foods as saturated fat, such as vegetable shortenings, crackers, candies, cookies, snack foods, fried foods, baked goods, and other foods made with partially hydrogenated vegetable oils. The American Heart Association recommends that these fats be minimized in the diet.

How and where do we store fats? If a human consumes more calories than he or she burns, most of the excess (regardless of whether these calories were consumed as carbohydrate, fat, or protein) gets converted to fat and stored in fat cells distributed throughout the body. A pound of body fat holds 3,600 kilocalories worth of energy. It is like a savings account for an uncertain future.

Given that our bodies can convert excess calories into body fat, regardless of whether the calories were initially ingested as carbohydrates or proteins, why is it still a more effective weight-management strategy to minimize dietary fat intake? The answer rests in the number of chemical conversions carbohydrates and proteins must undergo to become body fat. In the case of carbohydrates, complex sugars must first be broken down into simple sugars—a process that requires energy. Then the simple

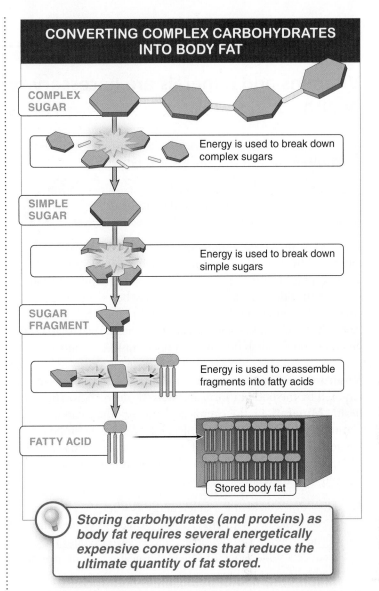

CONVERTING COMPLEX CARBOHYDRATES INTO BODY FAT

COMPLEX SUGAR

Energy is used to break down complex sugars

SIMPLE SUGAR

Energy is used to break down simple sugars

SUGAR FRAGMENT

Energy is used to reassemble fragments into fatty acids

FATTY ACID

Stored body fat

Storing carbohydrates (and proteins) as body fat requires several energetically expensive conversions that reduce the ultimate quantity of fat stored.

FIGURE 22-14 Inefficient conversion to body fat. By the time carbohydrates can be stored as body fat, much of the original energy has been lost in fueling the conversion.

sugars must be broken down and the fragments reassembled as fatty acids—another process that requires energy. By the time those fatty acids can be stored as body fat, much of the original energy stored in the carbohydrates has been lost in fueling all the chemical conversions (**FIGURE 22-14**). And for someone trying to minimize body fat, that's good news. Storing protein as body fat also requires several energetically expensive conversions that reduce the ultimate quantity of fat stored.

TAKE-HOME MESSAGE 22·6

Carbohydrates are the primary fuel on which animal bodies run. Dietary fats function primarily as a dense source of energy that can be efficiently stored in the body.

22·7

Vitamins and minerals are necessary for good health.

> " Vitamins can double your health!
>
> —Dr. Atkins, on *The Larry King Show* (making perhaps the most nonsensical nutritional claim ever) "

It would be nice if we could take a pill that would make us more healthy or fit. Vitamins are not such a miracle pill. They're a bit like security guards at a museum: above a certain number, they don't make the museum any better, but in their absence, the museum is likely to become a whole lot worse. And while vitamin supplements are not a health panacea, vitamins and minerals do have an important role in nutrition.

Vitamins are organic compounds that are essential nutrients required by the body in small amounts for normal growth and health. **Minerals** are the chemical elements, other than those commonly found in organic molecules—carbon, hydrogen, oxygen, and nitrogen—some of which are required in the diet in small amounts. There are three features common to all vitamins and minerals.

1. They don't yield any usable energy. Rather, they serve as collaborators with enzymes to enable the processing of the proteins, carbohydrates, and fats we eat, and they catalyze a wide range of other chemical reactions around the body.

2. They need to be consumed in much smaller amounts than proteins, carbohydrates, and fats in our diet. This is because they tend to serve as reaction catalysts and so can be recycled and used again and again.

3. If we have a healthful diet, we tend to consume sufficient quantities of vitamins and minerals in our food.

Although their biological roles are frequently similar, vitamins and minerals have a fundamental chemical difference. Vitamins are organic molecules, meaning they contain carbon, whereas minerals are inorganic nutrients. Because vitamins are organic, they are more fragile, easily destroyed by heat and other chemical or physical extremes. Minerals, on the other hand, are elements, so they can't be broken down further or lose their chemical identity. They stay in your body until they are excreted. In fact, the only way they can be lost is if they are leached away—such as from food into the water as the food is cooked and the water is then thrown away. Seventeen minerals

have been identified that are essential to the human diet. They are described in **FIGURE 22-15**.

Thirteen vitamins essential to humans, also described in Figure 22-15, have been discovered. They fall into two groups based on whether they are soluble in fat or water. The water-soluble vitamins include eight vitamins that are part of the vitamin B complex, plus vitamin C. There is some variation among species in the ability to manufacture (rather than needing to ingest) vitamins. Cats and dogs, for instance, do not need to consume vitamin C.

There are four fat-soluble vitamins: A, D, E, and K. Because they are stored in fatty tissue and the liver until they are needed, they don't need to be consumed as regularly as water-soluble vitamins. Also, because excess water-soluble vitamins can be removed by the kidney and excreted in urine, they tend to be less likely to reach toxic levels than fat-soluble vitamins.

Currently, more than half of the U.S. population takes regular vitamin supplements (**FIGURE 22-16**). Should so many people be taking these supplements? It is difficult to give a single answer to this question. Nonetheless, it is well established that in the United States, few adults suffer from any vitamin and mineral deficiency diseases. This is because nearly all adults get all of the nutrients they need from the food they eat. For this reason, nutritionists believe that high doses of vitamins and minerals are not therapeutic, and they suggest that most people do not need to take regular supplements.

Usually, taking vitamin supplements is a costly but harmless behavior. The consumption of increasing amounts of vitamins often just leads to a plateau of maximum benefit, after which greater consumption has no additional benefits. Occasionally, however, taking vitamin and mineral supplements is both costly and harmful: in many cases, above a certain point, additional consumption of fat-soluble vitamins can lead to toxicity and cause serious health problems. Excessive consumption of vitamin A, for example, can lead to hair loss in men, while over-consumption of vitamin D can lead to growth retardation. Liver damage, too, is a common result of excessive vitamin and mineral consumption. Moreover, research has definitively discredited claims that vitamin E supplementation slows or prevents aging or improves physical performance, and no supplement has been demonstrated to "relieve stress"—despite the extravagant claims of marketers.

ESSENTIAL VITAMINS AND MINERALS IN THE HUMAN DIET

VITAMIN	SOURCE	MAJOR FUNCTION
Water-soluble		
B_1 (thiamin)	Liver, legumes, whole grains	Coenzyme in cellular respiration
B_2 (riboflavin)	Dairy foods, meat, eggs, green leafy vegetables	Coenzyme in FAD
B_6 (pyridoxine)	Liver, whole grains, dairy foods	Coenzyme in amino acid metabolism
B_{12} (cobalamin)	Liver, meat, dairy foods, eggs	Formation of nucleic acids, proteins, and red blood cells
Biotin	Liver, yeast, bacteria in gut	Found in coenzymes
C (ascorbic acid)	Citrus fruits, tomatoes, potatoes	Formation of connective tissues; antioxidant
Folic acid	Vegetables, eggs, liver, whole grains	Coenzyme in formation of heme and nucleotides
Niacin	Meat, fowl, liver, yeast	Coenzyme in NAD and NADP
Pantothenic acid	Liver, eggs, yeast	Found in acetyl CoA
Fat-soluble		
A (retinol)	Fruits, vegetables, liver, dairy foods	Found in visual pigments
D (cholecalciferol)	Fortified milk, fish oils, sunshine	Absorption of calcium and phosphate
E (tocopherol)	Meat, dairy foods, whole grains	Muscle maintenance; antioxidant
K (menadione)	Intestinal bacteria, liver	Blood clotting

MINERAL	SOURCE	MAJOR FUNCTION
Calcium (Ca)	Dairy foods, eggs, green leafy vegetables, whole grains	Found in bones and teeth; blood clotting; muscle action
Chlorine (Cl)	Table salt (NaCl), meat, eggs, vegetables, dairy foods	Water balance; principal negative ion in extracellular fluid
Chromium (Cr)	Meat, dairy foods, whole grains, legumes, yeast	Glucose metabolism
Cobalt (Co)	Meat, tap water	Found in vitamin B_{12}; formation of red blood cells
Copper (Cu)	Liver, meat, fish, shellfish, legumes, whole grains, nuts	Found in enzymes and electron carriers; hemoglobin production
Fluorine (F)	Most water supplies	Found in teeth; helps prevent tooth decay
Iodine (I)	Fish, shellfish, iodized salt	Found in thyroid hormones
Iron (Fe)	Liver, meat, green vegetables, eggs, whole grains, legumes	Found in many enzymes, hemoglobin, and myoglobin
Magnesium (Mg)	Green vegetables, meat, whole grains, nuts, milk, legumes	Required by many enzymes; found in bones and teeth
Manganese (Mn)	Organ meats, whole grains, legumes, nuts, tea, coffee	Activates many enzymes
Molybdenum (Mo)	Organ meats, dairy foods, whole grains, green vegetables	Found in some enzymes
Phosphorus (P)	Dairy foods, eggs, meat, whole grains, legumes, nuts	Found in nucleic acids, ATP, and phospholipids
Potassium (K)	Meat, whole grains, fruits, vegetables	Nerve and muscle action; principal positive ion in cells
Selenium (Se)	Meat, seafood, whole grains, eggs, milk, garlic	Fat metabolism
Sodium (Na)	Table salt, dairy foods, meat, eggs	Nerve and muscle action; water balance
Sulfur (S)	Meat, eggs, dairy foods, nuts, legumes	Found in proteins and coenzymes; detoxification
Zinc (Zn)	Liver, fish, shellfish, and many other foods	Found in some enzymes and some transcription factors

FIGURE 22-15 Overview of essential vitamins and minerals.

FIGURE 22-16 Is supplementation necessary? Shopping the vitamin aisle for health.

So, we can conclude that most people in the United States have no need to take vitamin and mineral supplements. Under special circumstances, however, supplementation is necessary.

- Women who lose unusually large amounts of blood during menstruation may need iron.

- Post-menopausal women and those allergic to milk may not get enough calcium in their diet to prevent bone degeneration.

- Pregnant and breast-feeding women may need additional vitamins and minerals to support a developing fetus or rapidly growing infant.

- Pregnant women may, in particular, need additional folate, which helps prevent neural tube defects.

Green leafy vegetables are a good source of folate.

- People on extremely low-calorie diets may need a vitamin and mineral supplement.

- People with limited consumption of milk or sun exposure may need additional vitamin D. Because of insufficient levels of ultraviolet energy from the sun at latitudes above 42 (covering a line approximately from the northern border of California across to Boston), individuals in these regions are unable to produce sufficient vitamin D from sun exposure alone.

- People with absorption problems (such as when taking antibiotics or with an infection or following surgery) may need vitamin and mineral supplementation.

Individuals who do not fall into these groups, however, generally get all of the essential vitamins and minerals simply by eating a varied diet, rich in nutritious foods.

TAKE-HOME MESSAGE 22·7

Vitamins and minerals are organic and inorganic molecules in the diet. They are used in the production and action of enzymes and other molecules involved in the processing of food and other biochemical reactions. While vitamins and minerals are essential in small amounts, most people in the United States do not benefit from taking them as supplements.

Food for Energy and Growth   Nutrients   Digestion and Absorption   Diet and Health

How do organisms "know" what to eat?

We take it for granted, but our bodies seem to "know" that we need food, and they seem to be able to sense whether we're consuming nutritionally valuable substances. Is this really true? To find out, researchers conducted a clever study. With some volunteer participants, they secretly gave one group of people sugar cookies while a second group got cookies that looked the same and tasted pretty good but were made with the low-calorie sugar substitute, NutraSweet. The researchers then noted how many cookies were eaten. Surprisingly, individuals in both groups ate the same number of cookies, suggesting that those eating the NutraSweet cookies might lose weight as a result of reduced caloric intake. In addition to having their cookie consumption monitored, however, study participants were also asked to keep diaries of all their eating in the days around the cookie-eating event. It turns out that those in the NutraSweet-cookie group ate more than those in the sugar-cookie group. So much more, in fact, that the total caloric intake of the two groups was identical over the period of days monitored (**FIGURE 22-17**). Similar studies have shown that individuals who switch from regular sodas to no-calorie, diet sodas increase their consumption of other foods, often unknowingly, so that their overall caloric intake is not reduced.

Why do our bodies seem to keep track of our caloric intake? It is because all animals are built to get hungry and to seek out food when in that state. Powerful, instinctual hunger kept our ancestors going in a tough, energetically demanding world. Recall from earlier in the chapter the Biosphere 2 study in which participants' diets were significantly reduced in calories. Increasingly, their thoughts and discussions were filled with food fantasies. Such hunger used to be a survival-enhancing feature in our genetic programming, but it is more of a bug in that programming now. Later in this chapter, we'll see that because most of us live in a world characterized by plentiful food, our tremendous ancestral appetites frequently lead to obesity and other health problems.

Our genes do more than instill a general hunger for calories. Humans and other animals also show a preference for fatty foods over carbohydrate- or protein-laden foods. We prefer fatty foods because our tongues have thousands of specific detectors—taste buds—that stimulate our brains when we eat foods like nuts, avocados, cheese, and red meat. With this system, a fatty meal stimulates many of the reward centers in the brain. These structures evolved because fat has the most

FIGURE 22-17 Experiment in human caloric intake.

CALORIC INTAKE STUDY

Sugar cookies **VS** NutraSweet cookies

EXPERIMENTAL GROUP
Researchers randomly divided subjects into two groups to study their caloric intake.

Group 1   Group 2

TREATMENT

Sugar cookies   NutraSweet cookies

Subjects were asked to keep diaries of all their eating in days around the cookie-eating event.

RESULTS (CALORIES CONSUMED)

Calories from sugar cookies

Calories from all other foods

Calories from NutraSweet cookies

Total calories consumed   Total calories consumed

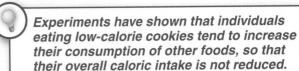

Experiments have shown that individuals eating low-calorie cookies tend to increase their consumption of other foods, so that their overall caloric intake is not reduced.

calories per serving. Our ancestral genes reward us whenever we find calories; in this quest for energy, fat deserves—and receives—the biggest reward.

To examine this in a more concrete way, let's return to the little shrew (**FIGURE 22-18**). Recall that our 5-gram shrew must consume about 8 kcal/day and that a pure source of carbohydrates or proteins carries about 4 kcal/gram, while a pure source of fat carries 9 kcal/gram. This means that a shrew can meet its energy requirements by finding and consuming 2.0 grams of a carbohydrate or protein. *Or* the shrew can find about 0.9 gram of a food that is primarily fat (such as insect larvae). Which is going to be easier? Clearly, the shrew (or any animal, for that matter) can meet its energy needs much more easily by seeking fats. Genetically based preferences for the taste of fats, then, can benefit shrews and humans, too (in their ancestral environment).

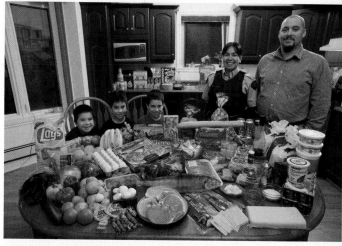

How would you describe this family's food preferences?

Animals have evolved to be sensitive to more than just total caloric intake or the fat (vs. protein or carbohydrate) content of food. It has been demonstrated in spiders, for example, that individuals will go out of their way, passing up valuable sources of food, in order to consume food items that contain certain rare but essential amino acids, so that their diet contains sufficient amounts of all of the essential amino acids. This suggests that there may actually be some underlying biological urges creating the various cravings and hunger pangs that we sometimes feel and that these feelings may not be restricted to humans. In Section 9-1, we describe how organisms have evolved to have very specific preferences when it comes to the foods they seek and prefer.

TAKE-HOME MESSAGE 22•8

Instincts cause animals to get hungry and to seek out food when in that state. Humans and other animals show a preference for fatty foods over carbohydrate- or protein-laden foods, a behavior reinforced by fat-laden meals stimulating many of the reward centers in the brain. These preferences probably evolved because fat has the most calories per serving.

| Proteins 4 kcal/gram | Carbohydrates 4 kcal/gram | Fats 9 kcal/gram |

Animals can meet their energy needs much more easily by seeking and consuming fats. This can significantly reduce the time spent looking for food.

FIGURE 22-18 Efficiency of a fat-rich diet.

Food for Energy and Growth · Nutrients · Digestion and Absorption · Diet and Health

❸ We extract energy and nutrients from food.

A cormorant catches a fish.

22·9

We convert food into nutrients in four steps.

The human digestive system is like an assembly line running backward. Imagine starting with an assembled car and dismantling all the parts: the tires, doors, windshield, steering wheel. The food entering the assembly line of the digestive system is like the intact car. It enters the assembly line and then passes through four distinct phases, during which the food is progressively chewed up and broken down, the nutrients absorbed by the body, and the non-usable portion of the raw materials discarded as waste products (**FIGURE 22-19**).

In the next several sections, we examine in detail the four stages in the processing of food: ingestion, digestion, absorption, and elimination. Throughout these sections, it will be useful to picture the digestive system as a long tube with an opening at each end, the mouth and the anus, and some glands along the way that produce the necessary chemicals to help the process along.

TAKE-HOME MESSAGE 22·9

The digestive process in humans includes four distinct phases during which food is progressively chewed up, broken down, and absorbed by the body, after which the non-usable portion of the raw materials is discarded as waste.

DIGESTIVE PROCESS FROM START TO FINISH

The digestive process in humans includes four distinct phases.

1 INGESTION
Food is taken into the body.

2 DIGESTION
Large pieces of food are dismantled by physically and chemically breaking them into absorbable molecules.

3 ABSORPTION
Energy-rich food molecules are taken into the cells of the body, where they can be used for energy and building materials.

4 ELIMINATION
The final remaining parts of the consumed foods—mostly indigestible materials—are discarded as waste products and much water reabsorption occurs.

FIGURE 22-19 There are four steps in the body's processing of food.

Ingestion is the first step in the breakdown of food.

It will take you longer to read about **ingestion,** the intake of food into your body, than it would to just do it (**FIGURE 22-20**). Typically lasting less than a minute, ingestion primarily involves four parts of your anatomy: your mouth, teeth, tongue, and esophagus. We'll look at each in some detail. To start, imagine that you take a big bite of a hamburger, containing bread, lettuce, and the meat.

Putting food in your mouth stimulates your salivary glands. Via tiny ducts throughout your mouth, the salivary glands secrete mucus that lubricates the food to help it pass into your stomach. They also secrete an enzyme called alpha-amylase that initiates the process of digestion. Alpha-amylase breaks the bonds holding together the starch molecule (a highly branched carbohydrate pieced together from hundreds of linked glucose molecules) and releases a bit of glucose that can be used for energy. About 20% of the ingested starch is broken down in the mouth. Protein and fat molecules, on the other hand, are not broken down at all.

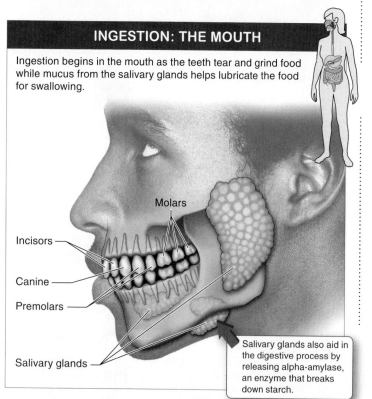

INGESTION: THE MOUTH

Ingestion begins in the mouth as the teeth tear and grind food while mucus from the salivary glands helps lubricate the food for swallowing.

Molars

Incisors

Canine

Premolars

Salivary glands

Salivary glands also aid in the digestive process by releasing alpha-amylase, an enzyme that breaks down starch.

FIGURE 22-20 Ingestion, the intake of food into the body, begins in the mouth.

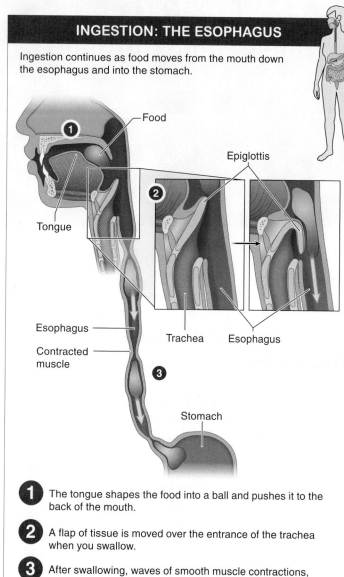

INGESTION: THE ESOPHAGUS

Ingestion continues as food moves from the mouth down the esophagus and into the stomach.

Food

Epiglottis

Tongue

Esophagus

Contracted muscle

Trachea

Esophagus

Stomach

1 The tongue shapes the food into a ball and pushes it to the back of the mouth.

2 A flap of tissue is moved over the entrance of the trachea when you swallow.

3 After swallowing, waves of smooth muscle contractions, called peristalsis, propel food down the esophagus and into the stomach.

FIGURE 22-21 Ingestion is complete when food passes from the mouth through the esophagus to the stomach.

You start chewing food in your mouth in order to tear and grind it into little bits. This is a first important step toward completely breaking down and harvesting the energy stored in the chemical bonds of the food. Several different types of teeth have evolved in mammals and other animal species that enable different types of food items to be processed. Incisor

Food for Energy and Growth   Nutrients   Digestion and Absorption   Diet and Health

and canine teeth in the front are used for biting and tearing food. Behind them are premolars and molars, used for grinding and crushing food. Just by looking at the type of teeth an animal has, we can learn a lot about its diet. Herbivores have molars primarily for grinding and crushing the tough cell walls of the plants they eat. Carnivores have sharp and lethal canines and incisors for killing and tearing apart the flesh of other animals.

Birds have no teeth. This explains why they can sometimes be seen eating gravel. Although the gravel has no nutritional value, it collects in the stomach, where it helps to grind up the food they eat. This is an important digestive step for birds because, without teeth, they must swallow their food whole. Consequently, when it gets to the stomach, it hasn't been ground up at all, which can reduce the efficiency of digestive enzymes.

While you are chewing your food, your tongue assists in the process by forming the food into a ball shape that can be swallowed. The ball of partly crushed, saliva-coated food is pushed to the back of your mouth by your tongue. There, your throat opens to two passageways into your torso, the **trachea** and the **esophagus** (**FIGURE 22-21**). The trachea, also called the windpipe, connects to your lungs, while the esophagus connects to your stomach. Food destined for your stomach is kept from entering your trachea by a fast but

Q *Why do many birds eat gravel?*

critical maneuver in which your voice box moves up (due to muscle contractions), causing a flap of tissue (called the epiglottis) to be pushed over the entrance to the trachea just as you begin to swallow. If the ball of food you swallow is too big, it can get stuck at the beginning of the esophagus, wedging against the flap of tissue in front of the trachea—and this can cause you to choke by blocking all air from getting into your lungs.

Once the ball of chewed food makes it into the esophagus, waves of smooth muscle contractions, called **peristalsis**, propel the food down the esophagus and into the stomach, where digestion continues. Because of peristalsis, it's not necessary for you to be sitting upright or standing when you eat. Even if you are standing on your head, the food is pushed down the esophagus to the stomach.

TAKE-HOME MESSAGE 22·10

Ingestion is the first phase of the digestive process. Usually lasting less than a minute, ingestion involves tearing and grinding food in preparation for passing it to the stomach. Digestion also begins during this phase, with some starch being broken down by enzymes in saliva.

22·11

Digestion dismantles food into usable parts.

Food is fuel. But it is useless to an animal until it has been completely broken down into its fundamental chemical constituents. Only then can it be absorbed into the bloodstream and used constructively by a body. The process of dismantling the large pieces of food, physically and chemically breaking them down into absorbable molecules, is digestion. It occurs primarily in the stomach and small intestine.

The Stomach Let's continue tracing the bite of hamburger as it moves through the digestive system. It empties from the esophagus directly into the **stomach,** a muscular J-shaped organ with thick, elastic walls that can expand greatly in size to accommodate a large meal—as much as 4 liters of material! At the point where the esophagus connects to the stomach, there is

a ring of muscle, called a **sphincter.** It seals off the stomach once the food has entered, preventing regurgitation of the stomach's acidic contents into the esophagus—even if you are eating while standing on your head. The stomach has three functions.

1. It physically breaks down and mixes food, through churning of the muscles surrounding it.

2. It secretes acid to further break down food, chemically, and to kill bacteria.

3. It begins some chemical digestion of proteins.

The presence of food in the stomach causes cells in crevices within the stomach lining, called gastric pits, to rapidly produce hydrochloric acid and a protein-dismantling enzyme known as

pepsin (FIGURE 22-22). The acid corrodes proteins in the food, breaking them into smaller pieces, which can then be broken into their constituent amino acids by the pepsin.

The burning sensation of indigestion occurs when the sphincter between the esophagus and the stomach doesn't completely prevent the acidic contents of the stomach from moving back up the esophagus. It usually occurs when a person eats too much or too quickly. Antacids can neutralize acid from the stomach. Remember, though, that the high acidity in the stomach is important for digestion, so while reducing it may alleviate heartburn, antacids can reduce the digestive efficiency of the stomach.

Q What is indigestion? How do antacids cure it?

The end result of all the churning and digesting is that the food you have eaten is no longer recognizable. It becomes a creamy, very acidic liquid called **chyme.** At the other end of the stomach is another ring of muscle. About every 20 seconds, it opens just a tiny bit and squirts a few tablespoonfuls of chyme into the small intestine. While some of the hamburger's carbohydrates and proteins have been partly or completely digested in the stomach, the lettuce is undigested, as are the lipids from the meat, which are suspended as greasy droplets within the chyme.

Besides helping to chemically break down food in your stomach, the strong acid also kills most of the bacteria that you might consume. Most bacteria just can't survive when the pH gets so acidic (although some microbes occasionally manage to sneak through by hiding in pockets of food with higher pH as the food passes through the stomach). In the StreetBio at the end of this chapter, we explore the ulcer-inducing effects of one species of bacteria that can live in your stomach.

Q Humans use heat for cooking and often marinate food in vinegar or lemon juice. How do these processes help with digestion?

Interestingly, across dozens and dozens of cultures, humans have developed common ways of preparing their food, including using heat and marinating food in acidic solutions, such as vinegar or lemon juice. Because harsh conditions such as heat and acid help to disrupt the tissue of food items, they increase the efficiency with which digestive enzymes can make contact with the food and break it down

The Small Intestine

Digestion only begins in the mouth and stomach. Most chemical digestion actually occurs in the **small intestine,** a long thin tube connected to the stomach in which most digestion takes place. It is about 20 feet long and winds all around your abdominal cavity (how else could 20 feet of tubing be packed into such a small area?). As we've seen, as a sphincter at the end of the stomach relaxes, creating an opening, small amounts of chyme are squirted from the stomach. The creamy substance slowly moves through the small intestine, pushed by the rhythmic contractions of peristalsis. As the chyme makes its way through the small intestine, the macromolecules are gradually digested, with help from the pancreas and the liver (FIGURE 22-23).

The **pancreas,** nestled at the point where the stomach connects to the small intestine, plays a central role in digestion by secreting pancreatic juice through a duct into the very beginning portion of the small intestine. This juice is a mixture of (1) chemicals that neutralize the acidic chyme, and

DIGESTION: THE STOMACH

Digestion is the process of dismantling large pieces of food, physically and chemically breaking them down into absorbable molecules.

Esophagus — Sphincter — Food — Churning muscle

A sphincter seals off the stomach once food has entered it, preventing the stomach's acidic contents from flowing back into the esophagus. Another sphincter seals off the end of the stomach from the small intestine.

Small intestine — Chyme

Gastric pits

1 Muscles in the stomach churn and physically break down and mix food.

2 Gastric pits produce hydrochloric acid to activate pepsin, which disassembles protein.

3 The food mixture, called chyme, then passes into the small intestine.

FIGURE 22-22 The role of the stomach in digestion.

Food for Energy and Growth   Nutrients   ▼ Digestion and Absorption   Diet and Health

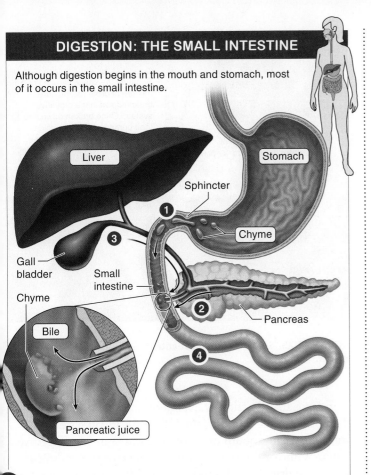

DIGESTION: THE SMALL INTESTINE

Although digestion begins in the mouth and stomach, most of it occurs in the small intestine.

Liver

Stomach

Sphincter

1

3

Chyme

Gall bladder

Small intestine

Chyme

2

Pancreas

Bile

4

Pancreatic juice

1 As a sphincter at the end of the stomach relaxes, small amounts of chyme are squirted into the small intestine.

2 The pancreas secretes pancreatic juice, which neutralizes the chyme and aids in the digestion of carbohydrates, proteins, and fats.

3 The liver produces bile, which travels from the gall bladder, where it is stored, to the small intestine, where it acts as a detergent to break up particles of fat.

4 Cells within the walls of the small intestine produce enzymes that further digest fats, carbohydrates, and proteins.

Digestion is completed in the small intestine, at which point carbohydrates, proteins, and fats have been broken down into simple sugars, amino acids, and fatty acids.

FIGURE 22-23 **The role of the small intestine in digestion.**

(2) enzymes that digest carbohydrates, proteins, and fats. Another organ that assists the small intestine with digestion is the **liver,** which produces **bile,** a juice that aids in the breakdown of fats. The liver sends the bile to the gall bladder, and from there it passes through a small duct into the small intestine, where the bile initiates the first step in fat digestion.

Remember, lipids are not water-soluble, so any fat from the hamburger is still suspended in the chyme, never dissolving into the watery substance of the digestive tract. Bile acts as a detergent that helps break up the suspended droplets of fat into much tinier particles. Once the lipids decrease in size, pancreatic enzymes can successfully break them down. In addition to the enzymes produced by the pancreas and the liver, the cells within the walls of the small intestine also generate enzymes that further digest fats, carbohydrates, and proteins. For a variety of reasons, people sometimes must have part of their small intestine surgically removed. Can you predict the effects this might have on digestion?

Digestion is completed in the small intestine when the consumed carbohydrates, proteins, and fats have been broken down into their component parts: simple sugars, amino acids, and fatty acids. These simple molecules can then be absorbed into the bloodstream, a process that we explore in the next section. But first let's look at a few cases in which digestion doesn't work properly or in which animals rely on some digestive assistance from bacteria, and a carnival trick that hinges on an understanding of digestion.

Intestinal Bacteria Have you noticed that certain types of food commonly give people gas? Some types of beans commonly cause such digestive distress. Enzyme deficiencies and metabolically versatile bacteria are the culprits. The beans contain the sugars raffinose and stachyose, which are indigestible by many people. And so when the sugars pass undigested through the small intestine and reach the large intestine, they are digested by bacteria. And the by-product of the bacterial feeding frenzy is gas, cramps, and flatulence. The product Beano contains enzymes that help digest the trouble-making sugars before our resident bacteria can get to them.

There is a wide variety of situations in which bacteria living inside animals similarly digest food molecules that the animals could not otherwise break down—and this has evolved as a benefit to the "host" animals as well as the bacteria. Living in termite guts, for example, are large colonies of symbiotic cellulose-digesting bacteria. The bacteria make it possible for the termite to eat wood and actually gain nutrients from it. The bacteria obtain energy by breaking down the cellulose in the wood into simple sugars that are valuable to the termite (as well as to the bacteria). If humans could figure out how to cultivate the same bacteria in our guts, perhaps we, too, could eat wood.

Leeches also have a symbiotic relationship with bacteria. As a leech sucks blood from an animal, bacteria—rather than its own enzymes—break down the blood proteins into their component amino acids, which the bacteria and the leech then share (**FIGURE 22-24**).

As a leech sucks blood from an animal, bacteria—rather than its own enzymes—break down the blood proteins into their component amino acids, which the bacteria and the leech then share.

FIGURE 22-24 Leeches and bacteria in partnership.

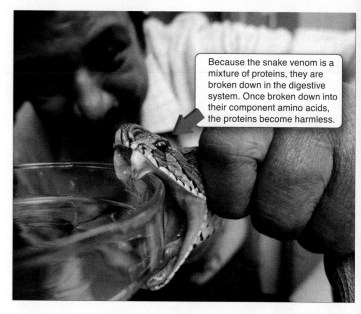

Because the snake venom is a mixture of proteins, they are broken down in the digestive system. Once broken down into their component amino acids, the proteins become harmless.

FIGURE 22-25 Snake venom must enter the bloodstream to cause ill effects.

Q *Snake venom is toxic, but if you drink it, in most cases it won't harm you. Why?*

Poisonous Proteins Snake venom is a mixture of toxic proteins. Yet if you "milked" a snake's venom into a glass and drank it, the toxin wouldn't necessarily harm you (**FIGURE 22-25**). At carnivals and entertainment parks, snake experts will sometimes do exactly this, with no ill effects. Because the venom is a mixture of proteins, it is broken down by the stomach acids and enzymes of the digestive system. Once broken down into their component amino acids, the poison proteins become harmless. Snake venom must enter the bloodstream to cause its ill effects. That is why snakes bite

with fangs that function as hypodermic needles, delivering the poison to the bloodstream. Of course, if you have any cuts inside your mouth or lesions elsewhere in your digestive system, some of the venom could get into your bloodstream when you drink it and poison you. For that reason, drinking venom isn't a wise stunt to attempt.

TAKE-HOME MESSAGE 22·11

Digestion—the process of dismantling large pieces of food, physically and chemically breaking them down into absorbable molecules—is the second phase of the breakdown of food in animals. It occurs primarily in the stomach and small intestine.

Food for Energy and Growth   Nutrients   Digestion and Absorption   Diet and Health

Absorption moves nutrients from your gut to your cells.

Chewing, tearing, churning, acidifying, dismantling. You put a lot of energy into reducing food to its simplest component molecules. Eventually, though, there is a payoff. That payoff is **absorption,** the process by which the energy-rich food particles are taken from the digestive tract into the bloodstream and then into the cells of the body, where they can be used for energy and building materials. Absorption occurs mainly in the small intestine; however, a few molecules are absorbed in the stomach, including aspirin and alcohol, which explains why drinking alcohol on an empty stomach can lead to unexpectedly rapid inebriation.

The secret to effective absorption is simple: surface area. For a molecule such as a sugar or an amino acid to be absorbed by the body, the molecule must be in direct contact with the cell membrane of the cell that is going to absorb it. The greater the number of cells that can come in contact with chyme passing through the small intestine, the greater the amount of nutrients that can be absorbed. For this reason,

the tremendous surface area of the small intestine allows for very efficient absorption of nutrients (**FIGURE 22-26**). How does the small intestine achieve this? There are four primary ways.

1. The small intestine is long. About 20 feet long, as we saw above.

2. Rather than being a straight, smooth tube, it has many folds.

3. The interior lining of the small intestine is made up of thousands of small finger-like projections, called villi. These create lots of nooks and crannies where chyme can come in contact with absorptive cells.

4. Each of the cells along the villi has hundreds of its own tiny thread-like projections, called microvilli. These create micro-nooks and micro-crannies that allow more of the molecules in chyme to directly touch the membranes of absorptive cells.

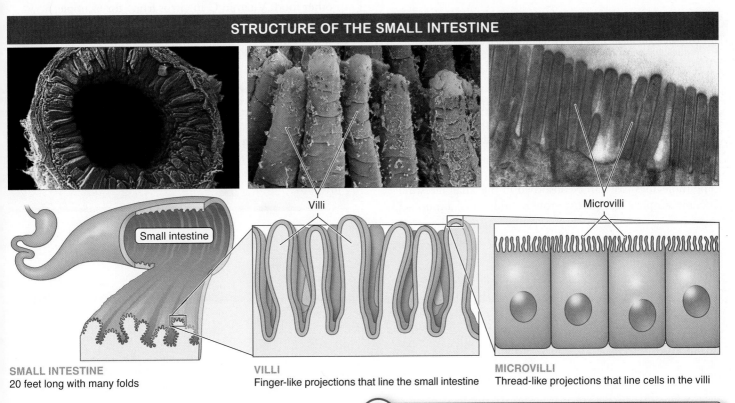

STRUCTURE OF THE SMALL INTESTINE

Villi

Microvilli

Small intestine

SMALL INTESTINE
20 feet long with many folds

VILLI
Finger-like projections that line the small intestine

MICROVILLI
Thread-like projections that line cells in the villi

FIGURE 22-26 The small intestine has a very large area for absorbing nutrients.

The tremendous surface area of the small intestine allows for very efficient absorption of nutrients.

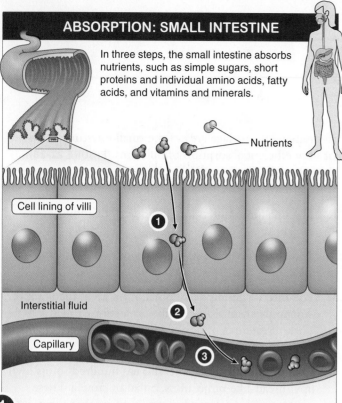

ABSORPTION: SMALL INTESTINE

In three steps, the small intestine absorbs nutrients, such as simple sugars, short proteins and individual amino acids, fatty acids, and vitamins and minerals.

Nutrients

Cell lining of villi

1

Interstitial fluid

Capillary

2

3

1 Nutrients are transported into the cells lining the villi.

2 Nutrients diffuse out of the cells and into the interstitial fluid bathing the cells.

3 Nutrients are picked up by the capillaries and move into the bloodstream, where they can be delivered to the organs and tissues that need them.

FIGURE 22-27 Absorption moves nutrients into the bloodstream.

fatty acids, vitamins, and minerals. When a nutrient molecule is small enough to be absorbed, it gravitates toward the villi lining the interior of the small intestine. The tiny particles become trapped in the microvilli and are drawn across the cell membrane into the cells (**FIGURE 22-27**). Then the nutrient diffuses out of the cell and into the interstitial fluid bathing the cells. Finally, from here the nutrients are picked up by capillaries and thus move into the bloodstream, where they can be delivered to the organs and tissues that need them.

There is a food myth that if certain foods are combined, digestion is impaired. This is not true. The myth ignores a couple of facts: the body is able to produce its digestive enzymes for fats, proteins, and carbohydrates simultaneously, and it can absorb nutrients regardless of which other nutrients are also in the digestive tract. In fact, the contrary is often true. Many foods enhance the absorption of nutrient molecules in other foods. Vitamin C in citrus fruits, for example, increases the efficiency of iron absorption from a meal of beef or beans.

Q Is it true that certain food combinations should not be eaten together?

TAKE-HOME MESSAGE 22·12

Absorption is the process by which energy-rich food particles are taken up from the digestive tract into the cells of the body, where they can be used for energy and building materials. It takes place primarily in the small intestine.

Ultimately, all of these surface-area-enhancing structural features give the small intestine a huge amount of surface area for absorption. If it were spread out as a flat surface, it would be about the size of a tennis court.

The molecules that can be absorbed in the small intestine include simple sugars, short proteins, individual amino acids,

Food for Energy and Growth   Nutrients   Digestion and Absorption   Diet and Health

22·13

Elimination removes unusable material from your body.

You are much better at conservation and recycling than you imagine. Especially when it comes to the fluids and solids you consume. The last phase in the breakdown of food, **elimination**, takes place as what's left of the chyme—mostly indigestible materials—leaves the small intestine and enters the **large intestine**, also called the **colon**. Much larger in diameter than the small intestine (about 3 inches, vs. 1 inch in the small intestine) but only about 3–6 feet long, the large intestine serves to absorb water, salts, and some vitamins (**FIGURE 22-28**). The last part of the large intestine is the rectum and serves as a storage compartment for the remaining parts of consumed food, the feces, which can then be defecated.

It is important to achieve just the right balance of water absorption in the large intestine. If too much is absorbed, the remaining indigestible material becomes too solid and can't move easily through the last part of the digestive system, causing constipation. Alternatively, if too little absorption occurs, the body loses more water and this causes diarrhea. Fiber—including gums and cellulose—cannot be digested or absorbed. For this reason, when fiber is consumed, it increases fecal mass and speeds the movement of chyme through the colon (**FIGURE 22-29**). With additional mass, more water is attracted, softening the feces and making it easier to eliminate (that's why too much fiber can lead to diarrhea). Fiber also binds to bile, causing some of it to be eliminated, thereby reducing the body's ability to absorb cholesterol from food.

Q Fiber is an indigestible carbohydrate. If we can't digest it, how can it be essential in our diet?

Huge colonies of bacteria live in the colon. Before we are born, our guts are sterile and free of bacteria. During birth, we acquire some of our mother's vaginal and fecal bacteria, and by the age of two we have acquired bacteria from food and the environment, so that all of the numerous species present in adults are already in residence by that age. We generally have more bacterial cells than our own body cells at any given time (see Figure 13-3). The bacteria are usually harmless and live off the undigested materials that end up in the colon. Bacteria

ELIMINATION: COLON

Colon

①

②

③

Small intestine

Rectum — Feces

① The remaining chyme—mostly indigestible materials—leaves the small intestine and enters the large intestine, or colon.

② Water, salts, and some vitamins are absorbed.

③ The rectum serves as a storage compartment for the feces, made up from dead bacterial cells and the final remaining, indigestible parts of consumed food.

FIGURE 22-28 Elimination is the final step in the digestive process.

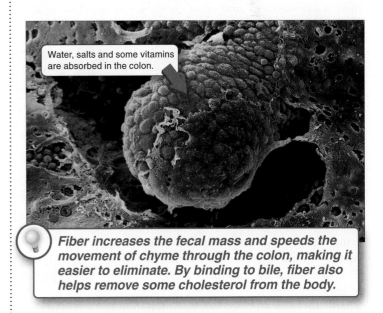

Water, salts and some vitamins are absorbed in the colon.

Fiber increases the fecal mass and speeds the movement of chyme through the colon, making it easier to eliminate. By binding to bile, fiber also helps remove some cholesterol from the body.

FIGURE 22-29 The last remnants of a meal in the colon.

also release important metabolic by-products such as vitamin K and one of the B vitamins, biotin. About half of the feces that we excrete each day is made up of dead bacterial cells, and the rest is mostly indigestible materials such as cellulose from the cell walls of plant matter and other types of fiber.

Q Why can taking antibiotics lead to vitamin deficiencies?

Antibiotics frequently (and unintentionally) kill a large proportion of the colon bacteria, in addition to whatever illness-causing microbe they were prescribed to kill. This can have multiple negative side effects. First, the transit of undigested materials through the colon may not be slowed down as much as usual, in which case less water is removed and diarrhea results. Also, a reduction in production of vitamin K and biotin can lead to deficiencies.

In the colon, water is removed from feces through osmosis. First, salts are pumped out of the colon, and then water moves out by simple diffusion (to an area where there are more ions). This process can be manipulated as a treatment for constipation. Laxatives contain magnesium salts that are so slowly absorbed that they are still largely intact when they reach the colon. Laxatives work by increasing the salt concentration in the colon, so that more water remains. This additional water makes it easier to excrete feces (but can cause diarrhea in some cases).

Q Laxatives contain salts. Why might this reduce constipation?

TAKE-HOME MESSAGE 22·13

The last phase of food breakdown takes place as the mostly indigestible materials leave the small intestine and enter the large intestine. There, water and ions are absorbed before the remaining materials are defecated.

22·14

Animals have some alternative means for processing their food.

Food, food everywhere, but not a bite to eat. Cellulose could feed the world: it's everywhere—the major carbohydrate making up the cell wall around plant cells is cellulose—and there is a tremendous amount of energy stored in its chemical bonds. But most animals don't produce enzymes that break down cellulose. If they can figure out a way to digest it—and some species have—they gain access to one of the most plentiful sources of chemical energy on the planet. Let's investigate how some animals have done it.

Ruminant animals, such as cows, bison, deer, goats, and sheep, have evolved complex four-part stomachs in which they are able to digest plant matter that humans cannot (**FIGURE 22-30**). First, the grazing animals chew on the plant material for a while, grinding the tough cell walls. Then they swallow it, and it passes into the first part of their stomach, which contains a huge pool of enzymes and cellulose-digesting bacteria. There, the plant material gets broken down, and much of the cellulose is digested. To increase their energy-extraction efficiency, the animals then regurgitate the food back into the mouth, chew it some more, and swallow it again. Called "chewing the cud," the additional chewing further breaks up the plant cell walls so that the bacteria can have easier access to the cellulose, digesting more of it. From the first part of the stomach, the food then passes through the remaining chambers, where some additional digestion takes place, before moving into the small intestine and continuing the usual path of animal digestion. Cellulose-digesting bacteria have some of the most dangerous working conditions on earth: although cellulose is the primary component of the ruminant diet, ruminants also get a significant amount of protein every day by digesting many of the bacteria working in their gut.

Q Silverfish are insect pests in libraries rather than in kitchens. Why might this be? (Hint: they are one of only a few species of animals to produce enzymes that digest cellulose.)

Some insects, including silverfish, produce cellulose-digesting enzymes. These enzymes make it possible for them to actually eat books and paper, which are made of plant products containing cell walls made from cellulose.

Food for Energy and Growth   Nutrients   Digestion and Absorption   Diet and Health

FOUR-PART STOMACH

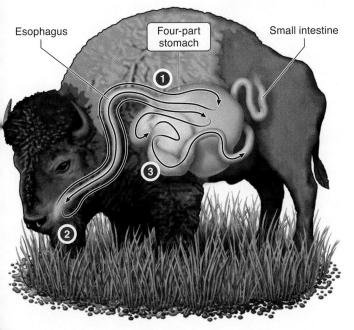

In ruminant animals, a complex four-part stomach has evolved in which they are able to digest the plant matter that humans cannot.

Cellulose-digesting bacteria

Esophagus — Four-part stomach — Small intestine

1. Plant material is swallowed and passed to the first part of the stomach, where it is broken down and digested by enzymes and cellulose-digesting bacteria.

2. Food is regurgitated, chewed more, then swallowed and passed to the first chamber again.

3. Food passes through the remaining chambers, where additional digestion takes place before it moves into the small intestine.

FIGURE 22-30 Ruminants can digest plant material that humans cannot.

There's more than one way to skin a plant. Other animals, without the large bacteria-filled stomach of ruminants, also employ cellulose-digesting bacteria to enable them to extract energy from cellulose. In these animals, including horses, rodents, rabbits, and koalas, the bacteria don't live in the stomach. Rather, they live farther down the digestive tract, within an outcropping of the small intestine called the cecum. This is a separate chamber where the food goes for a while and the cellulose gets digested, before the food continues down the intestine. In animals that don't break down cellulose, the cecum is much smaller. The cecum is almost non-existent in the meat-eating coyote, while the similarly-sized koala has a cecum that is 2 meters long, where bacteria can convert shredded eucalyptus leaves into usable food (**FIGURE 22-31**). In

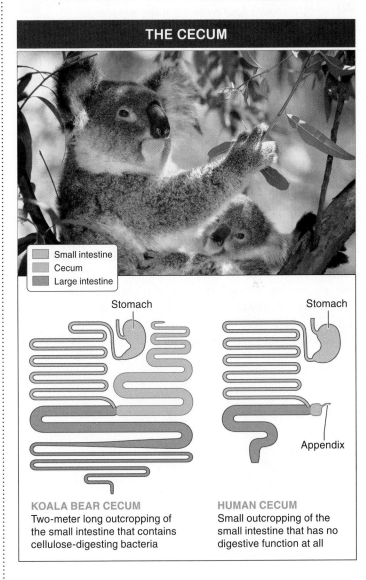

THE CECUM

- Small intestine
- Cecum
- Large intestine

Stomach   Stomach

Appendix

KOALA BEAR CECUM
Two-meter long outcropping of the small intestine that contains cellulose-digesting bacteria

HUMAN CECUM
Small outcropping of the small intestine that has no digestive function at all

FIGURE 22-31 Koalas can eat foods that are indigestible for humans. The cecum is the site of cellulose digestion in some animals.

Rabbits and rodents have mastered another way to increase their ability to extract energy from their food: they pass it through their digestive system twice.

FIGURE 22-32 Coprophagy increases nutritional intake from foods high in cellulose.

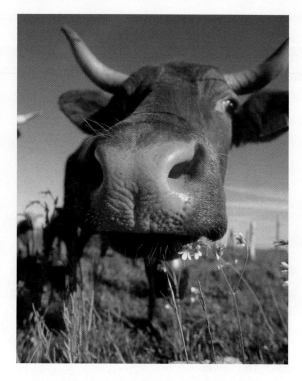

There are about 150 different domestic and wild ruminant species including cows, goats, deer, buffalo, bison, giraffe, and elk.

humans, no cellulose-digesting bacteria live in the cecum (which is called the appendix in humans). Recent research suggests, however, that the appendix may play a role in immune function.

Rabbits and rodents can't increase their cellulose-digesting efficiency by regurgitating their food and chewing the cud, because the cellulose-digesting bacteria reside in the small intestine, not the stomach. But they've mastered another way to increase their ability to extract energy from their food: they pass it through their entire digestive system twice (**FIGURE 22-32**). Called **coprophagy,** eating some of their feces allows them to

significantly increase their nutritional intake from their cellulose-laden diet.

TAKE-HOME MESSAGE 22·14

Most animals don't produce enzymes that break down cellulose. In ruminant animals, complex four-part stomachs have evolved in which the animals can digest plant matter that humans cannot, in part due to the presence of symbiotic cellulose-digesting bacteria. Other animals have alternative methods of utilizing cellulose-digesting bacteria.

Food for Energy and Growth   Nutrients   Digestion and Absorption   Diet and Health

④ What we eat profoundly affects our health.

Two sweet foods with very different nutritional composition.

22·15

What constitutes a healthy diet?

Choosing a healthy diet can be very difficult. There are more than 50,000 different foods that a person can choose from each day. And we not only must select which foods to eat, we must also consider how much of each to consume each day. Fortunately, there is not a single "best" solution that every person must adhere to in order to ensure good health. Rather, there are many different ways, making it possible to work within any person's particular likes and dislikes.

At the most basic level, just two requirements—quality and quantity—must be satisfied in the design of a healthy diet (**FIGURE 22-33**). First, a diet must contain sufficient amounts of each of the six categories of nutrients: water, proteins, carbohydrates, lipids, vitamins, and minerals (described in Sections 22-4–22-8). And second, a healthy diet must contain sufficient energy to support an individual's metabolic needs without containing a surplus of calories. But it is not easy to find the best strategy to satisfy these requirements.

Laboratory rodents—including those in longevity studies in which the animals have lived significantly longer than any wild rodent—have no such trouble with choosing a healthy diet. They are fed a diet that consists simply of water and special

💡 *A healthy diet should contain sufficient amounts of each of the six categories of nutrients and just enough energy to support an individual's metabolic needs.*

FIGURE 22-33 Food quality and quantity are the main factors to consider in choosing a healthy, balanced diet.

food pellets. The food pellet formulation is the result of decades of research on animal nutrition. It includes carefully controlled amounts of each nutrient and does not vary from the time an animal reaches maturity until it dies. Each day, the rodents receive a specific number of the pellets, and each day the rodents eat them. Humans (thankfully?) do not subsist on a single food item. But for that reason, one of the most important principles guiding selection of a healthy diet is *balance*.

Balance in a diet is important because no one food is completely adequate. Milk, for example, is a very good source of protein and calcium, but does not contain sufficient iron for most adults. Meats, on the other hand, are rich in iron (as well as protein) but generally are poor sources of calcium. Every type of food, in fact, while providing some nutritional value, also falls short in some other essential nutrient, whether a protein or a specific vitamin or mineral. For this reason, nutritionists recommend consuming a variety of foods from each of the basic food groups—including (1) grains, (2) vegetables, (3) fruits, (4) milk and other dairy products, and (5) meats, poultry, and beans—consuming small quantities of unsaturated fats such as olive and canola oil, and exercising daily to manage body weight (**FIGURE 22-34**).

The U.S. Department of Agriculture (USDA) has established dietary guidelines, which it updates every five years. These highlight the most important issues with respect to determining the ideal quantity and quality of food consumed. In addition to

urging people to take steps to ensure that their food is safe to eat, they also recommend the following.

1. Keep your weight within the recommended range.

2. Be physically active.

3. Choose a variety of fruits, vegetables, grains—particularly whole grains—and nonfat or low-fat milk and milk products.

4. Keep your diet low in saturated fat, cholesterol, and total fat.

5. Keep your diet low in sugars relative to complex carbohydrates and fiber.

6. Keep your diet low in salt.

7. If you consume alcoholic beverages, do so in moderation.

Food labels are an often overlooked tool that can help in adhering to these guidelines and selecting a balanced diet. Ingredient lists, too, are very valuable, listing every ingredient in order of amount (by weight). Ultimately, following these guidelines can help reduce the incidence and severity of chronic diseases such as stroke and other manifestations of cardiovascular disease, diabetes, and cancer.

Q Why is it increasingly difficult to maintain a healthy diet we get older?

Complicating the USDA's dietary guidelines is the fact that we need to reduce our caloric intake as we get older. Metabolic rate falls slowly but surely, beginning around age 30. Consequently, without an increase in activity, eating the same amount of food—even if it is a healthy diet—leads to a surplus of calories, a surplus that becomes larger and larger with each passing year. On average, most adults gain about half a pound every year throughout their thirties, forties, and fifties.

It is important to note that people who do not consume meat, poultry, fish, and/or milk products can still have a balanced diet. Legumes, seeds, and nuts can provide many of the same nutrients found in meat, including protein. Dark leafy vegetables can provide iron, another nutrient plentiful in meat. And in fact, because such diets tend to be lower in fat content, they can be valuable in helping to maintain a healthy body weight.

TAKE-HOME MESSAGE 22·15

A balanced diet contains adequate amounts of essential nutrients and energy, but not surplus amounts, and is low in substances—including saturated fats, cholesterol, sugar, salt, and alcohol—that can have adverse health effects when consumed in greater quantities.

RECOMMENDED DAILY FOOD INTAKE

GRAINS | VEGETABLES | FRUITS | OILS | DAIRY | MEAT & BEANS

Because no one food is completely adequate, nutritionists recommend consuming a variety of foods from each of the basic food groups.

FIGURE 22-34 What nutritionists recommend.

Food for Energy and Growth | Nutrients | Digestion and Absorption | Diet and Health

Obesity can result from too much of a good thing.

Jerry and Louis Kahn are two brothers who really love to eat. The pair tip the scales at about 500 pounds each—and their hunger never subsides. What is unusual about the Kahns' difficulty controlling their weight is that doctors have pinpointed the exact physiological source of their problem. They both possess an altered gene that renders their bodies unable to recognize the internal measure of food intake and register "enough," much like a broken thermostat that never shuts off a heater. Jerry and Louis are eternally hungry because their brains never get the "we're full" message from their stomachs.

Like the Kahns, we all have inherited genes from our parents that significantly influence our body weights. The thing is, we don't need to carry a defective gene to become obese. All humans inherit dozens (possibly hundreds) of genes that influence body weight, and even in their "normal" condition, these genes are likely to lead to weight problems (**FIGURE 22-35**). But this raises a couple of questions. Why would it be in our genetic interests to have huge appetites? Why would natural selection favor such genes? To answer these questions, we must consider the harsher, less predictable environment in which *Homo sapiens* evolved.

Our ancestors lived off the land by hunting animals and gathering plants. Under such conditions, it was unclear where the next meal was coming from. Powerful, instinctual hunger kept our ancestors going in that tough, energetically demanding world. Imagine a time when the individuals of a population varied in their appetites. Some individuals thought of food day and night, and ate whenever they could. Others became satiated once their daily needs were met. Of these types, which included individuals with the biggest surplus of energy stored in their thighs and buttocks when food became scarce? Who weathered the famine, with calories left over for reproducing? Who is most likely to be your ancestor? In every case, it is the enthusiastic and not the restrained eaters. Recent studies using PET scans (positron emission tomography, a type of imaging) have supported this, demonstrating that just the sight of food sets off activity in the brain's pleasure centers—a mechanism that generally leads to the consumption of food when it is available.

The consequence of our perpetual hunger is not news: one of every four Americans is obese. In terms of size, plumpness gets labeled "obesity" when our body mass index hits 30. **Body mass index,** or **BMI,** equals body weight in

Why has natural selection favored genes for large appetites?

FIGURE 22-35 Are your genes making it difficult for you to maintain a healthy weight?

kilograms divided by height in meters squared (kg/m^2). A BMI of 30 translates to about 209 pounds if you are 5 feet 10 inches tall, and 180 pounds if you are 5 feet 5 inches. With a BMI of 25 or higher, you are only considered "overweight." BMI isn't the only way to evaluate obesity, and it has its problems. Because the measure does not consider body composition, professional athletes and bodybuilders with unusually large muscle mass have BMIs that fall within the obese range. Still, it is a useful and easily obtained measure (**FIGURE 22-36**). Repeatedly, around the world, as societies get richer and as individuals age, they tend to become fatter. Most of us would reduce our risk of heart disease, stroke, and diabetes if we lost even as little as

BODY MASS INDEX (BMI)

Height	UNDER WEIGHT (<18.5) 18	HEALTHY WEIGHT (18.5–24.9) 19	20	21	22	23	24	OVERWEIGHT (25–29.9) 25	26	27	28	29	OBESE (>30) 30	31	32	33	34	35
6′4″	148	156	164	172	180	189	197	205	213	221	230	238	246	254	263	271	279	287
6′3″	144	152	160	168	176	184	192	200	208	216	224	232	240	248	256	264	272	279
6′2″	141	148	155	163	171	179	186	194	202	210	218	225	233	241	249	256	264	272
6′1″	136	144	151	159	166	174	182	189	197	204	212	219	227	235	242	250	257	265
6′0″	132	140	147	154	162	169	177	184	191	199	206	213	221	228	235	242	250	258
5′11″	129	136	143	150	157	165	172	179	186	193	200	208	215	222	229	236	243	250
5′10″	126	132	139	146	153	160	167	174	181	188	195	202	209	216	222	229	236	243
5′9″	122	128	135	142	149	155	162	169	176	182	189	196	203	209	216	223	230	236
5′8″	118	125	131	138	144	151	158	164	171	177	184	190	197	203	210	216	223	230
5′7″	115	121	127	134	140	146	153	159	166	172	178	185	191	198	204	211	217	223
5′6″	112	118	124	130	136	142	148	155	161	167	173	179	186	192	198	204	210	216
5′5″	108	114	120	126	132	138	144	150	156	162	168	174	180	186	192	198	204	210
5′4″	105	110	116	122	128	134	140	145	151	157	163	169	174	180	186	192	197	204
5′3″	102	107	113	118	124	130	135	141	146	152	158	163	169	175	180	186	191	197
5′2″	98	104	109	115	120	126	131	136	142	147	153	158	164	169	175	180	186	191
5′1″	95	100	106	111	116	122	127	132	137	143	148	153	158	164	169	174	180	185
5′0″	92	97	102	107	112	118	123	128	133	138	143	148	153	158	163	168	174	179

Body Weight (Pounds)

FIGURE 22-36 One indicator of healthy body weight: body mass index. The BMI indicates the ratio between height and body weight; the chart shows healthy body-weight ranges.

10 pounds. But because of the "famine-fearing" genes we carry, this is easier said than done.

From the cellular perspective, the specific causes of obesity are an increase in the size and number of fat cells an individual carries. Excess calories can be converted to fat regardless of whether they come from fats, carbohydrates, or proteins. Whatever the source, the fat molecules are added right to the fat cells in the body's adipose tissue. Fat cells increase in number primarily during the late years of childhood and the early teens (**FIGURE 22-37**). After that, the cells tend to grow in size rather than number with excess caloric intake, although when a fat cell becomes too large it will divide. The reverse, unfortunately, is not true. When people lose weight, their fat cells become smaller but are never lost completely. Consequently, it is especially important to avoid obesity early in life.

FIGURE 22-37 It's important to maintain a healthy body weight during childhood.

Fat cells increase in number during the years of childhood and early teens, making it especially important to avoid obesity then.

Food for Energy and Growth   Nutrients   Digestion and Absorption   Diet and Health

The problems of obesity are not restricted to humans. Most primates in zoos are also overweight, as are many pets and most laboratory research animals. In each case, the reason is the same as for humans. In their natural world, food is limited and unpredictable. Animals overeat when they do not need to expend much energy to acquire food and food is plentiful. In the next section, we explore some weight-loss diets and why they are almost universally unsuccessful.

22·17

Weight-loss diets are a losing proposition.

 I can reason down or deny everything, except this perpetual Belly: feed he must and will, and I cannot make him respectable.

—Ralph Waldo Emerson, *Representative Men*, 1850

Weight loss is both a simple and a complicated problem. It is simple because there is one complete and perfect plan that guarantees success; it requires only five words of description: "Eat less. Move around more." Regardless of the genes it carries, any animal of any species will lose weight when it expends more calories than it consumes. The equation holds whether the calories are consumed in hamburgers or in fresh, organic vegetables. Similarly, it doesn't matter whether energy is expended in the weight room or on the couch.

But weight loss is also complex: while we know that eating less and moving around more are all that is necessary, and while almost all short-term "diets" work, in the long-run, with very few exceptions, they fail. (**FIGURE 22-38**). More than half of the advice books currently on the *New York Times* bestseller list promise new plans for losing weight. Five years ago that was also true—although the bestsellers were different books. It may seem as if there are plenty of new ideas about how to lose weight, yet the problem has not gone away. Rather, it has gotten worse.

Current interventions designed to facilitate weight loss range from mild to extreme. They fall into three categories: drugs, surgery, and behavior modification. Each has both promising and problematic elements (**FIGURE 22-39**).

Drugs and Other Chemical Interventions

Xenical. The most promising of recently developed weight-control drugs is Xenical, a product that interferes with fat digestion by binding to lipases (fat-digesting enzymes) and

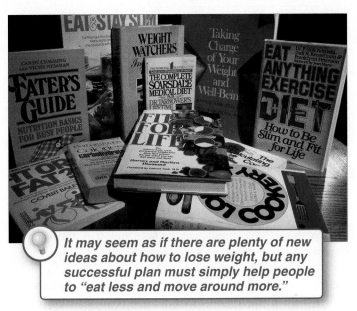

It may seem as if there are plenty of new ideas about how to lose weight, but any successful plan must simply help people to "eat less and move around more."

FIGURE 22-38 Weight-loss diets make for popular reading.

blocking them from doing their job. As a consequence, some of the fat in the digestive system passes through the body without absorption. In randomized, double-blind, placebo-controlled clinical studies—the gold standard for experimental design—Xenical has succeeded in helping people lose about 10 pounds over the course of one year. In the second year, these people regained some of their weight, but still ended up a bit lighter and with reduced circulating cholesterol and blood pressure. These findings are promising, but no long-term studies have been conducted to assess the permanence of the weight loss or potential side effects. Additionally, at a cost of more than $1,000 per year, Xenical is too expensive for most people to use.

Meridia. Approved for the treatment of obesity, this appetite-suppressant has shown promise as a weight-loss product. It reduces the rate at which the chemical serotonin, associated

DRUGS AND OTHER CHEMICAL INTERVENTIONS

SURGERY

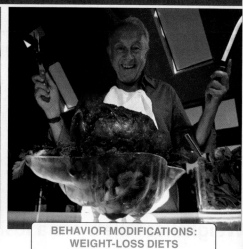

BEHAVIOR MODIFICATIONS: WEIGHT-LOSS DIETS

FIGURE 22-39 What are the promises and perils of weight-loss interventions?

with satiation, is removed from the space between nerve cells in the brain. Concerns over possible adverse effects on the cardiovascular system, however, have prompted some opposition to continued availability of this prescription drug.

Olestra and NutraSweet. Some artificially created molecules, such as Olestra and NutraSweet, can trick our taste buds into responding as if a molecule of sugar or fat, respectively, were present. Olestra, for example, is designed to have a taste and texture similar to fats, but in an indigestible molecule (see Section 2-13). After stimulating the taste buds that normally respond to fats, it ultimately is excreted, without having yielded any energy (read: without having deposited unwanted fat in your body). Still, as the NutraSweet cookie study described earlier in this chapter illustrates, our bodies have been built to detect reductions in caloric intake and to respond by increasing consumption. We're not tricked quite so easily. For this reason, low-calorie versions of food are unlikely to be successful on their own in generating permanent weight loss.

Caffeine and other stimulants. A variety of products claim to increase the expenditure of energy without an offsetting increase in appetite. This approach is theoretically sound, but there are no published data on either the safety or efficiency of these unregulated products. While clinical trials demonstrate that stimulants such as caffeine can produce short-term weight loss in the range of 5–10 pounds, long-term studies reveal that most of the short-term losses do not last.

Placebo. During clinical studies for diet pills, one observation was quite unexpected. As we learned in Chapter 1, researchers testing new compounds always have a "placebo" group. Subjects in this group go through all the same motions but get pills with none of the test drug. Because the placebo pills and

the test drug pills are identical in appearance, no one knows which patients are getting the drug candidate and which are getting blanks. The goal is to separate the effects of the test drug from the effects of the monitoring process. As expected, some new drugs work and others fail, but here's the strangest finding: people in placebo groups always lose weight. In a study on the effectiveness of Xenical, for instance, more than 25% of the people in the placebo group lost at least 10 pounds. How can this be? While those in the placebo group aren't using drugs, they are keeping track of their weight and are more aware of their food intake than usual. This mindfulness may be the only "secret" behind the success of some crazy and non-scientific diets that advocate, for example, only eating food of a certain color (but "as much as you want") on a certain day. Careful monitoring proves to be a crucial component of weight control.

Surgery

Liposuction. Liposuction is fast becoming one of the most popular surgical procedures in the United States, with close to half a million performed each year. In this procedure, doctors directly remove fat cells from various parts of the body, using a hollow tube and a suction device. Over time, however, individuals who have undergone liposuction tend to regain all the lost weight. In fact, the only follow-up study on liposuction found that within a few months, nearly half of the patients weighed more than they did before the surgery. This is because body weight is a function of caloric intake and energy expenditure; fat cells can be removed, but without a change in the inputs and outputs, eventually the body will achieve the same composition.

Bariatric surgery and stomach banding. More invasive surgical procedures are also possible. The most effective is also the most extreme. In a type of surgical procedure known as bariatric surgery, surgeons bypass a significant portion of the small

Food for Energy and Growth · Nutrients · Digestion and Absorption · Diet and Health intestine and seal off, by stomach banding, most of a person's stomach. This has two effects. First, it reduces the amount of food people can eat before becoming full—they actually become violently ill if they consume more than a few tablespoons at one time. And second, it reduces the ability of their small intestine to digest and absorb nutrients. Before all of the nutrients that they consume can be absorbed, the food material passes through the shortened digestive system and is excreted. The surgery carries significant risks, though, and leads to major nutritional deficiencies in almost a third of all cases. Still, something can be said for bariatric surgery that cannot be said unequivocally for any drug or diet: it works. One study of more than 600 patients found that after 14 years, the average weight loss was 100 pounds! Additionally, many health problems such as diabetes, high cholesterol, and high blood pressure went away.

Behavior Modification: Weight-Loss Diets

Portion control and general caloric restriction. Can we change our eating habits permanently? To answer this question, researchers put a group of monkeys on a very low-calorie diet. The monkeys shed pounds initially, then stabilized at much lower weights for two years. After two years they were given unlimited access to food. Did they maintain their new weights? Absolutely not. After spending close to 10% of their lives at a constant, low weight, these monkeys quickly returned to their original, pre-diet weights.

This monkey example suggests that there might be a "set point" for body weight. A variety of human and non-human studies do, in fact, reveal that just like a thermostat for a room, when weight is below the set point, the body induces calorie-seeking behavior, and when weight is above the set point, the mind and body are free to pursue other goals. In a human study equivalent to the hungry monkey study, researchers observed a group of successful dieters over time. The newly skinny people had lost an average of 70 pounds per person through a comprehensive program. Three years after completing the program, the participants had, on average, regained all of their lost weight.

Low-carbohydrate diets. These are the latest in a long series of fad diets that enjoy popularity before being discarded for failing to deliver on the claims of their proponents and the promise of their short-term success. They are based on the incorrect assumption that carbohydrates universally cause rapid increases in blood sugar, followed by large releases of insulin from the pancreas, leading to immediate and efficient conversion of the blood sugar into fats that are stored throughout the body. While this scenario is correct for some carbohydrates, other carbohydrates, such as whole wheat pasta, produce less of an insulin response than a similar amount of high-protein beef. Similarly, many high-fiber fruits and vegetables are also rich in carbohydrates yet increase blood sugar levels only very gradually

and elicit very small insulin responses. As a consequence, blanket avoidance of carbohydrates can lead to insufficient fiber intake as well as vitamin and mineral deficiencies. Unlimited consumption of fat, too, can lead to a caloric surplus and weight gain. Low-carbohydrate diets do lead reliably to impressive initial weight loss. This is because in the absence of dietary carbohydrates, glycogen (and the large amount of water bound to it) in the liver and muscles is quickly used up.

General Problems with Weight-Loss Diets The main problems with most popular weight-loss diets are that (1) they focus on reducing weight (even weight due to water) rather than reducing body fat; (2) they reduce muscle mass, the body tissue best able to burn fat; (3) because they reduce body weight too rapidly, they trigger several defense mechanisms designed to preserve the body's energy reserves; and (4) they don't focus enough on the other side of the energy equation: exercise. (**FIGURE 22-40**). This generally leads to four problems.

GENERAL PROBLEMS WITH WEIGHT-LOSS DIETS
- They focus on reducing weight (even weight due to water) rather than body fat.
- They reduce muscle mass, the body tissue best able to burn fat.
- Because they reduce body weight too rapidly, they trigger several defense mechanisms designed to preserve the body's energy reserves, generally leading to even more problems.
- They don't focus enough on the other side of the energy equation: exercise.

FIGURE 22-40 Weight-loss diets often fail.

1. *Nutritional deficiencies.* Consider how a family facing a financial crunch may be forced to defer important work, such as fixing the car's brakes. Similarly, when the body goes into efficiency mode to combat a shortage of calories, a variety of systems get modulated down or turned off. Hungry lab animals, for example, almost completely lose their sex drive and may be less adept at fighting infection. Nearly all popular diets are seriously deficient in vitamins, minerals, and fiber.

2. *Metabolic rate reduction.* Sudden caloric restriction leads to a rapid reduction in basal metabolic rate, and this lower rate remains for several weeks after resuming normal caloric intake. With a reduced BMR, your body burns fat at a slower rate.

3. *Loss of muscle mass and body fluids rather than body fat.* Low-calorie diets lead to weight loss, but as much as 45% of the weight loss comes from the loss of muscle mass. Muscle tissue is significantly more metabolically active than the relatively inert fat cells. As a consequence, the body's fat-burning capacity is significantly reduced along with its muscle mass. Weight loss, as we've noted, is also commonly due to loss of the water bound to glycogen in muscles and the liver.

4. *Increased lipoprotein lipase activity.* With a reduction in caloric intake, your body increases the activity of an enzyme called lipoprotein lipase. This enzyme is responsible for converting nutrients in the bloodstream to fats for storage.

As with the metabolic rate reduction, the increased activity of lipoprotein lipase continues for weeks following resumption of a normal diet.

An evaluation by the National Institutes of Health of *all* the major diet programs concluded that there was no good evidence that any of the programs reliably led to long-term weight loss. A large study published in the *New England Journal of Medicine* came to a similar conclusion in 2009. The claims made by weight-loss programs rely on anecdotal accounts of individuals that are not at all representative of the average outcome. Unfortunately, this means that there are no easy solutions to the problem of weight control. As long as we live in our modern, zoo-like environment of plenty, we're going to struggle with natural systems that relentlessly seek out and efficiently store calories.

TAKE-HOME MESSAGE 22·17

Weight loss is both a simple and a complicated problem. There is only one complete and perfect plan that guarantees success: reduced caloric intake and increased caloric expenditure. Interventions designed to facilitate weight loss involve drugs, surgery, or behavior modification, none of which is reliably successful.

22·18

Diabetes is caused by the body's inability to regulate blood sugar effectively.

A finely tuned, responsive machine. When it functions properly, the human body can resemble such a machine. Nowhere is this more true that in the processing of food. After you digest and absorb food, there's an increase in the amount of glucose circulating in your bloodstream. This triggers the release of insulin by your pancreas. Insulin is a storage-stimulating hormone that causes your body's cells, especially muscle cells and fat cells, to pull the glucose in. They can then either use it for energy or convert it to glycogen or fat for storage until the energy is needed some other time. This leads to a reduction in glucose in the bloodstream and brings your blood sugar level back down to normal.

Foods differ in the extent to which they cause a surge in blood sugar and subsequent release of insulin. Foods that cause a rapid and large surge—such as orange juice, honey, and white potatoes—are classified as having a high **glycemic**

index and are less desirable in the diet. More desirable are foods that cause only a slow, moderate increase, having a low glycemic index. These include whole grains and beans. With a reduced insulin response comes more efficient utilization of the sugar and lipids in the bloodstream and a reduction in fat storage. Insulin surges can also be reduced by eating smaller meals or, if you consume foods that have a high glycemic index, eating them with other foods as part of a meal.

Even finely tuned machines can malfunction. More than 10 million Americans (and 100 million people worldwide) have problems with their insulin-response systems, referred to as **diabetes.** These problems are chiefly of two types (**FIGURE 22-41**): either (1) the pancreas doesn't secrete enough insulin in response to an increase in blood sugar, or (2) the pancreas secretes plenty of insulin, but the cells of the body don't respond to it, usually due to a deficiency in glucose receptors on their

Food for Energy and Growth | Nutrients | Digestion and Absorption | Diet and Health

Insulin—a hormone produced by the pancreas in response to increased blood sugar—causes your body's cells to pull glucose in from blood vessels.

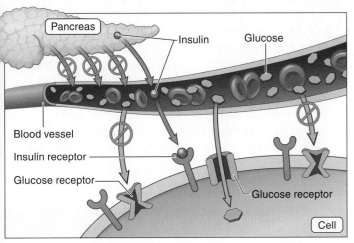

TYPE 1 DIABETES

The pancreas doesn't secrete enough insulin in response to an increase in blood sugar.

TYPE 2 DIABETES

The pancreas secretes plenty of insulin, but the cells of the body don't respond to it, usually due to a deficiency in glucose receptors on the cell membranes.

FIGURE 22-41 Diabetes is a disruption in the body's regulation of blood sugar.

Why must diabetics inject insulin rather than taking it in pill form?

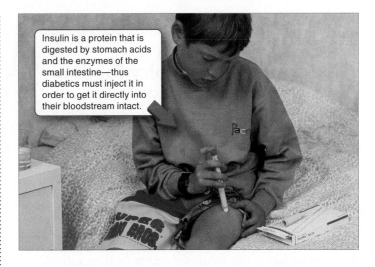

Insulin is a protein that is digested by stomach acids and the enzymes of the small intestine—thus diabetics must inject it in order to get it directly into their bloodstream intact.

FIGURE 22-42 Type 1 diabetes is treated with insulin injections.

insulin, thus they can be treated by insulin injections (**FIGURE 22-42**). (Unfortunately, because insulin is a protein, it is digested by stomach acids and the enzymes of the small intestine, so diabetics must inject the insulin in order to get it into their bloodstream intact.) The second type of diabetes (type 2) is about 10 times more common. It generally develops after the age of 40, and in about 90% of cases is a consequence of obesity. It appears that chronic and excessive amounts of sugar in the diet (and, later, in the bloodstream) reduce the sensitivity and/or number of cellular insulin receptors that help control blood sugar. This causes even greater releases of insulin, which can, ultimately, wear out the insulin-producing cells of the pancreas. Type 2 diabetes is treated by minimizing the glucose fluctuations in the bloodstream. Weight loss is also encouraged, as it reduces insulin resistance.

Because chronically high levels of blood sugar affect nearly all the cells of the body, the health effects can be far-reaching and severe. Cells in the eye lens can become deformed, causing blurry vision; blood vessels can be damaged, causing circulatory system and kidney malfunction; and nerves can also be damaged. Taken together, the varied problems resulting from diabetes make it the sixth leading cause of death in the United States.

TAKE-HOME MESSAGE 22·18

Digesting and absorbing food leads to an increase in the amount of glucose circulating in the bloodstream, which triggers the release of insulin by the pancreas, causing the body's cells, especially muscle cells and fat cells, to pull the glucose in for energy or storage. Problems with regulation of blood sugar, called diabetes, affect millions of people and are caused by heredity and poor diet.

cell membranes. In both cases, blood sugar remains high, and a host of problems can occur as a result of such persistence of glucose in the bloodstream.

The first type of diabetes (called type 1) is hereditary and usually occurs in children. Generally, people with type 1 diabetes have a pancreas that doesn't secrete enough

Food and infection: spicy foods are natural antibiotics.

Have you ever tasted salsa so spicy that it brought tears to your eyes? After you gulped down a beverage to extinguish the fire in your mouth, did you ignore the distress signals from your taste buds and head right back for more? Why would anyone seek out such culinary torture? The answer is surprisingly simple, although not immediately apparent. We'll start by asking the question: what *are* spicy foods?

Spices come from plants. Plants are rooted in the ground, and their immobility makes them easy targets for their natural enemies. But although they can't run away, they don't just give in to those organisms that want to eat them. They fight back chemically. Plants have evolved to produce a large number of toxic compounds to help in this fight. The presence of these noxious chemicals makes the plant toxic to would-be predators, either killing them outright or being so unpleasant-tasting that predators search elsewhere for a meal.

Humans, somewhat unexpectedly, actually seek out these toxins. We don't think of them as toxins, though. We call them spices, and as long as they're not too toxic, they make our food taste better. There is also a deeper, more evolutionarily relevant reason we find our food to be more appealing with spices added. They help us in our own battles with natural enemies. "Food poisoning," it turns out—which affects about 1 out of 10 people in the United States each year—is a misleading term. It isn't the food that poisons us. Instead, it is microorganisms, particularly bacteria, that poison us. Humans and plants must perpetually fight against infection from microorganisms. This task is difficult because bacteria find easy entry into our bodies via the food we eat. After sitting out at room temperature for just a few hours, food can acquire huge amounts of bacteria. But by adding spices to our food, we take advantage of the plant defenses to strike back at the microbes, killing them before they make it to our digestive systems.

The "spices kill bugs" theory emerged from extensive observations and analyses. It has generated several predictions that have been tested.

Prediction 1: The magnitude of spice use in any part of the world should be related to the amount of microbial growth in that part of the world.

Observations: Put another way, this is a prediction that in warm, wet countries (where microbial growth occurs more readily), spice use should be greatest, while in cooler climates, spice use should be less. In an analysis of more than 4,500 meat-based recipes and 2,100 vegetable-

based recipes from 36 countries, this prediction was overwhelmingly supported. There is a strong correlation between regions with high average temperatures and their use of spices with antimicrobial effects (**FIGURE 22-43**). Spices were included in every single recipe, for example, from Ethiopia, Kenya, Greece, India, Indonesia, Iran, Malaysia, Morocco, Nigeria, and Thailand. Conversely, two-thirds of all recipes from Finland and Norway called for no spices at all.

SPICE USE AND CLIMATE

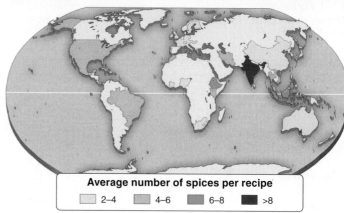

Average number of spices per recipe

2–4	4–6	6–8	>8

 There is a strong correlation between regions having high average temperatures (where microbial growth occurs more readily) and their use of spices with antimicrobial effects.

FIGURE 22-43 Fighting natural enemies. Antimicrobial spices are used much more where temperatures are high.

Food for Energy and Growth | Nutrients | Digestion and Absorption | Diet and Health

SPICE USE AND ANTIMICROBIAL PROPERTIES

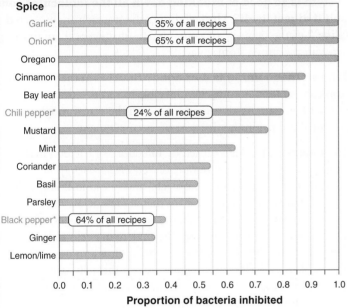

Spice

Proportion of bacteria inhibited

- Garlic* — 35% of all recipes
- Onion* — 65% of all recipes
- Oregano
- Cinnamon
- Bay leaf
- Chili pepper* — 24% of all recipes
- Mustard
- Mint
- Coriander
- Basil
- Parsley
- Black pepper* — 64% of all recipes
- Ginger
- Lemon/lime

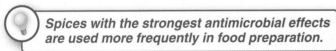

Spices with the strongest antimicrobial effects are used more frequently in food preparation.

* The four most commonly used spices are shown in red.

FIGURE 22-44 Recipe ingredients with antimicrobial properties. (Photo shows woman with drying chili peppers.)

Two observations suggest that this relationship between spice use and climate cannot be attributed to the fact that more spices grow in the countries with hotter, wetter climates. First, onion and garlic, two of the most potent antimicrobial spices, grow in all of the countries studied but are used more frequently in the warmer countries. And second, although the warmer countries do have larger numbers of local spices to choose from, they use a greater proportion of the available spices than do the cooler countries.

Prediction 2: Spices with the strongest antimicrobial effects should be used most, and the weaker antimicrobial agents used less frequently.

Observations: In a test of 42 spices, in which each was added to individual plates of bacteria, nearly all exhibited antimicrobial properties—sometimes quite dramatically—when used in the amounts called for in recipes. For example, the toxic compound in cilantro was twice as effective at killing *Salmonella* bacteria as was the commonly used antibiotic drug gentamicin. Most of the spices tested were broad in their effects, too, killing most of the 30 different types of common food-borne bacteria tested. Overall, onions and black pepper, which had the best antimicrobial effects (they killed all species of bacteria they came into contact with), were used most frequently, appearing in 65% of all recipes. They were followed by black pepper (in 64% of all recipes), garlic (in 35% of all recipes), chili peppers (24%), and lemon and lime juice (23%). Other commonly used spices include parsley, ginger, bay leaf, coriander, and cinnamon (**FIGURE 22-44**).

Prediction 3: Because bacterial growth is faster and more common on meat than on vegetables, meat recipes should call for more spices than vegetable recipes.

Observations: The vegetable recipes called for, on average, 2.4 spices, while the meat recipes called for almost twice as many, with an average of 3.9.

Research on the connection between the use of spices and their antimicrobial properties continues. Nonetheless, it seems to be quite likely that humans did initially incorporate spices into food preparation because of their antimicrobial properties. Given that refrigeration is a very recent invention, consumption of food that had been "sanitized" by spices ensured the spice-consumers greater survival and reproduction. This example shows how seemingly arbitrary behaviors may reflect evolutionary adaptations.

TAKE-HOME MESSAGE 22·19

Plants produce toxic compounds that make the plant distasteful to would-be predators, either killing them outright or being so unpleasant-tasting that predators search elsewhere for a meal. Humans seek out these toxins, using them as spices that help us fight off illness-inducing microorganisms.

Knowledge You Can Use

When digestion breaks down. Microbes, stress, and stomach ulcers.

Q: **If the digestive system is so good at breaking down all the molecules sent through it, why doesn't it digest itself?** The cells lining the stomach are protected by a layer of highly alkaline (i.e., the opposite of acidic) mucus that keeps them from coming in direct contact with the strong stomach acids.

Q: **What happens if the stomach lining is damaged?** Breaches in the protective layer of mucus in the stomach render the stomach vulnerable to ulcers—from small erosions in the digestive tract lining to life-threatening holes all the way through to the abdominal cavity. Ulcers can also form in the first part of the small intestine.

Q: **What causes these ulcers?** Ulcers are caused by infections of bacteria living in the stomach and the first part of the small intestine. Called *Helicobacter pylori,* these bacteria live in the tiny spaces between the stomach- and intestine-lining cells, where they create cocoon-like areas around themselves that are less acidic than their surroundings. The bacteria then damage the mucus and the top layer of cells, while stimulating increased secretions of acids. This exposes the underlying cells to harsh gastric juices, hydrochloric acid, and digestive enzymes. The result is a minor irritation at first, but over time, the harsh chemicals can eat right through the cells, at which point they damage the underlying capillaries—causing the ulcer to bleed—and can damage the nerves in the area, too, causing extreme pain.

Q: **But isn't it stress that causes stomach ulcers?** Until about 1990, it was not clear that ulcers were caused by bacterial infection. Instead, it was believed that psychological stress played a much more important role in causing stomach ulcers. Because antibiotics can kill *H. pylori* and cure most ulcers within two weeks, however, it now seems clear that the role of stress in causing stomach ulcers is relatively small.

Q: **What can you conclude?** While stress is off the hook as the culprit, ulcers are still not completely understood. Consider, for instance, that as many as 50% of people in the world have *H. pylori* living in their digestive systems, yet only about 10% of people will develop an ulcer at some point in their lives. Clearly, there are additional factors beyond infection. And research increasingly reveals that stress does reduce the immune system's effectiveness and can increase susceptibility to illness. We explore this link in Chapter 26.

1 Food provides the raw materials for growth and the fuel to make it happen.

Animals must eat for two reasons: to acquire the energy needed for all growth and activity, and to acquire the raw materials required for life. Carnivores consume only other animals. Herbivores consume only plants. And omnivores consume both plants and animals. The minimal energetic needs of an individual not engaged in any activity are called the basal metabolic rate, or BMR.

2 Nutrients are grouped into six categories.

Water is probably the single most important component of a balanced diet, while proteins, carbohydrates, and fats provide calories and raw materials. Vitamins and minerals are organic and inorganic molecules (respectively) in the diet that are used in the production and action of enzymes and other molecules. Humans and other animals show an evolved preference for fatty foods over carbohydrate- or protein-laden foods.

3 We extract energy and nutrients from food.

The digestive process in humans includes four distinct phases. (1) Ingestion involves tearing and grinding food in preparation for passing it to the stomach. (2) Digestion, the process of dismantling large pieces of food, physically and chemically breaking them down into absorbable molecules, occurs primarily in the stomach and small intestine. (3) Absorption, in the small intestine, is the process by which energy-rich food particles are taken into the cells of the body. (4) Water and ions are absorbed before the indigestible portions of consumed food are defecated. Most animals don't produce enzymes that break down cellulose, although many have symbiotic bacteria that do this for them.

4 What we eat profoundly affects our health.

Ancestral humans experienced unpredictable food supplies, leading to the evolution of strong appetites. In the modern industrial world, such instincts have problematic consequences for weight control. Although there is, in theory, one complete and perfect plan that guarantees successful weight control—reduced caloric intake and increased caloric expenditure—the many interventions designed to help people lose weight are rarely successful. Problems with regulation of blood sugar, called diabetes, affect millions of people and are often caused by poor diet. Somewhat ironically, but for good evolutionary reasons, humans seek out toxic compounds that are produced by plants to ward off predators. Such compounds, used as spices, help us fight off illness-inducing microorganisms.

KEY TERMS

1. Based on the types of diet they consume, spiders and owls are considered:
   a) carnivores.
   b) omnivores.
   c) herbivores.
   d) primary producers.
   e) fluid-feeders.

2. Basal metabolic rate:
   a) depends to a large degree on how active an individual is.
   b) does not vary across mammalian species.
   c) is a measure of the minimal energetic needs of an individual not engaged in any activity.
   d) is the same for males and females of any given species.
   e) All of the above are correct.

3. Water has many functions in animal bodies. These include all of the following except:
   a) lubricating many joints, the spinal cord, and the eyes.
   b) serving as a solvent for many vitamins and minerals.
   c) transporting nutrients and waste materials throughout the body.
   d) regulating growth and development.
   e) All of the above are functions of water in animal bodies.

4. Why do dieters lose large amounts of "water weight" during the first few days of a diet?
   a) The first, most accessible, molecules that can be broken down for energy are glycogen molecules in muscles and liver. And because large amounts of water are bound to glycogen, as the glycogen is removed from tissues, so too is the water.
   b) Dieters tend to reduce their consumption of all food and beverages—including their consumption of water—during the first days of a diet.
   c) Dieting causes a slight increase in body temperature, which leads to increased evaporative cooling and the loss of water.
   d) The fat cells of the body are primarily filled with water. As these cells are utilized for energy, the water is also lost.
   e) Actually, dieters do not lose "water weight" during the first few days of a diet. This is a myth.

5. On food packages, "fiber" refers to plant material that we can't fully digest but is important for maintaining a healthy digestive tract. "Fiber" refers to a type of:
   a) carbohydrate.   d) amino acid.
   b) nucleic acid.   e) protein.
   c) lipid.

6. Proteins are an essential component of a healthy diet for humans (and other animals). Their most common purpose is to serve as:
   a) fuel for running the body.
   b) raw material for growth.
   c) inorganic precursors for enzyme construction.
   d) organic precursors for membrane construction.
   e) long-term energy storage.

7. Vitamin and mineral supplements are generally necessary for individuals in all of the following categories except:
   a) post-menopausal women.
   b) healthy people with good diets.
   c) people on extremely low-calorie diets.
   d) pregnant women.
   e) people with limited milk consumption or sun exposure.

8. Most mammals (including humans) prefer the taste of fats to carbohydrates and proteins. Why?
   a) Fats are more easily digested than proteins or carbohydrates.
   b) Fats were much less available than proteins and carbohydrates in most ecosystems in which humans and other mammals evolved.
   c) The caloric content of a gram of fat is more than double that of a gram of protein or carbohydrate.
   d) The vitamin and mineral content of a gram of fat is more than double that of a gram of protein or carbohydrate.
   e) Many individuals lack the enzymes (such as lactase) to break down polysaccharides into their component sugars.

9. Why do birds eat gravel?
   a) Gravel contains most of the essential minerals for a bird's diet.
   b) Birds have poor vision and have difficulty distinguishing gravel from small seeds.
   c) By chewing on gravel, birds are able to sharpen their teeth, increasing their ability to crack open hard nuts or catch their prey.
   d) The gravel collects in the stomach, where it helps to grind up the food they eat.
   e) Because they have such a small brain relative to body size, birds tend to be the least intelligent of all vertebrates.

10. Across dozens of cultures, humans have developed common ways of preparing their food, including using heat and marinating food in acidic solutions, such as vinegar or lemon juice. How might these be adaptations that help with digestion?
    a) Harsh conditions such as heat and acid help to disrupt the tissue of food items. This increases the efficiency with which digestive enzymes can make contact with the food molecules and break them down.
    b) These methods of food preparation reduce the necessity of producing chyme and so increase the caloric efficiency of food intake.
    c) Because even the weakest acids are toxic to all bacteria, these methods of food preparation reduce the incidence of dietary-induced bacterial infection.
    d) These methods increase the body's ability to extract energy from normally indigestible cellulose.
    e) These methods of food preparation reduce the need for water consumption.

11. Which of the following statements about the small intestine is incorrect?

   a) It is the primary site of digestion and absorption of nutrients into the bloodstream.

   b) It is the chief site of absorption of water by the digestive system.

   c) It is the longest part of the digestive tract.

   d) It receives secretions from the gall bladder.

   e) It is the part of the digestive tract where all food macromolecules can be broken down into absorbable monomers.

12. To leave the digestive tract and enter the cells of the body, a substance must cross a cell membrane. During which stage of digestion does this take place?

   a) peristalsis   d) chemotaxis

   b) absorption   e) ingestion

   c) elimination

13. Digestion and absorption:

   a) involve the breakdown of food into small nutrient molecules (absorption) and the passage of those molecules into the bloodstream (digestion).

   b) both occur primarily in the large intestine, or colon.

   c) are terms that describe the same process.

   d) both occur primarily in the stomach.

   e) involve the breakdown of food into small nutrient molecules (digestion) and the passage of those molecules into the bloodstream (absorption).

14. In the mammalian digestive system, vitamin-synthesizing symbiotic bacteria live primarily in the:

   a) small intestine.   d) large intestine.

   b) esophagus.   e) stomach.

   c) mouth.

15. Though essentially the same organ, the human appendix is much smaller than a koala's cecum. This is because:

   a) humans take supplements to obtain enough vitamins and do not need the extra vitamins produced by the bacteria housed in the appendix.

   b) humans aid the digestive process by marinating and cooking foods, so they do not require a large appendix to aid food digestion.

   c) humans maintain bacteria in their intestine rather than in their appendix, so the organ does not need to be as large as a koala's cecum.

   d) in humans, no cellulose-digesting bacteria live in the cecum—called the appendix—and it has no digestive function at all.

   e) humans get a greater proportion of their nutrients from meat than do koalas, so they do not need as large an organ to digest the plant matter they eat.

16. Cows have large populations of bacteria in their digestive systems. Which of the following best explains why?

   a) The mutualistic microbes combat the harmful microbes that may enter a cow's body on its food.

   b) Cows are able to use cellulose-producing bacteria to help them digest their food.

   c) Most cows actually do not have large populations of bacteria in their digestive systems. Only infected cows have these microbes.

   d) Scientists put the microbes there, so that they can study how the microbes affect cows' digestion.

   e) The microbes metabolize the cellulose in the plants that cows eat.

17. The spices that many humans use to season their food:

   a) are generally compounds produced by plants to reduce their risk of being eaten.

   b) are actually dead microorganisms.

   c) consist primarily of amino acids.

   d) are the chief cause of ulcers.

   e) can only be grown in tropical regions of the world.

SHORT-ANSWER QUESTIONS

1. What are the six groups of nutrients? What is their primary role in human health?

2. What are the four distinct phases used by humans to extract nutrients from food? For each phase, what significant activity takes place that contributes to nutrient harvesting and absorption?

3. Describe how some mammals, which do not have enzymes to break down cellulose, are able to extract nutrients from cellulose-containing food.

4. Describe the two forms of diabetes. What are the risk factors and treatments?

See Appendix for answers. For additional study questions, go to www.prep-u.com.

23

Nervous and Motor Systems

Actions, reactions, sensations, and addictions: meet your nervous system

❶ What is the nervous system?

The cat responds to a stimulus in the environment (possibly a dog, in this case) by raising hairs on its back, called hackles.

23•1 --------------------------------------

Why do we need a nervous system?

Imagine a world without pain. Think of all that you could achieve. You could work harder, run farther, and just plain feel better. Maybe that's why so many products are marketed as "painkillers."

But would it really be a better world? Think again.

The case of three-year-old Gabby Gingras tells us that we wouldn't really be happier in a pain-free world. Gabby feels no pain. She was born that way. At first it seemed like a blessing: just after birth, when nurses drew blood from her, she did not cry but instead slept peacefully through the procedure. When she falls down, she doesn't cry. But rather than being a gift that makes her life easier, Gabby's inability to feel pain is a crippling curse. As she has grown older, some unexpected consequences of her condition make this clear. First, she inadvertently damaged her eyes—permanently scratching one of her corneas—by poking her fingers into them. Later, chewing on a plastic toy, she cracked several of her teeth. Another girl, also born without the ability to feel pain, encountered even more severe problems. Holding her hand over a hot stove, she was severely burned—moving her hand only when she smelled the burning flesh. This condition is called "heritable sensory autonomic neuropathy," and it reveals that, no matter how unpleasant pain is to experience, it does have a very large benefit. The pains we feel alert us to the need to extricate ourselves from a dangerous situation and can prevent much greater suffering in the long run (**FIGURE 23-1**).

No one likes to feel pain, and yet those who cannot do so inevitably experience suffering far greater than the pain they are spared. Why are we built this way? Why is the experience of pain a necessary part of being a living animal? Pain tells us that some aspect of our environment is not hospitable and that we must take action to remove ourselves from it. If an animal is biting or stinging you, you try to get away from the animal. And what happens if your hand touches something hot? You don't even have to think about it: you quickly pull your hand away. In short, bad stuff happens to animals. The survival and well being of organisms depends on their awareness of the world around them, and the ability to limit exposure to physically harmful situations.

Present in all multicellular animals other than sponges, the **nervous system** is a network of cells that collects information about the organism's internal and external environments, processes that information, and sends signals to effectors, which are muscles and glands that are capable of responding to the information. Our nervous system

What Is the Nervous System?   How Do Neurons Work?   The Senses   Muscular and Skeletal Systems

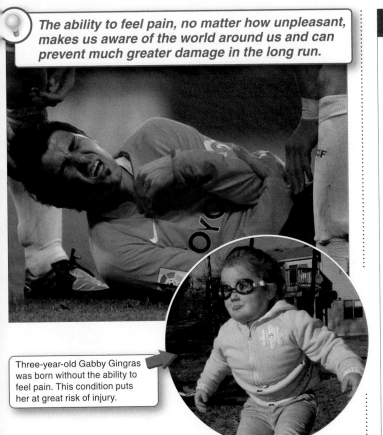

💡 *The ability to feel pain, no matter how unpleasant, makes us aware of the world around us and can prevent much greater damage in the long run.*

Three-year-old Gabby Gingras was born without the ability to feel pain. This condition puts her at great risk of injury.

FIGURE 23-1 Avoiding danger. The sensation of pain gives us important information about the world.

FUNCTIONS OF THE NERVOUS SYSTEM

The nervous system—present in almost all multicellular animals—has three primary functions.

RECEIVE INPUT
The nervous system collects information about the internal and external environment.

Stimulus

PROCESS INFORMATION
The nervous system interprets the incoming stimuli and determines a response.

INITIATE RESPONSE
The nervous system sends signals to muscles and glands in response to the internal and external environment.

Cellular response

FIGURE 23-2 Overview of nervous system functions.

accomplishes these tasks by letting us see, hear, feel, taste, smell, remember (and forget!), think about, act on, and react to various events and stimuli around us. (Plants, conversely, do not have nervous systems.)

Nervous systems have three critical features (**FIGURE 23-2**):

1. They receive input from the surrounding world.
2. They process that information.
3. They initiate responses to the internal and external environment when necessary.

In this chapter, we examine the organization and structures found in the nervous system, and the diversity of nervous system specializations that have evolved in the animal world, including specializations which allow humans to discern light from dark, to identify subtle differences in touch, temperature,

and color, and to use language and abstract reasoning to perform and coordinate complex social behaviors. We also explore how the nervous system, interacting with the muscular and skeletal systems, can generate movement. And we examine how various drugs (legal and illegal) affect, often adversely, the function of the nervous system.

TAKE-HOME MESSAGE 23·1

Present in all multicellular animals other than sponges, the nervous system is a network of cells that collects information about the organism's internal and external environments, processes that information, and sends signals to muscles and glands in response to the information.

The Brain   Drugs Hijack Pleasure Pathways

Neurons are the building blocks of all nervous systems.

In all vertebrates, the nervous system is divided into two components: the peripheral nervous system and the central nervous system (**FIGURE 23-3**). The **peripheral nervous system (PNS)** is the network of sensory cells modified to receive information from the environment and the cells that transmit signals to effectors, the organism's muscles and glands that are capable of responding to that stimulus. But the information received by the body's sensory cells does not generally go straight to the cells that control the muscles and glands. First it passes through the **central nervous system (CNS),** which is made up of the spinal cord and brain. Not directly connected to sensory organs or to muscles, the central nervous system processes information that it receives from sensory cells about the organism's surroundings and sends out instructions to other nervous tissue to act in response to that sensory information. Later in this chapter we discuss the elaborate specializations—from memory to language and abstract reasoning—that have evolved in the most complex vertebrate brains.

The **neuron**—the type of cell specialized for generating and conducting electrical impulses—is the building block of all nervous systems (**FIGURE 23-4**). No matter how complex or

NEURON STRUCTURE

Neurons—individual cells that specialize in carrying electrical signals—are the building blocks of the nervous system. They are composed of three distinct elements.

Stimulus

DENDRITES
Sense and respond to stimulation from outside the cell and send that information toward the cell body

CELL BODY
Contains the nucleus and other cellular machinery

AXON
Long tube-like projection that extends from the cell body and transmits signals to other cells

Signal

GLIAL CELLS
Support cells that protect, insulate, and nourish the neurons

FIGURE 23-4   The neuron is the building block of the nervous system.

THE VERTEBRATE NERVOUS SYSTEM

In vertebrates, the nervous system is divided into the central nervous system and the peripheral nervous system.

CENTRAL NERVOUS SYSTEM
Composed of the neurons and other supporting cells that make up the brain and spinal cord
- Brain
- Spinal cord

PERIPHERAL NERVOUS SYSTEM
Composed of neurons that detect stimuli and neurons that transmit signals to the muscles and glands
- Neurons (bundled together into nerves)

FIGURE 23-3   Organization of the vertebrate nervous system.

simple that system is, it consists of neurons. Each neuron is very small and has but a single option at any point in time: "fire" or "don't fire" (meaning that the neuron either generates an electrical signal that can convey information to nearby cells, or the neuron does not). But, put together a few hundred billion neurons, and things start to get interesting. Taken together, groups of neurons bundled together with connective tissue—into structures called **nerves**—connect us to our world by enabling us to sense light, sound, touch, tastes, and smells and to respond to all of that sensory information. The accumulated information carried by all of our neurons—whether they are firing or not firing—is also responsible for information storage and retrieval and all thought in our brain.

Neurons are powerful cells, but they are also fragile. In the time it takes you to read this sentence, one of your neurons will die. If you read it again, another one will die. And neither will be replaced; unlike most cells in your body, very few neurons are able to replace themselves. This need not be cause for alarm, though. Even with about 9,000 neurons dying on a good day—significantly more if you consume any alcohol or happen to inhale any gasoline fumes—the 100 billion to one trillion that you're born with are more than enough for you to keep your wits about you.

Even though they perform such varied and significant functions, neurons are relatively standard eukaryotic cells. Each has a **cell body** that contains all of the typical machinery of a eukaryotic cell, including a nucleus, mitochondria, endoplasmic reticulum, and so on. But neurons also have two specialized structures that make them unusually adept at interacting with the external environment and with other cells.

The first of these two important specializations is the **dendrite.** The dendrite is the part of the neuron that is like an antenna: it senses and responds to stimulation from outside the cell and sends that information toward the cell body of the neuron. Numerous dendrites branch out from the neuron cell body, like a complex antenna system; the tree-shaped dendrites of a neuron branch extensively.

The neuron's second important specialization is the **axon.** The axon is a long—sometimes *very* long—tube-like extension of the main cell body that transmits the signals picked up by the dendrites to the rest of the organism's body. The end of the axon is specially modified in a way that allows it to transmit the signals to another cell. An axon can transmit a signal, much as an electrical wire does, over great distances. The longest cells in the world are neurons. Some neurons are several feet long. The sciatic (sigh-AT-ick) nerve, for example, runs from your spinal cord all the way to the tips of your toes. Most of this distance is covered by a single axon.

> If neurons rarely (if ever) divide, how can people get brain tumors, which are the result of unstoppable cell division?

Although neurons do all the actual work of the nervous system, they do it with a lot of help from other cells. In the brain, for example, in addition to the neurons there are equal numbers of non-neuronal cells, called **glial cells,** that function like a support staff to protect, insulate, and nourish the neurons. Unlike neurons, glial cells regularly divide in the adult brain. Not surprisingly, then, virtually all brain tumors in adults are formed from glial cells, the supporting cells of the brain.

Just as big corporations keep their big computers locked up in super-clean, secure rooms to keep them functioning at an optimal level, support cells line the blood vessels that supply the brain to isolate the brain cells from potentially harmful molecules in the blood. Called the "blood-brain barrier," this semi-permeable barricade allows essential nutrients and gases to pass through, while barring harmful molecules such as metabolic wastes produced throughout the body. The blood-brain barrier is not perfect, though. Many small molecules, including anesthetics and alcohol, can make it through to influence the brain. The barrier also can be broken down by hypertension, radiation, and a variety of infectious organisms.

We said at the beginning of this section that neurons are the building blocks of the nervous system, but there isn't just one type of neuron. Neurons come in three types, with names that reveal their functions (**FIGURE 23-5**):

1. **Sensory neurons** collect information from an animal's environment and have dendrites modified to respond directly to internal and external stimulation. This stimulation can include temperature, touch, taste, smell, light, or sound.

2. **Motor neurons** stimulate action by conveying signals to muscles or glands and initiating a body's response to stimuli.

TYPES OF NEURONS

SENSORY NEURONS
- Collect information from an animal's environment
- Dendrites modified to respond to external stimulation, such as temperature, touch, taste, smell, light, or sound

MOTOR NEURONS
- Initiate an animal's response to stimuli
- Stimulate action by conveying signals to muscles or glands

INTERNEURONS
- Interpret signals coming in from sensory neurons and relay them to motor neurons
- Located only in the brain and the spinal cord

FIGURE 23-5 Three types of neurons work together in the vertebrate nervous system.

The Brain   Drugs Hijack Pleasure Pathways

OVERVIEW OF NERVOUS SYSTEM INTERACTION

1 A sensory neuron on your hand senses an irritation (as a mosquito lands on you) and sends a signal to convey this information to your spinal cord.

2 In the spinal cord, the signal is sent through an interneuron to your brain. The signal is interpreted and a response is determined (that you want to make the mosquito go away) and then sent through another interneuron back down your spinal cord to a motor neuron.

3 The signal is sent through the motor neuron to a muscle, swatting at the mosquito.

PERIPHERAL NERVOUS SYSTEM

Stimulus

Sensory neuron

Cellular response

Motor neuron

CENTRAL NERVOUS SYSTEM

Brain

Interneurons

Spinal cord

FIGURE 23-6 The peripheral nervous system interacts with the central nervous system.

3. **Interneurons** integrate the signals coming in from the sensory neurons and relay them to the motor neurons. These "middlemen" are located only in the brain and the spinal cord.

Let's look at how these three types of neurons interact. When a sensory neuron in the peripheral nervous system, perhaps in your hand, senses an irritation (such as a mosquito landing on your skin), it sends a signal to convey this information to the spinal cord, where the sensory neuron connects with an interneuron that extends to the brain (**FIGURE 23-6**). The signal is interpreted and a response is determined (probably that you want to make the mosquito go away), and this is sent through another interneuron back down your spinal cord to a motor neuron that is attached to a muscle. The signal from the brain to the muscle causes you to swat at the mosquito—removing the source of irritation. This whole process takes only a tiny fraction of a second.

Some signals can generate a response without any processing by the brain, traveling directly from a sensory neuron to an interneuron in the spinal cord which connects directly to a motor neuron. This kind of direct sensory-motor response is called a **reflex,** and it causes reaction to a sensation that does not need to be processed through the brain. Reflexes enable an organism to respond faster to an imminent danger (**FIGURE 23-7**).

In the next section, we explore the details of how changes in the internal and external environment stimulate a neuron and trigger a response.

Reflexes enable an organism to respond faster to an imminent danger.

FIGURE 23-7 **Quick reaction.** Reflexes can generate a response to a stimulus without need for processing of the signal by the brain.

TAKE-HOME MESSAGE 23·2

In all vertebrates, the nervous system is divided into the peripheral nervous system and the central nervous system. The neuron is a type of cell specialized for carrying electrical signals and is the building block of all nervous systems. Each neuron is very small, but groups of neurons bundled together enable us to sense light, sound, touch, tastes, and smells and to respond to them.

What Is the Nervous System?   How Do Neurons Work?   The Senses   Muscular and Skeletal Systems

❷ How do neurons work?

The branching neurons (colorized green) found in the cerebellum are some of the largest and most complex cells in the mammalian brain.

23·3 -

Dendrites receive external stimuli.

"Fire!" "Don't fire!" "Fire!" "Don't fire!" Dendrites are on the receiving end of an almost constant barrage of (sometimes conflicting) signals. But this is their job. These highly branched tendrils are one of the two types of projections that extend from a neuron's cell body. (The other projection, the axon, is discussed in more detail in Section 23-4.) A neuron may have hundreds or even thousands of dendrites, which give it a huge amount of surface area over which to make connections with other neurons and receive signals.

Dendrites receive external stimuli in one of two ways. Those on motor neurons and interneurons generally connect with and receive signals from other neurons. Sensory neuron dendrites, on the other hand, are modified to respond to a specific external stimulus such as a touch or sound, light, or a

> ❝ The trees grew heavy with blackbirds, branches like dendrites of the nervous system fattening, deep in twittering nerve dusk, waiting for some important message. ❞
>
> —Thomas Pynchon, *Gravity's Rainbow*, 1973

chemical (**FIGURE 23-8**). In each case, sensory receptors in the cell membrane of the dendrite respond to the stimulation by briefly opening up little channels. These channels allow the passage of charged ions (usually sodium ions), momentarily altering the electrical charge within the cell from the negative charge that it carries prior to stimulation, when it is at rest. Opening the channels may make the neuron more negatively charged (that is, the electrical charge within the cell relative to that in the fluid surrounding the cell becomes even more negative, or "hyperpolarized"), which says, "Don't fire!" Or it may make the neuron more positively charged (or "depolarized"), which says, "Fire!"

As stimuli cause channels to open in the dendrites of a neuron—some of which may make the neuron more negatively charged, while others may make the neuron more positively charged—the changes in the cell's electrical charge occurring in all of these dendrites converge at the cell body. The cell body then integrates them, much like tallying the votes in an election. If the sum total of signals coming in is sufficiently positive—exceeding a threshold favoring "Fire!"— then the neuron initiates an **action potential,** an electrical signal that travels down its axon. If the sum total is negative, no action potential is generated.

DENDRITES RECEIVE EXTERNAL STIMULI

Dendrites

Stimulus

1

Positively charged ions

Receptor proteins

Cell membrane

Axon

Ion channels

2

3

Positively charged ions tell the neuron "Fire!" while negatively charged ions tell the neuron "Don't fire!"

Action potential

1 Receptor proteins within the cell membrane of the dendrite respond to stimuli by briefly opening up little channels.

2 Open channels allow the passage of ions, momentarily altering the electrical charge within the cell from the negative charge it carries prior to stimulation, when it is at rest.

3 Signals from all of the dendrites of a neuron converge. If the sum total of signals coming in is significantly positive, then the cell initiates an action potential that travels down the axon.

FIGURE 23-8 "Fire!" (or "Don't fire!"). Dendrites receive signals and forward them to the cell body.

An action potential is an all-or-nothing event. It either occurs or doesn't occur as the result of dendrite stimulation. But our experience of sensations is not "all or nothing." We are able to feel gradations of intensity. A 10-pound

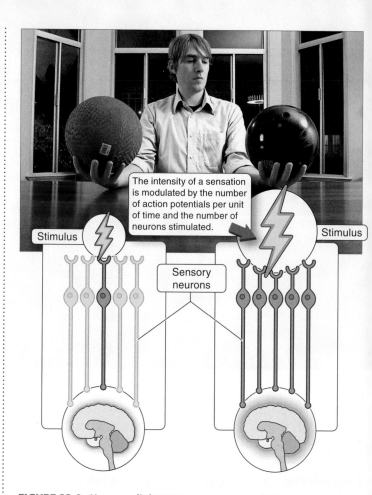

The intensity of a sensation is modulated by the number of action potentials per unit of time and the number of neurons stimulated.

Stimulus

Sensory neurons

Stimulus

FIGURE 23-9 **Heavy or light?** We experience gradations of sensation depending on the number of neurons that fire.

bowling ball resting in your right hand will feel very heavy (and perhaps cooler and smoother) compared with a lightweight rubber ball in your left hand (**FIGURE 23-9**). How can the "fire" versus "don't fire" event still produce such a range of sensations? The intensity of the sensation an individual feels is modulated by the number of action potentials per unit of time and the number of neurons stimulated. The rubber ball causes a small number to fire, and the bowling ball causes many more to fire.

TAKE-HOME MESSAGE 23·3

Dendrites receive external stimuli in one of two ways. Dendrites on motor neurons and interneurons generally connect with and receive signals from other neurons, whereas sensory neuron dendrites are modified to respond to a specific external stimulus such as a touch or sound, light, or a chemical.

844   CHAPTER 23 • NERVOUS AND MOTOR SYSTEMS

What Is the Nervous System?   How Do Neurons Work?   The Senses   Muscular and Skeletal Systems

23·4

The action potential propagates a signal down the axon.

We owe a great deal to giant squids. Much of what we know about human nervous systems has come from studying squid neurons. Neurons function almost exactly the same in all animals, and giant squids just happen to also have giant neurons. While a human neuron might be 0.02 millimeters in diameter, a squid's may be more than 100 times wider, up to double the thickness of a human hair. This makes squid neurons much easier to manipulate and observe.

Regardless of the species under observation, each neuron has one axon. This projection leaves the cell body and can extend several feet or more. At its end, the axon branches into several (or hundreds of) axon terminals, also called **terminal buttons,** which are knob-like ends of the axon, positioned very close to a muscle cell or gland or the dendrites of another neuron. And in response to an action potential, these axon terminals release the contents of vesicles, small sacs of chemicals inside the axon terminal, into the space between the cells, potentially influencing adjacent cells (**FIGURE 23-10**).

We've said that axons are like the electrical wires of the nervous system. In your home, electrical wires are usually covered with rubber. Besides reducing the likelihood of someone receiving an electric shock from the current running through the wire, this insulation also has another function: it causes the electrical charge to move through the wire more quickly and reduces dissipation of the signal. Axons are similarly insulated, by a fatty coating called the **myelin sheath,** preventing the action potential from weakening as it travels down the axon. But, unlike wire insulation, there are gaps in the fatty insulation provided by the myelin sheath. And as the action potential moves down an axon, it is at gaps in the myelin sheath that ion channels in the axon membrane allow charged sodium ions to rush in. In doing so, the ions make the cell's charge sufficiently positive in that region to cause the opening of ion channels at the next gap in the myelin sheath, thereby propagating the action potential along the axon.

Because the fatty myelin is white, in cross sections of the brain, some areas, where axons are densely packed together, appear white (**FIGURE 23-11**). Other parts, where there are more cell bodies and dendrites, appear gray. These different regions are often referred to as white matter and gray matter.

What do you think would happen to signals traveling down an axon in your leg—perhaps 3 feet long long—if the myelin sheath insulator were removed? Would a signal from your brain telling your muscles to wiggle your toes ever arrive? No. The

FIGURE 23-10 An action potential moves down an axon.

THE AXON

The myelin sheath prevents the action potential from weakening as it travels down the axon.

As the action potential moves down an axon, at gaps in the myelin sheath, ion channels allow sodium ions (which carry a positive charge) to rush in, changing the cell's charge to positive in that region and thus propagating the action potential.

Action potential

Axon

Myelin sheath

Terminal buttons

Action potential

Sodium ions

The Brain   Drugs Hijack Pleasure Pathways

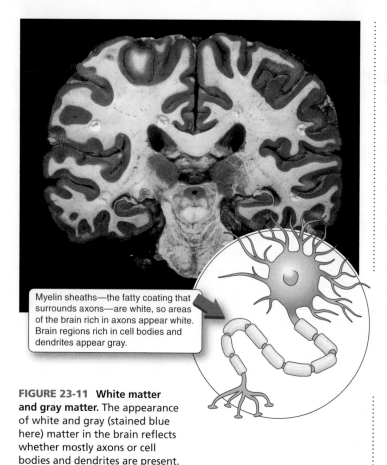

Myelin sheaths—the fatty coating that surrounds axons—are white, so areas of the brain rich in axons appear white. Brain regions rich in cell bodies and dendrites appear gray.

FIGURE 23-11 White matter and gray matter. The appearance of white and gray (stained blue here) matter in the brain reflects whether mostly axons or cell bodies and dendrites are present.

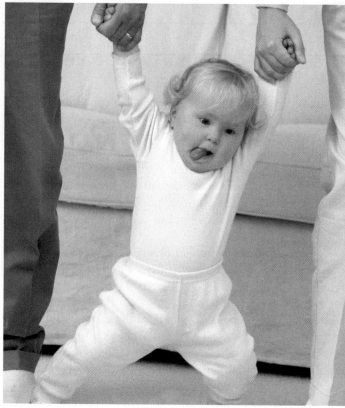

FIGURE 23-12 Unsteady on her feet. Incomplete development of the myelin sheath makes walking difficult for infants.

signal would dissipate before making it to your toe muscles, and your toes would not wiggle. This effect of the lack of myelin on an axon can be seen in babies when they first start trying to walk at around 10 or 11 months of age. At that time, myelin hasn't completely formed around all of their axons and consequently, their gross motor control isn't very good (**FIGURE 23-12**). So, although their brain may be saying, "Walk!" the signal never makes it to the leg muscles. Walking is especially difficult to master because the areas of the brain that control the feet and legs don't develop until after the areas controlling the rest of the body.

Q *Some symptoms of multiple sclerosis resemble difficulties that babies have when learning to walk. Why?*

Multiple sclerosis (MS) is a disease that affects the central nervous system. In MS, myelin is gradually lost, leaving scar tissue called sclerosis. As myelin is lost, the neuron gradually loses its ability to conduct electrical impulses. This makes it progressively more difficult for the brain to send signals to muscles—the same difficulty babies have when first learning to walk—and can lead to a gradual loss in motor control, balance and coordination, and bladder and bowel control.

TAKE-HOME MESSAGE 23·4

Each neuron has one axon, a projection that leaves the cell body and can extend several feet or more. At its end, an axon branches into numerous axon terminals (terminal buttons), positioned close to a muscle cell or gland or the dendrites of another neuron. In response to an action potential, the axon terminals release chemicals into the extracellular space, potentially influencing adjacent cells.

846 CHAPTER 23 • NERVOUS AND MOTOR SYSTEMS

What Is the Nervous System?   How Do Neurons Work?   The Senses   Muscular and Skeletal Systems

At the synapse, neurons interact with other cells.

An action potential moving rapidly down an axon quickly runs out of axon. This is the end of one neuron but not necessarily the end of the signal. As we've seen, the end of an axon—the axon terminal or terminal button—is always right next to another neuron or a muscle cell or a gland. The point where they meet is called a **synapse,** and several possible things can happen there. The signal arriving at the end of the axon may stimulate an action potential in an adjacent cell, it may cause a muscle to contract or relax, or it may initiate a secretion by a gland. Or the signal may even end then and there. In each case, though, the events at the synapse are remarkably similar across all animal species. Let's explore them in sequence (**FIGURE 23-13**).

1. *Sacs called vesicles release neurotransmitters into the synaptic cleft.* The axon terminal is filled with a couple of hundred little

sacs, called **vesicles.** These sacs are filled with chemicals called **neurotransmitters,** the chemical workhorses of the nervous system that transmit signals to adjacent cells. When the action potential reaches the axon terminal, the vesicles merge with the axon's cell membrane, called the **presynaptic membrane,** open up, and dump their contents out of the end of the axon and into the **synaptic cleft,** the space between the axon and whatever is next to it (a muscle cell, gland cell, or neuron).

2. *Neurotransmitter diffuses and binds to nearby receptor sites.* As the neurotransmitter molecules float around in the fluid in the synaptic cleft, they diffuse away from the axon until they bump into receptor sites on the adjacent neuron, muscle, or gland. Some of the neurotransmitter molecules attach to receptor sites on the **postsynaptic membrane** of the adjacent cell.

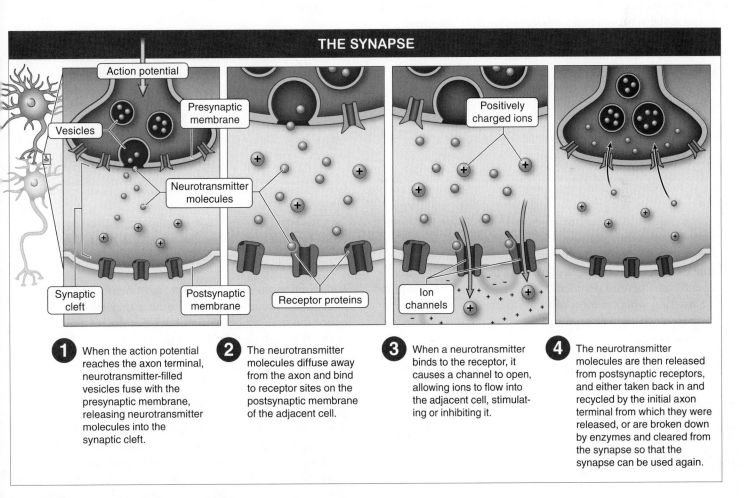

THE SYNAPSE

1 When the action potential reaches the axon terminal, neurotransmitter-filled vesicles fuse with the presynaptic membrane, releasing neurotransmitter molecules into the synaptic cleft.

2 The neurotransmitter molecules diffuse away from the axon and bind to receptor sites on the postsynaptic membrane of the adjacent cell.

3 When a neurotransmitter binds to the receptor, it causes a channel to open, allowing ions to flow into the adjacent cell, stimulating or inhibiting it.

4 The neurotransmitter molecules are then released from postsynaptic receptors, and either taken back in and recycled by the initial axon terminal from which they were released, or are broken down by enzymes and cleared from the synapse so that the synapse can be used again.

FIGURE 23-13 **The sequence of events when an action potential reaches the synapse.**

3. *Gates open in the postsynaptic cell membrane and the signal is passed to the postsynaptic cell.* When neurotransmitter binds to a receptor in the postsynaptic cell membrane, this causes a gate to open, which allows ions (often sodium ions) to flow into the adjacent cell, which may be a neuron, a muscle cell, or a gland cell. Opening the chemical gates allows the signal to be passed from the neuron's axon to the adjacent cell. This chemical change in the postsynaptic cell can cause an electrical change and, consequently, initiate an action potential (if the adjacent cell is a neuron), a contraction (if it's a muscle), or a secretion (if it's a gland).

4. *Neurotransmitter is released from the postsynaptic cell receptors and recycled or broken down.* The receptors then release the bound neurotransmitter molecules back into the fluid in the synaptic cleft. Eventually, the neurotransmitter molecules are either taken back up through the presynaptic membrane and recycled by the axon terminal from which they were released, or they are broken down within the synaptic cleft by enzymes, clearing out the area so that the synapse can be used again.

We've just looked at the general sequence of events that occurs at the synapse in all animals, noting how the signal may be propagated to an adjacent neuron, or how it may lead to a muscle contraction or gland secretion. We now focus on how signal propagation occurs at the synapse between two neurons. Several outcomes are possible, and they depend on what neurotransmitter is released and what type of receptor it binds to on the postsynaptic membrane. In some cases, the released neurotransmitters are excitatory and excite the next cell, increasing the likelihood that it will fire its own action potential. In other cases, the neurotransmitters are inhibitory and reduce the likelihood that the next cell will produce an action potential. And for some neurotransmitters, whether it is excitatory or inhibitory depends on the receptor. With the giant web of connections between neurons—each neuron synapses with hundreds or thousands of other neurons—the ultimate outcome of whether an action potential is initiated depends on a neuron democratically weighing all of its inputs and assessing whether most of its synapses are urging it to fire (pass on the signal) or not to fire (stop the signal from getting through).

At first it might seem odd that the total of all the signals received by a cell might tell it not to do anything, not to fire a signal. Why would it be useful to inhibit activity and effectively block information from being passed along? This option is not just useful, but essential to the nervous system's capacity to control which signals get through. By having a synapse where two neurons meet (rather than one long, continuous "wire" constantly conducting electrical signals), it is possible to modulate and filter some of the overwhelming amount of sensory information coming into the brain. It's like call-screening for your brain.

At synapses, not all signals are propagated. Some sensory "noise" may be filtered out—reducing the barrage of stimuli to the brain.

FIGURE 23-14 Like call-screening for your brain. Not every signal is propagated.

An example makes this process clearer. Focus carefully, for a moment, on the environment you're in. Listen. Look. Feel. Are your shoes a bit tight? Can you hear the hum of an air conditioner? Are sirens audible in the distance? Is the guy sitting two rows behind you tapping his foot? All of these sounds and feelings were there a minute ago, yet you probably weren't aware of them, and that's not necessarily a bad thing. It's hard to think clearly when you're distracted by a constant barrage of sights and sounds. This "filtering" characteristic of the nervous system is one of the main reasons that organisms don't have single, long neurons running from their sensory receptors right to their brain or muscles. It's not always best to have every signal propagated (**FIGURE 23-14**).

With continuous stimulation, too, most neurons gradually reduce the amount of neurotransmitter they release, and thus reduce the strength of the signal. It's as if the neurons are saying, "Enough already. We get the message."

TAKE-HOME MESSAGE 23·5

At the synapse, a neuron interacts with other cells. In response to an action potential, neurotransmitters are released into the synaptic cleft, diffuse, and may bind to receptors on an adjacent neuron, muscle cell, or gland, potentially stimulating an action potential, muscle contraction, or secretion. Neurotransmitters may then be taken back in by the axon terminal or enzymatically broken down in the synaptic cleft.

23·6

There are many types of neurotransmitters.

The neurotransmitters released by neurons can be thought of as the chemicals that initiate or modify a wide variety of actions, moods, feelings, or other sensations. Some make us feel happy or sad, restless or sedate. Some stimulate muscles to contract. Others influence learning, memory. In all, about 25 neurotransmitters have been identified, each of which has a sort of personality based on its specific actions. A detailed discussion of all 25 neurotransmitters is beyond the scope of this book. Here we discuss four that are particularly important.

Why are curare-tipped poison arrows so lethal?

Acetylcholine Acetylcholine is the neurotransmitter released by motor neurons at the point where they synapse with muscle cells. When enough acetylcholine binds to a muscle cell, the muscle contracts. A poison called curare, found in some South American plants, is used on arrow tips to make them more lethal. Curare works by blocking the receptor sites where acetylcholine normally binds to muscle cells. Once it gets into an animal's system, curare causes death from lack of oxygen very quickly, because it makes it impossible for the skeletal muscles to contract (**FIGURE 23-15**).

Glutamate Another excitatory neurotransmitter is glutamate. Although its mechanism of action isn't well understood, it appears to be involved with learning and memory. Mice that were genetically engineered to have more sensitive glutamate receptors, for instance, learned tasks better and became much better at running mazes than normal mice.

Dopamine Dopamine is important in initiating and coordinating movement. Loss of dopamine neurons may be responsible for Parkinson's disease, for which the symptoms include tremors of a hand or foot, stiffness or inflexibility of muscles, and impaired balance and coordination. Dopamine is also one of the body's chief "happiness" neurotransmitters. Its release in certain parts of the brain is associated with feelings of intense pleasure. In studies of brain functioning, for example, when subjects are shown their favorite food items, the levels of dopamine released in the brain skyrocket. We explore dopamine in greater detail later in this chapter.

Serotonin Serotonin generally functions as an inhibitory neurotransmitter. It affects appetite, sleep, anxiety, and mood, and produces feelings of contentment and satiation when released. Women make serotonin only about two-thirds as

A hunter collects shavings of a plant from the genus *Strychnos*, from which curare is extracted, a lethal poison that blocks acetylcholine binding sites and prevents muscle contraction.

FIGURE 23-15 Hunting with curare-tipped arrows. A nomad from the Nukak-Maku tribe in the Amazon jungle hunts for monkeys using a blowgun and darts tipped with curare. Red arrow: A hunter collects shavings of a plant from the genus Strychnos, from which curare is extracted, a lethal poison that blocks acetylcholine binding sites and prevents muscle contraction.

quickly as men, an observation that may be related to why depression is twice as common among women as men. As we see later in the chapter, antidepressant medications such as Prozac increase the amount of serotonin in the synapse and are effective at elevating the mood of someone who is depressed.

TAKE-HOME MESSAGE 23·6

About 25 neurotransmitters have been identified, each of which has several actions, depending on the synapse where it occurs. Acetylcholine is the neurotransmitter released by motor neurons at the point where they synapse with muscle cells. Glutamate is an excitatory neurotransmitter involved with learning and memory. Dopamine is important in initiating and coordinating movement and in producing feelings of intense pleasure. Serotonin, an inhibitory neurotransmitter, affects appetite, sleep, anxiety, and mood, and produces feelings of contentment and satiation.

❸ Our senses detect and transmit stimuli.

The North African fennec fox (Vulpes zerda) *has large ears to help it shed body heat. The ears also help the animal hear its prey, which is often hiding underground.*

23·7 --

Sensory receptors are our windows to the world around us.

Q | **Why *do* animals have only one head? Why is it in the front?**

Did you ever wonder why animals tend to have only one head and why it's always in the front of the body? When organisms became bilaterally symmetrical—that is, having mirror-image left and right sides—suddenly they had a "front" and a "back." As such animals move through their environment, the "front" part of the animal encounters new things in the environment first; with the sensory equipment up there, the organism is able to decide what to do—eat or run—as quickly as possible (**FIGURE 23-16**), which may have conferred evolutionary benefits. And as the decisions to be made get more and more complex, the circuitry required to "make up its mind" becomes more complex. In fact, only then does it really become necessary to have a mind. And so the brain and head (which always go hand in hand) have tended to become more and more pronounced.

Our senses—sight, hearing, smell, taste, and touch—make us physically aware of the environment around us. They are our windows to the world. Each of our senses puts us in touch with and brings us information about a different and unique

💡 *Sensory equipment is concentrated at the "front" of bilaterally symmetrical animals because this part of the animal encounters new things in the environment first.*

FIGURE 23-16 Eyes up front. Most of an animal's sensory organs are located in its head.

What Is the Nervous System?   How Do Neurons Work?   The Senses   Muscular and Skeletal Systems

THE FIVE SENSES

Hearing

Touch

Taste

Sight

Smell

> Our senses—sight, hearing, smell, taste, and touch—are our windows to the world. Each brings us information about a different slice of the world, but the senses have much in common.

FIGURE 23-17 Making us aware of our environment: the senses. (Note that most of the body parts pictured have more than one function; the elephant's trunk, for example, enables smell, but also has numerous other functions, including lifting, touching, and drinking.)

slice of the world, but the senses also have much in common (**FIGURE 23-17**).

The process by which all our senses work is basically the same. A receptor—commonly a modified dendrite on a sensory neuron (in the eye, nose, tongue, ear, or skin)—is stimulated by some aspect of the outside world (light, odor, taste, sound, or touch). This outside stimulus causes a change in the neuron, causing the sensory neuron to either (1) fire an action potential itself, which shoots down the axon and ultimately reaches a part of the brain where the signal is perceived as a particular smell or sound, for example, or (2) alter its rate of neurotransmitter secretion so that it increases or reduces the rate of firing of action potentials in a neighboring cell.

All of the specific senses are variations on this theme, fine-tuned by natural selection to give an animal specific information about its environment to help it respond appropriately. The following sections present details on each of the primary five senses.

TAKE-HOME MESSAGE 23·7

The process by which all our senses work is basically the same. A modified dendrite on a sensory neuron is stimulated by some aspect of the outside world, causing the sensory neuron to fire an action potential (that shoots down the axon and ultimately reaches a part of the brain where the signal is perceived as a particular smell or sound, for example) or to alter its rate of neurotransmitter secretion (so that it increases or reduces the rate of action potentials in a neighboring cell).

The Brain   Drugs Hijack Pleasure Pathways

Taste: an action potential serves up a taste sensation to the brain.

Look at your tongue in the mirror. It is covered with bumps. Embedded within these bumps are taste buds—more than 10,000 in all. Within each taste bud are 60–80 sensory receptor cells, called **chemoreceptors** (which are modified epithelial cells that synapse with sensory neurons), stimulated when particular chemicals in food dissolve in saliva and bind to proteins on the cell surface. Much as a lock will open only when the proper key is inserted, particular taste receptors allow only specific food molecules, with exactly the right shape, to bind (**FIGURE 23-18**).

Taste chemoreceptors fall into five groups, depending on which type of molecule chemically stimulates them: sweet, salty, sour, bitter, or a recently discovered, but difficult to describe, savory taste called umami. These different types of chemoreceptor occur all across the tongue (although the different groups tend to be concentrated in different regions of the tongue). A rich variety of tastes is possible because most foods stimulate unique combinations of the different taste receptors. Foods also release molecules into the air in the mouth, which stimulate smell receptors within the nasal cavity.

Not all animals use their mouths to taste things. Some insects have chemoreceptors on their legs, and they "taste" things

> **Q** How can artificial sweeteners taste like sugar while not actually being sugar?

just by touching them. Other animals have taste receptors on their antennae or tentacles. Regardless of where the food meets the taste receptors, the process is the same: chemical binding triggers an action potential that delivers a taste sensation to the brain.

Because of the way we sense taste, it's possible to fool your brain. Your brain never actually "knows" the true identity of the food on your tongue. Rather, it senses a particular taste based solely on the combination of receptor cells that is stimulated. If a molecule that is not sugar has a chemical structure closely resembling sugar, it can stimulate the same taste-bud receptors and be perceived by the brain as sugar (**FIGURE 23-19**). Many non-nutritive sugar-substitute molecules such as saccharin and sucralose do exactly this. They have three-dimensional arrangements of atoms that are similar to sugar molecules such as sucrose, glucose, or fructose, but have structures that cannot be broken down by any enzymes in the human body. Consequently, when we consume them, we sense the sweet taste of sugar but don't actually derive any energy from the molecules. Instead, they pass through our digestive tract unaltered.

TASTE

Taste buds · Chemoreceptor cells · Food molecules · Positively charged ions

Action potential sent to brain

Tongue · Sensory neurons

Taste receptor proteins · Ion channels

A particular taste is sensed when the chemoreceptor proteins that correspond to that taste are stimulated by the food molecules dissolved in saliva.

FIGURE 23-18 From taste buds to delicious flavor. How the sensation of taste is generated in the brain.

What Is the Nervous System? · How Do Neurons Work? · The Senses · Muscular and Skeletal Systems

Aspartame also resembles sugar closely enough to stimulate sugar receptors in taste buds. Molecularly, however, it is quite different: it is made from two amino acids. It can be broken down and releases energy (and hence contains calories), but is so efficient at stimulating sweet-taste receptors that it can generate a strong sugary taste even when used in tiny amounts.

FIGURE 23-19 **Fooling the brain.** Sugar substitutes stimulate receptor cells that produce a sweet taste.

TAKE-HOME MESSAGE 23·8

On your tongue, there are about 10,000 taste buds, each of which contains 60–80 chemoreceptors, which are stimulated when particular chemicals in food bind to receptor proteins on the cell surface. Some animals have chemoreceptors on their antennae or tentacles, and the binding of chemicals to these receptors similarly triggers an action potential that delivers a taste sensation to the brain.

23·9

Smell: receptors in the nose detect airborne chemicals.

Our sense of smell works in almost exactly the same way as our sense of taste. Neurons that can detect smells have dendrites modified with tiny, hair-like projections. These dendrites—densely packed within the nasal cavity—are covered with chemoreceptors. Airborne chemicals move through mucus in the nasal cavity and bind to the smell receptors, triggering action potentials that shoot down the axon, all the way into the smell center of the brain, where the signal is perceived as a particular odor. There are more than a thousand different types of receptors—modified neurons—in a human nose, each capable of detecting a different scent (**FIGURE 23-20**). (These neurons are actually

SMELL

Action potential sent to brain

Nasal cavity

Chemoreceptor cells

Smell receptor proteins

Ion channels

Airborne molecules

Positively charged ions

A smell is sensed when the chemoreceptor proteins that trigger perception of that particular smell are stimulated by the appropriate airborne molecules in the nasal cavity.

FIGURE 23-20 **How the sensation of smell is generated.**

853

the only neurons in the body in direct contact with the outside world.)

In humans, the senses of smell and taste are closely connected, because the air in the mouth, throat, and nasal passages circulates around all these areas. You may have noticed that when you have a cold and your nose is stuffed up, you taste little beyond the basic salt, sweet, bitter, and sour tastes on your tongue, and you can't smell anything at all. Your senses of taste and smell are dulled when you have a cold because increased mucus in your nasal passageways reduces the rate at which airborne chemicals can reach the smell receptors and taste receptors on dendrites in your nose and on your tongue.

Animals vary greatly in their sensitivity to smells, and humans don't fare too well in the competition. Recent evidence even suggests that fewer and fewer of the genes coding for the different smell receptors in humans function properly anymore. Interestingly, human females are significantly better than males at detecting, distinguishing, and identifying odors, a sensitivity that is even greater during the days surrounding ovulation.

Dogs are among the most smell-sensitive vertebrates, having as many as 40 times more smell receptors than a human—hence their tremendous proficiency at detecting drugs or explosives (**FIGURE 23-21**). Some moths, such as gypsy moths and silkworm moths, put even dogs to shame and may be the champions of chemoreception. The tiny hairs on the males' antennae can detect just a few molecules of the sex attractant released by females. By moving in the direction of

Dogs have as many as 40 times more smell receptors than a human—hence their keen sense of smell, which gives them tremendous proficiency at detecting drugs or explosives.

FIGURE 23-21 **Smelling champ: the bomb-sniffing dog.**

increasing concentration of the airborne chemicals, a male can track down a female two miles away. Similarly, salmon use smell to help them navigate from the ocean back into the exact streams where they were born, a trip that can be hundreds of miles long. Snakes have chemoreceptors on their tongue and are actually "smelling" their environment as they stick their tongue out.

TAKE-HOME MESSAGE 23·9

Neurons that can detect smells have dendrites modified with tiny, hair-like projections covered with chemoreceptors, densely packed within the nasal cavity.

23·10

Vision: seeing is the perception of light by the brain.

What humans lack in smell proficiency, we more than make up for in visual acuity. Vision is one of the senses in which our capabilities exceed those of most other animals. Still, as with nearly every trait, there are plenty of species—including many birds and some spiders, for example—whose abilities exceed ours. In any case, despite the great diversity of species with light-sensing capabilities, the basic functioning of light-

absorbing cells is quite consistent, although in some ways the process works in a fashion opposite what we see for other sensory reception. Here's how these cells work (**FIGURE 23-22**).

Within the eye or other light-detecting structure, there are light-sensitive neurons, called **photoreceptor cells,** with light-sensitive molecules embedded in their cell membranes.

854   CHAPTER 23 • NERVOUS AND MOTOR SYSTEMS

What Is the Nervous System?   How Do Neurons Work?   The Senses   Muscular and Skeletal Systems

VISION

- Photoreceptor cell
- Sodium channel
- Na⁺
- Light-sensitive molecule
- Inhibitory neurotransmitters
- Optic nerve

IN THE DARK

1. Sodium channels, located within photoreceptor cell membranes, are open, allowing the photoreceptor cells to continuously release inhibitory neurotransmitters.

2. The inhibitory transmitters reduce the ability of adjacent neurons to excite the neurons that signal the brain.

3. An action potential is not sent through the optic nerve and light is not perceived by the brain.

- Photoreceptor cell
- Sodium channel
- Na⁺
- Light-sensitive molecule
- Inhibitory neurotransmitters
- Optic nerve

IN LIGHT

1. Light energy causes light-sensitive molecules to change shape, closing sodium channels in the photoreceptor cell membranes.

2. The closing of sodium channels reduces the amount of inhibitory neurotransmitter released by the photoreceptor cells.

3. No longer inhibited, adjacent neurons excite the neurons that signal the brain.

4. An action potential is sent through the optic nerve and light is perceived by the brain.

In the dark, these photoreceptor cells continuously release an inhibitory neurotransmitter. Like the depressing of a brake pedal, this inhibitory message reduces the ability of adjacent cells to excite the neurons that signal the brain. In a sense, darkness blocks the ability of optic nerves to send visual signals to the brain.

When light hits one of the light-sensitive molecules in the membrane of a photoreceptor cell, the light energy causes some of the chemical bonds in the molecule to become stretched. (A similar capture of light energy occurs in plants during photosynthesis.) This closes sodium channels in the photoreceptor cell membranes.

The light-induced closing of sodium channels in the photoreceptor cell membranes reduces the amount of inhibitory neurotransmitter released by the cells. This, in a convoluted way, can lead to the perception of light by the brain: the photoreceptor cells no longer block the ability of adjacent neurons to excite the neurons that send visual signals to the brain. And the particular wavelength perceived by the brain depends on which version of the light-sensitive molecules bound to the photoreceptor cells was stimulated by the light (and reduced the photoreceptor's inhibition of adjacent neurons).

Three different types of eyes have evolved (**FIGURE 23-23**). The simplest, called **eye cups,** are found in the flatworms such as planaria, which live in ponds and streams. Eye cups are made up of photoreceptors, and although they cannot form images, they are able to detect the presence and intensity of light. Unless light is directly in front of the worm, it shines more intensely on one eye than the other. This allows the animal to sense which direction the light is coming from. Usually, this information tells the animal which way to move: toward or away from the light. Planaria, for example, move away from the light.

Insects have much more refined visual capabilities (**FIGURE 23-24**). They possess **compound eyes** made of dozens to thousands of separate light-sensing units, each with its own lens that directs light onto about a dozen photoreceptors. The photoreceptors then send signals along neurons. When the signals finally reach the brain, the brain interprets these signals as an image. Because some insect photoreceptor cells—such as those in honeybees—contain a broader range of light-sensitive pigments than is found in humans, these insects can see wavelengths of light in the ultraviolet spectrum that are invisible to us.

FIGURE 23-22 How the sensation of vision is produced.

Photoreceptor cells

Photoreceptor cells

Lenses

Photoreceptor cells

Lens

EYE CUPS
Contain photoreceptor cells that are able to detect the presence and intensity of light, but cannot form images

COMPOUND EYES
Contain many separate light-sensing units—each with its own lens—that direct light on to about a dozen photoreceptor cells

SINGLE-LENS EYES
Contain a single lens that focuses light on to highly sensitive photoreceptor cells

FIGURE 23-23 Eye structure suits the needs of the organism. Shown: flatworm, red damselfly, glowing reef squid.

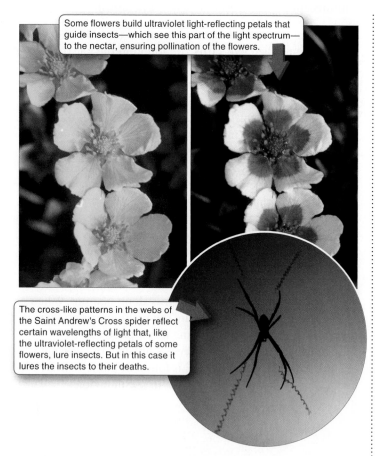

Some flowers build ultraviolet light-reflecting petals that guide insects—which see this part of the light spectrum—to the nectar, ensuring pollination of the flowers.

The cross-like patterns in the webs of the Saint Andrew's Cross spider reflect certain wavelengths of light that, like the ultraviolet-reflecting petals of some flowers, lure insects. But in this case it lures the insects to their deaths.

FIGURE 23-24 Seeing with compound eyes. Insects can see wavelengths of light in the ultraviolet spectrum. The flower shown is Silverweed (*Potentilla anserina*). In daylight it appears uniformly yellow, but in ultraviolet light it appears red and white.

Plants sometimes capitalize on this ability of insects to detect the ultraviolet spectrum by constructing flowers with UV-reflecting petals that look like the landing lights at an airport, guiding insects to their nectar reward (while ensuring pollination of the flowers). Devious spiders capitalize on this ability, too. Some build webs with UV-reflecting threads that trick insects into thinking the web is a flower. Once it flies into the web, the insect finds no nectar and ends up as a meal for the spider.

Q Insects don't just fly into spiders' webs accidentally. Sometimes they do it on purpose. Why?

The image-forming, **single–lens eye** has evolved independently twice, once in a group of molluscs—including squid—and again in vertebrates. In each case, light hits the eye and enters the eye's interior through an **iris.** The pupil, an opening in the iris, opens and closes to control the amount of light that gets into the eye. Once the light is through the pupil, a lens focuses it on the eye's photoreceptor cells (**FIGURE 23-25**).

The lens focuses the light onto the **retina,** nervous tissue containing light-sensitive cells that lines the inner surface of the eye and transmits impulses to the vision center of the brain via the **optic nerve.** The two types of photosensitive cells in the retina are **rods,** which are highly sensitive to even tiny amounts of light and make it possible to see at night and in low–light situations, and **cones,** which are less sensitive to light and so are more effective during daylight. Humans have

What Is the Nervous System?   How Do Neurons Work?   The Senses   Muscular and Skeletal Systems

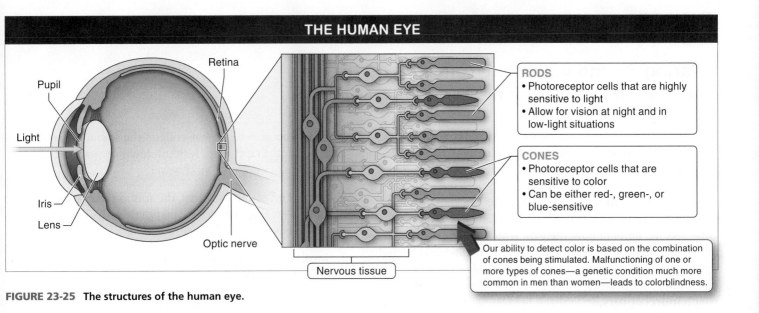

THE HUMAN EYE

Pupil

Light

Iris

Lens

Retina

Optic nerve

Nervous tissue

RODS
• Photoreceptor cells that are highly sensitive to light
• Allow for vision at night and in low-light situations

CONES
• Photoreceptor cells that are sensitive to color
• Can be either red-, green-, or blue-sensitive

Our ability to detect color is based on the combination of cones being stimulated. Malfunctioning of one or more types of cones—a genetic condition much more common in men than women—leads to colorblindness.

FIGURE 23-25 **The structures of the human eye.**

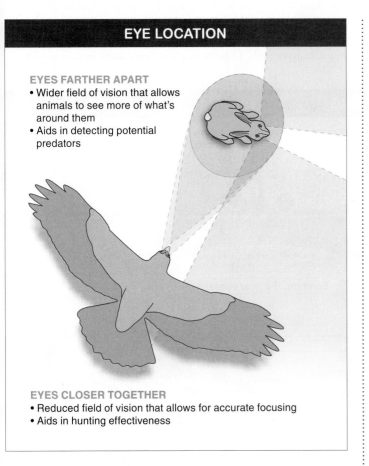

EYE LOCATION

EYES FARTHER APART
• Wider field of vision that allows animals to see more of what's around them
• Aids in detecting potential predators

EYES CLOSER TOGETHER
• Reduced field of vision that allows for accurate focusing
• Aids in hunting effectiveness

FIGURE 23-26 **The hunter and the hunted.** Eye placement may indicate whether an animal is predator or prey.

three kinds of cone cells: red-, green-, and blue-sensitive. Our ability to detect color is based on the combination of cones being stimulated. Some individuals (usually men) produce non-functioning red or green cones—the result of mutant

genes. In either of these cases, it is impossible for the individual to distinguish red from green and so the person is said to be **color blind.**

The location of the eyes of the body of an animal is an evolutionary adaptation. Some animals have their eyes close together in the front of their head. Others have them closer to the sides of their head (**FIGURE 23-26**). The farther apart the eyes are, the wider the animal's field of vision. That is, the animal can see more of what's around it. This is particularly important for small animals preyed on by other animals. It's about as close as they can get to having eyes in the back of their head, and so keeps them safer. Predators—such as owls or hawks—on the other hand, have both eyes right in the front. This reduces their field of vision, but allows super-accurate focusing on exactly where the prey is, a characteristic that makes them excellent hunters. Winning the award for strangest eye-placement is the flounder. As they develop, one of their eyes migrates gradually from one side of their body to the other. When these marine flatfish lie camouflaged on the ocean bottom (like a plate on a table), both eyes are then on the same side of the body, looking up.

TAKE-HOME MESSAGE 23·10

Vision results from the stimulation of light-sensitive sensory neurons, called photoreceptor cells. The photoreceptor cells have a variety of molecules, embedded within their membranes, that are chemically altered by light. Signals are conveyed to the brain and interpreted as an image. The particular wavelength perceived depends on which version of the light-sensitive molecules in the photoreceptor cell membranes is stimulated.

The Brain

Drugs Hijack Pleasure Pathways

Hearing: sound waves are collected by the ears and stimulate auditory neurons.

Hearing is yet another variation on a theme. As with the previous senses described, something in the external world stimulates modified neurons, and the stimulation initiates an action potential that passes along a series of neurons until it reaches the brain. In this case, the stimuli from the outside world are sound waves, tiny fluctuations in air pressure, collected and amplified by the ears, which then pass the information to the brain. While tastes and smells are detected by chemoreceptors and sight is made possible by photoreceptors, hearing is a result of the stimulation of **mechanoreceptors,** specialized neurons with receptors that respond to mechanical pressure.

Although there is some variation in the details of how hearing works in different species, this general, six-step hearing model is consistent (**FIGURE 23-27**).

1. The outer part of the ear collects the sound waves and, because of its shape, funnels them down the **ear canal,** a channel that conducts sound waves.

2. At the end of the ear canal, the sound waves bang into the **eardrum**—a thin membrane that divides the outer ear from the middle portion of the ear—causing it to vibrate.

3. Small bones on the other (inner) side of the eardrum pass the vibrations on to the inner ear membrane.

4. The vibrations are conducted by fluid inside the inner ear, which consists of fluid-filled canals in the bones of the skull. The semicircular canals function in balance, and the coiled cochlea, is involved in hearing. This fluid movement bends hair-shaped receptor cells, which release neurotransmitters. (The more vigorous their bending—in

HEARING

1 Sound waves are funneled down the ear canal.

2 Sound waves cause the eardrum to vibrate.

3 Vibrations pass to the inner ear membrane.

4 Fluid in the inner ear conducts the vibrations, bending hair-shaped receptor cells, releasing neurotransmitters.

5 The neurotransmitters cause auditory neurons to fire an action potential.

6 The signal is passed to the brain where it is interpreted as sound.

Inner ear · Sound waves · Semicircular canals · Cochlea · Ear · Eardrum · Ear bones · Fluid-filled chambers · Receptor cells · Auditory neurons · Action potential sent to brain

FIGURE 23-27 The process of hearing.

response to stronger sound waves—the greater the amount of neurotransmitter released.)

5. Auditory neurons then respond to the neurotransmitters released by the hair cells by firing an action potential.

6. The signal continues along a path of neurons to the brain, where it is interpreted as sound.

> **How can you get motion sickness without moving at all?**

The fluid in the semicircular canals of the inner ear also acts like an inner motion detector, telling your body about its orientation, whether it is moving, and in which direction. It's not a foolproof system, though. Sitting in an IMAX theater watching a movie filmed from the seat of a roller coaster, shown on a huge screen, it is possible to feel motion sickness without actually moving. Your eyes tell your brain that you are moving, while your inner ear senses no motion at all. The conflicting signals can confuse your brain and lead to feelings of nausea.

> **How can loud music lead to hearing loss?**

Long-term exposure to loud noises, including music, can be damaging to hearing, because such stimulation can wear out the cochlea of the inner ear. The hair cells in the inner ear are very fragile and irreplaceable, so chronic over-stimulation due to loud noises can damage them. This reduces their ability to release neurotransmitters and stimulate auditory neurons, causing hearing loss (**FIGURE 23-28**).

Chronic overstimulation due to loud noises can damage the hair cells in the inner ear, reducing their ability to stimulate auditory neurons, leading to hearing loss.

FIGURE 23-28 Loud noises can cause hearing loss.

ECHOLOCATION

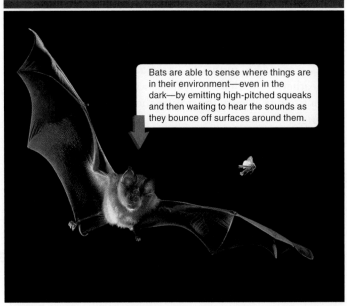

Bats are able to sense where things are in their environment—even in the dark—by emitting high-pitched squeaks and then waiting to hear the sounds as they bounce off surfaces around them.

FIGURE 23-29 Hearing through echolocation.

Are ears necessary for hearing? Not really. Most insects, for example, don't have ears but still can hear a wide range of sounds, often with even greater sensitivity than humans. They do it with delicate hairs on antennae or other parts of the body that bend slightly in response to sound waves, much like the inner-ear hair cells described above. These insects tend to produce noises (that is, communicate by sound) by rubbing parts of their body together, rather than using their mouth. Male mosquitoes actually identify females by the vibrations of their wings as they fly. Cricket chirping, on the other hand, require a bit more work; like miniature violinists, crickets rub their wings together to create their special mating calls.

Among the mammals, bats have a unique system for hearing, called **echolocation.** Most bats spend nearly all of their time in the dark, and such a sensitive call-and-response system of hearing has evolved in them that they can sense where everything is in their environment, even with terrible sight. They do this by emitting high-pitched squeaks (that are generally inaudible to humans) and then waiting to hear the sounds as they bounce off surfaces around them. This system is so sensitive that they can detect even a small moth as it flies in their vicinity (**FIGURE 23-29**).

> **Q Do blind people have more sensitive hearing?**

Recent research has revealed that individuals who go blind as infants, before the age of two, have significantly more sensitive hearing. They are up to 10 times better at hearing pitch changes than individuals who are not blind or who go blind later in life. Apparently, with the onset of blindness, parts of the brain normally used for processing visual information take up new duties, particularly in the detection and processing of sound. The earlier in life that this reallocation of brain responsibilities occurs, the greater the improvements in hearing.

23·12

Touch: the brain perceives pressure, temperature, and pain.

The last of the traditional five senses in humans is touch. Touch is actually a class of sensations generated by numerous different types of sensory neurons that are sensitive to pressure (mechanoreceptors), temperature (thermoreceptors), or pain (pain receptors). These sensory receptors are located throughout the body and are found in particularly dense concentrations in places such as the fingertips in primates or the side of the body (called the lateral line) in most types of fish.

Whether they are mechanoreceptors or pain receptors or thermoreceptors—and any given part of the body usually has many of each of these sensory neuron types—they function similarly. External stimulation, such as the prick of a pin, the

tickle from a feather, or the heat of a pan, can cause a change in the shape of the neuron's membrane, momentarily altering its permeability. This change in permeability then increases or decreases the rate at which ions enter the cell, converting the stimulus into action potentials and, ultimately, sensations perceived by the brain (**FIGURE 23-30**).

Pain-killing drugs such as morphine reduce the ability of various pain receptors to send their signals to the brain. They do this by blocking the receptors' ability to respond to stimuli, thereby blocking neurons in the brain from sensing stimuli that would normally be identified as pain. It's as if the phone line between that part of the body and the brain is cut.

FIGURE 23-30 How the sensation of touch is produced.

860 CHAPTER 23 · NERVOUS AND MOTOR SYSTEMS

What Is the Nervous System?   How Do Neurons Work?   The Senses   Muscular and Skeletal Systems

Many amputees experience "phantom pain" that seems to come from their missing limb as neurons in the brain that had synapses with touch receptors in the lost limb are stimulated, usually by nearby neurons. Watching in a mirror as the person tries to move the phantom limb—called mirror therapy—can reduce the pain.

FIGURE 23-31 **Phantom pain.** Neurons in the brain can perceive pain in a body part that is no longer present.

Q Amputees sometimes feel real pain where their limb once was. How can this be?

Conversely, and eerily, most amputees report that they sometimes experience tingling, prickly sensations or even shooting pains that come from where their amputated limb once was. Called "phantom pain," these sensations are very real and occur when neurons in the brain that used to represent touch receptors in the lost limb are firing, usually due to stimulation from other, nearby neurons (**FIGURE 23-31**).

TAKE-HOME MESSAGE 23·12

Touch is a class of sensations generated by mechanoreceptors, thermoreceptors, and pain receptors located throughout the body. Stimulation of these receptors causes a change in the shape of the sensory neuron's membrane, altering its permeability, generating action potentials, and causing the perception of touch by the brain.

23·13 ─────────────────────────────

Other senses help animals negotiate the world.

Traditionally, we think of the senses as being limited to taste, smell, vision, hearing, and touch. But in actuality, there are several more senses that some animals use. As with the five senses described above, these additional senses are made possible by neurons that are specially modified to respond to external stimuli by generating action potentials that convey information to the brain about the outside world.

Balance and Motion Many invertebrates (including jellyfish, lobsters, and crayfish) and vertebrates have sensory cells that enable them to orient themselves with respect to gravity and to detect changes in velocity or orientation. These sensory cells are always some sort of hair cells that can be pushed in one direction or another, much as grass blows in the wind. The force exerted on the hair cells (which, as we've seen, are located in the inner ear in vertebrates) gives information about the movement of the organism. In a variation on the sense of touch, in many mammals the sensations detected by whiskers can also convey information about balance and motion.

Electricity Marine animals of many types are sensitive to tiny electrical changes in the water around them. Sharks have sensory cells, embedded within sacs in their skin, that are open to the shark's external surroundings. These cells are so sensitive to electrical changes around them that they can sense the muscle contractions of a fish swimming nearby. This ability to sense changes in electrical charge helps sharks to track down prey.

Magnetism Compass needles point north because of the faint magnetic field produced by the earth. A wide range of species, from birds to eels and sharks to migrating beluga whales, and even some bacteria, are able to detect this magnetic field and use it to help them navigate (**FIGURE 23-32**). In some clever but devious experiments, researchers placed strong magnets around some bird cages, deflecting the magnetic field. This caused the birds to shift their orientation within the cages by exactly the amount that the magnetic field had been moved. Very little is known about how sensory cells have evolved to detect and respond to magnetism.

The Brain · · · · · Drugs Hijack Pleasure Pathways

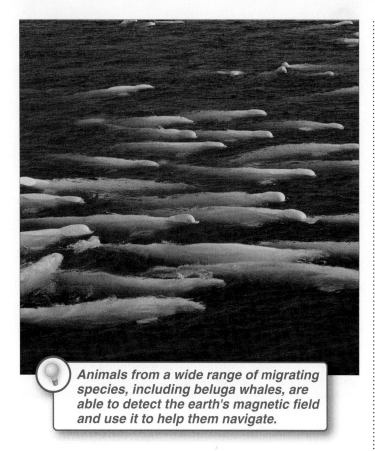

Animals from a wide range of migrating species, including beluga whales, are able to detect the earth's magnetic field and use it to help them navigate.

FIGURE 23-32 **Traveling south.** Beluga whales during migration.

Heat Unlike the way you sense heat by touching a hot plate or feeling warm when it's hot outside, pythons, vipers, and some other snakes can "see" heat differences in their environments without having to touch it. Using "pit organs" located on either side of the head, they can sense—even in complete darkness—a mouse or other prey animal near them, solely from the body heat that it produces (**FIGURE 23-33**).

Pit organ

Using "pit organs" located on either side of the head, pit vipers can sense—even in complete darkness—a prey animal solely from the body heat that it produces.

FIGURE 23-33 **Some snakes can "see" heat.**

TAKE-HOME MESSAGE 23·13

Among animals, there are several senses in addition to the five found in humans, including those that perceive and respond to balance and motion, electricity, magnetism, and heat production in the animal's environment.

862 CHAPTER 23 • NERVOUS AND MOTOR SYSTEMS

What Is the Nervous System?   How Do Neurons Work?   The Senses   Muscular and Skeletal Systems

These eastern gray kangaroos have powerful leg muscles that propel them forward.

❹ The muscular and skeletal systems enable movement.

23·14 --

Muscles generate force through contraction.

Running, flying, swimming, crawling, walking, digging, dancing. Animals, with very few exceptions, move. And in vertebrates, this movement is generally initiated by cells of the nervous system that stimulate contractions in muscle tissue that pull on a rigid skeletal system. In this section, we examine the three types of muscle tissue, how contractions are generated within that tissue, and how input from the nervous system can initiate and control muscle contractions. We'll also investigate how the size and strength of muscles reflects their use and how physical training can increase muscle strength.

As we saw in Section 20-10, muscle tissue is made up of elongated cells capable of generating force when they contract, and there are three types of muscle tissue.

1. *Skeletal muscle* is responsible for generating most of the movement we see in animals. Skeletal muscle attaches to bones and is controlled by individual neurons attached to each muscle fiber. It makes up about 40% of human body weight.

2. *Cardiac muscle* causes the heart to pump blood through the body. Not initiated by the nervous system or under conscious control, cardiac muscle contractions and relaxations occur continuously throughout life, with the muscle cells containing more energy-releasing mitochondria than other types of muscle cells.

3. *Smooth muscle,* which is not under conscious control and is able to contract without stimulation from the nervous system, surrounds blood vessels and many internal organs. Smooth muscle generates slower contractions that can gradually move blood, food, or other substances through vessels and organs.

In the rest of this section, we focus on the type of muscle that is controlled by the nervous system: skeletal muscle. The muscular system of humans contains about 700 skeletal muscles in all. To facilitate movement, skeletal muscles are attached to bones by connective tissue. Often, a muscle tapers at each end into tendons, which attach the muscle at the two ends—the "insertion" and the "origin" of the muscle—to bones. The

863

contraction of the muscle then pulls the attachment points closer together and causes a movement of the bone. The biceps muscle of the upper arm, for example, has its origin in the shoulder and its insertion in one of the bones of the forearm. Contraction can rotate the forearm or bring the lower part of the arm closer to the shoulder. Two muscles generally work in opposition so that as one moves a bone in one direction, the other—the triceps in the upper arm—has its insertion and origin located so that its contraction moves the bone in the opposite direction (**FIGURE 23-34**).

Let's look more closely at the structure of a muscle and at the cellular mechanism by which muscle fibers contract. A muscle comprises a bundle of fibers. Each fiber is a single cell, but with multiple nuclei and with numerous **myofibrils,** cylindrical organelles that shorten when they contract. A myofibril contains repeating units called

sarcomeres, which is where the contraction takes place. The **sarcomeres** are composed of large numbers of long filaments, overlapping and parallel to each other. The filaments come in two types: thin filaments made mostly from the protein **actin,** and thick filaments made mostly from the protein **myosin.** There may be 100,000 sarcomeres in a biceps muscle cell.

The sarcomere shortens in a four-step process (**FIGURE 23-35**):

1. *Detach:* A link between a myosin and an actin filament parallel to it is broken as a molecule of ATP binds to the myosin.

2. *Reach:* As the ATP breaks down, energy released alters the shape of the myosin into a higher-energy shape— much like bending a twig, which is in a higher-energy shape because it can release energy as it snaps back to its original shape.

3. *Reattach:* In its altered shape, the myosin reaches farther down the actin filament, where it reattaches.

4. *Pull back:* The myosin then snaps back to its original shape, pulling the actin filament as it does so and shortening the fiber. This last step is considered the "power stroke."

As the contraction process occurs across numerous sarcomeres in a muscle cell, the entire muscle can shorten. From the perspective of energy, the potential energy of ATP is converted to the kinetic energy of sarcomere-shortening, which can do work (for instance, as your arm curls a dumbbell).

Nervous system control over skeletal muscle occurs as neurons, at their synapses with muscle cells, release the neurotransmitter acetylcholine. Acetylcholine causes the muscle cell membrane to open its sodium channels, which depolarizes the muscle cell. Deeper inside the muscle cell, the depolarization causes the opening of calcium channels in the cell's endoplasmic reticulum. Calcium stored in the modified endoplasmic reticulum rushes into the cytoplasm, diffuses toward the myofibrils, and binds to a molecule surrounding the actin. When calcium binds to the protein molecule it acts as a switch and moves another molecule that normally covers binding sites on the actin molecule. After the binding sites are exposed, myosin can attach to actin, and contraction can occur.

When a muscle contracts, the duration between a contraction and a relaxation is called a **twitch.** Muscle fibers within a muscle vary in how quickly they can twitch, with two general types. Fast-twitch fibers, which can contract very quickly and tend to function anaerobically, have relatively weak endurance. They are capable of contracting

SKELETAL MUSCLE GENERATES MOVEMENT

Biceps

Triceps

Upper arm bone

Lower arm bones

Origin point

Tendons

Insertion point

Two muscles generally work in opposition so that contracting one muscle moves a bone in one direction, while contracting the other muscle moves the bone in the opposite direction.

1 A contraction of the biceps brings the lower part of the arm closer to the shoulder.

2 A contraction of the triceps pulls the lower part of the arm away from the shoulder.

FIGURE 23-34 Movement: the work done by skeletal muscles.

What Is the Nervous System?   How Do Neurons Work?   The Senses   ▼ Muscular and Skeletal Systems

FIGURE 23-35 Muscle fibers contract to generate force.

and relaxing about 10 times faster than slow-twitch fibers, which are surrounded by rich oxygen-delivering capillary beds and large numbers of oxygen-storing myoglobin molecules, and can sustain activity for much longer periods of time. Although most muscles have approximately equal proportions of fast-twitch and slow-twitch fibers, there is some variation among the fibers of different muscles, as well as among different individuals. It has been shown, for example, that world-class sprinters have significantly more fast-twitch fibers in their leg muscles, while world-class long distance runners tend to have more slow-twitch fibers in their leg muscles (**FIGURE 23-36**).

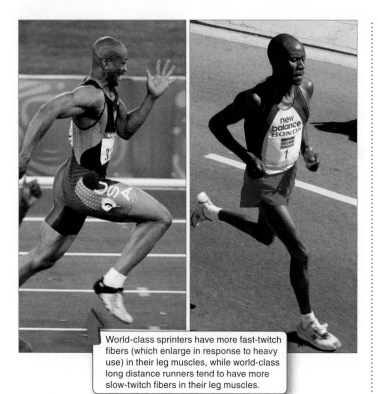

World-class sprinters have more fast-twitch fibers (which enlarge in response to heavy use) in their leg muscles, while world-class long distance runners tend to have more slow-twitch fibers in their leg muscles.

FIGURE 23-36 Fast-twitch and slow-twitch muscles.

When muscles are used for high-intensity work against increasing resistance, as in many weight-training programs, muscle fibers increase in size as the fast-twitch fibers become thicker. Endurance training, on the other hand, does not cause an increase in the size of muscle cells.

Q Marathon runners tend to have smaller leg muscles than sprinters. Why?

TAKE-HOME MESSAGE 23·14

Muscle tissue—including skeletal, cardiac, and smooth muscle—is made up of elongated cells capable of generating force when they contract. A muscle fiber is a single cell containing myofibrils that shorten with the making and breaking of links between parallel actin and myosin filaments.

23·15

Skeletal systems enable movement, among several other important functions.

By serving as a structural frame, the skeletal system interacts with the muscular system to enable movement. But this is just one of many important functions of a skeleton (**FIGURE 23-37**). A skeletal system can also provide support for an organism, providing shape and structure and a means of securing the organs and other structures within the animal's body. And in addition to enabling movement and providing support, a skeletal system offers protection—the brain, for example, is protected from harm within the skull, and the heart is protected within the rib cage. Additionally, in some organisms, including humans, the skeletal system provides a site for production of important blood and immune cells, a process that occurs in bone marrow. Bones also serve as a reservoir of some minerals, such as calcium, absorbing excess quantities from the bloodstream or releasing minerals when their concentration in the blood is low (see Section 24-5).

There are three distinct types of skeletal systems (**FIGURE 23-38**). In a *hydrostatic skeleton*—such as is found in earthworms, jellyfish, and squid—pressure created within a fluid-

filled cavity creates sufficient rigidity that the muscles surrounding it can generate movement, including, in earthworms, the ability to dig. An *exoskeleton* is a rigid outer covering that supports and protects an animal's body. An exoskeleton may be the shell of a turtle, the rigid calcium-based covering of some molluscs, or the polysaccharide-based, chitinous exoskeleton of insects, crabs and lobsters, and spiders. Exoskeletons can also be valuable in reducing some animals' vulnerability to drying out. The third type of skeleton—an *endoskeleton*—is a support structure of hard mineralized tissue, as is found in echinoderms (such as sea stars and sand dollars), and in all vertebrates including humans. The vertebrate endoskeleton serves as a site for production of blood and immune cells and as a reservoir of some minerals.

The composition of the endoskeleton varies among echinoderms and vertebrates. Echinoderm endoskeletons consist of a rigid, calcium-based structure, similar to bone. Among the vertebrates, the jawless fishes and sharks have a flexible but strong skeleton made from cartilage. The other

What Is the Nervous System? | How Do Neurons Work? | The Senses | Muscular and Skeletal Systems

FUNCTIONS OF THE SKELETAL SYSTEM

STRUCTURAL SUPPORT
Provides shape and structure, including securing organs in place

PROTECTION
Shields vulnerable tissue—such as the brain and heart—from external insults

ENABLING MOVEMENT
Muscles, which are connected to bones, generate movement when they contract

CELL PRODUCTION
Produces blood cells in bone marrow

MINERAL RESERVOIR
Elements such as calcium can be released from or stored in bones in response to deficiencies or excesses in the bloodstream

FIGURE 23-37 The skeletal system serves multiple purposes.

vertebrates have a skeletal system made primarily from bone, a harder, but still resilient connective tissue material (described in Section 20-8).

Most vertebrate skeletons are divided into an axial skeleton, which includes the skull, sternum, ribs, and vertebrae, and an appendicular skeleton, which includes the limbs

TYPES OF SKELETAL SYSTEMS

HYDROSTATIC SKELETON
A fluid-filled cavity with sufficient rigidity so that muscles surrounding it can generate movement

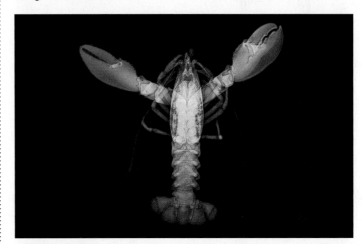

EXOSKELETON
A rigid outer covering that supports and protects an animal's body

ENDOSKELETON
An internal support structure composed of hard mineralized tissue

FIGURE 23-38 There are three distinct types of skeletal systems in animals. Shown: bell jellyfish, lobster, and toad.

The Brain　　　　　Drugs Hijack Pleasure Pathways

VERTEBRATE SKELETON STRUCTURE

AXIAL SKELETON
Includes the skull, sternum, ribs, and vertebrae

APPENDICULAR SKELETON
Includes the limbs, the pelvic girdle, and the pectoral girdles (of the shoulder region)

FIGURE 23-39 Vertebrate skeletons are divided into axial and appendicular regions.

OSTEOPOROSIS

Healthy bone

Osteoporotic bone

Osteoporosis results in reduced bone density and a change in the chemical composition of bone, leading to an increased risk of bone fracture.

FIGURE 23-40 Osteoporosis weakens bone.

(or fins, in the case of fishes), the pelvic girdle, and the pectoral girdles (of the shoulder region) (**FIGURE 23-39**).

At the locations in the skeleton where bones meet, several types of joints occur. These may allow movement while maintaining support, such as is seen in the shoulder, hip, knee, and elbow joints. Or they may enable little movement (such as the joints between vertebrae) or no movement at all (such as the "joints" that are the sutured connections between the bones of the skull). Arthritis is a condition in which joints have become damaged. There is a variety of forms of arthritis. In the most common type, osteoarthritis, a breakdown of connective tissue, usually cartilage, reduces the cushioning of the bones and can lead to inflammation of tissue around the joint, and accompanying pain.

Another type of breakdown in the skeletal system is osteoporosis, a disease that occurs as the density of bone is

Q What is osteoarthritis? Why is it so painful?

reduced and the chemical composition of the bones changes (**FIGURE 23-40**). Occurring most commonly in women, particularly following menopause, osteoporosis increases the risk of bone fractures and falls. Dietary modifications, including increased calcium and vitamin D that can strengthen bones, along with lifestyle changes such as increased exercise that can build bone mass and strengthen muscles, can reduce osteoporosis and the risks associated with it.

TAKE-HOME MESSAGE 23·15

Among animals, three distinct types of skeletal systems occur: hydrostatic skeletons, exoskeletons, and endoskeletons. The vertebrate skeletal system can enable movement, provide support, offer protection, provide a site for production of important blood and immune cells, and serve as a reservoir of minerals, including calcium.

868 CHAPTER 23 • NERVOUS AND MOTOR SYSTEMS

What Is the Nervous System?　　How Do Neurons Work?　　The Senses　　Muscular and Skeletal Systems

❺ The brain is organized into distinct structures dedicated to specific functions.

An fMRI image of the brain and spinal cord of an adult male.

23·16

The brain is organized into several distinct regions.

Looks can be deceiving. Especially when it comes to brains. Take the human brain, for example. You'd hardly know that you were looking at something far more complex and powerful than the most advanced supercomputers ever built. In an adult, it is only a bit over 3 pounds, or 1.4 kilograms. It's fairly uniform in color, a drab whitish-gray, the surface is soft and gently wrinkled, and it's just a bit stiffer than Jell-O.

From a cellular perspective, all animal brains function in the same general way. A neuron is a neuron is a neuron. But this isn't the whole picture. Although the brain is made up primarily from the same type of cells as the rest of the nervous system (the spinal cord and the peripheral nervous system), close inspection reveals several distinct regions within the brain. Each region is characterized by neurons that are shaped slightly differently, that have different axon and dendrite branching patterns and complexities, and that use different neurotransmitters at their synapses. Each of these regions is the control center for various activities in the body.

Among different species, evolutionary changes have resulted in differences in the relative amount of the brain dedicated to various structures. These differences have, in turn, led to corresponding differences in abilities and behaviors. In the cerebral cortex, for example, humans have significantly more neurons than do other species. This extra brain matter in this

particular part of the brain (which we examine in more detail later in this chapter) is associated with many abilities that are particularly well developed in humans, including abstract thought, perception, and language. Similarly, the unusually large number of neurons (relative to overall brain size) devoted to the smell-sensing section of a rat's brain give it a particularly powerful sense of smell. This powerful sense, which is much more sensitive to scent stimuli than is a human's sense of smell, contributes to the rat's abilities to find food.

In this and the next two sections, we explore the three principal regions of the brain—the hindbrain, the midbrain, and the forebrain—and the functions they control (**FIGURE 23-41**).

Hindbrain The central nervous system is made up of the brain and spinal cord. The spinal cord extends from the brain down through the backbone (though not down the entire length of the backbone), protected by the vertebral column. Branching off from the spinal cord at regular intervals are bundles of axons, some carrying motor information to muscles and glands, others carrying in sensory information from the senses to the brain. The top of the spinal cord is the beginning of the brain. Here, the spinal cord expands into the **hindbrain.** Three important structures are located in the hindbrain: the **medulla,** the **pons,** and the **cerebellum.** Because these structures are not involved in higher thought,

PRINCIPAL REGIONS OF THE BRAIN

FOREBRAIN

CEREBRAL CORTEX
Involved in abstract thought, problem solving, and language

THALAMUS
Receives sensory input and relays some signals to the cerebral cortex while blocking others

HYPOTHALAMUS
Regulates many fundamental drives, including hunger and thirst, sexual activity, and maintenance of body temperature; controls the hormone secretions of the tiny pituitary gland

MIDBRAIN
Filters and evaluates motor and sensory neuron signals

HINDBRAIN

CEREBELLUM
Coordinates motor activity

PONS
Pathway for motor and sensory neuron signals

MEDULLA
Pathway for motor and sensory neuron signals; regulates basic physiological functions such as respiration, heart rate, and digestion

Brainstem

Spinal cord

FIGURE 23-41 The brain is divided into three main regions: forebrain, midbrain, and hindbrain.

hindbrain damage can lead to paralysis without harming consciousness.

Medulla and Pons. Running through these structures are the many motor neurons traveling from the brain to the spinal cord and the many sensory neurons traveling from the body into the brain. Additionally, within the medulla are lots of collections of neurons that regulate basic physiological functions such as respiration, heart rate, and digestion. Consequently, injury to these structures—such as occurred when President John F. Kennedy was assassinated in 1963—nearly always leads to death.

Cerebellum. This structure coordinates numerous types of motor activity. When it works properly, graceful motion is possible. The coordination of many complex movements is overseen by the cerebellum. Knitting or typing, for example, involve a wide range of complex muscle movements that must be executed in precise sequences. Once learned, these movements run on "auto-pilot": we don't have to think consciously about these activities because the cerebellum directs them (**FIGURE 23-42**). If you are typing rapidly and suddenly think consciously about the motions your fingers are engaged in, you start to make all kinds of errors. Why? Because your conscious thought draws on a part of the brain other than the cerebellum.

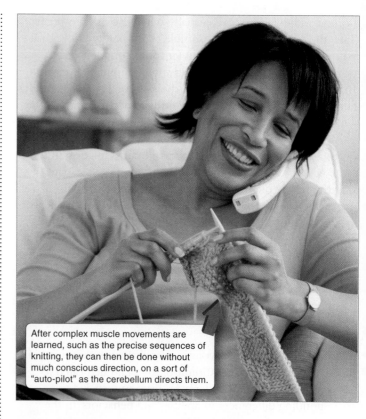

After complex muscle movements are learned, such as the precise sequences of knitting, they can then be done without much conscious direction, on a sort of "auto-pilot" as the cerebellum directs them.

FIGURE 23-42 Coordinated by the cerebellum. Once learned, knitting does not require conscious thought.

What Is the Nervous System? | How Do Neurons Work? | The Senses | Muscular and Skeletal Systems

Midbrain The **midbrain,** along with the medulla and pons of the hindbrain, makes up the brainstem. Most of the sensory information and motor neuron connections coming into and out of the brain pass through the midbrain. These receptors and effectors frequently have synapses with each other, as the midbrain helps filter and evaluate the importance of each signal. The midbrain is greatly enlarged and plays a more significant role in cold-blooded animals, such as fishes and frogs, than it does in warm-blooded animals.

Forebrain In humans, the **forebrain** is the largest region of the brain. It includes two control and relay structures, the thalamus and hypothalamus, as well as the cerebrum. The cerebral cortex, which makes up the bulk of the cerebrum, is responsible for most of what we consider "higher" thought, including perception, memory, language, intelligence, and personality.

Thalamus and Hypothalamus. The **thalamus** is one of the primary switchboards in the brain. It receives most of the visual, auditory, and touch input and, like a secretary deciding which calls to let through, relays some signals to the cerebral cortex while blocking others. The **hypothalamus** (part of the limbic system, discussed later in this section) is one of the chief regulatory centers of the brain. It regulates many fundamental drives, including hunger and thirst, sexual activity, and maintenance of body temperature. It also controls the hormone secretions of the tiny pituitary gland, located right next to it, which play important roles in reproduction and development.

> " The mind is its own place, and in itself
> Can make a heaven of hell, a hell of heaven. "
>
> —John Milton, *Paradise Lost,* 1667

In the 1950s, James Olds discovered something very peculiar about the hypothalamus. When he inserted a tiny electrode into the hypothalamus of a rat's brain, the animal seemed to experience great pleasure (**FIGURE 23-43**). Of course, Olds couldn't be certain that it was pleasure that the rats were experiencing, but he hypothesized that this was so by noting how the rats would work very hard (for instance, by learning to run very complex mazes) to get the stimulation. When he set up the apparatus so that an animal could administer the stimulation to its own brain simply by pushing a lever, the rats became lever addicts, pushing the lever more than a hundred times a minute for many hours. They would even choose to push the lever over eating food or drinking water, with some rats starving to death while pushing the lever rather than taking even a short break to eat.

This discovery that the brain has "pleasure centers" or "do-it-again centers" was important because it revealed a mechanism

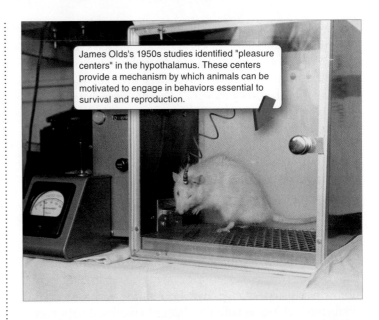

James Olds's 1950s studies identified "pleasure centers" in the hypothalamus. These centers provide a mechanism by which animals can be motivated to engage in behaviors essential to survival and reproduction.

FIGURE 23-43 Olds's experiments led to the discovery that the brain has "pleasure centers."

by which animals could be motivated to engage in evolutionarily important behaviors by which they might increase their own reproductive success relative to other individuals in the population. Drinking when an animal is thirsty or eating when it is hungry produces stimulation in this brain area, thereby reinforcing behaviors essential to survival and reproduction.

In a disturbing experiment with potential ethical implications, researchers recently implanted small transmitters and electrodes into the brains of rats that enabled the researchers to stimulate the rats' whiskers by remote control. This stimulus generated sensory signals about the direction in which the rats were moving. The researchers also implanted electrodes enabling the stimulation of the animals' pleasure centers. Together, this apparatus made it possible to guide, via remote control, the direction in which the animals moved, rewarding them when they moved in the desired direction. The researchers were able to direct the rats like robots over fences, through pipes, and up trees, from several hundred yards away.

Q How could you direct a rat's movements via remote control?

Cerebral Cortex. For humans, the **cerebral cortex** is the most sophisticated part of the brain. Involved in abstract thought, problem solving, language, and more, this is the part of the brain that is most responsible for the traits that most set us apart from the rest of the animal species.

One of the most dramatic demonstrations of the complexity of the cerebral cortex resulted from a tragic accident and apparently miraculous recovery. In 1848, a railroad worker named Phineas Gage was packing explosives into a hole when

The Brain   Drugs Hijack Pleasure Pathways

they exploded unexpectedly, blasting a three and a half foot iron bar right through his face, just below his left eye, through the front part of his head, and out through the top of his skull (**FIGURE 23-44**). Amazingly, he recovered from the accident. Soon after his recovery, though, it became clear that something in Gage's personality had changed dramatically as a result of the injury. Before the accident he was serious and industrious, but after the accident he became vulgar, unpleasant, and irresponsible. He also became much more uninhibited than he had previously been.

Gage died about 13 years after the accident, and his skull was preserved. Recent analyses of the skull indicate that Gage suffered from severe damage to part of his frontal cortex. In other case studies of patients with damage to the same part of their frontal cortex, such as that caused by certain tumors, similar personality changes have been noted, with patients frequently exhibiting radically changed emotional responses. As we'll see in Section 23-17, modern brain imaging techniques are enabling us to learn more about the functions of specific brain regions, without the need to study individuals with tumors or other brain injuries.

The highly folded cerebral cortex is by far the largest brain structure, covering all of the brain except for the cerebellum (**FIGURE 23-45**). The cerebral cortex makes up 80% to 85% of the brain mass in humans, with about 10 billion neurons and hundreds of billions of synapses. Although the brain (including the cerebral cortex) looks fairly symmetrical, functions are not divided in a symmetrical way. The brain is divided into a left and a right hemisphere, connected by a broad, thick band of neurons, called the **corpus callosum.** The **left hemisphere** in most, but not all, individuals is the

Damage to Phineas Gage's frontal cortex radically altered his personality.

FIGURE 23-44 **Phineas Gage's accident.** Gage suffered damage to his frontal cortex, which caused dramatic behavior changes.

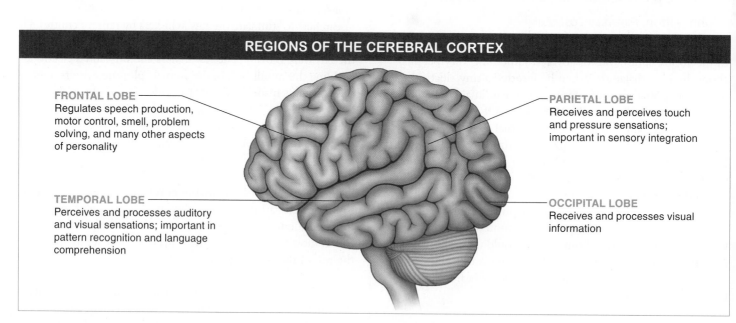

REGIONS OF THE CEREBRAL CORTEX

FRONTAL LOBE
Regulates speech production, motor control, smell, problem solving, and many other aspects of personality

TEMPORAL LOBE
Perceives and processes auditory and visual sensations; important in pattern recognition and language comprehension

PARIETAL LOBE
Receives and perceives touch and pressure sensations; important in sensory integration

OCCIPITAL LOBE
Receives and processes visual information

FIGURE 23-45 **The lobes of the cerebral cortex.**

What Is the Nervous System?   How Do Neurons Work?   The Senses   Muscular and Skeletal Systems

site of areas specializing in language, logic, and mathematical skills, while the **right hemisphere** is more commonly home to larger areas dedicated to emotions, intuitive thinking, and artistic expression.

Each hemisphere of the cerebral cortex has four different lobes: frontal, temporal, parietal, and occipital. Each lobe is associated with specific functions (but each also has many other subareas that control a variety of additional functions; see Figure 23-45):

1. *Frontal lobe:* important in speech production, motor control, smell, problem solving, and many aspects of personality.

2. *Temporal lobe:* perceives and processes auditory and visual sensations; also important in pattern recognition and language comprehension. Damage to part of the right temporal lobe—usually due to a stroke or tumor—has been implicated in a condition known as prosopagnosia or face blindness. Individuals with this condition find it difficult or impossible to recognize faces.

3. *Parietal lobe:* receives and perceives touch and pressure sensations; also important in **sensory integration,** the process of incorporating information from all of the senses to form a single perception of something.

4. *Occipital lobe:* receives and processes visual information.

Limbic System. Within the forebrain, near the center of the brain, is a set of structures that together make up the **limbic system.** It includes parts of the cerebral cortex and two structures deeper within the center of the brain, the **hippocampus** and the **amygdala,** and is responsible for many of our physiological drives and instincts. Together, these structures also play an important role in emotions, learning, and memory, which we discuss later in the chapter.

TAKE-HOME MESSAGE 23·16

There are several distinct regions in the brain, each of which is the control center for various activities in the body. The hindbrain regulates basic physiological functions such as respiration, heart rate, and digestion, and coordinates numerous types of motor activity. The midbrain, part of the brainstem, helps filter and evaluate the importance of sensory and motor information. In humans, the forebrain is the largest region of the brain, responsible for most of what we consider higher thought, including perception, memory, language, intelligence, and personality.

23·17

Measuring brain activity helps us understand how tasks are allocated.

How many times have you heard someone say, "We only use 10% of our brain!" Besides being just plain silly, this pervasive myth is completely false. But it prompts some reasonable questions: Which parts of the brain *are* we using? Do we use some more than others? Do mental tasks or physical sensations require the use of a specific part of the brain, or do they use neurons from all over the brain? Until relatively recently, we didn't have the tools to address these questions, but now we do.

Most computers have lights that blink when the machine is active. A brain, however, just sits there; no lights flash, no sounds are made. Nothing. At least, nothing obviously visible to the naked eye. Helping us to better understand how the brain functions, there has been a revolution in **brain imaging technologies,** which capture pictures of the brain as it functions, revealing activity patterns (based on increased metabolism) in the different regions of the brain. Two techniques in particular are making it possible to see how the

brain works on various tasks. One is called PET scanning (positron emission tomography) and the other is called fMRI scanning (functional magnetic resonance imaging). Both examine the brain while it is in action and capture an image of the brain's activity.

Both PET scans and fMRI scans provide valuable information about the activity in the brain, but do so by different means. In a **PET scan,** radioactive glucose is injected into the subject. The radioactivity can then be traced in the brain as the subject performs a task. Because areas with more metabolic activity require more fuel, more of the radioactive glucose moves to those areas. In the image, areas of the brain are colored differently, depending on their rate of metabolic activity during the task. In an **fMRI scan,** a giant magnet detects the relative amounts of oxygenated blood and deoxygenated blood in various parts of the brain. When parts of the brain are active, more blood flows to them and the sensitive magnet can pick up the change. As with

The Brain   Drugs Hijack Pleasure Pathways

the PET scans, an image can be obtained that is colored to indicate different levels of metabolic activity in various parts of the brain. Because no radioactivity is required, fMRI scans are generally preferable to PET scans.

At any given time during the day, you are not using all of your muscles. But over the course of a day, you use most of them. Similarly, for any particular task, not all regions of the brain are called into action, but over the course of a day all of your neurons are used. Some interesting discoveries have been made about how human brains allocate various tasks.

Seeing your favorite foods activates brain reward centers. Subjects shown images of their favorite foods show increased brain activity in the pleasure centers of the forebrain (**FIGURE 23-46**). Researchers have also found that recovering drug addicts have a similar response to images of a syringe (or even an anti-drug advertisement), often prompting them to relapse. Both cases underscore the power of advertisements.

Altruistic behavior activates reward centers. When playing a game called "Prisoner's Dilemma," in which people gain rewards based on their decisions to cooperate or act selfishly, brain activity in the forebrain's reward center is increased when a player chooses to cooperate. This may indicate that our brains are built to produce a physiological "prodding" toward kindness in certain situations.

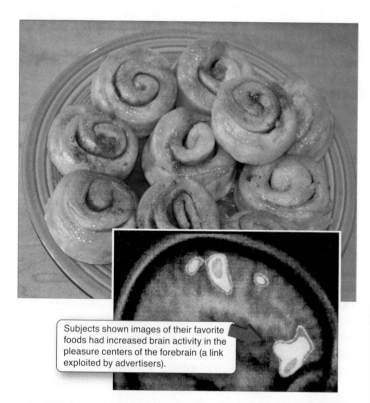

Subjects shown images of their favorite foods had increased brain activity in the pleasure centers of the forebrain (a link exploited by advertisers).

FIGURE 23-46   Does the thought of eating one of these cinnamon rolls increase the activity of your brain?

Colored regions indicate metabolic activity, with black areas representing decreased activity. In Alzheimer's disease, areas associated with thinking and understanding show particularly reduced activity.

PET scan of brain of healthy individual

PET scan of brain of individual with Alzheimer's disease

FIGURE 23-47   PET scan showing the effect of Alzheimer's on the brain.

People with Alzheimer's disease exhibit significantly reduced brain activity. When compared with healthy individuals of the same age, Alzheimer's patients show decreased activity throughout the parts of the brain associated with thinking and understanding, while they show normal activity in the areas active in movement and sensory perception (**FIGURE 23-47**).

Females and males respond differently to emotional situations. PET scans were made while women and men were asked to reflect on the saddest images in their lives. In both sexes, the limbic system glowed brightly. In the women, though, the activity covered an area eight times larger than that in the men!

Language tasks are localized in different parts of the brain. Language uses very different parts of the cerebral cortex, depending upon whether someone is hearing, depending on whether someone is hearing, speaking, reading, or generating new words. Interestingly, among bilingual people, their second language is stored in a slightly different part of the brain if they acquired it past a certain age. We explore language in more detail in the next section.

TAKE-HOME MESSAGE 23·17

PET scans and fMRI scans make it possible to detect and visualize metabolic activity in brain tissue and to see how the brain works during various tasks. These technologies help us understand how tasks are processed by different regions of the brain and how individuals vary in their patterns of brain activity for similar tasks.

What Is the Nervous System?   How Do Neurons Work?   The Senses   Muscular and Skeletal Systems

Specific brain areas are involved in the processes of learning, language, and memory.

Brains are capable of myriad amazing feats. Learning and memory, along with the use of complex language, are among the most sophisticated and enigmatic of these functions. But while these abilities rank among the greatest mysteries of the brain, we're unlocking more and more of the secrets every day.

Language What is language exactly? In its most broad interpretation, **language** is simply the means of communication between individuals of any species. In humans, language has evolved its most complex manifestation. Words and sentences allow us to convey not just simple information, but also complex thoughts such as things distant in space or time, something rarely if ever seen in other species. Try conveying to a friend, without using words, the details of the first birthday party you remember attending or the things you saw on a trip to a foreign country. Language also makes it possible for us to articulate abstract ideas. Could you explain democracy or the concept of natural selection without language? Language is fundamental to who we are as a species. Let's investigate some of the biology behind it.

Several distinct brain structures, and two in particular, are necessary for the acquisition and use of language. One is required for the understanding of speech, including the linking of words with meaning (**FIGURE 23-48**). The other controls the actual production of speech. In more than 95 of every 100 people, it is the left hemisphere that is responsible for both of these functions. The discrete parts used for controlling the muscles involved in the actual process of speaking are in the front part of the left frontal lobe, a region called **Broca's area.** The region responsible for understanding speech is called **Wernicke's area,** and it is located in the left temporal lobe. People with damage to Wernicke's area (from a stroke or head injury) are able to produce sounds properly, such as when repeating things they hear, but they cannot understand speech and can speak only gibberish. It's as if they've lost the ability to link words with their meanings.

Brain science is still in its infancy, and we're still discovering some perplexing and unexpected things about this most complex of all organs. Consider this: in 2008, an American woman named Cindy Lou Romberg had a chiropractic adjustment that apparently aggravated a severe brain injury

SPEECH CENTER IN THE BRAIN

BROCA'S AREA
Coordinates the muscles necessary for speech production

WERNICKE'S AREA
Responsible for language comprehension

FIGURE 23-48 Areas of the brain controlling the ability to produce speech and understand language.

Q Do men or women have a better chance of language recovery following a stroke? Why?

that she had suffered 17 years earlier. Much to her surprise, she found that she suddenly had a foreign accent! In her life she had never spoken with such an accent—which sounds like a sort of mixture of German, French, and Russian—nor had she ever studied any foreign languages or even been to Europe (**FIGURE 23-49**). It appeared that parts of her language production areas had been damaged, and this altered the way she spoke. Although the exact mechanism for this change is not understood, this strange phenomenon has been reported several other times, the first being in 1941 when a Norwegian woman had a stroke and afterward spoke with what sounded like a German accent. Interestingly, women are much more likely to regain the ability to speak after a stroke. This may be related to the fact that, on average, women have a thicker corpus callosum, the band of fibers connecting the left and right hemispheres of the brain. The additional thickness may facilitate another part of the brain's ability to take over language functions after the stroke-induced death of brain tissue.

The Brain · Drugs Hijack Pleasure Pathways

Following a chiropractic adjustment that apparently aggravated an earlier brain injury, Cindy Lou Romberg suddenly acquired a foreign accent!

FIGURE 23-49 Changing accent. Cindy Lou Romberg never studied any foreign languages or traveled to Europe, but a brain change has caused her to now speak with a mixture of a German, French, and Russian accent.

MEMORY CENTER IN THE BRAIN

AMYGDALA
The area of the brain that appears to associate emotional feelings and sensory input with memories

HIPPOCAMPUS
The area of the brain that is important in the storage and retrieval of memories and the transfer of short-term memories

FIGURE 23-50 Areas of the brain associated with memories.

Another recent discovery suggests that children have a propensity to learn language regardless of what language they are exposed to. In a study of children raised by parents who spoke using sign language only, observations of their children revealed that the infants actually "babbled" with their hands. Much as babies with parents who speak begin to put together nonsense words made up from actual fragments of words and sounds, from age six months to one year, the babies of signing parents used their hands to produce fragments of hand signs. The babies of speaking parents did not exhibit such hand babbling.

Learning and memory are understood even less well than language. Still, certain cellular changes seem to occur in neurons when we learn and remember things. Two parts of the limbic system are critical in storing memories, the amygdala and the hippocampus. The amygdala seems to associate emotional feelings and sensory input with memories (**FIGURE 23-50**). This is why it is not uncommon for certain smells or tastes, for example, to elicit memories. The hippocampus is also important in the storage and retrieval of memories, as well as the transfer of short-term memories—things that are stored in our brain only briefly, such as a phone number or the name of a person we have just met—into long-term memories that can be recalled

days, years, or even decades later. Memories and associations of sensations are stored throughout much of the cerebral cortex, too.

Humans don't have a monopoly on powerful memory. When it comes to remembering where they've put things and where they can find food, many birds and non-human mammals are also quite accomplished. Each fall, for example, red squirrels each hide more than 3,000 acorns and other nuts (**FIGURE 23-51**). Come winter, each squirrel is able to remember the locations of more than 80% of those nuts and recover them for food. Similarly, birds such as the black-capped chickadee store large numbers of nuts for the winter. Researchers looking for neurological changes in these birds found that the hippocampus is significantly larger in the fall, when the birds must remember all of their nut-stash locations, than in the spring, when they no longer need to rely on stored nuts for food.

For many years, it was believed that no new neurons are added to the human brain once development is completed in early childhood. While this is largely true, recent observations suggest that some parts of the hippocampus are an exception, adding cells even into adulthood, possibly as a function of use. On the flip side, amnesia usually comes from

What Is the Nervous System?   How Do Neurons Work?   The Senses   Muscular and Skeletal Systems

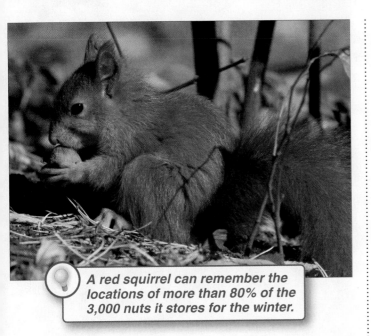

A red squirrel can remember the locations of more than 80% of the 3,000 nuts it stores for the winter.

FIGURE 23-51 A good memory for hiding places. A red squirrel never forgets the location of its acorn stash.

damage to the amygdala or hippocampus from a stroke or head injury.

What happens to the neurons at a cellular level during the processes of learning and forming memories? When repeated action potentials are generated by a neuron, changes occur at the synapse. There are two types of change that generally occur. One is called **long-term depression** and the other is called **long-term potentiation.** In each, as neurotransmitters are repeatedly released by the presynaptic membrane, the adjacent neuron responds by initiating an action potential, but also by becoming less likely (long-term depression), or more likely (long-term potentiation) to respond to future stimulation with an action potential. That's the learning: future responses are modified by past experience. This makes sense when we consider that perhaps the simplest form of learning comes from repeated attempts at doing something, during which the individual becomes better and better at it.

"Use it or lose it." That is a frequent assertion by weightlifters in reference to their muscles. The same expression might be used about the memory-forming components of our limbic system. Using fMRI brain scans, researchers in England recently discovered that the brains of London cab drivers have a larger hippocampus than those of non-cabbies. The researchers believe that this may be a result of the formation of new neurons, due to the greater demands placed on the hippocampus as the cab drivers navigate the streets of London. Their hypothesis was supported by the observation that the longer an individual had been a cab driver, the larger his hippocampus was.

Q Can we generate new brain cells? How?

The synapse isn't just the site of "normal" signal propagation. We'll explore next how, by tinkering with the synapse and modifying the amount or duration of stimulation occurring, it is possible to use drugs and medications to artificially create feelings of happiness, satiation, euphoria, and more. It's also possible to create medically valuable anesthetics and deadly toxins.

TAKE-HOME MESSAGE 23·18

Learning and memory, along with the use of complex language, are among the most sophisticated functions of the brain. Although brain science is still in its infancy, we are gaining a clearer picture of the brain structures—primarily, for language, in the left frontal and left temporal lobes and, for learning and memory, in the amygdala and hippocampus—that are chiefly responsible for these functions.

The Brain   Drugs Hijack Pleasure Pathways

❻ Drugs can hijack pleasure pathways.

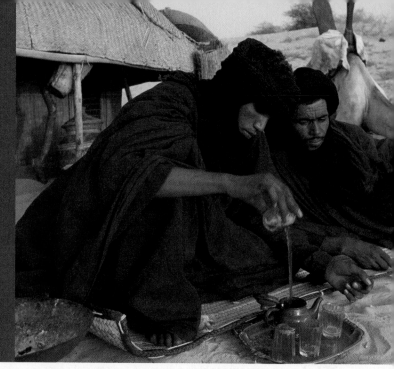

Two men preparing tea in the desert of Timbuktu, Mali. Worldwide, more caffeine-containing tea is consumed every day than any beverage other than water.

23·19

Our nervous system can be tricked by chemicals.

Stimulation of the reward centers in the brain spurs animals to behave in certain ways. We're built this way on purpose: when we behave in ways important to our evolutionary fitness, our brain releases neurotransmitters such as dopamine. Exposed to such neurotransmitters, our pleasure centers produce the sensation of bliss. And that bliss spurs us to seek out that feeling again once it fades. Usually this system works well.

Our brain's signaling system can be tricked, however, and with potentially disastrous consequences. Drugs—whether recreational or therapeutic, whether found in nature or made in the laboratory—can work by mimicking neurotransmitters. When we take a pleasure-causing drug, our brain experiences the same sensations as if appropriately released neurotransmitters were flooding the system. The brain cannot distinguish this artificial high from a real high. There are several different methods by which drugs can influence our nervous system. We'll explore some of them here.

Cocaine When someone snorts a bit of cocaine, it crosses the blood-brain barrier and quickly reaches the brain's pleasure centers. Once there, the cocaine binds to the sites on the presynaptic membrane where dopamine is normally reabsorbed

from the synaptic cleft by the cells that originally released it. As long as these reuptake sites are blocked by the drug, dopamine released by that neuron remains in the synaptic cleft, repeatedly stimulating the postsynaptic cell and causing non-stop activity in the pleasure center (**FIGURE 23-52**).

Prozac and Zoloft Antidepressants work by an almost identical mechanism to that of cocaine. In addition to dopamine, another neurotransmitter important in our brain's pleasure centers is serotonin. The antidepressants Prozac and Zoloft block serotonin from being reabsorbed and recycled by the presynaptic cells that released it, prolonging its effect (see Figure 23-52). This is why these drugs are called **selective serotonin reuptake inhibitors (SSRIs).** The net result is that people taking these drugs generally experience an elevated mood because of serotonin's prolonged stay in the synaptic cleft.

Morphine and Heroin Some chemical messengers we ought to be especially thankful for are the endorphins, our body's natural painkillers. Produced by our brain, endorphins block pain messages arriving from throughout the body. Under a variety of situations of extreme stress—such as if an individual has just been seriously injured in a fight or is in

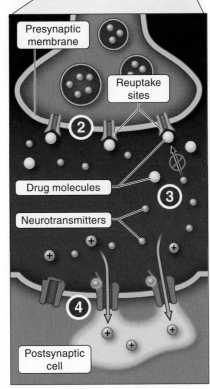

REUPTAKE INHIBITORS

1 After the drug is taken, it crosses the blood-brain barrier and quickly reaches the brain's pleasure centers.

Blood-brain barrier

Blood vessel

Drug molecules

Neurons in the brain

2 Drug molecules bind to sites on the presynaptic membrane where neurotransmitters are normally reabsorbed by the cells that originally released them.

Presynaptic membrane

Reuptake sites

3 As long as reuptake sites are blocked by drug molecules, the neurotransmitters previously released by that neuron remain in the synaptic cleft.

Drug molecules

Neurotransmitters

4 The neurotransmitters repeatedly stimulate the postsynaptic cell and cause non-stop activity in the pleasure centers of the brain.

Postsynaptic cell

FIGURE 23-52 Prolonging pleasure sensations. Reuptake inhibitors cause prolonged action of a neurotransmitter in the synapse.

mile 12 of a half-marathon—the body responds by releasing endorphins.

The popular opiates morphine and heroin mimic endorphins and bind to their receptor sites. With a large enough dose, opiate users can give themselves an "endorphin rush" and feelings of euphoria far more intense than anything possible with their own natural supply of these pleasure compounds. The respiratory slow-down that comes with heroin use can occur quickly and, with large doses of heroin, can be fatal.

Nicotine One of the most commonly used drugs is nicotine. Shortly after entering the bloodstream, nicotine begins mimicking one of the body's most common and important neurotransmitters, acetylcholine. Fooled by the nicotine binding to acetylcholine receptors, cells release adrenaline and other stimulating chemicals, including pleasure-causing dopamine. Nicotine causes rapid surges, then rapid depletions, of these chemicals, leaving smokers happy for a short while but soon yearning for another cigarette.

When we consume drugs such as those described above, our bodies soon respond to the perception that there are larger

Some people use a nicotine patch that supplies nicotine to the bloodstream to help reduce the severity of physical symptoms associated with cigarette smoking cessation.

879

FIGURE 23-53 Can a gene nudge you toward risk-taking?

amounts than usual of certain neurotransmitters. Usually the response is a reduction in sensitivity to the drug. Although tolerance is inevitable, its magnitude and consequences vary with the type of drug. In one study, volunteers were injected with a uniform daily dose of heroin and monitored for their level of euphoria. Initially they were ecstatic, but their bodies reacted by reducing the number of receptors that bind heroin. With fewer and fewer receptors, the euphoric heroin effects dropped almost to zero in just three weeks. Similar changes occur in response to using caffeine, nicotine, or alcohol.

Do human drug addictions and dependencies reflect differences in our genes? Recent data suggest that they might at least be influenced by the alleles a person carries. In one study of 283 individuals, a third of the people who smoked had a version (i.e., an allele) of an important gene that almost none of the non-smokers carried. This

> **Q Can a gene nudge you toward risk-taking?**

gene, labeled D4DR, codes for the receptor that enables the pleasure centers of our brain to respond to dopamine. The allele of the D4DR gene found among one-third of the smokers in the study was the same one we discussed in the StreetBio feature at the end of Chapter 7, one that appears to cause individuals to exhibit a variety of personality traits associated with risk-taking and novelty-seeking behavior (**FIGURE 23-53**). Do you think that you carry it?

In the next section we look at a popular and effective drug that acts not by blocking neurotransmitter reuptake, but rather by blocking the postsynaptic receptors.

TAKE-HOME MESSAGE 23·19

Our brain's signaling system can be tricked by drugs, whether recreational or therapeutic, that mimic neurotransmitters. Such drugs—including cocaine, Prozac, heroin, and nicotine—can produce euphoric sensations, can reduce depression, and can block pain, but the effects often come with significant health risks.

23·20

A brain slows down when it needs sleep. Caffeine wakes it up.

Many drugs can interfere with normal neuron functioning, and caffeine is perhaps the most frequently used drug of all with this effect. Worldwide, more caffeine-containing tea is consumed every day than any beverage other than water. A close second is coffee (**FIGURE 23-54**). And in the United States, 90% of the soda consumed contains caffeine. The average American drinks about a hundred gallons a year of these three beverages. From philosophers and writers to scientists and musicians, caffeine has been revered as a necessity for stimulating the creative juices. In his Coffee Cantata of 1732, J. S. Bach wrote, "Ah! How sweet coffee tastes! Lovelier than a thousand kisses, sweeter far than muscatel wine!"

> **"** If it weren't for coffee, I'd have no discernible personality at all.
>
> —David Letterman **"**

The centuries of strong praise are well founded. Caffeine has powerful effects on nearly every animal species. For instance, while all rats can eventually be trained to race through mazes, some learn quickly while others languish in remedial maze-running classes. What they all have in common, however, is

880 CHAPTER 23 • NERVOUS AND MOTOR SYSTEMS

What Is the Nervous System?   How Do Neurons Work?   The Senses   Muscular and Skeletal Systems

FIGURE 23-54 Many people take pleasure in drinking tea and coffee.

that when they are given a caffeine pick-me-up before their maze lessons, they learn the solutions faster and remember them better.

How does caffeine work its magic? As long as we are awake, our brain is working hard and consuming about 20% of the energy we take in. Much as a running motor generates exhaust fumes, however, all of this neural activity leads to a buildup of cellular waste products. Neuron "exhaust" takes the form of a variety of molecules, including one called adenosine. As a cell releases adenosine, it fills adenosine receptors on nearby cells, particularly those in the brainstem. When a molecule of adenosine binds to an adenosine receptor, this reduces a neuron's likelihood of initiating an action potential. Adenosine has been described as putting a brake on neuron activity. Consequently, as the production of adenosine continues throughout our day, more and more receptors on more and more neurons are filled, and the neurons in our brain become less likely to fire, regardless of how strongly they are stimulated. We perceive this as tiredness. Then, as we sleep, the cellular waste products such as adenosine are reabsorbed and recycled. Upon awaking, we feel better because we literally are more clear-headed.

Caffeine has its effect by blocking the message to reduce activity and to sleep. Here's how it accomplishes this effect. The caffeine we ingest quickly circulates to our brain, and once there, it diffuses around the cells. Because the shape of the caffeine molecule is similar to that of the adenosine molecule, the caffeine slips into some of the receptors intended for adenosine (**FIGURE 23-55**). It doesn't have the

HOW CAFFEINE WORKS

Adenosine

Adenosine receptors

Action potential not fired

ADENOSINE IN THE BRAIN

1 Activity in the brain leads to a buildup of a cellular waste product known as adenosine that binds to receptors on nearby cells.

2 As more adenosine receptors become filled with adenosine, the neurons in our brain become less likely to fire. We perceive this as tiredness.

Caffeine molecules

Adenosine

Adenosine receptors

Action potential fired

CAFFEINE IN THE BRAIN

3 Ingested caffeine circulates to the brain and binds to receptors intended for adenosine.

4 Adenosine receptors bound to caffeine do not reduce our neurons' ability to fire, and we feel alert.

FIGURE 23-55 How caffeine reduces the feeling of fatigue.

The Brain   Drugs Hijack Pleasure Pathways

same effect as adenosine, however. Adenosine receptors with bound caffeine molecules do not reduce a neuron's propensity to respond to other stimuli with an action potential. Thus, when many of the adenosine receptors are blocked by caffeine, the adenosine is unable to pass on the message that we need to sleep. Instead, we feel surprisingly alert as caffeine interrupts one of the normal sleep-signaling systems.

Surprisingly, caffeine seems to be safe for most people. Despite considerable searching for ill effects, there is no clear evidence that moderate consumption of caffeine increases our risk of anything beyond the occasional jitters. For healthy people,

there appears to be no increased risk of heart, lung, or kidney disease or even cancer.

TAKE-HOME MESSAGE 23·20

Normal neural activity leads to a buildup of cellular waste products. One of these, adenosine, fills adenosine receptors on nearby neurons, reducing the likelihood that a cell will initiate an action potential and causing fatigue. Caffeine binds to the adenosine receptors, without reducing their likelihood of firing, thus blocking the fatigue-inducing message of adenosine.

23·21

Alcohol interferes with many different neurotransmitters.

So far, we've seen that drugs frequently can alter our brain functioning by mimicking the neurotransmitters used by our neurons during normal functioning. Their specific effects are quite predictable, as long as we know the neurotransmitter that the drug mimics. Their work is like a surgical strike, altering our neurochemistry in one specific way.

But what happens if the drug is more of an everyman, looking enough like many different neurotransmitters to impersonate them all? This is the case with alcohol. More specifically, it is the case with ethanol, the "alcohol" molecule in alcoholic beverages. Alcohol is a great neurotransmitter impersonator, fooling at least four different receptor molecules. Let's look at some of its effects (**FIGURE 23-56**).

1. Alcohol slows us down, "relaxing" our neurons. By blocking receptors for glutamate (see Section 23-6), one of the brain's chief excitatory neurotransmitters, alcohol slows our reaction times and slurs our speech. It may also have more serious effects: many animals can't learn as well when their glutamate receptors are blocked.

2. Alcohol gives us a pleasant buzz. Acting like cocaine—but much weaker—alcohol blocks dopamine reuptake, increasing the concentration of this neurotransmitter that is active in the reward centers of our brain.

3. Alcohol blocks pain. By stimulating the release of endorphins—neurotransmitters that block pain messages—alcohol causes the same feeling that has been called "runner's

EFFECTS OF ALCOHOL
- Slows reaction time and slurs speech by blocking receptors for glutamate
- Provides a pleasant buzz by blocking dopamine reuptake
- Blocks pain by stimulating the release of endorphins
- Increases feelings of happiness by modifying and increasing the efficiency of our serotonin receptors

FIGURE 23-56 Alcohol impersonates several neurotransmitters, with several consequences.

high." Resembling morphine and heroin in this respect, but again at a greatly reduced magnitude, alcohol spurs our body to produce a little opiate-like high.

882 CHAPTER 23 • NERVOUS AND MOTOR SYSTEMS

What Is the Nervous System?   How Do Neurons Work?   The Senses   Muscular and Skeletal Systems

Alcohol intake lowers inhibitions and, in excess, can increase the likelihood of risky behavior.

4. Alcohol makes us happier, at least while it's in our system. Much like Prozac, alcohol modifies and increases the efficiency of our serotonin receptors, increasing the contentment that accompanies serotonin release at synapses in the brain. Interestingly, rats that have been bred for a high preference for alcohol turn out to have lower serotonin levels than normal rats. One possible interpretation for this is that the alcohol-seeking animals are trying to compensate for their lack of serotonin stimulation by looking for the alcohol effects.

For most people, moderate alcohol consumption is pleasant and does not have significant health risks. For some, however, alcohol abuse and alcoholism can lead to serious problems. Nearly 14 million Americans abuse alcohol, and the consequences can be serious. Beyond the effects it creates by mimicking neurotransmitters, alcohol has a variety of other physiological effects in our bodies that can become harmful when alcohol is consumed in large amounts or for long periods of time. These include increasing the risk for some types of cancer, increasing the risk of liver disease (because the liver must metabolize and detoxify all the ethanol molecules that are consumed), increasing the likelihood of harm to the fetus during pregnancy, increasing the likelihood of taking part in risky sexual and other behaviors, and increasing the risk of automobile crashes.

TAKE-HOME MESSAGE 23·21

Alcohol affects the functioning of multiple neurotransmitters—including glutamate, endorphins, dopamine, and serotonin—slowing reaction times, slurring speech, blocking pain, and increasing contentment.

The Brain | Drugs Hijack Pleasure Pathways

Knowledge You Can Use

Don't move a muscle! (Injecting the toxic bacterial protein, Botox, can help.)

Q: What is Botox? Botox refers to "botulinum toxin," a protein produced by several species of bacteria. It is the most toxic substance known—less than a microgram is lethal if injected in a person or inhaled. (For comparison, an inch-long human hair weighs more than 200 micrograms.) Botox is also an increasingly popular drug used in cosmetic procedures, with more than a billion dollars spent on it worldwide each year.

Q: What makes it toxic? What gives it medical value? When injected in muscles, Botox blocks the release of acetylcholine, the neurotransmitter that stimulates muscle contraction. Botox does this by interfering with the fusion of acetylcholine-filled vesicles with the presynaptic neuron's membrane, preventing release of acetylcholine into the synapse and thus its effect on muscle cells. A tiny amount of Botox can prevent a muscle from contracting for three or four months! (This feature of Botox makes it an effective treatment for muscle spasms.)

Q: Why would a healthy person want to get near the most toxic substance known? Tiny injections of Botox can smooth lines in the forehead and between the eyebrows. The injections can also reduce "crow's feet" wrinkles around the eyes. Extolling its ability to make them look younger, many people seek out Botox treatments, including high-profile celebrities such as actress Jenny McCarthy, who said, "I love Botox, I absolutely love it . . . I get it minimally, so I can still move my face. But I really do think it's a savior."

Q: Wait a minute! "I get it minimally, so I can still move my face"? What is the downside to Botox? Because Botox essentially paralyzes muscles, it can lead to a variety of problems. At the extreme, if Botox spreads to muscles other than those intended, it can interfere with the muscles needed for swallowing and breathing—muscles you can't afford to be without for more than a few minutes, let alone a few months. Most of the 180 reported cases of life-threatening problems resulting from Botox injections between 1997 and 2006 stemmed from problems of this nature. Less life-threatening, but disturbing to many, is the severe reduction in individuals' ability to move parts of their face that can result from Botox injections, often causing droopy eyelids or a mask-like face and inability to express emotions.

① What is the nervous system?

Nervous systems are found in nearly all animal species. Primarily utilizing cells called neurons, they (1) receive input from the surrounding world, (2) process that information, and (3) initiate responses to the environment when necessary.

② How do neurons work?

Neurons are cells specialized for receiving information via their dendrites and transmitting this information through action potentials down their axons. An action potential is a self-propagating, all-or-none change in the membrane potential that travels down an axon, causing the release of neurotransmitters, which diffuse across the synapse, bind to receptors, and excite or inhibit the postsynaptic cell—which may be a muscle, a gland, or another neuron.

③ Our senses detect and transmit stimuli.

All of our senses are variations on a theme: sensory cells respond to physical or chemical stimuli by opening or closing channels within the membranes of receptor cells and stimulating or blocking action potentials that, when received by the brain, are perceived as taste, smell, light, sound, or touch.

④ The muscular and skeletal systems enable movement.

Muscle tissue—including skeletal, cardiac, and smooth muscle—is made up of elongated cells capable of generating force when they contract. A muscle fiber is a single cell containing myofibrils that shorten with the making and breaking of bonds connecting parallel actin and myosin filaments. Muscles are attached to parts of the skeletal system, which, in vertebrates, can enable movement, provide support, offer protection, provide a site for production of important blood and immune cells, and serve as a reservoir of minerals, including calcium.

⑤ The brain is organized into distinct structures dedicated to specific functions.

There are several distinct regions in the brain—the hindbrain, midbrain, and forebrain—each of which is the control center for various activities in the body. The forebrain, the largest region of the brain, is responsible for most of what we consider higher thought, including perception, memory, language, intelligence, and personality. PET scans and fMRI scans make it possible to detect and visualize metabolic activity in brain tissue and to see how the brain works on various tasks.

⑥ Drugs can hijack pleasure pathways.

Drugs that interfere with the functioning of neurotransmitters can have various effects, some of which are diseases and some of which are sought-after euphoric or excited states. The drug's interference can involve blocking or over-facilitating the release of a neurotransmitter, increasing or decreasing the rate at which neurotransmitter is removed from the synaptic cleft, or blocking or over-facilitating the binding of neurotransmitter to its receptors.

KEY TERMS

1. Animal nervous systems have several principal features. These include all of the following except:
   a) They coordinate long-term growth and development in an organism.
   b) They receive input from the world around the organism.
   c) They initiate responses to the information they receive from the world, when necessary.
   d) They process the information from the world that an organism receives.
   e) All of the above are principal features of animal nervous systems.

2. Which of the following statements about plants and nervous systems is correct?
   a) Plants can feel pain in their trunks and stems, where they have neurons, but not in their leaves.
   b) Plants can feel pain in their leaves, where they have neurons, but not in their trunks or stems.
   c) Plants can feel pain because they have a nervous system that extends throughout all of their tissues.
   d) Plants can feel pain in their trunks, where they have neurons, but not in their stems or leaves.
   e) Plants cannot feel pain because they do not have nervous systems.

3. What is the difference between a nerve and a neuron?
   a) A nerve is a bundle of neurons, whereas a neuron is a single cell.
   b) Nerves have synapses with muscle cells, whereas neurons have synapses with other neurons.
   c) Nerves have dendrites that can be modified into sensory cells, whereas neurons do not have dendrites.
   d) "Nerve" is the name given to nervous system cells specialized for receiving and transmitting information, whereas "neuron" describes a nerve cell in humans.
   e) There is no difference. They are different words for the same structure.

4. In a neuron, the cell body:
   a) contains the nucleus, mitochondria, and other cell organelles.
   b) does not contain a nucleus.
   c) has a membrane that is impermeable to water and intracellular solutes.
   d) is highly modified and coated in a fatty myelin sheath.
   e) is considered the primary structure of the "central" nervous system.

5. Dendrites:
   a) conduct action potentials away from the cell body.
   b) are present in mammalian nervous systems but not in the nervous systems of other vertebrates.
   c) receive information from other neurons or from the external environment.
   d) are coated in a fatty substance called the myelin sheath, which speeds up the rate at which signals are conducted.
   e) are bundles of axons.

6. In individuals with multiple sclerosis, myelin is gradually lost. What symptoms would you expect these individuals to exhibit?
   a) Their membranes have reduced numbers of sodium channels.
   b) Their sensory neurons lose the ability to initiate action potential.
   c) Their brain becomes smaller.
   d) They are able to continue athletic activity long after pain would cause most individuals to stop.
   e) Their neurons gradually lose their ability to conduct electrical impulses.

7. Which of the choices below properly describes the difference between the gray and white matter of the nervous system?
   a) The white matter is composed of non-myelinated fibers, and the gray matter is composed of myelinated fibers.
   b) The white matter is composed of neuron bodies, and the gray matter is composed of axons and dendrites.
   c) The white matter is composed of sensory neurons, and the gray matter is composed of motor neurons.
   d) The white matter is composed of myelinated fibers, and the gray matter is composed of non-myelinated fibers.
   e) None of the above is correct.

8. The synapse consists of:
   a) a release of neurotransmitter into a synaptic cleft.
   b) a presynaptic neuron and its neurotransmitters.
   c) the membrane depolarization that occurs at gaps in the myelin sheath.
   d) the interface between a neuron and another neuron or muscle cell or gland.
   e) None of the above.

9. Neurotransmitters in a synaptic cleft have all of the following possible fates except:
   a) reuptake by the presynaptic neuron.
   b) enzymatic breakdown in the synaptic cleft.
   c) inactivation by acetylcholine in the synaptic cleft.
   d) binding to a receptor in the postsynaptic cell membrane.
   e) All of the above are possible fates of neurotransmitters in a synaptic cleft.

10. An action potential in the optic nerve triggered by light striking the eye is the same as:
    a) an action potential triggered by air vibrating in the ear.
    b) an action potential triggered by salt on the tongue.
    c) an action potential triggered by an odorous substance entering the nose.
    d) Answers a), b), and c) are correct.
    e) None of the above is correct.

11. When you put a piece of chocolate on your tongue, your brain registers a sensation of sweetness. What aspect of a molecule is responsible for its having a particular taste?
    a) the molecule's shape
    b) the total number of protons in the molecule
    c) the number of hydrogen bonds in the molecule (more hydrogen bonds = sweeter taste)
    d) the ratio of covalent bonds to ionic bonds joining the atoms of the molecule
    e) the speed of melting in your mouth

12. Because cone cells are less sensitive to light than are rod cells:
    a) they are better suited for daylight vision.
    b) they are better suited for night vision.
    c) they are better suited for peripheral vision.
    d) Both a) and c) are correct.
    e) Both b) and c) are correct.

13. Sensory receptors in your skin include:
    a) mechanoreceptors, thermoreceptors, and pain receptors.
    b) mechanoreceptors, thermoreceptors, and electromagnetic receptors.
    c) chemoreceptors, thermoreceptors, and electromagnetic receptors.
    d) mechanoreceptors, thermoreceptors, chemoreceptors, and pain receptors.
    e) mechanoreceptors, thermoreceptors, chemoreceptors, electromagnetic receptors, and pain receptors.

14. The connective tissue that connects a muscle to a bone is also known as:
    a) collagen.   d) a tendon.
    b) a ligament.   e) None of the above.
    c) cartilage.

15. Which of the following is not one of the many functions of an endoskeleton?
    a) storage of important vital minerals
    b) production of blood and immune cells
    c) protection of the body's internal structures
    d) supporting the animal against gravity
    e) All of the above are important functions of an exoskeleton.

16. The brain is divided into which three main regions?
    a) hindbrain, cerebellum, and hypothalamus
    b) midbrain, cerebrum, and brainstem
    c) hypothalamus, medulla oblongata, and cerebrum
    d) brainstem, cerebellum, and cerebrum
    e) hindbrain, midbrain, and forebrain

17. The blood-brain barrier:
    a) is formed from muscle tissue.
    b) is a semi-permeable barricade that allows essential nutrients and gases to pass through.
    c) prevents harmful molecules such as metabolic wastes from passing into the brain.
    d) restricts the passage of molecules to neurons but not to glial cells.
    e) Both b) and c) are correct.

18. A boy is born with a specific brain defect in which the two hemispheres of his cerebrum are no longer able to "talk" to each other (they are no longer connected). This boy is born without a:
    a) hippocampus.   d) corpus callosum.
    b) brainstem.   e) hypothalamus.
    c) medulla oblongata.

19. Caffeine blocks what type of receptors in the human nervous system?
    a) dopamine
    b) adenosine
    c) acetylcholine
    d) serotonin
    e) glutamate

20. Which of the following is not an effect of alcohol on the nervous system?
    a) Alcohol increases the activity of some serotonin receptors, boosting the effective serotonin level in the synapse.
    b) Alcohol stimulates endorphin release.
    c) Alcohol blocks glutamate receptors, leading to slurred speech and reduced reaction times.
    d) Alcohol leads to modestly increased dopamine levels.
    e) Alcohol blocks reuptake of acetylcholine, creating an energized feeling.

SHORT-ANSWER QUESTIONS

1. Compare and contrast the structure and role of neurons and glial cells of the nervous system.

2. Describe the structure of the myofibril of skeletal muscle fibers that makes contraction possible. What changes occur that allow contraction?

3. List the primary types of sensory receptor cells, their functions, and which of the five traditional senses they are associated with.

See Appendix for answers. For additional study questions, go to www.prep-u.com.

Hormones

Mood, emotions, growth, and more: hormones as master regulators

❶ Hormones are chemical messengers regulating cell functioning.

A heart-pounding moment: The rock climber swings by one hand on the rock face.

24·1

The "cuddle" chemical: oxytocin increases trust and enhances pair bonding.

"Trust me." It's easy enough to say, but can be very difficult to do. Recently, however, some researchers discovered a way to actually make people more trusting. Here's how they did it.

Study participants, called investors, were given an amount of money. Each investor could keep the money or transfer some or all of it to another person, called a trustee. Any amount the investor chose to transfer to the trustee was tripled, and the trustee could then return to the investor some portion of the significantly increased pot of cash. Or, the trustee could simply opt to keep it all. For those with the investor role, this created a dilemma in making a decision about what to do: by trusting the other player, they could lose some or all of their money. But trusting behavior might reward the investor with a much greater payoff.

Using a double-blind experimental design, the researchers created two different groups of investors. In one group, before making their decision whether to entrust some of their money to the trustee, the investors used a nasal spray to inhale

a dose of oxytocin—a chemical normally found in humans and other vertebrates, but in smaller amounts than used in the study. Investors in the other group received a placebo, rather than oxytocin, from the inhaler.

The results were dramatic and unambiguous. The investors inhaling the oxytocin were significantly more trusting than those receiving the placebo: more than twice as many of those receiving oxytocin entrusted the maximum amount of their money to the trustee, compared with investors who did not inhale oxytocin. And more than twice as many of those in the placebo group transferred the smallest amounts of cash to the trustee, apparently exhibiting an increased fear of betrayal.

This result is consistent with some findings of research in other animals. In those studies, exposure to oxytocin reliably caused animals to let down their guard, initiate interaction, and facilitate social attachment with other individuals at a much higher rate than they typically would. It appears that

Hormones Are Chemical Messengers   Hormones Are Produced in Glands   Wide-Ranging Effects of Hormones   Chemicals Can Disrupt Hormone Function

FIGURE 24-1 Complex emotions and behaviors can be influenced by chemical signals, such as the hormone oxytocin.

Oxytocin, a chemical signal produced in the body, can influence complex emotions and behaviors, such as increasing trust, making milk available to nursing babies, and forming social attachments.

this chemical may be having a similar effect on humans in the investor-trustee study.

One particularly clever and valuable feature of this study's experimental design is that in a follow-up study, the same methods were used but with one exception: the investors were told that the "trustee" in the game was a computer rather than another person. In these cases, the investors receiving oxytocin did not transfer increased amounts of money to the trustee; they behaved exactly like those in the placebo group. This finding suggests that oxytocin specifically increased the investors' trust of another human, rather than just increasing their willingness to take a financial risk.

Researchers believe that these findings give some insight about the biological basis for trust and that they might even lead to effective treatments for people with extreme shyness. And the results provide a pretty clear demonstration that complex emotions and behaviors can be influenced by chemical signals produced in the body. Oxytocin influences much more in humans than a propensity for trust (**FIGURE 24-1**). Other research has demonstrated that oxytocin plays significant roles in facilitating birth, making milk available to nursing babies, and increasing the propensity to form social

attachments—an effect that has caused some researchers to refer to oxytocin as "the cuddle drug." And although it remains to be seen whether used-car dealers can make potential customers trust them by pumping oxytocin through the air-conditioning systems of showrooms, some journalists have called oxytocin "trust in a bottle."

In this chapter, we see that oxytocin is just one of several dozen influential chemical signals in vertebrates and many other eukaryotes, as we explore just what these chemicals are, where they are produced, and how they have their effects. We also explore the pervasive influence of these molecules in nearly every aspect of vertebrate life, from emotions to physical structures to behavior to health and physiology.

TAKE-HOME MESSAGE 24·1

Complex emotions and behaviors can be influenced by chemical signals produced in the body. Exposure to oxytocin, for example, causes humans to be more trusting of others, as well as facilitating birth, making milk available to nursing babies, and increasing the propensity to form social attachments.

Hormones are chemical messengers that travel through extracellular fluids to influence cells elsewhere in the body.

You wouldn't use the postal service to notify the fire department that your house is burning down. Even with overnight delivery, the information wouldn't arrive in time to be of use. Similarly, you probably wouldn't use the phone to convey all the complex details of a contractual agreement or architectural plans—the mail service might be preferable, to ensure that the details are conveyed precisely. For almost all types of communication, some modes of delivery are more effective than others.

Animals need ways to respond to the outside world: ways of sending signals about certain conditions and giving instructions to tissues in response to those conditions. There are two systems in animals for carrying out this internal communication and regulation (**FIGURE 24-2**). As we saw in Chapter 23, the nervous system generally is responsible for controlling rapid movement and sensations in response to environmental changes. In multicellular animals, including humans, there is another system, as well, with a special type of messenger. **Hormones** (from the Greek word meaning "that which sets in motion or urges forward") are a type of chemical messenger, secreted by cells into the extracellular fluid, including the bloodstream, and influencing the actions

of non-adjacent cells, elsewhere in the body, as part of an internal communication and regulation system. Oxytocin, described in Section 24-1, is an example of an animal hormone.

Cells that secrete hormones are called **endocrine cells,** and the cells that receive their signals are called **target cells.** The hormone-secreting cells may be individual cells such as the endocrine cells in the lining of the stomach and small intestine, which aid in digestion. Larger collections of hormone-secreting cells—including the pituitary gland, the pancreas, and the ovaries and testes—are called **endocrine glands.** Together, all of the hormone-secreting cells in an animal make up its **endocrine system** (**FIGURE 24-3**).

While the nervous system controls rapid movements and sensations, the glands of the endocrine system have the ability to secrete chemical signals into the bloodstream that influence cells that are close by, even adjacent, and cells that are far away. In contrast to the nervous system, the endocrine system is generally responsible for longer-term, slower regulation, such as growth and development, as well as a variety of secretions (see Figure 24-2). It's important to note, however, that there

INTERNAL COMMUNICATION IN ANIMALS

Animals have two systems for carrying out internal communication in response to external conditions.

THE NERVOUS SYSTEM
- Messages are sent via chemical and electrical signals down the axons of neurons and across synapses to target cells.
- Generally responsible for controlling rapid movement and sensations in response to environmental changes

THE ENDOCRINE SYSTEM
- Messages are sent via chemical signals (hormones) secreted by endocrine cells into the extracellular fluid, including, often, the bloodstream, and influencing target cells at a distance.
- Generally responsible for slower, longer-term regulation, such as growth and development as well as a variety of secretions

FIGURE 24-2 The endocrine and nervous systems work together in animals.

Hormones Are Chemical Messengers   Hormones Are Produced in Glands   Wide-Ranging Effects of Hormones   Chemicals Can Disrupt Hormone Function

OVERVIEW OF THE ENDOCRINE SYSTEM

The endocrine system consists of all of the hormone-secreting cells—including larger collections of cells called endocrine glands—in an animal.

Hypothalamus

Pineal gland

Pituitary gland

Thyroid gland

Adrenal glands

Pancreas

Gonads
• Ovaries (in females)
• Testes (in males)

HORMONE SECRETION

Endocrine gland

Bloodstream

Hormones

Endocrine glands have the ability to secrete hormones into the bloodstream that can influence cells that are nearby, even adjacent, and cells that are far away.

Target cells

FIGURE 24-3   Organization of the endocrine system.

are some nervous system cells that secrete hormones, so the systems are not completely separate and distinct but rather can overlap in function somewhat. Interestingly, although they don't have nervous systems, most plants do have endocrine systems (see Chapter 19), suggesting that endocrine systems predate nervous systems evolutionarily.

When a hormone gets to a target cell, it elicits a response. There is a huge variety of possible responses, depending on the hormone and on the target cell. Commonly, the hormone's effect on a target cell is to alter the animal's physiology in a way that helps the organism maintain homeostasis. In doing so, the hormone may alter the target cell's metabolism or growth, it

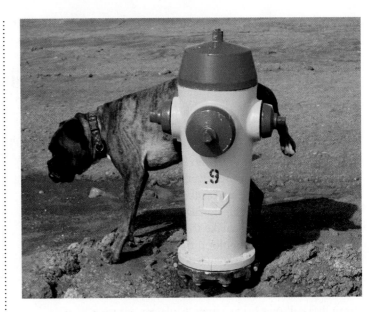

FIGURE 24-4   High hopes. The dog marks its territory and also exaggerates its size by lifting its leg during urination.

may spur cell division, or it may initiate some developmental pathway. In this chapter, we investigate how the chemical nature of each hormone influences the way that molecule regulates the functioning of target cells.

Another type of chemical messenger, called a **pheromone,** is considered an "ecto-hormone," because it is transported to the outside of an animal and can cause a behavioral or physiological change in another individual. Pheromones serve a large number of different purposes. These include alarm pheromones, such as those that signal the presence of a predator and can trigger aggression or flight in a group of individuals; territorial pheromones, such as those found in dogs' urine, that mark the boundaries of a territory; and trail-marking pheromones, such as those produced by ants and that serve as a guide to the nest (**FIGURE 24-4**). And the first pheromones discovered were sex pheromones, signaling sexual receptivity. In some butterfly species, males can detect a female's pheromones from more than six miles away, and the males fly in the direction of increasing pheromone concentration to locate the female.

TAKE-HOME MESSAGE 24·2

Hormones are chemical messengers, secreted by endocrine cells and endocrine glands into the extracellular fluid, that influence the actions of cells, called target cells, elsewhere in the body, as part of an internal communication and regulation system.

Hormones can regulate target tissues in different ways.

If you turn on a radio, you can hear music. This is because, somewhere, a radio station is broadcasting a signal and your radio picks up that signal. If you turn the radio off, the music stops. The signal from the radio station, however, is still there. But without the proper receiver, the signal goes unnoticed. Hormones, one of the body's two chief methods of signaling, function much like radio signals. Glands produce and release hormones, which then make their way through the body, often distributed by the bloodstream, and bump into cells throughout the body. But, like a person without a radio, a cell doesn't respond to a hormone unless it has a specific receptor for that hormone. The hormone may even diffuse right through a cell that has no intracellular receptors.

There are dozens of hormones and even more ways that they regulate target tissue, but the general process by which hormones affect a particular cell doesn't vary much:

1. *Signal is sent.* A hormone is release by a gland.

2. *Signal is received.* Although a hormone has no effect on most tissue it comes in contact with, cells with the proper receptor in the cytoplasm or on the plasma membrane receive the signal.

3. *Cell responds.* When a hormone binds to an appropriate receptor, it causes a response in the target cell. The response can be a change in gene expression in the target cell's nucleus. The cell may start (or stop) producing a protein, or it may alter the rate at which it produces the protein. A single hormone may cause different responses in different target cells.

Most hormones are one of two types: (1) peptide and protein hormones (such as insulin), or (2) steroid hormones (such as estrogen and testosterone). Differences in the chemical structure of these two types of hormones determine whether or not a hormone can pass through the cell membrane (**FIGURE 24-5**). Peptide and protein hormones, the most common type of hormones, are water-soluble, as opposed to lipid-soluble. This means that they cannot pass through membranes, which are high in lipids. Steroid hormones are built from cholesterol and, consequently, are lipid-soluble. They can diffuse right through cell membranes and into the cytoplasm.

PEPTIDE AND PROTEIN HORMONES vs. STEROID HORMONES

Most hormones are one of two types, and differences in their chemical structure influence the method by which they regulate activity in a cell.

PEPTIDE AND PROTEIN HORMONES

1. Peptide and protein hormones are water-soluble, and therefore cannot pass through cell membranes.

2. The hormones bind to receptors embedded within the cell membrane.

3. Once a hormone binds to a receptor, its alteration of the receptor causes any one of a number of changes within the cell.

A hormone can regulate a target cell only if the cell has a receptor for the hormone.

Peptide hormone
Steroid hormone
Hormone receptor
Cell membrane
Cellular response
Cell nucleus
DNA
Hormone receptor
Cellular response

STEROID HORMONES

1. Steroid hormones are lipid-soluble, and therefore can pass through cell membranes.

2. The hormones then bind to receptors located within the cytoplasm or nucleus of the cell.

3. If not already in the nucleus, the hormone-receptor complex will generally pass into the nucleus.

4. Once in the nucleus, the hormone-receptor complex may bind to DNA, influencing gene expression.

FIGURE 24-5 Most hormones belong to one of two main groups, differing in chemical properties. Hormones influence gene expression in different ways, depending on their chemical structure.

Hormones Are Chemical Messengers   Hormones Are Produced in Glands   Wide-Ranging Effects of Hormones   Chemicals Can Disrupt Hormone Function

The chemical structure of the hormone determines how it regulates activity in target tissue. For example, the receptors for peptide and protein hormones are large glycoproteins embedded within cell membranes. Part of the receptor faces toward the outside of the cell; this is the part of the receptor to which the hormone binds. The receptor molecule also extends through the cell membrane, and another part of it extends into the cell's cytoplasm. Once a peptide or protein hormone binds to a receptor on the outside of the cell, it alters the receptor (perhaps changing its shape) and causes any one of a number of changes within the cell. It may activate an enzyme, initiating or speeding a reaction in the cell. Or it may alter the cell's membrane permeability, causing it to absorb or secrete certain molecules. Or it may alter proteins within the cell, causing them to move into the nucleus, where they may bind directly to the DNA and influence the rate of transcription of one or more genes.

The receptors for steroid hormones are proteins in the cytoplasm or nucleus of target cells. The hormone passes into the cell and binds to its receptor. If it is not already in the nucleus, the hormone-receptor complex generally passes into the nucleus. Once there, it may bind to the DNA, influencing the rate of transcription of one or more genes.

By traveling through the bloodstream, peptide, protein, and steroid hormones secreted by glands in one part of the body are able to regulate cell function in another part of the body. However, some glands produce regulators that act more locally. Called **paracrine regulators,** these molecules generally diffuse from the tissue in which they are produced, through intracellular fluid, and into nearby tissue, binding to receptors on or in the neighboring cells and influencing their activity. *Prostaglandins* are one of the most important and common groups of paracrine regulators, produced by almost every cell and nearly every organ in an animal's body. Prostaglandins have numerous effects, including dilation or constriction of blood vessels and influencing tissue inflammation (in which increased plasma and leukocytes move from the blood into tissues).

> Why might long-term, heavy use of aspirin cause stomach bleeding?

One of the chief reasons that aspirin is such an effective pain reliever is that it inhibits an enzyme necessary for the production of prostaglandins (**FIGURE 24-6**). As a consequence, aspirin reduces inflammation (and the pain that often accompanies it). But, because aspirin also inhibits another, similar enzyme that is involved in

> Unlike hormones, paracrine regulators—such as prostaglandins—influence cells nearby or adjacent to the cells in which they are produced. Prostaglandins, which influence nearby tissue in many ways, have been implicated in causing painful inflammation that is associated with arthritis.

FIGURE 24-6 Arthritis hurts. Prostaglandins can cause sometimes painful inflammation in the body.

maintaining the lining of the stomach, taking too much aspirin can cause stomach bleeding and other problems. The development of the drug celecoxib, sold as Celebrex, has been hugely beneficial to people suffering from arthritis, who need regular, long-term anti-inflammation medication. Celecoxib inhibits the prostaglandin-producing enzyme without inhibiting the stomach-lining-maintaining enzyme, making long-term use of this painkiller possible.

TAKE-HOME MESSAGE 24·3

Hormones can regulate the activities of a target tissue only if the cells have a receptor for the hormone. Most hormones are one of two types: (1) peptide and protein hormones, which cannot pass through cell membranes, and interact with receptors embedded in the membrane, or (2) steroid hormones, which can diffuse through cell membranes, then interact with their receptors in the cytoplasm or nucleus of the target cell. Both types of hormones, once bound to a receptor, cause changes in the target cell, including influencing the rate of transcription of genes.

② Hormones are produced in glands throughout the body.

Hormone-secreting cells in the anterior pituitary. The nuclei of the cells are stained dark green. The red granules contain hormones to be secreted.

24•4

Where do hormones come from? 1. The hypothalamus controls secretions of the pituitary.

As we have seen, animals have two systems by which they send signals and regulate body functions in response to their external environment. And although one system or the other tends to be more effective for each particular signaling task, there is considerable interaction between the nervous system and the endocrine system. The **hypothalamus,** part of the underside of the brain, functions as a liaison between the two systems (**FIGURE 24-7**). It receives input from neurons throughout the brain and the rest of the body, and using this information about the external environment and the physiological state of the body, sends out the appropriate hormones (and nervous signals) to regulate nearly every aspect of the organism's physiology, including body temperature, hunger, thirst, and water balance.

Attached to the hypothalamus by a thin stalk is a gland about the size of a pea, called the **pituitary gland.** Signals from the hypothalamus directly influence the pituitary gland. The hypothalamus may release hormones that cause the pituitary

to increase its production and release of hormones. Or the hypothalamus may direct the pituitary to reduce or stop the release of hormones.

Closer inspection of the pituitary gland reveals that it is actually two separate glands that appear to be fused together. The two regions, however, look different, originate from different embryonic tissues, produce different hormones, and are regulated differently. We consider the two regions separately.

The **posterior pituitary** has a fibrous appearance, because it contains a large amount of nervous tissue, particularly axons coming straight from the hypothalamus—from which the posterior pituitary develops. The posterior pituitary produces no hormones of its own. Instead, two important peptide hormones are produced in neurons within the hypothalamus and travel down the axon tracts into the posterior pituitary, from which they are then released:

Hormones Are Chemical Messengers   Hormones Are Produced in Glands   Wide-Ranging Effects of Hormones   Chemicals Can Disrupt Hormone Function

HYPOTHALAMUS
Receives input from neurons throughout the brain and the rest of the body; releases hormones that regulate nearly every aspect of an organism's physiology.

ANTERIOR PITUITARY
Produces numerous hormones—many of which direct endocrine glands elsewhere to release hormones—including:
• Thyroid-stimulating hormone
• Follicle-stimulating hormone
• Luteinizing hormone
• Prolactin
• Adrenocorticotropic hormone
• Growth hormone

POSTERIOR PITUITARY
Releases two important hormones produced within the hypothalamus:
• Oxytocin
• Antidiuretic hormone

FIGURE 24-7 Function of the endocrine system glands: hypothalamus and pituitary glands.

1. *Oxytocin,* the "cuddle hormone," which we discussed in Section 24-1, influences people's trust in others and increases the propensity to form social attachments, as well as directing the ejection (or "let–down") of milk for nursing babies and stimulating muscular contractions in the uterus during childbirth.

2. *Antidiuretic hormone (ADH)* influences water retention by the kidneys. With increased levels of ADH, more water is saved, reducing the amount of urine produced while increasing its concentration.

The **anterior pituitary** has a more glandular appearance than the posterior pituitary, developing not from nervous tissue but rather from epithelial cells near the roof of the mouth during embryonic development. The anterior pituitary produces numerous hormones, in response to commands by the hypothalamus. Many of the anterior pituitary hormones direct endocrine glands elsewhere to release hormones. Some of the most important hormones produced by the anterior pituitary in mammals include the following:

1. *Thyroid-stimulating hormone (TSH)* causes the thyroid to produce thyroxine, which is important in cellular respiration, and which we discuss further in Section 24-5.

2. *Follicle-stimulating hormone (FSH)* stimulates follicles in the ovaries to begin development, and *luteinizing hormone (LH)* triggers ovulation. In males, LH stimulates testosterone production. FSH stimulates sperm maturation and LH stimulates testosterone production.

3. *Prolactin* stimulates the mammary glands to produce milk.

4. *Adrenocorticotropic hormone (ACTH),* also known as *corticotropin,* stimulates the adrenal gland to produce cortisol and other stress–related hormones.

5. *Growth hormone* has several effects, including stimulating the liver to release chemicals that spur the growth of bones, cartilage, and many other tissues.

Improper functioning of the pituitary can lead to some anomalies in growth and development. Excessive production of growth hormone during childhood, for example, can cause extreme growth, called gigantism, with some individuals reaching 8 feet in height! If the increased exposure to growth hormone doesn't occur until adulthood, only the hands, face, and feet tend to respond with unusual growth. Similarly, individuals with reduced or no production of growth hormone during childhood develop a condition

FIGURE 24-8 Pituitary malfunction can affect stature in humans.

Excessive production of growth hormone during childhood can cause extreme growth, with some individuals reaching 8 feet in height.

Reduced production or an absence of growth hormone during childhood can lead to pituitary dwarfism.

Improper functioning of the pituitary can lead to anomalies in growth and development.

called pituitary dwarfism, in which the individual may not grow more than 4 feet tall (**FIGURE 24-8**). Early diagnosis of these conditions and treatment with human growth hormone (produced using recombinant DNA technology) can restore normal growth. See Section 5-11 for a discussion of human growth hormone and recombinant DNA technology.

Although the hypothalamus and pituitary gland control much of the hormone secretion in the body, there are several other endocrine glands with important regulatory roles, which we explore in the sections that follow. And it is important to keep in mind that the hypothalamus and pituitary don't necessarily *control* all of the hormone secretions; they themselves are, in turn, regulated in large part by the glands that they regulate, through numerous feedback loops. See Section 20-3 for a discussion of feedback loops.

TAKE-HOME MESSAGE 24•4

The hypothalamus functions as a liaison between the nervous system and endocrine system. It receives input from neurons throughout the brain and the rest of the body, and using this information about the internal and external environments, it sends out the appropriate hormones (and nervous signals), often directing the pituitary gland to release hormones with important regulatory control over body tissues.

24•5

Where do hormones come from? 2. Other endocrine glands also produce and secrete hormones.

The hypothalamus and pituitary gland play large roles in the regulation of body functions in animals, but they are joined by many other glands in using hormones to signal and regulate physiology. From the anxiety a person may experience at the thought of public speaking, to the changes in wake and sleep patterns that occur when flying to a new time zone, to the changes in metabolism people experience as they get older, endocrine glands throughout the body are responsible for detecting and

Q Why is adrenaline given to people experiencing the severe airway restriction of an asthma attack?

responding to signals reflecting an organism's internal and external environments. Here we explore the signals of some of the most important endocrine glands (**FIGURE 24-9**).

Adrenal Glands Regulating an organism's response to stress is largely a function of the secretions of the two adrenal glands, which sit just above the kidneys and secrete the hormones cortisol and adrenaline, among others. Simply the

Hormones Are Chemical Messengers | Hormones Are Produced in Glands | Wide-Ranging Effects of Hormones | Chemicals Can Disrupt Hormone Function

THE ENDOCRINE GLANDS (PART 2)

In addition to the hypothalamus and pituitary, many other glands use hormones to signal and regulate physiology.

PINEAL GLAND
- Releases melatonin
- Regulates wake and sleep cycles

THYROID GLAND
- Releases thyroxine
- Influences the speed and efficiency of cellular metabolism
- Regulates calcium levels in the blood

ADRENAL GLANDS
- Release adrenaline and cortisol
- Regulate organism's response to stress

PANCREAS
- Releases insulin and glucagon
- Maintains blood glucose levels within a narrow range

Ovaries (in females)

Testes (in males)

GONADS
- Release the sex steroids, including testosterone, estrogen, and progesterone
- Responsible for numerous physical, behavioral, and emotional features, including much sexual behavior, development, and growth

FIGURE 24-9 Function of the endocrine system glands: pineal, thyroid, adrenals, pancreas, and gonads.

sight of a predator is enough to initiate the "fight-or-flight" response—the secretions of adrenaline and cortisol that prepare the body for action (**FIGURE 24-10**). Within seconds, these secretions—in a case of positive feedback—can cause an increase in heart rate, an increased rate of glycogen breakdown in the liver and skeletal muscles, the release of stored fatty acids, goose bumps, and a dilation of the bronchioles in the lungs that enables greater absorption of oxygen, for delivery to needy tissues.

The stress pathways are modulated by negative feedback loops. As an animal takes action in response to a stressful situation, and the source of the stress is removed, the secretions of

Simply the sight of a predator is enough to initiate the "fight-or-flight" response in an animal, and within seconds, secretions of adrenaline and cortisol generate a number of physiological changes that prepare the body for action.

FIGURE 24-10 **Who will win in this conflict?** Adrenal glands influence the fight-or-flight response in animals.

cortisol and adrenaline are reduced. This is how the stress response usually works in nature. But when there is no outlet by which an organism can deal with the stress, long-term consequences of a chronic stress response include ulcers, cardiovascular problems, decreased immune function, and the risk of illness. With increased understanding of the stress response and its general function in nature as a short-term physiological state that helps organisms quickly and effectively respond to stressful situations, researchers are gaining insights into how to better treat anxiety and depression.

Pineal Gland The 17th century philosopher René Descartes believed that the pineal gland was where the soul connected with the body—which he believed largely because the pea-sized gland was located near the center of the brain, was (he thought) unique to humans, and was singular (that is, there was just one, not one on the left side of the brain and another on the right). This view has been abandoned (and we now know that the pineal gland is present in all vertebrates), but there's still considerable scientific interest in this gland. The pineal gland has neuron connections with the retina of the eye, and it controls the secretions of the hormone melatonin, which is derived from the amino acid tryptophan and affects diurnal-nocturnal wake and sleep patterns, called *circadian cycles.*

Although the exact mechanism by which melatonin influences circadian cycles is not understood, it has been shown to have slight benefits in synchronizing individuals' sleep and wake cycles to the environment and in treating some types of insomnia, and is now sold throughout the United States.

Thyroid Gland One of the largest endocrine glands in humans, the **thyroid gland,** is found in the neck, just below the point where, in men, the Adam's apple is. It secretes hormones—including thyroxine—that influence the speed and efficiency at which body cells break down macromolecules in the diet and use the energy released from food to produce proteins. In short, it controls most of what we think of as metabolism. As a consequence, poor thyroid function is believed to be at the root of many metabolic disorders, with underactive thyroid responsible for fatigue and weight gain, and overactive thyroid responsible for jitteriness, rapid heartbeat, weight loss, and irritability.

Goiter is a common health problem caused by an enlargement of the thyroid gland (**FIGURE 24-11**). There are several causes of goiters, and they are particularly common in areas with low consumption of foods containing iodine. When iodine intake is low, the thyroid is unable to produce thyroxine (which contains iodine). This causes thyroxine levels in the body to drop. In the absence of the normal negative feedback telling the body to slow its production of thyroxine, the hypothalamus and anterior pituitary produce increasing amounts, respectively, of thyroxine-releasing hormone and thyroxine-stimulating hormone. These cause the thyroid to swell into a visible lump—a goiter—as it tries unsuccessfully to make thyroxine. In the United States, the widespread use of table salt fortified with iodine prevents most iodine deficiencies, but such deficiencies are common in Asia, central Africa, and parts of South America.

The thyroid is also responsible for regulating levels of calcium in the blood. Calcium is necessary for building and maintaining bones and teeth, and influences the functioning of nerves and muscles. When there is too much calcium in the blood, the thyroid increases its release of **calcitonin,** a hormone particularly important in babies and children, which causes bones to take up the excess calcium. Additionally, embedded in the surface of the thyroid are four small structures, the **parathyroid glands,** that produce parathyroid hormone, which plays a central role in regulating calcium levels in adults (**FIGURE 24-12**). Throughout life, bone is continually broken down and remade as minerals are lost and added. Parathyroid

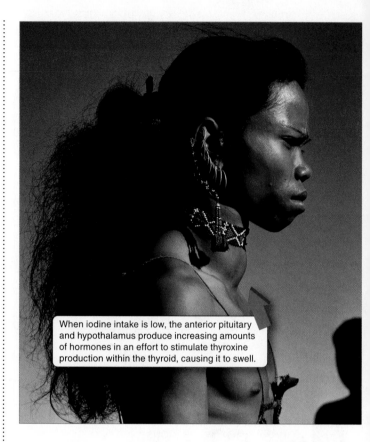

When iodine intake is low, the anterior pituitary and hypothalamus produce increasing amounts of hormones in an effort to stimulate thyroxine production within the thyroid, causing it to swell.

FIGURE 24-11 An enlargement of the thyroid gland in the neck is called a goiter.

hormone is important in stimulating much of this continued turnover of bone, including reabsorption of old bone and production of new bone. Parathyroid hormone further regulates blood calcium levels by reducing calcium loss in the urine, by regulating the release of calcium from bone, and in conjunction with vitamin D (from the diet and produced in skin cells in response to exposure to the sun), helping to increase the body's ability to utilize calcium in the diet.

Pancreas Located next to the stomach and connected to the small intestine via a short duct, the pancreas is an endocrine gland that is most important in controlling the levels of blood glucose. As we saw in Section 22-18, the pancreas maintains blood glucose within narrow ranges—a typical blood glucose concentration in humans is 90 mg/100 mL—through the coordinated secretions of insulin and glucagon (**FIGURE 24-13**).

Following a meal (particularly one rich in carbohydrates), the concentration of blood glucose rises. This stimulates release of insulin by cells in the pancreas. Insulin in the bloodstream causes the liver and other tissues—primarily muscle—to take up glucose, which reduces the blood glucose level. As blood glucose levels fall, there is a reduction in insulin secretion.

900 CHAPTER 24 • HORMONES

Hormones Are Chemical Messengers   Hormones Are Produced in Glands   Wide-Ranging Effects of Hormones   Chemicals Can Disrupt Hormone Function

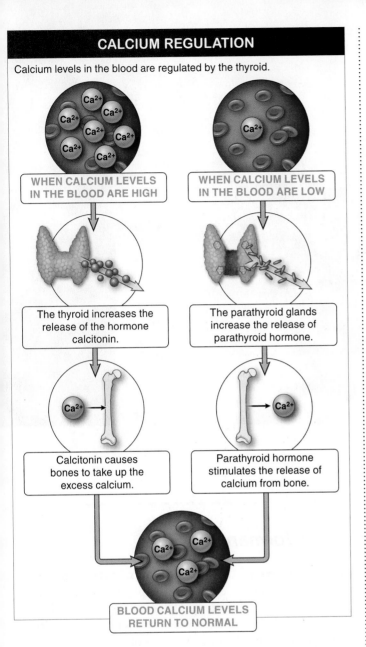

CALCIUM REGULATION

Calcium levels in the blood are regulated by the thyroid.

WHEN CALCIUM LEVELS IN THE BLOOD ARE HIGH

The thyroid increases the release of the hormone calcitonin.

Calcitonin causes bones to take up the excess calcium.

WHEN CALCIUM LEVELS IN THE BLOOD ARE LOW

The parathyroid glands increase the release of parathyroid hormone.

Parathyroid hormone stimulates the release of calcium from bone.

BLOOD CALCIUM LEVELS RETURN TO NORMAL

FIGURE 24-12 The body's use of calcium is regulated by the thyroid and parathyroid glands.

Conversely, after fasting for a few hours, the blood glucose level gradually drops. The reduced blood glucose triggers release of glucagon by some cells in the pancreas. Glucagon has the reverse effect of insulin, causing the liver to convert stored glycogen into glucose, which is released into the bloodstream. Rising blood glucose concentration then causes the pancreas to reduce its glucagon secretion, maintaining homeostasis through negative feedback.

Gonads The sex steroids, including testosterone, estrogen, and progesterone, are produced largely by the gonads—the testes in males and the ovaries in females. These hormones are

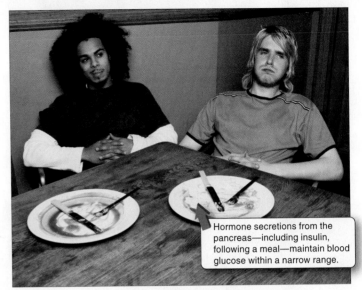

Hormone secretions from the pancreas—including insulin, following a meal—maintain blood glucose within a narrow range.

FIGURE 24-13 Even after a heavy meal, a healthy person can maintain blood glucose levels within a narrow range.

responsible for numerous physical, behavioral, and emotional features, including much sexual behavior and growth, sexual development (beginning embryonically, but playing a significant role in triggering puberty and continuing into adulthood), and maintenance of gamete production throughout organisms' reproductive lives. In Chapter 25 we discuss the sex hormones in detail.

In the next section, we investigate further some of the gonadal hormones and see how closely linked they are to athletic performance and the physical attributes necessary to excel physically. We'll also see a dark side to hormones, in noting some examples of the dramatic physical changes and improvements to athletic performance that have resulted from illegal use of hormone supplements. Later in the chapter, we also note the extreme health consequences that accompany such abuse of these hormones.

TAKE-HOME MESSAGE 24·5

Endocrine glands throughout the body are responsible for detecting and responding to signals reflecting an organism's internal and external environments. The adrenal glands regulate responses to stress. The pineal gland regulates wake and sleep cycles. The thyroid gland influences the speed and efficiency of cellular metabolism. The pancreas maintains blood glucose within a narrow range. And the gonads produce hormones responsible for numerous physical, behavioral, and emotional features, including much sexual behavior, development, and growth.

Growth hormones influence stature.

❸ Hormones influence nearly every facet of an organism.

24·6

Hormones can affect *physique and physical performance.*

The Tour de France is one of the most grueling tests of physical strength and endurance. The annual bike race occurs over the course of three weeks, as riders cover more than 2,200 miles (3,500 km), in 21 separate races, or stages. In 2006, an American rider named Floyd Landis, in 11th place overall, turned in a performance in stage 17 that was so improbably fast that some cycling commentators called it "the greatest performance ever." His victory brought him within 30 seconds of the overall lead, and propelled him, over the course of the final four stages, to the Tour de France victory (**FIGURE 24-14**).

But his glory was not to last. Less than a week after his victory, it was announced that Landis had tested positive for unusually high levels of testosterone. A second test confirmed this finding. The typical ratio of testosterone relative to another hormone (epitestosterone) in men is 1:1 or 2:1. While the Tour de France allows ratios of up to 4:1, Landis's level was 11:1. Moreover, the lab tests detected a synthetic form of testosterone in his bloodstream, in addition to the naturally produced hormone. Landis was stripped of his title and banned from the sport for two years.

While the revelation that a competitor had resorted to illegal supplementation in an effort to boost physical performance was disappointing, it was certainly not a new or isolated occurrence. The recent history of sports is littered with drug scandals, usually involving athletes' use of testosterone or variants of that male hormone. The winner of the gold medal in the 100-meter race in the 1988 Olympics, Ben Johnson, for example, was stripped of his medal and the world record when he tested positive for a synthetic steroid hormone similar to testosterone. In 2003, 104 Major League Baseball players (of 750 players in the league) tested positive for illegal performance-enhancing drugs. In 2005, 111 professional football players tested positive for banned substances. And the scandals are not limited to men. Marion Jones won five Olympic gold medals in 2000, only to have all of them taken away when she admitted that she had illegally taken performance-enhancing drugs, including a muscle-building "designer steroid" called tetrahydrogestrinone, or "the clear."

And so it is clear that many athletes seek out ways to increase the amount of certain hormones in their bodies. The question

Hormones Are Chemical Messengers | Hormones Are Produced in Glands | ▼ Wide-Ranging Effects of Hormones | Chemicals Can Disrupt Hormone Function

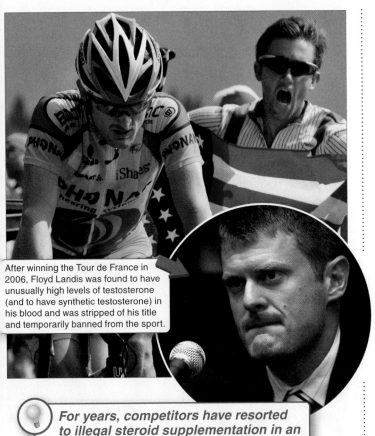

After winning the Tour de France in 2006, Floyd Landis was found to have unusually high levels of testosterone (and to have synthetic testosterone) in his blood and was stripped of his title and temporarily banned from the sport.

For years, competitors have resorted to illegal steroid supplementation in an effort to boost physical performance.

FIGURE 24-14 Unsporting conduct. Many athletes have tested positive for illegal testosterone supplementation.

is, do these hormones actually affect a person's physique and physical performance? And, if so, how do they do it?

When it comes to testosterone (and many structurally similar steroid hormones), the answer to the first question is a definitive *yes*. Testosterone does affect the composition of the body. Experimental studies of testosterone supplementation in men reported gains of 5–12.5 pounds in body weight within 10 weeks. The gains were due primarily to increases in lean muscle mass, with the greatest increases occurring in the shoulders, upper chest, and upper arms, where there are the highest concentrations of testosterone receptors. In randomized, controlled studies, researchers also documented strength increases of 5% to 20%, in both experienced and novice athletes.

Testosterone has also been shown to influence locomotor performance—speed and endurance, in particular—in animals. In an experimental study on lizards (the northern fence lizard, *Sceloporus undulatus*), two to three weeks of supplemental testosterone administration caused a 24% increase in sprinting speed and a 17% increase in stamina.

Use of testosterone, or testosterone doping, causes changes in physique and physical performance by activating processes that lead to increases in muscle mass. Produced primarily by the testes in males (but also by the adrenal glands of both males and females), testosterone binds to receptors in target cells, then moves to the nucleus and influences gene expression. The cells respond to testosterone by increasing protein synthesis and cell division, resulting, in the case of muscle cells, in increased muscle mass (and simultaneously reducing the rate of production of fat-storage cells). Additional responses to testosterone include the development of secondary sex characteristics, including stimulating the growth of chest and facial hair and deepening the voice—effects seen in both males and females in response to testosterone supplementation (**FIGURE 24-15**).

As we'll see later in the chapter, there are numerous adverse effects to supplemental steroid hormones, including increased

THE EFFECTS OF TESTOSTERONE

INCREASE IN LEAN MUSCLE MASS

IMPROVED SPEED AND STAMINA

REDUCED PRODUCTION OF FAT-STORAGE CELLS

DEVELOPMENT OF SECONDARY SEX CHARACTERISTICS

THE ADVERSE EFFECTS OF SUPPLEMENTAL TESTOSTERONE

- Increased blood pressure and risk of heart disease
- Kidney and liver damage
- Development of breast tissue in males
- Atrophy (shrinkage) of the testes
- Increased risk of many types of cancer

FIGURE 24-15 The normal effects of testosterone in the body, and the harmful effects of testosterone supplementation.

blood pressure and risk of heart disease, as well as damage to the kidneys and the liver (where the steroids are metabolized), development of breast tissue in males, and atrophy (shrinkage) of the testes as negative feedback leads to reduced production of testosterone in response to the increased levels of circulating testosterone. Also, because testosterone increases cell division—such as by increasing muscle mass—it increases the risk of unrestrained cell division in many tissues and, consequently, increases the risk of many types of cancer.

TAKE-HOME MESSAGE 24·6

Hormones affect a person's physique and physical performance. Testosterone, for example, increases muscle mass while reducing fat storage and can increase speed and stamina. It produces these changes by influencing gene expression and protein synthesis in cells with testosterone receptors.

24·7

Hormones can affect *mood*.

In a randomized, controlled, and double-blind study of testosterone, researchers injected 47 men each week for six weeks with large amounts of testosterone, after which the researchers made numerous measurements on each subject's physical state. The testosterone caused more than physical changes, as summarized by one of the subjects after he had been receiving the testosterone for about six weeks: "I feel great! I'm confident, positive, happy, and productive. I want to be on this stuff forever!"

Not only do hormones affect our physical traits and physical performance, but they can also influence how we *feel*. Many hormones have pronounced effects on **moods,** defined as relatively long-lasting emotional states (shorter-lasting than a person's temperament, but longer-lasting and less specific than a single emotion). Here we describe just a few of the documented effects of hormones on mood in humans.

Estrogen   In women, the levels of estrogen in the bloodstream change throughout life. And the incidence of depression follows a similar pattern. The large increases in estrogen levels at puberty, the sharp drop off in estrogen levels after a woman gives birth, and the reduced estrogen levels at the onset of menopause are all associated with increased occurrence of depression (**FIGURE 24-16**). Related observations have demonstrated that estrogen is effective at reducing depression when taken as part of hormone replacement therapy in women going through menopause.

Interestingly, researchers investigating the effect of hormones on mood discovered that women exposed to their partner's semen during sex rated their mood as happier than those using condoms. The effect is believed to be a consequence of the mood-altering effects of the testosterone and estrogen that are present in semen and absorbed through the vagina. With unprotected sex, however, the potential for sexually transmitted diseases or unwanted pregnancy must also be

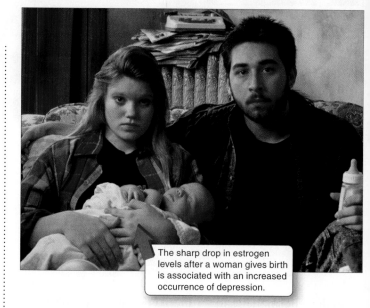

The sharp drop in estrogen levels after a woman gives birth is associated with an increased occurrence of depression.

FIGURE 24-16   Drastic changes in estrogen levels affect mood. For example, the changes can cause "the baby blues" in some women shortly after giving birth.

factored into any long-term assessment of mood, complicating the research findings.

Testosterone   Many studies have demonstrated a link between testosterone and mood in human males. In the study on testosterone administration described above, for example, testosterone caused increased ratings of a variety of feelings, characterized as hypomania, including the men's increased self-esteem and a sense that they were overflowing with new ideas. During the period when receiving the testosterone, the men were described by their significant others as energetic, euphoric, confident, and charismatic. In a small number of cases, however, subjects became uncharacteristically aggressive and exhibited verbal hostility. The researchers even had to withdraw one subject from the study when he became "alarmingly" aggressive—consistent with anecdotal claims of "'roid rage" resulting from taking supplemental testosterone.

Hormones Are Chemical Messengers   Hormones Are Produced in Glands   Wide-Ranging Effects of Hormones   Chemicals Can Disrupt Hormone Function

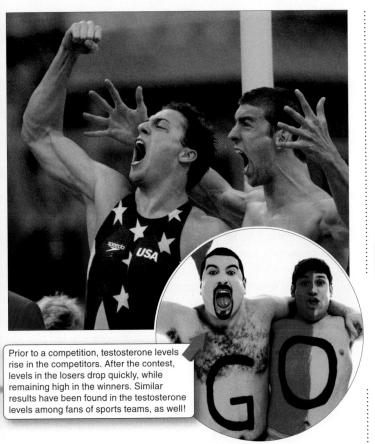

Prior to a competition, testosterone levels rise in the competitors. After the contest, levels in the losers drop quickly, while remaining high in the winners. Similar results have been found in the testosterone levels among fans of sports teams, as well!

FIGURE 24-17 Biological victory dance. Testosterone levels surge in competitors and in fans, too.

Exposure to cortisol for two weeks or more caused rodents to exhibit anxiety-like behavior, including reluctance to enter a brightly lit area.

FIGURE 24-18 Hiding in the dark. Rodents exposed to cortisol show anxious behavior.

Several studies on male athletes in a variety of competitive settings, including tennis and wrestling, have documented that testosterone levels—and the mood changes they influence—rise in competitors prior to a competition. After the contest, testosterone levels in the losers of the competition drop quickly and dramatically, while testosterone levels in the winners remain high and sometimes even increase (**FIGURE 24-17**).

> How can the exhilaration of watching your favorite team win a game match the feeling you get from winning a sports contest yourself?

Recent studies reveal that sports fans share in this biological "victory dance." Measurements of testosterone levels in male fans of Brazilian and Italian soccer teams during World Cup finals revealed that the testosterone levels of the fans of the winning team rose, but not those of the losing team. This finding has been replicated in fans of a college basketball team.

Melatonin In randomized, controlled, double-blind studies, researchers have demonstrated that under certain conditions, oral melatonin can induce hypnotic, sedative-like effects and improve sleep efficiency. Other studies have shown that, in comparison with placebo treatment, melatonin supplementation significantly reduced subjects' self-reported vigor, while increasing their fatigue and confusion.

Cortisol Two separate observations suggest that the hormone cortisol has significant effects on mood. First, researchers have noted that the majority of individuals suffering from Cushing's disease, a condition in which the adrenal glands release unusually large amounts of cortisol, experience depression and anxiety. And second, individuals receiving cortisone (a chemical variant of cortisol that is converted to cortisol in the body) as part of a treatment to reduce inflammation of various tissues also experience anxiety and depression at atypically high rates.

As a consequence of these observations, researchers conducted a controlled study to test whether the stress hormone actually causes anxiety. To do this, they exposed rodents to cortisol by adding it to the animals' drinking water. Exposure to cortisol for two weeks or more, they found, caused the animals to take significantly longer to emerge from small, dark compartments into a brightly lit area—a measure of anxiety-like behavior in rodents—as compared with animals not exposed to the cortisol (**FIGURE 24-18**).

TAKE-HOME MESSAGE 24·7

Many hormones, including estrogen, testosterone, melatonin, and cortisol, have pronounced effects on moods.

Hormones can affect *behavior.*

It can be hard to imagine how a little more or a little less of a chemical could influence an animal's behavior, but experimental research on hormones and behavior has documented literally *thousands* of such effects. The scholarly journal *Hormones and Behavior,* for example, now nearing its 60th volume, publishes 10 issues a year, each containing 25 or more articles describing laboratory and field studies on hormones and their influences on the development and expression of behaviors (**FIGURE 24-19**). In these studies, researchers take a variety of experimental approaches. Just two of these are described here.

Genetic manipulation of hormone levels. Researchers bred some lab mice so that the animals no longer made aromotase, an enzyme necessary essential to the production of the hormone estrogen. With this deficiency, the lower-estrogen animals had two striking behavioral changes: they ran excessively on the exercise wheels in their cages and, when they were sprayed lightly with water, they spent significantly longer grooming themselves than do typical mice. Both of these behaviors are indicators of obsessive-compulsive disorder in mice. The animals also had lower-than-usual levels of a brain chemical called COMT, which also is a typical finding in obsessive-compulsive men.

Q Is castration an effective and humane treatment for sex offenders?

Physiological supplementation of hormone levels. In a second type of experimental approach to studying hormone effects on behavior, researchers implanted testosterone capsules (with tiny pin-prick-sized holes) in male juncos, a type of song bird. The researchers monitored the birds' behavior and documented that the male birds produced a song that was more attractive to females and also produced more offspring than control-group males that received a capsule containing no testosterone. The increased reproductive success did not come without a cost, however. Male birds with testosterone implants spent less time with their offspring and gave the offspring less food. The testosterone-supplemented birds were also more susceptible to disease and had shorter life spans. In similar studies, male birds with supplemented testosterone tended to have increased muscle mass and maintained larger territories than non-supplemented males.

The dramatic and close link between hormones and behavior has even caused people in many countries to debate the possibility of castrating sex offenders to modify their behavior (**FIGURE 24-20**). Whether or not castration—the removal of the testes, with a resultant near-

Thousands of research articles have described the wide variety of hormone effects on behavior.

FIGURE 24-19 The influence of hormones on behavior is an area of active scientific research.

Castrated sex offenders experience a dramatic drop in testosterone levels but whether the procedure prevents future crimes is uncertain.

FIGURE 24-20 Is castration of convicted sex offenders an ethical procedure?

Hormones Are Chemical Messengers | Hormones Are Produced in Glands | Wide-Ranging Effects of Hormones | Chemicals Can Disrupt Hormone Function

complete drop in testosterone levels—can reliably rehabilitate violent sex offenders is hotly debated. In the Czech Republic, one of the very few countries where sex offenders may be castrated, 94 prisoners have undergone castration in the past decade. None of these men have been reported to commit any further offenses. Similarly, in a Danish study of 900 castrated sex offenders, the rate of repeat offense dropped to approximately 2%, from close to 80% among non-castrated sex offenders.

Opponents of the castration of sex offenders argue that the evidence cannot be trusted, because it partly relies on self-reporting by the castrated men. We just can't be sure of the effectiveness of castration in completely stopping sex offenders from committing additional offenses. Moreover, opponents argue that having such an option is coercive, because many convicted offenders will feel obligated to opt for the surgery, leading to an unacceptable violation of the prisoners' rights. Some argue for the reversible form of castration that is achieved by injection of chemicals that block the effects of testosterone, but this is opposed by many on the grounds that it relies on the offenders, once released from prison, voluntarily undergoing their treatment, which they may stop at any point.

TAKE-HOME MESSAGE 24·8

Many studies—including genetic manipulations and physiological alterations of hormone levels—describe laboratory and field research demonstrating hormone influences on the development and expression of behaviors.

24·9

Hormones can affect *cognitive performance.*

Repeat this sentence five times, as quickly as you can: "A box of mixed biscuits in a biscuit mixer." Researchers found that, at the midpoint in their ovulatory cycle, women in the study group could do this in about 14 seconds. During this time, female estrogen levels are at their highest and about 50 times higher than they are in men. During the period just after menstruation, women in this study took 17 seconds to complete the task. During the post-menstruation period, estrogen levels in women are at their lowest, but are still about 3 times higher than in men, and at both times, women were able, on average, to recite the tongue twister faster than men.

The methods used in this widely reported study have been criticized for several reasons, including (1) the study was not blind, because the researchers knew what phase of their reproductive cycle the subjects were in, and the subjects knew why they were being tested, and (2) actual measures of estrogen were not taken—the subjects just reported what point they were at in their reproductive cycle. Nonetheless, this type of research has led to numerous, better-controlled research efforts to evaluate whether cognitive abilities—mental processes involving perception, memory, judgment, and reasoning—are influenced by hormones, with particular emphasis on the reproductive hormones estrogen and testosterone.

Studies on the effects of hormones on cognitive performance have focused on two primary types of measures, designed to reflect different aspects of cognition: (1) motor and verbal tasks, and (2) spatial tasks (**FIGURE 24-21**).

1. *Motor and verbal tasks* include tests of articulation speed, such as the tongue twister noted above, or complex wrist and hand movements and fine-muscle movements, such as those required in surgery and machine repair.

Most tests of hormone effects on motor and non-verbal tasks involve comparisons of the performances of men and women or of girls and boys at these tasks. There is consistent and significant evidence that females perform better than males and that the disparity between male and female performances is greatest at points of high estrogen levels in the female reproductive cycle and smallest at the points of lowest estrogen levels.

2. *Spatial tasks* include tests such as predicting the folded shapes of cardboard boxes when they are unfolded and flat, and mental rotations, in which a pair of two- or three-dimensional objects are compared to see whether they represent the same object, either rotated or as a mirror image.

In humans and other animal species, performance on tests of spatial ability is, on average, higher in males than females. A large body of evidence suggests that this performance difference reflects effects of testosterone—although the mechanisms for this effect are poorly understood. Some of the suggestive findings include:

Repeat this sentence five times, as quickly as you can:

"A box of mixed biscuits in a biscuit mixer."

Identify which of the four shapes on the right represent the target shape on the left in alternative positions.

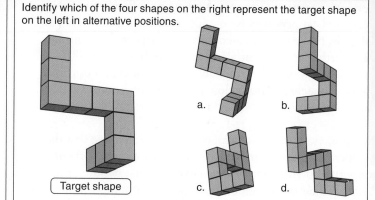

a.

b.

Target shape

c.

d.

MOTOR AND VERBAL TASKS
- Females tend to perform better than males on tests of articulation speed and fine-muscle movement.
- The disparity between male and female performance is greatest at points of high estrogen levels in the female reproductive cycle and least at the points of lowest estrogen levels.

SPATIAL TASKS
- Males tend to perform better than females on tests of spatial ability, such as mental rotations of two- or three-dimensional objects.
- Evidence suggests that this performance difference reflects effects of testosterone—although the mechanisms by which testosterone affects spatial ability are poorly understood.

FIGURE 24-21 Different talents. Men and women have slightly different abilities in certain areas, based on the abundance or lack of the hormones testosterone and estrogen.

- As men get older and their testosterone levels decrease, so too does their performance on tests of spatial ability.

- In older men, testosterone supplementation improves performance on spatial tasks, while chemical castration (administration of chemicals that reduce the production of testosterone) for treatment of prostate cancer causes a decrease in spatial abilities.

- Women with one form of a condition called congenital adrenal hyperplasia have higher than typical levels of circulating testosterone and increased performance on tests of spatial ability.

As with tests of motor and verbal tasks, it is not clear exactly how—or whether—performance on tests of spatial ability affects individuals in contexts more relevant to everyday life. Recently, there has been discussion about the observation in a National Geographic Society study that more than three-quarters of the winners of "Geography Bee" contests are boys and that 118 of the 120 finalists in the National Geography Bee have been boys (**FIGURE 24-22**). While interest in such competitions is unquestionably influenced by cultural and societal forces, the researchers suggested that the results stem from male-female differences in spatial abilities—based on the belief that spatial abilities translate into an ability to read and interpret maps. An author of the study, Lynn Liben, commented that "it's not true that every woman is worse than every man or every girl is worse than every boy. But at the group level, it is true." Girls remain more likely to make the honor roll and to perform well in school.

Beyond tests of motor and verbal tasks and tests of spatial ability, another component of cognitive performance is

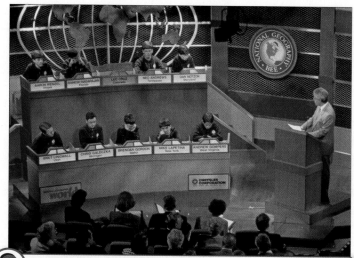

? *Of the 120 finalists in the National Geography Bee over the past 12 years, 118 have been boys. Researchers suggest that this disparity is linked to male-female differences in spatial abilities. Can this hypothesis be tested experimentally?*

FIGURE 24-22 Showing an interest in geography.

Hormones Are Chemical Messengers | Hormones Are Produced in Glands | Wide-Ranging Effects of Hormones | Chemicals Can Disrupt Hormone Function

memory. Numerous studies report a strong role for estrogen in memory, suggesting as a possible mechanism the fact that estrogen increases the growth of neurons and the connections between them. A recent study in rodents, for example, showed that treatment with a high dose of estrogen improved a maze-running task that tests memory.

The stress hormone, cortisol, has also been implicated in memory abilities. Most studies have reported a relationship that resembles an inverted "U." Up to a point, increased cortisol improves memory (and removing the adrenal gland, which produces most of the body's cortisol, impairs performance on tests of memory, but abilities are restored when cortisol is supplemented to typical levels). Excess cortisol and other stress hormones, however, consistently reduce performance on tests of memory. Optimum memory performance seems to require moderate levels of cortisol and other stress hormones.

24·10

Hormones can affect *health and longevity.*

Sometimes the links between cause and effect in biological systems appear straightforward. Take, for example, the results from one of the most appalling "experiments" ever conducted. In the early 1900s, many men committed to sanitariums were castrated. In a case-controlled study, the castrated men were compared with non-castrated, institutionalized men, born in the same year and with the same estimated IQ. It turned out that the median longevity of the castrated men, at 69.3 years, was almost 14 years longer than that of the control group.

Similarly, data from analyses of more than 1,000 cats (both males and females) showed that sterilized cats live significantly longer than those not sterilized. Among females, the intact animals lived a mean of 3.0 years, while those with their ovaries removed had a mean life span of 8.2 years (**FIGURE 24-23**). Laboratory mice, too, have significantly lengthened life spans when sterilized. And in similar experiments, female fruit flies that were exposed briefly to high temperature or X rays experienced a dramatic reduction in ovary size, a severe drop in egg-laying rate, and an accompanying 73% increase in life span. Each of these results on sterilization and longevity suggest that reducing levels of circulating reproductive hormones increases longevity.

The link between reproductive hormones and longevity is also supported by experiments in which mice were fed diets significantly reduced in calories. Researchers found that the amounts of luteinizing hormone, estrogen, and progesterone in the bloodstream were significantly reduced among calorie-restricted females compared with controls—animals given access to as much food as they wanted. Similarly, the researchers found testosterone levels in males on the low-

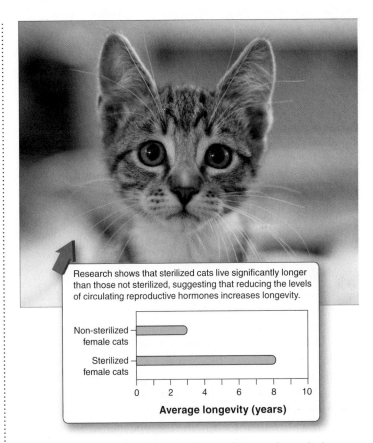

Research shows that sterilized cats live significantly longer than those not sterilized, suggesting that reducing the levels of circulating reproductive hormones increases longevity.

Non-sterilized female cats	
Sterilized female cats	

Average longevity (years)

FIGURE 24-23 Long-lived pets. Sterilization increases longevity in cats.

calorie diet were reduced to less than one-third of those found among animals with free access to food. Mice on the low-calorie diet lived more than 40% longer than those with unlimited access to food.

Hormones probably have their significant impact on longevity because the rate of cancer—in rodents as well as in humans—is closely related to the concentrations of circulating reproductive hormones, such as estrogen:

- Increased lifelong exposure to estrogen is associated with increased rates of cell division and, consequently, increased cancer risk.

- High concentrations of estrogen in the bloodstream are associated with increased incidence of endometrial cancer.

- Women taking oral contraceptives and women giving birth to higher numbers of children—both of which reduce a woman's exposure to estrogen and other hormones produced by developing follicles—have decreased incidences of ovarian cancer. An analysis of 20 studies assessing the relationship between oral contraceptive use and ovarian cancer reported that five years of taking oral contraceptives reduced women's lifetime risk of cancer by approximately 50% (**FIGURE 24-24**).

There is similar evidence of increased cancer risk linked to circulating levels of progesterone and testosterone.

These seemingly straightforward results, however, lead us to an example that illustrates the extreme complexity and interrelatedness of the body's physiological systems. It would seem, given the results above, that longevity should be decreased by hormone replacement therapy, which can take a variety of forms but generally involves supplementation of the hormone estrogen (or estrogen and progesterone) following menopause—which, typically beginning in the mid to late forties, is characterized by the cessation of monthly ovulation and a reduced production of estrogen and progesterone by the ovaries. In fact, though, almost all studies of hormone replacement have found that the treatment reduces the annual risk of death by about 50% and leads to increased longevity.

How can this increased longevity be reconciled with observations on the adverse effects of estrogen, as described above? It turns out that estrogen reduces circulating levels of cholesterol—by a mechanism not yet understood—which in turn reduces the risk of death from heart disease, the top killer of elderly women. Heart disease kills 10 times more women than do reproductive-system cancers, so any treatment that reduces heart disease is likely to increase longevity, *even if it significantly increases the risk of cancers of the reproductive system.* Estrogen replacement therapy in post-menopausal women also lowers the rate of bone loss, significantly reducing health problems related to osteoporosis.

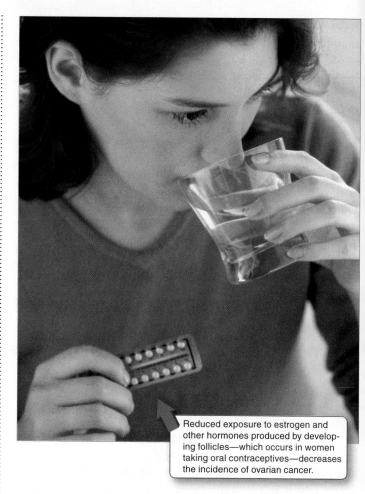

Reduced exposure to estrogen and other hormones produced by developing follicles—which occurs in women taking oral contraceptives—decreases the incidence of ovarian cancer.

FIGURE 24-24 Use of birth control pills decreases the incidence of ovarian cancer.

And so, in the end, while there are several strong links between hormones and health and longevity, the complex and myriad ways in which hormones can affect health make it difficult to make simple predictions about the influence of any hormone on health and longevity.

TAKE-HOME MESSAGE 24·10

Hormones affect health and longevity in complex ways. Sterilization of animals, for example, reduces levels of circulating reproductive hormones and increases longevity, usually due to reduced cancer mortality. But in other cases, such as hormone replacement therapy in women, the relationship is reversed, with treatment reducing the annual risk of death by about 50% and increasing longevity.

Hormones Are Chemical Messengers   Hormones Are Produced in Glands   Wide-Ranging Effects of Hormones   Chemicals Can Disrupt Hormone Function

❹ Environmental contaminants can disrupt normal hormone functioning.

Bald eagle populations were harmed by agricultural use of the pesticide DDT.

24·11

Chemicals in the environment can mimic or block hormones, with disastrous results.

Beginning in 1939 and continuing for more than three decades, the chemical DDT was used as a pesticide against insects, with widespread agricultural use. It is extremely effective in killing a variety of insects, including mosquitoes, which made it popular in strategies against malaria—a disease transmitted by insects. Unfortunately, after DDT killed the intended insect pests, it remained in the environment. Animals that consumed insects exposed to DDT ingested the chemical, which was stored in their body tissues, particularly fat cells. And when those animals were consumed by others, the DDT was passed on. Because larger animals ate larger numbers of animals carrying DDT, they stored more and more of the toxic chemical.

In predators such as bald eagles, peregrine falcons, and pelicans, the DDT disrupted the development and functioning of the reproductive tract and impaired the birds' ability to produce properly functioning eggshells—the shells would crack under the weight of the parent incubating the egg (**FIGURE 24-25**). These problems led to serious population

Predatory birds consuming insects exposed to the pesticide DDT had reduced ability to produce properly functioning eggshells, leading to serious population declines.

Normal peregrine falcon egg

Peregrine falcon egg affected by DDT

FIGURE 24-25 Effects of DDT. The endocrine disruptor DDT causes thinning of eggshells in some birds.

declines in many bird species and may have led to the complete demise of some species.

Publication of the book *Silent Spring,* by the biologist Rachel Carson, in 1962 called attention to the negative environmental effects of the widespread use of DDT. Highlighting the many harmful effects of the pesticide, Carson's book represented the beginning of the environmental movement and incited such a public outcry that the use of DDT was eventually banned completely in the United States—a ban that is cited as instrumental in the rebound of bald eagle populations.

The discovery that DDT can disrupt normal reproduction in wildlife—and could potentially have negative effects on humans, as well—signaled the beginning of concern over **endocrine disruptors,** chemicals manufactured by humans that, when taken up by organisms, can mimic, block, or otherwise interfere with their hormones, leading to harmful effects. Endocrine disruptors' effects are a consequence of their close chemical similarity to hormones, particularly estrogen. Often, endocrine disruptors can directly bind to the same receptors as estrogen.

There are several types of endocrine disruptors, in addition to DDT. These include **PCBs (polychlorinated biphenyls),** which are effective as industrial coolants and lubricants; **phthalates,** which are commonly found in soft toys and cosmetics; and **bisphenol A,** found in some plastic water bottles and baby bottles (**FIGURE 24-26**).

Endocrine disruptors are found in thousands of other consumer products, too, and have been detected in numerous natural habitats, sometimes carried in runoff water from industrial manufacturing processes or as airborne pollutants. Exposure to endocrine disruptors has been implicated in a variety of adverse physiological effects, often related to the chemicals' feminizing effects, which has led to some endocrine disruptors being referred to as "gender-bending chemicals." In addition to birds, a variety of animal groups seem to be adversely affected by endocrine disruptors.

Mammals. Populations of Baltic ringed seals have declined significantly over the past 100 years. This is due, in part, to the presence of large concentrations of pollutants, including PCBs and DDT, in their habitats, which has interfered with female reproductive functioning in many ways, leading to partial or complete sterility in 70% of the animals.

Fish. In a variety of fish species, including carp, rainbow trout, and flounder, exposure to endocrine disruptors in sewage runoff is known to interfere with reproductive functioning. In some cases, the exposure has led to such a high degree of feminization of males that production of *egg* proteins occurs at

THE ADVERSE EFFECTS OF ENDOCRINE DISRUPTORS

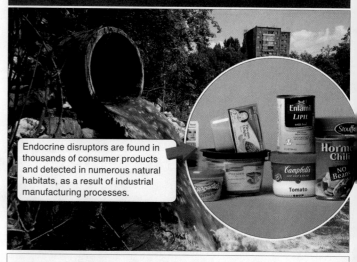

Endocrine disruptors are found in thousands of consumer products and detected in numerous natural habitats, as a result of industrial manufacturing processes.

A variety of animal groups appear to have been adversely affected by endocrine disruptors.

MAMMALS
In populations of Baltic ringed seals, endocrine disruptors have interfered with female reproductive functioning, leading to partial or complete sterility in 70% of the animals.

FISH
In a variety of fish species, including carp, rainbow trout, and flounder, exposure to endocrine disruptors in sewage runoff has been shown to interfere with reproductive functioning.

INVERTEBRATES
In marine invertebrates, endocrine disruptors have led to the production of defective shells, as well as the masculinization of female genitals, reducing fertility.

FIGURE 24-26 Some consumer products contain chemicals that act as endocrine disruptors in wildlife.

greater concentrations in males than is typically found in females.

Invertebrates. A group of chemicals called tributyltin compounds, or TBTs, are used to reduce the growth of

Hormones Are Chemical Messengers   Hormones Are Produced in Glands   Wide-Ranging Effects of Hormones   Chemicals Can Disrupt Hormone Function

organisms, particularly microorganisms, on the hulls of ships. TBTs, however, have a side effect of acting as endocrine disruptors in several marine species. Oysters, for example, when exposed to TBTs, produce defective shells, and in numerous other marine invertebrates, females' genitals become masculinized and the animals have reduced fertility. These impacts have led to a worldwide decline in populations of gastropods such as sea snails and limpets.

It is clear that large numbers of synthetic and natural chemicals used by humans have endocrine-disrupting functions in both natural and laboratory populations of animals. It remains controversial, however, whether these chemicals cause endocrine disruption and health problems in humans. Although no direct links have been found, many studies are underway—so far, with conflicting or inconsistent results—and the U.S. government has taken many steps to restrict the use of the endocrine disruptors described here.

TAKE-HOME MESSAGE 24·11

Endocrine disruptors are chemicals manufactured by humans that, when taken up by organisms, can mimic, block, or otherwise interfere with their hormones. These chemicals can lead to a variety of adverse physiological effects, often related to their feminizing effects. Although endocrine disruptions have been demonstrated in numerous animal species, it remains controversial whether these chemicals cause endocrine disruption and health problems in humans.

Knowledge You Can Use

Are pheromones real-life "love potions?"

Q: **What are sex pheromones?** Sex pheromones, such as those produced by female gypsy moths, are chemical messengers released into the environment to announce to males over a wide area that a female is ready to reproduce.

Q: **Do humans produce them?** The jury is out on this question. In 1971, data were published suggesting that among women living in college dormitories, pheromones, probably released from underarms, could shorten or lengthen the reproductive cycle in other women (see Section 25-7). But, despite ample evidence of sex pheromones in other species, the evidence of their existence in humans is still hotly debated.

Q: **What about the claims made in other studies?** A study published in 2002 claimed that human pheromones could increase the sexual attractiveness of women to men. In the double-blind, placebo-controlled study, one group of women had a purported human sex pheromone added to their perfume, while women in a control group had a placebo added. The women then recorded, over the next 3 months, their "sociosexual" behaviors—which included kissing, dating, sexual activity, and male approaches—which were then compared with observations from the same women *prior* to receiving the pheromone or placebo. The results? More than three times as many pheromone users as placebo users (74% vs. 23%) experienced an increased frequency of sociosexual behaviors. The researchers concluded that the pheromone acted as a sex attractant.

Q: **Can we be certain of the claims of this one study?** The double-blind and placebo-controlled aspects of this study represent important attempts at making a rigorous test of the authors' hypothesis. But the study has been criticized on several grounds. The authors tested only a small number of women (n = 36), within a limited age range (27.8 ± 6.7 years), over only a 3-month period. Perhaps more important, they did not disclose in their published report the chemical preparation added to the perfumes. Additionally, a co-author of the authors of this study synthesized the proprietary chemical, and currently markets it for profit. And reanalyses of the results by others challenge the significance of the results. Still, the results do suggest that there may be something in the air.

❶ Hormones are chemical messengers regulating cell functioning.

Hormones are chemical messengers, secreted by endocrine cells and endocrine glands into extracellular fluid, that influence the actions of target cells elsewhere in the body—including by influencing gene transcription; this is part of an internal communication and regulation system. Most hormones are one of two types: (1) peptide and protein hormones cannot pass through cell membranes, and their receptors are embedded in the membranes; (2) steroid hormones can diffuse through cell membranes, and their receptors are in the cytoplasm or nucleus. Complex emotions and behaviors can be influenced by hormones.

❷ Hormones are produced in glands throughout the body.

Endocrine glands throughout the body are responsible for detecting and responding to signals that reflect an organism's internal and external environments. The hypothalamus functions as a liaison between the nervous and endocrine systems, often directing the pituitary gland to release hormones with important regulatory control over body tissues. The adrenal glands regulate organisms' responses to stress. The pineal gland regulates wake and sleep cycles. The thyroid gland influences the speed and efficiency of cellular metabolism. The pancreas maintains blood glucose levels. And the gonads produce hormones responsible for numerous physical, behavioral, and emotional features, including much sexual behavior, development, and growth.

❸ Hormones influence nearly every facet of an organism.

Hormones affect a person's physique and physical performance, behavior, moods, and cognitive abilities, as well as health and longevity. Hormones produce these changes by influencing gene expression and protein synthesis in cells with appropriate receptors.

❹ Environmental contaminants can disrupt normal hormone functioning.

Endocrine disruptors are chemicals manufactured by humans that, when taken up by organisms, can mimic, block, or otherwise interfere with their hormones. They can lead to a variety of adverse physiological effects, often related to the chemicals' feminizing effects. Although endocrine disruptions have been demonstrated in numerous animal species, it remains controversial whether these chemicals cause endocrine disruption and health problems in humans.

KEY TERMS

anterior pituitary p. 897
bisphenol A, p. 912
calcitonin, p. 900
endocrine cell, p. 892
endocrine disruptor, p. 912

endocrine gland, p. 892
endocrine system, p. 892
hormone, p. 892
hypothalamus, p. 896
mood, p. 904

paracrine regulator, p. 895
parathyroid glands, p. 900
PCBs (polychlorinated biphenyls), p. 912
pheromone, p. 893

phthalates, p. 912
pituitary gland, p. 896
posterior pituitary, p. 896
target cell, p. 892
thyroid gland, p. 900

1. The target cells of the hormone _____ are located in a woman's breasts and uterus. This hormone causes its target cells to contract, which releases milk from the breast cells to feed an infant and causes the painful contractions of the uterus that push out the newborn during labor.
   a) progesterone
   b) oxytocin
   c) estrogen
   d) ACTH
   e) prolactin

2. Human sex hormones are classified as which type of biological molecule?
   a) enzyme
   b) protein
   c) carbohydrate
   d) lipid
   e) nucleic acid

3. Why are steroid hormone complexes with their receptors able to directly bind to DNA to influence gene expression, whereas peptide hormones must influence gene expression indirectly?
   a) Peptide hormones are made from amino acids, which are also used to make proteins, and proteins cannot bind to DNA. Steroid hormones are not made from amino acids, and therefore they can directly interact with DNA.
   b) Steroid hormones are cholesterol-based and therefore can block arteries, causing cardiovascular disease. Directly binding to DNA allows them to complete their function and to be removed from the circulatory system as soon as possible.
   c) Steroid hormones are lipid-based, allowing them pass through the lipid-composed cell membrane to enter the cell and directly bind to DNA. Peptide hormones are not lipid-based and therefore cannot pass through the cell membrane.
   d) Steroid hormones are smaller than peptide hormones and can fit through the holes in the cell membrane to enter the cell.
   e) Neither steroid nor peptide hormones directly bind to DNA; both influence gene expression indirectly.

4. The _____ is a pea-sized gland located below the hypothalamus in the brain and is one of the controlling glands of the endocrine system.
   a) testis
   b) pancreas
   c) thyroid gland
   d) adrenal gland
   e) pituitary gland

5. The hypothalamus secretes which two hormones into the posterior pituitary gland, from which they enter the bloodstream and act on their target cells?
   a) ADH and TSH
   b) oxytocin and ADH
   c) prolactin and oxytocin
   d) pheromone and ACTH
   e) FSH and LH

6. The following pairs link a human gland with the hormone(s) it secretes. Which pairing is incorrect?
   a) adrenal cortex: cortisol
   b) thyroid: oxytocin
   c) pancreas: insulin
   d) ovary: estrogen and progesterone
   e) testis: testosterone

7. The pituitary gland is actually a fusion of two glands. Which of the following statements about its origins is correct?
   a) The posterior pituitary is an outgrowth of the cerebellum; the anterior pituitary develops from the pineal gland.
   b) The anterior pituitary is an outgrowth of the hypothalamus; the posterior pituitary is an outgrowth of the cerebellum.
   c) The posterior pituitary is an outgrowth of the hypothalamus; the anterior pituitary is an outgrowth of the cerebellum.
   d) The posterior pituitary is an outgrowth of the hypothalamus; the anterior pituitary develops from a fold of tissue at the roof of the embryonic mouth.
   e) The anterior pituitary is an outgrowth of the hypothalamus; the posterior pituitary develops from a fold of tissue at the roof of the embryonic mouth.

8. The _____ gland releases melatonin, which is a hormone important for reproduction in certain mammals.
   a) thyroid   d) pancreatic
   b) adrenal   e) pineal
   c) pituitary

9. The target tissues or organs of insulin are:
   a) the testes and ovaries.
   b) muscles and the liver.
   c) blood and bones.
   d) blood and the pancreas.
   e) muscles and the pancreas.

10. Blood samples from an individual who has fasted for 24 hours would have:
    a) high levels of insulin and low levels of glucagon.
    b) high levels of both insulin and glucagon.
    c) low levels of both insulin and glucagon.
    d) high levels of glucagon and low levels of insulin.
    e) high levels of glucagon and standard levels of insulin.

11. Many female bodybuilders take steroids (testosterone) to increase muscle mass and achieve their body shape. The consequences can include all of the following except:
    a) increased competitiveness and aggressiveness.
    b) increased concentration.
    c) decreased object memory.
    d) decreased fertility.
    e) increased hair growth.

12. If a high dose of time-released testosterone is given to a male songbird, which of the following is not a likely effect?
    a) He would obtain a larger territory than males with lower levels of circulating testosterone.
    b) He would get into many fights with larger males.
    c) He would have a longer life span than most other males.
    d) He would enjoy increased reproductive success.
    e) He would develop a greater muscle mass than other males of similar body weight.

SHORT-ANSWER QUESTIONS

1. Compare and contrast peptide and protein hormones with steroid hormones.

2. How do the hypothalamus, posterior pituitary, and anterior pituitary interact, and what role do they play in the endocrine system?

3. In what ways do estrogen and testosterone influence mood? How can sex hormones, including these two hormones, affect life expectancy?

4. What are the general effects of endocrine disruptors? Why can even small quantities in the environment be harmful to some organisms?

5. For each gland, list the hormone(s) they produce and their function.

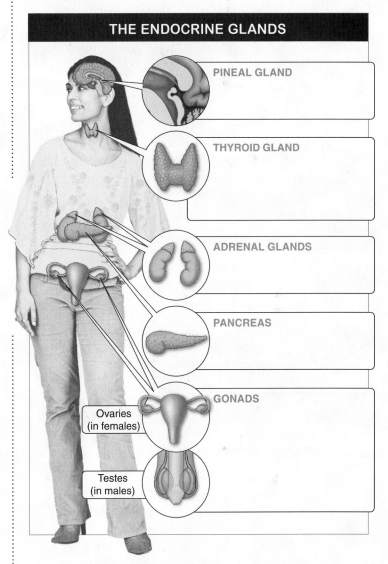

THE ENDOCRINE GLANDS

PINEAL GLAND

THYROID GLAND

ADRENAL GLANDS

PANCREAS

GONADS

Ovaries (in females)

Testes (in males)

See Appendix for answers. For additional study questions, go to www.prep-u.com.

25

Reproduction and Development

From two parents
to one embryo
to one baby

❶ How do animals reproduce?

The endangered black rhinoceros and calf.

25·1

Reproductive options (and ethical issues) are on the rise.

Thirty-year-old Diane Blood wanted to have a child with her husband, Stephen. And then the High Court in England ruled that she could not. The problem: her husband was dead.

Stephen Blood had died of bacterial meningitis two years earlier, but when he was in a coma the day before he died, his wife asked the doctors to take sperm from him, and the sperm sample was frozen and stored. The Human Fertilisation and Embryology Authority, however, ruled that because he hadn't given written consent, his sperm could not be used.

This case illustrates a type of ethical and legal quandary that is becoming increasingly common (**FIGURE 25-1**). Technology is making conception and pregnancy possible in many situations where they previously were not possible. But along with many happy outcomes, there are also numerous complex legal battles and, as yet, few consistent legal decisions on such matters. Here are some examples.

Q Are frozen embryos divided up like other marital assets at divorce?

- Do couples have the right to make contracts with a surrogate mother, a woman who carries and gives birth to their child? And, if so, can they pay her a salary to do so? In North Dakota, the surrogate actually becomes the legal parent of the child. In Washington, DC, and in many states, a couple can pay the surrogate's expenses, but nothing more.

- Do egg donors have any rights (and responsibilities) with respect to the children conceived with their eggs? Is the situation the same for sperm donors? Several states have ruled differently on these issues.

- Do children conceived from sperm or egg donors have a right to know who the donor was?

- If a couple has embryos created and frozen for later implantation but then gets divorced, who retains custody of the embryos? In one Tennessee case, custody was given to the mother, against the wishes of the father. A Texas court, on the other hand, refused to give frozen embryos to the mother. With almost half a million frozen embryos in the United States, this is likely to be an increasingly common issue for courts to decide.

In this chapter, we describe how men produce sperm and women produce eggs, as well as the process by which fertilization occurs (or does not occur). We also explore the early stages of development, following fertilization, including

Advances in assisted reproductive technology are giving rise to complex legal battles and ethical dilemmas.

FIGURE 25-1 In the headlines: ethical issues and reproductive technologies.

the steps by which an embryo is triggered to develop as a male or a female. We also investigate the perils and promise of a variety of assisted reproductive technologies.

But first, a happy resolution to the case we opened with. Diane Blood was eventually allowed to take the sperm to another country where she could be inseminated (after re-mortgaging her house to pay for the expensive legal battles). The law in England still prevents storage of sperm from a man without his written consent, but an appeals court made an exception in her case, and Diane Blood was able to conceive a child (and, three and a half years later, another child) with her husband's sperm.

TAKE-HOME MESSAGE 25·1

Technology is making conception and pregnancy possible in many situations where they previously were not possible. But it is simultaneously giving rise to complex legal battles and ethical dilemmas

25·2

There are costs and benefits to having a partner: asexual versus sexual reproduction.

The term reproduction, the biological process by which new organisms are produced from existing organisms, usually conjures images of a male and a female, contributing equal amounts of genetic material and producing offspring together. And for most animals, this is how it's done. But recall from Section 6-14 that there are two fundamentally different ways in which organisms can reproduce. While the vast majority of plants and animals reproduce sexually, prokaryotes and many plant and animal species reproduce asexually—and some can reproduce in both ways.

Asexual reproduction involves the production of offspring by a single individual without a contribution of genetic material from another individual. There are several types of

> Do female turkeys need males to reproduce?

asexual reproduction in animals, including parthenogenesis, budding, and fragmentation (**FIGURE 25-2**).

Parthenogenesis. In **parthenogenesis,** a female's egg develops into a new organism without ever having to be fertilized by a sperm cell. Some species can reproduce asexually or sexually, depending on

TYPES OF ASEXUAL REPRODUCTION

Asexual reproduction involves the production of offspring by a single individual without contribution of genetic material from another individual.

PARTHENOGENESIS
A female's egg develops into a new organism without ever having to be fertilized by a sperm cell.

BUDDING
An offspring grows right out of the body of the parent.

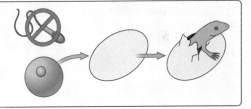

FRAGMENTATION
A parent breaks into multiple pieces, and each develops into a fully functioning, independent individual.

FIGURE 25-2 Asexual reproduction: parthenogenesis, budding, and fragmentation.

environmental conditions; parthenogenesis allows them to utilize resources as quickly as possible. Aphids, for example, produce eggs that develop into normal adults without fertilization in the spring, when food is plentiful. When food is more limited, the eggs are fertilized before development. Hammerhead sharks and, occasionally, turkeys also have the capability to reproduce by parthenogenesis (although turkeys resulting from asexual reproduction tend to be less healthy). Other animal species, including the desert grassland whiptail lizard, are exclusively asexual, and all of the individuals in the species are female. Among these lizards, though, ovulation rates are increased by female-female courtship rituals and behavior called "pseudocopulation" that resembles the male-female mating seen in related species.

Budding. In budding, an offspring grows directly out of the body of the parent. Hydras, predatory cnidarians, reproduce by budding.

Fragmentation. In fragmentation, a parent breaks into multiple pieces, each of which develops into a fully functioning, independent individual. Fragmentation is seen among many species of flatworms, as well as some sea stars. Among some sea stars, for example, if even a tiny part of one arm breaks off, it can develop into a complete individual.

In contrast to asexual reproduction, **sexual reproduction** involves two individuals contributing genetic material to produce offspring (**FIGURE 25-3**). The genetic material is

SEXUAL REPRODUCTION

Sexual reproduction involves two individuals contributing genetic material to produce offspring. The genetic material is contained in gametes, the reproductive cells.

EGG
• Female gamete
• Haploid (one copy of each chromosome)

SPERM
• Male gamete
• Haploid (one copy of each chromosome)

FERTILIZATION

FERTILIZED EGG
• Diploid (two copies of each chromosome)

FIGURE 25-3 **In sexual reproduction, two parents contribute genetic material to the offspring.** The fusion of female gamete (egg) and male gamete (sperm) forms a zygote that potentially develops into offspring.

contained in gametes, the reproductive cells. The male gamete is called a **sperm** (or sperm cell) and the female gamete is called an egg or **ovum** (*pl.* **ova**). Recall from

SEXUAL vs. ASEXUAL REPRODUCTION

SEXUAL REPRODUCTION

ADVANTAGES
• Offspring are genetically different from each other and from either parent.
• Genetic diversity among offspring can be an evolutionary adaptation, increasing fitness in changing environments.

DISADVANTAGES
• Finding a partner and mating can be difficult and time-consuming.
• Only half of an individual's alleles will be passed to its offspring.

ASEXUAL REPRODUCTION

ADVANTAGES
• Reproduction is fast and efficient.
• All of an individual's alleles are passed on to its offspring.

DISADVANTAGES
• With a changing environment, individuals producing genetically diverse offspring are more likely to have offspring suited to the environment.

FIGURE 25-4 **Genetic variation versus efficiency: advantages and disadvantages of sexual and asexual reproduction.**

How Do Animals Reproduce?   Male and Female Reproductive Systems   Sex Can Lead to Fertilization   Human Development

Section 6-11 that the cellular division process of meiosis produces gametes, cells that contain only half as many sets of chromosomes as other body cells (the somatic cells). When the male and female gametes fuse in **fertilization,** the full chromosome number is restored to the diploid condition. Both the production of the gametes and the combination of genetic material from two individuals at fertilization tend to increase the genetic diversity among offspring. We explore sexual reproduction in greater detail in the remainder of this chapter.

An important feature of sexual reproduction is that it leads to offspring that differ genetically from each other and from either parent (see Figures 6-21 and 6-23). This genetic diversity among an individual's offspring can be an evolutionary adaptation, increasing fitness in changing environments. If an environment is gradually changing, individuals producing diverse offspring increase the likelihood that one of their offspring will be suited, genetically, to the new environment. There are, however, disadvantages to sexual reproduction. The two main drawbacks are that (1) finding a partner and mating can be time-consuming and dangerous, and (2) an individual

contributes only half of the alleles that its offspring carry (**FIGURE 25-4**).

With asexual reproduction, the advantages and disadvantages are more or less reversed. It can be fast and easy, because it involves only a single individual. And if an organism's environment is stable, it is beneficial for offspring to carry all of the genes that their parent carried. If an environment is changing, however, asexually reproducing organisms may be at a disadvantage.

TAKE-HOME MESSAGE 25·2

Organisms can reproduce in two ways: asexually or sexually—or both. Asexual reproduction, which can be fast and efficient, leads to offspring genetically identical to the parent; it occurs in all prokaryotes and in many plant and animal species. Sexual reproduction, which leads to offspring that are genetically different from each other and from either parent, occurs in the vast majority of plant and animal species.

25·3

Fertilization can occur inside or outside a female's body.

Sexual reproduction, as we've seen, leads to the production of genetically diverse offspring and so can have evolutionary advantages. But because sexual reproduction requires male and female gametes to come together at fertilization, it also presents a challenge: the male and female gametes must somehow get to each other. Two general strategies have evolved as a consequence of this challenge: **external fertilization,** in which the sperm and egg unite outside the male's and female's bodies, and **internal fertilization,** in which the sperm are deposited directly in the female's reproductive tract and meet and unite with eggs inside the female's body (**FIGURE 25-5**).

The first vertebrates evolved in the oceans. In this environment, it was possible for females to produce and release batches of eggs right into the water. Males could then release sperm into the water, where fertilization could take place. Many aquatic invertebrates—including sea urchins and

clams—along with most fishes and amphibians use external fertilization to bring sperm and eggs together.

Although seawater is not harmful to sperm or eggs, one potential problem for organisms using external fertilization is that the tiny gametes of one sex can be very quickly washed away from those of the other sex when the gametes are released into water. For this reason, males and females of a species tend to produce very large numbers of gametes and release their gametes at the same time and very near each other. A variety of cues help to synchronize the release of gametes by males and females, including water temperature, the phase of the moon, day length, chemicals released by one or the other sex, and courtship rituals.

Among the most extreme tactics employed for ensuring that sperm and eggs are released at the same time and in the same place is something called

Q Male frogs clutch onto female frogs for months at a time without letting go. Why?

Reproductive Technology

EXTERNAL FERTILIZATION
The sperm and egg unite outside of the male's and the female's body.

INTERNAL FERTILIZATION
Sperm are deposited directly in the female's reproductive tract and unite with the eggs inside the female's body.

FIGURE 25-5 Methods of fertilization. Frogs deposit large quantities of sperm and eggs into the water, where some are fertilized. In mammals, such as bears, fertilization takes place within the reproductive tract of the female.

amplexus, used by most species of frogs. In amplexus, the male embraces the female frog from behind, wrapping his front legs around her body. He then holds on until the female releases her eggs, at which point he releases his sperm and fertilizes them. This doesn't sound all that remarkable, except that males will sometimes hold on to a female for weeks or even months at a time!

As we learned in Chapter 11, the colonization of land by vertebrates opened up a huge number of new niches, but presented one huge problem for animals. External fertilization just doesn't work well on land. First, gametes cannot be moved around (and thus toward each other) without water. Secondly, and even more important, gametes quickly dry out on land. For these reasons, there was strong selective pressure on land-colonizing vertebrates for a new method to evolve: internal fertilization.

Used by nearly all terrestrial animals, internal fertilization solves the problem of gamete desiccation (drying out) by having males deposit their sperm directly in the reproductive tract of females. This deposit is usually accomplished by the male placing his reproductive organ within the female's reproductive tract, in the act of **copulation.** Inside the female's body, there is sufficient moisture for the sperm to remain viable until one or more are able to fertilize her eggs.

Once an egg is fertilized by a sperm, the fertilized egg is called a zygote. Following the first division into two cells (and

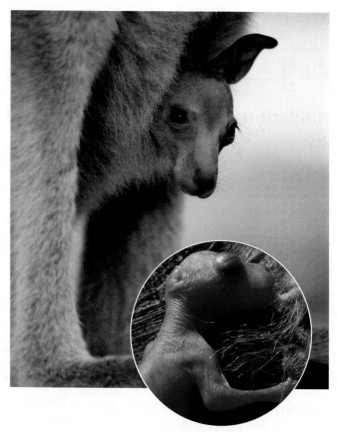

The kangaroo is a viviparous animal. The embryo develops inside the womb of the mother for approximately 33 days when it emerges blind, hairless and just a few centimeters long. It finishes development in its mother's protective pouch—staying in the protective environment for many months.

OVIPARITY
- Most embryonic development takes place within an egg outside the mother's body.
- Embryo is nourished by nutrients in the egg's yolk
- Examples: all birds; also some fishes, amphibians, reptiles, insects, and spiders

OVOVIVIPARITY
- Most embryonic development takes place within an egg that remains in the mother's body until it hatches (or is released just before hatching).
- Embryo is nourished by nutrients in the egg's yolk
- Examples: some sharks, fishes, amphibians, reptiles, and invertebrates

VIVIPARITY
- Most embryonic development takes place inside the mother, and live offspring are born.
- Embryo is nourished by nutrients in the mother's blood
- Examples: nearly all mammals; also some fishes, amphibians, and reptiles

FIGURE 25-6 Three strategies for protecting and nourishing a developing embryo.

continuing to approximately 8 weeks of development in humans), it is called an **embryo.** The embryo must, at some point in its development, leave the female's body. There are three different strategies for this (**FIGURE 25-6**).

1. Oviparity, a strategy in which the fertilized egg moves outside the body and most embryonic development continues there. The embryos are nourished by nutrients contained in the egg's yolk, and live offspring emerge or hatch from the egg. This developmental strategy is most familiar to us among birds (all bird species are oviparous), but it also occurs among most fishes, amphibians, reptiles, insects, and spiders.

2. Ovoviviparity, a less common strategy, in which most embryonic development takes place inside an egg, with the embryo nourished by the egg's yolk, but the egg itself remains in the female's body until it hatches (or is released just before hatching). This strategy is used by many aquatic organisms, including sharks and some other fishes, and some species of amphibians, reptiles, and invertebrates.

3. Viviparity, a strategy in which the embryo develops inside the mother, nourished by nutrients carried in her blood, and live offspring are born. This strategy is perhaps most familiar to us because it is used by humans and nearly all other mammals, but it is also occurs among some reptiles, amphibians, and fishes.

TAKE-HOME MESSAGE 25·3

Sexual reproduction requires fertilization, which occurs externally in most fishes and amphibians, and internally in most other vertebrates, including humans. Among those species having internal fertilization, development of the embryo can be nourished by yolk within an egg (that may or may not be retained within the female's body during development) or, remaining in the mother's body, by nutrients carried in her blood.

2 Male and female reproductive systems have important similarities and differences.

"From Here to Eternity," 1953

25•4

Sperm are made in the testes.

Beginning at puberty and continuing for their entire lives, men produce sperm, often more than 100 million per day. The process of sperm production, called **spermatogenesis,** is similar among most mammals and requires 9-10 weeks in humans. In this section, we examine the structures of the male reproductive system and the production of sperm and **semen,** a fluid expelled at ejaculation that usually contains sperm. We begin with an examination of the male reproductive structures and the role each plays in the process of sperm formation and fertilization (**FIGURE 25-7**).

Male Reproductive Structures Externally, a male has just two reproductive structures, the penis and the scrotum. The **penis** has three columns of tissue—one on either side and a third on the bottom side—that can become engorged with blood, causing erection and making copulation possible. In most animal species, including dogs, walruses, and most primates other than humans, a bone (known as a baculum) is present in the penis and contributes to its stiffness. The **scrotum,** generally on the outside of the body in the pelvis region, is a sac containing the two **testes** (*sing.* **testis;** also called testicles), the site of sperm production. Each testis is made up of highly coiled **seminiferous tubules,** lined with cells, called spermatogonia, that are the site of sperm

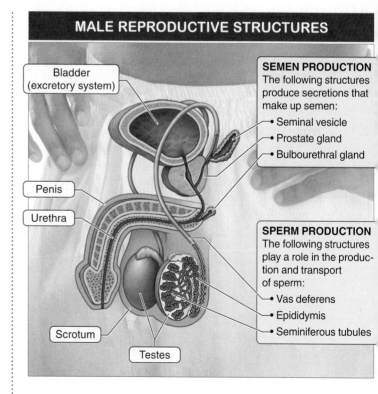

MALE REPRODUCTIVE STRUCTURES

Bladder
(excretory system)

Penis

Urethra

Scrotum

Testes

SEMEN PRODUCTION
The following structures produce secretions that make up semen:
- Seminal vesicle
- Prostate gland
- Bulbourethral gland

SPERM PRODUCTION
The following structures play a role in the production and transport of sperm:
- Vas deferens
- Epididymis
- Seminiferous tubules

FIGURE 25-7 The structures of the male reproductive system.

How Do Animals Reproduce? Male and Female Reproductive Systems Sex Can Lead to Fertilization Human Development

production. It is in cells between the seminiferous tubules where **testosterone,** the principal male sex hormone, and other androgens are produced. Testosterone stimulates sperm production.

Connected to the seminiferous tubules is the **epididymis,** a 15- to 20-foot-long coiled tube, in each testis, where sperm mature. The epididymis in each testis is linked to a **vas deferens,** a tube of smooth muscle tissue that passes from the testis into the body. The vas deferens from each testis connects to a single ejaculatory duct, which continues into the urethra, a duct passing through the penis and through which semen and urine are expelled.

Three other important male reproductive structures produce secretions that make up semen. These include the **prostate gland,** located just below the urinary bladder, which secretes

into the urethra a milky, basic (as opposed to acidic) fluid containing enzymes and sperm nutrients that makes up just under one-third of the volume of the ejaculate. A pair of **seminal vesicles,** secrete into the semen nutrients for the sperm, as well as substances that increase sperm motility and make the female reproductive tract more hospitable to sperm. And finally, a pair of **bulbourethral glands,** located just below the urethra near the base of the penis, contribute the remaining 1% or so of the ejaculate, as well as a mixture of mucus and sugar that lubricates the tip of the penis prior to copulation.

Gametogenesis in Males
Recall from Sections 6-10 through 6-14 that gametes are produced by cells that undergo meiosis. Diploid cells, the spermatogonia, are present in the highly coiled seminiferous tubules of the testes (**FIGURE 25-8**). Each spermatogonium divides by mitosis to produce two cells.

FIGURE 25-8 Gametogenesis in males. Sperm are continuously produced in the testis by meiosis.

927

STRUCTURE OF SPERM

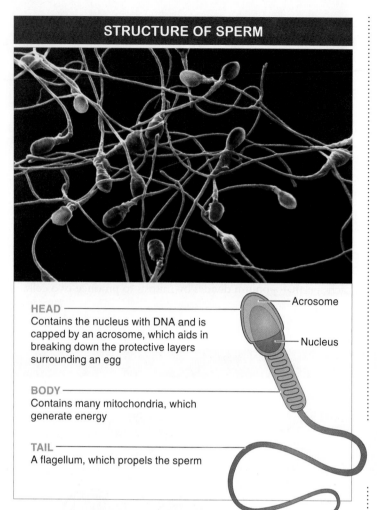

HEAD
Contains the nucleus with DNA and is capped by an acrosome, which aids in breaking down the protective layers surrounding an egg

BODY
Contains many mitochondria, which generate energy

TAIL
A flagellum, which propels the sperm

FIGURE 25-9 Sperm structure reflects its function.

One of these cells is another spermatogonium, so the male never runs out of a store of sperm-producing cells; the other is a **primary spermatocyte,** which undergoes meiosis, in the first step of sperm production. Each primary spermatocyte produces two cells in the first meiotic division. These two cells are called **secondary spermatocytes,** and they then complete the second meiotic division, each producing two spermatids. The four spermatids produced by each spermatogonium, as products of meiosis, are haploid. As each spermatid matures into a sperm cell, it moves from the seminiferous tubules to the epididymis, where, over the course of approximately 18 hours, the sperm become motile—that is, they become able to move.

Each sperm cell consists of three primary parts: (1) the head region, containing the sperm cell's nucleus with its DNA, plus a cap-like **acrosome** containing enzymes that can break down the protective layers surrounding an egg; (2) the body region, which contains many energy-generating mitochondria; and (3) the tail, a flagellum that propels the sperm through the fluid in the female reproductive tract (**FIGURE 25-9**).

Sperm production is tremendously sensitive to numerous factors. Two of the most important factors are hormones and temperature. The optimum temperature for sperm production is approximately two degrees lower than body temperature. This accounts for why, in most mammals, the testes hang outside the body, where their temperature can be controlled by moving them closer to or farther from the heat of the body. It also accounts for the fact that men exposed to hot tubs or hot baths for 30 minutes or more each week generally show signs of infertility, with fewer numbers of sperm as well as lower motility of the sperm they do have. Fortunately, the condition almost always can be reversed by reducing exposure to the hot tubs or baths.

Q Do hot tu reduce a ma fertility?

The path that sperm take from the male to the female is as follows (**FIGURE 25-10**):

THE PATH OF SPERM

During ejaculation, sperm move from the male body as follows:

At ejaculation, approximately 300 million sperm cells are expelled as part of a fluid, called semen.

1 MATURATION
Sperm mature in the epididymis.

2 STORAGE AND TRANSFER
Muscle contractions cause sperm to move from the epididymis through the vas deferens.

3 DELIVERY
Sperm move through the ejaculatory duct into the urethra, where they can be expelled.

FIGURE 25-10 The pathway taken by sperm during ejaculation.

How Do Animals Reproduce?   Male and Female Reproductive Systems   Sex Can Lead to Fertilization   Human Development

1. *Maturation:* sperm mature in the epididymis, within each testis.

2. *Storage and transfer:* during ejaculation, sperm move from the epididymis (in each testis) through the vas deferens. Their movement is generated by contractions of the muscular tissue that makes up the vas deferens.

3. *Delivery:* sperm moving from each vas deferens then pass through the ejaculatory duct and into the urethra. During copulation, sperm are expelled from the urethra into the female reproductive tract.

At ejaculation, the sperm are expelled as part of the semen. Although there are approximately 300 million sperm cells in the fluid of a single ejaculation, the sperm make up only about 1% to 5% of the total volume of ejaculated fluid. In the next section, we explore the question of why so many sperm are present in an ejaculation and the observation that a significant proportion of sperm is not actually capable of fertilizing an egg.

TAKE-HOME MESSAGE 25·4

In adult men, sperm are continuously produced in the testes by meiosis. Semen—consisting of sperm cells and fluids that nurture and aid the sperm in fertilization—is ejaculated during copulation.

25·5

There is unseen conflict among sperm cells.

In her book *The Chimpanzees of Gombe: Patterns of Behavior,* published in 1986, Jane Goodall reported female copulatory rates of "an average of between five and six copulations per female per hour in the early morning, after which the rate dropped gradually to about two per hour in the midmorning, rose very slightly during the afternoon, and tapered off to one per hour in the evening." These observations were consistent with the realization that researchers had come to in the 1970s that if females (of any species, not just chimps) mate with more than one male, there may be competition among the males' sperm.

A chimp's testicles are 15 times bigger than a gorilla's! Why?

The idea of sperm competition, or "sperm wars" as they have been called, gives rise to several testable predictions. One simple prediction is this: when a female is likely to mate with more than one male, the males that produce more sperm are likely to be more successful at fertilizing the female's eggs. Some interesting observations support this prediction. For example, gorillas have golf-ball-sized testes, while chimpanzees' testes are closer in size to baseballs. Gorilla testicles account for only 0.02% of body weight, while chimp testes account for 0.30%, 15 times as much. Why the huge difference? Gorilla groups are relatively small, and all females within a group mate with just one male, the dominant silverback. In contrast, as Jane Goodall noted, fertile chimpanzee females may have sex dozens of times a day with many different males. Consequently, the tiny testes of the gorilla are perfectly adequate, but for a chimp male to win these sperm competitions, he must produce significantly more sperm (**FIGURE 25-11**). Similarly, among fruit bats, males of species that

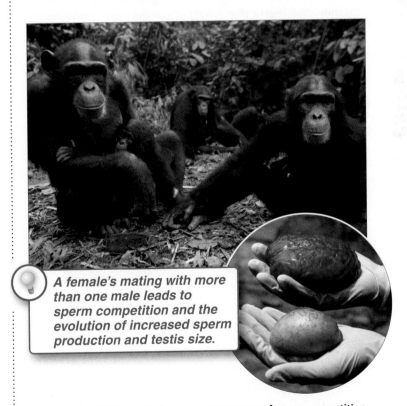

A female's mating with more than one male leads to sperm competition and the evolution of increased sperm production and testis size.

FIGURE 25-11 The evolutionary consequences of sperm competition among males. Female mating behavior influences the size of males' testes and sperm production. The inset shows the size of a male chimp's brain (top) relative to one of its testicles.

live in large social groups have significantly larger testes than males of species that live in smaller groups.

Sperm competition has given rise to several other adaptations.

- Physical barriers to copulation, such as the mating plugs produced by the coagulation of semen in many species that prevent sperm from other males entering the female's reproductive tract.

 Why do male fruit flies produce toxic semen?

- Toxic semen components, such as the protein in fruit fly semen that suppresses further mating by the female for several days (ensuring a male's paternity), as well as the fruit fly semen components that can incapacitate the sperm of other males (and even decrease the female's lifespan by about 10%).

- Large numbers of sperm (20% to 30% of the sperm in each ejaculate in humans) differing structurally from the sperm that are able to move along the female reproductive tract and fertilize an egg. These sperm have been described as "kamikaze sperm," adapted to preventing other males' sperm from reaching and fertilizing an egg. More recent research suggests, however, that these non-fertilizing sperm may simply be abnormal sperm that reflect errors during meiosis.

- Genital morphology, such as the claspers and scrapers of dung flies, as well as the "shovel penis" of some dragonfly species that make it possible for males to dislodge the sperm of previous males that have mated with a female (**FIGURE 25-12**).

This unseen conflict between males is an area of considerable investigation as researchers try to understand the physical and behavioral consequences of such competition. It seems that females are not passive players in these battles and that, in many cases, the female will eject the sperm from undesirable males.

Sperm competition can influence the evolution of genital morphology that aids in displacing other males' sperm.

FIGURE 25-12 **Sperm wars.** This damselfly, *Calopteryx virgo,* has a "shovel penis" that can scrape away the sperm deposited by a rival. Inset shows micrograph of damselfy penis.

TAKE-HOME MESSAGE 25·5

When females mate with more than one male, sperm competition occurs and can lead to a variety of adaptations, including increased sperm production and testis size, semen that can create a physical barrier to subsequent mating, toxic semen components, and penis morphology that aids in the displacement of rival males' sperm.

Eggs are made in the ovaries (and the process can take decades).

From a genetic perspective, making eggs barely differs from making sperm. In the female gonads—the **ovaries** rather than the testes—diploid cells undergo meiosis to produce haploid eggs, and in the process, a great deal of variation is generated so that each haploid egg has a unique genetic makeup. When the haploid egg is fertilized by a sperm, the diploid condition is restored.

But the process of egg production differs from sperm production in several key ways. Eggs are produced in much smaller numbers; each egg is considerably larger than a sperm cell; and the production process can take decades rather than days, even though it begins at a much younger age. Let's explore the specifics, beginning with a description of the female reproductive system (**FIGURE 25-13**).

Female Reproductive Structures Externally, a female has just two structures, the **clitoris** and the **labia,** which develop from the same embryonic tissue that in males produces the penis and scrotum. There is also a vaginal opening. Internally, the **vagina** is a tube-like chamber into which sperm are released during copulation. The vagina connects with the **uterus,** also called the womb, which resembles an upside-down pear. The lower, narrowest portion of the uterus is called the **cervix.** The lining of the uterus, rich with blood vessels, is the **endometrium,** and this is where a fertilized

egg implants and is nourished. The uterus is also where an embryo develops throughout pregnancy.

Connecting to the top of the uterus on the left and right sides are the **Fallopian tubes,** or **oviducts.** Each Fallopian tube extends outward and is funnel-shaped near its end where the ovaries lie, held in place by thin membranes. Each ovary is about the size of a large olive.

Gametogenesis in Females The process of gametogenesis in females, called **oogenesis** (pronounced oo-oh-GEN-eh-sis), starts in the ovaries prior to birth—that is, while the female is still a fetus (**FIGURE 25-14**). Here, diploid cells called **oogonia** (*sing.* **oogonium**) multiply by mitosis. Each oogonium then begins meiosis, but stops at prophase I, at which point the cell is called a **primary oocyte** and is contained within a **follicle**—the small structure in which an egg will form. At birth, there are approximately one million follicles present in a female's ovaries, each follicle containing a primary oocyte.

The primary oocytes remain in their hibernation-like state until puberty. At that point, periodic bursts of **follicle-stimulating hormone (FSH)** cause several primary oocytes to complete meiosis I. Unlike in the production of sperm, however, when the primary oocyte divides into two cells, although the pairs of homologous chromosomes split evenly,

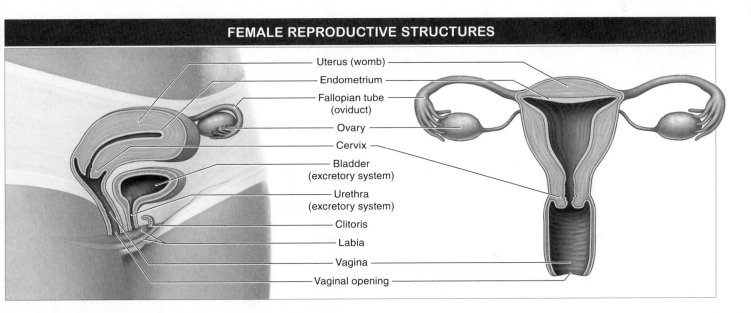

FEMALE REPRODUCTIVE STRUCTURES

- Uterus (womb)
- Endometrium
- Fallopian tube (oviduct)
- Ovary
- Cervix
- Bladder (excretory system)
- Urethra (excretory system)
- Clitoris
- Labia
- Vagina
- Vaginal opening

FIGURE 25-13 The structures of the female reproductive system.

FIGURE 25-14 Gametogenesis in females.

nearly all of the cytoplasm goes to one of the cells, now called a **secondary oocyte.** The other cell, known as a **polar body,** gets almost no cytoplasm and eventually disintegrates. At this point, meiosis again stops.

When females **ovulate,** generally a single follicle in one ovary ruptures, releasing the secondary oocyte—which still has not completed meiosis. The secondary oocyte, which at this point can be called an egg, is swept by cilia into the Fallopian tube and carried down toward the uterus. If sperm have been deposited in the vagina during copulation, it is in the Fallopian tube that the sperm, swimming up from the vagina and through the uterus, are most likely to fertilize the egg. It is only *after* fertilization that a secondary oocyte is triggered to finally complete meiosis—once again with an unequal division of cytoplasm. One of the resulting cells, the ovum, receives most of the cytoplasm, while the other receives almost none. This second polar body disintegrates just as the

first polar body did. The haploid ovum now fuses with the haploid nucleus of the sperm, forming a diploid fertilized egg, called a zygote.

In the next section, we see how the development of follicles, the preparation of the uterus for implantation, and ovulation are coordinated by hormone secretions.

TAKE-HOME MESSAGE 25·6

Genetically, the production of eggs barely differs from sperm production. In the ovaries, diploid cells begin to undergo meiosis, a process that continues in the Fallopian tubes following ovulation, and produces genetically varied haploid gametes. A much smaller number of eggs than sperm are produced, however, and each egg is considerably larger than a sperm cell.

932   CHAPTER 25 • REPRODUCTION AND DEVELOPMENT

How Do Animals Reproduce?   Male and Female Reproductive Systems   Sex Can Lead to Fertilization   Human Development

Hormones direct the process of ovulation and the preparation for gestation.

If you are female, here's something you may have noticed if you are living in a dormitory (or are in prison): when women live in close proximity, over time their reproductive cycles become synchronized so that they menstruate at approximately the same time and, perhaps less obviously, ovulate at the same time. This issue was first addressed in a scientific publication in 1971, when Martha McClintock reported findings—inspired by her own experiences—based on data from 135 female students living in a dormitory at Wellesley College in Massachusetts. Similar observations have been reported in other animal species, and subsequent studies implicate airborne chemicals, called **pheromones** (probably released from women's underarms), that can shorten or lengthen the reproductive cycle in other women. It's not clear why such synchrony of reproductive cycles would occur, however. And other researchers have argued that the different lengths of women's cycles make it impossible for them to become truly synchronized. The jury is still out on this hotly contested issue.

Hormones regulate the timing and development of egg production, called the **ovarian cycle,** which occurs approximately every 28 days. Hormones also regulate another aspect of the reproductive cycle, the **menstrual cycle,** during which the uterus prepares for the possible implantation and nurturing of a fertilized egg, and sheds its lining when fertilization does not occur. We describe each of these cycles and the ways in which each influences the other (**FIGURE 25-15**).

Q *What does the process of being an egg donor entail?*

Females have about one million follicles, or potential eggs, when they are born, but most women ovulate fewer than 500 times over the course of their life. This leaves a lot of potential eggs lying around. In the normal course of events, these follicles just disintegrate, but in recent decades, modern medicine has taken to tinkering with the reproductive cycle to make it possible for a woman to donate her eggs to another woman. The process involves several steps.

First, if you choose to be a donor, each day for about a week, you have an injection of a drug called Lupron, which suppresses your own reproductive cycle. The suppression is followed by a week of injections of a fertility drug that contains large amounts of two hormones, LH (luteinizing

THE REPRODUCTIVE CYCLE

OVARIAN CYCLE

Follicle · Corpus luteum · Ovulation

MENSTRUAL CYCLE

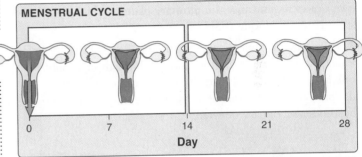

HORMONE LEVELS

Follicle-stimulating hormone (FSH) · Luteinizing hormone (LH) · Progesterone · Estrogen

FIGURE 25-15 The stages of the female reproductive cycle and associated hormonal changes.

hormone) and FSH, which induces one to two dozen follicles to develop in your ovaries. A doctor examines your ovaries by ultrasound to count the number of developing follicles and to estimate their size. Finally, you are given an injection of human chorionic gonadotropin, which stimulates ovulation, the night before the egg "retrieval." The following morning, before the eggs have been released from the follicles, the doctor inserts a tiny needle into each follicle within the ovaries and sucks out the eggs, one by one. This process takes about half an hour. The donor's role is now over. The eggs are placed in a Petri dish, mixed with sperm to fertilize them, and the fertilized eggs are allowed to divide for 2-6 days before several are transferred to the recipient's uterus—with the hope that they will implant and a successful pregnancy will occur.

In the normal monthly cycle, without injections, hormones direct the development of a follicle and the release of an egg (ovulation), while simultaneously preparing the uterus for implantation. Let's follow the changes in hormone levels and their effects during the 28-day cycle (see Figure 25-15).

1. *Menstruation.* Traditionally, the first day of menstrual bleeding, a woman's "period," or **menstruation,** is considered the first day of the menstrual cycle. Three to five days of bleeding occur as the lining of the uterus is sloughed off.

2. *FSH produced.* As the uterine lining sheds, the levels of **estrogen,** the chief female sex hormone, drop. Reduced levels of estrogen cause the pituitary gland to release follicle-stimulating hormone (FSH).

3. *Follicle develops.* FSH, just as its name indicates, causes a few follicles in the ovaries to grow and develop, although only one follicle reaches full maturity. Within this one follicle, the primary oocyte completes its first meiotic division and becomes a secondary oocyte.

4. *Estrogen produced.* As the follicles develop, they produce estrogen, gradually increasing the level of estrogen in the blood.

5. *LH released.* The high levels of estrogen trigger the release of a burst of luteinizing hormone (LH) and of more FSH.

6. *Ovulation.* The burst of LH triggers ovulation, causing the ovum to erupt from the follicle and out of the ovary. This release occurs approximately halfway through the cycle, around day 14, and signals the end of what is called the **follicular phase** of the reproductive cycle.

7. *Progesterone produced.* As the second half, or **luteal phase,** of the reproductive cycle begins, the follicle cells that had surrounded the ovum develop into a structure called the **corpus luteum** (Latin for "yellow body"). These cells begin secreting smaller amounts of estrogen, but increasing amounts of progesterone.

8. *Endometrium thickens.* **Progesterone,** just as its name suggests (*pro* = for; *gestare* = to bear), causes the body to prepare for gestation of an embryo, in case fertilization occurs. Progesterone's primary effect is to cause a thickening of the endometrium, or lining of the uterus. The endometrium becomes increasingly rich with blood vessels and deposits of glycogen that can nourish a developing embryo.

At this point, the process can go in one of two directions, depending on whether or not the egg is fertilized (**FIGURE 25-16**).

THE FATE OF AN EGG

The fate of an egg and the preparation of the endometrium can go in one of two directions, depending on whether or not the egg is fertilized.

IF THE EGG IS NOT FERTILIZED

The corpus luteum degenerates.

Progesterone levels decrease.

The endometrium sloughs off and is shed, along with the egg, as menstruation begins.

IF THE EGG IS FERTILIZED

The zygote secretes hCG, preserving the corpus luteum.

Progesterone levels remain high.

The endometrium thickens in preparation for implantation.

FIGURE 25-16 Two possible fates for an egg. Shown here: an egg moving down the oviduct.

How Do Animals Reproduce?   Male and Female Reproductive Systems   Sex Can Lead to Fertilization   Human Development

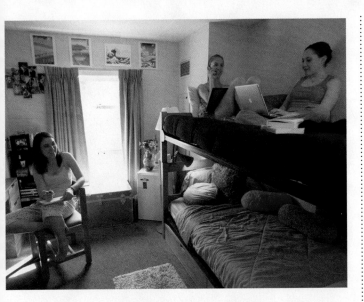

Jury is still out. In 1971 Martha McClintock reported that women living together in a dormitory at Wellesley College experienced synchronized menstrual cycles. It is not clear why such synchrony would occur, and some researchers disagree that synchronization is possible.

If the egg is not fertilized, the egg disintegrates and the corpus luteum degenerates about 12 days after ovulation, sloughs off, and it is shed, along with the disintegrating egg, as menstruation begins. Abruptly removing this source of estrogen and progesterone causes the lining of the uterus to slough off, and menstruation begins. With continuing reduction in estrogen levels, the pituitary gland is spurred to release FSH and the process begins again.

If the egg is fertilized, which usually occurs in the Fallopian tube, the zygote begins development and after several days begins to secrete **human chorionic gonadotropin (hCG).** This hormone prevents degradation of the corpus luteum, which continues to secrete progesterone, thereby maintaining the endometrium. In the next section, we investigate what happens next in development of the embryo.

Reproductive cycling continues from puberty, usually in the early teens, until **menopause**—the cessation of ovulation and menstruation—usually between ages 45 and 55. It is not clear whether there is any evolutionarily adaptive value to menopause. In most species other than humans, females remain fertile throughout their entire adult life. Menopause may be a consequence of the relatively recent (on an evolutionary time scale) increase in human longevity. Regardless of the evolutionary explanation, oocyte depletion seems to influence the onset of menopause.

TAKE-HOME MESSAGE 25·7

In the ovaries, a cell within a follicle is stimulated to develop into a fertile egg by coordinated secretions of the hormones estrogen, FSH, and LH. The preparation of the uterus for implantation of a fertilized egg is coordinated by progesterone.

❸ Sex can lead to fertilization, but can also spread sexually transmitted diseases.

Sperm fertilizing an egg.

25·8

In fertilization, two cells become one.

For fertilization to occur, it's not enough for sperm cells to be in the same general location as an egg—there are some specific events that must occur. The process of fertilization in vertebrates involves three separate steps: penetration, activation, and fusion of the nuclei (**FIGURE 25-17**). And before a sperm can take that first step and penetrate an egg, it must find it.

FERTILIZATION

SPERM

Granulosa cells

Zona pellucida

Sperm nucleus

Acrosome

EGG

Enzymes

Plasma membrane

Egg nucleus

Zygote nucleus

❶ PENETRATION
A sperm pushes its way through the granulosa cells, and enzymes within its acrosome digest the zona pellucida.

❷ ACTIVATION
The plasma membrane of the sperm and egg fuse, making it impossible for other sperm to fuse with the egg.

❸ NUCLEI FUSION
The haploid nucleus of the egg fuses with the haploid nucleus of the sperm, forming a diploid zygote.

FIGURE 25-17 Fertilization is the fusion of one sperm with an egg.

How Do Animals Reproduce?   Male and Female Reproductive Systems   Sex Can Lead to Fertilization   Human Development

Recently, researchers discovered that sperm have receptors, like chemical sensors, that cause the sperm cells to swim toward a chemical attractant that is released by the egg. This attractant, in essence, says, "I'm over here!"

After ovulation, the egg is still surrounded by some smaller cells, called granulosa cells. These cells stand between the sperm and the egg, but they're not the only barrier. Between the granulosa cells and the egg's membrane, there is a glycoprotein layer called the **zona pellucida** (pronounced puh-LOO-sih-duh). As sperm approach the egg, release of calcium by cells surrounding the egg appears to increase the swimming speed and tail movements of the sperm, in a process known as sperm activation. A second phase of sperm activation occurs as a sperm cell pushes its way through the granulosa cells, and the acrosome (at the head of the sperm) dissolves and releases digestive enzymes that help the sperm digest its way through the zona pellucida.

Once the sperm gets through the zona pellucida, the oocyte is activated, and the plasma membranes of the sperm and egg fuse. This fusion has a couple of important consequences. First, it changes the egg membrane in such a way that it is impossible for any other sperm to also fertilize the egg. After all, it would be a genetic disaster for the fertilized egg to have

more than two sets of chromosomes. Second, the fusion of the plasma membranes of sperm and egg induces the egg to complete its second meiotic division. On doing so, one haploid egg is formed, along with one smaller polar body. The latter disintegrates or is ejected from the egg.

In many species, stripping away the zona pellucida makes it possible for the egg to be fertilized by sperm from different species. This suggests that something in the zona pellucida, perhaps recognition sites, makes it possible for the egg to be fertilized only by sperm from the same species.

And, finally, the haploid nucleus of the egg fuses with the haploid nucleus of the sperm, creating a diploid cell—the **zygote.**

TAKE-HOME MESSAGE 25·8

At fertilization, a sperm penetrates the protective zone around the egg, the egg blocks additional sperm entry, and the sperm and egg membranes fuse. The egg then completes its second meiotic division, and the haploid nuclei of the egg and sperm fuse, forming a diploid zygote.

25·9

Numerous strategies can help prevent fertilization.

Pregnancy depends on the occurrence of a great many events, relating to the production of sperm and eggs, their coming together in fertilization, and implantation of the zygote in the uterus. **Contraception,** or birth control, is the attempt to prevent pregnancy. Although a wide variety of contraception methods are used—with varying degrees of effectiveness—each method generally represents one of three general strategies: (1) preventing ovulation, (2) preventing fertilization, or (3) preventing implantation. **FIGURE 25-18** summarizes various methods of contraception, how they work, and their failure rates.

Preventing Ovulation

Birth control pills. Available since 1960, birth control pills are among the most effective of all methods of contraception, with a failure rate of 1% to 8%; that is, among 100 women using birth control pills over the course of one year, there would be 1-8 pregnancies. (If taken every day at exactly the same time, they are 99+% effective; the

Q How do birth control pills work?

problem is that not all women are consistent in taking them.) Among 100 women using no contraception, there would be about 85 pregnancies during one year.

Two chief varieties of birth control pills are available, one that contains synthetic versions of the hormones estrogen and progesterone, and one that contains only a synthetic progesterone. The estrogen-progesterone pill prevents ovulation by keeping estrogen levels just high enough so that the release of FSH by the pituitary gland is never triggered. As long as FSH is never released, eggs never develop and ovulation does not occur. The progesterone component of the pill causes just enough development of the lining of the uterus that a plug of mucus forms at the connection between the vagina and uterus, blocking sperm from getting through.

Taking the birth control pill at the same time every day is essential. If more than 24 hours go by between

METHODS OF CONTRACEPTION

METHOD	HOW IT WORKS
PREVENTING OVULATION	
• Birth control pills	A pill containing synthetic hormones prevents the release of FSH by the pituitary gland, thus preventing egg development and ovulation (effectiveness: 92–99%).
• Hormone implants or injections	Synthetic hormones are inserted under the skin to prevent the release of FSH by the pituitary gland, thus preventing egg development and ovulation (effectiveness: 97–99%).
PREVENTING FERTILIZATION	
• Condoms	A thin rubber or natural membrane sheath placed on the penis or inside the vagina, covering the cervix, prevents sperm from coming in contact with an egg (effectiveness: male condoms: 85–98%; female condoms: 79–95%).
• Diaphragm/cervical cap	A dome-shaped piece of rubber placed in the vagina blocks the cervix and prevents sperm from coming in contact with an egg (effectiveness: 84–94%).
• Sterilization	A medical procedure permanently alters the reproductive system to prevent the release of sperm or block the movement of eggs down the Fallopian tubes (effectiveness: >99%).
• Abstinence	Individuals refrain from sexual intercourse (effectiveness: complete abstinence: 100%; abstinence during days when fertility is likely, based on analysis of female's menstrual cycle pattern: 75–99%).
PREVENTING IMPLANTATION	
• Intrauterine device (IUD)	A small plastic or metal device inserted into the uterus by a doctor prevents a fertilized egg from implanting (effectiveness: >99%).
• "Morning-after" pills	A pill containing a dose of estrogen 50 times higher than that found in birth control pills can stop ovum development or implantation (effectiveness: >75%).

FIGURE 25-18 Preventing pregnancy.

taking pills, the estrogen level in the body begins to drop; if it gets below a critical level, FSH release by the pituitary is triggered, which can lead to ovulation and the risk of pregnancy.

The long-term health consequences of using birth control pills include a slightly elevated risk of cardiovascular disease, particularly among women who smoke. However, because birth control users have a reduced risk of pregnancy—a condition that carries with it some significant health risks—and a reduced risk of ovarian and endometrial cancers, women's overall mortality risk is reduced while on the pill.

Although the birth control pill is one of the most commonly used methods of contraception, recent research has revealed that the hormones may actually alter women's attraction to men. When not taking birth control pills, most women prefer the odor of men possessing certain genetic combinations that are most different from their own. When taking the pill, however, their preference switches and they prefer the odor of men with genetic combinations most similar to their own. It remains to be seen how significant any effect of birth control pills is on women's mate preferences, and much additional research in this area is under way.

Hormone injections or implants. Injections or capsule implants, just under the skin, of synthetic estrogen and progesterone, or progesterone only, represent a slight variation on birth control pills. The prevention of pregnancy works in the same way, but with the added convenience of not having to take a pill every day. Some implants, in fact, need to be implanted and removed only once every three years. Consequently, these methods are slightly more effective than birth control pills, because much of the user error is eliminated.

Preventing Fertilization

Condoms. The condom—a thin rubber or natural membrane sheath placed on the penis or inside the vagina, covering the cervix, that prevents sperm from coming in contact with an

How Do Animals Reproduce?   Male and Female Reproductive Systems   Sex Can Lead to Fertilization   Human Development

egg—is one of several barrier methods of contraception, which keep sperm from coming in contact with an egg. Condoms have the added benefit of being one of the only methods of contraception that offer effective protection against sexually transmitted diseases, including HIV/AIDS. (See the next section for further discussion of this topic.)

Diaphragm or cervical cap. A diaphragm or cervical cap—a dome-shaped piece of rubber placed in the vagina, blocking the cervix—also prevents pregnancy by blocking sperm from reaching an egg. The use of spermicidal creams with a diaphragm or cervical cap (and with a condom as well) can increase their effectiveness, resulting in a failure rate of 6% to 16%.

Sterilization. Sterilization is the permanent alteration of the reproductive system to prevent the release of sperm or the movement of eggs down the Fallopian tubes. In a tubal ligation, the woman's oviducts are cut and tied off so that eggs cannot reach the uterus. In a vasectomy, the vas deferens on each side is cut and tied off so that sperm cannot reach the urethra, thereby causing a man's semen to carry no sperm. There are no side effects in either case. Each of these procedures, however, should be considered permanent (although in rare cases, the procedure can be successfully reversed).

Abstinence. Abstinence—not having sexual intercourse—is the most effective method of preventing pregnancy. In practice, however, abstaining from intercourse can prove difficult, particularly in the context of a long-term relationship. And temporary abstinence during the times when conception is most likely (often called the "rhythm method"), while theoretically effective, has a failure rate as high as 25%, probably due to variation in the time of ovulation and the fact

Q What is the "morning-after" pill?

that sperm can live for 72 hours (and possibly longer) in the female reproductive system.

Preventing Implantation

Intrauterine device (IUD). The intrauterine device, or IUD, is a small plastic or metal device that is inserted by a doctor into the uterus. The IUD (which can be left in for 3-4 years) does not prevent fertilization from occurring but instead prevents a fertilized egg from implanting in the uterus. IUDs have a failure rate of just under 1%. Some women experience side effects from IUDs (including cramps and other pain) and may need to have the device removed.

"Morning-after" pills. Although not recommended as a long-term strategy for contraception, the morning-after pill, a dose of estrogen 50 times greater than that found in birth control pills, can stop ovum development or implantation. The morning-after pill has a failure rate of up to 25% and is recommended only for cases of rape and emergency situations in which other methods of contraception have failed. In contrast to the large hormone content of morning-after drugs, another drug, known as RU486, is considered an anti-hormone drug. It blocks progesterone receptors in the uterus, thereby causing the lining of the uterus to be sloughed off. This can end a pregnancy any time during the first seven weeks. In addition to causing abdominal pain and cramping, RU486 can also have other adverse effects, including nausea, vomiting, and fever.

TAKE-HOME MESSAGE 25·9

Pregnancy can be prevented by numerous methods, each of which acts in one or more ways to prevent ovulation, fertilization, or implantation.

25·10

Sexually transmitted diseases reveal battles between microbes and humans.

To many microbes, the human genitals and reproductive tract represent a desirable place to find shelter, nourishment, and opportunities for reproducing and dispersing. Unfortunately, these microbes can cause problems for humans in the form of **sexually transmitted diseases (STDs).** STDs produce symptoms of varying severity, from mild to extreme discomfort to sterility or even death. It is

estimated that more than 300 million new cases of STDs occur each year worldwide.

Sexually transmitted diseases are caused by bacteria, viruses, fungi, protists, and even some arthropods. The organisms are passed from the mucous membranes (of the genitals, as well as of the anus and mouth) of one individual to those of another

FIGURE 25-19 The most common STDs.

CAUSE	EXAMPLES	SYMPTOMS	TREATMENT
BACTERIUM	• Gonorrhea	Often none; sometimes painful urination, genital discharge, or irregular menstruation	Several antibiotics can successfully cure gonorrhea; however, drug-resistant strains are increasing.
	• Syphilis	Often no symptoms for years; eventual sores, skin rash, and if untreated, organ damage	Penicillin, an antibiotic, can cure a person in the early stages of syphilis.
	• Chlamydia	Often none; sometimes painful urination, genital discharge	Chlamydia can be easily treated and cured with antibiotics.
VIRUS	• HIV/AIDS	Initial symptoms range from none to flu-like; late stages involve severe infections and death	Currently no cure. Antiretroviral treatment can slow progression. Drug-resistant strains occur.
	• Genital herpes	Often none; outbreaks include sores on genitals, flu-like symptoms	Currently no cure. Antiviral medications can shorten and prevent outbreaks.
	• Human papilloma virus (HPV)	Often none; some types can lead to genital warts, others can cause cervical cancer	A vaccine prevents HPV, and is recommended for girls age 11–12. Warts and cancerous lesions can be removed.
PROTIST	• Trichomoniasis	Painful urination and/or vaginal discharge in women; often no symptoms in men	Trichomoniasis can usually be cured with prescription drugs.
FUNGUS	• Yeast infections	Genital itching or burning, and/or vaginal discharge in women; genital itching in men	Yeast infections can usually be cured with antifungal suppositories or creams.
ARTHROPOD	• Crab lice	Visible lice eggs or lice crawling or attached to pubic hair, itching in the pubic and groin area	Crab lice can be treated with over-the-counter lotions.

during sexual contact; sometimes they are transmitted by needles used for drug injections.

Some of the most common STDs, their symptoms, and treatments are listed in **FIGURE 25-19**. Although most are curable with antibiotics, antifungal drugs, or anti-protozoan drugs, two characteristics of STDs make them nearly impossible to completely eradicate from a population: (1) their symptoms may be mild or completely absent at times, causing many people to unwittingly pass an infection to their partners, and (2) to prevent reinfection, both partners must be treated simultaneously. Furthermore, because most microbes have such high reproductive rates, populations of a microbe can evolve quickly and become resistant to existing drugs, reducing the long-term effectiveness of treatments. Consequently, the treatment of STDs represents one of the most pressing public health issues in the world today.

TAKE-HOME MESSAGE 25·10

Sexually transmitted diseases (STDs) are caused by a variety of organisms, including bacteria, viruses, protists, fungi, and arthropods. Worldwide, more than 300 million people are infected each year. The effects of being infected with an STD range from non-existent, to mild to extreme discomfort, sterility, or even death.

How Do Animals Reproduce? Male and Female Reproductive Systems Sex Can Lead to Fertilization Human Development

Developing human fetus five months after fertilization.

4 Human development occurs in specific stages.

25·11

Early embryonic development occurs during cleavage, gastrulation, and neurulation.

How do you build a complete human, with specialized cells, tissues, and organs, when at fertilization there is just a zygote, a single cell that doesn't resemble a human at all? This question is studied and answered by developmental biology, the branch of science that seeks to understand and explain how a complex organism develops from a single cell. To be sure, the genes in that initial cell are important, and the environmental conditions in which the cell develops are also critically important. These factors interact as the development of humans and most other vertebrates proceeds in a carefully coordinated sequence of three stages: cleavage, gastrulation, and neurulation.

Cleavage The first phase, **cleavage,** is the early cell division, by mitosis, of the zygote, beginning shortly after fertilization (**FIGURE 25-20**). It starts when, about 30 hours after fertilization, the zygote divides into two cells. Then, about 30 hours later, it divides again, becoming four cells. This continues through numerous divisions. Although the number of cells increases significantly during cleavage, there is little or no growth in overall size. Rather, the fertilized egg is partitioned into more

and more cells that are smaller and smaller. These multiple cell divisions are fueled by nutrients that were in the egg. At the cleavage stage, it is difficult to distinguish between species as dissimilar as sea urchins and humans.

After about six days of continuous cell division, the cells form a hollow ball, called a **blastula**—the mammalian version is called a **blastocyst**—of approximately a thousand cells. The cells secrete fluid into the center, where there is an inner mass of cells that will form the embryo. The outer cells also produce human chorionic gonadotropin (hCG), which keeps the corpus luteum from disintegrating, so that it continues to produce progesterone and thereby maintain the lining of the uterus for implantation.

The blastocyst grows rapidly and forms membranes that surround and protect it. These include the **amnion,** which surrounds the embryo, and the **chorion,** which, along with the endometrium, forms the **placenta,** the structure that connects the developing embryo to the wall of the uterus

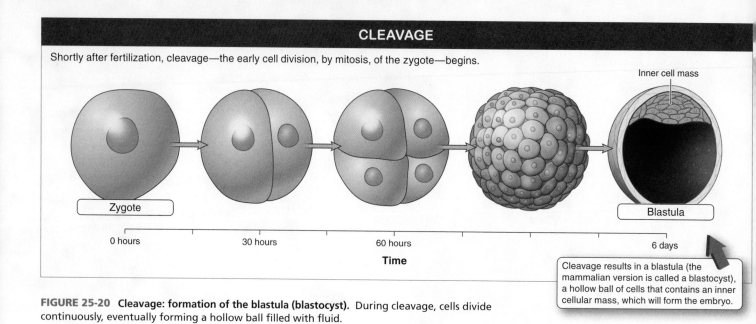

CLEAVAGE

Shortly after fertilization, cleavage—the early cell division, by mitosis, of the zygote—begins.

Inner cell mass

Zygote

Blastula

0 hours   30 hours   60 hours   6 days

Time

Cleavage results in a blastula (the mammalian version is called a blastocyst), a hollow ball of cells that contains an inner cellular mass, which will form the embryo.

FIGURE 25-20 Cleavage: formation of the blastula (blastocyst). During cleavage, cells divide continuously, eventually forming a hollow ball filled with fluid.

(see Figure 25-25). The placenta is packed with blood vessels that bring nourishment to the embryo and remove wastes generated by the embryo.

Gastrulation In the second phase of development, **gastrulation,** three distinct **germ layers** of tissue form. Picture a beach ball—a hollow sphere. Now imagine making a fist and slowly pushing inward on the beach ball. This resembles the

process of gastrulation. The indentation is called the blastopore and is located almost opposite from the point at which the sperm entered the egg. The blastopore will become the anus in vertebrates. At this point the entire mass of cells is called a gastrula (**FIGURE 25-21**).

Three distinct layers of tissue form during gastrulation. The cells in these layers have not yet differentiated (that is, they all

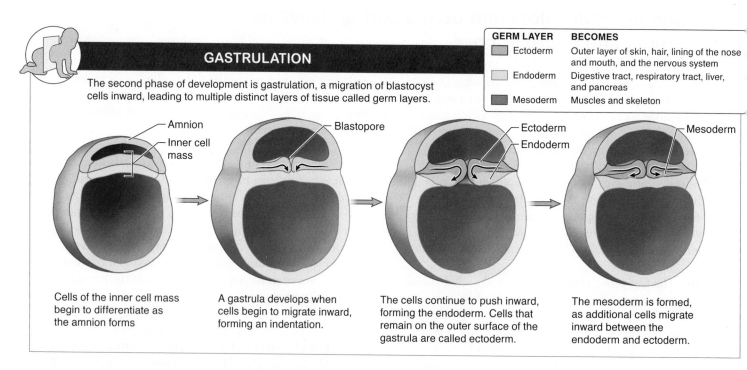

GASTRULATION

The second phase of development is gastrulation, a migration of blastocyst cells inward, leading to multiple distinct layers of tissue called germ layers.

GERM LAYER	BECOMES
Ectoderm	Outer layer of skin, hair, lining of the nose and mouth, and the nervous system
Endoderm	Digestive tract, respiratory tract, liver, and pancreas
Mesoderm	Muscles and skeleton

Amnion
Inner cell mass

Blastopore

Ectoderm
Endoderm

Mesoderm

Cells of the inner cell mass begin to differentiate as the amnion forms

A gastrula develops when cells begin to migrate inward, forming an indentation.

The cells continue to push inward, forming the endoderm. Cells that remain on the outer surface of the gastrula are called ectoderm.

The mesoderm is formed, as additional cells migrate inward between the endoderm and ectoderm.

FIGURE 25-21 Gastrulation: formation of three germ layers. During gastrulation, three distinct layers of tissue form that will eventually make up the structures of the body.

look similar to one another), but they have become determined, which means that the type of tissue they will become, their ultimate developmental fate, is irreversibly decided. Prior to determination, cells are referred to as "totipotent" and have the capacity to develop into any type of tissue in the body.

Here's a summary of what happens during gastrulation.

1. First, the blastocyst begins to fold inward forming an indentation, the blastopore. The blastopore is located almost opposite the point at which the sperm entered the egg.

2. As the cells continue to push inward, they are called **endoderm,** and they form the lining of what will eventually become the digestive tract; the blastopore will become the anus. Endoderm cells will also form the liver, the pancreas, and the lining of the respiratory tract. At this point, the entire mass of cells is called a **gastrula.**

3. The cells that remain on the outer surface of the gastrula are called **ectoderm** and will ultimately form the outer layer of skin, the hair, the nervous system, and the lining of the nose and mouth.

4. Some additional cells migrate inward, between the endoderm and ectoderm, forming a third type of tissue, called **mesoderm,** which will ultimately give rise to muscles and the skeleton.

The specific details of gastrulation vary slightly from one species to the next. The general outcome, however—the formation of endoderm, mesoderm, and ectoderm—occurs throughout the vertebrates.

Neurulation and the Formation of Adult Structures

As an embryo begins its third week of development, the three types of tissue formed during gastrulation begin to develop into the various organs and tissues. At this time, within the mesoderm and running the length of the embryo, just above the digestive tract, a structure called the notochord forms. The **notochord** is a flexible rod that develops in all chordates and gives support to surrounding tissue. In vertebrates, the notochord's function is ultimately taken over by the backbone.

Just above the notochord, ectoderm folds in for the entire length of the embryo, first forming a groove and then becoming a long hollow tube, called the **neural tube.** The process is referred to as **neurulation** and the resulting neural tube ultimately develops into the entire nervous system, including the brain (located opposite the original position of the blastopore) and the spinal cord (**FIGURE 25-22**).

As the neural tube is developing, blocks of mesoderm tissue, called somites, begin to form down the length of the embryo. These somites will form the vertebrae and the muscles of the body. Next to the somites, spaces form that will become the

NEURULATION

During the third week of development, the three types of tissues formed during gastrulation begin to develop into the various organs and tissues of the organism.

GERM LAYER	BECOMES
Ectoderm	Outer layer of skin, hair, lining of the nose and mouth, and the nervous system
Endoderm	Digestive tract, respiratory tract, liver, and pancreas
Mesoderm	Muscles and skeleton

Notochord

Groove

Neural tube

Somites

Coelom

Amnion

Cells within the mesoderm form the notochord, which runs the length of the embryo.

The ectoderm folds inward, forming a groove that runs the entire length of the embryo.

Neurulation is completed with the formation of the neural tube. Somites and the coelom develop from the mesoderm.

FIGURE 25-22 Neurulation: formation of organs and tissues from the germ layers. During neurulation, the germ layers begin to develop into the organs and tissues of the body.

Reproductive Technology

body cavity, or **coelom** (pronounced SEE-lum). Within the coelom, many of the organs will form. At this point, toward the end of the third week of development, the embryo is only 2 millimeters (less than one-tenth of an inch) in length. Further development and specialization occur as some cells are programmed to die, in essence "sculpting" the body the way that a sculptor would create a statue.

Other cells may be induced to develop into one particular cell type or another by neighboring cells that send signals, possibly proteins, to turn certain genes on or off. This process was demonstrated dramatically by researchers who transplanted cells from the top of a newt blastopore in one embryo to another developing embryo. In the recipient embryo, the

blastopore cells induced the development of nearby cells to form a second neural tube!

TAKE-HOME MESSAGE 25•11

Soon after fertilization, cleavage takes place and many rapid cell divisions occur without overall growth. Following cleavage is gastrulation, in which a gut begins to form, along with three distinct germ layers with specific developmental fates. In neurulation, mesoderm forms a supporting rod called the notochord, and above that, an infolding of ectoderm forms a neural tube, which will become the brain and spinal cord.

25•12

How does an embryo become male or female?

During the first few weeks after fertilization, surprisingly little distinguishes boys from girls. Then, about four weeks into embryo development in mammals, a gene carried on the Y chromosome, called SRY (for **s**ex-determining **r**egion on the **Y**-chromosome), can initiate development of the embryo as a male (**FIGURE 25-23**). The gene is expressed in the tissue that will form the gonads, and in most cases in which SRY is expressed, the gonads develop as testes. (There is a gene on the X chromosome that also influences sex determination and, in rare cases, can alter typical sex development.) If SRY is not present, as in females who do not carry a Y chromosome, ovaries develop instead. Once activated, SRY also stimulates numerous other genes involved in testes formation.

Once the fetal gonads develop, they start producing steroid hormones. If testes, they produce testosterone. If ovaries, they produce estrogen. The presence of high levels of testosterone causes the ducts connecting the gonads and the outside of the body to develop into the male internal reproductive organs, including the vas deferens (on each side), ejaculatory duct, and prostate. In the absence of testosterone, these ducts become the female reproductive organs, including the uterus, cervix, and Fallopian tubes.

Following development of the internal reproductive organs, undifferentiated external genitals develop. If testosterone is present and is modified slightly (by an enzyme called 5-alpha-reductase) into dihydrotestosterone (DHT), it causes the external genitals to become the penis and scrotum. In the

Q Can someone with a Y chromosome still develop as a female?

absence of DHT, female external genitals develop, including the clitoris, labia, and vagina. Sex differentiation is generally complete by about the 12th week of development in humans.

At several points in development, the development of an embryo as male or female can be disrupted. Disruptions of this type occur in several genetic disorders.

Androgen insensitivity syndrome. Some XY individuals (approximately 1 in 20,000) carry a non-functioning copy of the androgen receptor. Although the SRY gene on the Y chromosome triggers the development of testes, this X-linked recessive trait causes the tissues of the body to be unresponsive to the normal effects of testosterone. Consequently, individuals with this syndrome develop what appears to be a typical female body. Internally, however, there is no uterus and no ovaries, but rather testes that remain inside the abdomen. Individuals with this condition are identified as female, and the condition is usually not detected until the girl fails to menstruate.

5-Alpha-reductase deficiency. Some XY individuals carry a non-functioning version of the gene for the enzyme that converts testosterone into DHT. Without DHT to direct the development of external male genitals, these individuals possess testes, but the external genitals develop as they would in a female. Consequently, individuals with this condition are generally identified as female at birth and in early childhood. At puberty, however, in response to the significantly increased testosterone production by the testes,

How Do Animals Reproduce? | Male and Female Reproductive Systems | Sex Can Lead to Fertilization | Human Development

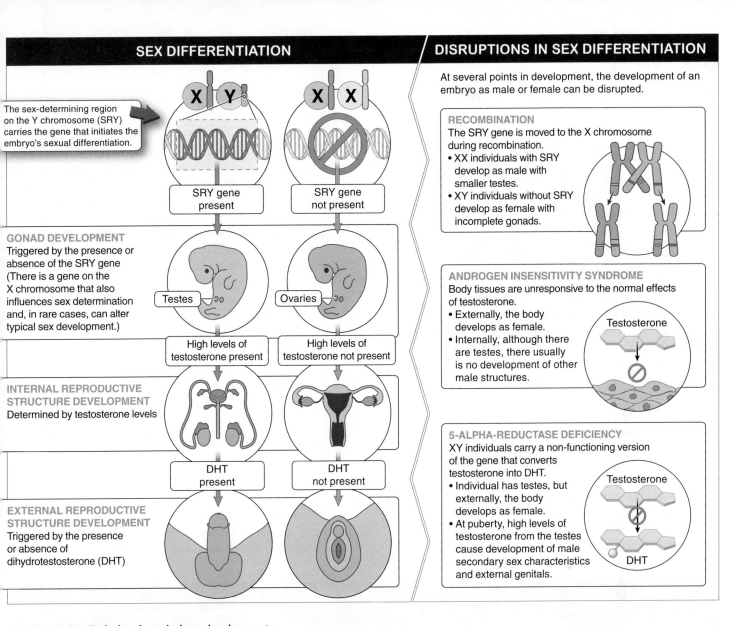

SEX DIFFERENTIATION

The sex-determining region on the Y chromosome (SRY) carries the gene that initiates the embryo's sexual differentiation.

SRY gene present

SRY gene not present

GONAD DEVELOPMENT
Triggered by the presence or absence of the SRY gene (There is a gene on the X chromosome that also influences sex determination and, in rare cases, can alter typical sex development.)

Testes

Ovaries

High levels of testosterone present

High levels of testosterone not present

INTERNAL REPRODUCTIVE STRUCTURE DEVELOPMENT
Determined by testosterone levels

DHT present

DHT not present

EXTERNAL REPRODUCTIVE STRUCTURE DEVELOPMENT
Triggered by the presence or absence of dihydrotestosterone (DHT)

DISRUPTIONS IN SEX DIFFERENTIATION

At several points in development, the development of an embryo as male or female can be disrupted.

RECOMBINATION
The SRY gene is moved to the X chromosome during recombination.
- XX individuals with SRY develop as male with smaller testes.
- XY individuals without SRY develop as female with incomplete gonads.

ANDROGEN INSENSITIVITY SYNDROME
Body tissues are unresponsive to the normal effects of testosterone.
- Externally, the body develops as female.
- Internally, although there are testes, there usually is no development of other male structures.

Testosterone

5-ALPHA-REDUCTASE DEFICIENCY
XY individuals carry a non-functioning version of the gene that converts testosterone into DHT.
- Individual has testes, but externally, the body develops as female.
- At puberty, high levels of testosterone from the testes cause development of male secondary sex characteristics and external genitals.

Testosterone

DHT

FIGURE 25-23 Typical and atypical sex development.

these individuals develop male secondary sex characteristics, including a deeper voice, facial hair, and increased muscle mass. The external genitals grow and often come to resemble a penis and scrotum more than a clitoris and labia.

Recombination leading to XX individuals with the SRY gene or XY individuals lacking SRY. It is possible, during the production of sperm by males, for crossing over to occur between the X and Y chromosomes. If this crossover causes the SRY gene to be moved to the X chromosome, and if the sperm cell carrying the X with SRY or the Y without SRY fertilizes an egg, irregular development occurs in the resulting individual. In XX individuals with the SRY gene, the individual appears to develop as a typical male. Although testes develop, however, they are smaller than average. These individuals are infertile (cannot produce sperm that can

fertilize an egg or eggs that can be fertilized) and also tend to be shorter than XY males. In XY individuals without the SRY gene, the gonads develop incompletely, resembling streaks of connective tissue, but these individuals appear to develop as a typical female. At puberty, however, they are taller than average, do not develop secondary sex characteristics, and do not menstruate.

TAKE-HOME MESSAGE 25·12

Mammalian embryos develop female internal and external reproductive organs unless a gene on the Y chromosome stimulates fetal gonads to develop as testes, leading to testosterone production, which then stimulates the development of male reproductive organs.

945

There are three stages of pregnancy.

The development of a human embryo and fetus is usually divided into three equal periods, of approximately three months each. (The **fetus** stage begins about 8 weeks after fertilization, when the organs and other major structures first form.) Each of these **trimesters** is characterized by specific features and developmental milestones (**FIGURE 25-24**).

The First Trimester We have already discussed several of the most significant events of the first trimester. This period is characterized by relatively little growth: at the end of the first three months, the fetus is only about two or three inches long and weighs about an ounce. Much more important than growth during the first trimester is development and the differentiation of cells into specialized types of tissues. Here are some of the chief milestones (times indicate how much time has passed since fertilization).

First month

30 hours: The first cleavage occurs.

60 hours: The second cleavage occurs. In both cleavages, there is no overall growth, just cell division.

6–7 days: The zygote reaches the uterus for implantation. At this time, the zygote has become a hollow ball of cells (a blastocyst) with a small inner mass of cells that will become the embryo.

2nd week: Gastrulation occurs, and three distinct tissue layers develop. At this point, the placenta also forms. This occurs as the two membranes around the blastocyst—the amnion around the embryo and the chorion around the amnion—grow. The chorion ultimately branches out and surrounds the lining of the uterus. Together, the chorion and endometrium form the placenta (**FIGURE 25-25**), a mass of tissue in which nutrients, respiratory gases, and waste products are transferred between the mother and the developing embryo. (Although there is a yolk sac in placental mammals, its size is reduced and the placenta takes over the yolk sac's role of nourishing the embryo.) The embryo is connected to the chorion by the body stalk, which will become the **umbilical cord.**

Although the mother's blood and embryo's blood do not mix, they come in very close contact at the placenta, and oxygen diffuses from mother to embryo as carbon dioxide diffuses from embryo to mother. The placenta also nourishes the embryo and secretes hormones, including hCG, which maintains the corpus luteum, ensuring continued secretions of progesterone and, consequently, maintenance of the endometrium.

3rd week: Neurulation, the formation of the neural tube—which will develop into the nervous system—from ectoderm, follows soon after gastrulation.

HUMAN EMBRYO DEVELOPMENT

FIRST TRIMESTER: MONTHS 1–3
• Cells begin to differentiate into specialized types of tissues.
• Major organs and structures begin to form, including the eyes, heart, liver, pancreas, and gall bladder, as well as the limbs.

SECOND TRIMESTER: MONTHS 4–6
• Significant muscle and bone growth occurs, with less new development relative to the first trimester.

THIRD TRIMESTER: MONTHS 7–9
• Significant development of the nervous system.

FIGURE 25-24 Development of the human embryo and fetus. The nine months of human fetal development are divided into three-month trimesters.

THE PLACENTA

The placenta is a mass of highly vascularized tissue in which nutrients, respiratory gases, and waste products are transferred between the mother and the developing embryo.

PLACENTA
- Endometrium (maternal)
- Chorion (embryonic)

Yolk sac | Embryo

Umbilical cord

Amnion

The mother's and embryo's blood do not mix. They come in close contact, however, allowing the diffusion of gases, nutrients, and waste molecules.

Maternal blood vessels | Embryonic blood vessels

FIGURE 25-25 Structure and function of the placenta.

4th week: The formation of major structures and organs, including the eyes and heart, begins. At this point, it is also possible to see the arm and leg buds.

Second month

During this time, the limbs take shape. The major organs, including the liver, pancreas, and gall bladder, can also be seen. In spite of such dramatic development and differentiation, though, very little growth has occurred

yet, and the weight of the embryo is about one gram, less than one-tenth of an ounce!

Third month

During the third month, the nervous system develops, as do some of the first reflexes, such as suckling. At this point, the corpus luteum finally degenerates. In the absence of the progesterone it has been producing, a new ovulatory cycle would typically (i.e., without pregnancy) occur, but because the placenta produces significant levels of estrogen and progesterone (which inhibit the production of FSH and LH), no ovulation occurs. The fetus's heartbeat usually becomes audible around the 10th week. The development of mammary glands in the mother's breasts is also stimulated at this time, in preparation for later milk production (**lactation**).

The Second Trimester The second trimester, months 4, 5, and 6 of a pregnancy, is a time of significant growth and less new development relative to the first trimester. During this time, as the bones get bigger and the muscles develop, the fetus moves around and the mother can often feel it kick. The heartbeat becomes much louder and can be heard easily with a stethoscope. Its amplified "whooshing" sounds like a freight train. Although the fetus cannot survive outside the womb at the end of the second trimester, its size has increased to about 600 grams (1.3 pounds) and 12 inches in length.

The Third Trimester The third trimester is all about growth, as the fetus ultimately becomes large enough to survive outside the mother—the minimum size for survival is generally about a pound and a half (3–4 kg). In addition to growth, during the third trimester there is significant development of the nervous system. The addition of new neurons occurs at the explosive rate of 15 million per hour, a rate that continues even after birth.

TAKE-HOME MESSAGE 25·13

The nine-month development of a human embryo and fetus is divided into three equal periods, or trimesters. The first trimester is primarily a time of development and differentiation of cells into specialized types of tissues, as the embryo implants in the uterus and the placenta forms. The second and third trimesters are characterized mostly by significant growth and rapid development of the fetus's nervous system.

Reproductive Technology

Pregnancy culminates in childbirth and the start of lactation.

Birth, also called parturition, is the culmination of pregnancy, and it occurs in three phases. The first is the initiation of contractions and the dilation, or opening, of the cervix. Toward the end of the third trimester, the fetus usually becomes positioned with its head down and its skull resting on the cervix. This positioning, along with the increasing size of the fetus, stretches the uterus. Although the exact process is not fully understood, fetal hormones then cause the placenta to produce hormones, including estrogen and prostaglandin, that stimulate contractions in the uterus. The stretching of the uterus causes the pituitary gland to release oxytocin, another hormone that causes contractions. The contractions are referred to as **labor.** The rate of contractions increases from one or two per hour over many hours or even days before the birth, to about one every two to three minutes when birth is about to occur. The contractions cause a gradual dilation of the cervix, with the opening increasing from just over an inch (about 3 cm) at the beginning of labor to 4 inches (about 10 cm) or more at the end (**FIGURE 25-26**).

The second phase of birth is the delivery of the baby. This generally occurs with the head passing first through the

> **Q** How long does breastfeeding last?

vagina, which is also called the birth canal. After delivery of the baby, there is a brief relaxation of the contractions before the third and final phase of the birth process. The contractions then resume and, after the placenta is sheared from the wall of the uterus, the contractions expel it through the birth canal. The umbilical cord is then clamped and cut, and clotting quickly stops any bleeding.

During pregnancy, mammary gland development is stimulated by estrogen, progesterone, and other hormones. After birth, the pituitary hormone prolactin stimulates milk production. Suckling by the infant, too, causes the release of prolactin and the hormone oxytocin, which further increases milk production. During the first few days, a yellowish fluid, called colostrum, is released. Colostrum is high in protein and contains numerous antibodies from the mother that protect the infant from some diseases (**FIGURE 25-27**). Gradually, the colostrum is replaced by milk, which is higher in fat and sugar, with less protein than colostrum. The average duration of breastfeeding varies a lot from one country, and one culture, to another—it is 12 weeks in the United States and as long as two to two and a half years in Bangladesh and Nepal, respectively. Among

THE PHASES OF BIRTH

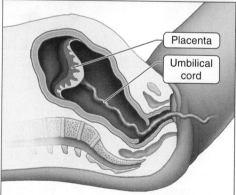

1 INITIATION OF CONTRACTIONS AND DILATION OF THE CERVIX
Hormones, including estrogen and prostaglandins, stimulate contractions in the uterus that cause a gradual opening of the cervix.

2 DELIVERY OF THE BABY
The baby's head passes through the vagina, or birth canal, followed by the rest of the body.

3 EXPULSION OF THE PLACENTA
Final contractions shear the placenta from the uterus wall and expel it through the birth canal.

FIGURE 25-26 Labor and birth.

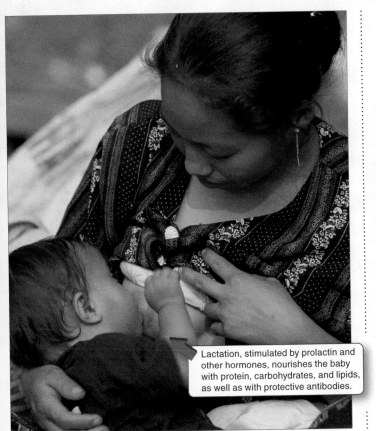

Lactation, stimulated by prolactin and other hormones, nourishes the baby with protein, carbohydrates, and lipids, as well as with protective antibodies.

FIGURE 25-27 Complete nutrition. Breastfeeding provides an infant with all the nourishment it needs, along with antibody protection from some diseases.

hunter-gatherer societies of humans, breastfeeding continued for as long as four years.

During lactation, the suckling of the infant prevents the pituitary from releasing a sufficient surge of LH to cause ovulation. For this reason, during lactation, a woman's fertility is significantly reduced. As a method of birth control this method (called "lactational amenorrhea") depends on several conditions being satisfied, including that the mother is exclusively breastfeeding (i.e., the baby is not getting nourishment in any other way), the baby is less than six months old, and no more than six hours pass between any two feedings.

Q Can breastfeeding be effective as birth control?

TAKE-HOME MESSAGE 25·14

Birth is the culmination of pregnancy and occurs in three phases. The first is the initiation of contractions and the dilation of the cervix. The second is delivery of the baby. The third is expulsion of the placenta. Lactation, stimulated by prolactin and other hormones, nourishes the baby with proteins, carbohydrates, and lipids and provides the infant with protective antibodies.

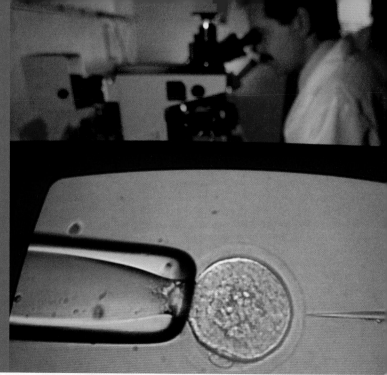

A single sperm is injected into the cytoplasm of an egg.

❺ Reproductive technology has benefits and dangers.

25·15

Assisted reproductive technologies are promising and perilous.

Just as technological advances have led to numerous developments in methods of preventing pregnancy, so, too, have they led to the development of techniques that help couples have children in situations where previously they might have remained infertile. In this section we examine some of these techniques, beginning more than a hundred years ago with the somewhat low-tech procedure that started it all.

In 1884, a woman came to see Dr. William Pancoast because she had not been able to conceive a child. After examining the couple, Dr. Pancoast determined that the husband was infertile. In the course of a discussion about the case by Dr. Pancoast and his students, someone suggested that semen should be collected from "the best-looking" member of the class and used to inseminate the woman. Dr. Pancoast agreed and arranged to see the patient again, under the pretense of another examination, at which point he injected the semen into the woman's uterus. Only when it became clear that the woman was pregnant did the doctor inform the husband of what he had done. The husband, however, was happy and requested only that the doctor not tell his wife how she had become pregnant. Eventually, a healthy son was born, the first recorded child born as the result of artificial insemination with a donor's sperm. From these inauspicious beginnings, there have been tremendous advances in the technologies available to couples experiencing difficulty having children.

Infertility is defined as a couple not being able to get pregnant after one year of trying—a definition that includes approximately 7% of married couples in the United States in any given year. There are many reasons for and causes of infertility—evenly divided between males and females—including low sperm counts and insufficient sperm motility, Fallopian tube damage or blockage, and ovulation problems. In 10% of cases, no cause can be found.

The technologies available are varied and include such interventions as surgery to repair blocked Fallopian tubes and hormone treatments to increase sperm counts or egg production. They also include a range of options called **assisted reproductive technology (ART),** the use of fertility treatments in which both sperm and egg are handled. These procedures typically involve removing eggs from a woman's ovaries, combining them with sperm to achieve fertilization in a Petri dish, and subsequently reinserting the now fertilized egg into the reproductive tract of that woman, or another woman. In many cases—such as the case described at the beginning of this chapter—the eggs, sperm, or fertilized eggs may be frozen for some period of time before completing the process (**FIGURE 25-28**). The methods used in ART include the following.

IVF-ET. This stands for in vitro fertilization–embryo transfer. It is the most common of all ART methods. Several secondary

How Do Animals Reproduce? | Male and Female Reproductive Systems | Sex Can Lead to Fertilization | Human Development oocytes are collected from a woman's ovaries and combined with sperm in a Petri dish. After several days, the fertilized eggs, at the eight-cell stage, are inserted into the woman's uterus, with the hope that they will implant and a pregnancy will result.

ZIFT. The technique of zygote intra-Fallopian transfer differs from IVF-ET in only two respects. After fertilization in a Petri dish, the fertilized eggs are transferred not to the uterus but to one of the Fallopian tubes instead. They also are transferred earlier, at the one-cell stage. Perhaps because surgery is needed to place the fertilized egg within the Fallopian tube, ZIFT is used by only 1% of couples seeking ART. In some cases, transfer to the Fallopian tube is not made until the fertilized egg is in the two- to four-cell stage (this is referred to as tubal embryo transfer). Some studies have shown ZIFT to have a higher implantation rate than IVF-ET.

GIFT. The method known as gamete intra-Fallopian transfer differs from ZIFT only in that the oocytes are immediately mixed with sperm and transferred to a Fallopian tube so that fertilization occurs in the body, rather than in a Petri dish.

In some cases, if the male's sperm counts are particularly low or if his sperm have low motility, a procedure called ICSI, or intracytoplasmic sperm injection, may be used in conjunction with IVF-ET or ZIFT. In this procedure, a single sperm is injected directly into an egg. While this method can be effective as a treatment for male infertility, there are concerns because

sperm selection is bypassed. That is, instead of one sperm "winning" in the competition to fertilize the egg, a sperm is selected by the individual doing the procedure. This may be why there's an increased incidence of genetically carried birth defects with ICSI.

Outside the definition of ART, but still intriguing, is the increasingly effective process for selecting the sex of a baby, known as "sperm sorting." In this method, a fluorescent dye that binds to the DNA is applied to a sperm sample. Because the X chromosome is larger than the Y chromosome (by about 3%), the X-chromosome-bearing sperm bind more dye. The dyed sperm are then given a small electric charge, based on which chromosome they carry, and as they are passed through a tube in single file, the sperm cells are deflected to a collecting tube on one side or the other, depending on their charge. The selected sperm carrying an X or Y sex chromosome can then be used in any of the ART methods described above. The purities of the X versus Y samples of sperm range from 70% to 90%.

TAKE-HOME MESSAGE 25·15

Assisted reproductive technology (ART) procedures typically involve removing eggs from a woman's ovaries, combining them with sperm to achieve fertilization, and reinserting the fertilized eggs into the woman's uterus or Fallopian tube. These technologies can enable previously infertile couples to have babies.

ASSISTED REPRODUCTIVE TECHNOLOGY (ART) METHODS

Assisted reproductive technologies can enable previously infertile couples to have babies.

1 Several eggs (secondary oocytes) are collected from a woman's ovaries.

The procedures typically begin with the removal of eggs from a woman's ovaries.

IN VITRO FERTILIZATION–EMBRYO TRANSFER (IVF–ET)

2 The eggs are combined with sperm in a Petri dish, where fertilization occurs.

3 Fertilized eggs at the 8-cell stage are inserted into the uterus.

ZYGOTE INTRA-FALLOPIAN TUBE TRANSFER (ZIFT)

2 The eggs are combined with sperm in a Petri dish, where fertilization occurs.

3 Fertilized eggs at the 1-cell stage are inserted into the Fallopian tube.

GAMETE INTRA-FALLOPIAN TUBE TRANSFER (GIFT)

2 The eggs are immediately mixed with sperm.

3 The mixture of sperm and eggs is inserted into the Fallopian tube, where fertilization occurs.

FIGURE 25-28 Technologies used in assisted reproductive technology.

Knowledge You Can Use

Business and science in conflict. Why is the number of multiple births—twins, triplets, and more—on the rise?

Q: Multiple births are in the news a lot. Are they on the rise? Yes! Between 1980 and 2008, the incidence of twins in the United States increased by 70%. The rate of triplets and higher increased even more.

Q: Why are there so many more multiple births? Consider this: if you are running a fertility clinic, one of the most important pieces of information that will lead to the success or failure of your clinic is the percentage of treated couples who become pregnant. Unfortunately, in most assisted reproductive technology procedures, this number is influenced by the number of embryos transferred into the woman: 5–10 transferred embryos are more likely to result in pregnancy than 1–4 transferred embryos. The problem is, though, that with 5–10 embryos transferred, the risk of "multiples"—twins, triplets, or more—also increases, as does the health risk to the mother and the babies. And so the decision regarding the number of embryos to transfer involves a trade-off between the perceived effectiveness of the clinic and the risk to the mother. This point was vividly illustrated in 2009 by the case of Nadya Suleman (called "Octomom" by the media), a California woman who gave birth to octuplets after eight embryos were implanted.

Q: Are fertility clinics bringing the rate back down to safer levels? In the past 10 years, the number of in vitro fertilization cycles in which four or more embryos were transferred dropped from 62% to 21%. This has significantly reduced the incidence of triplets, but the rate of twins has remained high. And although, for women under 35, the American Society of Reproductive Medicine now recommends the transfer of just a single embryo during ART procedures, for women above 35, it still recommends three to five embryos be transferred.

How do animals reproduce?

Animals can reproduce asexually or sexually. Asexual reproduction can be fast and efficient, but leads to offspring genetically identical to the parent. Sexual reproduction occurs in the vast majority of animal species and leads to offspring that are genetically different from one another and from either parent.

Male and female reproductive systems have important similarities and differences.

In adult men, sperm are continuously produced in the testes by meiosis. Semen, consisting of sperm cells and accessory fluids that nurture the sperm and aid in fertilization, is ejaculated during copulation. In adult women, diploid cells in the ovaries undergo meiosis to produce genetically varied haploid eggs. Fewer eggs than sperm are produced, and eggs are much larger than sperm.

Sex can lead to fertilization, but can also spread sexually transmitted diseases.

At fertilization, a sperm penetrates the egg. The egg blocks additional sperm entry, and the sperm and egg membranes fuse. The haploid nuclei of the egg and sperm then fuse, forming a diploid zygote. Pregnancy can be prevented by preventing ovulation, fertilization, or implantation.

④ Human development occurs in specific stages.

Fertilization is followed by cleavage of the zygote, with many rapid cell divisions but without growth. Next, in gastrulation, a gut begins to form, along with three distinct germ layers with specific developmental fates. In neurulation, mesoderm forms the notochord, and ectoderm forms a neural tube, which will become the brain and spinal cord. Mammalian embryos develop female reproductive organs unless a gene on the Y chromosome stimulates the fetal gonads to develop as testes, leading to the further development of male reproductive organs. The development of human embryos is divided into three trimesters. The first is primarily a time of development and differentiation; the second and third are characterized mostly by significant growth. Birth is the culmination of pregnancy, and lactation, stimulated by prolactin and other hormones, nourishes the baby and provides protective antibodies.

⑤ Reproductive technology has benefits and dangers.

Assisted reproductive technology procedures typically involve removing eggs from a woman's ovaries, combining them with sperm to achieve fertilization in a Petri dish, and reinserting the fertilized eggs into the woman. They can enable couples to have babies who previously would have been infertile.

KEY TERMS

1. Some animals are primarily asexual in their reproduction, but have the ability to switch to sexual reproduction under certain conditions. What adaptive advantage might an animal that generally reproduces asexually have by also being able to reproduce sexually?
   a) to increase the genetic diversity of its offspring during periods of stress
   b) to confuse its predators
   c) to give the animal some variety in its life
   d) to increase its own likelihood of survival
   e) Only a) and d) are correct

2. Amplexus is a tactic that occurs in most species of frogs. The most likely reason that this tactic has evolved is:
   a) the gametes of terrestrial animals can quickly dry out in non-aquatic environments.
   b) it enables internal fertilization to occur without the necessity of viviparity.
   c) it ensures that the sperm and eggs are released at the same time and in the same place, increasing the likelihood of fertilization.
   d) it reduces the negative effect of salt water on gametes.
   e) All of the above are correct.

3. Meiosis occurs in the _____ in female humans and in the _____ in male humans.
   a) follicles; seminiferous tubules
   b) somatic cells; germ cells
   c) uterus; prostate gland
   d) follicles; prostate gland
   e) Fallopian tube; vas deferens

4. Which three sets of accessory glands add secretions to the semen in human males?
   a) the seminal vesicles, the prostate gland, and the bulbourethral glands
   b) the ejaculatory duct, the prostate gland, and the vas deferens
   c) the seminal vesicles, the prostate gland, and the urethra
   d) the seminal vesicles, the prostate gland, and the epididymis
   e) the ejaculatory duct, the prostate gland, and the bulbourethral glands

5. When individual females mate with multiple males within short periods of time:
   a) a male that produces more sperm than other males has an increased probability of reproductive success.
   b) internal fertilization cannot occur.
   c) there is selection for a reduction in the size of the male testes.
   d) the male gametes experience reduced desiccation.
   e) All of the above are correct.

6. The tissue that develops into the penis in males, develops into _____ in females.
   a) the vagina
   b) the labia
   c) the clitoris
   d) the oviduct
   e) the ovary

7. The completion of meiosis II in the oocyte of human females occurs:
   a) before birth.
   b) during menstruation.
   c) after the oocyte is fertilized by a sperm.
   d) a few hours before ovulation.
   e) at ovulation.

8. The corpus luteum:
   a) secretes chorionic gonadotropin.
   b) is reabsorbed when fertilization occurs.
   c) is the only source of the hormones that maintain pregnancy
   d) secretes progesterone but not estrogen.
   e) is the initial source of progesterone during pregnancy.

9. In mammalian fertilization, the extracellular layer of the egg that functions, in part, as a sperm receptor is called the:
   a) endoderm.
   b) jelly coat.
   c) acrosome.
   d) egg plasma membrane.
   e) zona pellucida.

10. The hormones present in birth control pills typically prevent pregnancy by:
    a) preventing formation of the endometrial lining of the uteru
    b) preventing ovarian follicles from maturing.
    c) preventing sperm from fertilizing the ovulated egg.
    d) causing the endometrium to be shed once a fertilized egg h implanted.
    e) preventing implantation of fertilized eggs in the endometrium.

11. Tying off the vas deferens leading from each testis will:
    a) prevent formation of sperm.
    b) decrease testosterone secretion.
    c) reduce secretion from the seminal vesicles.
    d) reduce secretions from the prostate gland.
    e) None of the above.

12. When do cells begin to lose their totipotency?
    a) anaphase of mitosis
    b) gastrulation
    c) late prophase I of meiosis
    d) cleavage
    e) neurulation

13. The phenotype of an individual who is genetically XY but is lacking the sex-determining region on the Y chromosome would be:
    a) a person who does not have testes but does have male external sex organs.
    b) completely male, because of low estrogen levels.
    c) either male or female, depending on whether the person carries the gene for DHT, which directs development of the penis.
    d) a person with ovaries and female secondary sex characteristics.
    e) completely male, because the person will produce testosterone, which masculinizes the internal and external reproductive organs.

14. In humans, fetal growth is slowest during which trimester?
    a) first
    b) second
    c) third
    d) fourth
    e) It occurs at the same rate in all trimesters.

15. In which of the following methods of assisted reproductive technology does fertilization occur within the woman's body?
    a) intracytoplasmic sperm injection
    b) in vitro fertilization–embryo transfer (IVF-ET)
    c) zygote intra-Fallopian transfer (ZIFT)
    d) gamete intra-Fallopian transfer (GIFT)
    e) All of the above.

SHORT-ANSWER QUESTIONS

1. In humans, how are male gametes formed? Where in the male reproductive system does this process occur?

2. What are germ layers? How many layers are there, what are they called, and what structures ultimately form from them?

3. Summarize the three stages of pregnancy and the major events that occur in each.

See Appendix for answers. For additional study questions, go to www.prep-u.com.

26

Immunity and Health

How the body defends and maintains itself

① Your body has different ways to protect you against disease-causing invaders.

Sneezing is one of the body's ways of expelling harmful substances that enter our body.

26·1

Three lines of defense prevent and fight pathogen attacks.

Most of us don't think about the germs that constantly attempt to invade our bodies until we hear that an illness is "going around." For example, in the spring of 2009, Mexico alerted the world to an outbreak of the H1N1 virus that caused numerous deaths—particularly among people under 25 years old and pregnant women. This outbreak was caused by a new strain of the influenza virus that the world's current population had never before encountered. The media showed footage of Mexico City residents wearing face masks and reported that schools and businesses were closing for extended periods of time. Within weeks, the virus had spread to the United States and around the world. Fortunately, however, as the flu strain began infecting people worldwide, researchers noted that although this influenza strain was strong, it was not as virulent as first suggested.

When you first heard about the H1N1 flu, did you think about washing your hands more frequently, wearing a face mask, and staying away from people who were coughing? The H1N1 flu example demonstrates that when we are aware of **pathogens,** disease-causing microorganisms, molecules, and viruses (sometimes referred to as "germs"), in our environment, we

Indian girls wearing protective masks outside a museum in the Indian city of Bangalore in August 2009, just after a 26-year-old woman died of Swine flu (H1N1 virus) in a nearby hospital.

Lines of Defense | Specific Immunity | Immune System Malfunction

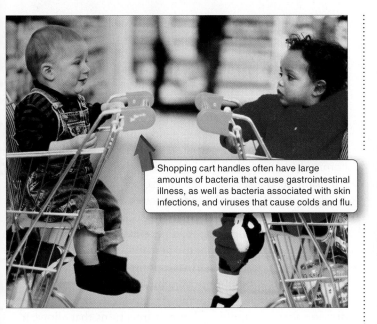

Shopping cart handles often have large amounts of bacteria that cause gastrointestinal illness, as well as bacteria associated with skin infections, and viruses that cause colds and flu.

FIGURE 26-1 Everyday encounters with pathogens. Shopping cart handles harbor germs.

may take precautions to avoid them. But we fail to notice most of the germs in our everyday lives. Think about the commonplace items that you and others touch. Did you know that shopping cart handles rank as one of the "germiest" items around? Shopping carts are often found to have fecal bacteria that cause gastrointestinal illness, bacteria associated with skin infections, and viruses that cause colds and flu, along with many non-pathogenic organisms (**FIGURE 26-1**). Not surprisingly, many stores now offer disinfectant wipes, and some states have even proposed legislation to make providing these wipes mandatory.

The vast majority of the microscopic organisms found on everyday items will not cause disease, but some will. That we don't notice or pay attention to surfaces that may be covered with germs, don't get sick frequently, and don't think too much about how our immune system protects us is a testament to the efficacy of this body system.

The human **immune system** provides protection against an enormous variety of pathogens, including many bacteria, fungi, viruses, and parasitic protists and worms (**FIGURE 26-2**). To protect the body from the various pathogens, the immune system needs to be able to rapidly recognize the general category of "non-self" or "stuff that doesn't belong in the body," as well as distinguish among specific disease-causing microbes or viruses. The immune system works within minutes to begin destroying a pathogen. In many cases this requires killing body cells that are infected with the pathogen. To accomplish this challenging protective task, there are three major divisions of the immune system (**FIGURE 26-3**).

1. Physical barriers provide the first defense against pathogens and can keep them out of the body. For example, skin acts as a nearly impenetrable barrier that keeps viruses, bacteria, and other pathogens from entering the body, and various chemicals secreted by epithelial surfaces stop the growth of many pathogens.

2. Non-specific immunity is the division of the immune system that provides the next defense, for situations in which pathogens make it past the physical barriers and into the body. This cellular system is sometimes referred to as the *innate system* (meaning "inborn"), because this division is ready to go at birth and does not require any previous

PATHOGENS

Viruses | Bacteria | Fungi | Parasitic protists | Parasitic worms

FIGURE 26-2 Examples of the foreign, "non-self" microbes and viruses that can harm the body.

The immune system protects us from a diverse group of pathogens—disease-causing viruses and microorganisms, often referred to as "germs."

DIVISIONS OF THE IMMUNE SYSTEM

PHYSICAL BARRIERS
- Form a nearly impenetrable wall, keeping pathogens from entering body tissues
- Consist of skin, mucous membranes, and their associated anti-pathogen secretions

Pathogens

Skin

NON-SPECIFIC IMMUNITY
- Recognizes and destroys pathogens that breach external barriers
- Does not distinguish among specific pathogens
- Response to infection within minutes

Pathogens

Non-specific immune system cells

SPECIFIC IMMUNITY
- Destroys pathogens that are not killed by non-specific defenses
- Recognizes specific pathogens and forms a memory of them
- Response to infection takes days

Pathogens

Specific immune system cells

After the specific immunity system forms a "memory" of a pathogen, it fights off the same pathogen more quickly in the future, often resulting in lifelong protection from that pathogen.

FIGURE 26-3 Layered defenses of the immune system block entry and fight invaders.

exposure to pathogens to act. Cells of the non-specific division of the immune system rapidly recognize pathogens that breach external barriers and are not part of the body's own tissue, but they do this without distinguishing the specific identity of one pathogen from another. Non-specific immunity is found in virtually all multicellular organisms, including plants, nematode worms, fruit flies, and humans.

3. Specific immunity, also called *adaptive immunity,* is the division of the immune system that deals with pathogens that either were missed by the non-specific system or cannot be overcome by that system. The specific division recognizes very specific infectious agents—not just bacteria in general but, for example, the specific *Staphylococcus aureus* that causes common skin infections; not just viruses in general but, for example, the specific varicella-zoster virus that causes chicken pox. Because the specific immunity part of your immune system must recognize the specific threat and then manufacture specific weapons to combat it, there is a time lag between your exposure to the pathogen and the specific immunity response to it. This response takes hours to days, unlike non-specific immunity, which responds immediately or within minutes. Once activated, however, the specific division forms a "memory" of past infections that allows it to fight off the same infection more quickly in the future. As a result, an individual often has lifelong protection from a pathogen he or she has previously encountered.

These three divisions of the immune system are collaborative. Once an invader is recognized by the non-specific system, chemical signals trigger the cells of the specific system to go to work. We first look more closely at the non-specific immune system that plays a necessary and immediate role in protecting the body's tissues.

TAKE-HOME MESSAGE 26·1

The immune system protects us from a diverse group of pathogens. There are three collaborative divisions to the immune system: a physical barrier, non-specific immunity, and specific immunity. Physical barriers and non-specific immunity are the first lines of defense and, as non-specific systems, recognize pathogens only as "non-self." The specific immunity line of defense recognizes individual species of pathogens and forms a memory of them.

Lines of Defense   Specific Immunity   Immune System Malfunction

External barriers prevent pathogens from entering your body.

Just as a high-security building may have walls and barbed wire to keep out potential intruders, your body has ways to prevent pathogens from entering your body, tissues, and cells. The **integumentary system** is made up of skin, sweat glands, oil glands, hair, and nails that protect you from mechanical stress caused by external forces such as friction or pressure, sunlight, dehydration, and, of course, pathogens (**FIGURE 26-4**).

> How dangerous is it to sit directly on a toilet seat in a public restroom?

Have you ever sat down on a public toilet seat only to wonder if you were going to contract some horrible disease from it (**FIGURE 26-5**)? The good news is that most human pathogens cannot survive outside the body for very

Pathogens do not pass through intact skin. So, while there may be germs on a toilet seat, your skin acts as a barrier that prevents entry.

FIGURE 26-5 A safe place to sit. Public restrooms are generally safe to use (but be sure to thoroughly wash your hands!).

THE INTEGUMENTARY SYSTEM

Hair

Nails

Skin surface

Hair

Oil glands

Sweat glands

Fat cells

Nerve fiber

Blood vessel

The integumentary system protects you from pathogens and external stresses such as friction, pressure, sunlight, and dehydration.

FIGURE 26-4 Providing a nearly impenetrable barrier: the integumentary system.

long, and a cold, smooth toilet seat is not an ideal place for them to survive. Additionally, pathogens need an access point. For example, HIV is transmitted through the membranes of the genitals (or, much less frequently, those of the mouth). The virus does not pass through intact skin on your buttocks! So while there may be germs on the toilet seat, your skin acts as a barrier that prevents entry. Many public bathrooms offer toilet seat covers that can act like a second skin, if the thought helps you relax while you do your business!

Skin is not exactly like a wall, however—skin is far more active than a protective wall. In addition to forming a nearly impenetrable barrier, skin cells actively secrete chemicals that inhibit bacterial growth (**FIGURE 26-6**). Sweat secreted onto the skin's surface, for example, contains **lysozyme,** an enzyme that can kill bacteria by damaging their cell walls. The protection provided by skin becomes really clear in burn victims: lacking skin in certain areas, they are susceptible to numerous pathogenic bacteria and fungi. Although we may not realize it, besides skin, the external and internal surfaces of

DEFENSE MECHANISMS OF THE INTEGUMENTARY SYSTEM

SKIN
Forms a nearly impenetrable barrier that keeps pathogens from entering the body

LYSOZYME AND OTHER ENZYMES
Lysozyme in saliva and tears, and digestive enzymes in the small intestine kill many bacteria

ACIDIC SECRETIONS
Stomach acids, acidic vaginal secretions, and acidic urine, all of which protect the digestive, reproductive, and urinary tracts from bacterial pathogens

CILIA
Hair-like extensions on the surface of the respiratory tract that move mucus-entrapped pathogens up and out of the lungs

TEARS
Fluid containing antiviral and antibacterial chemicals that washes away microorganisms from around the eyes

EAR WAX
Sticky substance that can trap microorganisms in the ear canal

FIGURE 26-6 Security barrier. The integumentary system provides multiple defenses to protect you from pathogens.

the body, such as eyes, ears, and the linings of the digestive and respiratory tracts, are also exposed to environmental stresses and forces. These body areas, too, are shielded by the integumentary system (and, as we'll see, by the cells of the non-specific defense system).

Consider, for example, how the digestive tract is protected. Imagine that minutes after you push a germ-laden shopping cart, you put your finger in your mouth to bite your nail. Are you guaranteed to get ill? No, because mucus (a major component of the saliva in your mouth) contains lysozyme. And even if this antibacterial chemical doesn't destroy potential invaders, they will quickly reach the stomach, a harsh environment containing both acid and digestive enzymes that can destroy a variety of pathogens.

The respiratory tract is also protected by the thick and sticky physical properties of mucus, which traps pathogens before they can reach the lungs. In the respiratory tract, hair-like extensions of the epithelial cells, called **cilia,** continually move mucus-entrapped pathogens up and out of the lungs. As the mucus moves up toward your throat, you continually swallow germs and send them to your stomach, where they are destroyed (or you spit them out). You hardly notice that all of this is going on, until sometimes you feel the urge to "clear your throat" or cough.

The eyes produce tears that physically wash away microorganisms, and tears also contain lysozyme and antiviral and antibacterial chemicals. Ear wax serves a protective function, too. Secretions produced by numerous glands inside the ear canal, combined with dead skin cells, make up this sticky substance. Its physical properties are effective at trapping microorganisms. The slight acidity and the lysozyme in ear wax also serve to inhibit the growth of some microorganisms that find their way into the ear canal.

Q What is the purpose of ear wax?

TAKE-HOME MESSAGE 26·2

Skin, part of the integumentary system, is a physical barrier that prevents pathogens from entering the body's cells. Cells that are not covered by skin but are exposed to the external environment are protected by defenses such as bacteria-destroying chemicals, acidic secretions, sticky mucus, and wax.

Lines of Defense   Specific Immunity   Immune System Malfunction

The non-specific division of the immune system recognizes and fights pathogens while signaling for additional defenses.

Sometimes security measures fail. When intruders break through a defensive wall surrounding a secure building, the building's security guards need to (1) identify the security breach, (2) call for backup, and (3) attack and remove the invader. Similarly, your body *recognizes* any security breaches, such as a wound to the skin or some spoiled food you've eaten, and then *responds* instantly to prevent an infection (**FIGURE 26-7**). Chemical signals are put out to call for backup cells, and molecular weapons are used to destroy both the pathogens and any cells they've infected. In this section, we examine the cells that perform these duties and the tools that they use to combat infection. First, let's examine the recognition stage.

An important first step in defending the body is for immune cells to distinguish invaders from the body's own cells, or "non-self" from "self." The surface receptors on the patrolling non-specific (innate) immune system cells recognize molecules, usually proteins, such as those found only on the surfaces of pathogens, and bind to them. This recognition is considered non-specific because immune cell receptors recognize and bind to classes of molecules shared by a wide array of organisms. For example, one receptor recognizes a protein contained in all bacterial flagella. Another receptor recognizes a molecule found in the cell walls of many types of fungi.

Your immune cells have combinations of receptors that can recognize virtually any pathogen that might cause infection, by recognizing surface molecules. Because your own cells do not contain these molecules, a cell that possesses any of them can be "marked" as an invader by the innate system cells.

While the cells of the innate system are the initial responders to a pathogen, there are never enough of them at the initial site of infection to ingest and kill all the invading pathogens. Thus, after recognizing the security breach and starting the response, the patrolling cells of the non-specific system sound the alarm and call for backup.

The chief way that cells of the immune system—both the specific and non-specific divisions—talk to one another is by secreting signaling proteins called **cytokines** in response to pathogens in the body. Cytokines secreted by one immune cell can bind to receptors on other immune cells and signal them to respond in various ways. For example, cytokine binding can cause immune cells to move closer to the site where the cytokines are being produced (*cyto* = cell; *kine* = to move). Cytokine-secreting cells use this as a way to recruit more immune cells to the site of infection.

Interferon is an important type of cytokine produced by cells infected by a virus. Interferon alerts other cells to turn on protective measures that help them resist viruses. These alerted cells take on an "antiviral state" in which they transcribe specific genes and translate them into proteins that can inhibit viral replication and degrade viral RNA.

RESPONDING TO PATHOGENS IN THE BODY

1 **IDENTIFY THE INTRUDER**
Non-specific immune system cells recognize molecules found only on the surface of pathogens and bind to them, marking the pathogens as invaders.

2 **CALL FOR BACKUP**
Immune system cells secrete signaling proteins called cytokines that recruit more immune cells to the site of the infection or warn them to protect themselves.

3 **ATTACK AND REMOVE**
Specialized immune system cells destroy, break down, and ingest both the pathogens and any cells they've infected.

FIGURE 26-7 **Sometimes the security measures fail.** The body recognizes and responds to invading pathogens.

As proteins on the cell surfaces of pathogens allow cells of the body's non-specific system to recognize an intruder, several different types of immune cells next begin to mount the non-specific system's response. Pathogens that breach the body's external defenses are met by **white blood cells,** specialized cells that play roles in both the specific and the non-specific divisions of the immune system (introduced in Section 21-6). These cells are made in the bone marrow and released into the bloodstream, where they patrol the body's tissues and search for invaders. Some white blood cells, called **phagocytes,** can engulf, ingest, kill, and break down foreign pathogens and particles. Three of the most important types of white blood cells—neutrophils, macrophages, and dendritic cells—act as phagocytes, with the dendritic cells also having an important role in stimulating the specific immunity system, as we'll see later. A fourth type of white blood cells, **natural killer (NK) cells,** are not phagocytes, but operate by killing body cells that have been infected by pathogens. Let's look more closely at these four types of white blood cells (**FIGURE 26-8**).

Neutrophils circulate in the blood and exit blood vessels at sites of injury and infection in tissues. These phagocytes ingest small organisms, primarily bacteria. They also produce hydrogen peroxide and bleach. Neutrophils normally make up between 50% and 70% of all white blood cells circulating in the bloodstream, and their numbers increase dramatically and rapidly during the first few days of some infections. Neutrophils are the kamikazes of the immune system—they destroy themselves as they ingest pathogens and live only 3-5 days, on average.

Macrophages are large ("macro") white blood cells that reside in and patrol the tissues. They engulf and digest whole pathogens (small organisms), as well as any debris that remains after the neutrophils have done their job. However, macrophages do not destroy themselves in the process. Instead, they serve as an important link between the non-specific and specific divisions of the immune system. Once they have ingested a pathogen, they "present" digested pieces of the pathogen on their cell surface, "advertising" the infection to cells of the specific system. We'll learn more about the role of "presenting cells" when we examine specific immunity in Section 26-9.

Q *What is pus?*

Neutrophils and macrophages employ chemical warfare to destroy pathogens. For example, both types of cells can produce hydrogen peroxide and hypochlorous acid (components of household bleach). These two chemicals are quite effective in killing bacteria and fungi, as you may know first-hand from using one or both to clean your room or house. Individuals who have defects in the pathway that produces these defensive chemicals are, not surprisingly, frequently stricken with bacterial and fungal infections. In the process of killing, neutrophils destroy themselves and become a major part of **pus,** the thick yellowish

THE WHITE BLOOD CELLS OF NON-SPECIFIC IMMUNITY

The non-specific immune system consists of several types of white blood cells that are made in the bone marrow and released into the bloodstream, where they patrol the body's tissues and search for invaders.

NEUTROPHILS
- Phagocytic cells that ingest small organisms, primarily bacteria
- Destroy both the pathogen and themselves in the process

Pathogens

MACROPHAGES
- Phagocytic cells that ingest whole pathogens as well as large debris such as dead cells
- Present pieces of pathogens on their surface, advertising the infection to cells of the specific immune system

DENDRITIC CELLS
- Phagocytic cells that present ingested pathogens to cells of the specific immune system

NATURAL KILLER (NK) CELLS
- Kill body cells infected by pathogens by poking holes in the cell membranes
- Also play a role in recognizing and killing cancer cells

Infected cell

FIGURE 26-8 Hardworking cells. Several types of white blood cells defend the body in the non-specific division of the immune system. Note that the neutrophil nucleus sometimes appears like a cluster of nuclei because it is multi-lobed, with the lobes connected by thin strands.

fluid we often notice at the site of infection. (Other components of pus include damaged cell debris from the invaded tissue and both live and dead pathogens.) Often, our bodies can clear these infections on their own or with some help from an **antiseptic,** a solution used on a body surface to kill or discourage growth of microorganisms, such as rubbing alcohol or hydrogen peroxide. But when there is excessive pus, combined with signs of a more serious infection, antibiotics might be needed to kill bacteria inside the body.

Dendritic cells are phagocytes that link the non-specific and specific divisions of the immune system by "presenting" the cells of the specific system with foreign matter. These phagocytic cells migrate to the lymph nodes, which are populated by cells of the specific immunity system.

Natural killer (NK) cells, which are not phagocytes, provide the first line of resistance to viruses by poking holes in the membranes of virus-infected cells so as to kill the cells, and in doing so, killing the viruses inside the cells. Their initial response may eliminate the viral infection, or at least slow it down until the specific system can respond to the virus in a more specific manner. Interestingly, NK cells also play a role in recognizing and killing cancer cells (**FIGURE 26-9**).

In addition to the cells we've learned about here, the non-specific system can also quickly recognize and destroy invaders thanks to some circulating defensive proteins, collectively called **complement proteins.** There are approximately 30 of these proteins that "complement" the cells of both the non-specific and specific immunity systems and can link the two systems. Foreign molecules, such as the components of bacterial cell walls, activate the complement proteins (**FIGURE 26-10**). Once activated, the complement proteins fight pathogens in several ways. For example, a particular combination of complement proteins can blast holes in the cell membranes of pathogenic organisms, allowing water and ions to pass through, but not larger molecules such as proteins. As a result, water rushes inward and the pathogen swells and lyses, or bursts. Other complement proteins help destroy pathogens by sticking to them and forming a coating that enhances the ability of phagocytes to bind to and engulf them.

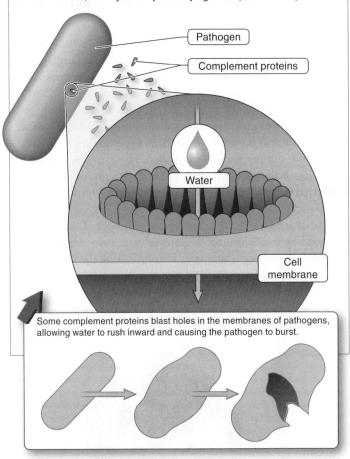

COMPLEMENT PROTEINS

A collective group of circulating proteins, called complement proteins, recognize pathogens and help fight them in various ways, including by sticking to them and increasing the ability of phagocytes to consume them, and by directly destroying them (shown here).

Pathogen

Complement proteins

Water

Cell membrane

Some complement proteins blast holes in the membranes of pathogens, allowing water to rush inward and causing the pathogen to burst.

FIGURE 26-10 Defensive proteins "complement" the other cells of the non-specific system to combat pathogens.

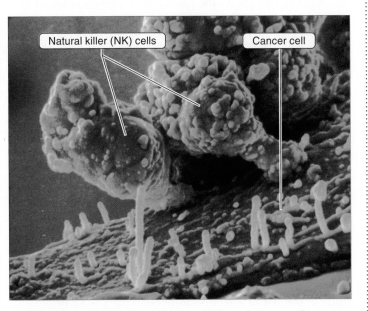

Natural killer (NK) cells

Cancer cell

FIGURE 26-9 **Attacking cancer.** Natural killer cells are attaching to a cancer cell.

TAKE-HOME MESSAGE 26·3

Non-specific immunity provides defenses against pathogens by recognizing molecules on their cell surfaces. Immune cells communicate with each other via chemical signals called cytokines. Non-specific immunity cells that secrete cytokines can recruit other cells to the site of infection or warn them to protect themselves. White blood cells of the non-specific system include phagocytes—such as neutrophils and macrophages that ingest and kill pathogens, and macrophages and dendritic cells that display pathogens to cells of the specific immunity system—and natural killer cells, which kill virus-infected cells and cancer cells. Complement proteins also non-specifically recognize invaders and help to destroy them.

The non-specific system responds to infection with the inflammatory response and with fever.

While we don't notice that our innate immune system is constantly on patrol for invaders, we definitely do notice when it responds at the site of an infection. A little response is quickly amplified into a noticeable one. Think about what happens when you get a splinter. Initially, you might only feel the pain of the splinter going into your finger. Within minutes, though, you feel pain and warmth, and see that the area around the splinter is red and swollen. The changes you are observing at the site of the splinter are the signs of an **inflammatory response.** The inflammatory response is a combination of events that leads to recruitment of phagocytes and other immune cells to assist with pathogen destruction, followed by tissue healing. Whenever tissues are damaged by an invading pathogen such as a virus infecting throat cells, or by a physical injury such as a wound to the skin, the inflammatory response is triggered.

This mast cell contains small round granules containing histamine. Release of histamine occurs at sites of infection as part of the immune response.

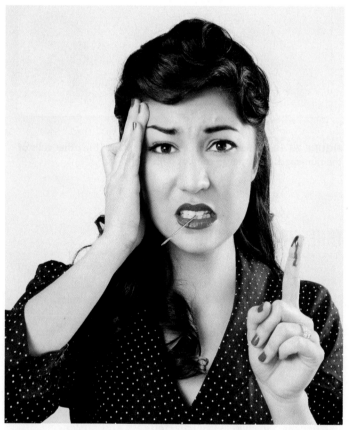

Following a wound—such as the cut shown here—the body responds with an inflammatory response that causes redness, heat, swelling, and pain. But the process clears away foreign invaders and allows for healing.

In the first century A.D., the Romans first described the four signs of inflammation: redness, heat, swelling, and pain. Whether it is a sore throat or wounded skin, these hallmarks of inflammation are always the same. Let's imagine a scenario in which you cut your finger with a small knife while slicing a bagel (**FIGURE 26-11**). Invading pathogens from the knife and the skin surface are quickly engulfed by the macrophages that reside in all tissues. The macrophages then release cytokines to recruit more phagocytes and two other types of white blood cells, which initiate inflammation. **Basophils,** which circulate in the blood, and **mast cells,** found in the tissues, trigger the inflammatory reaction by releasing **histamine,** a molecule that causes nearby non–injured blood vessels to (1) dilate (open up and become wider) and (2) become leaky.

When blood vessels dilate, the flow of blood increases and allows for a faster, greater supply of defensive molecules and cells that can fight infection. The increased blood supply at the site of injury causes the *redness* and *heat* associated with inflammation. The increased leakiness of the blood vessels makes it easier for neutrophils to exit the blood and enter tissue at the site of infection to begin destroying any invading pathogens. The leakiness is the reason for the

Lines of Defense | Specific Immunity | Immune System Malfunction

1 After you cut your finger with a knife, invading pathogens from the knife and the skin's surface enter your body.

2 Macrophages residing in tissues surrounding the cut begin engulfing the pathogens and releasing cytokines, recruiting more phagocytes and other white blood cells to the area.

3 Basophils, which circulate in the blood, and mast cells, found in the tissues, trigger the inflammatory reaction by releasing histamine.

4 Histamine causes nearby non-injured blood vessels to dilate, increasing the flow of blood and allowing for a greater supply of defensive molecules and cells that can fight infection.

5 Histamine also causes the blood vessels to become more leaky, allowing neutrophils to more easily exit the blood and enter the site of infection.

6 The inflammatory response continues until the pathogens have been eliminated and the skin grows back, forming an impenetrable barrier once again.

Inflammatory response causes redness, heat, swelling, and pain, but ultimately leads to tissue healing.

FIGURE 26-11 Reacting to injury. An inflammatory response causes redness, heat, swelling, and pain, but ultimately leads to tissue healing.

swelling, as fluid leaking from the blood vessels accumulates in the tissue.

Macrophages and neutrophils then begin an immediate response to destroy pathogens and also release cytokines. The various cytokines not only amplify the response by recruiting more immune cells but also can affect other cell types. For example, some of the cytokines released from macrophages, neutrophils, and mast cells can activate neurons and are therefore the cause of *pain*. Pain is also caused by the increased pressure on nerve endings resulting from the localized tissue swelling.

As we've seen, macrophages residing in the injured tissue initially recognize an invader and produce cytokines to attract neutrophils to the site of injury or invasion. As many as 70% of the white blood cells circulating in the bloodstream are neutrophils, and these plentiful cells move from the blood and into the tissue at the site of an injury. The blood vessels make it easier for them to reach the injured tissue, as cells lining the vessels near the site of inflammation become "sticky" to neutrophils (red blood cells do not stick). This stickiness slows down the neutrophils so that they can exit the leaky vessel at the site where they are needed.

Complement proteins also play a role in inflammation. Just as cytokines (secreted by macrophages) trigger the inflammatory response, activated complement proteins also can trigger initial reactions. Activated complement proteins at the site of infection cause mast cells to release histamine and further amplify the inflammatory response by attracting additional phagocytes. As mentioned in Section 26-3, complement proteins also directly affect pathogens by attacking their membranes and making it easier for phagocytes to engulf them.

So what about that cut on your finger? A scab temporarily forms to cover the wound, much like a natural Band-Aid, and prevents more pathogens from entering. Thanks to the inflammatory process, any pathogens initially entering the wound were immediately destroyed. At the end of the inflammatory process, collagen fibers are secreted by nearby cells to close the wound in a more stable fashion, and the scab falls off. Skin begins to grow back to form an impenetrable barrier once again. And you are more cautious about cutting bagels!

Sometimes an infection is overcome quickly by the inflammatory response and is confined to the site of damage. However, if pathogens are not quickly destroyed, macrophages will be constantly stimulated and continue to release cytokines. Some cytokines can cause a **fever,** an elevated body temperature, if their concentration is high enough—a situation that both stimulates the immune response and reduces the rate at which many pathogenic bacteria can divide. The fever-causing cytokines travel through the bloodstream and affect a region of the brain, called the hypothalamus, that functions as the body's thermostat (see Section 23-16). Just as you can change the settings on your home thermostat, your body's thermostat can also be set higher, thus leading to a fever (**FIGURE 26-12**).

Q Why do chills and sweating sometimes occur together when you have a fever?

When your body's thermostat is set higher with a fever, you feel cold and your body responds with rapid periods of muscle contractions and relaxations (shivers and chills). Chills are the body's way of trying to warm up to the higher temperature setting of the thermostat. When your fever "breaks," the thermostat is being reset to normal. You feel sweaty because your body is now too hot; sweating is a way to cool down. Anti-inflammatory medicines such as aspirin, acetaminophen, and ibuprofen help to lower a fever. They block steps in the biochemical pathways promoted by the fever-producing cytokines. A very high fever (105° F or higher) is extremely dangerous and can be fatal. At such high temperatures, proteins can denature (unfold) and critical biochemical processes can malfunction, causing cellular stress and, in small children, seizures.

Chemicals released by immune system cells can trigger a fever, which can inhibit pathogen growth.

FIGURE 26-12 Turning up the thermostat. Fever slows the growth of pathogens.

In the StreetBio at the end of Chapter 20, we described the new perspective on when to treat and when not to treat symptoms, called "Darwinian medicine." From this perspective, many protective responses that have evolved in organisms are recognized as having value in fighting illness. And consequently, treating symptoms such as fever, which is actually part of the immune system response to infection, can hinder our efforts at fighting infection. This idea was supported, for example, by the observation that chicken pox lasted longer, on average, in patients taking aspirin than in patients taking a non-fever-reducing placebo.

Q Is it always wise to treat a fever with aspirin or other medication?

TAKE-HOME MESSAGE 26·4

Inflammation is a major way in which pathogens are eliminated by the non-specific (innate) immunity system. The four recognizable signs of the inflammatory response (redness, heat, swelling, and pain) are related to the changes in blood vessels that enhance the recruitment of phagocytes and complement proteins to the site of inflammation. Fever-promoting cytokines cause the hypothalamus to set the body temperature higher, which may help the body fight an infection by stimulating the immune responses and inhibiting the growth of some pathogens.

Lines of Defense   Specific Immunity   Immune System Malfunction

A selection of cells from the bloodstream, including red blood cells (red), three T lymphocytes (orange), and activated platelets (green).

❷ Specific immunity develops after exposure to pathogens.

26·5

The specific division of the immune system forms a memory of specific pathogens.

Often, a pathogen can be eliminated by the non-specific system's inflammatory response. Sometimes, however, the pathogen has molecularly "disguised" itself in some way and is not recognized as a pathogen by the non-specific system, or the infection is persistent. Luckily, the specific division of the immune system is also there to protect us. Recall that non-specific defenses first *recognize* pathogens and then *respond*. The same is true for the specific division, but the recognition is more specific, and the types of cells and molecular weapons used in the response differ from those deployed by the innate division—in a sense, there is a trade-off between the speed of the non-specific response and the slower, but much more precise, response of the specific immunity system. The specific immunity system forms a memory (it "adapts" over one's lifetime), so the body's response to a specific pathogen occurs more quickly in future encounters. But the specific immunity system doesn't work alone; only by working together can the specific and non-specific systems completely defend us from the constant barrage of pathogens that surround us.

The memory of the specific division of the immune system results in **immunity,** a state of long-term protection against a specific pathogen. There are two ways in which we can acquire immunity to a particular pathogen. The first is to become sick with the disease (**FIGURE 26-13**). For example, people who contracted chicken pox when they were young cannot get chicken pox again; they are immune to it. Fortunately, there is a second way to gain immunity, without having to suffer through the disease and its unpleasant symptoms. A vaccine for chicken pox has been widely used since the mid-1990s. A **vaccine** is a weakened or harmless form of a specific pathogen that is administered to an individual to induce immunity, without subjecting the individual to the disease. Vaccines trick the body into thinking it has the full-blown disease, and the body mounts a specific immunity response. An individual who receives the chicken pox vaccine and is later exposed to the virus will not get the disease, because the body already has a memory of this virus (meaning that a group of cells—memory cells—are already primed to recognize and rapidly respond to the virus). On encountering the virus, there will be no lag time in responding. Vaccine technology has been a major success in medicine.

Today we have vaccines against numerous viruses (such as polio, measles, rubella, mumps, and rotavirus) and bacteria (such as tetanus, cholera, and meningitis). These vaccines are less available in the developing world and thus, worldwide, many people die each year from what are now preventable illnesses.

GETTING SICK

Exposure to a pathogen causes the body to form a memory of the pathogen, producing the cells necessary to rapidly respond to the pathogen if encountered again. Shown here: a toddler with chicken pox.

GETTING A VACCINATION

Exposure to a weakened or harmless form of a pathogen via a vaccine allows the body to form a memory of the pathogen without the risk of symptoms. The body then produces the cells necessary to rapidly respond to the pathogen if encountered again.

FIGURE 26-13 Two paths to immunity: contracting and fighting an illness, or receiving a vaccine.

 The memory of the adaptive system gives you immunity to a pathogen following exposure to it (ideally, with the exposure as a vaccine, rather than as an illness).

An **antigen** is any molecule that induces a specific immune response. A single pathogen often contains many different antigens (for example, the different glycoproteins, lipoproteins, and polysaccharides of a single bacterium can all be antigens). The body responds to antigens by making **antibodies,** circulating proteins that recognize specific antigens. (You can remember it like this: antigen is short for *anti*body *gen*erating.) Antibodies provide protection by enhancing the non-specific system's ability to recognize and destroy bacteria or viruses and the body cells they infect (**FIGURE 26-14**). Antibody levels peak within the first 2 weeks after encountering a pathogen or receiving a vaccine. We discuss the body's ability to recognize and destroy antigens in Section 26-8.

Even though antibody production eventually diminishes, the specific immunity system retains a memory of the disease. If the same antigen is encountered again, it will take the body only 1–2 days to begin producing large amounts of specific antibodies that aid in destruction of the pathogen; within just 7–9 days, there will be massive amounts of the antibodies. So, if a friend exposes you to chicken pox after you've already had the vaccine, your body won't need 2 weeks to respond: it will quickly kick into high gear and start antibody production immediately!

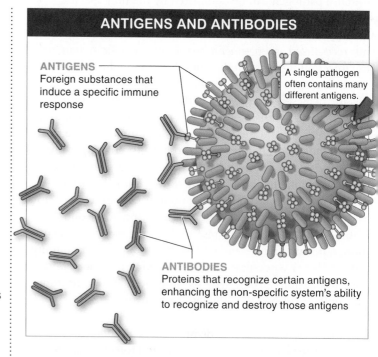

ANTIGENS AND ANTIBODIES

ANTIGENS
Foreign substances that induce a specific immune response

A single pathogen often contains many different antigens.

ANTIBODIES
Proteins that recognize certain antigens, enhancing the non-specific system's ability to recognize and destroy those antigens

FIGURE 26-14 Antibodies are proteins that recognize foreign molecules called antigens.

Lines of Defense | Specific Immunity | Immune System Malfunction

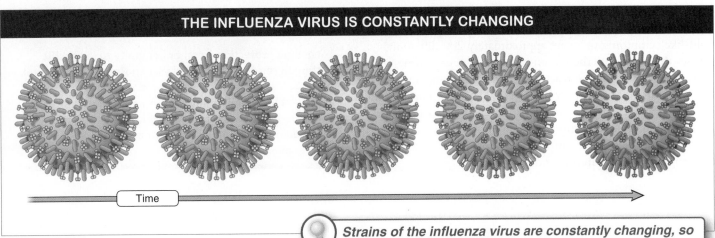

THE INFLUENZA VIRUS IS CONSTANTLY CHANGING

Time

FIGURE 26-15 Because the influenza virus changes so rapidly, flu vaccinations need to be given annually.

Strains of the influenza virus are constantly changing, so the body encounters a slightly different form with each new flu season, and therefore a different set of antigens.

Any vaccine must contain an antigen. In the case of the flu vaccine, for example, it is commonly an influenza virus that has been inactivated by heat or a live, weakened form of the virus that does not cause the flu. Although you can get the flu at any time of year, the flu season occurs in winter, so it makes sense to have the vaccine administered in autumn to give your body time to make antibodies that can protect you throughout the winter flu season.

Each year there are many different versions, or strains, of the influenza virus, which are constantly changing. With each new flu season, the body encounters a slightly different form of influenza and, therefore, a different set of antigens. As the virus adapts to changing conditions and evolves, the best protection is to get a flu shot each year (**FIGURE 26-15**). Yet, even with these preventive measures, a person may still get the flu. Although it is commonly thought that the flu shot itself can give someone the flu, this is simply not true. So, why do individuals sometimes get the flu after having the vaccination? There are several possible reasons. First, scientists developing the vaccine must make predictions, well before the flu season, about how the influenza virus will change in the upcoming season. Sometimes the vaccine "matches" the current virus, and sometimes it may be less than perfect. Second, different strains of the flu virus can circulate at the same time, and the vaccine may protect an individual from just one strain. Lastly, a person might already be infected with the flu at the time of vaccination.

Q Why don't people develop immunity to the common cold?

If the specific immune response can protect a person from illness during a future encounter with a specific pathogen, why is it that every winter you develop the runny nose, cough, and sore throat of the common cold? Why don't you develop immunity to this most annoying and recurrent disease? Just like the influenza virus, the rhinovirus ("nose virus"), one of the viruses that cause the common cold, continually changes (**FIGURE 26-16**). Your immune system mounts a response to each version of

There are approximately 200 different viruses that produce cold-like symptoms. Each time you catch a cold, you are reacting to a different version of the same virus or an entirely new virus.

FIGURE 26-16 **A constant challenge.** Many different, rapidly changing viruses cause the common cold.

the virus. Although rhinoviruses are a frequent cause of the common cold, they are not the only viruses that produce cold-like symptoms; there are approximately 200 different viruses that can cause the common cold. Thus, each time you catch a cold, you are reacting to a different version of the same virus or an entirely new virus. The sheer number of pathogens and their ability to adapt and evolve over time are two challenges that the immune system constantly faces. Nonetheless, the specific immunity system stands up to this challenge, as detailed in the next few sections.

26·6

Lymphocytes fight pathogens on two fronts.

Lymphocytes are the white blood cells responsible for the specific immunity response. These cells can be found circulating in the blood and lymphatic systems, and they reside in lymphatic organs such as the lymph nodes and spleen. (See Section 21-9 to review the lymphatic system.) In contrast to blood, which contains various types of white blood cells, 99% of the lymph is made up of lymphocytes. Lymphocytes have **antigen receptors,** proteins on their plasma membranes that stick out from the cell surface and can bind to specific antigens—any one lymphocyte binding to just one type. The presence of antigen receptors allows lymphocytes, collectively, to recognize and react to a wide array of antigens.

There are two major types of lymphocytes. Both develop in the bone marrow, but one type leaves the bone marrow and continues to mature in the thymus, a lymphatic organ located in the upper chest. These lymphocytes are named for where they mature and so are called T lymphocytes, or **T cells.** The other type of lymphocyte remains and matures in the bone marrow, and these are fittingly named B lymphocytes, or **B cells** (**FIGURE 26-17**).

The other cells that normally circulate in the lymphatic system are dendritic cells, which use the lymphatic system for the sole purpose of meeting up with lymphocytes. Recall that dendritic cells display digested pieces of pathogens, or antigens, to adaptive immune cells.

Immune system reactions are comparable to a military battle. In real-life combat, it is advantageous to attack by both land and air to win a battle. Like the armed forces, the specific

THE WHITE BLOOD CELLS OF SPECIFIC IMMUNITY

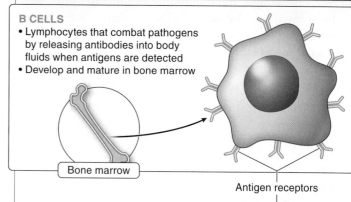

B CELLS
- Lymphocytes that combat pathogens by releasing antibodies into body fluids when antigens are detected
- Develop and mature in bone marrow

Bone marrow

Antigen receptors

T CELLS
- Lymphocytes that combat pathogens by directly destroying the infected cells
- Develop in bone marrow and mature in the thymus

Bone marrow — Thymus

FIGURE 26-17 B cells and T cells. These two types of lymphocytes are responsible for the specific immunity response. They are named for the location in the body where they mature (the bone marrow and thymus).

immune system has major divisions, too. Lymphocytes fight pathogens on two fronts: humoral and cell-mediated immunity (**FIGURE 26-18**).

Lines of Defense   Specific Immunity   Immune System Malfunction

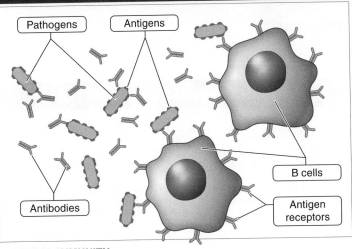

HUMORAL IMMUNITY
- Protection against pathogens and toxins found in body fluids, such as blood and lymph
- Carried out by B cells that secrete antibodies into body fluid, making it easier for phagocytes to engulf and destroy invading pathogens

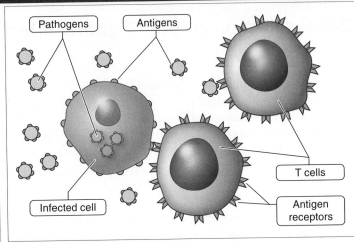

CELL-MEDIATED IMMUNITY
- Protection against pathogens and toxins found within body cells
- Carried out by T cells that directly destroy invading pathogens as well as the infected cells

FIGURE 26-18 Fighting invaders in body fluids and within cells. B cells are responsible for humoral immunity (antibody-mediated immunity) and T cells are responsible for cell-mediated immunity.

1. *Humoral immunity,* also referred to as antibody-mediated immunity, is protection against pathogens and toxins found in body fluids, such as blood and lymph. The word *humoral* (to give just a quick history lesson) comes from "humors"—the term Greeks and Romans used for body fluids. Blood was one of the four humors (the other three were phlegm, yellow bile, and black bile). Antibodies are secreted into the body fluids by cells derived from B cells following detection of an antigen. The antibodies circulating in blood and lymph defend against pathogens and toxins, making it easier for phagocytes to engulf them.

2. *Cell-mediated immunity* is protection from pathogens located *inside* body cells and is carried out by T cells. Your body cells have molecules on their cell membranes that identify them as "self" to the cells of your immune system—as cells that belong. But body cells that have been infected by a pathogen (and many cancer cells) present some different proteins (antigens) on their membranes. T cells recognize and bind to these antigens, initiating an immune response that kills the cells (and, usually, the pathogen within).

Both B and T cells have antigen receptors on their surfaces. These receptors differ in structure and are characterized by both diversity and specificity. There are endless variations of these receptors. It is estimated that our lymphocytes can recognize billions of different pathogens. But each individual lymphocyte doesn't bear billions of different antigen receptors. Instead, each lymphocyte has only one type of receptor that recognizes only one antigen, and it has many copies of this receptor on its surface. To defeat a specific pathogen, numerous identical lymphocytes (bearing the same antigen receptor) are needed.

You may be starting to ask yourself, do we have trillions of immune cells? How does the body have room for all of these individual armies of lymphocytes ready to face any enemy it might—or might not ever—encounter? The answer is that the body doesn't store vast quantities of identical lymphocytes. It makes copies of these lymphocytes *only if* the antigen is encountered. In the next section we see how the body does this.

TAKE-HOME MESSAGE 26·6

Two types of lymphocytes are associated with the specific immunity system: B cells and T cells. B cells are responsible for the humoral (antibody-mediated) response, and T cells for the cell-mediated response. Because of the diversity and specificity of lymphocyte receptors, almost any pathogen can be recognized by the body's B and T cells.

Clonal selection helps in fighting infection now and later.

Just about every lymphocyte in an individual is unique because of its specific antigen receptor. Although the immune system is *ready* to encounter any antigen, many lymphocytes will never meet the antigen they are capable of recognizing. But when a lymphocyte does come into contact with the antigen specific to its receptor, a sequence of events begins— and it doesn't end until the antigen is destroyed.

When a B or T cell binds to its antigen, the cell and its descendants divide numerous times to create a population of genetically identical cells (clones) with the same antigen specificity. This process, known as **clonal selection,** ensures that there are enough B and T cells to recognize and respond to a specific pathogen that has invaded the body.

Recognizing a new pathogen is an important first step, but the specific immunity system has two additional challenges: to *respond* to and *remember* the invader. Clonal selection generates many lymphocytes that can recognize the same pathogen, but these lymphocytes function in two different ways. Some attack the antigen (these are called effector cells) and some are involved in creating a memory of the invasion (the memory cells). We discuss the effector cells first.

The responders, or **effector cells,** recognize an antigen and immediately take some action that leads to its destruction. For example, **plasma cells,** derived from B cells, are the effector cells in the humoral response because they secrete antibodies. And T cells that directly kill infected cells are the effector cells in the cell-mediated response. During the immune system's first interaction with a pathogen, called the **primary response,** effector cells are not immediately available. The cells of the primary immune response must first be generated through clonal selection, which takes 2 weeks to produce effective numbers (**FIGURE 26-19**).

Also produced during the primary response is the second type of lymphocytes, the **memory cells.** Like effector cells, they are produced through clonal selection. The job of these lymphocytes is to remember an antigen so that, if the body is infected with the same antigen in the future, it will be ready to attack it. Thus, memory cells hang around in the lymph and blood and wait for their specific antigen to show up again. There are both B and T memory cells, and they have the same antigen specificity as the effector cells produced in the primary response. While effector cells live less than a week, memory cells remain and circulate for a long time. The

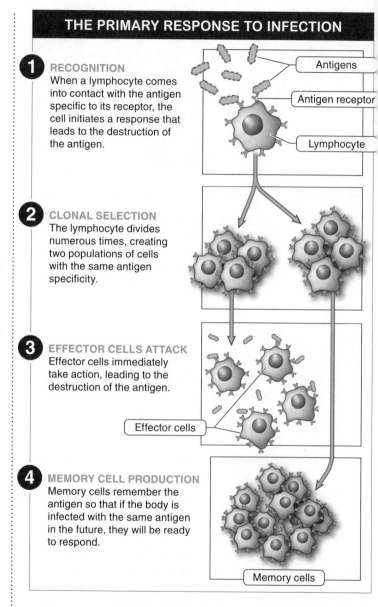

THE PRIMARY RESPONSE TO INFECTION

1 RECOGNITION
When a lymphocyte comes into contact with the antigen specific to its receptor, the cell initiates a response that leads to the destruction of the antigen.

Antigens
Antigen receptor
Lymphocyte

2 CLONAL SELECTION
The lymphocyte divides numerous times, creating two populations of cells with the same antigen specificity.

3 EFFECTOR CELLS ATTACK
Effector cells immediately take action, leading to the destruction of the antigen.

Effector cells

4 MEMORY CELL PRODUCTION
Memory cells remember the antigen so that if the body is infected with the same antigen in the future, they will be ready to respond.

Memory cells

FIGURE 26-19 Fighting now and later. The primary response leads to destruction of an antigen and generation of memory cells to fight the antigen should it ever be encountered again.

lifespan of memory cells is variable, but they may exist for years and possibly even for the individual's lifetime.

With this understanding of how effector cells and memory cells act in the primary immune response, let's look at what happens when a five-year-old kindergartener comes to school

THE SECONDARY RESPONSE TO INFECTION

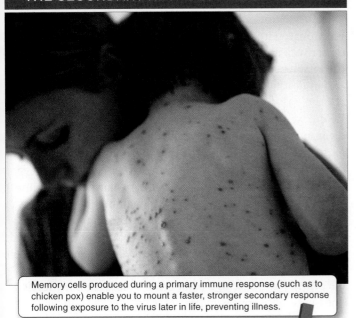

Memory cells produced during a primary immune response (such as to chicken pox) enable you to mount a faster, stronger secondary response following exposure to the virus later in life, preventing illness.

FIGURE 26-20 **Another encounter with the same antigen.** Because of memory cells, the secondary response is able to fight an antigen quickly and effectively.

not knowing that he has a chicken pox infection. Imagine that the kindergarten teacher had chicken pox as a small girl. At that time, her specific immunity system produced a population of chicken pox memory cells during her primary immune response. When the teacher interacts with the infected boy, these specific memory cells go through clonal selection and give rise to new B and T effector and memory cells. This **secondary response,** the creation of B and T effector cells, occurs rapidly (beginning after as little as 1–2 days) and produces a more intense response (peaking at 7–9 days) than the primary response that occurred in her childhood (**FIGURE 26-20**). Because the B cells of humoral immunity and the T cells of the cell-mediated response work immediately to destroy the virus, the teacher won't even miss a day of work, because this secondary immune response attacks the chicken pox virus so rapidly and effectively.

TAKE-HOME MESSAGE 26·7

When the body encounters a specific antigen, the lymphocytes recognizing this antigen divide to produce many cells through clonal selection. During a primary response, effector cells respond to and facilitate removal of the antigen. Memory cells produced during the primary response are ready to go through clonal selection if a secondary response is necessary.

26·8

The structure of antibodies reflects their function.

At this point you've learned that B cells are the effectors of the humoral response and that they produce antibodies, which are proteins that enhance the non-specific system's ability to recognize and destroy bacteria or viruses and infected body cells. We now examine the structure and function of antibodies to learn exactly how they work with the non-specific division of the immune system to protect us against pathogens.

During the primary immune response, a B cell with a highly specific receptor recognizes an antigen. The B cell receptors

are actually membrane-bound antibodies on the cell surface. All antibodies are Y-shaped, whether they are functioning as receptors or as soluble proteins released by B cells into lymph and blood. The diversity and specificity of antibodies come from variations in this Y-shaped structure.

Each antibody consists of four polypeptide chains joined together: two long (also called heavy) chains and two short (or light) chains (**FIGURE 26-21**). The top of the "Y" is the region that varies from antibody to antibody. But there are only

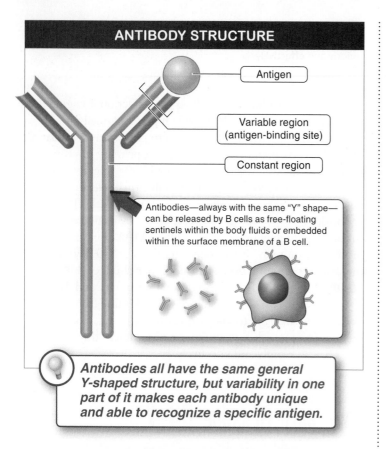

ANTIBODY STRUCTURE

Antigen

Variable region (antigen-binding site)

Constant region

Antibodies—always with the same "Y" shape—can be released by B cells as free-floating sentinels within the body fluids or embedded within the surface membrane of a B cell.

Antibodies all have the same general Y-shaped structure, but variability in one part of it makes each antibody unique and able to recognize a specific antigen.

FIGURE 26-21 Variations on a molecular theme. The shape of the top of the "Y" varies from one antibody to another and fits with only one antigen.

about five variants for the lower part, the base of the "Y," and so this is referred to as the constant region of an antibody. In the variable region, each antibody has a unique three-dimensional shape that dictates which specific antigen it will "fit." An enormous diversity of antibodies is needed to recognize a correspondingly enormous group of antigens that the immune system may encounter. Different antibodies can recognize different antigens on a given pathogen. Keep in mind that antibodies recognize *antigens,* not pathogens. And there are antigens that are not part of pathogens. An antigen is anything that an antibody recognizes, including snake venom toxins, bacterial toxins that cause food poisoning, pollen, and various chemicals (such as latex).

Any foreign cells introduced into the body will elicit an immune response, even if the cells are part of a life-saving medical treatment. Consider organ transplants. Transplanted cells have surface molecules that are seen as antigens ("non-self") by the recipient's immune system. Although the transplanted cells are not pathogens, the recipient's immune system identifies them as invaders, and an immune response begins. Medicines are needed to suppress the immune system's attack on and eventual destruction of a transplanted organ.

The immune system is also the reason that people in need of blood transfusions must have a proper match of blood type. As we saw in Section 7-10, if a transfusion is made between individuals with incompatible blood types, antibodies from the donor will attach to antigens on the surface of the foreign (i.e., the recipient's) red blood cells and mount an attack that can end in death.

Before we describe how antibodies work with the non-specific division of the immune system, let's briefly review the humoral response. When the humoral response begins, clonal selection produces two types of B cells: effector B cells that attack immediately and memory B cells that are inactive in the short run but will recognize a particular antigen in the future. As we mentioned in Section 26-7, the effector B cells that secrete antibodies are called plasma cells, and they can secrete hundreds to thousands of antibodies per second as a consequence of their extensive endomembrane system (see Section 3-17). During the primary response to a pathogen invasion, antibody levels don't peak until approximately 2 weeks after the antigen is recognized. In a secondary response, however, antibody levels rise more quickly and in larger numbers because of the memory B cells produced during the primary response. Furthermore, antibody production reaches higher levels and production is more sustained in this secondary response. Antibody levels can be up to 1,000 times higher in a secondary response than in the primary response

Now let's consider the main ways in which the antibodies themselves function (**FIGURE 26-22**).

As we've seen, the immune system pumps out tons of antibodies during a humoral response, but antibodies don't *directly* kill the pathogen. Instead, they use the non-specific cells of the non-specific immune system (such as macrophages and neutrophils) to kill the pathogen. When the antigens on the surface of a pathogen have an antibody attached to them, the pathogen is easily ingested by phagocytes of the innate system. The antibodies act as beacons that make pathogens highly conspicuous to patrolling phagocytes.

Besides "marking" a pathogen—or marking free-floating antigens that are not part of a pathogen, such as a snake venom toxin—for destruction, antibodies act in two other important ways: (1) they cause pathogens or antigens to clump together, making it easier for phagocytes to find and ingest them; and (2) they coat the surfaces of pathogens and prevent them from binding to and entering body cells, thus blocking the infection from spreading.

Lastly, antibodies have a role in recruiting another player of the non-specific system when bound to the surface of a pathogen: complement proteins. Recall that some proteins of

Lines of Defense   Specific Immunity   Immune System Malfunction

ANTIBODY FUNCTIONS

Antibodies function in several ways to help destroy pathogens and soluble antigens.

PHAGOCYTE SIGNALING
Antibodies bind to antigens on the surface of pathogens, making it easier for phagocytes to find the pathogens and destroy them.

ANTIGEN CLUMPING
Antibodies make pathogens and soluble antigens clump together, making it easier for phagocytes to find them and destroy them.

PREVENTION OF CELL ENTRY
Antibodies coating the surface of pathogens prevent the pathogens from entering body cells, thus blocking the infection from spreading.

COMPLEMENT PROTEIN SIGNALING
Antibodies recruit complement proteins, which poke holes in pathogen membranes, causing the pathogen cells to burst.

FIGURE 26-22 **Antibodies fight pathogens in several ways.**

Antibodies produced by the mother and present in her breast milk get into the baby's bloodstream and protect the baby for the first few months of life.

FIGURE 26-23 **An excellent reason to breastfeed an infant.** Passive immunity transfers immunity from mother to child.

the complement system can poke holes in membranes and cause cells to lyse (burst). Antibodies indirectly lead to pathogen lysis through their recruitment of these complement proteins.

> **Q** Do newborn babies have any protection from diseases?

Would isolating antibodies from one person's blood and giving them to another person who has not yet encountered that disease protect the recipient? Yes. But, it would only be short-term protection, because the memory B cells that have the ability to make more antibodies are not transferred. Transferring antibodies with a given specificity is termed *passive immunity*. This is in contrast to vaccination, in which the immune system develops long-term, *active immunity*. An example of passive immunity occurs during pregnancy—antibodies produced by the mother are transferred to the baby's bloodstream and protect the baby for the first few months of life.

How do we know about passive immunity? In some regions of the developing world where measles is still prevalent, infants breastfeeding from mothers who have either had the measles or received the measles vaccine have antibodies in their bloodstream in the first few months of life and are protected from the disease during these months (**FIGURE 26-23**). This protection only lasts while the antibodies are still present. (Remember, infants are also born with the non-specific immune system, which provides much protection in addition to that of their immature specific immunity system.) Interestingly, passive immunity is also the key to treating snake bites. The anti-venom injection given at the site of the bite is actually a solution of antibodies to the venom antigens.

TAKE-HOME MESSAGE 26·8

Each antibody has a unique structure that recognizes a specific antigen. Plasma cells secrete high levels of antibodies into the blood and lymph. Antibodies are effective in helping to destroy pathogens and soluble antigens by enhancing ingestion by phagocytes, preventing more cell infection, and enhancing complement-driven lysis. Passive immunity is just short-term protection, because only antibodies are transferred, not the B cells that make the antibodies.

Cytotoxic T cells and helper T cells serve different functions.

The specific immunity response, as we've seen, is made up of both the humoral response (B cells) and the cell-mediated response (T cells). Why the two-pronged approach? Aren't antibodies sufficient? In a word: *no.* Consider a viral infection. Antibodies, circulating in blood and lymph, can recognize and bind to a specific virus in these body fluids. A virus that is coated with antibodies cannot effectively bind to and enter a host cell, which is a required event in viral infection. This antibody coating is effective in slowing infection, but what happens to all the body cells that already have viruses hiding inside them? Antibodies cannot enter these cells—it is the role of the T cell-mediated response to fight pathogens that are already inside cells. We focus here on this T cell-mediated response, and begin by examining the two major types of T cells, both of which are lymphocytes:

1. **Cytotoxic T cells,** which are the effectors of the cell-mediated response; they directly kill cells infected with pathogens.

2. **Helper T cells,** which do not directly kill infected cells but, instead, stimulate other immune cells. They are required in the stimulation of B cells to produce antibodies and of cytotoxic T cells to kill infected cells.

We'll follow a viral infection through the cell-mediated response to demonstrate how T cells function (**FIGURE 26-24**).

When a pathogen enters the body, the phagocytes and NK cells of the non-specific system respond. Meanwhile, dendritic cells and macrophages call on the specific system by "advertising" antigens to circulating lymphocytes. Dendritic cells and macrophages (as well as B cells) that "present" digested particles of pathogens on their cell surfaces are called **antigen-presenting cells.** The role of presenting cells is essential to T cell functioning, because T cells can only recognize an infected cell by the antigens presented on its plasma membrane.

Imagine a dendritic cell in your throat that has engulfed a respiratory virus and is presenting an antigen (digested virus particle) on its cell surface. If this presenting cell is to increase the likelihood of "meeting up" with a T cell that will recognize this specific antigen, hanging out in the tissues of your throat is not very effective. It is more effective for the

FIGURE 26-24 Helper T cells and cytotoxic T cells work together to recognize and respond to pathogens.

T CELL-MEDIATED RESPONSE

1 PRESENTATION
An antigen-presenting cell displays digested particles of a virus to a helper T cell that recognizes the viral antigen being presented.

2 ACTIVATION
Binding to the antigen-presenting cell activates the helper T cell, which then produces cytokines that activate cytotoxic T cells, as well as the B cells of the humoral response.

B cell development occurs only in response to the signals from helper T cells.

3 CLONAL EXPANSION
Both helper T cells and cytotoxic T cells undergo clonal expansion, producing vast amounts of memory and effector cells with specificity for the viral antigen.

Cytotoxic T cells (memory and effector cells)

Helper T cells (memory and effector cells)

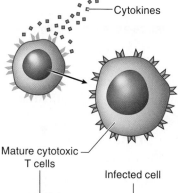

4 MATURATION
Other cytokines produced by the helper T cells make the cytotoxic T cells mature and ready to fight the pathogen at the site of infection.

Cytokines

Mature cytotoxic T cells

Infected cell

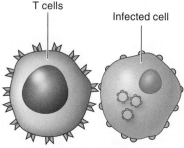

5 DESTRUCTION
Mature cytotoxic effector cells circulate throughout the body, destroying cells infected with the specific viral antigen.

Lines of Defense | Specific Immunity | Immune System Malfunction

presenting cell to circulate in the lymph nodes and spleen where lymphocytes circulate.

A dendritic cell circulating through a lymph node or the spleen may bump into T cells with specificity for the viral antigen being presented. The T cell receptor recognizes the antigen, and the T cell "locks" onto the antigen-presenting cell. Once this binding has taken place, the helper T cell has been "activated." Activated helper T cells produce signaling molecules (cytokines), most notably interleukin 2 (IL-2), that activate the other type of T cell, cytotoxic T cells. Both helper T cells and cytotoxic T cells undergo clonal expansion, producing vast numbers of memory and effector cells with specificity for this respiratory virus antigen. Other cytokines produced by the activated helper T cells provide the final signals that make the cytotoxic T cells "mature" and ready to fight the pathogen at the site of infection. You may notice this process occurring; the rapid division of lymphocytes in the lymph nodes is often pronounced and sometimes produces "swollen glands." The T cells then leave the lymph nodes or spleen and circulate throughout the body. (Helper T cells also are required to stimulate B cells to produce antibodies; B cell development occurs only in response to these signals from helper T cells.)

Mature cytotoxic effector cells are like newly trained soldiers, ready to fight the enemy, but first they need to detect where the enemy is hiding. Consider that infected cell in the throat again. Is it revealing that it's under attack? Yes! The infected cell displays some of the pathogen's molecules on its cell surface receptors, advertising the infection to the now numerous cytotoxic T cells that are able to recognize the specific respiratory virus.

How do the cytotoxic effector cells fight the internal pathogen? They do something drastic—they kill the throat cell that is infected. The weapons that they use are proteins: some punch holes in the cell's plasma membrane, and others promote the cell's self-destruction, or **apoptosis.** This programmed cell death does not explode the cell—sending virus particles everywhere. Just the opposite—it is a neatly organized, well-orchestrated process carried out by enzymes that break down macromolecules inside the cell and fragment the cell into smaller vesicles. Phagocytes then clean up the

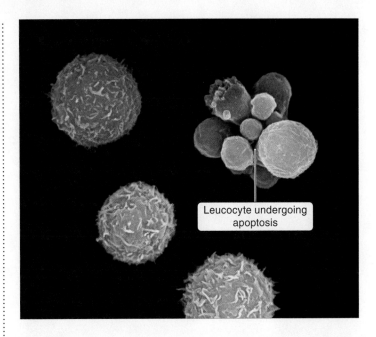

Leucocyte undergoing apoptosis

FIGURE 26-25 Programmed cell death. Shown are four leukocytes (white blood cells). The one at the top right is undergoing apoptosis.

debris (**FIGURE 26-25**). So, while some body cells are lost in the battle, ultimately it is for the good of the entire organism.

Because memory helper T cells and memory cytotoxic T cells are also made during the throat infection, this same virus cannot cause illness again. Remember, this is specific immunity, and memory cells will leap into action to make more effector cells if the virus is encountered again.

TAKE-HOME MESSAGE 26·9

Antibodies, produced by B cells, cannot destroy pathogens that are inside cells. The specialization of cytotoxic T cells is required to kill infected cells. Antigen-presenting cells display antigens to circulating helper T cells and cytotoxic T cells, to alert the specific immunity system to an infection. In turn, helper T cells produce cytokines that instruct cytotoxic T cells to mature and respond to the infection.

❸ Malfunction of the immune system causes disease.

The human immunodeficiency virus (HIV).

26·10

Autoimmune diseases occur when the body turns against its own tissues.

What happens when the immune system malfunctions? Genetic defects, environmental influences, or even viruses can trigger immune dysfunction. And in many cases, such as autoimmune diseases, a combination of causes is suspected, but not completely understood. **Autoimmunity** occurs when an individual's immune system responds inappropriately to the individual's own cells and tissues as if they were pathogens, mistaking "self " for "non-self." If immunity can be compared to warfare, then autoimmunity is equivalent to an army turning its weapons upon its own citizens. Lymphocyte receptors wrongly recognize an individual's own molecules or cellular structures as antigens, and the humoral and/or cell-mediated immune responses can be initiated by these **autoantigens.** Most autoimmune diseases result in significant tissue and organ damage, and some can even result in death.

Type 1 diabetes (or juvenile diabetes) is an example of an autoimmune disorder. It is diagnosed in more than 13,000 young people in the United States each year. Symptoms include high blood glucose levels, weight loss, unquenchable thirst, frequent urination, fatigue, and weakness. In this disease,

AUTOIMMUNITY: TYPE 1 DIABETES

Type 1 diabetes is an autoimmune disorder in which cytotoxic T cells destroy one's own pancreatic cells.

Healthy pancreatic cells

Cytotoxic T cells

T cell receptors incorrectly recognize healthy pancreatic cells as antigens, initiating a cell-mediated immune response against them.

FIGURE 26-26 **Type 1 diabetes is an all-too-common autoimmune disorder.**

Lines of Defense   Specific Immunity   Immune System Malfunction

cytotoxic T cells destroy the person's own pancreatic cells. Antibody production leads to even more damage through complement-mediated lysis and macrophage ingestion of pancreatic cells. Without a normal pancreas, a person cannot make insulin (**FIGURE 26-26**). Without insulin, cells in need of glucose are not able to take it up from the blood, even though glucose is plentiful. In turn, the body breaks down muscle and fat tissues to provide cells with needed energy, and blood glucose levels remain high. The exact cause of the autoimmune reaction is not understood. Treatment for individuals with type 1 diabetes is insulin injections or implantation of an insulin pump, which directly monitors blood glucose levels and releases insulin as needed.

In some disorders, including type 1 diabetes, the immune system destroys a single cell type or a single organ. In other disorders, the damage is spread throughout the body. When the insulation (myelin) that surrounds nerve fibers of the brain and spinal cord is under immune attack, the resulting disorder is called **multiple sclerosis (MS)** (see Section 23-4). Individuals with MS usually begin to exhibit symptoms between 20 and 40 years of age, and these symptoms include blurred vision, weakness in the arms and legs, trouble with balance, and tingling sensations (**FIGURE 26-27**). This disorder tends to affect women more than men, and it affects more than 300,000 people in the United States. There is no cure for MS, but anti-inflammatory drugs can reduce the severity of some symptoms. Many new drugs are being investigated, including some that block cytokines and hence the inflammatory response.

Rheumatoid arthritis is another autoimmune disease that affects women more frequently than men, and usually strikes between ages 40 and 60. (This form of arthritis is a far less common cause of joint inflammation than osteoarthritis, which is not an autoimmune disease.) The linings of joints are the autoantigens of this immune attack—leading to pain and severe joint swelling that can result in deformities. Various

Multiple sclerosis is the result of an autoimmune attack on the insulation that surrounds the nerve fibers of the brain and spinal cord.

FIGURE 26-27 An autoimmune disorder: multiple sclerosis.

pharmaceuticals are available to help reduce symptoms, and joint replacement surgeries also provide relief for individuals suffering from rheumatoid arthritis.

TAKE-HOME MESSAGE 26·10

When lymphocytes bear receptors that inappropriately recognize structures of a person's own body, autoimmunity develops. Autoimmune responses can do significant damage to specific organs or to tissues throughout the body, depending on where the antigens are located.

26·11

AIDS is an immune deficiency disease.

Autoimmune diseases demonstrate how immune recognition can fail and have devastating effects on the body. Here we examine a case in which recognition of a true pathogen occurs, but the *response* is deficient. Normally, the immune system destroys body cells that are infected with a virus. But what if the infected cells are immune cells that are critical for mounting a normal immune response? The **human immunodeficiency virus (HIV)**, which causes **AIDS (acquired immune deficiency syndrome)**, infects immune system cells, including

helper T cells—cells that are crucial to survival. With AIDS, a deficiency of helper T cells leads to complete failure of the specific immunity response. As a result of this failure, individuals are prey to, and may die from, infections that a healthy immune system would have no trouble defeating.

HIV infection occurs through contact with blood, semen, vaginal fluid, or breast milk from an infected person. Thus, using clean (not shared) intravenous needles and using condoms are effective precautionary measures against HIV infection. People who become infected with HIV often do not have immediate symptoms and often do not know they are infected. Because individuals are contagious once they are infected, this initial lack of symptoms contributes to the spread of the disease. Let's examine the details of how immunity diminishes as the immune system loses its battle against HIV.

Different viruses infect different kinds of body cells. HIV infects helper T cells, macrophages, and dendritic cells. When an individual is first infected by HIV, a normal specific immunity response is mounted, and infected helper T cells are killed by both humoral and cell-mediated responses. More than 99% of the virus is destroyed in this primary response. Although many helper T cells are lost, new helper T cells arise. As you might expect, antibodies against HIV are made in a humoral response and can easily be detected in blood tests within months of the initial infection. Antibody detection marks the end of the first phase of HIV infection, the *acute phase* (**FIGURE 26-28**).

Unfortunately, the viruses that were not destroyed by the primary response can lie dormant inside infected helper T cells and macrophages. An infected person then enters a period in which he or she is infectious but doesn't have outward symptoms, called the *chronic phase.* This period is variable but rarely exceeds 12 years. Although the infection may seem inactive, a battle is going on within the immune system. Some of the HIV viruses lie dormant but others replicate and infect new helper T cells. Helper T cells that are infected are killed by the viral infection or are destroyed by the immune system's normal responses. New helper T cells arise, and new viruses infect them. This cycle continues, but it is not a balanced situation. Sooner or later, the number of viruses climbs and the number of helper T cells decreases, and serious clinical symptoms appear. (This process is like an army valiantly fighting a battle but ultimately running out of soldiers.)

A severe shortage of helper T cells marks the progression from HIV infection to AIDS. Without helper T cells, B cells and cytotoxic T cells cannot be activated (recall from Section 26-9 that helper T cells stimulate the production of B cells and cytotoxic T cells). Common pathogens that are normally kept at bay in a healthy individual—such as a parasitic protist that causes diarrhea, a fungus that causes "thrush" on the tongue and throat, and viruses that can cause skin lesions, diarrhea, and swelling—ultimately lead to debilitating illness and death.

Q Why is there no vaccine against AIDS yet?

As we saw in Section 13-18, HIV is an RNA-containing virus that mutates rapidly. Even within a single host, the virus's surface proteins can change with each new round of replication

IMMUNE SYSTEM DEFICIENCY: HIV

ACUTE PHASE

1 HIV infects helper T cells, macrophages, and dendritic cells.

HIV virus · Helper T cell · Macrophage · Dendritic cell

2 Humoral and cell-mediated immune responses eliminate over 99% of the virus.

Antibodies against HIV, made in the humoral response, can be detected in blood tests within months of the initial infection.

CHRONIC PHASE

3 Viruses not destroyed by the primary response can lie dormant inside infected helper T cells or replicate and infect new helper T cells.

4 Infected helper T cells are destroyed by the viral infection or by the immune system's normal responses.

5 New helper T cells arise, yet new viruses infect them. Eventually, the number of viruses climbs and the number of helper T cells decreases.

A severe shortage of helper T cells marks the progression from HIV infection to AIDS.

AIDS

6 Without helper T cells, B cells and cytotoxic T cells cannot be activated.

B cell · Helper T cell · Cytotoxic T cell

7 Common pathogens that are normally kept at bay in a healthy individual lead to serious illness and, ultimately, death.

Common pathogens

FIGURE 26-28 The progression from HIV infection to AIDS.

Lines of Defense · Specific Immunity · Immune System Malfunction

(**FIGURE 26-29**). These changing surface proteins pose recognition problems for the pool of cytotoxic T cells derived through clonal selection to recognize the original virus. Antibodies made against the original virus do not recognize newer, mutated versions. The ever-changing HIV makes developing vaccines against it challenging, too. Consider a vaccine that is made using a surface glycoprotein of HIV as the antigen. The vaccine becomes obsolete immediately, because the virus antigen is changing too quickly. More than 25 years after isolating the virus, this traditional method of making vaccines against viral antigens has failed because of the constantly mutating HIV. Interestingly, some people have a mutation in a T cell receptor that makes it more difficult for the virus to enter their helper T cells. Ongoing studies of individuals who are naturally resistant to HIV are helping scientists develop new potential vaccines and drug treatments.

Current therapies for HIV infection have been successful at increasing the length and quality of life for those infected. The regimen, called combination therapy, includes numerous drugs that affect HIV's ability to replicate or infect new cells. These drugs keep the virus number low and maintain a suitable number of helper T cells. HIV resistance to the drugs, however, is a fear shared by both patients and clinicians. Nonetheless, the lifespan for individuals taking combination therapy is increasing and getting close to normal. Although there is not a cure yet, individuals who have access to treatment are able to live with HIV as a chronic condition.

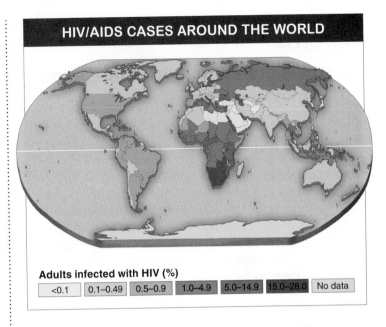

HIV/AIDS CASES AROUND THE WORLD

Adults infected with HIV (%)

| <0.1 | 0.1–0.49 | 0.5–0.9 | 1.0–4.9 | 5.0–14.9 | 15.0–28.0 | No data |

FIGURE 26-30 HIV/AIDS is widespread in sub-Saharan Africa.

(Unfortunately, treatment is unavailable for millions infected in developing nations.) New therapies aim to find latent viruses that hide inside helper T cells, sometimes for decades, and eliminate them. In the future, HIV may be a disease that can be cured, but for now it continues to be a life-long condition and a challenge to scientists.

Looking at a map depicting HIV/AIDS cases around the world, we can see just how widespread this virus is. Sub-Saharan Africa is the region most severely affected. In some countries in this region, such as Swaziland and Lesotho, close to 25% of the adult population is infected with HIV. In South Africa, more than 5 million people, or almost 20% of its adult population, are infected (**FIGURE 26-30**). In contrast, less than 1% of the U.S. population is infected with HIV. Not everyone who is HIV-infected has AIDS, however. For example, estimates indicate that of the more than one million people infected by HIV in the United States, in fewer than 40,000 cases has the infection progressed to AIDS.

TAKE-HOME MESSAGE 26·11

AIDS is an immune system disease caused by the human immunodeficiency virus (HIV), which infects helper T cells—immune cells that are crucial to survival. As helper T cells are killed by the infection or by the body's own cells in response to the infection, the deficiency of helper T cells leads to complete failure of the specific immunity response, resulting in illness and death from infections that a healthy immune system could defeat. There is currently no vaccine for HIV, because traditional vaccine methods do not work against this rapidly mutating virus, nor is there a cure for AIDS.

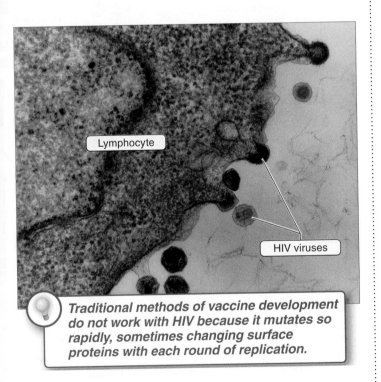

Lymphocyte

HIV viruses

Traditional methods of vaccine development do not work with HIV because it mutates so rapidly, sometimes changing surface proteins with each round of replication.

FIGURE 26-29 An ever-changing foe. Surface proteins on the HIV virus change rapidly as the virus replicates, leaving the body to fight an almost impossible-to-identify enemy.

Allergies are an inappropriate immune response to a harmless substance.

A three-year-old girl bites into a peanut butter sandwich. She immediately develops hives around her mouth and begins vomiting. She is having an allergic reaction. This is only the second time she's eaten peanut butter. Unfortunately, her story is not unusual. The Centers for Disease Control and Prevention (CDC) estimates that approximately 3 million children in the United States have food allergies, 90% caused by just eight foods: peanuts, tree nuts, milk, eggs, fish, shellfish, soy, and wheat. **Allergies** are an inappropriate immune response to what should be a harmless substance.

In discussing antibodies earlier in the chapter, we did not focus on the groups of antibodies that differ in their constant (heavy) region at the base of the "Y." There are five classes of antibodies, differing in their chemical structure in this region. When antibodies of one of these classes bind to mast cells (the white blood cells found in tissues), they cause the mast cells to release histamine and cytokines, both of which cause local blood vessels to become dilated and leaky. Recall that this dilation and leakiness are standard parts of the inflammatory response and are useful for recruiting other immune cells to the site of infection.

This class of antibodies can cause much harm to the body, however, if they are made in response to an **allergen,** an antigen that causes an allergic response. Upon first encounter, an allergen induces a normal humoral response: memory cells form and plasma cells secrete antibodies specific to the allergen. The antibodies bind to the surface of mast cells and can remain bound for months and maybe even years. The mast cells are now "sensitized" to the allergen. While the first exposure often goes unnoticed, the second exposure can be damaging and potentially life-threatening. In the second exposure, the allergen binds to the antibody that is still attached to the mast cells—which are now "activated." This time, allergen binding causes the mast cells to release histamine, which causes the blood vessels to dilate and become leaky, and inflammation ensues (**FIGURE 26-31**).

The effect of different allergens reflects which particular mast cells have been exposed to the allergen and thus activated. Most allergic reactions occur in the digestive or respiratory tracts, because this is where the body first encounters an allergen that is eaten or inhaled. Allergic reactions associated with food often lead to vomiting or diarrhea, but can also lead to hives and other symptoms if the allergen enters the bloodstream. Respiratory allergens, such as pollen and dust, can cause a runny nose and teary eyes ("hay fever") in the upper respiratory tract, or can result in asthma, a chronic inflammatory disease of the lower respiratory tract that causes wheezing, coughing, and

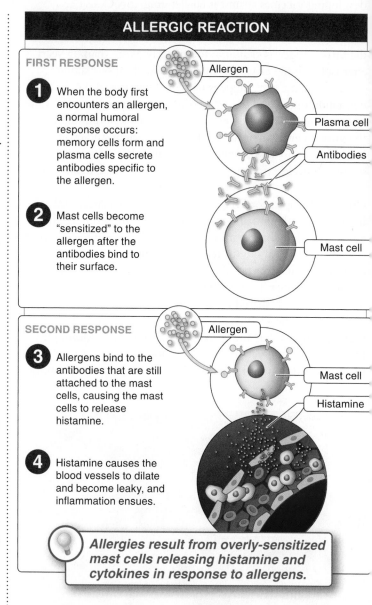

ALLERGIC REACTION

FIRST RESPONSE

Allergen

1 When the body first encounters an allergen, a normal humoral response occurs: memory cells form and plasma cells secrete antibodies specific to the allergen.

Plasma cell

Antibodies

2 Mast cells become "sensitized" to the allergen after the antibodies bind to their surface.

Mast cell

SECOND RESPONSE

Allergen

3 Allergens bind to the antibodies that are still attached to the mast cells, causing the mast cells to release histamine.

Mast cell

Histamine

4 Histamine causes the blood vessels to dilate and become leaky, and inflammation ensues.

Allergies result from overly-sensitized mast cells releasing histamine and cytokines in response to allergens.

FIGURE 26-31 Allergens induce a humoral response in some individuals.

shortness of breath. Allergic eczema, a chronic skin disorder characterized by scaly and itchy rashes, is a result of allergens that bind to mast cells in the skin.

Taking an antihistamine can alleviate some allergies, as these medicines block the inflammatory effects of histamine. Other medicines block mast cells from releasing histamine. Steroids are prescribed for more severe allergies. Steroids block the production of cytokines from immune cells, thus preventing

Lines of Defense   Specific Immunity   Immune System Malfunction

he migration of more inflammatory cells, such as macrophages and neutrophils, to the site of inflammation. Additionally, the eroids can block the killing ability of these phagocytes, esulting in less damage to the inflamed tissue.

An individual with a severe allergic response may experience **anaphylactic shock,** a life-threatening allergic reaction that is ystemic, meaning that it is not localized to the site of exposure. Anaphylactic shock can lead to severe respiratory distress, as the hroat swells and asthma develops. Swelling in various tissues neans there is less fluid in the blood system, and this can lead to angerously low blood pressure. Individuals with severe allergies ften carry with them a dose of adrenaline (also called pinephrine), a chemical found naturally in our bodies (see ection 24-5) and also manufactured by several drug companies. Epinephrine, which can be injected if needed, reverses the effects of histamine on blood vessels, but it must be injected quickly, because death can occur rapidly from anaphylactic shock.

A common method of testing for allergies is called *skin allergy esting,* in which microscopic amounts of one or more potential llergens are injected under the skin—usually on the back or he forearm. The development of a rash can indicate a ypersensitivity to that allergen, enabling the person to take teps to reduce exposure to the allergen (**FIGURE 26-32**).

Allergies are on the rise in the industrialized world, asthma specially. Asthma results in an airway that is swollen and nflamed and leads to chest tightness, coughing, wheezing, and reathing difficulty. The CDC estimates that the incidence of

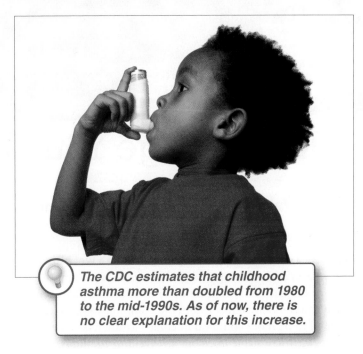

The CDC estimates that childhood asthma more than doubled from 1980 to the mid-1990s. As of now, there is no clear explanation for this increase.

FIGURE 26-33 Asthma. Individuals with asthma may need to inhale medications to counteract the airway restriction associated with this allergic response.

childhood asthma more than doubled from 1980 to the mid-1990s, by that time affecting about 1 in 14 American adults and almost 1 in 10 children (**FIGURE 26-33**).

As is true for many complex diseases, there are both genetic and environmental factors associated with asthma. But our genes are not changing fast enough to explain the increase in occurrence of asthma—which has led scientists to examine the environmental factors that have changed in the past few decades. Determining which environmental factors cause asthma is not a simple task. Numerous correlations have been proposed, including increased air pollution, increased antibiotic or acetaminophen use in infancy, less exposure to infections (due to better hygiene), use of vaccines, rising global temperatures, diets lacking vitamin D, increased exposure to cleaning sprays, indoor dust, cigarette smoke . . . and the list goes on. As yet, there is no simple or clear explanation of why asthma is on the rise in developed countries.

TAKE-HOME MESSAGE 26·12

In individuals who are sensitive, an allergen induces a humoral response in which one class of antibodies binds to and activates mast cells. A second exposure to the allergen leads to activated mast cells releasing histamine and cytokines, resulting in allergy-related symptoms. Swelling and inflammation can be localized or can be systemic and lead to anaphylactic shock.

IGURE 26-32 Screening for allergies. Allergens are injected under he skin on which a grid has been drawn. If a bump or rash develops n any of the squares, an allergy may be suspected.

Knowledge You Can Use

Fact or fallacy? How best to avoid getting sick.

Q: Can I catch a cold from going out with wet hair in the winter? No. Your grandmother was wrong about this one! To catch a cold, you must be infected with a pathogen (such as a rhinovirus) that causes the common cold. Colds do tend to be more common in colder weather, because the viruses are more stable in colder air with low humidity. And droplets of water and virus (such as those that escape when we sneeze and cough) remain airborne slightly longer in dry air than in humid summer air. Also, because people are indoors more often during winter, the increased population in confined quarters increases the incidence and ease of transmission. So while the virus is affected by the colder weather, your immune system is not. Dry your hair before you leave the house if you don't want icicles in it, but not as strategy for combating the common cold.

Q: Can I catch a cold because I am not sleeping enough? This gets an emphatic *yes!* In randomized, controlled studies in which individuals were given nasal drops containing rhinovirus, individuals getting less sleep were significantly more likely to develop colds than those

sleeping 7 hours or more. And simply resting in bed or having an interrupted night's sleep doesn't count. Seven hours or more of good-quality sleep seems to be important to the immune system, particularly for the production and functioning of cytokines. Interestingly, there is also evidence that individuals who sleep 7–8 hours a night have the lowest rates of heart disease. Although eating well and exercising are most often associated with good health, sleep, too, is important, and neglecting it can increase your vulnerability to illness.

Q: Can drinking herbal teas, eating chicken soup, or taking "Airborne" help me ward off the common cold? *Herbal teas and chicken soup?* Not exactly. There are some symptom-reducing benefits of hot fluids, including keeping nasal passages moist, preventing dehydration, and soothing a sore throat. And one study showed that chicken soup with vegetables seemed to have an anti-inflammatory effect. But while these effects can make an infection less unpleasant by reducing the symptoms, they don't decrease the likelihood of catching a cold or shorten its duration. *Airborne?* Remember the very first section of the first chapter of this book? There is not a shred of evidence that Airborne can ward off colds or boost your immune system.

❶ Your body has different ways to protect you against disease-causing invaders.

The immune system protects the body from a diverse group of pathogens. There are three collaborative divisions of the immune system: physical barriers, non-specific immunity, and specific immunity. Physical barriers, part of the integumentary system, prevent pathogens from entering the body's cells; cells not covered by skin but exposed to the external environment are protected by defenses such as bacteria-destroying chemicals, acidic secretions, sticky mucus, and wax. Non-specific (innate) immunity defends against pathogens by recognizing combinations of receptors on their cell surfaces. White blood cells of the non-specific system include phagocytes—such as neutrophils and macrophages that ingest and kill pathogens, and macrophages and dendritic cells that display pathogens to cells of the specific immunity system—and natural killer cells that kill cancer cells and virus-infected cells. Complement proteins non-specifically recognize invaders and help destroy them. Inflammation is a major way in which the innate system eliminates pathogens. The four signs of the inflammatory response (redness, heat, swelling, and pain) are related to changes in blood vessels that enhance recruitment of phagocytes and complement proteins to the site of inflammation.

❷ Specific immunity develops after exposure to pathogens.

Long-term protection, or immunity, from a specific pathogen can form in two ways: exposure to the natural pathogen or exposure to a vaccine with an altered version of the pathogen. Exposure to an antigen results in production of antibodies. The specific (adaptive) immunity system responds continually to numerous pathogens that can change over time, through the action of two types of lymphocytes: B cells and T cells. B cells are responsible for the humoral (antibody-mediated) response, and T cells for the cell-mediated response. When the body encounters an antigen, the lymphocytes recognizing this antigen divide to produce many cells through clonal selection. During a primary response, effector cells respond to and facilitate removal of the antigen, and memory cells are produced that are ready to go through clonal selection if a secondary response is necessary. Plasma cells secrete high levels of antibodies into the blood and lymph. Each antibody has a unique structure that recognizes a specific antigen. Antibodies help destroy pathogens and soluble antigens by enhancing ingestion by phagocytes, preventing more cell infection, and enhancing complement-driven cell lysis, but they cannot destroy pathogens that are inside cells. Cytotoxic T cells undergo specialization to kill infected cells. Antigen-presenting cells display antigens to helper T cells and cytotoxic T cells, to alert the adaptive immune system to an infection. In turn, helper T cells produce cytokines that allow cytotoxic T cells to mature and respond to the infection.

❸ Malfunction of the immune system causes disease.

When lymphocytes bear receptors that inappropriately recognize structures of a person's own body, autoimmunity develops and significantly damages specific organs or tissues throughout the body. AIDS is an immune system disease caused by the human immunodeficiency virus (HIV), which infects helper T cells. As these cells are killed by the infection or by the body's own cells in response to the infection, the deficiency of helper T cells leads to complete failure of the specific immunity response and thus illness and death from infections that a healthy immune system could defeat. In individuals who are sensitive, allergens induce a humoral response in which one type of antibody binds to mast cells, activating them. With a second exposure to the allergen, activated mast cells release histamine and cytokines, resulting in allergy-related symptoms. Swelling and inflammation can be localized or can be systemic and lead to anaphylactic shock.

KEY TERMS

1. Which of the following statements about the integumentary system is incorrect?
   a) It is one of the body's three lines of defense against infectious pathogens.
   b) It confers specific immunity on an individual because it confers protection against individual pathogens.
   c) It includes sweat glands.
   d) It is responsible for the production of tears and ear wax.
   e) It helps protect the digestive system from pathogens.

2. Which of the following statements about how complement proteins kill bacteria is incorrect?
   a) Bound complement proteins are able to recruit other complement proteins to come to the site of bacterial infection.
   b) Complement proteins aggregate to form larger protein complexes that create holes in the bacterial cell surface.
   c) Bacterial death results from membrane holes created by complexes between complement and surface proteins.
   d) Complement proteins surround and bind to the entire surface of a bacterium, marking it to be engulfed by phagocytes and cytotoxic T cells.
   e) Complement proteins are able to recognize and bind directly to the surface of bacteria's cell surface proteins.

3. Which of the following statements about the inflammatory response is incorrect?
   a) The release of histamine by mast cells initiates inflammation.
   b) Cells lining blood vessels near inflamed tissue become "stickier" to neutrophils.
   c) Pain can occur with inflammation, as increased pressure in an inflamed area stimulates local neurons.
   d) The release of histamine causes blood vessels to constrict, reducing blood loss in an injured area.
   e) Four signs of inflammation are swelling, redness, heat, and pain.

4. Vaccines:
   a) activate a primary response in the vaccinated individual.
   b) lead to the creation of memory B cells that provide a rapid secondary response against a specific infectious agent.
   c) are sometimes made of no more than the unique antigens from a pathogen's surface.
   d) All of the above are correct.
   e) Only b) and c) are correct.

5. The major difference between T cells and B cells is that:
   a) T cells develop in the thymus, whereas B cells develop in the bone marrow.
   b) T cells do not interact with the innate immune system, but B cells do.
   c) T cells bind directly to foreign antigens, whereas B cells produce proteins (antibodies) that are secreted and bind to the foreign antigens.
   d) All of the above are major differences between T cells and B cells.
   e) Both a) and c) are major differences between T cells and B cells.

6. Why don't people develop immunity to the common cold?
   a) Actually, many people do develop immunity to the common cold and get sick only from bacterial infections.
   b) There are at least 200 different viruses that can cause the common cold, and they change over time.
   c) Only non-specific immunity helps individuals fight the common cold, and specific immunity is not an effective defense against viruses.
   d) The rhinovirus that causes the common cold has no surface antigens and so can move through the body without being detected.
   e) The pathogen that causes the common cold attacks and kills memory cells, continually "erasing" the immune system's memory of it.

7. Antibodies:
   a) are produced by helper B cells.
   b) are produced by helper T cells.
   c) are produced by the B cell bound by a specific antigen.
   d) are produced by plasma cells.
   e) are made in the bone marrow.

8. The polypeptides that make up the structure of an antibody consist of:
   a) two heavy chains and two light chains, shaped like a "Y," with a lower constant region and an upper variable region.
   b) two heavy chains and two light chains, shaped like a "Y," each with an upper constant region and a lower variable region.
   c) one heavy chain and one light chain, shaped like a "Y," each with a lower constant region and an upper variable region.
   d) one heavy chain and one light chain, shaped like a "Y," each with an upper constant region and a lower variable region.
   e) Both b) and d) can be correct, depending on the type of antibody.

9. Which of the following is not a function of helper T cells?
   a) They stimulate B cells to proliferate and produce antibodies.
   b) They activate cytotoxic T cells.
   c) They stimulate B cells to secrete cytokines.
   d) They recognize antigens presented on macrophage surfaces.
   e) All of the above are functions of helper T cells.

10. Autoimmunity is:
    a) one of three lines of defense in the vertebrate immune system.
    b) responsible for muscular dystrophy, which occurs when immune cells destroy the myelin sheath, reducing motor control and balance.
    c) the culprit in rheumatoid arthritis, which occurs when immune attack on the linings of joints causes inflammation.
    d) a consequence of a body's inability to produce antigens, leading it to attack its own cells as if they were pathogens.
    e) All of the above statements about autoimmunity are correct.

11. As the human immunodeficiency virus (HIV) begins to kill the host's _____, the host's immune system begins to fail.
    a) thymus cells
    b) spleen cells
    c) red blood cells
    d) white blood cells
    e) liver cells

12. Hay fever affects millions of individuals every year and is caused by an allergic reaction to pollen. Which of the following is not a step of the process in which a pollen grain causes an allergic reaction in an individual?
    a) Mast cells burst when they encounter the pollen during the initial exposure, releasing histamine and other chemicals.
    b) During the first exposure, B cells are activated by the pollen and differentiate into antibody-secreting plasma cells.
    c) During the second exposure, the pollen grains are recognized by previously created antibodies on mast cells.
    d) A type of antibody, specific to the pollen grain, is produced during the initial attack, and these antibodies adhere to mast cells, where they remain.
    e) Histamine and other allergen chemicals cause itchy eyes and a runny nose.

SHORT-ANSWER QUESTIONS

1. Generally, the second time a person is exposed to a particular pathogen, his or her immune system is able to respond to the pathogen more quickly and effectively. Why?

2. Why is it necessary to get only a single vaccine against the pathogen causing chicken pox, while a flu shot is necessary every year?

See Appendix for answers. For additional study questions, go to www.prep-u.com.

PHOTO CREDITS ———————————————————————

Lanting Photography, (R) A. Barry Dowsett/Photo Researchers. **p. 148:** *Figure 4-32* hybrid medical animation/Photo Researchers. **p. 151:** *photo* Martin Harvey/Getty Images; *Figure 4-35* Tobias Bernhard/Getty Images. **p. 152:** *Figure 4-37* Cephas Picture Library/Alamy, *(T inset)* SciMAT/ Photo Researchers, *(B inset)* Romilly Lockyer/Getty Images. **p. 153:** *Figure 4-38 (L)* FoodCollection/age fotostock, *(M)* Tim Hill/Alamy, *(R)* FoodCollection/age fotostock. **p. 155:** *photo* Plush Studios/Getty Images.

CHAPTER 5   pp. 158–159: *photo* Phanie/Photo Researchers. **p. 160:** *photo* Denis Galante/Corbis. **p. 161:** *Figure 5-1* Vasna Wilson/*Virginian-Pilot*; *Figure 5-2 (L)* Reprinted with permission, September 2008 *Discover* magazine. Copyright © Discover Magazine. All rights reserved, *(R)* Reprinted through the courtesy of the Editors of TIME Magazine © 2008 Time Inc., *(B)* Reprinted by permission of The Wall Street Journal, © 2008 Dow Jones & Company, Inc. All Rights Reserved Worldwide. License number 2038930425822. **p. 162:** *Figure 5-3* A. Barrington Brown/Photo Researchers, *(inset)* Science Source/Photo Researchers. **p. 164:** *Figure 5-5 (TL)* Courtesy of the author, *(TM)* Sian Irvine/Getty Images, *(TR)* Eye of Science/Photo Researchers, *(BL)* Visuals Unlimited/ Corbis, *(BR)* John White. **p. 166:** *Figure 5-8 (from top)* Courtesy of the author; John White; Eye of Science/Photo Researchers; Sian Irvine/Getty Images; Visuals Unlimited/Corbis. **p. 167:** *Figure 5-9 (from top)* Courtesy of the author; Eye of Science/Photo Researchers; Dr. Dennis Kunkel/ Getty Images; Fancy/Veer/Corbis; Dr. Dennis Kunkel/Visuals Unlimited. **p. 169:** *photo* Julia Kuskin/Photonica/Getty Images. **p. 174:** *photo* Uli Westphal 2008. **p. 175:** *Figure 5-15* Eye of Science/Photo Researchers. **p. 177:** *Figure 5-17 (L)* Mika/zefa/Corbis, *(M)* Robert Llewellyn/Corbis, *(R)* Tom Stewart/Corbis. **p. 178:** *Figure 5-18* Tommy Moorman. **p. 179:** *photo* Mario Tama/Getty Images; *Figure 5-19 (TL)* Getty Images, *(TM)* Jim West/Alamy, *(TR)* Charles O'Rear/Corbis, *(BL)* AP Photo/*Beloit Daily News*, Tom Holoubek, *(BR)* Landov. **p. 184:** *Figure 5-26* AJPhoto/Photo Researchers. **p. 185:** *Figure 5-27* MGM/courtesy Everett Collection. **p. 186:** *Figure 5-28* AP Photo. **p. 187:** *Figure 5-29* AP Photo/Examiner, Amy Elrod. **p. 188:** *photo* Betsie Van der Meer/Getty Images. **p. 189:** *photo* Jim Richardson/Corbis; *Figure 5-30* Ed Young/Corbis, *(inset)* John Doebley. **p. 190:** *Figure 5-31 (clockwise from left)* Martin Ruegner/Digital Vision/Getty Images; Scottish Crop Research Institute, Dundee; Professor Peter Beyer/Humanitarian Board for Golden Rice/www.goldenrice. org. **p. 191:** *Figure 5-32 (L)* BSIP/Photo Researchers, *(M)* Lance Nelson/ Corbis, *(R)* Steve Percival/Photo Researchers. **p. 192:** *Figure 5-33* Dr. Morley Read/Science Photo Library. **p. 193:** *Figure 5-35* Frank Whitney/ Getty Images; *Figure 5-36* Dr. Garth Fletcher. **p. 194:** *Figure 5-37* Reuters/Corbis; *Figure 5-38* Reuters/Corbis. **p. 196:** *photo* Digital Vision/ Alamy. **p. 197:** *Figure 5-39 (L)* Neville Chadwick/Science Photo Library, *(M)* Tom Grill/Corbis, *(R)* David Parker/Science Photo Library. **p. 199:** *Figure 5-42* Vo Trung Dung/Corbis Sygma. **p. 200:** *Figure 5-43 (clockwise)* Sian Irvine/Dorling Kindersley/Getty Images, Visuals Unlimited/Corbis, Eye of Science/Photo Researchers, John White, Courtesy of the author, *(tree of life)* David M. Hillis, Derrick Zwickl, and Robin Gutell, University of Texas. **p. 202:** *Figure 5-45 (TL)* John Chadwick/AP Photo, *(TR)* Ben Margot/AP Photo, *(BL)* Jack Smith/AP Photo, *(BM)* David J. Phillip/AP Photo, *(BR)* Advanced Cell Technologies/AP Photo. **p. 203:** *Figure 5-46* Amblin/Universal/The Kobal Collection. **p. 204:** *(T)* Anthony Marsland/ Getty Images; *(B)* Lauren Nicole/Getty Images.

CHAPTER 6   pp. 208–209: *photo* AP Photo. **p. 210:** *photo* Steve Gschmeissner/Photo Researchers. **p. 211:** *Figure 6-2* AP Photo/Gerald Herbert, *(inset)* Dr. Peter Landsorp/Visuals Unlimited. **p. 213:** *Figure 6-4*

CNRI/Photo Researchers. **p. 216:** *photo* Sisse Brimberg/Getty Images. **p. 217:** *photo* Tanya Constantine/Getty Images. **p. 218:** *Figure 6-7 (L)* Mike Hill/Alamy, *(inset)* Science Photo Library/Photo Researchers, *(R)* Dan Guravich/Photo Researchers, *(inset)* Biology Media/Photo Researchers; *photo* Micro Discovery/Corbis. **p. 219:** *photo* David Scharf/ Getty Images. **pp. 220–221:** *photos* Courtesy T. Wittman. **p. 223:** *Figure 6-11* GJLP/CNRI/Science Photo Library. **p. 224:** *Figure 6-13* Kevin Laubacher/Taxi/Getty Images. **p. 225:** *photo* Dr. Yorgos Nikas/Photo Researchers. **p. 231:** *Figure 6-18* Dr. Dennis Kunkel/Phototake. **p. 233:** *Figure 6-21* Margot Granitsas/Photo Researchers. **p. 234:** *Figure 6-22* Stephen Dalton/NHPA. **p. 234:** *Figure 6-23* Dr. Kari Lounatmaa/Photo Researchers. **p. 235:** *photo* Cormac Hanley/Getty Images. **p. 236:** *Figure 6-24* Biophoto Associates/Photo Researchers. **p. 237:** *Figure 6-26 (L)* Tui De Roy, *(M)* imagebroker/Alamy, *(R)* A. B. Sheldon/Root Resources. **p. 238:** *photo* Michael Patrick O'Neill/Alamy. **p. 239:** *photo* Visuals Unlimited/Corbis. **p. 240:** *Figure 6-27* CNRI/Photo Researchers; *Figure 6-28* Saturn Stills/Photo Researchers; *Figure 6-29 (L)* Mika/zefa/Corbis, *(R)* L. Willatt/East Anglian Regional Genetics Service/Photo Researchers. **p. 244:** *photo* Jupiterimages/Brand X/Alamy.

CHAPTER 7   pp. 248–249 *photo* Robert B. Carr/Bruce Coleman USA. **p. 250:** *photo* Dr. Karl Fredga, Department of Genetics, Uppsala University, Sweden. **p. 251:** *Figure 7-1* Isabelle Rozenbaum/age fotostock. **p. 252:** *Figure 7-4* © BNPS.CO.UK. **p. 253:** *Figure 7-5 (row 1, L)* Les3photo8/Dreamstime.com, *(row 1, R)* Gabriela Medina/Getty Images, *(row 2, L)* Geoff du Feu/Alamy, *(row 2, R)* Custom Medical Stock Photo/Alamy, *(row 3, L & R)* Kevin Winter/Getty Images. **p. 256:** *Figure 7-8* Content Mine International/Alamy. **p. 258:** *Figure 7-10* Jeff Wyoming/photolibrary. **p. 260:** *photo* John Gillmoure/Corbis. **p. 262:** *Figure 7-14* Michael K. Nichols/Getty Images. **p. 264:** *Figure 7-16* Yann Arthus-Bertrand/Corbis. **p. 265:** *photo* Gideon Mendel/Corbis. **p. 266:** *Figure 7-18* Wellcome Images. **p. 270:** *Figure 7-22* Corbis. **p. 271:** *Figure 7-23* Lennart Nilsson. **p. 273:** *Figure 7-25* AP Photo/Rob Carr. **p. 274:** *Figure 7-26 (T)* Juniors Bildarchiv/age fotostock, *(B)* Grant Heilman Photography/Alamy. **p. 275:** *photo* Charles Maraia/Getty Images. **p. 277:** *Figure 7-28* Mina Chapman/Corbis. **p. 278:** *photo* Patrick J. Miller.

CHAPTER 8   pp. 280–281: *photo* Steve Bloom Images/Alamy. **p. 282:** *photo* Frans Lanting Photography. **p. 283:** *Figure 8-1* Graphic Science/ Alamy. **p. 285:** *photo* Tui De Roy/Minden Pictures/Getty Images. **p. 287:** *Figure 8-5* Getty Images; *Figure 8-6* Mary Evans Picture Library/Alamy. **p. 290:** *Figure 8-8* Hulton Archive/Getty Images; *Figure 8-9* Photo by Louie Fasciolo/Bernard J. Shapero Rare Books. **p. 291:** *photo* Tom Brakefield/Science Faction/Getty Images. **p. 292:** *Figure 8-10* Renee Lynn/Corbis. **p. 294:** *Figure 8-11 (L inset)* Florida Images/Alamy, *(R inset)* Courtesy Oregon State University. **p. 295:** *Figure 8-12* J. D. Talasek/Phototake. **p. 296:** *Figure 8-13* Victor McCusick. **p. 297:** *Figure 8-14* Ross Warner/Alamy. **p. 299:** *Figure 8-16 from left)* Deanne Fitzmaurice; Jason Homa/Getty Images; Paul Costello/Getty Images; Paul Burns/Blend Images/Getty Images; Jacob Langvad/Stone/Getty Images. **p. 300:** *Figure 8-17* Max Nash/AFP/Getty Images; *Figure 8-18* Benn Mitchell/Riser/Getty Images. **p. 302:** *photo* Yann Arthus-Bertrand/ Corbis. **p. 304:** *Figure 8-22* J & B Photographers/Animals Animals—Earth Scenes. **p. 307:** *Figure 8-25* Patricia McDonough; *Figure 8-26* Grant Heilman/Grant Heilman Photography. **p. 308:** *Figure 8-27* Barros & Barros/Getty Images; *Figure 8-28* Gary Vestal/Photographer's Choice/ Getty Images. **p. 310:** *Figure 8-29* RubberBall/Alamy; *Figure 8-30* Michael Durham/Minden Pictures/Getty Images. **p. 311:** *photo* Gerald

p. 442: *photo (T)* Dr. David Wachenfeld/Auscape/Minden Pictures, *(B)* Zeva Oelbaum/Peter Arnold.

CHAPTER 12 **p. 446–447:** *photo* Katinka Matson. **p. 448:** *photo* Frans Lanting Photography; *Figure 12-1 (from left)* David Pearson/Alamy, Douglas Pulsipher/Alamy, Michael and Patricia Fogden/Minden Pictures. **p. 449:** *Figure 12-2* William James Warren/Getty Images; *Figure 12-3 (from left)* Photodisc/Alamy, Chad Ehlers/Alamy, Herbert Hopfensperger/age fotostock. **p. 451:** *photo* Frans Lanting/Corbis; *Figure 12-5* Charles F. Delwiche. **p. 452:** *Figure 12-6 (L)* Hans Strand/Corbis, *(R)* Gallo Images/Getty Images. **p. 453:** *Figure 12-7 (L)* Alistair Dove/Alamy, *(M)* Verbiesen Henk/age fotostock, *(R)* Daniel Vega/age fotostock. **p. 454:** *Figure 12-8* Barry Turner/Alamy; *Figure 12-9 (T)* The Irish Image Collection/Design Pics/Corbis, *(B)* Matthew Mawson/Alamy. **p. 455:** *Figure 12-10 (L)* Ed Reschke/Peter Arnold, *(M)* DEA/Dani-Jeske/Getty Images, *(R)* Juan Carlos Muñoz/age fotostock; *photo* Bjorn Forsberg/npl/Minden Pictures. **p. 456:** *Figure 12-11* Peter Arnold/Alamy. **p. 457:** *photo* Jeff Vanuga/Corbis; *Figure 12-12* Kevin Phelan. **p. 458:** *Figure 12-13 (from left)* Bohemian Nomad Picturemakers/Corbis, Design Pics/Alamy, Jouan & Rius/naturepl.com, Takahiro Miyamoto/Getty Images. **p. 459:** *Figure 12-14 (from left)* Thomas Kitchin and Victoria Hurst/AllCanadaPhotos. com, Alan and Linda Detrick/Photo Researchers, Jouan & Rius/naturepl.com, blickwinkel/Alamy; *Figure 12-15 (L)* Brad Mogen/Visuals Unlimited, *(R)* Stephen P. Parker/Photo Researchers. **p. 460:** *Figure 12-16* Darrell Gulin/Corbis. **p. 461:** *Figure 12-17 (T)* Gary Randall/Getty Images, *(M)* Kathleen Phelan, *(B)* Philippe Bourseiller/Getty Images. **p. 462:** *photo* Andy Small/Corbis; *Figure 12-18 (from left)* Ferruccio Carassale/Grand Tour/Corbis, blickwinkel/Alamy, Grand Tour/Corbis, Jack Dykinga/Getty Images. **p. 463:** *photo* John Fairhall/Auscape/Minden Pictures. **p. 464:** *Figure 12-20* Topic Photo Agency/age fotostock. **p. 465:** *Figure 12-21 (top row from left)* Kim Taylor/naturepl.com, Rolf Nussbaumer/naturepl.com, Andrew Darrington/Alamy, Sharkawi Che Din/Alamy; *(bottom row from left)* blickwinkel/Alamy, Mark Moffett/Minden Pictures. **p. 466:** *Figure 12-22* Tony Hertz/Corbis. **p. 468:** *photo* Dezorzi/Corbis. **p. 469:** *Figure 12-24 (from left)* Scott Camazine/Alamy, Steve Bloom Images/Alamy, Manfred Danegger/Peter Arnold. **p. 470:** *Figure 12-25 (TL)* Joe McDonald/Visuals Unlimited, *(TR)* Wildlife GmbH/Alamy, *(M)* Howard Grey/Getty Images, *(B)* Gertrud and Helmut Denzau/naturepl.com. **p. 471:** *Figure 12-26* Ed Reschke/Peter Arnold. **p. 472:** *photo* Jan Vermeer/Foto Natura/Minden Pictures; *Figure 12-27 (from left)* Andrew Parkinson/Corbis, Yva Momatiuk and John Eastcott/Photo Researchers, Glen Threlfo/Minden Pictures. **p. 473:** *Figure 12-29 (from left)* Steve Austin/Papilio/Corbis, Visuals Unlimited/Corbis, Visuals Unlimited/Corbis. **p. 474:** *Figure 12-30* Ingo Arndt/Minden Pictures. **p. 475:** *Figure 12-31* AP Photo/Oregon State University; *Figure 12-32* D. Hurst/Alamy. **p. 476:** *Figure 12-33* Visuals Unlimited/Corbis. **p. 477:** *Figure 12-34* Jim Brandenburg/Minden Pictures. **p. 478:** *photo* Mary Ellen Mark.

CHAPTER 13 **pp. 482–483:** *photo* Lee D. Simon/Photo Researchers. **p. 484:** Stephanie Schuller/Photo Researchers. **p. 485:** *Figure 13-2 (from left)* CNRI/Photo Researchers, *(inset)* Phototake/Alamy; Federico Veronesi/Getty Images, *(inset)* Agriculture et Agroalimentaire Canada; Science Source/Photo Researchers, *(inset)* Courtesy K.O. Stetter, R. Huber, and R. Rachel, University of Regensburg, Germany. **p. 486:** *Figure 13-3* Courtesy Jay Phelan; *photo* Frans Lanting/Corbis. **p. 487:** *Figure 13-4 (T from left)* Dennis Kunkel/Alamy, Dennis Kunkel/Alamy, Biodisc/Visuals Unlimited/Alamy, *(bottom)* Eye of Science/Photo Researchers. **p. 488:** *photo* Visuals Unlimited/Corbis. **p. 489:** *Figure 13-5* Dennis Kunkel/Alamy; *Figure 13-6 (L)* mediacolor/Alamy, *(R)* Raymond Otero/Visuals Unlimited. **p. 492:** *Figure 13-9* Mediablitz Images. **p. 493:** *Figure 13-10 (from left)* Dodie Ulery, *(M)* Thomas Dressler/age fotostock, *(R)* Reino Hanninen/Alamy. **p. 494:** *Figure 13-11* Original map by Dr. John Snow, *(inset)* Justinc. **p. 495:** *Figure 13-12* ImageState Royalty Free/Alamy. **p. 496:** *Figure 13-14* AGStockUSA/Alamy. **p. 497:** *photo* George Steinmetz/Corbis; *Figure 13-15* Dennis Kunkel/Visuals Unlimited. **p. 498:** *Figure 13-16* Russ Bishop/age fotostock; *Figure 13-17* Tim Mantoani/Masterfile. **p. 499:** *Figure 13-18* Salvador de Sas/epa/Corbis. **p. 500:** *photo* Steve Gschmeissner/Photo Researchers; *Figure 13-19* Microfossil Image Recovery and Circulation for Learning and Education (MIRACLE) Project, Micropalaeontology Unit of the Earth Sciences Department, University College, London. **p. 501:** *Figure 13-20 (from left)* Visuals Unlimited/Corbis, C-FH/Grant Heilman, Images&Stories/Alamy. **p. 502:** *Figure 13-21* M. I. Walker/Photo Researchers. **p. 503:** *Figure 13-22)* Eye of Science/Photo Researchers, *(top inset)* Peter Arnold/Alamy, *(bottom inset)* Phototake/Alamy. **p. 504:** *photo* NIBSC/Photo Researchers; *Figure 13-23 (M)* SPL/Photo Researchers, *(R)* Phototake. **p. 506:** *Figure 13-25 (T)* St. Louis Post Dispatch, *(B)* Reuters/Corbis. **p. 507:** *Figure 13-27* Bettmann/Corbis, *(inset)* nagelestock.com/Alamy. **p. 509:** *Figure 13-29* Dr. Klaus Boller/Photo Researchers. **p. 510:** *photo* Tommy Moorman.

CHAPTER 14 **pp. 514–515:** *photo* Frans Lanting Photography. **p. 516:** *photo* Barrett & MacKay/age fotostock; *Figure 14-1* Frans Lanting/Corbis. **p. 518:** *Figure 14-3* Tom Nebbia/Corbis. **p. 519:** *Figure 14-4* Juan Carlos Muñoz/age fotostock. **p. 520:** *Figure 14-5* R. Wittek/age fotostock. **p. 521:** *Figure 14-7* John McColgan, Bureau of Land Management, Alaska Fire Service. **p. 522:** *Figure 14-8* Bill Stormont/Corbis; *Figure 14-9* AP Photo/Dario Lopez-Mills. **p. 523:** *Figure 14-10* Lynn M. Stone/Naturepl.com; *Figure 14-11* age fotostock/Fotosearch. **p. 524:** *Figure 14-12* Dirk Anschutz/Getty Images. **p. 525:** *Figure 14-13* National Museum of Natural History, Smithsonian Institution; *Figure 14-14* Martin Bwenetti/AFP/Getty Images. **p. 526:** *photo* Frans Lanting/Corbis. **p. 527:** *Figure 14-15 (T)* Dave Watts/Naturepl.com, *(M)* Colin Preston/naturepl.com, *(B)* Joe McDonald/Visuals Unlimited. **p. 528:** *Figure 14-16* Greg Katsoulis. **p. 529:** *Figure 14-17 (L)* Martin Harvey/Alamy, *(M)* Terry Wall/Alamy, *(R)* D. R. Schrichte/SeaPics. com. **p. 530:** *Figure 14-18 (L)* Gunter Marx Photography/Corbis, *(M)* Philippe Clement/naturepl.com, *(R)* Gary Meszaros/Photo Researchers, *(inset)* iStockPhoto.com/jeridu. **p. 531:** *photo* Jim Brandenburg/Minden Pictures. **p. 532:** *photo* Gabriela Staebler/zefa/Corbis. **p. 533:** *Figure 14-19* Condé Nast Archive/Corbis. **p. 535:** *Figure 14-21 (T)* Renaud Visage/Getty Images, *(B)* W. Perry Conway/Corbis. **p. 537:** *photo* Eric Fougére/Kipa/Corbis. **p. 538:** *photo* Getty Images. **p. 543:** *Figure 14-27 (T)* Yadid Levy/Anzenberger Agency/Jupiterimages, *(M)* Sean Gallup/Getty Images, *(B)* Michael S. Yamashita/Getty Images; *Figure 14-28* Keren Su/Getty Images. **p. 544:** *photo* Elke Hesser/Getty Images.

CHAPTER 15 **pp. 548–549:** *photo* Georgette Douwma/Getty Images. **p. 550:** *photo* Frans Lanting/Corbis; *Figure 15-1* Thomas Marent/Minden Pictures. **p. 551:** *Figure 15-2* Steve Allen/Getty Images. **p. 552:** *Figure 15-3 (top row from left)* Jacques Jangoux/Alamy, Ted Med/Getty Images, Fritz Poelking/photolibrary, *(middle row from left)* John Warburton-Lee Photography/Alamy, Michael Melford/Getty Images, Visions LLC/photolibrary, *(bottom row from left)* Dan Lamont/Corbis, Frans Lanting/Corbis, Peter Arnold/Alamy. **p. 553:** *Figure 15-4 (top row)* Martin Siepmann/

photolibrary, Frans Lanting/Corbis, (bottom row) Troy Plota/Getty Images, Momatiuk-Eastcott/Corbis, Mark Conlin/V&W/Image Quest Marine. **p. 554:** *photo* Frans Lanting/Corbis. **p. 555:** *Figure 15-6* moodboard/Corbis. **p. 556:** *Figure 15-7* Craig Aurness/photolibrary, *photo* Frans Lanting/Corbis. **p. 557:** *Figure 15-8* Jacques Descloitres, MODIS Land Rapid Response Team, NASA/GSFC. **p. 558:** *Figure 15-9 (L)* Courtesy NASA/Goddard Space Flight Center Scientific Visualization Studio, *(R)* Sandy Felsenthal/Corbis. **p. 561:** *photo* Martin Harvey/Corbis. **p. 562:** *Figure 15-13 (L)* AJPhoto/Photo Researchers, *(R)* Eye of Science/Photo Researchers. **p. 568:** *Figure 15-19* AP Photo/Gautam Singh, *photo* P. Manner/zefa/Corbis. **p. 569:** *photo* Stephen Frink/Corbis. **p. 569:** *Figure 15-20* Mitsuhiko Imamori/Minden Pictures. **p. 570:** *Figure 15-21* Jim Brandenburg/Minden Pictures. **p. 574:** *Figure 15-24 (top row)* Anthony Bannister Gallo Images/Corbis, Suzanne L. and Joseph T. Collins/Photo Researchers, *(bottom row)* Michael & Patricia Fogden/Minden Pictures, Gail Shumway/Getty Images. **p. 575:** *Figure 15-25 (T)* Fred Bavendam/Minden Pictures, *(B)* John Downer/naturepl.com; *Figure 15-26* Dr. Bruce Robison/Minden Pictures. **p. 576:** *Figure 15-27 (T)* Gallo Images/Alamy, *(B)* Eye of Science/Photo Researchers. **p. 577:** *Figure 15-28* Biosphoto/Heuclin Daniel/Peter Arnold. **p. 578:** *Figure 15-29 (T)* Darlyne A. Murawski/Getty Images, *(B)* Arco Images GmbH/Alamy. **p. 579:** *photo* W. Perry Conway/Corbis. **p. 581:** *Figure 15-31 (inset)* Siede Preis/Getty Images. **p. 582:** *photo* NASA image by Robert Simmon, based on Landsat data provided by the UMD Global Land Cover Facility.

CHAPTER 16 pp. 586–587: *photo* Peet Simard/Corbis. **p. 588:** *photo* Martin Harvey/Corbis; *Figure 16-1* Burger/Phanie/Photo Researchers, *(inset)* Inga Spence/Getty Images. **p. 589:** *Figure 16-2 (clockwise from top left)* Wildscape/Alamy, Suzanne Long/Alamy, Jeff Vanuga/Corbis, The Photo Works. **p. 590:** *Figure 16-3 (from left)* Alfred Pasieka/Photo Researchers, DLILLC/Corbis, NASA. **p. 591:** *Figure 16-4* Dennis Macdonald/photolibrary.com. **p. 593:** *Figure 16-7 (TR)* blickwinkel/Alamy, *(BL)* Michael and Patricia Fogden/Corbis, *(BR)* DeAgostini/Getty Images. **p. 594:** *Figure 16-8* Courtesy Edward O. Wilson. **p. 595:** *Figure 16-9* Danny Lehman/Corbis. **p. 597:** *photo* Gallo Images/Corbis; *Figure 16-11* Tom Uhlman/Alamy. **p. 600:** *Figure 16-14* Marcelo Sayao/epa/Corbis; *Figure 16-15* Frans Lanting Photography. **p. 601:** *photo* Frans Lanting/Corbis. **p. 602:** *Figure 16-16 (from left)* USGS Photo by Harry Glicken, USGS Photo by Harry Glicken, Don Geyer/Alamy; *Figure 16-17* Denis Scott/Corbis. **p. 603:** *Figure 16-18* Jany Sauvanet/Photo Researchers, *(inset)* Gale S. Hanratty/Alamy. **p. 604:** *Figure 16-20 (from left)* John Mitchell/Photo Researchers, Michael P. Gadomski/Photo Researchers, Wil Meinderts/Minden Pictures. **p. 605:** *Figure 16-21* Jack Picone/Alamy. **p. 606:** *Figure 16-22* Anil Risal Singh-UNEP/Peter Arnold. **p. 607:** *Figure 16-25* Will and Deni McIntyre/Corbis. **p. 609:** *Figure 16-28 (both photos)* NASA. **p. 610:** *Figure 16-30 (all photos)* NASA. *Figure 16-31* AP Photo/Elise Amendola, *(I)* New Line/Photofest. **p. 613:** *Figure 16-34* Frans Lanting/Corbis. **p. 614:** *photo* JASON LEE/X01757/Reuters/Corbis. **p. 615:** *Figure 16-35 (T)* Cyril Ruoso/Minden Pictures, *(B)* Kim Taylor/Minden Pictures, *(inset)* Medical-on-Line/Alamy; *Figure 16-36 (L)* Gerry Ellis/Minden Pictures, *(R)* Robert Harding Picture Library/Alamy. **p. 616:** *Figure 16-37* Tommy Moorman. **p. 618:** *photo* Peter Arnold/Alamy.

CHAPTER 17 pp. 622–623: *photo* Paul Edmondson/Corbis. **p. 624:** *photo* Steve Terrill/Corbis. **p. 625:** *Figure 17-1 (from left)* Lonely Planet Images/Getty Images, Shalom Ormsby/Getty Images, De Agostini Picture Library/Getty Images, Frans Lanting/Frans Lanting Photography. **p. 627:**

photo David T. Webb, Ph. D. **p. 629:** *Figure 17-5 (L)* Eye of Science/Photo Researchers, *(L, inset)* Mark Bolton/Corbis, *(C)* Dr. Gerald Van Dyke/Getty Images, *(R)* Dennis Kunkel Microscopy, Inc./Visuals Unlimited, *(R, inset)* Doug Wilson/Corbis; *Figure 17-6* Steve Gschmeissner/Photo Researchers. **p. 630:** *Figure 17-7 (L)* Image Source/Corbis, *(L, inset)* Dennis Kunkel Microscopy, Inc., *(C)* Keith van-Loen/Alamy, *(C, inset)* Biophoto Associates/Photo Researchers, *(R)* Pete Ryan/Getty Images, *(R, inset)* Biophoto Associates/Photo Researchers. **p. 631:** *photo* Radius Images/Corbis. **p. 632:** *Figure 17-9 (L)* Robert Pickett/Corbis, *(R)* AgStock Images/Corbis; *Figure 17-10* Susumu Nishinaga/Photo Researchers. **p. 633:** *Figure 17-11* Wayne Lawler/Ecopix. **p. 634:** *Figure 17-14 (from left)* AgStock Images/Corbis, Dorling Kindersley/Getty Images, Gabor Geissler/Getty Images, Robert & Jean Pollock/Getty Images. **p. 636:** *Figure 17-16 (top row, from left)* Anna Kern/Etsa/Corbis, Niall Benvie/Corbis, Mark Bolton/Corbis, *(middle row, from left)* Michael Sedam/Photolibrary, John and Lisa Merrill/Corbis, Ehlers/Getty Images, *(bottom row, from left)* Frank Krahmer/Corbis, Micha Pawlitzki/Corbis, DLILLC/Corbis. **p. 637:** *Figure 17-17* AP Photo/Jody Kurash. **p. 638:** *Figure 17-18 (L)* Photo 24/Brand X/Corbis, *(inset)* Grant Heilman Photography/Alamy, *(C)* Jonathan Buckley/Getty Images, *(R)* Martin Oeggerli/Visuals Unlimited. **p. 639:** *photo* KOJI NAKAMURA/amanaimages/Corbis. **p. 640:** *Figure 17-20* AP Photo/Minot Daily News, Marvin Baker. **p. 641:** *Figure 17-21* Jim Richardson/National Geographic Stock; *Figure 17-22* Darrell Gulin/Corbis. **p. 642:** *Figure 17-23 (L)* Mary Hobbs/Alamy, *(R)* Jane Legate/Photolibrary; *Figure 17-24* Envision/Corbis. **p. 644:** *Figure 17-27 (L)* Clive Nichols/Getty Images, *(R)* Coke Whitworth/Getty Images. **p. 645:** *photo* Steve Gschmeissner/Photo Researchers; *photo* Dennis Drenner/Visuals Unlimited. **p. 646:** *Figure 17-29* Dr. Merton Brown/Visuals Unlimited. **p. 647:** *Figure 17-30* Momatiuk-Eastcott/Corbis. **p. 649:** *Figure 17-33* Radius Images/Corbis. **p. 651:** *Figure 17-35* George D. Lepp/Corbis. **p. 652:** *photo* Kevin Steele/Aurora Photos/Corbis.

CHAPTER 18 pp. 656–657: *photo* Steve Gschmeissner/Science Photo Library. **p. 658:** *photo (T)* James Randklev/Corbis; *photo (B)* Ingo Arndt/Minden Pictures. **p. 659:** *Figure 18-1* David Muench/Corbis, *(inset)* Copyright © Regents of the University of Minnesota. All rights reserved. **p. 660:** *Figure 18-2 (L)* Marc Vassallo © 2001 by The Taunton Press, Inc., *(C)* Bon Appetit/Alamy. *(R)* Arco Images GmbH/Alamy. **p. 662:** *Figure 18-4* Lori Greig/Getty Images **p. 663:** *Figure 18-5* Peter Ginter/Science Faction/Corbis **p. 665:** *photo Tulip, 1988* © Copyright The Robert Mapplethorpe Foundation. Courtesy Art + Commerce; *Figure 18-7 (L)* Frans Lanting/Frans Lanting Photography, *(C, L)* Imagemore Co., Ltd./Corbis, *(C, R)* Frank Lukasseck/Corbis, *(R)* Imagemore Co., Ltd./Corbis. **p. 666:** *Figure 18-9* nik wheeler/Alamy, *(inset)* John Glover/Photolibrary. **p. 668:** *photo (T)* Peter Arnold, Inc./Alamy, *photo (B)* Dennis Kunkel Microscopy, Inc./PHOTOTAKE/Alamy; *Figure 18-11* Robert Clare/Alamy, *(inset)* Bob Sacha/Corbis. **p. 670:** *photo* Herbert Zettl/Corbis; *Figure 18-13* Martin Harvey/Corbis. **p. 671:** *Figure 18-14 (L)* Nic Bothma/epa/Corbis, *(R)* Martin Harvey/Alamy, *(inset)* Irene Terry, University of Utah. **p. 672:** *Figure 18-15* Adam Jones/Visuals Unlimited, *(inset)* Micro Discovery/Corbis. **p. 677:** *photo (L)* John Oeth/Alamy; *photo (R)* Bill Beatty/AGPix. **p. 678:** *photo* Cindy Kassab/Corbis; *Figure 18-20* Photolibrary. **p. 680:** *Figure 18-22 (L)* Scott Stulberg/Corbis, *(C)* David Muench/Corbis, *(R)* ImageClick, Inc./Alamy. **p. 681:** *Figure 18-23 (T)* Dr. Brad Mogen/Visuals Unlimited, *(B)* Biodisc/Visuals Unlimited/Corbis, *(R)* Oxford Scientific/Photolibrary; *photo* Digital Vision/Getty Images. **p. 683:** *Figure 18-25 (R)* Alan Schein Photography/Corbis, *(C)* Edi Engeler/epa/Corbis, *(L)* Steve Babineau/NBAE via

Getty Images. **p. 684:** *Figure 18-27* Nils–Johan Norenlind/Getty Images. **p. 685:** *Figure 18-28* Charles O. Cecil/Alamy. **p. 686:** *photo* Food Collection/Stock Food.

CHAPTER 19   pp. 690–691: *photo* Cathlyn Melloan/Getty Images. **p. 692:** *photo* D. Hurst/Alamy. **p. 693:** *Figure 19-1* Bob Gibbons/Science Photo Library. **p. 694:** *Figure 19-3* Yoshio Niikura/amanaimages/Corbis. **p. 695:** *Figure 19-4* AP Photo/Anchorage Daily News, Bill Roth. **p. 696:** *Figure 19-5* Stuart Westmorland/Corbis. **p. 697:** *Figure 19-7* Lindholdt Foto/iStockphoto. **p. 698:** *Figure 19-8 (L)* Grant Faint/Getty Images, *(R)* Colin Underhill/Alamy; *Figure 19-9* Tom Thulen/Alamy. **p. 699:** *Figure 19-10* Crady von Pawlak/Corbis; *Figure 19-11* Garry DeLong/Photolibrary. **p. 700:** *Figure 19-12* John Kaprielian/Photo Researchers. **p. 701:** *Figure 19-13* Martin Shields/Photo Researchers; *Figure 19-14* Peter Arnold, Inc./Alamy. **p. 702:** *Figure 19-15* Courtesy of Roger P. Hangarter, Chancellor's Professor of Biology, Indiana University. **p. 703:** *Figure 19-16* Foto Grebler/Alamy. **p. 705:** *photo* Tony Wharton/Frank Lane Picture Agency/Corbis. **p. 706:** *Figure 19-18 (L)* J S Sira/Gap Photo/Visuals Unlimited, *(C)* Biosphoto/Mayet Jean/Peter Arnold, *(R)* Martin Shields/Photo Researchers; *Figure 19-19* Gerry Bishop/Visuals Unlimited. **p. 707:** *Figure 19-20* Olivier Voisin/Photo Researchers; *Figure 19-21* Gregory G. Dimijian, M.D./Photo Researchers. **p. 708:** *photo* Frans Lanting/Corbis; *Figure 19-22 (L)* Frans Lanting/Corbis, *(C)* Simon Fraser/Science Photo Library, *(R)* Christopher Talbot Frank/Corbis. **p. 709:** *Figure 19-23* Arco Images GmbH/Alamy, *(inset)* Tim Laman/NGS Image Collection; *Figure 19-24* Paul Nicklen/Getty Images. **p. 710:** BSIP/Photoshot.

CHAPTER 20   pp. 714–715: *photo* Visuals Unlimited/Corbis. **p. 716:** *photo* Alexander Demianchuk/Reuters/Corbis. **p. 717:** *Figure 20-1* AP Photo/Sue Ogrocki. **p. 718:** *Figure 20-2 (L)* Emilio Suetone/Hemis/Corbis, *(R)* AP Photo/Sergei Chuzavkov. **p. 719:** *photo* Anup Shah/npl/Minden Pictures. **p. 722:** *Figure 20-6 (T)* Paul Nicklen/Getty Images, *(B)* Doug Allan/Getty Images; *Figure 20-7 (L)* Tim Farrell/Star Ledger/Corbis, *(R)* Chris Johns/Getty Images. **p. 723:** *Figure 20-9 (from left)* Doug Allan/npl/Minden Pictures, Michael & Patricia Fogden/Minden Pictures, Simon King/npl/Minden Pictures, John–Francis Bourke/Corbis. **p. 724:** *Figure 20-10* TS Corrigan/Alamy. **p. 728:** *Figure 20-14* Peter Dasilva/epa/Corbis. **p. 729:** *photo* Keren Su/Corbis; *Figure 20-15* Hiroya Minakuchi/Minden Pictures. **p. 730:** *photo* Frans Lanting/Frans Lanting Photography. **p. 731:** *Figure 20-17 (T)* Image Quest Marine/Alamy, *(bottom, from left)* Dennis Kunkel Microscopy, Inc., Visuals Unlimited/Corbis *(all)*. **p. 733:** *Figure 20-19 (TL)* Quest/Photo Researchers, *(BL)* Photo Quest Ltd/Science Photo Library/Corbis, *(C)* George J. Sanker/DRK photo, *(TR)* Dennis Kunkel Microscopy, Inc, *(MR & BR)* Visuals Unlimited/Corbis; *photo* Clifford White/Corbis. **p. 735:** *Figure 20-22 (T)* Joe McDonald/Corbis, *(bottom, from left)* Photo Quest Ltd/Science Photo Library/Corbis, *(both)* Visuals Unlimited/Corbis. **p. 737:** *Figure 20-24* D. Robert & Lorri Franz/Corbis; *photo* Eric Grave/Photo Researchers. **pp. 738–739:** *Figure 20-25 (top row, from left)* MIXA/Alamy, Stuart O'Sullivan/Getty Images, Jose Luis Pelaez, Inc./Blend Images/Corbis, Andersen Ross/Blend Images/Corbis, Mark Andersen/Getty Images, Radius Images/Alamy, *(bottom row, from left)* Mike Kemp/Getty Images, Hola Images/Getty Images, Radius Images/Alamy, Caroline Schiff/Getty Images, Andersen Ross/Getty Images, RubberBall/Alamy. **p. 740:** *photo* Jupiterimages/Brand X/Alamy.

CHAPTER 21   pp. 744–745: *photo* Susumu Nishinaga/Photo Researchers. **p. 746:** *photo* Christopher Furlong/Getty Images. **p. 748:** *Figure 21-2* Chris Newbert/Minden Pictures; *Figure 21-3 (T)* Daniel J.

McCauley IV, *(B)* Ruoso Cyril/Peter Arnold. **p. 749:** *Figure 21-4* Ralph Hutchings/Visuals Unlimited, *(inset)* David M. Phillips/Photo Researchers. **p. 752:** *photo* Dennis Kunkel Microscopy, Inc.; *Figure 21-6* Dietmar Busse/Getty Images. **p. 755:** *Figure 21-9 (L)* Eyecandy Images/IPNstock.com, *(R)* BSIP/Phototake. **p. 756:** *Figure 21-10* Alix/Photo Researchers. **p. 757:** *Figure 21-11* Fancy Photography/Veer. **p. 758:** *Figure 21-12 (L)* Dr. Fred Hossler/Visuals Unlimited, *(C)* Dennis Kunkel Microscopy, Inc/Phototake, *(R)* CNRI/Photo Researchers; *Figure 21-13* AP Photo/Eckehard Schulz. **p. 759:** *photo* Luca Trovato/Jupiterimages. **p. 760:** *Figure 21-14* Popperfoto/Getty Images, *(inset)* imagebroker/Alamy. **p. 761:** *Figure 21-15* Frans Lanting/Frans Lanting Photography. **p. 762:** *Figure 21-16 (L)* Science Photo Library, *(R)* SPL/Photo Researchers. **p. 763:** *Figure 21-17 (T)* Banana Stock/Jupiterimages, *(B)* Digital Vision/Superstock. **p. 765:** *Figure 21-18* Dietmar Busse/Getty Images, *(inset)* Michael Abbey/Photo Researchers. **p. 766:** *Figure 21-20* Phototex/NEWSCOM. **p. 767:** *Figure 21-21* Everett Collection; *photo* Corbis. **p. 768:** *photo* Paul Souders/Corbis. **p. 772:** *Figure 21-26* Fancy/Veer/Corbis. **p. 773:** *Figure 21-27* Dennis Kunkel Microscopy, Inc.; *Figure 21-28* Dr. Bahman Guyuron. **p. 774:** *Figure 21-29* Yva Momatiuk & John Eastcott/Minden Pictures. **p. 775:** *photo* Frans Lanting/Frans Lanting Photography. **p. 776:** *photo* Image Source/Getty Images; *Figure 21-31 (L & R)* Pr. M. Brauner/Photo Researchers. **p. 777** *Figure 21-32* IMAX/Photofest. **p. 778:** *photo* Julian Herbert/Getty Images. **p. 780:** *Figure 21-36 (T)* Loungepark/Getty Images; *(B)* Image Source Ltd/age fotostock; *Figure 21-37* Lennart Nilsson. **p. 781:** *Figure 21-38 (L)* Dorling Kindersley; *(R)* Foodfolio/Jupiterimages. **p. 782:** *photo* Danita Delimont/Alamy; *Figure 21-39* Design Pics Inc./Alamy. **p. 783:** *Figure 21-40* Alison Wright/Corbis. **p. 784:** *Figure 21-41* imagebroker/Alamy. **p. 785:** *Figure 21-42* Doug Allan/Minden Pictures. **p. 786:** *photo* Mark M. Lawrence/Corbis.

CHAPTER 22   pp. 790–791: *photo* Marcus Wilson-Smith/age fotostock. **p. 792:** *photo* Michael Freeman/Corbis. **p. 794:** *Figure 22-2 (T)* Gunter Zlesler/Peter Arnold, *(M)* Fred Bavendam/Minden Pictures, *(B)* Alan & Sandy Carey/zefa/Corbis; *Figure 22-3* Adrian Hepworth/NHPA, *(inset)* Alex Wild. **p. 795:** *Figure 22-4* CDO Ranching and Development L.P., *(inset)* Joseph Sohm/Visions of America/Corbis. **p. 796:** *Figure 22-5 (T & BL)* Loungepark/Getty Images, *(BR)* Image Source Ltd/age fotostock; *Figure 22-6* Heinrich van den Berg/Getty Images. **p. 797:** *photo* Frans Lanting/Corbis; *Figure 22-7* Thomas Mangelsen/Minden Pictures. **p. 799:** *Figure 22-8* Judith Haeusler/Getty Images; *Figure 22-9 (T)* FoodCollection/age fotostock, *(B)* Riou/PhotoCuisine/Corbis. **p. 801:** *Figure 22-10* Image Source/Corbis; *Figure 22-11 (L)* Lew Robertson/Corbis, *(C)* John E. Kelly/Jupiterimages, *(R)* LWA-Stephen Welstead/Corbis. **p. 802:** *Figure 22-12* Owen Franken/Corbis. **p. 803:** *Figure 22-13 (L)* Bobbi Fabian/Getty Images, *(R)* Tim Hill/Photolibrary. **p. 806:** *Figure 22-16* Callum Bennetts/Alamy; *photo* Rubberball/Jupiterimages. **p. 807:** *Figure 22-17* Tommy Moorman. **p. 808:** *Figure 22-18* Oxford Scientific (OSF)/Photolibrary; *photo* Peter Menzel www.menzelphoto.com. **p. 809:** *photo* Steve Allen/Getty Images. **p. 810:** *Figure 22-20* Image Source/Veer. **p. 812:** *Figure 22-22* Science Photo Library/Alamy. **p. 814:** *Figure 22-24* Wayne G. Lawler/Photo Researchers; *Figure 22-25* Deshakalyan Chowdhury/AFP/Getty Images. **p. 815:** *Figure 22-26 (L)* Dr. Richard Kessel & Dr. Gene Shih/Visuals Unlimited, *(both)* SPL/Photo Researchers. **p. 817:** *Figure 22-29* SPL/Photo Researchers. **p. 819:** *Figure 22-30* Ladislav Janicek/zefa/Corbis, *(inset)* Dr Kari Lounatmaa/Photo Researchers; *Figure 22-31* Wayne Lynch/age fotostock. **p. 820:** *Figure 22-32* Annie Griffiths Belt/Corbis, *photo* S.Picavet/Jupiterimages. **p. 821:** *photo* Sean Justice/Corbis; *Figure 22-33* Envision/Corbis, *(inset)* Mango Productions/

ANSWERS --

Chapter 1

1. b; 2. b; 3. d; 4. e; 5. c; 6. e; 7. a; 8. a; 9. b; 10. a; 11. d; 12. c; 13. b; 14. e; 15. a; 16. d; 17. a

Short-Answer Questions

1. To provide proper controls, a group of participants must receive a placebo that superficially resembles the medication. The control group should be treated exactly the same as the experimental group, with one exception: the control group receives a placebo instead of the drug. This provides a basis of comparison between the experimental and control groups.

2. There are many possible answers. Four possibilities are: adding a control group; extending the test for a longer period of time; standardizing the subjects to make sure that other variables are not responsible for the weight loss; repeating the study.

3. The common use of the term "theory" often implies that it is simply a hunch about something. In a scientific context, "theory" is applied only when a hypothesis has received significant support from multiple sources over time.

Chapter 2

1. d; 2. e; 3. d; 4. e; 5. b; 6. a; 7. c; 8. a; 9. d; 10. c; 11. b; 12. a; 13. a; 14. a; 15. a; 16. a; 17. a; 18. e; 19. e; 20. d; 21. b

Short-Answer Questions

1. a) The sodium atom has one electron in its outermost shell; the fluorine atom has seven electrons in its outermost shell. b) An ionic bond forms between these two atoms. Neither atom has a full outer electron shell, and both are unstable. The atoms interact to achieve a full outer shell of electrons: the single electron in the outermost shell of the sodium is transferred to the outermost shell of the fluorine. Each atom becomes an ion, and the oppositely charged ions attract each other.

2. First, cohesion is a result of polar water molecules easily bonding together by hydrogen bonds; this allows one water molecule to "connect" with the next as water makes its way up from the soil to the leaves of a tall tree. Second, water has a large capacity to hold heat and resists large fluctuations in temperature; this is because added energy, in the form of heat, does not increase the movement of water molecules, as occurs in most substances. Instead, hydrogen bonds between water molecules are briefly broken and then re-form with nearby water molecules. Third, ice is less dense than water, so it floats; this is because polar water molecules are held apart by hydrogen bonds when the temperature drops (see Figure 2-15). Fourth, water is an excellent solvent because water molecules are polar. Polar molecules with charged regions are attracted to the charged regions of other polar molecules. Many substances contain polar molecules, which easily dissolve in water.

3. Water is a polar molecule and is attracted to other polar molecules, or molecules with charged regions. Oil consists of non-polar molecules.

As a result, polar water molecules will not interact with oil, and water by itself will not be able to dissolve oily dirt.

4. Lettuce and celery contain carbohydrates, which provide a source of energy or fuel for the body. Strawberries also contain carbohydrates, but more monosaccharides versus the complex carbohydrates of lettuce and celery. Walnuts and chicken are sources of protein. The amino acid building blocks of protein are used to build many structures and molecules required by all cells. The salad dressing contains lipids, which provide the body with energy.

Chapter 3

1. e; 2. b; 3. e; 4. a; 5. d; 6. d; 7. c; 8. a; 9. d; 10. d; 11. b; 12. d; 13. c; 14. e; 15. b; 16. b; 17. e; 18. b

Short-Answer Question

1. See the organelle review table, Figure 3-39 on page 117.

Chapter 4

1. a; 2. e; 3. e; 4. c; 5. a; 6. c; 7. a; 8. b; 9. d; 10. c; 11. b; 12. e; 13. b; 14. b; 15. a; 16. a; 17. e; 18. d

Short-Answer Questions

1. The plant can split the water molecules in the "photo" reactions of photosynthesis, producing oxygen gas, which can be used for aerobic respiration by both the plant and the mouse. The carbon dioxide produced as a by-product of aerobic respiration by the plant and the mouse can be used by the plant in the "synthesis" reactions, which ultimately produce glucose for the plant.

2. a) Water molecules are split during the "photo" reactions and oxygen gas is released. Measuring the amount of O_2 provides an indication of the rate of the "photo" reactions. b) Plants incorporate CO_2 in the "synthesis" reactions. Using the energy from the "photo" reactions, plants modify the CO_2 to (eventually) form glucose. The "synthesis" reactions are driven by the energy from the "photo" reactions. c) With additional CO_2, the rate of the "synthesis" reactions will increase, which in turn will increase the amount of energy needed from the "photo" reactions.

3. Photosynthesis involves the production of glucose, and cellular respiration involves the breakdown of glucose. Growth in plants is dependent on the rate of photosynthesis. The faster this process occurs, the more glucose is made, the more plant material can be synthesized, and the more the plant grows. If a plant is growing, the rate of photosynthesis exceeds the rate of cellular respiration.

Chapter 5

1. e; 2. e; 3. b; 4. c; 5. d; 6. d; 7. e; 8. b; 9. c; 10. b; 11. a; 12. e; 13. c; 14. a; 15. d; 16. c

Short-Answer Questions

1. Thymine makes up 30% of the bases. Cytosine and thymine have only one complementary base, so the base and its complement occur in

equal numbers. Because cytosine makes up 20%, its complementary base, guanine, is also 20%. The total of cytosine and guanine is 40%, so the remaining bases total 60%. Because thymine and adenine must occur in equal numbers, half of this total (30%) must be thymine and the other half (30%) adenine.

2. The mRNA is UAG CUG CCU AGG. mRNA allows instructions from DNA to be delivered to ribosomes in the cytoplasm, where it directs the assembly of the protein it encodes.

3. The sequence of codons of the mRNA is translated into a sequence of amino acids that forms a polypeptide chain. As each codon of the mRNA is read by a ribosome, a transfer RNA with an anticodon complementary to the mRNA codon adds a specific amino acid to the growing polypeptide chain.

4. This is an example of a point mutation. The adenine in the fourth codon from the left has been replaced with thymine. This change results in coding for a different amino acid, changing the type of protein produced by the gene—because the amino acid sequence has changed.

5. First, recombinant DNA technology is used to make certain medicines, such as insulin, growth hormone, and erythropoietin, with much less expense; this enables more people to purchase and benefit from these medicines. Second, there have been many efforts to cure some diseases caused by genetic abnormalities using gene therapy; although this technology has not met with success, the future still holds potential. Third, genetic testing can be conducted on parents to identify whether they are at risk of producing offspring with certain genetic diseases. Prenatal genetic screening can be conducted to determine whether a baby will be born with a genetic disease. Adults can also be tested to determine whether they carry genes that put them at risk of developing a disease. With genetic screening, preventive measures and treatments can be undertaken.

Chapter 6

1. c; 2. b; 3. d; 4. d; 5. c; 6. a; 7. b; 8. e; 9. d; 10. b; 11. b; 12. c; 13. d; 14. e; 15. c; 16. a; 17. e; 18. d

Short-Answer Questions

1. Crossing over occurs as sister chromatids of homologous chromosomes come together and swap equivalent segments containing the same genes (but possibly different alleles) during the first prophase of meiosis. This results in an uneven distribution of genetic material from maternal and paternal chromosomes. Gametes could potentially receive more genes from one (either) biological parent than the other. Also, the random division of the homologues (with respect to whether they are maternal or paternal) at anaphase I can lead to gametes having greater than or less than exactly 50% maternal and 50% paternal genetic material. For every gamete having a higher percentage of its genetic material from the maternal side, there is a gamete having an equally higher percentage of paternal genetic material.

2. There cannot be any essential genetic information on the Y chromosome—because all females are able to live without a Y chromosomes—but there is on the X chromosome. Receiving only the Y chromosome means that essential genetic information from the X chromosome is absent.

3. An organism is more likely to reproduce asexually in the absence of adverse environmental pressures. Should some environmental

pressure develop, the organism may start reproducing sexually, producing genetically diverse offspring that are better able to survive environmental pressures. An experiment could be conducted with an organism that has the capacity to switch between sexual and asexual reproduction. This organism could be placed in an environment with ideal conditions and another with adverse conditions. If the hypothesis is correct, the organism will reproduce asexually under ideal conditions and sexually under adverse conditions.

Chapter 7

1. a; 2. b; 3. e; 4. e; 5. a; 6. c; 7. e; 8. a; 9. c; 10. e; 11. e; 12. d; 13. d; 14. b; 15. d; 16. a

Short-Answer Questions

1. a) SMA must be a recessive genetic disorder, because the phenotype of both parents is normal—that is, they are not affected by SMA. For two unaffected parents to have children with the disease, both parents' genotypes must be heterozygous. This is an example of a disease-causing allele that doesn't always reveal itself in a population. b) Individuals who are heterozygous for a recessive genetic disorder (i.e., are carriers) will not necessarily have children with the disease. However, this example demonstrates heterozygous parents with children who inherit the disease-causing allele from both parents, resulting in SMA. The probability of having another biological child with SMA is the same as it was for each of the first two children. The probability of inheriting the recessive allele from the mother is 0.5, and the probability of inheriting the recessive allele from the father is 0.5. Therefore the overall probability is 0.25, 25%, or 1 in 4.

2. The phenotype, or color of the blooms, is affected by differences in the environment. Hydrangea flower color varies with the type of soil, because the pH of the soil affects the pigmentation of the blooms.

3. a) Genetic disorders that involve genes on the X chromosome affect men differently from women. If a female inherits an allele that produces a non-functional protein on one of her X chromosomes, she may not be affected *if* the second X chromosome has the normal allele. However, because males have only one X chromosome, they have only one chance to receive the normal allele.

b)

	X^H	X^H
X^h	$X^h X^H$	$X^h X^H$
Y	$X^H Y$	$X^H Y$

There is a 0% chance that a son will have hemophilia. A son inherits his X chromosome from his mother. Because the mother is carrying two functional alleles, either X would provide a functional allele.

Chapter 8

1. e; 2. a; 3. b; 4. c; 5. d; 6. d; 7. e; 8. a; 9. e; 10. e; 11. b; 12. a; 13. c; 14. b; 15. d; 16. b; 17. b; 18. e; 19. d; 20. d; 21. c

Short-Answer Questions

1. Evolution is a change in allele frequencies in a population. Natural selection is one of four evolutionary agents, characterized by variation, heritability, and differential reproductive success for a trait.

2. Genetic drift is a random change in allele frequencies. In small populations, random deviations from the expected genotype frequencies

among offspring are less likely to be counterbalanced by deviations in the opposite direction from the expected genotype frequencies.

3. First, environments can change quickly. Natural selection may be too slow to adapt the species to a constantly changing environment. Second, variation is needed as the raw material of selection. If there is no mutation to give rise to an allele that would help make an individual more fit, the species will never be perfectly adapted. (Why, for instance, are there no mammals with wheeled appendages?) Third, evolution produces "more fit" individuals in each generation. If the optimum solution required organisms to get worse before they could evolve to "perfection," selection would never lead to such a solution.

4. In the 1940s, when penicillin was first used to treat bacterial infections, it was uniformly effective in killing *Staphylococcus aureus.* Today, more than 90% of isolated *S. aureus* strains are resistant to penicillin. Because penicillin has become such a pervasive toxin in the environment of *Staphylococcus,* natural selection has led to an increase in the frequency of alleles that make the bacteria resistant. Today, nearly a third of "staph" infections are resistant to antibiotics. The meaning of such unintentional natural selection "experiments" is clear and consistent: evolution is occurring all around us.

Chapter 9

1. b; 2. d; 3. e; 4. b; 5. d; 6. d; 7. c; 8. a; 9. d; 10. e; 11. c; 12. a; 13. a; 14. b; 15. e; 16. b

Short-Answer Question

1. Males provide more parental care, consistent with the two predictions about sex roles and parental investment. First, the sex that invests more will be more discriminating. Second, the sex that invests less will compete among themselves for access to the higher-investing sex.

Chapter 10

1. a; 2. d; 3. e; 4. e; 5. a; 6. d; 7. d; 8. a; 9. e; 10. a; 11. d; 12. d; 13. e; 14. b; 15. c; 16. a; 17. c

Short-Answer Questions

1. The biological species concept focuses on reproductive populations, or groups of individuals that can mate with each other and are unable to breed with other reproductively isolated groups. The morphological species concept focuses on physical characteristics of the organisms to distinguish one species from another. Many living organisms don't fit neatly into a species as defined by the biological species concept. An example is many of the living organisms that divide asexually, such as bacteria. For these organisms, because they do not require a partner to mate, reproductive compatibility is not a useful diagnostic tool for discriminating among species.

2. Biologists would rely on physical features or characteristics to create evolutionary trees and establish relationships between groups of organisms. Today, with the advent of technology, DNA sequencing (examining the base-pair sequence of DNA) is used to construct evolutionary trees. In either case, the trees define which groups of organisms are most closely related, but not which groups are more advanced than others.

3. These adaptations could be considered an "evolutionary innovation" in which a specific trait or group of traits allows an organism to fill a new niche or an unoccupied niche. This is one trigger of adaptive radiation—the huge, rapid expansion of a species, often diversifying

into many more species. The specific traits of tall, flat teeth and a square jaw allowed the horse to efficiently crop grasses and vegetation from the ground. With areas of grasslands plentiful, these mammals were able to expand and flourish in this niche.

Chapter 11

1. d; 2. c; 3. e; 4. d; 5. c; 6. c; 7. a; 8. c; 9. b; 10. c; 11. e; 12. d; 13. b; 14. b; 15. a; 16. b; 17. d; 18. e.

Short-Answer Questions

1. In all animals, the ability to obtain food, whatever method that may be, has evolved through natural selection. For the sloth, it would make no sense for it to have developed the ability to spring at great speeds, because its food source (vegetation) is stationary. The cheetah, by contrast, must use high speeds to catch its prey, which also can run fast. If the cheetah were to occupy the same niche as the sloth, its ability to run would not improve its ability to obtain vegetation, so it might lose this running ability over many generations.

2. Much of the energy derived from food is utilized for heat production, so endotherms require more food to maintain a constant internal temperature. Ectotherms depend on an external heat source to maintain their body temperature, so they do not need energy derived from food to generate heat.

3. The snake, like other ectotherms, depends on an outside source of heat, so placing an insulating sweater on the snake will prevent heat from reaching its body, keeping it from warming up. For the same reason, ectotherms do not have insulating feathers or fur.

4. The slug has a radula for scraping food from surfaces, has a broad foot on which it glides, and produces a protective slime. Slugs lack the body segmentation found in segmented worms.

Chapter 12

1. a; 2. b; 3. b; 4. c; 5. a; 6. b; 7. e; 8. c; 9. c; 10. c; 11. d; 12. b; 13. d; 14. b; 15. d.

Short-Answer Questions

1. Non-vascular plants lack tissue that can conduct water and dissolved nutrients, tissue that *is* found in vascular plants. Because diffusion can transport water only over very short distances, non-vascular plants are much smaller than vascular plants. Non-vascular plants must live in an environment that is wet for at least some parts of the year, and become dormant when it is dry.

2. Mycorrhizal fungi are associated with the roots of plants, benefiting them by transporting phosphorus and nitrogen from the soil to the cells of the plant roots. In exchange, the fungus takes some sugar from the plant. This relationship enhances the overall health of the plant.

3. Plants expend considerable energy producing a fruit, which contains the seeds. Once a fruit is eaten, it is digested by the animal and the seeds are excreted unharmed, and thus relocated to an area distant from the parent plant. The plant pays the animal with a meal, and in return, the animal transports the seeds.

Chapter 13

1. a; 2. b; 3. c; 4. e; 5 d; 6. a; 7. a; 8. d; 9. b; 10. a; 11. c; 12. b; 13. e; 14. b; 15. e; 16. e; 17. e; 18. b.

Short-Answer Question

	Prokaryotes		Eukaryotes	Viruses
	Bacteria	Archaea	Protists	
Unicellular, colonial, or multicellular?	Unicellular	Unicellular	Unicellular or colonial	Not cells
Plasma membrane?	Present	Present	Present	Absent
Peptidoglycan in cell wall?	Present	Absent	Absent	Absent
Flagella? What type?	Yes; spins like a propeller	Yes; spins like a propeller, but has a chemical composition different from that of bacteria	Yes; waves from side to side and has a chemical composition different from that of bacteria or archaea	No flagellum
Presence of nucleus?	Absent	Absent	Present	No nucleus
Intracellular organelles?	Absent	Absent	Present	No organelles
Type of genetic material (DNA, RNA, or both possible)?	DNA	DNA	DNA	DNA or RNA
Chromosome structure (linear or circular)?	Usually circular	Usually circular	Linear	Linear or circular

Chapter 14

1. a; 2. e; 3. a; 4. b; 5. e; 6. d; 7. b; 8. d; 9. c; 10. c; 11. e; 12. d; 13. a; 14. b; 15. c.

Short-Answer Questions

1. Density-dependent factors are limitations on a population's growth resulting from competition among individuals for a finite amount of resources, such as food and space for living and breeding, and an increased risk of disease and predation. Density-independent factors are forces such as hurricanes and droughts that kill off many individuals in a population, regardless of the size of the population.

2. An organism with a type I survivorship curve is relatively large, has only a few offspring, invests a lot in each offspring, and lives a relatively long life. If the organism had a type III survivorship curve, it would have a high probability of dying early in life and would produce many offspring and provide very little parental care.

3. Species that lack natural enemies and live in an environment with low risk of mortality from other sources breed at a later age; late-onset genetic disorders are selected out and individuals are healthier in old age. Species that breed at an early age pass on adverse genetic traits that are expressed after their normal age of breeding; they do not live long after the normal age of breeding. If breeding is delayed, as in the fruit flies in the experiments described in the chapter, age-related disorders that interfere with breeding are selected out and the life span will be extended.

Chapter 15

1. d; 2. e; 3. a; 4. a; 5. e; 6. d; 7. e; 8. a; 9. d; 10. a; 11. a; 12. a; 13. d; 14. e; 15. b; 16. b.

Short-Answer Questions

1. Heated air rises and cools at the equator (0° latitude); as it cools, it cannot hold as much water and loses it as precipitation. Air moves north and south from the equator and begins to fall at about 30° latitude north and south, warming and absorbing moisture. This creates very dry conditions at these latitudes, and deserts are found there. Air continues to move toward the poles and begins to rise again at 60° latitude, cooling and losing its moisture through precipitation, making these locations very wet. Air again falls near the poles, making these areas very dry. Temperature and amount of rainfall are the primary determinants of the kind of biome found in any terrestrial location.

2. Energy flows through each trophic level. Photosynthetic organisms, the primary producers, trap energy from the sun in the chemical bonds of food. Primary consumers, the herbivores, eat photosynthetic organisms, and these animals are consumed by secondary consumers, the carnivores. Carnivores can be consumed by tertiary consumers, the top carnivores. A natural ecosystem can support only a few top carnivores because only about 10% of the energy is available to each subsequent trophic level.

3. An organism's niche includes the space it requires to live in, the kinds and amount of food it eats, the time of day and of year it reproduces, the amount of moisture and temperature it requires, as well as other criteria. Two organisms that occupy the same niche compete, with two different possible outcomes: one species may drive the other to extinction (competitive exclusion) or both species may change their behavior or undergo a morphological change so they are restricted within their own niche, dividing the resources between them (resource partitioning).

Chapter 16

1. e; 2. c; 3. d; 4. a; 5. e; 6. e; 7. d; 8. d; 9. b; 10. a; 11. e; 12. c; 13. b; 14. e.

Short-Answer Questions

1. The greatest biodiversity, both aquatic and terrestrial, is in equatorial regions. Less biodiversity is found with increasing latitude. Habitat destruction and degradation are the greatest threats to biodiversity.

2. The biotic and abiotic nature of the habitat was altered, but species were not driven to extinction. If species had been made extinct, the ecosystem disturbances would not have been reversible.

3. Most of the deforestation of tropical rain forests is a result of clearing land to make way for agriculture; mining and pollution also contribute. The biodiversity of the planet is greatly affected by rain forest deforestation because no other terrestrial ecosystem has the extent of biodiversity found in these forests.

Chapter 17

1. b; 2. b; 3. d; 4. a; 5. d; 6. d; 7. a; 8. a; 9. b; 10. b; 11. a; 12. c; 13. e.

Short-Answer Questions

1. Both groups are autotrophic, photosynthesizing plants that inhabit a wide range of environments, and play a vital role in human survival by providing foods, medicines, housing, and many other products. Monocots have one cotyledon, which distinguishes them from eudicots, which have two cotyledons. The venation, which is bundles of xylem and phloem, of leaves are another distinguishing

characteristic, with monocots having parallel venation and eudicots having a branching pattern. Vascular bundles are arranged in a random pattern within stems of monocots, while they are arranged in a circular pattern in stems of eudicots. A vast majority of eudicots are capable of secondary growth, while only a small percentage of monocots are capable of secondary growth. Flowering parts of flowers occur in multiples of 3 for monocots and multiples of 4 and 5 for eudicots. Finally, monocots typically form fibrous root systems while eudicots form taproots from which rootlets grow.

2. Water is pulled from the roots up through xylem to the leaves. When a water molecule evaporates from a leaf it pulls on its neighboring water molecule, which is held together by hydrogen bonding. This in turn causes all the other water molecules within this xylem tube, which all have hydrogen bonds with their neighboring water molecules, forming an interconnected column of water, to be pulled up the xylem. The ability of water to form hydrogen bonds between water molecules allows it to have tension and cohesion and therefore the ability to be pulled up from leaves as water evaporates.

3. Since vascular bundles of monocots are randomly spread out within the stem, a shallow cut would sever only those vascular bundles near the surface. Vascular bundles of eudicots, on the other hand, usually form a ring structure, typically closer to the surface. Since their vascular tissue is close to the surface a shallow cut is likely to sever all of their vascular tissue, preventing the movement of fluids and causing the plant to die.

Chapter 18

1. a; 2. b; 3. e; 4. a; 5. e; 6. a; 7. e; 8. e; 9. d; 10. a; 11. b; 12. c; 13. c; 14. b

Short-Answer Questions

1. A single strawberry plant, within a year or so, can completely fill a large area as the plant reproduces asexually and populates the patch with genetically identical, strawberry-producing clones.

2. Planting a potato produces a new plant asexually, so the new plant is genetically identical to the plant from which the potato came. If the parent plant is healthy and productive, this can help a farmer produce new crops that are equally productive. Seeds, on the other hand, are the product of sexual reproduction, so the new plant may not resemble the "mother plant" from which the seeds were collected; the properties of the new generation will depend also on the male parent, of unknown productivity. The farmer should choose potatoes for planting that come from the parent plant with the greatest productivity and vigor.

Chapter 19

1. a; 2. a; 3. c; 4. b; 5. b; 6. e; 7. a; 8. e; 9. d; 10. a; 11. d

Short-Answer Questions

1. This phenomenon is called phototropism, growth in response to a light source. When light hits a plant from a particular direction, auxins produced in the plant move away from the light source and end up on the opposite, shaded side of the stem. There, the auxins stimulate a slightly greater rate of growth than on the side with less auxin. As a consequence, the uneven growth causes the plant to bend toward the light.

2. The hormone ethylene is a gas that speeds the rate at which fruit ripens. Ethylene can help with shipping fruits internationally because if bananas, for example, are picked in Central America before they are ripe (when they are green), and just prior to their delivery, ethylene is injected into the cargo hold of the ship; this initiates the ripening of all the fruit simultaneously.

3. Spicy foods, such as mustard, frequently come from plants and get their flavor from secondary compounds that may make the plant toxic or unpalatable to an insect, representing an anti-herbivore adaptation. The fact that the chemicals are not, in some cases, toxic to humans may be a consequence of our larger body size relative to the intended herbivores'.

4. See Figure 19-2, page 693.

Chapter 20

1. a; 2. c; 3. d; 4. a; 5. a; 6. a; 7. d; 8. e; 9. b; 10. d; 11. a

Short-Answer Questions

1. Homeostasis is the maintenance of a constant internal environment within a narrow range of conditions around a set point for variables such as temperature, pH, and concentrations of solute, water, CO_2, O_2, and glucose, among many others. Homeostasis allows for the normal functioning of an organism's cells. Body temperature is normally controlled by a negative feedback mechanism (thermoregulation). Hyperthermia occurs when the body temperature rises above its normal range. If high enough, this can interfere with the structure and activity of the enzymes involved in the body's metabolic activities, resulting in metabolic dysfunction, death of cells, organ failure, and, ultimately, death of the organism.

2. Cells of similar type are organized into tissues; tissues are organized into organs that perform specialized functions; and organs are organized into organ systems, arranged in an integrated manner to achieve common goals. There are four types of tissue. *Connective tissues* support and help form body structures. *Epithelial tissues* form internal and external body coverings, providing protection, synthesizing and releasing chemical products, and controlling movement of substances within the body. *Muscle tissues* have the ability to contract, generating body movements and moving materials within the body. *Nervous tissue* conducts electrical impulses, allowing communication within the organism.

3. *Connective tissue proper* includes (a) *loose connective tissue,* which has cells embedded in a semi-fluid matrix, with many collagen fibers that bind and hold organs in place, as well as storing fat and insulating, cushioning, and protecting the body; and (b) *dense connective tissue,* which has many more collagen fibers than loose connective tissue and thus has greater strength, forming tendons, which connect muscles to bones, and ligaments, which connect bones to each other. *Special connective tissue* includes (a) *bone,* composed of cells within a solid matrix interspersed with many collagen fibers, forming a rigid structure that supports and protects the body; (b) *cartilage,* composed of cells within a matrix (not as hard as bone) made up of collagen, elastin, and proteins connected to carbohydrate chains; and (c) *blood,* which has a fluid matrix called plasma, with suspended red blood cells, white blood cells, and platelets.

4. *Skeletal muscles* are made up of cells (fibers) that have alternating light and dark bands (striations) and contain many nuclei; the muscles are attached to bones, generating force for their movement, and are controlled voluntarily. *Smooth muscles,* which are not striated and have smaller cells, are found in the walls of hollow organs; contractions allow movement of liquids and solids within the organs, and are involuntary. *Cardiac muscle* is found in the walls of the heart and consists of striated, small, branched cells with a single nucleus; contractions generate pressure to move blood in the cardiovascular system, and are involuntary.

Chapter 21

1. d; 2. c; 3. a; 4. b; 5. a; 6. e; 7. e; 8. b; 9. e; 10. e; 11. a; 12. b; 13. e; 14. a; 15. c; 16. a; 17. c; 18. d; 19. d; 20. a; 21. c

Short-Answer Questions

1. Single-celled organisms, such as bacteria, are in direct contact with their environment, and direct diffusion of gases, nutrients, and wastes can take place at an adequate rate to maintain these organisms physiologically. In larger organisms made up of multiple cells, many of which are not in direct contact with the outside environment, direct diffusion is no longer feasible. With the development of a circulatory system, nutrients and gases can be brought in close proximity to cells, where diffusion can take place. An open circulatory system is characterized by having only one type of extracellular fluid; a closed circulatory system has two different extracellular fluids: interstitial fluid, bathing cells, and blood, which is contained only within the blood vessels.

2. In a single-circuit cardiovascular system, the heart has two chambers, one receiving blood that has traveled through the body, and the other moving blood to the gills and then through the blood vessels of the rest of the body. As blood moves through capillaries and other blood vessels, it slows down considerably, which slows down the delivery of substances to tissues and removal of waste products. A double-circuit system has one circuit that moves blood through the lungs and another that moves blood through the rest of the body. This system allows blood to be re-pressurized after it has traveled through the lungs, and this would be the better choice to supply tissues with high energy demands: blood can be delivered and removed at a faster rate.

3. *Red blood cells (erythrocytes):* Their primary function is to carry oxygen. They are suspended in plasma and contain iron-bearing hemoglobin, which binds, carries, and releases the oxygen. *White blood cells (leukocytes):* These are part of the body's immune system; their primary function is to seek out and destroy foreign organisms, including viruses and bacteria. *Platelets:* These cellular fragments circulate in blood and take part in plugging tears and holes in blood vessels and preventing leakage of blood. They do this by sticking together to form a clot.

4. Aquatic animals move water across their gills, which have capillaries that use a countercurrent mechanism. Blood moves through the capillaries in the opposite direction to the water flow, and this allows for a more efficient gas exchange: absorption of O_2 by and release of CO_2 from blood. In animals that breathe air, fresh air enters the lungs and moves into the alveoli. Gas exchange occurs there: O_2 in the air diffuses into capillaries in the walls of the alveoli, and CO_2 diffuses out of the blood and into the air, to be exhaled from the lungs.

Chapter 22

1. a; 2. c; 3. d; 4. a; 5. a; 6. b; 7. b; 8. c; 9. d; 10. a; 11. b; 12. b; 13. e; 14. d; 15. d; 16. e; 17. a

Short-Answer Questions

1. *Water:* important in the transport of nutrients and wastes; acts as a solvent for amino acids, sugars, minerals, and many vitamins; and takes part in some chemical reactions. *Proteins:* the source of amino acids, which are the building blocks of body proteins, such as hemoglobin, muscle cells, and enzymes. Proteins also can act as an energy source.

Carbohydrates: energy-rich chemicals used by cells, through cellular respiration, as their primary energy source. Cellulose (fiber), which cannot be digested by humans, stimulates movement of food through the intestines. *Fats:* long-term energy-storage molecules, stored as fat tissue under the skin (which also provides body insulation) and elsewhere. *Vitamins and minerals:* required in very small quantities, but playing an important role in the proper functioning of enzymes and other processes.

2. *Ingestion:* intake of food through the mouth. The structures of the mouth cut food into small pieces and grind and mix it with saliva, so that it can be transported through the esophagus to the stomach by peristaltic action. *Digestion:* breakdown of food in the mouth, stomach, and small intestine into its most basic components, which can be readily absorbed and used by cells. Digestion is accomplished by a combination of physical breakdown of food into smaller pieces and chemical breakdown by enzymes. *Absorption:* uptake of usable nutrients through the wall of the small intestine and into the bloodstream, and then transport to cells of the body. *Elimination:* finally, in the large intestine, absorption of water, salts, and vitamins, storage of feces in the rectum, and elimination through defecation.

3. Animals that consume cellulose-containing foods such as grasses and leaves have, either in their stomach or in their cecum, bacteria that can break down cellulose into a usable form.

4. Type 1 diabetes, usually beginning in childhood, results from the inability of the pancreas to produce enough insulin; treatment is injection of insulin so that cells can absorb glucose. Type 2 diabetes, generally beginning later in life, occurs when cells become less responsive to insulin or the number of insulin receptors is reduced. Risk factors include obesity and chronic consumption of high amounts of sugar. Treatment includes weight loss and minimizing glucose fluctuations.

Chapter 23

1. a; 2. e; 3. a; 4. a; 5. c; 6. e; 7. d; 8. d; 9. c; 10. d; 11. a; 12. a; 13. a; 14. d; 15. e; 16. e; 17. e; 18. d; 19. b; 20. e.

Short-Answer Questions

1. Neurons are the impulse-conducting cells of the central and peripheral nervous systems. An impulse travels along the axon away from the cell body, eventually arriving at a synapse with another neuron, a muscle cell, or a gland cell. Glial cells are supporting cells found in the central and peripheral nervous systems. They help neurons function by protecting, insulating, and nourishing them, but do not play a direct role in impulse conduction. Without glial cells, neurons would not be able to function, survive, and grow. Glial cells are capable of dividing throughout life, while neurons, with a few exceptions, are not.

2. Each skeletal muscle fiber consists of numerous myofibrils, which are made up of many sarcomeres—the units of contraction. Each sarcomere contains thin and thick filaments, made of different types of protein. Thin filaments consist of two rows of small globular actin molecules, and thick filaments are made up of myosin; each myosin molecule looks much like a double-headed golf club. Myosin molecules are overlapping, with the globular heads projecting along the entire length of the fiber. The four-part change that allows contraction consists of: (1) *Detach:* A link between a myosin and an actin filament parallel to it is broken as a molecule of ATP binds to the myosin. (2) *Reach:* As the ATP breaks down, energy released alters the shape of the myosin into a higher-

energy shape. (3) *Reattach:* In its altered shape, the myosin reaches farther down the actin filament, where it reattaches. And (4) *Pull back:* The myosin then snaps back to its original shape, pulling the actin filament as it does so and shortening the fiber, in the "power stroke."

3. There are five primary types of sensory receptors. *Mechanoreceptors* measure mechanical stress and are associated with hearing and touch. *Thermoreceptors* measure temperature and are found in the skin; they are part of our perception of touch. *Photoreceptors* measure light and are found in the eyes, functioning in sight. *Pain receptors* detect pain, which can be caused by extremes of heat or tissue damage; they are part of the perception of touch. *Chemoreceptors* detect chemicals; they are found in the mouth and nose and function in taste and smell.

Chapter 24

1. b; 2. d; 3. c; 4. e; 5. b; 6. b; 7. d; 8. e; 9. b; 10. d; 11. b; 12. c

Short-Answer Questions

1. Both types of hormones circulate in extracellular fluids and influence changes in target cells (cells with a receptor for a particular hormone). Peptide and protein hormones cannot pass through the cell membrane of target cells; they attach to membrane receptors on the target cell, which causes a change within the cell. Steroid hormones, however, can pass through the cell membrane of target cells; they then attach to a receptor in the cytoplasm or nucleus.

2. The hypothalamus integrates sensory information, received by the brain, on the internal and external conditions of the organism. Once the hypothalamus has evaluated the information, it produces hormones that travel to the pituitary gland, which is attached by a thin stalk to the hypothalamus. These hormones cause the pituitary either to release or to stop the release of specific hormones. The pituitary gland is made up of two parts, the anterior and posterior pituitary; these produce hormones that influence other endocrine glands to produce other hormones.

3. Drops in estrogen level in females, such as during menopause and after giving birth, as well as the spike in estrogen that occurs at puberty, have been correlated with depression. In cases of low estrogen, supplements can be taken to help return estrogen levels to normal and reduce the occurrence of depression. Males who take supplemental testosterone may experience elevated self-esteem and overflowing of new ideas, and feel energetic, euphoric, confident, and charismatic; others find that they are more aggressive. Human and animal studies show that castrated males, who produce almost no testosterone, and females that have been sterilized and do not produce estrogen and other sex hormones, live longer than those producing normal levels of these hormones. However, among post-menopausal women taking hormone supplements, mortality decreases, illustrating the complexity of this issue.

4. Some manufactured chemicals, such as DDT and PCBs, can mimic, block, or interfere with the functioning of hormones. These endocrine disruptors can build up in organisms that feed on other, contaminated organisms, and collect in tissues (such as fat tissue, in the case of DDT). As a result, even in small quantities, the chemicals may harm some organisms.

5. See Figure 24-9 on page 899.

Chapter 25

1. a; 2. c; 3. a; 4. a; 5. a; 6. c; 7. c; 8. e; 9. e; 10. b; 11. e; 12. b; 13. d; 14. a; 15. d

Short-Answer Questions

1. Human males produce sperm by the process of spermatogenesis, which occurs in the testes, located in the scrotum. Spermatogonia, cells in the seminiferous tubules, divide by mitosis, each cell producing a new spermatogonium and a primary spermatocyte. The primary spermatocyte undergoes a first meiotic division, producing two secondary spermatocytes, each of which divides by a second meiotic division to produce four haploid sperm. Sperm move to the epididymis, where they mature and become motile.

2. Germ layers are the three layers of tissue—endoderm, mesoderm, and ectoderm—that form in the embryo during gastrulation. *Endoderm* is the inner tissue layer that forms the digestive tract, liver, pancreas, and the lining of the respiratory tract. *Mesoderm* is the middle tissue layer that gives rise to muscle and the skeletal system. *Ectoderm* is the outer tissue that gives rise to the outer layer of skin, hair, the nervous system, and the lining of the nose and mouth.

3. *First trimester:* During the first three months of development, minimal growth of the embryo takes place, but vital cell differentiation and development occur. The fertilized egg (zygote) divides and eventually forms three cell layers, from which all the organs and their associated systems will develop, as well as all body structures. This is also the stage during which the zygote implants in the uterus and the placenta forms. *Second trimester:* Significant growth occurs during the fourth through six months. The bones of the skeletal system grow and muscles develop, making possible fetal movement. *Third trimester:* The fetus primarily grows during these last three months of pregnancy. Growth and development of the nervous system also take place. During this stage, the fetus becomes an individual that can survive outside the womb.

Chapter 26

1. b; 2. d; 3. d; 4. d; 5. e; 6. b; 7. d; 8. a; 9. e; 10. c; 11. d; 12. a.

Short-Answer Questions

1. During the specific division of the immune system's primary response to an antigen on a pathogen, a type of lymphocyte called memory cells is produced through clonal selection. These lymphocytes "remember" an antigen. The second time a person is exposed to the pathogen, the memory cells, hanging around in the lymph and blood cells, are ready to attack it, mounting a much faster and more vigorous attack.

2. The specific division of the immune system recognizes very specific infectious agents, such as the virus that causes chicken pox. As a consequence of a vaccine for this illness, the immune system forms a "memory" of the virus that allows it to fight off the virus in the future before the virus can cause the chicken pox. The chicken pox virus antigens remain relatively constant over time. The influenza virus, on the other hand is not so constant. Each year there are many different versions, or strains, of the influenza virus, all of which are constantly changing. And so with each new flu season, the body encounters a slightly different form of influenza and, therefore, a different set of antigens. For this reason, previously formed memory cells are not helpful in fighting the new virus.

GLOSSARY

A note about notation: The word or phrase being defined is in boldface type; it is followed by the number (in parentheses) of the chapter or chapters where it is discussed. In some cases, derivations are given. Abbreviations: Gk., Greek; Lat., Latin; *sing.,* singular; *pl.,* plural; *dim.,* diminutive (a smaller version of the object named); *pron.,* pronounced.

A

abscisic acid (19) A plant hormone that has the general effect of inhibiting growth and reproductive activities.

absorption (22) The process by which biological macromolecules in food particles are taken up from the cells lining the digestive tract and then move into the bloodstream.

acid (2) Any fluid with a pH below 7.0, indicating the presence of more H⁺ ions than OH⁻ ions. [Lat., *acidus,* sour]

acquired immune deficiency syndrome (AIDS) (13, 26) Infectious human disease caused by a retrovirus, HIV (human immunodeficiency virus), which compromises the immune system by attacking T cells, leaving an individual susceptible to multiple infections as well as cancers.

acrosome (25) Cap-like structure covering the head region of a sperm; it contains enzymes for penetrating the outer membrane of an egg, enabling fusion of the nuclei to occur.

actin (23) A protein of muscle tissue; makes up the thin filaments.

action potential (23) An electrical signal that travels along an axon, from a neuron to another neuron, a muscle cell, or a gland cell.

active transport (3) Molecular movement that depends on the input of energy, which is necessary when the molecules to be moved are large or are being moved against their concentration gradient.

adaptation (8) The process by which, as a result of natural selection, organisms become better matched to their environment; also, a specific feature, such as the quills of a porcupine, that makes an organism more fit.

adaptive radiation (10) The rapid diversification of a small number of species into a much larger number of species, able to live in a wide variety of habitats.

additive effects (7) Effects from alleles of multiple genes that all contribute to the ultimate phenotype for a given characteristic.

adenosine triphosphate (ATP) (4) A molecule that temporarily stores energy for cellular activity in all living organisms; ATP is composed of a sugar molecule and a chain of three negatively charged phosphate groups.

adult (11) In complete metamorphosis, the third and final stage of insect development.

aging (14) An increased risk of mortality with increasing age; generally characterized by multiple physiological breakdowns.

alleles (5, 7) Alternative versions of a gene. [Gk., *allos,* another]

allergen (26) An antigen that causes an allergic response.

allergy (26) An inappropriate immune response to what should be a harmless substance.

allopatric speciation (10) Speciation that occurs as a result of a geographic barrier between groups of individuals that leads to reproductive isolation and then genetic divergence. [Gk., *allos,* another + *patris,* native land]

allopolyploidy (10) A special case of polyploidy, in which through asexual propagation and subsequent repeated hybridization the increased number of chromosome sets in an individual are derived from multiple different species. [Gk., *allos,* another + *polys,* many + *ploion,* vessel]

alternation of generations (18) In plants, the life cycle that is characterized by an extended period in which the plant has a multicellular haploid form and a period in which it has a multicellular diploid form.

altruistic behavior (9) A behavior that comes at a cost to the individual performing it and benefits another. [Lat., *alter,* the other]

amino acid (2) One of 20 molecules built of an amino group, a carboxyl group, and a unique side chain; proteins are constructed of combinations of amino acids. [Gk., *Ammon,* name of ancient Libyan god, near whose temple a compound known as "sal ammoniacus," or "ammonium salt," was prepared]

amino group (2) A nitrogen atom bonded to three hydrogen atoms.

amnion (25) During animal development, the membrane enclosing the fluid-filled sac surrounding an embryo.

amniotes (11) Terrestrial vertebrates—reptiles, birds, and mammals—that produce eggs (called amniotic eggs) that are each protected by a water-tight membrane and a shell.

amphibians (11) Members of the class Amphibia; amphibians are ectotherms (that is, they are cold-blooded), with a moist skin, lacking scales, through which they can fully or partially absorb oxygen. They were the first terrestrial vertebrates; the young of most species are aquatic, and the adults are true land animals. [Gk., *bios,* life + *amphi,* on both sides]

amygdala (23) Part of the brain's limbic system; associates emotional feelings and sensory input with memories.

analogous (10) Describes characteristics (such as bat wings and insect wings) that are similar because they were produced by convergent evolution, not because they descended from a common structure in a shared ancestor. [Gk., *analogos,* proportionate]

anaphase (6) The third phase of mitosis, in which the sister chromatids are pulled apart by the spindle fibers, with a full set of chromosomes going to opposite sides of the cell; in meiosis, the homologues separate in anaphase I and the sister chromatids separate in anaphase II. [Gk., *ana,* up + *phasis,* appearance]

anaphylactic shock (26) A life-threatening allergic reaction that causes severe respiratory distress, as the throat swells and asthma develops. With swelling in various tissues, there is less fluid in the bloodstream, and this can lead to dangerously low blood pressure.

anecdotal observation (1) Observation of one or only a few instances of a phenomenon.

angiosperms (12) Vascular, seed-producing flowering and fruit-bearing plants, in which the seeds are enclosed in an ovule within the ovary. [Gk., *angeion,* vessel, jar + *sperma,* seed]

animals (11) Members of the kingdom Animalia, which are eukaryotic, multicellular, and heterotrophic (that is, they cannot produce their own food); many of these organisms have body parts specialized for different activities and can move during some stage of their lives. [Lat., *animal,* a living being]

anterior pituitary (24) A gland of the endocrine system that produces numerous hormones, including thyroid-stimulating hormone (TSH), luteinizing hormone (LH), follicle-stimulating hormone (FSH), prolactin, adrenocorticotropic hormone (ACTH), and growth hormone. Many of the hormones of the anterior pituitary gland direct endocrine glands elsewhere to release other hormones.

anther (12, 18) The part of the stamen, the male reproductive structure of a flower, that produces pollen. [Gk., *anthos,* blossom]

antibody (26) A protein produced by the specific immunity system in response to an antigen. Circulating antibodies recognize and bind to specific antigens.

antigen (26) Any molecule that induces a specific immunity response.

antigen receptor (26) Protein on the plasma membrane of a lymphocyte that sticks out from the cell surface and can bind one specific type of antigen.

antigen-presenting cells (26) Dendritic cells and macrophages that ingest bacteria and viruses, destroying them and "presenting" digested particles of the pathogens on their cell surface.

antiseptic (26) Solution such as rubbing alcohol or hydrogen peroxide that discourages growth of microorganisms.

apical meristem (17) Growth region at the tip of a plant root or stem; division of cells in this meristem causes the root or stem to increase in length.

apoptosis (6, 26) Programmed cell death, which takes place particularly in parts of the body where the cells are likely to accumulate significant genetic damage over time and are therefore at high risk of becoming cancerous. Also occurs in the specific immune response, as cytotoxic effector cells destroy infected body cells. [Gk., *apoptosis,* falling away]

archaea (10) A group of prokaryotes that are evolutionarily distinct from bacteria and that thrives in some of the most extreme environments on earth; one of the three domains of life. [Gk., *archaios,* ancient]

arteriosclerosis (21) A disease process, following development of atherosclerosis, in which calcium deposits harden the arteries.

artery (21) A blood vessel that transports blood from the heart, at higher pressure than veins, to the capillaries of the body.

arthropods (11) Members of the invertebrate phylum Arthropoda; characterized by a segmented body, an exoskeleton, and jointed appendages. [Gk., *arthron,* joint + *pous,* foot]

asexual reproduction (6, 25) A type of reproduction common in prokaryotes and plants, and also occurring in many other multicellular organisms, in which the offspring inherit their DNA from a single parent.

assisted reproductive technology (ART) (25) The use of fertility treatments in which both sperm and egg are handled.

atherosclerosis (21) A disease process in which plaques develop in the arteries, reducing the flow of blood and increasing the risk of blood clots.

atom (2) A particle of matter than cannot be further subdivided without losing its essential properties. [Gk., *atomos,* indivisible]

atomic mass (2) The mass of an atom; the combined mass of the protons, neutrons, and electrons in an atom (the mass of the electrons is so small as to be almost negligible).

atomic number (2) The number of protons in the nucleus of an atom of a given element.

atrium (21) A chamber of the heart that collects blood returning from the lungs or the rest of the body.

autoantigen (26) An individual's own molecule or cellular structure that is incorrectly recognized as an antigen by a lymphocyte receptor, thus initiating a humoral and/or cell-mediated immune response.

autoimmunity (26) Inappropriate response of an individual's immune system to the individual's own cells and tissues as if they were pathogens.

auxins (19) In plants, a small group of naturally occurring hormones (and a larger group of synthetic variants) that promote cell division, stem elongation, and formation of roots. Auxins also influence plant orientation, making sure the correct ends are up and down.

axon (20, 23) A projection from a neuron that transmits impulses away from the cell body.

B

B cell (26) A type of lymphocyte, maturing in the bone marrow, that is involved in humoral immunity; fights invaders in body fluids.

background extinctions (10) Extinctions that occur at lower rates than at times of mass extinctions; background extinctions occur mostly as the result of aspects of the biology and competitive success of the species, rather than catastrophe.

basal metabolic rate (BMR) (22) The amount of energy expended by a living organism at rest in a neutral temperature environment.

base (chemistry) (2) Any fluid with a pH above 7.0, that is, with more OH$^-$ ions than H$^+$ ions.

base (genetics) (2, 5) One of the nitrogen-containing side-chain molecules attached to a sugar molecule in the sugar-phosphate backbone of DNA and RNA. The four bases in DNA are adenine (A), thymine (T), guanine (G), and cytosine (C); the four bases in RNA are adenine (A), uracil (U), guanine (G), and cytosine (C); the information in a molecule of DNA and RNA is determined by its sequence of bases.

base pair (5) Two nucleotides on complementary strands of DNA that form a pair, linked by hydrogen bonds; the pattern of pairing is adenine (A) with thymine (T) and cytosine (C) with guanine (G); the base-paired arrangement forms the "rungs" of the double-helix structure of DNA.

basophil (26) A type of white blood cell that initiates inflammation.

behavior (9) Any and all of the actions performed by an organism, often in response to its environment or to the actions of another organism.

bilateral symmetry (11) A body structure with left and right sides, which are mirror images. [Lat., *bi-,* two + *latus,* side]

bile (22) A juice that aids in the breakdown of fats; it is produced by the liver, sent to the gall bladder, and passed through a small duct into the small intestine, where it initiates the first step in fat digestion.

binary fission (6) A type of asexual reproduction in which the parent cell divides into two genetically identical daughter cells; bacteria and other prokaryotes reproduce by binary fission. [Lat., *binarius,* consisting of two + *fissus,* divided]

biodiversity (10) The variety and variability among all genes, species, and ecosystems. [Gk., *bios,* life + Lat., *diversus,* turned in different directions]

biodiversity hotspots (16) Regions of the world with significant reservoirs of biodiversity that are under threat of destruction.

biofuels (4) Fuels produced from plant and animal products.

biogeography (8) The study and interpretation of distribution patterns of living organisms around the world. [Gk. *bios,* life + *geo-,* earth + *graphein,* to write down]

biological literacy (1) The ability to use scientific inquiry to think creatively about problems with a biological component, to communicate these thoughts to others, and to integrate these ideas into one's decision making.

biological species concept (10) A definition of species described as populations of organisms that interbreed, or could possibly interbreed, with each other under natural conditions, and that cannot interbreed with organisms outside their own group.

biology (1) The study of living things. [Gk., *bios*, life + *logos*, discourse]

biomass (15) The total mass of all the living organisms in a given area. [Gk., *bios*, life]

biomes (15) The major ecological communities of earth; terrestrial biomes, such as rainforest or desert, are defined and usually described by the predominant types of plant life in the area, which are mostly determined by the weather; aquatic biomes are usually defined by physical features such as salinity, water movement, and depth. [Gk., *bios*, life]

biotechnology (5) The modification of organisms, cells, and their molecules for practical benefits. [Gk., *bios*, life + *technologia*, systematic treatment]

biotic (15) Relating to living organisms; the biotic environment, or community, consists of all the living organisms in a given area. [Gk., *bios*, life]

bisphenol A (24) A chemical found in some plastic water bottles and baby bottles; a known endocrine disruptor.

bivalve molluscs (11) Molluscs with two hinged shells; examples are clams, scallops, oysters and molluscs. [Lat., *bi-*, two]

blastocyst (25) The mammalian blastula.

blastula (25) An early stage of embryonic development produced by cleavage of a fertilized egg (zygote). A spherical layer of cells encloses a large fluid-filled space where the embryo forms. [Gk., *blastos*, sprout]

blind experimental design (1) An experimental design in which the subjects do not know what treatment (if any) they are receiving.

blood (20, 21) A connective tissue with a liquid extracellular matrix containing blood cells; contained in a closed circulatory system, and important in the transport of respiratory gases, vitamins and minerals, nutrients, hormones, components of the immune system, and metabolic wastes.

blood pressure (21) The force with which blood flows through the arteries.

body mass index (22) Body weight in kilograms divided by height in meters squared (kg/m^2); often used as an index of a healthy weight for an individual based on the person's height.

bone (20) A rigid connective tissue that protects and provides support.

bottleneck effect (8) A change in allele frequencies of a population caused by a sudden reduction in population size (often due to famine, disease, or rapid environmental disturbance).

Bowman's capsule (20) A ball-like structure surrounding the blood-filtering unit of a nephron in the kidney. It is connected to a single, long, urine-collecting tube that excretes its filtered fluid into a collecting duct.

brain imaging technologies (23) Techniques used to reveal activity patterns (based on increased metabolism) in different regions of the brain. See also **fMRI scan; PET scan.**

Broca's area (23) The discrete part of the brain, located, in most people, in the front part of the left frontal lobe, that is used for controlling the muscles responsible for the process of speaking.

bryophytes (12) Three groups of plants (the liverworts, hornworts, and mosses) that lack vascular tissue and move water and dissolved nutrients by diffusion. [Gk., *bruon*, tree-moss, liverwort + *phytas*, plant]

buffer (2) A chemical that can quickly absorb excess H^+ ions in a solution (preventing it from becoming too acidic) or quickly release H^+ ions to counteract increases in OH^- concentration.

bulbourethral gland (25) A male reproductive gland, one on each side of the body, that contributes mucus and sugar to the ejaculate and lubricant to the tip of the penis prior to copulation.

C

C4 photosynthesis (4) A method (along with C3 and CAM photosynthesis) by which plants fix carbon dioxide, using the carbon to build sugar; serves as a more effective method than C3 for binding carbon dioxide under low carbon dioxide conditions, such as when plants in warmer climates close their stomata to reduce water loss.

calcitonin (24) A hormone released from the thyroid gland that causes bones to take up excess calcium from the bloodstream.

calorie (22) The energy required to raise the temperature of 1 gram of water by 1° C; the kilocalorie, made from 1,000 calories, is commonly used as a measure of the amount of energy in a particular food.

Calvin cycle (4) In photosynthesis, a series of chemical reactions in the stroma of chloroplasts, in which sugar molecules are assembled. [from the name of one of its discoverers, Melvin Calvin, 1911–1997]

CAM (crassulacean acid metabolism) (4) Energetically expensive photosynthesis in which the stomata are open only at night to admit CO_2, which is bound to a holding molecule and released to enter the Calvin cycle to make sugar during the day; in this type of photosynthesis, found in many fleshy, juicy plants of hot, dry areas, water loss is reduced because the stomata are closed during the day.

cancer (6) Unrestrained cell growth and division. [Lat., *cancer*, crab; by extension, the disease cancer]

capillaries (21) Tiny blood vessels that bring blood close enough to cells to allow the diffusion of molecules into and out of the blood.

capsid (13) The protein container surrounding the genetic material (DNA or RNA) of a virus. [Lat., *capsa*, box, case]

capsule (13) A layer surrounding the cell wall of many bacteria; the capsule may restrict the movement of water out of the cell and thus allow bacteria to live in dry places, such as the surface of the skin. The capsule contributes to the virulent characteristics of some bacteria, making them resistant to phagocytosis by the host's immune system. [Lat., *capsula*, small box or case]

carbohydrate (2) One of the four types of biological macromolecule, containing mostly carbon, hydrogen, and oxygen; carbohydrates are the primary fuel for cellular activity and form much of the cell structure in all life forms. [Lat., *carbo*, charcoal + *hydro-*, pertaining to water]

carboxyl group (2) A carbon atom bonded to two oxygen atoms.

cardiac muscle (20) A type of muscle tissue, located only in the heart, that causes the heart to pump blood through the body. Cardiac muscle cells, which are fused together and connected by gap junctions, contain many more mitochondria than other types of muscle cells.

cardiovascular disease (21) Progressive deterioration of the arteries and other degradations of the circulatory system; the leading cause of death and disability in the United States.

carnivores (15, 22) Predatory animals (and some plants) that consume only animals. [Lat., *carnis*, of flesh + *vorare*, to devour]

carotenoids (4) Pigments that absorb blue-violet and blue-green wavelengths of light and reflect yellow, orange, and red wavelengths of light. [Lat., *carota*, carrot]

carpel (12, 18) The female reproductive structure of a flower, including the stigma, style, and ovary. [Gk., *karpos*, fruit]

carrier (7) An individual who carries one allele for a recessive trait and who does not exhibit the trait; if two carriers mate they may produce offspring who do exhibit the trait.

carrying capacity (K) (14) The ceiling on a population's growth imposed by the limitation of resources for a particular habitat over a period of time.

cartilage (20) A dense connective tissue with an extracellular matrix rich in collagen, elastin, and proteins bound to long carbohydrate chains, with a hardness between that of bone and of tendons; strong, but also flexible, cartilage is found in the ears and tip of the nose in humans, and it cushions the bones in joints throughout the body.

cartilaginous fishes (11) Fish species characterized by a skeleton made completely of cartilage, not bone. [Lat., *cartilago,* gristle]

cell (3) The smallest unit of life that can function independently; a three-dimensional structure, surrounded by a membrane and, in the case of prokaryotes and most plants, a cell wall, in which many of the essential chemical reactions of the life of an organism take place. [Lat., *cella,* room]

cell body (20, 23) The part of a cell, such as a neuron, that contains the nucleus and other organelles.

cell cycle (6) In a cell, the alternation of activities related to cell division and those related to growth and metabolism.

cell theory (3) A unifying and universally accepted theory in biology that holds that all living organisms are made up of one or more cells, and that all cells arise from other, pre-existing cells.

cell wall (3) A rigid structure, outside the cell membrane, that protects and gives shape to the cell; found in many prokaryotes and plants.

cellular respiration (4) The process by which all living organisms extract energy stored in the chemical bonds of molecules and use it for fuel for their life processes.

cellulose (2) A complex carbohydrate, indigestible by humans, that serves as the structural material for a huge variety of plant structures; it is the single most prevalent organic compound on earth. [Lat., *cellula, dim.* of *cella,* room]

central nervous system (CNS) (20, 23) The part of an organism's nervous system that includes the brain and spinal cord and coordinates all nervous activity.

central vacuole (3) In plants, a large, fluid-filled organelle, surrounded by a membrane, important in nutrient storage, waste management, predator deterrence, sexual reproduction, and physical support. [Lat., *vacuus,* empty]

centromere (6) After replication, the region of contact between sister chromatids, which occurs near the center of the two strands. [Gk., *centron,* the stationary point of a pair of compasses, thus the center of a circle + *meris,* part]

cephalopods (11) Molluscs in which the head is prominent and the foot has been modified into tentacles; examples are octopuses and squids. Cephalopods have a reduced or absent shell and possess the most advanced nervous system of the invertebrates. [Gk., *kephale,* head + *pous,* foot]

cerebellum (23) The part of the vertebrate hindbrain that controls muscle coordination.

cerebral cortex (23) The part of the vertebrate brain involved in abstract thought, problem solving, language, and more; the brain structure most responsible for the traits that set humans apart from other animal species.

cervix (25) The low, narrow portion of the uterus leading to the vagina. [Lat., *cervix,* neck]

character displacement (15) An evolutionary divergence in one or more of the species that occupy a niche that leads to a partitioning of the niche between the species. Changes in characteristics, such as behavioral or body plan, of two or more very similar species that have overlapping geographical locations result in a reduction of competition between species.

chemical energy (4) A type of potential energy in which energy is stored in chemical bonds between atoms or molecules.

chemolithotrophs (13) Bacteria that can use inorganic molecules such as ammonia, hydrogen sulfide, hydrogen, and iron as sources of energy. [Gk., *lithos,* stone, rock + *trophē,* food]

chemoorganotrophs (13) Bacteria that consume organic molecules, such as carbohydrates, as an energy source. [Gk., *trophē,* food]

chemoreceptor (23) A type of sensory cell that detects chemical changes in the organism's internal or external environment.

chitin (2) (*pron.* KITE-in) A complex carbohydrate, indigestible by humans, that forms the rigid outer skeleton of most insects and crustaceans. [Gk., *chiton,* undershirt]

chlorophyll (4) A light-absorbing pigment molecule in chloroplasts. [Gk., *chloros,* pale green + *phyllon,* leaf]

chlorophyll a (4) The primary photosynthetic pigment, chlorophyll *a* absorbs blue-violet and red light; because it cannot absorb green light and instead reflects those wavelengths, we perceive the reflected light as the color green.

chlorophyll b (4) A photosynthetic pigment similar in structure to chlorophyll *a,* chlorophyll *b* absorbs blue and red-orange wavelengths and reflects yellow-green wavelengths.

chloroplast (3, 4) The organelle in plant cells in which photosynthesis occurs. [Gk., *chloros,* pale green + *plastos,* formed]

cholesterol (2, 3) One of the sterols, lipids important in regulating growth and development; cholesterol is an important component of most cell membranes, helping the membrane to maintain its flexibility. [Gk., *chole,* bile + *stereos,* solid + *-ol,* chemical suffix for an alcohol]

chorion (25) During animal development, the outer membrane surrounding an embryo, which, with the endometrium, forms the placenta.

chromatid (6) One of the two strands of a replicated chromosome. [Gk., *chroma,* color]

chromatin (3) A mass of long, thin fibers consisting of DNA and proteins in the nucleus of the cell. [Gk., *chroma,* color]

chromosomal aberration (5) A type of mutation characterized by a change in the overall organization of genes on a chromosome, such as the deletion of a section of DNA; the moving of a gene from one part of a chromosome to elsewhere on the same chromosome or to a different chromosome; or the duplication of a gene, with the new copy inserted elsewhere on the chromosome or on a different chromosome. [Lat., *aberrare,* to wander]

chromosome (5) A linear or circular strand of DNA on which are found specific sequences of base pairs; the human genome consists of two copies of each of 23 unique chromosomes, one from the mother and one from the father. [Gk., *chroma,* color + *soma,* body]

chyme (22) A liquid mass of partially digested food that passes from the stomach through the small intestine.

cilia (*sing.* **cilium**) (3, 26) Short projections from the cell surface, often occurring in large numbers on a single cell, that beat against the intercellular fluid to move the fluid past the cell. [Lat., eyelid]

class (10) In the hierarchical taxonomic system developed by Carolus Linnaeus (1707–1778), a classification of organisms consisting of related orders.

cleavage (25) In embryonic development, the early cell division of the zygote, which begins shortly after fertilization.

climax community (15) A stable and self-sustaining community that results from ecological succession.

clitoris (25) Erectile sexual organ of female mammals; develops from the same embryonic tissue that produces the penis.

clonal selection (26) Process in which a B cell or T cell binds to its antigen and divides numerous times to create a population of cells with the same antigen specificity. This process ensures that there are sufficient numbers of B and T cells to recognize and respond to a specific pathogen that has invaded the body.

clone (5) A genetically identical DNA fragment, cell, or organism produced by a single cell or organism. [Gk., *klon*, twig]

clone library (5) A collection of cloned DNA fragments; also known as a gene library.

cloning (5) The production of genetically identical cells, organisms, or DNA molecules.

closed circulatory system (21) A circulatory system in which blood is contained in vessels and is separate from the interstitial fluid that bathes cells.

code (5) In genetics, the base sequence of a gene.

codominance (7) The case in which the heterozygote displays characteristics of both alleles.

codons (5) Three-base sequences in mRNA that link with complementary tRNA molecules, which are attached to amino acids; a codon with yet another sequence ends the process of assembling a protein from amino acids.

coelom (25) (*pron.* SEE-lum) The body cavity; it forms from the mesoderm in embryonic development.

coevolution (15) The concurrent appearance over time, through natural selection, of traits in interacting species that enable each species to become adapted to the other; an example is the 11-inch-long tongue of a moth that feeds from the 11-inch-long nectar tube of an orchid.

cohesion–tension mechanism (17) In vascular plants, the force driving fluid flow in the xylem; results from evaporation of water from leaves, which pulls water up from the roots.

collagen (20) A protein in the matrix of connective tissue, synthesized and secreted by connective tissue cells (fibroblasts).

collenchyma cell (17) A long, stringy cell with unevenly thickened cell walls that contributes to a plant's flexibility. Collenchyma cells are a type of ground tissue.

colon (22) See **large intestine**.

colonizers (15) Species introduced into an area that has been disturbed and is undergoing the process of either primary or secondary succession. The identity of a colonizing species varies depending on the stage and type of succession.

color blind (23) In humans, describes the inability to distinguish between colors that most individuals can see—most commonly, the inability to distinguish between the colors red and green; occurs mostly in males.

commensalism (15) A symbiotic relationship between species in which one benefits and the other neither benefits nor is harmed. [Lat., *com*, with + *mensa*, table]

communication (9) An action or signal on the part of one organism that alters the behavior of another organism.

community (in ecology) (15) The biotic environment; a geographic area defined as a loose assemblage of species with overlapping ranges.

competitive exclusion (15) The case in which two species battle for resources in the same niche until the more efficient of the two wins and the other is driven to extinction in that location.

complement protein (26) A type of circulating, defensive protein that can create holes in the membranes of pathogens or destroy pathogens by sticking to them and forming a coating that enhances the ability of phagocytes to bind to and engulf them.

complementarity (6) The characteristic of double-stranded DNA that the base on one strand always has the same pairing partner, or complementary base, on the other strand.

complementary base (6) A base on a strand of double-stranded DNA that is a pairing partner to a base on the other strand: adenine (A) is the complementary base to thymine (T), and guanine (G) is the complementary base to cytosine (C).

complex carbohydrate (2) A carbohydrate that contains multiple simple carbohydrates linked together; types of complex carbohydrates include starch, which is the primary form of energy storage in plants, and glycogen, which is the primary form of short-term energy storage in animals.

composting (17) Deliberate mixing of decaying organic matter, from leaves, food scraps, and manure, used to provide nutrients to soil.

compound (2) A substance composed of atoms of different elements in specific ratios, held together by ionic bonds. [Lat., *componere*, to put together]

compound eye (23) A group of light-sensing cells found in many invertebrates, made up of dozens to thousands of separate light-sensing units, each with its own lens that focuses light onto about a dozen photoreceptors.

cone (23) In the retina, a highly light-sensitive cell type that enables color vision.

conformer (20) An organism that, for a given physiological variable, has no set point for the variable and allows it to fluctuate with external changes in the environment.

connective tissue (20) A type of animal tissue that consists of cells embedded in a large amount of extracellular material, called matrix, which together contribute to body structure and support; includes tendons, ligaments, fat, blood, bone, and cartilage.

connective tissue proper (20) A type of connective tissue, including fat tissue, tendons, and ligaments, that has a semi-fluid, flexible matrix and functions like packing material.

conjugation (13) The process by which a bacterium transfers a copy of some or all of its DNA to another bacterium, of the same or another species. [Lat., *coniugatio*, connection]

conservation biology (16) An interdisciplinary field, drawing on ecology, economics, psychology, sociology, and political science, that studies and devises ways of preserving and protecting biodiversity and other natural resources.

contact inhibition (3) The limiting factor of cell growth that occurs when normal cells come into contact; in cancer cells, contact inhibition does not take place and the cells continue to divide.

contraception (25) The attempt to prevent pregnancy by preventing ovulation, fertilization, or implantation. Also called *birth control*.

control group (1) In an experiment, the group of subjects not exposed to the treatment being studied but otherwise treated identically to the experimental group.

convergent evolution (8, 10) A process of natural selection in which features of organisms not closely related come to resemble each other as a consequence of similar selective forces; many marsupial and placental species resemble each other as a result of convergent evolution. [Lat., *con-*, together with + *vergere*, turn + *evolvere*, to roll out]

coprophagy (22) A nutritional strategy, common in rabbits and rodents, in which animals consume some of their feces, thereby increasing their ability to extract energy from food by passing it through their digestive system twice.

copulation (25) The act of placing the male reproductive organ within the female's reproductive tract.

coronary arteries (21) The blood vessels that deliver oxygen and nutrients to the heart.

cork cell (17) A cell of the protective outer covering of some plants, containing a waxy substance impermeable to water and resistant to fire and decay.

corpus callosum (23) In the brain, the broad, thick band of neurons connecting the left hemisphere to the right hemisphere.

corpus luteum (25) A structure that develops from a follicle after ovulation; it secretes hormones to maintain pregnancy. [Lat., *corpus*, body + *luteum*, yellow]

cortex (17) In vascular plants, the ground tissue located between the epidermis and the xylem and phloem.

cotyledon (17, 18) Part of the plant embryo within the seed; this structure usually becomes the first embryonic leaf or leaves of the plant. Also called *seed leaf*.

covalent bond (2) A strong bond formed when two atoms share electrons; the simplest example is the H_2 molecule, in which each of the two atoms in the molecule shares its lone electron with the other atom. [Lat., *con-*, together + *valere*, to be strong]

critical experiment (1) An experiment that makes it possible to determine decisively between alternative hypotheses.

cross (7) The breeding of organisms that differ in one or more traits.

crossing over (6) The exchange of some genetic material between a paternal homologous chromosome and a maternal homologous chromosome, leading to a chromosome carrying genetic material from each; also referred to as recombination.

cuticle (12, 17) A waxy layer produced by epidermal cells and found on leaves and shoots of terrestrial plants, protecting them from drying out. [Lat., *cuticula, dim.* of *cutis*, skin]

cytokine (26) A type of signaling protein secreted by cells of the immune system: the chief way in which cells of the specific and non-specific immunity systems communicate with one another.

cytokinesis (6) In the cell cycle, the stage following mitosis in which cytoplasm and organelles duplicate and are divided into approximately equal parts and the cell separates into two daughter cells; in meiosis, two diploid daughter cells are formed in cytokinesis following telophase I and four haploid daughter cells are formed in cytokinesis following telophase II. [Gk., *kytos*, container + *kinesis*, motion]

cytokinins (19) In plants, a group of hormones that stimulate cell division throughout the body and throughout the lifetime of the plant.

cytoplasm (3) The jelly-like fluid that fills the inside of the cell; in eukaryotes, the cytoplasm contains the organelles. [Gk., *kytos*, container + *plasma*, anything molded]

cytoskeleton (3) A network of protein structures in the cytoplasm of plants and animals that serves as scaffolding, adding support and giving animal cells of different types their characteristic shapes; the cytoskeleton serves as tracks guiding the intercellular traffic flow and, because it is flexible and can generate force, gives cells some ability to control their movement.

cytotoxic T cell (26) A type of lymphocyte, acting in the cell-mediated response, that directly kills body cells infected with a pathogen.

D

daughter cells (6) Cells produced by the division of a parent cell.

decomposers (12, 15) Organisms, including bacteria, fungi, and detritivores, that break down and feed on once-living organisms.

decomposition (17) The process of breaking down organic material into the individual elements of which it is made.

demographic transition (14) A pattern of population growth characterized by the progression from high birth and death rates (slow growth) to high birth rates and low death rates (fast growth) to low birth and death rates (slow growth).

denaturation (2) The disruption of protein folding, in which secondary and tertiary structure are lost, caused by exposure to extreme conditions in the environment such as heat or extreme pH (that is, a strong acid or a strong base); denaturation causes proteins to lose their function; also the disruption of DNA, also known as DNA melting, in which the bonds linking complementary bases are broken and the two strands separate from each other.

dendrite (20, 23) A branched projection from a neuron that receives signals from the external environment or from other neurons. [Gk., *dendron*, tree]

dendritic cell (26) A type of white blood cell that links the non-specific and specific divisions of the immune system by engulfing foreign matter and then presenting the digested remnants of the pathogen on its cell surface.

density-dependent factors (14) Limitations on a population's growth that are a consequence of population density.

density-independent factors (14) Limitations on a population's growth without regard to population size, such as floods, earthquakes, fires, and lightning.

deoxyribonucleic acid (DNA) (2, 5) A nucleic acid, DNA carries information about the production of particular proteins in the sequences of its nucleotide bases.

dermal tissue (17) The outer covering that protects the surface of a plant.

desert (15) A type of terrestrial biome; a type of dry climate, with very little rainfall, in which water loss through evaporation exceeds water gain through precipitation; typically found at 30° north and south latitude.

desmosome (3) Irregularly spaced connections between adjacent animal cells that, in the manner of Velcro, hold cells together by attachments but are not water-tight; they provide mechanical strength and are found in muscle tissue and in much of the tissue that lines the cavities of animal bodies. [Gk., *desmos*, bond + *soma*, body]

detritivores (15) Organisms that break down and feed on once-living organic matter; this group includes scavengers such as vultures, worms, and a variety of arthropods. [Lat., *detritus*, worn out + *vorare*, to devour]

deuterostomes (11) Bilaterally symmetrical animals with defined tissues in which the gut develops from back to front; the anus forms first, and the second opening formed is the mouth of the adult animal. [Gk., *deuteros*, second + *stoma*, mouth]

diabetes (22) A condition in which an individual does not adequately regulate their blood sugar levels; usually results from insufficient insulin secretion from the pancreas in response to an increase in blood sugar, or inadequate response of the cells of the body to insulin in the bloodstream.

diaphragm (21) A large sheet of muscle that separates the chest cavity from the abdominal cavity, allowing for increased volume when contracted during inhalation. [Gk., *dia*, through + *phrasein*, to enclose]

diaphragm (contraceptive) (25) A dome-shaped piece of rubber placed in the vagina that blocks the cervix and prevents sperm from coming in contact with an egg.

diastolic pressure (21) The second blood pressure reading; a measure of the force that blood exerts on the artery walls while the heart is between beats.

dicot (17) One of the two major groups of flowering plants; dicot seedlings have two cotyledons (seed leaves).

differential reproductive success (8) The situation in which individuals have greater reproductive success than other individuals in a population; along with variation and heritability, differential reproductive success is one of the three conditions necessary for natural selection.

differentiated (25) Describing cells that, during development, begin to take on specific structures or functions.

diffusion (3) Passive transport in which a particle (the solute) is dissolved in a gas or liquid (the solvent) and moves from an area of higher solute concentration to an area of lower solute concentration. [Lat., *diffundere,* to pour in different directions]

digestion (22) The physical and chemical breakdown of food into its fundamental macromolecular components for absorption or elimination.

diploid (6) Describes cells that have two copies of each chromosome (in many organisms, including humans, somatic cells are diploid). [Gk., *diplasiazein,* to double]

direct fitness (9) The total reproductive output of an individual.

directional selection (8) Selection that, for a given trait, increases fitness at one extreme of the phenotype and reduces fitness at the other, leading to an increase or decrease in the mean value of the trait.

disaccharides (2) Carbohydrates formed by the union of two simple sugars, such as sucrose (table sugar) and lactose (the sugar found in milk). [Gk., *di-,* two + *sakcharon,* sugar]

dispersers (15) Organisms able to move away from their original home.

disruptive selection (8) Selection that, for a given trait, increases fitness at both extremes of the phenotype distribution and reduces fitness at middle values.

DNA probe (5) A short sequence of radioactively tagged single-stranded DNA that contains part of the sequence of the gene of interest, used to locate that gene in a gene library; the probe binds to the complementary base pair on a gene in the library, which is identified by the radioactive tag on the probe.

domain (10) In modern classification, the highest level of the hierarchy; there are three domains, bacteria, archaea, and eukarya.

dominant (7) Describes an allele that masks the phenotypic effect of the other, recessive, allele for a trait; the phenotype shows the effect of the dominant allele in both homozygous and heterozygous genotypes. [Lat., *dominari,* to rule]

dorsal hollow nerve cord (11) The central nervous system of vertebrates, consisting of the spinal cord and brain. [Lat., *dorsum,* back]

double-blind experimental design (1) An experimental design in which neither the subjects nor the experimenters know what treatment (if any) individual subjects are receiving.

double bond (2) The sharing of two electrons between two atoms; for example, the most common form of oxygen is the O_2 molecule, in which two electrons from each of the two atoms of oxygen are shared.

double fertilization (12, 18) In angiosperms, two sperm are released by a pollen grain: one fuses with an egg to form a zygote, and the other fuses with two nuclei, forming a triploid endosperm.

double helix (2) The spiraling ladder-like structure of DNA composed of two strands of nucleotides; the bases protruding from each strand like "half-rungs" meet in the center and bind to each other (via hydrogen bonds), holding the ladder together. [Gk., *heligmos,* wrapping]

dynamic equilibrium (16) A situation on islands in which the number of species present remains constant over time, while the composition of species may change.

E

ear canal (23) The channel from the outer ear to the middle ear that conducts sound waves.

eardrum (23) The thin membrane that divides the outer ear from the middle ear.

echolocation (23) The ability of some animals (including bats) to sense the location of objects by producing sounds and then detecting echoes bounced off the objects.

ecological footprint (14) A measure of the impact of an individual or population on the environment by calculation of the amount of resources—including land, food and water, and fuel—consumed.

ecology (14) The study of the interaction between organisms and their environments, at the level of individuals, populations, communities, and ecosystems. [Gk., *oikos,* home + *logos,* discourse]

ecosystem (15) A community of biological organisms and the non-living environmental components with which they interact.

ectoderm (25) The outermost embryonic cell layer during gastrulation; it eventually forms skin, hair, the nervous system, and the lining of the nose and mouth. [Gk., *ektos,* outside + *derma,* skin]

ectotherms (11, 20) Organisms that rely on the heat from an external source to raise their body temperature and seek the shade when the air is too warm. [Gk., *ektos,* outside + *thermē,* heat]

effector (20) A structure that can be triggered in response to a stimulus; aids in the maintenance of homeostasis by opposing or reducing changes in the internal environment in response to changes in the external environment.

effector cell (26) In the specific (adaptive) immunity system, a type of cell that recognizes an antigen and immediately takes some action that leads to its destruction; plasma cells, which are antibody-secreting, modified B cells, are the effector cells of the cell-mediated response.

egg (25) A female gamete. Also called *ovum (pl. ova).*

electromagnetic spectrum (4) The range of wavelengths that produce electromagnetic radiation, extending (in order of decreasing energy) from high-energy, short-wave, gamma rays and X rays, through ultraviolet light, visible light, and infrared light, to very long, low-energy, radio waves. [Lat., *specere,* to look at]

elastin (20) A protein in the matrix of connective tissue, synthesized and secreted by connective tissue cells (fibroblasts), that gives the tissue flexibility.

electron (2) A negatively charged particle that moves around the atomic nucleus.

electron transport chain (4) The third step of cellular respiration, in which high-energy electrons are passed from molecule to molecule, at every step releasing energy that is used to make ATP.

element (2) A substance that cannot be broken down chemically into any other substances; all atoms of an element have the same atomic number. [Lat., *elementum,* element, or first principle]

elimination (22) The last phase in the breakdown of food; the absorption of water, salts, and some vitamins in the large intestine, followed by defecation of remaining waste material.

El Niño (15) A sustained surface temperature change in the central Pacific Ocean that occurs every two to seven years; this event can start a chain reaction of unusual weather across the globe that can result in flooding, droughts, famine, and a variety of extreme climate disruptions. [Spanish, *the child;* a reference to the Christ child, because of the appearance of the phenomenon at Christmastime]

embryo (18, 25) The multicellular, developing, fertilized egg of a eukaryote. In humans, at about eight weeks following fertilization the embryo is called a fetus.

embryo sac (18) The part of the female reproductive structure of a flower that contains an egg and is the site of fertilization.

empirical (1) Describes knowledge that is based on experience and observations that are rational, testable, and repeatable. [Gk., *empeiria*, experience]

endangered species (16) As defined by the Endangered Species Act, species in danger of extinction throughout all or a significant portion of their range.

Endangered Species Act (ESA) (16) A United States law that defines "endangered species" and is designed to protect those species from extinction.

endemic (16) Describes species peculiar to a particular region and not naturally found elsewhere. [Gk., *en*, in + *demos*, the people of a country]

endocrine cell (24) A hormone-secreting cell. Endocrine cells are part of the endocrine system.

endocrine disruptor (24) A chemical manufactured by humans that, when taken up by organisms, can mimic, block, or otherwise interfere with their hormones, leading to harmful effects.

endocrine gland (20, 24) A collection of epithelial cells that produces hormones and releases them into the bloodstream or other fluids of the body.

endocrine system (24) Organ system comprising glands and cells that secrete hormones, which are chemical messengers that act on target cells to regulate body functions and maintain homeostasis.

endocytosis (3) A cellular process in which large particles, solid or dissolved, outside the cell are surrounded by a fold of the plasma membrane, which pinches off, forming a vesicle, and the enclosed particle now moves into the cell; the three types of endocytosis are phagocytosis, pinocytosis, and receptor-mediated endocytosis. [Gk., *endon*, within + *kytos*, container]

endoderm (25) The innermost embryonic cell layer during gastrulation; it eventually forms the lining of the respiratory and digestive tracts, the liver, and the pancreas. [Gk., *endon*, within + *derma*, skin]

endomembrane system (3) A system of organelles (the rough endoplasmic reticulum, the smooth endoplasmic reticulum, and the Golgi apparatus) that surrounds the nucleus; it produces and modifies necessary molecules, breaks down toxic chemicals and cellular by-products, and is thus responsible for many of the fundamental functions of the cell. [Gk., *endon*, within + Lat., *membrana*, a thin skin]

endometrium (25) The lining of the uterus where a fertilized egg implants and is nourished.

endosperm (12, 18) Tissue of a mature seed that stores certain carbohydrates, proteins, and lipids that fuel the germination, growth, and development of the embryo and young seedling. [Gk., *endon*, within + *sperma*, seed]

endosymbiosis theory (3) Theory of the origin of eukaryotes that holds that in the past two different types of prokaryotes engaged in a close partnership and eventually one, capable of performing photosynthesis, was subsumed into the other, a larger prokaryote; the smaller prokaryote made some of its photosynthetic energy available to the host, and over time the two became symbiotic and eventually a single more complex organism in which the smaller prokaryote had evolved into the chloroplast of the new organism (a similar scenario can be developed for the evolution of mitochondria). [Gk., *endon*, within + *symbios*, living together]

endotherms (11, 20) Organisms that use the heat produced by their cellular respiration to raise and maintain their body temperature above air temperature. [Gk., *endon*, within + *thermē*, heat]

energy (4) The capacity to do work, which is the moving of matter against an opposing force. [Gk., *energeia*, activity]

energy pyramid (15) A diagram that illustrates the path of energy through the organisms of an ecosystem; each layer of the pyramid represents the biomass of a trophic level.

enzymatic protein (3) See **enzyme**

enzyme (2, 3) A protein that initiates and accelerates a chemical reaction in a living organism; enzymatic proteins take part in chemical reactions on the inside and outside surfaces of the plasma membrane. [Gk., *en*, in + *zyme*, leaven]

epidermis (17) The layer of tightly packed, very thin cells that covers and protects a plant's roots, leaves, and stems.

epididymis (25) A tube in each testis where the sperm mature.

epithelial tissue (20) A thin tissue that covers and protects the surfaces of an animal's body. Also called *epithelium*.

epithelium (20) See **epithelial tissue.**

erythrocytes (21) See **red blood cells.**

esophagus (22) The passageway from the throat to the stomach through which food travels.

essential amino acid (22) An amino acid that is not made by the body and so must be consumed in food.

estuary (15) A tidal water passage, linked to the sea, in which salt water and fresh water mix; estuaries are characterized by exceptionally high productivity. [Lat., *aestus*, tide]

estrogen (25) One of the primary female sex hormone; important in female development and the female reproductive cycle.

ethanol (4) The end product of fermentation of yeast; the alcohol in beer, wine, and spirits. [contraction of the full chemical name, ethyl alcohol]

ethylene (19) In plants, a gas that functions as a hormone that speeds up the rate at which fruit ripens.

eudicot (17) A large monophyletic subset of the dicots (plants in which two cotyledons form) and one of the two major groups of flowering plants.

eukaryote (3) An organism composed of eukaryotic cells. [Gk., *eu*, good + *karyon*, nut, kernel]

eukaryotic cell (3) A cell with a membrane-bound nucleus containing DNA, membrane-bound organelles, and internal structures organized into compartments.

eutrophication (15) The process in which excess nutrients dissolved in a body of water lead to rapid growth of algae and bacteria, which consume much of the dissolved oxygen and, in time, can lead to large-scale die-offs. [Gk., *eu*, good + *trophe⁻*, food]

evolution (8) A change in allele frequencies of a population. [Lat., *evolvere*, to roll out]

exocrine gland (20) A collection of epithelial cells that secretes products onto the surface of the epithelium.

exocytosis (3) A cellular process in which particles within the cell, solid or dissolved, are enclosed in a vesicle and transported to the plasma membrane, where the membrane of the vesicle merges with the plasma membrane and the material in the vesicle is expelled to the extracellular fluid for use throughout the body. [Gk., *ex*, out of + *kytos*, container]

exoskeleton (11) A rigid external covering such as found in some invertebrates, including insects and crustaceans. [Gk., *ex*, out of]

exotic species (16) Species introduced by human activities to areas other than the species' native range.

experimental group (1) In an experiment, the group of subjects exposed to a particular treatment; also known as the treatment group.

exponential growth (14) Growth of a population at a rate that is proportional to its current size.

external fertilization (25) The process in which sperm and egg unite outside the bodies of the male and female.

extinction (10) The complete loss of all individuals in a species. [Lat., *extinguere,* to extinguish]

extracellular fluid (20) A body fluid that is outside the cells; as distinct from intracellular fluid. See also **blood; interstitial fluid.**

extremophiles (13) Bacteria and archaea than can live in extreme physical and chemical conditions. [Lat., *extremus,* outermost + Gk., *philios,* loving]

eye cup (23) A group of simple, light-sensing cells found in flatworms such as planaria.

F

facilitated diffusion (3) Diffusion of molecules through the phospholipid bilayer of the plasma membrane that takes place through a transport protein (a "carrier molecule") embedded in the membrane; molecules that require the assistance of a carrier molecule are those that are too big to cross the membrane directly or are electrically charged and would be repelled by the middle layer of the membrane.

Fallopian tube (25) The tube that conveys eggs from an ovary to the uterus. Also called *oviduct.*

family (10) In the system developed by Carolus Linnaeus (1707–1778), a classification of organisms consisting of related genera.

fatty acid (2) A long hydrocarbon (a chain of carbon-hydrogen molecules); fatty acids form the tail region of triglyceride fat molecules.

female (9) In sexually reproducing organisms, a member of the sex that produces the larger gamete.

fermentation (4) The process by which glycolysis occurs in the absence of oxygen; the electron acceptor is pyruvate (in animals) or acetaldehyde (in yeast) rather than oxygen.

fertilization (6, 25) The fusion of two reproductive cells.

fetus (25) Developmental stage in humans, from the end of the embryonic period, approximately eight weeks after fertilization, until birth.

fever (26) An elevated body temperature in response to infection; enhances the immune response and slows the growth of pathogens.

fibrous roots (17) A root system in which numerous roots branch out directly from the plant stem; found primarily in monocots.

filament (12, 18) The supporting stalk of the anther of a stamen found in angiosperm flowers. [Lat., *filum,* thread]

filtrate (20) Fluid that accumulates in Bowman's capsule in the vertebrate kidney; it contains salts, sugars, amino acids, vitamins, and many other molecules, all at the same concentration as in the blood.

first law of thermodynamics (4) A physical law that states that energy cannot be created or destroyed; it can only change from one form to another.

fitness (8) A relative measure of the reproductive output of an individual with a given phenotype compared with the reproductive output of individuals with alternative phenotypes.

fixation (8) The point at which the frequency of an allele in a population is 100% and, therefore, there is no more variation in the population for this gene.

fixed action pattern (9) An innate sequence of behaviors, triggered under certain conditions, that requires no learning, does not vary, and once begun runs to completion; an example is egg-retrieval in geese.

flagella (*sing.* **flagellum**) (3) Long, thin, whip-like projections from the cell body of a prokaryote that aid in cell movement through the medium in which the organism lives; in animals, the only cell with a flagellum is the sperm cell. [Lat., *flagellum,* whip]

flatworms (11) Worms with flat bodies that are members of the phylum Platyhelminthes; characterized by well-defined head and tail regions, with some having clusters of light-sensitive cells for eyespots; most are hermaphroditic and are protostomes that do not molt; examples are tapeworms and flukes.

fleshy fruit (12) A fruit that consists of the ovary and some additional parts of the flower; when fleshy fruits, an attractive food, are eaten by animals, the seeds may be widely dispersed.

flower (12) The part of an angiosperm that contains the reproductive structures; the flower consists of a supporting stem with modified leaves (the petals and sepals) and usually contains both male and female reproductive structures.

fluid mosaic (3) A term that describes the structure of the plasma membrane, which is made up of several different types of molecules, many of which are not fixed in place but float, held in proper orientation by hydrophilic and hydrophobic forces.

fMRI scan (23) Functional magnetic resonance imaging scan; a brain imaging technology. A giant magnet detects the relative amounts of oxygenated and deoxygenated blood in different parts of the brain, which vary with brain activity.

follicle (25) In an ovary, the small structure in which an egg forms.

follicle-stimulating hormone (FSH) (25) A hormone that stimulates the production of eggs.

follicular phase (25) The first half of the reproductive cycle in women, culminating in ovulation.

food chain (15) The path of energy flow from primary producers to tertiary consumers.

food web (15) A more precisely described path of energy flow from primary producers to tertiary consumers than the food chain, reflecting the fact that many organisms are omnivores and occupy more than one position in the chain.

forebrain (23) The largest region of the vertebrate brain; includes two control and relay structures, the thalamus and hypothalamus, and the cerebrum.

fossil (8) The remains of an organism, usually its hard parts such as shell, bones, or teeth, which have been naturally preserved; also, traces of such an organism, such as footprints. [Lat., *fossilis,* that which is dug up]

fossil fuels (4) Fuels produced from the decayed remains of ancient plants and animals; fossil fuels include oil, natural gas, and coal.

founder effect (8) A change in the allele frequencies of a population resulting from the isolation of a small subgroup of a larger population; all the descendants of the smaller group will reflect the allele frequencies of the subgroup, which may be different from those of the larger source population; the founder effect is one cause of genetic drift.

fruit (18) The mature ovary of a flower that houses seeds for dispersal. See also **fleshy fruit.**

fundamental niche (15) The full range of environmental conditions under which an organism can live.

G

gametes (6, 25) Haploid cells from two individuals that, as sperm and egg, will combine at fertilization to produce offspring; also called reproductive cells. [Gk., *gamete,* wife]

gametophyte (12) The plant structure that produces gametes (sperm and eggs); the haploid life stage of plants and some algae, which may be either male (producing sperm) or female (producing eggs). [Gk., *gamete,* wife + *phytas,* plant]

gap junction (3) A junction between adjacent animal cells in the form of a pore in each of the plasma membranes surrounded by a protein that links the two cells and acts like a channel between them to allow materials to pass between the cells.

gastropods (11) Molluscs that are members of the class Gastropoda; most have a single shell, a muscular foot for locomotion, and a radula used for scraping food from surfaces; examples are snails and slugs. [Gk., *gaster*, belly + *pous*, foot]

gastrula (25) The mass of cells, made up of three layers, formed during the gastrulation phase of embryonic development.

gastrulation (25) The second phase of embryonic development in which cells form distinct layers.

gene (5) The basic unit of heredity; a sequence of DNA nucleotides on a chromosome that carries the information necessary for making a functional product, usually a protein or an RNA molecule. [Gk., *genos*, race, descent]

gene flow (8) A change in the allele frequencies of a population due to movement of some individuals of a species from one population to another, changing the allele frequencies of the population they join; also known as migration.

gene library (5) A collection of cloned DNA fragments; also known as a clone library.

gene therapy (5) A therapy designed to treat or cure a disease by insertion of a functional gene to replace a defective version of that gene.

genetic drift (8) A random change in allele frequencies over successive generations; a cause of evolution.

genetic engineering (5) The manipulation of an organism's genetic material by adding, deleting, or transplanting genes from one organism to another.

genome (5) The full set of DNA present in an individual organism; also can refer to the full set of DNA present in a species.

genotype (5, 7) The genes that an organism carries for a particular trait; also, collectively, an organism's genetic composition. [Gk., *genos*, race, descent + *typos*, impression, engraving]

genus (*pl.* **genera**) (10) In the system developed by Carolus Linnaeus (1707–1778), a classification of organisms consisting of closely related species. [Lat., *genus*, race, family, origin]

germ layers (25) The three distinct layers of cells formed during gastrulation.

germinate (18) In plant spores or seeds, to begin growing after a period of dormancy.

gibberellins (19) In plants, a large group of hormones that regulate a plant's growth processes, primarily by stimulating cell division and cell elongation.

gills (21) Organs in fishes and other aquatic animals in which gases are exchanged between water and blood capillaries.

gland (20) A collection of epithelial cells that produces secretions for use elsewhere in the body.

glial cells (20, 23) Cells of nervous tissue that support and provide nutrients to neurons. Also called *neuroglia*.

glomerulus (20) The blood-filtering unit of the nephron; a mass of capillaries, surrounded by Bowman's capsule and connected to a single, long, urine-collecting tube that excretes its filtered fluid into a collecting duct.

glycemic index (22) A measure of the extent to which foods cause a surge in blood sugar and subsequent release of insulin.

glycerol (2, 3) A small molecule that forms the head region of a triglyceride fat molecule. [Gk., *glykys*, sweet + *-ol*, chemical suffix for an alcohol]

glycogen (2) A complex carbohydrate consisting of stored glucose molecules linked to form a large web, which breaks down to release glucose when it is needed for energy. [Gk., *glykys*, sweet + Gk., *genos*, race, descent]

glycolysis (4) In all organisms, the first step in cellular respiration, in which one molecule of glucose is broken into two molecules of pyruvate; for some organisms glycolysis is the only means of extracting energy from food, and in most organisms it is followed by the Krebs cycle and the electron transport chain. [Gk., *glykys*, sweet + *lysis*, releasing]

Golgi apparatus (3) An organelle, part of the endomembrane system, structurally like a flattened stack of unconnected membranes, each known as a Golgi body; the Golgi apparatus processes molecules synthesized in the cell and packages those molecules that are destined for use elsewhere in the body. [*pron.* GOHL-jee; from the name of the discoverer, Camillo Golgi, 1843–1926]

gonads (6) The ovaries and testes in sexually reproducing animals. [Gk., *gonē*, offspring]

gram stain (13) A test used by microbiologists in identifying an unknown bacterium; the dye that is used stains the layer of peptidoglycan outside the cell wall purple, but those bacteria in which the layer of peptidoglycan is covered by a membrane are not colored by the dye; bacteria that take a Gram stain are known as Gram-positive bacteria, those that do not are known as Gram-negative bacteria.

gravitropism (19) Growth in plants in response to the pull of gravity. [L., *gravidus*, heavy + Gk., *tropikos*, turn]

ground tissue (17) Those parts of a plant that are not dermal tissue or vascular tissue; makes up the bulk of the plant and is where most of the plant's metabolic activities take place.

group selection (9) The process, extremely uncommon in nature, which brings about an increase in the frequency of alleles for traits (e.g., behaviors) that are beneficial to the persistence of the species or population while simultaneously being detrimental to the fitness of the individual possessing the trait (or engaging in the behavior).

growth rate (*r*) (14) The birth rate minus the death rate; the change in the number of individuals in a population per unit of time.

guard cell (17) One of the pair of plant cells that surround and control the opening of stomata, through which carbon dioxide and water can pass.

gymnosperms (12) Vascular plants that do not produce their seeds in a protective structure, but are usually found on the surface of the scales of a cone-like structure; the gymnosperms include conifers, cycads, gnetophytes, and ginkgo. [Gk., *gymnos*, naked + *sperma*, seed]

H

habitat (15) The physical environment of organisms, consisting of the chemical resources of the soil, water, and air, and physical conditions such as temperature, salinity, humidity, and energy sources. [Lat., *habitare*, to dwell or inhabit]

hair (11) Dead cells filled with the protein keratin that collectively serve as insulation covering the body or a part of the body; present in all mammals.

haploid (6) Describes cells that have a single copy of each chromosome (in many species, including humans, gametes are haploid). [Gk., *haploeides*, single]

hazard factor (14) An external force on a population that increases the risk of death.

heart (21) A muscular pump that, with each contraction, propels blood at high pressure to lungs, gills, or other body organs and tissues.

heat stroke (20) A potentially life-threatening medical condition caused by extreme hyperthermia, characterized by an inability of the organism to maintain homeostasis.

heliotropism (19) In plants, a growth in response to a light source in which leaves and flowers orient themselves in relationship to the sun's rays. [Gk., *helios*, sun + *tropikos*, turn]

helper T cell (26) A type of lymphocyte that stimulates B cells to produce antibodies and cytotoxic T cells to kill infected cells.

hematocrit (21) The proportion of blood that is made up from red blood cells; determined by spinning a blood sample in a centrifuge.

hemoglobin (21) An oxygen-carrying protein molecule in red blood cells. [Gk., *haima*, blood + Lat., *globus*, ball]

hemolymph (21) The single fluid of an open circulatory system that surrounds all cells and transports nutrients, gases, and waste products.

herbivores (15, 22) Animals that eat plants; also known as primary consumers. [Lat., *herba*, grass + *vorare*, to devour]

heredity (7) The greater resemblance of offspring to parents than to other individuals in the population, a consequence of the passing of characteristics from parents to offspring through their genes. [Lat., *heres*, heir]

heritability (8) The transmission of traits from parents to offspring via genetic information; also known as inheritance.

hermaphrodite (6) An organism that produces both male and female gametes. [from the names of the Greek god Hermes and goddess Aphrodite]

heterotherm (20) An animal that has a body temperature that fluctuates as the environmental temperature changes. [Gk., *heteros*, other + *thermē*, heat]

heterozygous (7) Describes the genotype of a trait for which the two alleles an individual carries differ from each other. [Gk., *heteros*, other + *zeugos*, pair]

hibernate (20) To go into a state of reduced metabolic activity for days or weeks, during which the animal's body temperature can drop considerably.

hindbrain (23) The region of the vertebrate brain that includes the medulla, pons, and cerebellum.

hippocampus (23) Part of the brain's limbic system; functions in long-term memory formation.

histamine (26) A molecule released by mast cells that assists in the inflammatory response by causing non-injured blood vessels to dilate and become leaky.

histones (6) Proteins around which the long, linear strands of DNA are wrapped; the histones serve to keep the DNA untangled and to enable an orderly, tight, and efficient packing of the DNA within the cell.

homeostasis (20) The body's use of physical and chemical processes to maintain a consistent internal environment. [Gk., *homos*, same + *stasis*, standing]

homeotherm (20) An animal that maintains a relatively constant body temperature. [Gk., *homos*, same + *thermē*, heat]

homologous (10) Describes features that are inherited from a common ancestor. [Gk., *homologia*, agreement]

homologous pair (homologues) (6) The maternal and paternal copies of a chromosome. [Gk., *homologia*, agreement]

homologous structures (8) Body structures in different organisms that, although modified extensively over time to serve different functions in different species, are due to inheritance from a common evolutionary ancestor.

homozygous (7) Describes the genotype of a trait for which the two alleles are the same. [Gk., *homos*, same + *zeugos*, pair]

honest signal (9) A signal, which cannot be faked, that is given when both the individual making the signal and the individual responding to it have the same interests; it carries the most accurate information about an individual or situation.

horizontal gene transfer (10) The transfer of genetic material directly from one individual to another not necessarily related individual.

hormone (19, 24) A chemical signal that responds to environmental variables, found in both plants and animals. In plants, hormones are produced in various locations and may have their effect in that location or may be transported to another part of the plant to regulate the plant's activities. In animals, hormones are usually secreted by endocrine glands and are transported by the bloodstream to target cells as part of an internal communication and regulation system. [Gk., *hormao*, that which sets in motion or urges forward]

host (13, 15) An organism in or on which a parasite lives.

human chorionic gonadotropin (hCG) (25) A hormone secreted by the embryo that keeps the lining of the uterus thickened for implantation.

Human Genome Project (5) A project to decode the three billion base pairs in the human genome and to identify all genes present in it.

human immunodeficiency virus (HIV) (13, 26) The virus responsible for AIDS, a deadly disease that destroys the human immune system. HIV is a retrovirus, a RNA-containing virus that is thought to have been introduced to humans from chimpanzees.

humus (17) (*pron.* HYOO-muss) The decomposing remains of plants and animals found in the uppermost region of soil; absorbs and releases water easily and releases many nutrients.

hybridization (genetics) (10) The interbreeding of closely related species. [Lat., *hybrida*, animal produced by two different species]

hybridization (molecular biology) (5) The process of joining two complementary strands of DNA from different sources; hybridization occurs when a DNA probe is used to match with a complementary sequence in a gene library. [Lat., *hybrida*, animal produced by two different species]

hybrids (10) Offspring of individuals of two different species. [Lat., *hybrida*, animal produced by two different species]

hydrogen bond (2) A type of weak chemical bond formed between the slightly positively charged hydrogen atoms of one molecule and the slightly negatively charged atoms of another (often oxygen or nitrogen atoms); hydrogen bonds are important in building multi-atom molecules, such as complex proteins, and are responsible for many of the unique and important features of water.

hydrophilic (2, 3) Attracted to water, as, for example, polar molecules that readily form hydrogen bonds with water. [Lat., *hydro-*, pertaining to water; Gk., *philios*, loving]

hydrophobic (2, 3) Repelled by water, as, for example, non-polar molecules that tend to minimize contact with water. [Lat., *hydro-*, pertaining to water, Gk., *phobos*, fearing]

hydroponically grown plant (17) A plant grown without soil, but in water enriched with essential plant nutrients.

hypertonic (3) Of two solutions, that with a higher concentration of solutes. [Gk., *hyper*, above + *tonos*, tension]

hyphae (*sing.* hypha) (12) (*pron.* HIGH-fee) Long strings of cells that make up the mycelium of a multicellular fungus. [Gk., *hypha*, web]

hyperthermia (20) A condition in which high external environmental temperature and humidity overwhelm the body's ability to dissipate heat, and body temperature becomes abnormally high; can lead to death. [Gk., *hyper*, above + *thermē*, heat]

hypothalamus (23, 24) A structure on the underside of the brain that functions as a liaison between the nervous and endocrine systems and serves as one of the chief regulatory centers of the brain. It regulates many fundamental drives, including hunger and thirst, sexual activity, and maintenance of body temperature. It also controls the hormone secretions of the pituitary gland, located next to it. [Gk., *hypo*, under + *thalamos*, inner room]

hypothermia (20) A condition in which body temperature becomes abnormally low; can lead to death. [Gk., *hypo*, under + *thermē*, heat]

hypothesis (*pl.* **hypotheses**) (1) A proposed explanation for an observed phenomenon. [Gk., *hypothesis*, a proposal]

hypotonic (3) Of two solutions, that with a lower concentration of solutes. [Gk., *hypo*, under + *tonos*, tension]

I

immune system (26) Body system consisting of disease-fighting white blood cells and external barriers such as skin, providing protection against an enormous variety of pathogens, such as bacteria, fungi, some viruses, parasitic protists, and worms.

immunity (26) State of long-term protection against a specific disease-causing microorganism or virus.

inclusive fitness (9) The sum of an individual's indirect and direct fitness.

incomplete dominance (7) The case in which the heterozygote has a phenotype intermediate between those of the two homozygotes; an example is pink snapdragons, whose appearance is intermediate between homozygous for white flowers and homozygous for red flowers.

indirect fitness (9) The reproductive output that an individual brings about through apparently altruistic behaviors toward genetic relatives.

infertility (25) The inability of a couple to get pregnant after one year of trying.

inflammatory response (26) The recruitment of phagocytes and other immune cells to assist with pathogen destruction, followed by tissue healing. Signs of the inflammatory response include redness, heat, swelling, and pain.

ingestion (22) The intake of food via the mouth, teeth, tongue, and esophagus.

inheritance (8) The transmission of traits from parents to offspring via genetic information; also known as heritability.

innate behaviors (9) Behaviors that do not require environmental input for their development; innate behaviors are present in all individuals in a population and do not vary much from one individual to another or over an individual's life span; also known as instincts. [Lat., *innatus*, inborn]

instincts (9) Behaviors that do not require environmental input for their development; instincts are present in all individuals in a population and do not vary much from one individual to another or over an individual's life span; also known as innate behaviors. [Lat., *instinctus*, impelled]

integumentary system (26) Body system consisting of skin, sweat glands, oil glands, hair, and nails that protects the body from mechanical stress caused by external forces such as friction or pressure, sunlight, dehydration, and pathogens. [Lat., *integere*, to cover]

interferon (26) An important cytokine produced by cells infected by a virus; alerts other cells to turn on protective measures that help them resist infection.

intermembrane space (3) In a mitochrondrion, the region between the inner and outer membranes. [Lat., *inter*, between + *membrana*, a thin skin]

internal fertilization (25) The process in which sperm are deposited in the female's reproductive tract and unite with one or more eggs.

interneuron (23) A type of neuron that acts as a middleman, integrating the signals coming in from sensory neurons and relaying them to a motor neuron; located in the brain and spinal cord.

interphase (6) In the cell cycle, the phase during which the cell grows and functions; during this phase, replication of DNA occurs in preparation for cell division. [Lat., *inter*, between + Gk., *phasis*, appearance]

interstitial fluid (20) An extracellular fluid that surrounds and bathes cells; consists mainly of water and also contains nutrients, raw materials, and waste products.

intron (5) A non-coding region of DNA.

invagination (3) The folding in of a membrane or layer of tissue so that an outer surface becomes an inner surface. [Lat., *in*, in + *vagina*, sheath]

ion (2) An atom that carries an electrical charge, positive or negative, because it has either gained or lost an electron or electrons from its normal, stable configuration. [Gk., *ion*, going]

ionic bond (2) A bond created by the transfer of one or more electrons from one atom to another; the resulting atoms, now called ions, are charged oppositely and so attract each other to form a compound.

iris (23) The colored portion of the vertebrate eye with an opening, called the pupil, that controls the amount of light reaching the eye's interior.

isotonic (3) Refers to solutions with equal concentrations of solutes. [Gk., *isos*, equal to + *tonos*, tension]

K

karyotype (6) A visual display of an individual's full set of chromosomes. [Gk., *karyon*, nut or kernel + *typos*, impression, engraving]

keystone species (15) A species that has an unusually large influence on the presence or absence of numerous other species in a community.

kilocalorie (kcal) (22) One thousand calories.

kin selection (9) Kindness toward close relatives, which may evolve as apparently altruistic behavior toward them, but which in fact is beneficial to the fitness of the individual performing the behavior.

kinetic energy (4) The energy of moving objects, such as legs pushing the pedals of a bicycle or wings beating against the air. [Gk., *kinesis*, motion]

kingdom (10) In the system developed by Carolus Linnaeus (1707–1778), one of the three categories—animal, plant, and mineral—into which all organisms and substances on earth were placed. In modern classification, there are six kingdoms: bacteria, archaea, protists, plants, animals, and fungi.

Krebs cycle (4) The second step of cellular respiration, in which energy is extracted from sugar molecules as additional molecules of ATP and NADH are formed. [from the name of the discoverer, Hans Adolf Krebs, 1900–1981]

L

labia (*sing.* **labium**) (25) Protective folds of skin surrounding the female genitals; develops from the same embryonic tissue that produces the scrotum.

labor (25) During childbirth, a series of contractions of the uterus.

lactation (25) Milk production in the mammary glands.

lamella (*pl.* **lamellae**) (21) Disk-like structure in gills, with elaborately branched capillaries.

landscape conservation (16) The conservation of habitats and ecological processes as well as species.

language (9, 23) A type of communication in which arbitrary symbols represent concepts and grammar; a system of rules dictates the way the symbols can be manipulated to communicate and express ideas.

large intestine (22) The last part of the vertebrate digestive system, larger in diameter but shorter in length than the small intestine. It serves to absorb water, salts, and some vitamins and, in its final compartment (the rectum), to store the indigestible parts of consumed food and symbiotic bacteria (the feces), which can then be defecated. Also called *colon.*

larva (11) In complete metamorphosis, the first stage of insect development; the larva is hatched by the egg, which eats to grow large enough to enter the pupa stage; the larva (for example, a caterpillar) looks completely different from the adult (a butterfly or moth). [Lat., *larva,* ghost]

lateral meristem (17) Growth region of a plant consisting of a layer of cells called cambium; division in this meristem causes a stem or root to become thicker, as opposed to longer.

leaf (17) The chief site of photosynthesis in most plants; leaves and stems form the shoot system.

learning (9) The alteration and modification of behavior over time in response to experience.

left hemisphere (23) The region of the brain that specializes, in most (but not all) humans, in language, logic, and mathematical skills.

leukocytes (21) See **white blood cells.**

lichens (12) Symbiotic partnership between fungi and chlorophyll-containing algae or cyanobacteria, or both.

life (10) A physical state characterized by the ability to replicate and the presence of metabolic activity.

life cycle (18) The series of stages experienced by an individual of a species throughout its development, each stage following the preceding stage through reproduction.

life history (14) The vital statistics of a species, including age at first reproduction, probabilities of survival and reproduction at each age, litter size and frequency, and longevity.

ligament (20) A connective tissue that binds bone to bone.

light energy (4) A type of kinetic energy made up of energy packets called photons, which are organized into waves.

lignin (17) A chemical in the cell walls of sclerenchyma cells of woody plants; it is indigestible to nearly all organisms and gives sclerenchyma cells their strength.

limbic system (23) The brain region that includes parts of the cerebral cortex and two structures deeper in the center of the brain, the hippocampus and the amygdala. It is responsible for many physiological drives and instincts.

linked genes (7) Genes that are close to each other on a chromosome, and so are more likely than others to be inherited together.

lipid (2) One of four types of macromolecules, lipids are insoluble in water and greasy to the touch; they are important in energy storage and insulation (fats), membrane formation (phospholipids), and regulating growth and regulating growth and development (sterols). [Gk., *lipos,* fat]

liver (22) An organ in vertebrates and some other animals that is important in the detoxification of toxic molecules, storage of glycogen, and synthesis of bile, hormones, and digestive enzymes.

lobe-finned fishes (11) Fish species characterized by two pairs of sturdy lobe-shaped fins on the underside of the body.

logistic growth (14) A pattern of population growth in which initially exponential growth levels off as the environment's carrying capacity is approached.

long-term depression (23) Long-lasting decrease in the sensitivity of a neuron, resulting from a period of intense stimulation.

long-term potentiation (23) Long-lasting increase in the sensitivity of a neuron, resulting from a period of intense stimulation.

lungs (21) Internal organs in most land vertebrates, with highly branched, moist respiratory surfaces where gases are exchanged between air and blood.

luteal phase (25) The second half of the reproductive cycle in women in which the follicle cell that had surrounded the ovum develops into the corpus luteum; culminates in pregnancy or the sloughing off of the uterine lining.

lymph (21) A clear fluid formed from interstitial fluid as it is filtered into the lymphatic vessels in vertebrates.

lymph nodes (21) In the lymphatic system, patches of connective tissue filled with pathogen-fighting white blood cells, through which lymph passes.

lymphocyte (26) A type of white blood cell that carries out the response of the specific division of the immune system.

lysosome (3) A round, membrane-enclosed, enzyme- and acid-filled vesicle in the cell that digests and recycles cellular waste products and consumed material. [Gk., *lysis,* releasing + *soma,* body]

lysozyme (26) Enzyme produced by skin cells and in tears that kills bacteria by damaging their cell walls.

M

macroevolution (10) Large-scale products of evolutionary change involving the origins of new groups of organisms; the accumulated effect of microevolution over a long period of time. [Gk., *macros,* large + Lat., *evolvere,* to roll out]

macromolecule (2) A large molecule, made up of smaller building blocks or subunits; four types of biological macromolecules are carbohydrates, lipids, proteins, and nucleic acids. [Gk., *macros,* large + Lat., *dim.* of *moles,* mass]

macrophage (26) A type of large ("macro") white blood cell that resides in tissues and ingests small organisms and large debris such as dead cells. Macrophages serve as an important link between the non-specific and specific divisions of the immune system.

male (9) In sexually reproducing organisms, a member of the sex that produces the smaller gamete.

mammary glands (11) Glands in all female mammals that produce milk for the nursing of young. [Lat., *mamma,* breast]

marsupials (11) Mammals in which, in most species, after a short period of embryonic life in the uterus, the young complete their development in a pouch in the female. [Gk., *marsipos,* pouch]

mass (2) The amount of matter in a given sample of a substance.

mass extinctions (10) Extinctions in which a large number of species become extinct in a short period of time, usually because of extraordinary and sudden environmental change. [Lat., *extinguere,* to extinguish]

mast cell (26) A type of white blood cell found in tissues that triggers the inflammatory response by releasing histamine.

mate guarding (9) Behavior by an individual that reduces the opportunity for that individual's mate to interact with other potential mates.

mating system (9) The pattern of mating behavior in a species, ranging from polyandry to monogamy to polygyny; mating systems are influenced by the relative amounts of parental investment by males and by females.

matrix (connective tissue) (20) A mass of non-living, extracellular material in which connective tissue cells are embedded.

matrix (mitochondrial) (3, 4) The space within the inner membrane, where the carriers NADH and $FADH_2$ begin the electron transport chain by carrying high-energy electrons to molecules embedded in the inner membrane.

maximum sustainable yield (14) The point at which the maximum number of individuals are removed from a population without impairing its growth rate, it occurs at half the carrying capacity.

mechanoreceptor (23) A type of sensory cell that responds to mechanical pressure.

medulla (23) The part of the vertebrate hindbrain that connects to the spinal cord; controls functions such as respiration, heart rate, and digestion.

meiosis (6) In sexually reproducing organisms, a process of nuclear division in the gonads that, along with cytokinesis, produces reproductive cells that have half as much genetic material as the parent cell, and that all differ from each other genetically. [Gk., *meioun,* to lessen]

memory cell (26) Long-lived B cells or T cells, produced in the primary immune response to a particular antigen, that enable rapid response to subsequent exposure to the same antigen.

Mendel's law of independent assortment (7) Allele pairs for different genes separate independently in meiosis, so the inheritance of one trait generally does not influence the inheritance of another trait (the exception, unknown to Mendel, occurs with linked genes). [from the name of its discoverer, Gregor Mendel, 1822–1884]

Mendel's law of segregation (7) During the formation of gametes, the two alleles for a gene separate, so that half the gametes carry one allele, and half of the gametes carry the other. [from the name of its discoverer, Gregor Mendel, 1822–1884]

menopause (25) The permanent cessation of ovulation and menstruation, prior to the end of an individual's life.

menstrual cycle (25) The cycle in which the uterus prepares for the implantation and nurturing of a fertilized egg, and sheds its lining if fertilization does not occur.

menstruation (25) The shedding of the uterine lining.

meristem (17, 18) Growth region of a plant, made up of undifferentiated cells that divide to form additional undifferentiated cells as well as other cells that differentiate to form specific plant tissues.

mesoderm (25) The middle embryonic cell layer during gastrulation; it eventually forms the muscles and skeleton. [Gk., *mesos,* middle + *derma,* skin]

messenger RNA (mRNA) (5) The ribonucleic acid that "reads" the sequence for a gene in DNA and then moves from the nucleus to the cytoplasm, where the next stage of protein synthesis will take place.

metamorphosis (11) The rebuilding of molecules from the larva stage to the adult, resulting in a change of form. [Gk., *metamorphoun,* to transform]

metaphase (6) The second phase of mitosis, in which the sister chromatids line up at the center of the cell; in meiosis, the homologues line up at the center of the cell in metaphase I and the sister chromatids line up in metaphase II. [Gk., *meta,* in the midst of + *phasis,* appearance]

microbe (10, 13) A microscopic organism; not a monophyletic group since it includes protists, archaea, and bacteria. [Gk., *micros,* small + *bios,* life]

microevolution (10) A slight change in allele frequencies in a population over one or a few generations. [Gk., *micros,* small + Lat., *evolvere,* to roll out]

microsphere (10) A membrane-enclosed, small, spherical unit containing a self-replicating molecule and carrying information, although no genetic material; microspheres may have been an important stage in the development of life. [Gk., *micros,* small + *sphaira,* ball]

midbrain (23) Part of the brainstem; a sensory integration and relay center through which most of the sensory information and motor neuron connections coming into and out of the brain pass.

migration (8) A change in the allele frequencies of a population due to the movement of some individuals from one population to another; an agent of evolutionary change caused by the movement of individuals into or out of a population. [Lat., *migrare,* to move from place to place]

mimicry (15) The evolution of an organism to resemble another organism or object in its environment to help conceal itself from predators. [Gk., *mimesis,* imitation]

mineral (22) A chemical element other than those commonly found in organic molecules (carbon, hydrogen, oxygen, and nitrogen); some minerals are required in the diet in small amounts.

mitochondrial matrix (4) See **matrix.**

mitochondrion (*pl.* **mitochondria**) (3) The organelle in eukaryotic cells that converts the energy stored in food in the chemical bonds of carbohydrate, fat, and protein molecules into a form usable by the cell for all its functions and activities. [Gk., *mitos,* thread + *chondros,* cartilage]

mitosis (6) The division of a nucleus into two genetically identical nuclei, along with cytokinesis, leads to the formation of two identical daughter cells. [Gk., *mitos,* thread + *phasis,* appearance]

mitotic phase (M phase) (6) The phase of the cell cycle during which first the genetic material and nucleus, and then the rest of the cellular contents, divide.

molecule (2) A group of atoms held together by covalent bonds. [Lat., *dim.* of *moles,* mass]

monocot (17) One of the two major groups of flowering plants; monocot seedlings have one cotyledon (seed leaf).

monogamy (9) A mating system in which most individuals mate and remain with just one other individual. [Gk., *monos,* single + *gamete,* wife]

monophyletic (10) A group containing a common ancestor and all of its descendants. [Gk., *monos,* single + *phylon,* race, tribe, class]

monosaccharides (2) The simplest carbohydrates and the building blocks of more complex carbohydrates; monosaccharides, which cannot be broken down into other monosaccharides, include glucose, fructose, and galactose; also known as simple sugars. [Gk., *monos,* single + *sakcharon,* sugar]

monotremes (11) Present-day mammals that retain the ancestral condition of laying eggs; monotremes are so called because they have a single duct, the cloaca, which the reproductive system, the urinary system, and the digestive system (for defecation) open into. [Gk., *monos,* single + *trema,* hole]

mood (24) A relatively long-lasting emotional state (shorter-lasting than a person's temperament, but longer-lasting and less specific than a single emotion).

morphological species concept (10) A concept that defines species on the basis of physical features such as body size and shape. [Gk., *morphē,* shape]

motor neuron (23) A type of neuron that stimulates action by conveying signals to muscles or glands and initiating a body's response to stimuli.

multiple allelism (7) The case in which a single gene has more than two possible alleles.

multiple sclerosis (MS) (26) Autoimmune disease in which the body attacks the myelin sheath surrounding nerve fibers of the brain and spinal cord, causing blurred vision, weakness in arms and legs, and trouble with balance.

muscle fiber (20) An individual muscle cell; typically contains multiple nuclei.

muscle tissue (20) A body tissue consisting of contractile cells (muscle fibers) that generate force and can facilitate movement.

mutagen (8) An agent capable of causing a mutation in DNA; may be chemical (as some insecticides) or physical (as with the energy from radiation). [Lat., *mutare,* to change + *genus,* race, family, origin]

mutation (5, 8) An alteration in the base-pair sequence of an individual's DNA; may arise spontaneously or following exposure to a mutagen. [Lat., *mutare,* to change]

mutualism (15) A symbiotic relationship in which both species benefit and neither is harmed. [Lat., *mutuus,* reciprocal]

mycelium (12) A mass of interconnecting hyphae that make up the structure of a multicellular fungus. [Gk., *mykes,* fungus]

mycorrhizae (12, 17) (*pron.* my-ko-RYE-zay) Root fungi, that is, symbiotic associations between roots and fungi in which fungal structures are closely associated with fine rootlets and root hairs. [Gk., *mykes,* fungus + *rhiza,* root]

myelin sheath (23) Fatty coating insulating the axon.

myofibril (23) A cylindrical organelle within muscle cells that can contract; contains repeating units, called sarcomeres, in which the contraction takes place.

myoglobin (21) An oxygen-binding protein in muscle that releases oxygen when demand is high and the partial pressure of oxygen is low.

myosin (23) A protein of muscle tissue; makes up the thick filaments.

N

NADPH (4) A molecule (nicotinamide adenine dinucleotide phosphate) that is a high-energy electron carrier involved in photosynthesis, which stores energy by accepting high-energy protons; NADPH is formed when the electrons released from the splitting of water are passed to NADP$^+$.

natural killer (NK) cell (26) A type of white blood cell that kills body cells infected by a pathogen.

natural selection (8) A mechanism of evolution that occurs when there is heritable variation for a trait and individuals with one version of the trait have greater reproductive success than do individuals with a different version of that trait.

nectar (18) A solution produced by a flower, rich in sugars and amino acids, that can serve as an attractant to animal pollinators.

negative feedback (20) A control mechanism in which sensors detect changes in the internal environment and trigger effectors to counteract the change; one of the chief strategies by which organisms maintain homeostasis.

nephron (20) The chief functional unit in the vertebrate kidney, consisting of a tubule and a mass of blood vessels that work together to accomplish the tasks of filtration, reabsorption, and excretion.

nerve (23) A group of neurons bundled together with connective tissue.

nervous system (23) Network of cells (neurons), present in all multicellular animals other than sponges, that collects information about the organism's internal and external environments, processes that information, and sends signals to muscles and glands in response to the information.

nervous tissue (20) A body tissue that specializes in storing and transmitting information.

neural tube (25) A long hollow tube formed during neurulation that ultimately develops into the nervous system.

neuroglia (20) See **glial cells.**

neuron (20, 23) The "excitable" cell within the nervous system that receives and transmits signals; made up of three distinctive elements: dendrites, a cell body, and an axon.

neurotransmitter (23) A chemical of the nervous system that transmits signals to adjacent cells.

neurulation (25) During embryonic development, the process of the folding in of the ectoderm for the entire length of the embryo, first forming a groove and then becoming the neural tube.

neutron (2) An electrically neutral particle in the atomic nucleus. [Lat., *neutro,* in neither direction]

neutrophil (26) A type of white blood cell that circulates in the blood and ingests small organisms, primarily bacteria. Neutrophils make up 50% to 70% of all white blood cells.

niche (15) The way an organism utilizes the resources of its environment, including the space it requires, the food it consumes, and timing of reproduction.

nitrogen fixation (17) Process by which the bonds between paired nitrogen atoms in molecules of nitrogen (N_2) are broken and the individual atoms are converted into a form, such as ammonia, that is usable by plants.

node (phylogeny) (10) The point on an evolutionary tree at which species diverge from a common ancestor. [Lat., *nodus,* knot]

node (plant structure) (17) A small lump of tissue on a stem from which a leaf, flower, cone, or additional stem (or branch) may grow.

nodule (17) In plant roots, a round lump containing plant cells and nitrogen-fixing bacteria.

nondisjunction (6) The unequal distribution of chromosomes during cell division; can lead to Down syndrome and other disorders caused by the possession in an individual of too few or too many chromosomes.

non-essential amino acid (22) An amino acid that can be produced by the body and so is not needed in the diet.

non-specific immunity (26) Division of the immune system that, through various types of non-specific immune cells, rapidly recognizes pathogens that breach external barriers and are not part of the body's own tissue, but does not distinguish between specific pathogens. Also called the *innate system* (meaning "inborn"), because it is functioning at birth and does not require any previous exposure to pathogens to act.

non-polar (3) Electrically uncharged.

non-vascular plants (12) Plants that do not have vessels to transport water and dissolved nutrients, but rely on diffusion; bryophytes are non-vascular plants. [Lat., *vasculum, dim.* of *vas,* vessel]

notochord (11) A rod of tissue from head to tail that stiffens the body when muscles contract during locomotion; primitive chordates retain the notochord throughout life, but in advanced chordates it is present only in early embryos and is replaced by the vertebral column. [Gk., *notos,* back + Lat., *chorda,* cord]

notochord (25) A flexible rod in chordates whose function in vertebrates is ultimately taken over by the backbone.

nuclear membrane (3) A membrane that surrounds the nucleus of a cell, separating it from the cytoplasm, consisting of two bilayers and perforated by pores enclosed in embedded proteins that allow the passage of large molecules from nucleus to cytoplasm and from cytoplasm to nucleus; also called the nuclear envelope.

nucleic acid (2, 5) One of the four types of biological macromolecules, the nucleic acids DNA and RNA store genetic information in unique sequences of nucleotides.

nucleolus (3) An area near the center of the nucleus where subunits of the ribosomes are assembled. [Lat., *nucleolus, dim.* of *nucleus,* kernel, small nut]

nucleotide (2, 5) A molecule containing a phosphate group, a sugar molecule, and a nitrogen-containing molecule; nucleotides are the individual units that together, in a unique sequence, constitute a nucleic acid.

nucleus (cell biology) (3) A membrane-enclosed structure in eukaryotic cells that contains the organism's genetic information as linear strands of DNA in the form of chromosomes. [Lat., *nucleus, dim.* of *nux,* nut]

nucleus (chemistry) (2) The central and most massive part of an atom, usually made up of two types of particles, protons and neutrons, which move about the nucleus. [Lat., *nucleus, dim.* of *nux,* nut]

null hypothesis (1) A hypothesis that proposes a lack of relationship between two factors. [Lat., *nullus,* none]

nuptial gift (9) A food item or other item presented to a potential mate as part of courtship. [Lat., *nuptialis,* of marriage]

nutrient (22) A substance used for energy, raw materials, and maintenance of the body's systems.

O

omnivores (15, 22) Animals that eat both plants and other animals and thus can occupy more than one position in the food chain. [Lat., *omnis,* all + *vorare,* to devour]

oogenesis (25) The process of egg production in females.

oogonium (*pl.* **oogonia**) (25) Diploid cell in the ovary that multiplies by mitosis. Each oogonium begins meiosis but pauses at prophase I, at which point the cell is called a primary oocyte.

open circulatory system (21) A circulatory system in which a single fluid, hemolymph, circulates to transport nutrients, gases, and waste products and also surrounds all cells.

optic nerve (23) The nerve that transports visual information from the retina of the eye to the thalamus and other parts of the brain.

order (10) In the system developed by Carolus Linnaeus (1707–1778), a classification of organisms consisting of related families.

organ (20) A structure that serves specialized functions and contains several types of tissue.

organ system (20) A group of organs that work together to accomplish physiological functions.

organelles (3) Specialized structures in the cytoplasm of eukaryotic cells with specific functions, such as the rough and smooth endoplasmic reticulum, Golgi apparatus, and mitochondria. [Gk., *organon,* tool]

osmoconformer (20) An organism that regulates water loss and gain by maintaining the solute concentration of its body fluids at the solute concentration of its environment.

osmoregulation (20) The regulation of water content and of the concentrations of dissolved solutes that influence osmosis; an important component of homeostasis in animals.

osmoregulator (20) An organism that regulates water loss and gain by maintaining the solute concentration of its body fluids within a narrow range that differs from that of its environment.

osmosis (3) A type of passive transport in which water molecules move across a membrane such as the plasma membrane of a cell; the direction of osmosis is determined by the relative concentrations of all solutes on either side of the membrane. [Gk., *osmos,* thrust]

ovarian cycle (25) The cycle in which a woman's hormones regulate the timing and development of egg production.

ovary (12, 18, 25) An enclosed chamber at the base of the carpel of a flower that contains the ovules; the female gonad. [Lat., *ovum,* egg]

oviduct (25) See **Fallopian tube.**

oviparity (25) A reproductive strategy in which the fertilized egg moves outside the body for embryonic development.

ovoviviparity (25) A reproductive strategy in which most embryonic development takes place in the female's body until the egg hatches (or is released just before hatching).

ovulate (25) To release a secondary oocyte from an ovarian follicle into a Fallopian tube from where it moves to the uterus.

ovule (12, 18) The structure within the ovary of flowering plants that gives rise to female egg cells. [Lat., *ovum,* egg]

ovum (*pl.* **ova**) (25) See **egg.**

Oxygen Revolution (13) The accumulation in the atmosphere of oxygen released by cyanobacteria and other photosynthetic organisms.

P

pair bond (9) A bond between an individual male and female in which they spend a high proportion of their time together, often over many years, sharing a nest or other refuge and contributing equally to the care of offspring.

pancreas (22) An organ that secretes digestive juice into the small intestine and hormones into the blood.

paracrine regulator (24) A chemical that is secreted from a cell and acts locally. Paracrine regulators generally diffuse through intracellular fluid from the tissue in which they are produced to nearby tissue, binding to receptors of neighboring cells and influencing their activity.

parasite (13, 15) An organism that lives in or on another organism, the host, and damages it. [Gk., *para,* beside + *sitos,* grain, food]

parasitism (15) A symbiotic relationship in which one organism (the parasite) benefits while the other (the host) is harmed.

parathyroid glands (24) Endocrine glands embedded in the surface of the thyroid gland that produce parathyroid hormone, which plays a central role in regulating calcium levels in adults. [Gk. *para,* beside + *thyra,* door]

parenchyma cell (17) A type of cell that carries out most of a plant's metabolic activities. Parenchyma cells are a type of ground tissue.

parent cells (6) Cells that divide to form daughter cells, which are genetically identical to the parent cell.

parthenogenesis (25) The asexual reproductive process in which a female's egg develops into a new organism without fertilization by a sperm cell.

passive transport (3) Molecular movement that occurs spontaneously, without the input of energy; the two types of passive transport are diffusion and osmosis.

paternity uncertainty (9) Describes the fact that among species with internal fertilization in the female, a male cannot be 100% certain that any offspring a female produces are his. [Lat., *pater,* father]

pathogen (21, 26) A disease-causing substance or organism, such as infectious bacteria, viruses, and fungi. Pathogens are sometimes referred to as "germs."

PCBs (polychlorinated biphenyls) (24) Chemicals used in industrial coolants and lubricants; known endocrine disruptors.

pedigree (7) In genetics, a type of family tree that maps the occurrence of a trait in a family, often over many generations.

penis (25) External male reproductive structure.

pepsin (22) A protein-dismantling enzyme produced by cells in the stomach lining.

peptide bond (2) A bond in which the amino group of one amino acid is bonded to the carboxyl group of another; two amino acids so joined form a dipeptide, several amino acids so joined form a polypeptide. [Gk., *peptikos,* able to digest]

peptidoglycan (13) A glycoprotein that forms a thick layer on the outside of the cell wall of a bacterium; in some bacteria the layer of peptidoglycan is covered by a membrane and so is not colored by a Gram stain.

peripheral nervous system (PNS) (20, 23) The part of an organism's nervous system that transmits information to and from the central nervous system; includes the sensory and motor neurons.

peristalsis (22) Waves of smooth muscle contractions that propel food along the digestive tract. [Gk., *peri*, around + *stellein*, to place]

permafrost (19) Soil that remains frozen for two or more years, so that plants' root growth is limited and any water that is present from precipitation or melting cannot drain well.

PET scan (23) Positron emission tomography scan; a brain imaging technology in which radioactive glucose is injected into the subject and the radioactivity is traced in the brain, as a way of measuring brain activity.

petal (18) One of the usually brightly colored leaf-like structures of a flower, located inside the ring of sepals; the color, shape, and size vary greatly among the flowering plants. The petals help to attract animal pollinators, with different colors generally appealing to different pollinator species.

pH (2) A logarithmic scale that measures the concentration of hydrogen ions (H^+) In a solution, with decreasing values indicating increasing acidity; water, in which the concentration of hydrogen ions (H^+) equals the concentration of hydroxyl ions (OH^-), is pH = 7, the midpoint of the scale. [abbreviation for "power of hydrogen"]

phagocyte (26) A type of white blood cell that can engulf, ingest, kill, and break down foreign pathogens and particles. [Gk., *phagein*, to eat + *kytos*, container]

phagocytosis (3, 13) One of the three types of endocytosis, in which relatively large solid particles are engulfed by the plasma membrane, a vesicle is formed, and the particle is moved into the cell.

pharyngeal slits (11) Slits in the pharyngeal region, between the back of the mouth and the top of the throat, for the passage of water for breathing and feeding. [Gk., *pharynx*, throat]

phenotype (5, 7) The manifested structure, function, and behaviors of an individual; the expression of the genotype of an organism. [Gk., *phainein*, to cause to appear + *typos* impression, engraving]

pheromone (9, 24, 25) Molecules released by an individual into the environment that trigger behavioral or physiological responses in other individuals. [Gk., *pherein*, to carry]

phloem (*pron.* FLOW-uhm) (17) In vascular plants, the tissue that conducts nutrients—sugar, in particular—throughout the plant.

phospholipid (2, 3) A lipid that is the major component of the plasma membrane; phospholipids are structurally similar to fats, but contain a phosphorus atom and have two, not three, fatty acid chains.

phospholipid bilayer (3) The structure of the plasma membrane; two layers of phospholipids, arranged tail to tail (the tails are hydrophobic and so avoid contact with water), with the hydrophilic head regions facing the watery extracellular fluid and intracellular fluid.

photoautotroph (13) Chlorophyll-containing bacteria, or other organisms, that use the energy from sunlight to convert carbon dioxide to glucose by photosynthesis. [Gk., *phos*, light + *autos*, self + *trophē*, food]

photon (4) The elementary particle that carries the energy of electromagnetic radiation of all wavelengths. [Gk., *phos*, light]

photoperiodism (19) A plant's response to the cycling of light and dark in a day; regulates flowering time and numerous other responses to seasonal changes.

photoreceptor cell (23) A type of cell that detects the presence of light.

photosynthesis (4) The process by which some organisms are able to capture energy from the sun and store it in the chemical bonds of sugars and other molecules the plants produce. [Gk., *phos*, light + *syn*, together with + *tithenai*, to place or put]

photosystems (4) Two arrangements of light-absorbing pigments, including chlorophyll, within the chloroplast that capture energy from the sun and transform it first into the energy of excited electrons and ultimately into ATP and high-energy electron carriers such as NADPH. [Gk., *phos*, light + *systema*, a whole compounded of parts]

phototropism (19) A growth response in plants, toward or away from a light source. [Gk., *phos*, light + *tropikos*, turn]

phthalates (24) Chemicals commonly found in soft toys and cosmetics; known endocrine disruptors.

phylogenetic tree (5) A grouping of organisms in a hierarchical system that reflects the evolutionary history and relatedness of the organisms. [Gk., *phylon*, race, tribe, class + Lat., *genus*, race, family, origin]

phylogeny (10) The evolutionary history of organisms.

phylum (10) In the system developed by Carolus Linnaeus (1707–1778), a classification of organisms consisting of related classes. [Gk., *phylon*, race, tribe, class]

physical barriers (immune system) (26) The first defense against pathogens, to keep them out of the body; for example, skin acts as a nearly impenetrable barrier that keeps viruses and bacteria from entering the body, and various chemicals secreted by epithelial surfaces stop the growth of many pathogens. See also **integumentary system.**

physiology (20) The study of the internal functions of organisms.

pigment (4) In photosynthesis, molecules that are able to absorb the energy of light of specific wavelengths, raising electrons to an excited state in the process. [Lat., *pigmentum*, paint]

pilus (*pl.* pili) (3) A thin, hair-like projection that helps a prokaryote attach to surfaces. [Lat., *pilus*, a single hair]

pinocytosis (3) One of the three types of endocytosis, in which dissolved particles and liquids are engulfed by the plasma membrane, a vesicle is formed and the material is moved into the cell; the vesicles formed in pinocytosis are generally much smaller than those formed in phagocytosis. [Gk., *pinein*, to drink + *kytos*, container]

pith (17, 18) The ground tissue close to the center of a stem.

pituitary gland (24) An endocrine gland, consisting of anterior and posterior parts, attached to the hypothalamus by a thin stalk and regulated by secretions from the hypothalamus. See also **anterior pituitary; posterior pituitary.**

placebo (1) An inactive substance used in controlled experiments to test the effectiveness of another substance; the treatment group receives the substance being tested, the control group receives the placebo. [Lat., *placebo*, I shall please]

placebo effect (1) A frequently observed and poorly understood phenomenon in which there is a positive response to treatment with an inactive substance.

placenta (6, 25) The organ formed during pregnancy (and expelled at birth) that connects the developing embryo to the wall of the uterus and allows the transfer of gases, nutrients, and waste products between mother and fetus; the placenta is so called from its shape. [Lat., *placenta*, a flat cake]

placentals (11) Mammals in which the developing fetus takes its nourishment from the transfer of nutrients from the mother through the placenta, which also supplies respiratory gases and removes metabolic waste products. [Lat., *placenta*, a flat cake]

plant (12) Members of the kingdom Plantae, which are multicellular eukaryotes having cell walls made up primarily of cellulose, contain true tissues, and produce their own food by photosynthesis; plants are sessile, and most inhabit terrestrial environments.

plasma (21) The liquid part of blood, containing dissolved metabolites and wastes, salts and ions, and proteins that transport lipids, vitamins, and other chemicals to the tissues where they are required.

plasma cell (26) A type of white blood cell (an effector B cell) that secretes antibodies as part of the specific immune system's response to a pathogen. Plasma cells can secrete hundreds to thousands of antibodies per second as a consequence of the cell's extensive endomembrane system.

plasma membrane (3) A complex, thin, two-layered membrane that encloses the cytoplasm of the cell, holding the contents in place and regulating what enters and leaves the cell; also called the cell membrane. [Gk., *plasma*, anything molded]

plasmid (5, 13) A circular DNA molecule found outside the main chromosome in bacteria.

plasmodesma (*pl.* plasmodesmata) (3) In plants, microscopic tube-like channels connecting the cells and enabling communication and transport between them. [Gk., *plassein*, to mold + *desmos*, bond]

platelets (21) Cellular fragments, components of the blood, formed by the pinching off of fragments from large cells (megakaryocytes) in the bone marrow; they lack organelles but are filled with enzymes and chemicals important for blood clotting.

pleiotropy (7) A phenomenon in which an individual gene influences multiple traits. [Gk., *pleion*, more + *tropos*, turn]

point mutation (5) A mutation in which one base pair in DNA is replaced with another or a base pair is either inserted or deleted.

polar (3) Having an electrical charge.

polar body (25) One of the two cells formed when a primary oocyte divides; it gets almost no cytoplasm and eventually disintegrates.

pollen grain (12, 18) A structure that contains the male gametophyte of a seed plant. [Lat., *pollen*, fine dust]

pollen tube (18) A long, tube-like structure formed by the growth of a single cell of the pollen grain after germination; it forms within the style of the female reproductive structure and carries the male gametes to the ovule.

pollination (12, 18) The transfer of pollen from the anther of one flower to the stigma of another flower. [Lat. pollen, *fine dust*]

polyandry (9) A polygamous mating system in which individual females mate with multiple males. [Gk., *polys*, many + *aner*, husband]

polygamy (9) A mating system in which for one sex some individuals attract multiple mates while other individuals of that sex attract none; among the opposite sex, all or nearly all of the individuals are able to attract a mate. [Gk., *polys*, many + *gamete*, wife]

polygenic (7) Describes a trait that is influenced by multiple different genes. [Gk., *polys*, many + *genos*, race, descent]

polygraph (21) The "lie detector" test; measures breathing rate, sweat gland activity, and heart rate to evaluate whether an individual is telling the truth.

polygyny (9) A mating system in which among the males some individuals attract multiple mates while other males attract none; among the females, all or nearly all of the individuals are able to attract a mate. [Gk., *polys*, many + *gune*, woman]

polymerase chain reaction (PCR) (5) A laboratory technique in which a fragment of DNA can be duplicated repeatedly. [Gk., *polys*, many + *meris*, part]

polyploidy (10) The doubling of the number of sets of chromosomes in an individual. [Gk., *polys*, many + *ploion*, vessel]

polysaccharides (2) Complex carbohydrates formed by the union of many simple sugars. [Gk., *polys*, many + *sakcharon*, sugar]

pons (23) Part of the vertebrate hindbrain that acts with the medulla to control body functions related to respiration, heart rate, and digestion.

population (8) A group of organisms of the same species living in a particular geographic region.

population density (14) The number of individuals of a population in a given area.

population ecology (14) A sub-field of ecology that studies the interactions between populations of organisms of a species and their environment.

positive correlation (1) A relationship between variables, in which they increase (or decrease) together. [Lat., *com*, with + *relatio*, report]

positive feedback (20) A control mechanism in which a deviation from normal internal conditions causes an increase or acceleration of the change.

post-anal tail (11) A tail that extends beyond the end of the trunk, a point that is marked by the anus; a characteristic of chordates. [Lat., *post*, after]

posterior pituitary (24) A gland of the endocrine system; releases several important peptide hormones—including oxytocin and antidiuretic hormone—that are produced in neurons of the hypothalamus.

postsynaptic membrane (23) The cell membrane of a neuron on the receiving side of a synapse, across from the presynaptic membrane.

postzygotic barrier (10) A barrier to reproduction caused by the infertility of hybrid individuals or the inability of hybrid individuals to survive long after fertilization. [Lat., *post*, after]

potential energy (4) Stored energy; the capacity to do work that results from an object's location or position, as in the case of water held behind a dam. [Lat., *potentia*, power]

predation (15) An interaction between two species in which one species eats the other. [Lat., *praedari*, to plunder]

prepared learning (9) Behaviors that are learned easily by all, or nearly all, individuals of a species.

pressure-flow mechanism (17) In vascular plants, the force driving the movement of sugar in the phloem; osmotic pressure moves material from sugar-production sites (sources) to sites where it is needed or stored (sinks).

presynaptic membrane (23) The cell membrane of an axon at the synapse.

prezygotic barrier (10) A barrier to reproduction caused by the physical inability of individuals to mate with each other, or the inability of the male's reproductive cell to fertilize the female's reproductive cell. [Lat., *prae*, before]

primary active transport (3) Active transport using energy released directly from ATP.

primary consumers (15) Herbivores, which consume the output of primary producers.

primary electron acceptor (4) In photosynthesis, a molecule that accepts excited, high-energy molecules from chlorophyll *a*, beginning the series of electron handoffs known as an electron transport chain.

primary growth (18) Plant growth that originates in the apical meristems of shoots and roots, increasing the height of the shoot, increasing the length of roots and branches, and producing new tissues. See also **secondary growth.**

primary oocyte (25) In female gametogenesis, a cell produced by meiosis, which then completes meiosis; it can become an egg (ovum).

primary producers (15) The organisms responsible for primary productivity, such as grasses, trees, and agricultural crops, which convert light energy from the sun into chemical energy (that is, food) through photosynthesis.

primary productivity (15) The amount of organic matter produced by living organisms, primarily through photosynthesis.

primary response (26) The immune system's first interaction with a pathogen.

primary spermatocyte (25) In sperm production, one of the two cells resulting from division of the spermatogonium; it undergoes meiosis in the first step of sperm production.

primary structure (2) The sequence of amino acids in a polypeptide chain.

probiotic therapy (13) A method of treating infections by introducing benign bacteria in numbers large enough to overwhelm harmful bacteria in the body. [Lat., *pro,* for, on behalf of + Gk., *bios,* life]

progesterone (25) A hormone secreted by the corpus luteum of the ovary that causes thickening of the endometrium to prepare for gestation. [Lat., *pro,* for + *gestare,* to bear]

prokaryote (3) An organism consisting of a prokaryotic cell (all prokaryotes are one-celled organisms). [Gk., *pro,* before + *karyon,* nut, kernel]

prokaryotic cell (3) A cell bound by a plasma membrane enclosing the cell contents (cytoplasm, DNA, and ribosomes); there is no nucleus or other organelles.

promoter site (5) A part of a DNA molecule that indicates where the sequence of base pairs that makes up a gene begins.

prophase (6) The first phase of mitosis, in which the nuclear membrane breaks down, sister chromatids condense, and the spindle forms; in meiosis, homologous pairs of sister chromatids come together and cross over in prophase I and the chromosomes in daughter cells condense in prophase II. [Gk., *pro,* before + *phasis,* appearance]

prostate gland (25) A gland in males that secretes enzymes and nutrients into the semen.

protein (2) One of the four types of biological macromolecules; constructed of unique combinations of 20 amino acids that result in unique structures and chemical behavior, proteins are the chief building blocks of tissues in most organisms. [Gk., *proteion,* of the first quality]

protein synthesis (5) The construction of a protein from its constituent amino acids, by the processes of transcription and translation.

prothallus (12) The free-living haploid life stage of a fern; the prothallus produces haploid gametes. [Gk., *pro,* before + *thallia,* twig]

protist (10) In modern classification, one of the four eukaryotic kingdoms, this group includes all the single-celled eukaryotes.

proton (2) A positively charged particle in the atomic nucleus; it is identical with the nucleus of the hydrogen atom, which lacks a neutron, and has atomic number 1. [Gk., *protos,* first]

protostomes (11) Bilaterally symmetrical animals with defined tissues in which the gut develops from front to back; the first opening formed is the mouth of the adult animal. [Gk., *protos,* first + *stoma,* mouth]

pseudoscience (1) Hypotheses and theories not supported by trustworthy and methodical scientific studies (but presented as if they were). [Gk., *pseudes,* false + Lat., *scientia,* knowledge]

pulmonary circuit (21) Flow of blood from the heart to the lungs and back to the heart; the returning blood is oxygenated.

punctuated equilibrium (10) Rapid periods of evolutionary change punctuated by longer periods in which there is relatively little evolutionary change.

Punnett square (7) A diagram showing the possible outcomes of a cross between two individuals; the possible crosses are shown in the manner of a multiplication table. [from the name of its designer, Reginald C. Punnett, 1875–1967]

pupa (11) In complete metamorphosis, the second stage of insect development, in which the larva is enclosed in a case and its body structures are broken down into molecules that are reassembled into the adult form. [Lat., *pupa,* a little girl]

pus (26) The thick, yellowish fluid at the site of an infection, made up of neutrophils, damaged cell debris from the invaded tissue, and both live and dead pathogens.

pyruvate (4) The end product of glycolysis.

Q

quaternary structure (2) Two or more polypeptide chains bonded together in a single protein; hemoglobin is an example of a protein molecule with this structure. [Lat., *quaterni,* four each]

R

radial symmetry (11) A body structure like that of a wheel, or pie, in which any cut through the center would divide the organism into identical halves. [Lat., *radius,* spoke of a wheel + Gk., *symmetria,* symmetry]

radiometric dating (8) A method of determining both the relative and the absolute ages of objects such as fossils by measuring both the radioactive isotopes they contain, which are known to decay at a constant rate, and their decay products.

rain shadow (15) An area in the lee of a mountain where there is no or reduced rainfall because the air passing over the mountain falls, becoming warmer and thus increasing the amount of moisture it can hold.

randomized (1) Describes a manner of choosing subjects and assigning them to groups on the basis of chance, that is, randomly.

ray-finned fishes (11) Fish species characterized by rigid bones and a mouth at the apex of the body; they are so called because their fins are lined with hardened rays.

realized niche (15) The environmental conditions in which an organism is living at a given time.

receptor-mediated endocytosis (3) One of the three types of endocytosis, in which receptors on the surface of a cell bind to specific molecules; the plasma membrane then engulfs both molecule and receptor and draws them into the cell.

receptor protein (3) A protein in the plasma membrane that binds to specific chemicals in the cell's external environment to regulate processes within the cell; for example, cells in the heart have receptor proteins that bind to adrenaline.

recessive (7) Describes an allele whose phenotypic effect is masked by a dominant allele for a trait. [Lat., *recessus,* retreating]

reciprocal altruism (9) Costly behavior directed toward another individual that benefits the recipient with the expectation that, at some later time, the recipient will behave in a similar manner, "returning the favor." [Lat., *reciprocare,* to move backward and forward + *alter,* the other]

recognition protein (3) A protein in the plasma membrane that provides a "fingerprint" on the outside-facing surface of the cell, making it recognizable to other cells; recognition proteins make it possible for the immune system to distinguish the body's own cells from invaders that may produce infection, and also help cells bind to other cells or molecules.

recombinant DNA technology (5) Technology that depends on the combination of two or more sources of DNA into a product; an example is the production of human insulin from fast-dividing transgenic *E. coli* bacteria in which has been inserted the human DNA sequence that codes for the production of insulin.

recombination (6) The exchange of some genetic material between a paternal homologous chromosome and a maternal homologous chromosome, leading to a chromosome carrying genetic material from each; also referred to as crossing over.

red blood cells (21) Hemoglobin-containing, oxygen-transporting blood cells, the most common type of blood cell. Also called *erythrocytes.*

reflex (23) An automatic response that occurs when signals travel directly from sensory neurons to the spinal cord, where they connect with motor neurons.

regulator (20) An organism that, for a given physiological variable, maintains homeostasis for that variable, keeping it within a narrow range, even in the face of external changes in the environment.

ruminant (22) A herbivorous animal with a four-chambered stomach. Ruminants include cows, bison, deer, goats, and sheep.

replication (6) The process in both eukaryotes and prokaryotes by which DNA duplicates itself in preparation for cell division.

reproductive cells (6) Haploid cells from two individuals that, as sperm and egg, will combine at fertilization to produce offspring; also called gametes.

reproductive investment (9, 14) Energy and material expended by an individual in the growth, feeding, and care of offspring.

reproductive isolation (10) The inability of individuals from two populations to produce fertile offspring together.

reproductive output (14) The number of offspring an individual or population produces.

resource partitioning (15) A division of resources that occurs when species that overlap some portion of a niche in which one or more species differ in behavior or body plan in a way that divides the resources of the niche between the species.

restriction enzymes (5) Enzymes that recognize and bind to different specific sequences of four to eight bases in DNA and cut the DNA at that point; restriction enzymes are important in biotechnology because they permit the cutting of short lengths of DNA, which can be inserted into other chromosomes or otherwise be utilized.

retina (23) Nervous tissue containing light-sensitive cells, on the inner surface of the vertebrate eye, which transmits impulses to the vision centers of the brain.

retrovirus (13) A virus containing RNA and also reverse transcriptase, a viral enzyme, which uses the viral RNA as a template to synthesize a single strand of DNA. [Lat., *retro,* backward + *virus,* slime]

ribonucleic acid (RNA) (2) A nucleic acid, RNA serves as a middleman in the process of converting genetic information in DNA into protein; messenger RNA (mRNA) takes instructions for production of a given protein from DNA to another part of the cell, whereas transfer RNA (tRNA) interprets the mRNA code and directs the construction of the protein from its constituent amino acids.

ribosomal subunits (5) The two structural parts of a ribosome, which function together to translate mRNA to build a chain of amino acids that will make up a protein.

ribosomes (3) Granular bodies in the cytoplasm, released from their initial positions on the rough endoplasmic reticulum, that copy the information in segments of DNA to provide instruction for the construction of proteins.

right hemisphere (23) The region of the brain dedicated, in most humans, to emotions, intuitive thinking, and artistic expression.

ring species (10) Populations that can interbreed with neighboring populations but not with populations separated by larger geographical distances; because the non-interbreeding populations are connected by gene flow through geographically intermediate populations, there is no clear point at which one species stops and another begins, and for this reason, ring species are problematic for the biological species concept.

RNA world hypothesis (10) A hypothesis that proposes that the world may have been filled with RNA-based life before it became filled with life based on DNA, the life of today.

rod (23) In the retina, a type of cell that enables vision in dim light.

root (12, 17) The part of a vascular plant, usually below ground, that absorbs water and minerals from the soil and transports them through vascular tissue to the rest of the plant, and that anchors the plant in place. The overall structure of a plant's roots is called the root system.

root meristem (18) A cluster of active, dividing embryonic cells at the tips of roots that generates new tissue and increases root length.

rough endoplasmic reticulum (3) An organelle, part of the endomembrane system, structurally like a series of interconnected, flattened sacs connected to the nuclear envelope; called "rough" because its surface is studded with ribosomes. [Gk., *endon,* within + *plasma,* anything molded; Lat., *reticulum, dim.* of *rete,* net]

roundworms (11) A worm phylum characterized by a long, narrow, unsegmented body and growth by molting; roundworms, also called nematodes, are protostomes with defined tissues; there are some 90,000 identified species.

rubisco (4) An enzyme (ribulose-1,5-bisphosphate carboxylase/oxygenase), important in photosynthesis, that fixes carbon atoms from CO_2 in the air, attaching them to an organic molecule in the stroma of the chloroplast; this fixation is the first step in the Calvin cycle, in which molecules of sugar are assembled. Rubisco is the most plentiful protein on earth.

S

sap (17) In vascular plants, (1) the fluid in the xylem that consists of water and dissolved minerals and sometimes sugars; (2) the fluid in the phloem that consists of water and dissolved sugars and other nutrients.

sarcomere (23) The fundamental unit of muscle contraction, made up of actin and myosin.

saturated fat (2) A fat in which each carbon in the hydrocarbon chain forming the tail region of the fat molecule is bound to two hydrogen atoms; saturated fats are solid at room temperature.

savanna (15) A type of terrestrial biome; a tropical or subtropical grassland with scattered woody plants, characterized by hot climate and distinct wet and dry seasons (rainfall is less than in the tropical seasonal forest biome).

science (1) A body of knowledge based on observation, description, experimentation, and explanation of natural phenomena. [Lat., *scientia,* knowledge]

scientific literacy (1) A general, fact-based understanding of the basics of biology and other sciences, the scientific method, and the social, political, and legal implications of scientific information.

scientific method (1) A process of examination and discovery of natural phenomena involving making observations, constructing hypotheses, testing predictions, experimenting, and drawing conclusions and revising them as necessary.

sclerenchyma cell (17) A type of cell that provides strength to plants, enabling them to grow tall; at maturity, the cell is not living. Sclerenchyma cells are a type of ground tissue.

scrotum (25) External sac that contains the testes.

second law of thermodynamics (4) A physical law that states that every conversion of energy is not perfectly efficient and invariably includes the transformation of some energy into heat.

secondary active transport (3) Active transport in which there is no direct involvement of ATP (adenosine triphosphate); the transport protein simultaneously moves one molecule against its concentration gradient while letting another flow down its concentration gradient.

secondary consumers (15) Animals that feed on herbivores; also known as carnivores.

secondary growth (18) In woody plants, plant growth that originates in lateral meristems, increasing the girth of stems and branches. It is the process by which dicots and some other angiosperms produce wood, acquiring increased water-conduction capacity and becoming thicker and sturdier. See also **primary growth.**

secondary oocyte (25) One of the two cells formed by division of a primary oocyte; it completes meiosis after fertilization.

secondary phloem (18) In woody plants, tissue produced by the vascular cambium, toward the outer circumference of the trunk or branch, during secondary growth; the cells conduct sugars throughout the plant body.

secondary response (26) The creation of B and T effector cells in response to a second exposure to a pathogen. The secondary response occurs rapidly and produces a more intense response than the primary response.

secondary spermatocyte (25) One of the two cells produced by the first meiotic division of a primary spermatocyte, which then complete the second meiotic division; each produces two spermatids.

secondary structure (2) The corkscrew-like twists or folds formed by hydrogen bonds between amino acids in a polypeptide chain.

secondary xylem (18) In woody plants, tissue produced by the vascular cambium, toward the inside of the trunk or branch, during secondary growth; the cells conduct water and minerals, while also providing structural support. Also called *wood.*

seed (12, 18) An embryonic plant with its own supply of water and nutrients encased within a protective coating.

segmented worms (11) A worm phylum characterized by grooves around the body that mark divisions between segments; segmented worms, also called annelids, are protostomes with defined tissues and do not molt; examples are earthworms and leeches.

selective serotonin reuptake inhibitors (SSRIs) (23) Antidepressant medications (including Prozac and Zoloft) that block serotonin from being reabsorbed and recycled by the cells (neurons) that released it, prolonging its effect. The net result for the individual is generally an elevated mood, because of serotonin's prolonged stay in the synapse.

semen (25) A fluid expelled at ejaculation that contains sperm along with enzymes and nutrients that foster survival of the sperm.

seminal vesicle (25) One of a pair of male reproductive glands that secrete sugar, enzymes, vitamin C, proteins, and immune suppressants into semen.

seminiferous tubules (25) Coiled tubes in the testes that are lined with the cells that divide to produce sperm.

sensory integration (23) The process of incorporating information from all of the senses to form a single perception.

sensory neuron (23) A type of neuron that collects information from an animal's environment; its dendrites are modified to respond directly to external stimulation—temperature, touch, taste, smell, light, or sound.

sepal (18) One of the leaf-like structures that grow in a ring around the outside of a flower, at the point where the flower is connected to the branch, stem, or stalk. Sepals protect the developing bud and usually are green, but sometimes are the same color as the petals.

sessile (11) Describes organisms that are fastened in place, such as adult mussels and barnacles. [Lat., *sedere,* to sit]

set point (20) A target value or range; in homeostasis, the normal range of values for a variable (such as temperature, pH, solute concentration).

sex-linked trait (7) A trait controlled by a gene on a sex chromosome.

sexual dimorphism (9) The case in which the sexes of a species differ in size or appearance. [Gk., *di-,* two + *morphē,* shape]

sexual reproduction (6, 25) A type of reproduction in which offspring are produced by the fusion of gametes from two distinct sexes.

sexual selection (8) The process by which natural selection favors traits, such as ornaments or fighting behavior, that give an advantage to individuals of one sex in attracting mating partners.

sexually transmitted disease (STD) (25) A disease passed from one person to another through sexual activity.

shoot (12, 17) The above-ground part of a plant, consisting of stems and leaves, and sometimes flowers and fruits. The stem contains vascular tissue and supports the leaves, the main photosynthetic organ of the plant. Also called *shoot system.*

shoot meristem (18) A cluster of active, dividing embryonic cells found at the tips of shoots that increases plant height and generates new tissues, including branches and buds.

sieve tube (17) A tube structure formed from specialized cells in the phloem that conducts sugar throughout the plant.

sign stimulus (9) An external signal that triggers the innate behavior called a fixed action pattern.

simple diffusion (3) Diffusion of molecules directly through the phospholipid bilayer of the plasma membrane that takes place without the assistance of other molecules; oxygen and carbon dioxide, because they are small and carry no charge that would cause them to be repelled by the middle layer of the membrane, can pass through the membrane in this way.

simple sugars (2) Monosaccharide carbohydrates, generally containing three to seven carbon atoms, which store energy in their chemical bonds and which biological cells can break down; cannot be broken down into other simple sugars; include glucose, fructose, and galactose.

single-gene trait (7) A trait that is determined by instructions on only one gene; examples are a cleft chin, a widow's peak, and unattached earlobes.

single-lens eye (23) The image-forming eye found in jellyfish and some molluscs.

sister chromatids (6) The two identical strands of a replicated chromosome.

skeletal muscle (20) A type of muscle tissue, usually attached to bones, that is responsible for generating most of the movement in animals; accounts for about 40% of human body weight. Also called *voluntary muscle.*

small intestine (22) A long, thin tube of the digestive tract between the stomach and large intestine; the part of the digestive system where most digestion and absorption take place.

smooth endoplasmic reticulum (3) An organelle, part of the endomembrane system, structurally like a series of branched tubes; called "smooth" because its surface has no ribosomes; smooth endoplasmic reticulum synthesizes lipids such as fatty acids, phospholipids, and steroids. [Gk., *endon,* within + *plasma,* anything molded; Lat., *reticulum, dim.* of *rete,* net]

smooth muscle (20) A type of muscle tissue found in the walls surrounding blood vessels, the stomach and intestines, bladder, and many other organs and inner "tubes" within the body. It generates slow, rhythmic contractions that can gradually move blood, food, or other substances through the organ; not under conscious control.

solute (3) A substance that is dissolved in a gas or liquid; in a solution of water and sugar, sugar is the solute. [Lat., *solvere,* to loosen]

solvent (3) The gas or liquid in which a substance in dissolved; in a solution of water and sugar, water is the solvent. [Lat., *solvere,* to loosen]

somatic cells (6) The (usually diploid) cells of the body of an organism (in contrast to the usually haploid reproductive cells). [Gk., *soma,* body]

special connective tissue (20) A type of connective tissue, including bone, cartilage, and blood, in which the matrix differs from that of connective tissue proper in that it is rigid or liquid.

speciation (10) The process by which one species splits into two distinct species; the first phase of speciation is reproductive isolation, the second is genetic divergence, in which two populations evolve over time as separate entities with physical and behavioral differences.

speciation event (10) A point in evolutionary history at which a given population splits into independent evolutionary lineages.

species (10) Natural populations of organisms that can interbreed and are reproductively isolated from other such groups; in the Linnaean system, the species is the narrowest classification for an organism. [Lat., *species,* kind, sort]

specific epithet (10) In the system developed by Carolus Linnaeus (1707–1778), a noun or adjective added to the genus name to distinguish a species; in the name *Homo sapiens, Homo* is the genus name and *sapiens* is the specific epithet. [Gk., *epithetos,* added]

specific immunity (26) Division of the immune system that recognizes and defends against very specific infectious agents—for example, not just all bacteria, but specific species, individually. Also called *adaptive immunity.*

sperm (18, 25) A male gamete.

spermatogenesis (25) The process of sperm production.

sphincter (22) A ring of muscle that opens or closes a passage between two chambers in the body, such as between the esophagus and the stomach.

spindle (6) A part of the cytoskeleton of a cell, formed in prophase (in mitosis) or in prophase I (in meiosis), from which extend fibers that organize and separate the sister chromatids.

spindle fibers (6) Fibers that extend from one pole of a cell to the other, which pull the sister chromatids apart in the anaphase stage of mitosis or the anaphase II stage of meiosis.

sporangia (*sing.* sporangium) (12) In many ferns, the structures on the underside of the leaves in which the spores are produced. [Gk., *spora,* seed + *angeion,* vessel]

spore (12, 18) A reproductive structure of non-vascular and some vascular plants that have an alternation of generations; spores are typically haploid, unicellular, and develop into either a male (producing sperm) or female (producing eggs) gametophyte. The eggs and sperm produced by gametophytes unite to produce the diploid generation (sporophyte) of the plant. [Gk., *spora,* seed]

stabilizing selection (8) Selection that, for a given trait, produces the greatest fitness at the intermediate point of the phenotypic range.

stamen (12, 18) The male reproductive structure of a flower, consisting of a head-like anther on a stalk-like filament. There are usually several stamens in a flower. [Lat., *stamen,* thread]

starch (2) A complex polysaccharide carbohydrate consisting of a large number of monosaccharides linked in line; in plants, starch is the primary form of energy storage.

statistics (1) A set of analytical and mathematical tools designed to further understanding of numerical data.

stem (17) Plant structure that supports and positions the leaves and flowers. The stem and leaves (and flowers) make up the shoot system.

stem cells (5, 21) Undifferentiated cells that have the ability to develop into any type of cell in the body; this property makes stem cells useful in biotechnology.

sterol (2) A lipid important in regulating growth and development; the sterols include cholesterol and the steroid hormones testosterone and estrogen, and are all modifications of a basic structure of four interlinked rings of carbon atoms. [Gk., *stereos,* solid + *-ol,* chemical suffix for an alcohol]

stigma (18) The region of the carpel, the female reproductive structure of a flower, that has a flat, sticky surface that functions as a landing pad for pollen.

stomach (22) A J-shaped digestive organ with thick, elastic walls; the part of the digestive system where food is mixed and partially digested.

stomata (*sing.* stoma) (4, 17) Small pores usually on the undersides of leaves that are the primary sites for gas exchange in plants; carbon dioxide (for photosynthesis) enters and oxygen (a by-product of photosynthesis) exits through the stomata. [Gk., *stoma,* mouth]

stroma (3, 4) In the leaf of a green plant, the fluid in the inner compartment of a chloroplast, which contains DNA and protein-making machinery. [Gk., *stroma,* bed]

style (18) The long, thin part of the carpel, the female reproductive structure of a flower, that holds up the stigma for pollen capture and through which a pollen tube will grow down into the ovary.

substrate (2) The molecule on which an enzyme acts; the active site on the enzyme binds to the substrate, initiating a chemical reaction; for example, the active site on the enzyme lactase binds to the substrate lactose, breaking it down into the two simple sugars glucose and galactose. [Lat., *sub,* under + *stratus,* spread]

succession (15) The change in the species composition of a community over time following a disturbance.

superstition (1) The irrational belief that actions not related by logic to a course of events can influence an outcome.

surface protein (3) A protein that resides primarily on the inner or outer surface of the phospholipid bilayer which constitutes the plasma membrane of the cell.

survivorship curves (14) Graphs showing the proportion of individuals of particular ages now alive in a population; survival curves indicate an individual's likelihood of surviving through a given age interval.

sympatric speciation (10) Speciation that results not from geographic isolation but as a result of polyploidy or hybridization and allopolyploidy; this type of speciation is relatively uncommon in animals but is common among plants. [Gk., *syn,* together with + *patris,* native land]

synapse (23) The site where a neuron communicates with another neuron, muscle cell, or gland [Gk., *syn,* together with + *haptein,* to fasten]

synaptic cleft (23) The space at the synapse between the axon terminal and whatever is next to it (neuron, muscle cell, or gland cell).

systematics (10) The modern approach to classification, with the broader goal of reconstructing the evolutionary history, or phylogeny, of organisms. [Gk., *systema,* a whole compounded of parts]

systemic circuit (21) Flow of blood from the heart to the body (other than the lungs) and back to the heart; returning blood is low in oxygen and high in carbon dioxide.

systolic pressure (21) The first blood pressure reading; a measure of the pressure when the heart contracts, pumping blood into the arteries.

T

T cell (26) A type of lymphocyte, maturing in the thymus, that is involved in cell-mediated immunity; fights invaders in body cells.

taproot (17) A thick primary root that grows deep into the soil and has smaller roots branching out from it; found primarily in dicots.

target cell (24) A cell that responds to a chemical regulatory signal, such as a hormone, typically when the regulatory chemical interacts with a receptor on or in the target cell.

telomere (6) A non-coding, highly repetitive section of DNA at the tip of every eukaryotic chromosome that shortens with every cell division; if it becomes too short, additional cell division can cause the loss of functional, essential DNA and therefore almost certain cell death. [Gk., *telos*, end + *meris*, part]

telophase (6) The fourth and last phase of mitosis, in which the chromosomes begin to uncoil and the nuclear membrane is reassembled around them; in meiosis, the sister chromatids arrive at the cell poles and the nuclear membrane reassembles around them in telophase I, and in telophase II the sister chromatids have been pulled apart and the nuclear membrane reassembles around haploid numbers of chromosomes. [Gk., *telos*, end + *phasis*, appearance]

temperate grassland (15) A type of terrestrial biome; a dry area with a hot season and a cold season (climatic conditions are less extreme than in the desert biome); vegetation is mostly grassland and shrubs.

tendon (20) A connective tissue that joins muscle to bone.

tendril (19) A specialized thread-like leaf or stem or branch that wraps around whatever it touches. Tendrils support the stem of the plant.

terminal buttons (23) Knob-like ends of an axon. Also called *axon terminals*.

tertiary consumers (15) Animals that eat animals that eat herbivores; also known as top carnivores. [Lat., *tertius*, third]

tertiary structure (2) The unique and complex three-dimensional shape formed by multiple twists of the secondary structure of the protein as amino acids come together and form hydrogen bonds or covalent sulfur-sulfur bonds. [Lat., *tertius*, third]

test-cross (7) A mating in which a homozygous recessive individual is bred to individuals of unknown genotype, showing the dominant phenotype; this type of cross can reveal the unknown genotype by the observed characteristics, or phenotype, of the offspring.

testis (*pl.* **testes**) (25) The male gonad.

testosterone (25) The principal male sex hormone; influences development of an embryo as male and the production of male secondary sex characteristics.

tetrapod (11) An organism with four legs; all terrestrial vertebrates are tetrapods. [Gk., *tetra-*, four + *pous*, foot]

thalamus (23) One of the primary switchboards in the brain. It receives most of the visual, auditory, and touch input, and relays some signals to the cerebral cortex while blocking others.

theory (1) An explanatory hypothesis for a natural phenomenon that is exceptionally well supported by empirical data. [Gk., *theorein*, to consider]

thermodynamics (4) The study of the transformation of energy from one type to another, such as from potential energy to kinetic energy. [Gk., *thermē*, heat + *dynamis*, power]

thermoregulation (20) The maintenance of body temperature within its normal range in homeostasis.

thigmotropism (19) Plant growth that occurs in response to touch or physical contact with an object. [Gk., *thigma*, touch + *tropikos*, turn]

thylakoid (3, 4) Interconnected membranous structures in the stroma of a chloroplast, where light energy is collected and the conversion of light energy to chemical energy in photosynthesis takes place. [Gk., *thylakis*, dim. of *thylakos*, bag]

thyroid gland (24) An endocrine gland, located in the neck in humans, that produces thyroxine, an iodine-containing hormone that influences growth and metabolism.

tight junction (3) A continuous, water-tight connection between adjacent animal cells; tight junctions are particularly important in the small intestine, where digestion occurs, to ensure that nutrients do not leak between cells into the body cavity and so be lost as a source of energy.

tissue (20) A group of similar cells that act together to perform specific functions in the body.

tonicity (3) For a cell in solution, a measure of the concentration of solutes outside the cell relative to that inside the cell. [Gk., *tonos*, tension]

topography (15) The physical features of a region, including those created by humans. [Gk., *topos*, place + *graphein*, to write down]

total reproductive output (9) The lifetime number of offspring produced by an individual.

trachea (22) A structure in the respiratory system that conducts air to the lungs. Also called *windpipe*.

trait (5, 8) Any characteristic or feature of an organism, such as red petal color in a flower.

transcription (5) The process by which a gene's base sequence is copied to mRNA.

transduction (13) A method of lateral transfer of DNA from one bacterial cell to another by means of a virus containing pieces of bacterial DNA picked up from its previous host that infects the recipient bacterium and passes along new genes to the recipient. [Lat., *trans*, on the other side of + *ducere*, to lead]

trans fat (2) An unsaturated fat that has been partially hydrogenated (meaning that hydrogen atoms have been added to make the fat more saturated and to improve a food's taste, texture, and shelf-life); the added hydrogen atoms are in a trans orientation, which differs from the cis ("near") orientation of hydrogen atoms in the unsaturated fat. [Lat., *trans*, on the other side of]

transfer RNA (tRNA) (5) RNA molecules in the cytoplasm that link specific triplet base sequences on mRNA to specific amino acids.

transformation (13) A method of lateral transfer of DNA from one bacterial cell to another in which a bacterial cell scavenges DNA released from burst bacterial cells in the environment. [Lat., *trans*, on the other side of + *formare*, to shape]

transgenic organism (5) An organism that contains DNA from another species.

translation (5) The process by which mRNA, which encodes a gene's base sequence, directs the production of a protein.

transmembrane protein (3) A protein that can penetrate the phospholipid bilayer of a cell's plasma membrane.

transport protein (3) A transmembrane protein that provides a channel or passageway through which large or strongly charged molecules can pass; transport proteins are of a number of shapes and sizes, making possible the transport of a wide variety of molecules.

treatment (1) Any condition applied to the subjects of a research study that is not applied to subjects in a control group.

triglyceride (2) A fat having three fatty acids linked to the glycerol molecule. [Gk., *tri-* three + *glykys,* sweet]

trimester (25) In human development, one of the three three-month periods of pregnancy.

trophic level (15) A step in the flow of energy through an ecosystem. [Gk., *trophe,* food]

tropical rain forest (15) A type of terrestrial biome; found between the Tropic of Cancer (23.5° north latitude) and Tropic of Capricorn (23.5° south latitude) and characterized by constant moisture and temperature that does not vary across the seasons; vegetation is dense.

tropical seasonal forest (15) A type of terrestrial biome; characterized by hot climate and distinct wet and dry seasons; trees shed their leaves in the dry season.

tropism (19) In plants, a growth response by which plants grow toward or away from environmental stimuli such as light, gravity, and physical impediments, by bending, curving, and twisting. [Gk., *tropikos,* turn] See also **gravitropism; phototropism; thigmotropism.**

true-breeding (7) Describes a population of organisms in which, for a given trait, the offspring of crosses of individuals within the population always show the same trait; thus, the offspring of pea plants that are true-breeding for round peas always have round peas.

turgor pressure (3) In plants, the pressure of the contents of the cell against the cell wall, which is maintained by osmosis as water rushes into the cell when it contains high concentrations of dissolved substances; turgor pressure allows non-woody plants to stand upright, and its loss causes wilting. [Lat., *turgere,* to swell]

twitch (23) In a muscle contraction, the duration of the period between muscle contraction and relaxation.

U

umbilical cord (25) A mass of tissue that connects the embryo to the placenta and through which nutrients and wastes are exchanged.

unsaturated fat (2) A fat in which at least one carbon in the hydrocarbon chain forming the tail region of the fat molecule is bound to only one hydrogen atom; unsaturated fats are liquid at room temperature.

uterus (25) Reproductive organ in female mammals where an embryo develops. Also called *womb.*

V

vaccine (26) Weakened or harmless form of a specific pathogen that is administered to an individual to induce immunity without subjecting the individual to the disease.

vagina (25) Tube-like chamber connecting the female external genitals to the uterus, into which sperm are released during copulation.

variables (1) The characteristics of an experimental system subject to change, for example time (the duration of treatment) or specific elements of the treatment such as the substance or procedure administered or the temperature at which it takes place. [Lat., *variare,* to vary]

vas deferens (25) A tube of smooth muscle tissue that passes from each testis into the body.

vascular cambium (18) In woody plants, the layer of lateral meristem cells that produces secondary xylem and secondary phloem.

vascular plants (12) Plants that transport water and dissolved nutrients by means of vascular tissue, a system of tubes that extends from the roots through the stem and into the leaves. [Lat., *vasculum, dim.* of *vas,* vessel]

vascular tissue (17) The part of a plant that conducts food, water, and nutrients throughout the plant body.

vein (21) A blood vessel that transports blood, at lower pressure than in arteries, from capillaries in the body to the heart.

ventricle (21) A chamber of the heart from which blood is pumped to the lungs, gills, or the rest of the body.

vesicle (3, 23) A small, membrane-bound sac within a cell. In neurons, a chemical-filled sac in the axon terminal that fuses with the presynaptic cell membrane to release its contents into the synaptic cleft. [Lat., *vesicula, dim.* of *vesica,* bladder]

vestigial structure (8) A structure, once useful to organisms but which has lost its function over evolutionary time; examples include the human appendix and molars in bats that now consume an exclusively liquid diet. [Lat., *vestigium,* footprint, trace]

viruses (10) Diverse and important biological entities that can replicate but which can conduct metabolic activity only by taking over the metabolic processes of a host organism and therefore fall outside the definition of life. [Lat., *virus,* slime]

vitamin (22) An organic compound that is an essential nutrient required by the body in small amounts.

viviparity (11) The characteristic of bearing young alive, giving birth to babies (rather than laying eggs). [Lat., *vivus,* alive + *parere,* to bear]

viviparity (25) A strategy in which the embryo develops inside the mother, and live offspring are born.

VNTRs (variable number of tandem repeats) (5) Regions of repeating sequences of bases in DNA that vary in the number of times the sequence repeats from individual to individual and, in a given individual, between homologues; identification of the number of repeats in several regions can serve as a DNA "fingerprint" unique to an individual.

W

waggle dance (9) Behavior of scout honeybees that indicates, by angle of the body relative to the sun and physical maneuvers of various duration, the direction to a distant source of food.

wax (2) A lipid similar in structure to fats but with only one long-chain fatty acid linked to the glycerol head of the molecule; because the fatty acid chain is highly non-polar, waxes are strongly hydrophobic.

Wernicke's area (23) The area of the brain responsible for understanding speech; located, in most people, in the left temporal lobe.

white blood cells (21, 26) Blood cells that defend against pathogens; the primary components of the immune response system. Also called *leukocytes.*

X

X and Y chromosomes (6) The human sex chromosomes.

xylem (*pron.* ZY-lum) (17) In vascular plants, the tissue that conducts water and dissolved minerals throughout the plant.

Z

zona pellucida (25) The glycoprotein layer between the granulosa cells and the egg's membrane.

zygote (18, 25) Diploid cell resulting when the sperm and egg fuse during fertilization.

INDEX

boldface indicates a definition; *italic* indicates a figure.